Study Card to Accompany Zumdahl's *Introductory Chemistry Series*

Measurements and Calculations

Table 2.2 The Commonly Used Prefixes in the Metric System
p. 19

Prefix	Symbol	Meaning	Power of 10 for Scientific Notation
mega	M	1,000,000.000000001	10^6
kilo	k	1000	10^3
deci	d	0.1	10^{-1}
centi	c	0.01	10^{-2}
milli	m	0.001	10^{-3}
micro	μ	0.000001	10^{-6}
nano	n	0.000000001	10^{-9}

Table 2.6 Some Examples of Commonly Used Units
p. 22

length	A dime is 1 mm thick. A quarter is 2.5 cm in diameter. The average height of an adult man is 1.8 m.
mass	A nickel has a mass of about 5 g. A 120-lb woman has a mass of about 55 kg.
volume	A 12-oz can of soda has a volume of about 360 mL. A half gallon of milk is equal to about 2 L of milk.

$1 \text{ cm}^3 = 1 \text{ mL}$
density of $H_2O(l) = 1.0$ g/mL
density = mass/volume
Avogadro's number = 6.022×10^{23}

Energy

Heat Required = Q = specific heat capacity × mass × ΔT
Specific heat capacity of $H_2O(l) = 4.184$ J/g °C
Kinetic energy = $mv^2/2$
Exothermic reactions produce heat
Endothermic reactions absorb heat

Kinds of Chemical Reactions

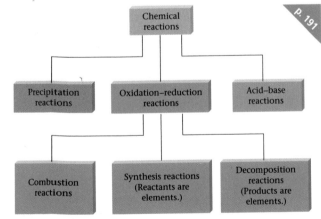

Figure 7.12 Summary of classes of reactions.
p. 191

Atomic Structure

Mass number (**A**)
(number of protons and neutrons)
$^{23}_{11}$Na ← Element symbol
Atomic number (**Z**)
(number of protons)
$A - Z = \#n^0$ $\#p^+ - \#e^- = \text{charge}$

Gases

STP: 0 °C, 1 atm
Volume of 1 mole of ideal gas at STP = 22.4 L
$PV = nRT$ (Ideal Gas Law)
$R = 0.08206$ L atm/K mol
Process at constant n and T: $P_1V_1 = P_2V_2$ (Boyle's law)
Process at constant n and P: $V_1/T_1 = V_2/T_2$ (Charles's law)
Process at constant T and P: $V_1/n_1 = V_2/n_2$
(Avogadro's law)

Types of Crystalline Solids

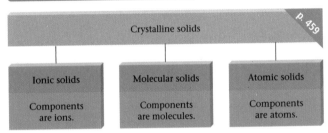

Figure 14.13 The classes of crystalline solids.
p. 459

Solutions

Mass percent = $\dfrac{\text{mass of solute}}{\text{mass of solution}} \times 100\%$ (p. 481)

M = molarity = $\dfrac{\text{moles of solute}}{\text{liters of solution}} = \dfrac{\text{mol}}{\text{L}}$ (p. 483)

Mass of solute = (molar mass of solute) × (L of solution) (Molarity)

Normality = $N = \dfrac{\text{number of equivalents}}{1 \text{ liter of solution}}$

$= \dfrac{\text{equivalents}}{\text{liter}} = \dfrac{\text{equiv}}{\text{L}}$ (p. 499)

Acids and Bases

Common Strong Acids: HCl, HNO_3, H_2SO_4, $HClO_4$, HI
Common Weak Acids: HSO_4^-, CH_3COOH (often written $HC_2H_3O_2$), HF
Common Strong Bases: NaOH, KOH
Common Weak Bases: NH_3

$K_w = 10^{-14} = [H^+][OH^-]$ (ion-product constant for water)
(p. 523)

$pH = -\log[H^+]$ (p. 526)

$pOH = -\log[OH^-]$ (p. 527)

$pH + pOH = 14.00$ (p. 529)

Equilibrium Constants

$aA + bB \rightleftharpoons cC + dD$, $K = [C]^c[D]^d/[A]^a[B]^b$ (p. 553)
A_2B_3 (s) $\rightleftharpoons 2A^{3+}(aq) + 3B^{2-}(aq)$, $K_{sp} = [A^{3+}]^2[B^{2-}]^3$
[X] = Molarity of X

Study Card to Accompany Zumdahl's *Introductory Chemistry* Series

Chemical Bonding

Table 12.4 Arrangements of Electron Pairs and the Resulting Molecular Structures for Two, Three, and Four Electron Pairs

p. 388

Number of Electron Pairs	Bonds	Electron Pair Arrangement	Ball-and-Stick Model	Molecular Structure	Partial Lewis Structure	Ball-and-Stick Model
2	2	Linear	180°	Linear	A—B—A	Cl—Be—Cl
3	3	Trigonal planar (triangular)	120°	Trigonal planar (triangular)	A—B—A (A above)	F—B—F with F
4	4	Tetrahedral	109.5°	Tetrahedral	A—B—A (A above, A below)	H—C—H with H, H
4	3	Tetrahedral	109.5°	Trigonal pyramid	A—B—A (A below)	N—H with H, H
4	2	Tetrahedral	109.5°	Bent or V-shaped	A—B—A	H—O—H

Common Lewis Dot Fragments

Oxidation–Reduction Reactions

Oxidation is loss of electrons (OIL)
Reduction is gain of electrons (RIG)

Rules for Assigning Oxidation States

p. 586

1. The oxidation state of an atom in an uncombined element is 0.
2. The oxidation state of a monatomic ion is the same as its charge.
3. Oxygen is assigned an oxidation state of −2 in most of its covalent compounds. Important exception: peroxides (compounds containing the O_2^{2-} group), in which each oxygen is assigned an oxidation state of −1.
4. In its covalent compounds with nonmetals, hydrogen is assigned an oxidation state of +1.
5. In binary compounds, the element with the greater electronegativity is assigned a negative oxidation state equal to its charge as an anion in its ionic compounds.
6. For an electrically neutral compound, the sum of the oxidation states must be zero.
7. For an ionic species, the sum of the oxidation states must equal the overall charge.

Table of Atomic Masses*

Element	Symbol	Atomic Number	Atomic Mass	Element	Symbol	Atomic Number	Atomic Mass	Element	Symbol	Atomic Number	Atomic Mass
Actinium	Ac	89	[227]§	Gold	Au	79	197.0	Praseodymium	Pr	59	140.9
Aluminum	Al	13	26.98	Hafnium	Hf	72	178.5	Promethium	Pm	61	[145]
Americium	Am	95	[243]	Hassium	Hs	108	[265]	Protactinium	Pa	91	[231]
Antimony	Sb	51	121.8	Helium	He	2	4.003	Radium	Ra	88	226
Argon	Ar	18	39.95	Holmium	Ho	67	164.9	Radon	Rn	86	[222]
Arsenic	As	33	74.92	Hydrogen	H	1	1.008	Rhenium	Re	75	186.2
Astatine	At	85	[210]	Indium	In	49	114.8	Rhodium	Rh	45	102.9
Barium	Ba	56	137.3	Iodine	I	53	126.9	Roentgenium	Rg	111	[272]
Berkelium	Bk	97	[247]	Iridium	Ir	77	192.2	Rubidium	Rb	37	85.47
Beryllium	Be	4	9.012	Iron	Fe	26	55.85	Ruthenium	Ru	44	101.1
Bismuth	Bi	83	209.0	Krypton	Kr	36	83.80	Rutherfordium	Rf	104	[261]
Bohrium	Bh	107	[264]	Lanthanum	La	57	138.9	Samarium	Sm	62	150.4
Boron	B	5	10.81	Lawrencium	Lr	103	[260]	Scandium	Sc	21	44.96
Bromine	Br	35	79.90	Lead	Pb	82	207.2	Seaborgium	Sg	106	[263]
Cadmium	Cd	48	112.4	Lithium	Li	3	6.9419	Selenium	Se	34	78.96
Calcium	Ca	20	40.08	Lutetium	Lu	71	175.0	Silicon	Si	14	28.09
Californium	Cf	98	[251]	Magnesium	Mg	12	24.31	Silver	Ag	47	107.9
Carbon	C	6	12.01	Manganese	Mn	25	54.94	Sodium	Na	11	22.99
Cerium	Ce	58	140.1	Meitnerium	Mt	109	[268]	Strontium	Sr	38	87.62
Cesium	Cs	55	132.90	Mendelevium	Md	101	[258]	Sulfur	S	16	32.07
Chlorine	Cl	17	35.45	Mercury	Hg	80	200.6	Tantalum	Ta	73	180.9
Chromium	Cr	24	52.00	Molybdenum	Mo	42	95.94	Technetium	Tc	43	[98]
Cobalt	Co	27	58.93	Neodymium	Nd	60	144.2	Tellurium	Te	52	127.6
Copper	Cu	29	63.55	Neon	Ne	10	20.18	Terbium	Tb	65	158.9
Curium	Cm	96	[247]	Neptunium	Np	93	[237]	Thallium	Tl	81	204.4
Darmstadtium	Ds	110	[271]	Nickel	Ni	28	58.69	Thorium	Th	90	232.0
Dubnium	Db	105	[262]	Niobium	Nb	41	92.91	Thulium	Tm	69	168.9
Dysprosium	Dy	66	162.5	Nitrogen	N	7	14.01	Tin	Sn	50	118.7
Einsteinium	Es	99	[252]	Nobelium	No	102	[259]	Titanium	Ti	22	47.88
Erbium	Er	68	167.3	Osmium	Os	76	190.2	Tungsten	W	74	183.9
Europium	Eu	63	152.0	Oxygen	O	8	16.00	Uranium	U	92	238.0
Fermium	Fm	100	[257]	Palladium	Pd	46	106.4	Vanadium	V	23	50.94
Fluorine	F	9	19.00	Phosphorus	P	15	30.97	Xenon	Xe	54	131.3
Francium	Fr	87	[223]	Platinum	Pt	78	195.1	Ytterbium	Yb	70	173.0
Gadolinium	Gd	64	157.3	Plutonium	Pu	94	[244]	Yttrium	Y	39	88.91
Gallium	Ga	31	69.72	Polonium	Po	84	[209]	Zinc	Zn	30	65.38
Germanium	Ge	32	72.59	Potassium	K	19	39.10	Zirconium	Zr	40	91.22

*The values given here are to four significant figures where possible.   §A value given in parentheses denotes the mass of the longest-lived isotope.

Basic Chemistry

w/ Solutions Manual & Study Guide

7e

Zumdahl | DeCoste

CENGAGE
Learning™

Australia • Brazil • Japan • Korea • Mexico • Singapore • Spain • United Kingdom • United States

CENGAGE
Learning™

Basic Chemistry: w/ Solutions Manual & Study Guide, 7e

Executive Editors:
Maureen Staudt
Michael Stranz

Senior Project Development Manager:
Linda deStefano

Marketing Specialist:
Courtney Sheldon

Senior Production/Manufacturing Manager:
Donna M. Brown

PreMedia Manager:
Joel Brennecke

Sr. Rights Acquisition Account Manager:
Todd Osborne

Cover Image:
Getty Images*

*Unless otherwise noted, all cover images used by Custom Solutions, a part of Cengage Learning, have been supplied courtesy of Getty Images with the exception of the Earthview cover image, which has been supplied by the National Aeronautics and Space Administration (NASA).

Basic Chemistry, Seventh Edition
Steven Zumdahl and Donald J. DeCoste

© 2010 Cengage Learning. All rights reserved.

Study Guide
Introductory Chemistry: A Foundation, Introductory Chemistry, Basic Chemistry, Seventh Edition
Steven Zumdahl and Donald J. DeCoste

© 2011 Cengage Learning. All rights reserved.

Student Solutions Manual
Introductory Chemistry: A Foundation, Introductory Chemistry, Basic Chemistry, Seventh Edition
Steven Zumdahl and Donald J. DeCost

© 2011 Cengage Learning. All rights reserved.

For product information and technology assistance, contact us at
Cengage Learning Customer & Sales Support, 1-800-354-9706
For permission to use material from this text or product,
submit all requests online at **cengage.com/permissions**
Further permissions questions can be emailed to
permissionrequest@cengage.com

This book contains select works from existing Cengage Learning resources and was produced by Cengage Learning Custom Solutions for collegiate use. As such, those adopting and/or contributing to this work are responsible for editorial content accuracy, continuity and completeness.

Compilation © 2010 Cengage Learning

ISBN-13: 978-1-111-29548-6

ISBN-10: 1-111-29548-4

Cengage Learning
5191 Natorp Boulevard
Mason, Ohio 45040
USA

Cengage Learning is a leading provider of customized learning solutions with office locations around the globe, including Singapore, the United Kingdom, Australia, Mexico, Brazil, and Japan. Locate your local office at:
international.cengage.com/region

Cengage Learning products are represented in Canada by Nelson Education, Ltd.
For your lifelong learning solutions, visit **www.cengage.com/custom**
Visit our corporate website at **www.cengage.com**

Printed in the United States of America

BRIEF CUSTOM CONTENTS

Student Solutions Manual

Study Guide

CONTENTS

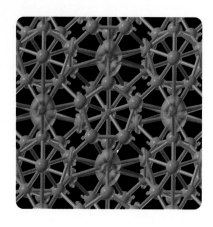

The seventh edition of *Introductory Chemistry* continues toward the goals we have pursued for the first six editions: to make chemistry interesting, accessible, and understandable to the beginning student. For this edition, we have included additional support for instructors and students to help achieve these goals.

Learning chemistry can be very rewarding. And even the novice, we believe, can relate the macroscopic world of chemistry—the observation of color changes and precipitate formation—to the microscopic world of ions and molecules. To achieve that goal, instructors are making a sincere attempt to provide more interesting and more effective ways to learn chemistry, and we hope that *Introductory Chemistry* will be perceived as a part of that effort. In this text we have presented concepts in a clear and sensible manner using language and analogies that students can relate to. We have also written the book in a way that supports active learning. In particular, the Active Learning Questions, found at the end of each chapter, provide excellent material for collaborative work by students. In addition, we have connected chemistry to real-life experience at every opportunity, from chapter opening discussions of chemical applications to "Chemistry in Focus" features throughout the book. We are convinced that this approach will foster enthusiasm and real understanding as the student uses this text. Highlights of the *Introductory Chemistry* program are described below.

New to This Edition

Building on the success of previous editions of *Introductory Chemistry,* the following changes have been made to further enhance the text:

Updates to the Student Text and Instructor's Annotated Edition

Changes to the student text and the accompanying Instructor's Annotated Edition are outlined below:

Instructor's Annotated Edition The marginal annotations have been revised and expanded to include point-of-use references to print and new media.

Section 8.4: Learning to Solve Problems We have added a new section that emphasizes the importance of conceptual problem solving in which students are shown how to think their way through a problem. The students will learn that this "big picture approach" produces more long-term, meaningful learning rather than simply memorizing specific steps that are soon forgotten.

Problem-Solving Approach in *Examples* Using the general conceptual problem-solving approach outlined in the new Section 8.4, we have introduced a series of questions into the in-chapter *Examples*. This more active approach helps students think their way through the solution to the problem. We use this approach for most of the quantitative *Examples* beginning in Section 8.4.

Section 9.4: The Concept of Limiting Reactants We have added a new section that helps students better understand the concept of a limiting reactant. Familiar examples such as making sandwiches and lemonade are used, as well as molecular-level illustrations of chemistry reactions. Students will learn how to think about limiting reactants before being asked to make mass–mass calculations to determine which reactant is limiting for a given reaction.

New Active Learning Questions We have written new Active Learning Questions for each chapter (over 170 new problems in all). In addition, many of the new problems include visual components such as graphs or molecular-level illustrations.

New End-of-Chapter Questions Using the "Chemistry in Focus" boxes We have written new end-of-chapter questions that specifically address topics covered in the "Chemistry in Focus" boxes (over 40 new questions in all).

Art Program We have revised almost every figure in the textbook to better serve visual learners. Most of the glassware, orbitals, graphs, and flowcharts have been redrawn.

"Chemistry in Focus" boxes Approximately 20% of the "Chemistry in Focus" boxes in the seventh edition are new, and many more have been revised, with up-to-date topics such as hybrid cars, artificial sweeteners, and positron emission tomography (PET).

End-of-Chapter Exercises We have replaced 20% of the end-of-chapter questions and problems and cumulative review exercises. As before, the margin of the Annotated Instructor's Edition includes answers to all of the Self-Check end-of-chapter exercises, along with additional examples for all Example problems. In the student edition, answers to Self-Check Exercises and to even-numbered exercises are provided at the back of the book.

NEW! ## Enhanced Teaching Resources for the Instructor

OWL: Online Web-based Learning by Roberta Day and Beatrice Botch of the University of Massachusetts, Amherst, and William Vining of the State University of New York at Oneonta (ISBN-10: 0-538-73740-9; ISBN-13: 978-0-538-73740-1). Developed at the University of Massachusetts, Amherst, and class-tested by tens of thousands of chemistry students, OWL is a fully customizable and flexible web-based learning system. OWL supports mastery learning and offers numerical, chemical, and contextual parameterization to produce thousands of problems correlated to this text. The OWL system also features a database of simulations, tutorials, and exercises, as well as end-of-chapter problems from the text. In addition, OWL now includes *ChemWork* assignments, which help students learn key chemical concepts while guiding them in the process to become problem solvers. (See description below.) With OWL, you get the most widely used online learning system available for chemistry with unsurpassed reliability and dedicated training and support. Also new in OWL is *Go Chemistry*™—27 mini-video lectures covering key chemistry concepts that students can view onscreen or download to their portable video player to study on the go! The optional **eBook**

in OWL (ISBN-10: 0-538-73739-5; ISBN-13: 978-0-538-73739-5) includes the complete electronic version of the text, fully integrated and linked to OWL homework problems. Most e-Books in OWL are interactive and offer highlighting, notetaking, and bookmarking features that can all be saved. In addition, the eBook includes links to Thinkwell® mini-video lectures. To view an OWL demo and for more information, visit **www.cengage.com/owl** or contact your Cengage Learning, Brooks/Cole representative.

ChemWork Offered in both OWL and *Enhanced WebAssign®*, *ChemWork* assignments offer students another opportunity to practice. These problems are designed for students to use in one of two ways: to *learn* the problem-solving process (while doing actual homework problems) or as a *capstone* assignment to determine whether they understand how to solve problems (perhaps in final preparation for an exam). *ChemWork* assignments test students' understanding of core concepts from each chapter. Students who solve a particular problem with no assistance can proceed directly to the answer and receive congratulations. However, students who need help can get assistance through a series of hints. The procedure for assisting students is modeled after the way a teacher would help with a homework problem in his or her office. The hints are usually in the form of interactive questions that guide students through the problem-solving process. Students cannot receive the right answer from the system; rather it encourages them to continue working on the problem through this system of multiple hints. *ChemWork* is chemically and numerically parameterized so that each student in the course receives a unique set of problems.

Enhanced WebAssign® *Enhanced WebAssign,* a robust, easy-to-use online learning system, includes algorithmic textbook problems with rich media learning resources, such as *ChemWork* assignments and Thinkwell® mini-video lectures. Instructors can create assignments from a ready-to-use database of textbook questions or write and customize their own exercises.

PowerLecture with ExamView® and JoinIn™ Instructor's DVD (ISBN-10: 0-538-73643-7; ISBN-13: 978-0-538-73643-5): PowerLecture is a one-stop digital library and presentation tool that includes:

- **Prepared Microsoft® PowerPoint® Lecture Slides** that cover all key points from the text in a convenient format that you can enhance with your own materials or with additional interactive video and animations from the CD-ROM for personalized, media-enhanced lectures.

- **Image Libraries** in PowerPoint® and JPEG formats that contain electronic files for all text art, most photographs, and all numbered tables in the text. These files can be used to print transparencies or to enhance PowerPoint® lectures.

- **JoinIn™ "Clicker" Slides** include questions that are written specifically for the use of *Introductory Chemistry* with the classroom response system of your choice, and allows you to seamlessly display student answers.

- **ExamView®** testing software, with all the test items from the Online Test Bank in electronic format. The electronic test bank by Steven S. Zumdahl and Donald J. DeCoste provides over 1600 multiple-choice, true-false, short-answer, matching, and completion questions. Approximately 200 questions from the previous edition have been made into algorithms, which enable you to create even more customized tests.

NEW!   ## Enhanced Learning Resources for the Student

Student Companion Website Accessible from **www.cengage.com/ chemistry/zumdahl,** this site provides online study tools, including practice tests and flashcards.

GoChemistry™ **for General Chemistry** (27-Module Set) (ISBN-10: 0-495-38228-0; ISBN-13: 978-0-495-38228-7) *GoChemistry*™ is a set of easy-to-use essential videos that can be downloaded to your video iPod or portable video player—ideal for the student on the go! Developed by award-winning chemists, these new electronic tools are designed to help students quickly review essential chemistry topics. Mini-video lectures include animations and problems for a quick summary of key concepts. Selected *GoChemistry* modules have e-flashcards to briefly introduce a key concept and then test student understanding of the basics with a series of questions. *GoChemistry* also plays on QuickTime, iTunes, and iPhones. Modules are also available separately. To purchase, enter ISBN 0-495-38228-0 at **www.ichapters.com.**

OWL for General Chemistry by Roberta Day and Beatrice Botch of the University of Massachusetts, Amherst, and William Vining of the State University of New York at Oneonta [OWL Instant Access (4 Semesters) ISBN-10: 0-495-05099-7; ISBN-13: 978-0-495-05099-5]. Developed at the University of Massachusetts, Amherst, and class-tested by tens of thousands of chemistry students, OWL is a fully customizable and flexible web-based learning system. OWL supports mastery learning and offers numerical, chemical, and contextual parameterization to produce thousands of problems correlated to this text. The OWL system also features a database of simulations, tutorials, and exercises, as well as end-of-chapter problems from the text. In addition, OWL now includes *ChemWork* assignments, which help students learn key chemical concepts while guiding them in the process to become problem solvers. (See description above.) With OWL, you get the most widely used online learning system available for chemistry with unsurpassed reliability and dedicated training and support. Also new in OWL is *GoChemistry*™—27 mini-video lectures covering key chemistry concepts that students can view onscreen or download to their portable video player to study on the go! The optional **eBook in OWL** (ISBN-10: 0-538-73739-5; ISBN-13: 978-0-538-73739-5) includes the complete electronic version of the text, fully integrated and linked to OWL homework problems. Most e-Books in OWL are interactive and offer highlighting, notetaking, and bookmarking features that can all be saved. In addition, the eBook includes links to Thinkwell® mini-video lectures. To view an OWL demo and for more information, visit **www.cengage.com/owl** or contact your Cengage Learning, Brooks/Cole representative.

Emphasis on Reaction Chemistry

We continue to emphasize chemical reactions early in the book, leaving the more abstract material on orbitals for later chapters. In a course in which many students encounter chemistry for the first time, it seems especially important that we present the chemical nature of matter before we discuss the theoretical intricacies of atoms and orbitals. Reactions are inherently interesting to students and can help us draw them to chemistry. In particular, reactions can form the basis for fascinating classroom demonstrations and laboratory experiments.

We have therefore chosen to emphasize reactions before going on to the details of atomic structure. Relying only on very simple ideas about the atom, Chapters 6 and 7 represent a thorough treatment of chemical reactions, including how to recognize a chemical change and what a chemical equation means. The properties of aqueous solutions are discussed in detail, and careful attention is given to precipitation and acid–base reactions. In addition, a simple treatment of oxidation–reduction reactions is given. These chapters should provide a solid foundation, relatively early in the course, for reaction-based laboratory experiments.

For instructors who feel that it is desirable to introduce orbitals early in the course, prior to chemical reactions, the chapters on atomic theory and bonding (Chapters 11 and 12) can be covered directly after Chapter 4. Chapter 5 deals solely with nomenclature and can be used wherever it is needed in a particular course.

Development of Problem-Solving Skills

Problem solving is a high priority in chemical education. We all want our students to acquire problem-solving skills. Fostering the development of such skills has been a central focus of the earlier editions of this text and we have maintained this approach in this edition.

In the first chapters we spend considerable time guiding students to an understanding of the importance of learning chemistry. At the same time, we explain that the complexities that can make chemistry frustrating at times can also provide the opportunity to develop the problem-solving skills that are beneficial in any profession. Learning to think like a chemist is useful to everyone. To emphasize this idea, we apply scientific thinking to some real-life problems in Chapter 1.

One reason chemistry can be challenging for beginning students is that they often do not possess the required mathematical skills. Thus we have paid careful attention to such fundamental mathematical skills as using scientific notation, rounding off to the correct number of significant figures, and rearranging equations to solve for a particular quantity. And we have meticulously followed the rules we have set down, so as not to confuse students.

Attitude plays a crucial role in achieving success in problem solving. Students must learn that a systematic, thoughtful approach to problems is better than brute force memorization. We foster this attitude early in the book, using temperature conversions as a vehicle in Chapter 2. Throughout the book we encourage an approach that starts with trying to represent the essence of the problem using symbols and/or diagrams, and ends with thinking about whether the answer makes sense. We approach new concepts by carefully working through the material before we give mathematical formulas or overall strategies. We encourage a thoughtful step-by-step approach rather than the premature use of algorithms. Once we have provided the necessary foundation, we highlight important rules and processes in skill development boxes so that students can locate them easily.

We have written a new section (Section 8.4: Learning to Solve Problems) so that students will better understand how to think their way through a problem. We discuss how to solve problems in a flexible, creative way based on understanding the fundamental ideas of chemistry and asking and answering key questions. We model this approach in the in-text *Examples* throughout the text.

Many of the worked examples are followed by Self-Check Exercises, which provide additional practice. The Self-Check Exercises are keyed to end-of-chapter exercises to offer another opportunity for students to practice a particular problem-solving skill or understand a particular concept.

We have expanded the number of end-of-chapter exercises. As in the first six editions, the end-of-chapter exercises are arranged in "matched pairs," meaning that both problems in the pair explore similar topics. An Additional Problems section includes further practice in chapter concepts as well as more challenging problems. Cumulative reviews, which appear after every few chapters, test concepts from the preceding chapter block. Answers for all even-numbered exercises appear in a special section at the end of the student edition.

Handling the Language of Chemistry and Applications

We have gone to great lengths to make this book "student friendly" and have received enthusiastic feedback from students who have used it.

As in the earlier editions, we present a systematic and thorough treatment of chemical nomenclature. Once this framework is established, students can progress through the book comfortably.

Along with chemical reactions, applications form an important part of descriptive chemistry. Because students are interested in chemistry's impact on their lives, we have included many new "Chemistry in Focus" boxes, which describe current applications of chemistry. These special interest boxes cover such topics as new technology to replace the incandescent lightbulb, using bees to detect drugs and bombs at airports, and analyzing isotopes in human hair to identify disaster victims' country of origin.

Visual Impact of Chemistry

In response to instructors' requests to include graphic illustrations of chemical reactions, phenomena, and processes, we use a full-color design that enables color to be used functionally, thoughtfully, and consistently to help students understand chemistry and to make the subject more inviting to them. We have included only those photos that illustrate a chemical reaction or phenomenon or that make a connection between chemistry and the real world. Many new photos enhance the seventh edition.

Choices of Coverage

For the convenience of instructors, four versions of the seventh edition are available: two paperback versions and two hardbound versions. *Basic Chemistry,* Seventh Edition, a paperback text, provides basic coverage of chemical concepts and applications through acid–base chemistry and has 16 chapters. *Introductory Chemistry,* Seventh Edition, available in hardcover and paperback, expands the coverage to 19 chapters with the addition of equilibrium, oxidation–reduction reactions and electrochemistry, radioactivity, and nuclear energy. Finally, *Introductory Chemistry: A Foundation,* Seventh Edition, a hardbound text, has 21 chapters, with the final two chapters providing a brief introduction to organic and biological chemistry.

Supplements for the Text

A main focus of this revision is to provide instructors and students with an unparalleled level of support. In addition to the media components described previously, we offer the following materials.

For the Student

Student Companion Website Accessible from **www.cengage.com/chemistry/zumdahl,** this site provides online study tools, including practice tests and flashcards.

Study Guide by Donald J. DeCoste of the University of Illinois contains Chapter Discussions and Learning Review (practice chapter tests) (ISBN-10: 0-538-73640-2; ISBN-13: 978-0-538-73640-4).

Solutions Guide by James F. Hall, University of Massachusetts, Lowell, contains detailed solutions for the even-numbered end-of-chapter questions and exercises and cumulative review exercises (ISBN-10: 0-538-73641-0; ISBN-13: 978-0-538-73641-1).

Introductory Chemistry in the Laboratory by James F. Hall contains experiments organized according to the topical presentation in the text. Annotations in the Annotated Instructor's Edition indicate where the experiments from this manual are relevant to chapter content. The lab manual has been updated and revised for this edition (ISBN-10: 0-538-73642-9; ISBN-13: 978-0-538-73642-8).

For the Instructor

Annotated Instructor's Edition The Annotated Instructor's Edition gathers a wealth of teaching support in one convenient package. The AIE contains all 21 chapters (the full contents of *Introductory Chemistry: A Foundation,* Seventh Edition). Annotations in the wrap-around margins of the AIE include:

- Answers to Self-Check Exercises, at point-of-use.

- Answers to all end-of-chapter questions and exercises, at point-of-use.

- Additional Examples with answers to supplemental worked-out Examples in the text.

- Technology Information about incorporating animations and video clips from the electronic support materials in lecture.

- Teaching Support Suggestions for specific lecture/instruction methods, activities, and in-class demonstrations to help convey concepts.

- An Overview of the chapter's learning objectives.

- Teaching Tips: Guidelines for highlighting critical information in the chapter.

- Misconceptions: Tips on where students may have trouble or be confused with a topic.

- Demonstrations: Detailed instructions for in-class demonstrations and activities. (These are similar to material in Teaching Support, and may be referenced in Teaching Support annotations.)

- Laboratory Experiments: Information on which labs in the Laboratory Manual are relevant to chapter content.

- Background Information: Explanations of conventions used in the text.

- Icons mark material correlations between the main text and the electronic support materials, the Test Bank, and the Laboratory Manual.

- Historical Notes: Biographical or other historical information about science and scientists.

PowerLecture with ExamView® and JoinIn™ Instructor's DVD (ISBN-10: 0-538-73643-7; ISBN-13: 978-0-538-73643-5): PowerLecture is a one-stop digital library and presentation tool that includes:

- **Prepared Microsoft® PowerPoint® Lecture Slides** that cover all key points from the text in a convenient format that you can enhance with your own materials or with additional interactive video and animations from the CD-ROM for personalized, media-enhanced lectures.

- **Image Libraries** in PowerPoint® and JPEG formats that contain electronic files for all text art, most photographs, and all numbered tables in the text. These files can be used to print transparencies or to enhance PowerPoint® lectures.

- **JoinIn™ "Clicker" Slides** include questions that are written specifically for the use of *Introductory Chemistry* with the classroom response system of your choice, and allows you to seamlessly display student answers.

- ***Complete Solutions Manual*** (James F. Hall, University of Massachusetts, Lowell) The *Complete Solutions Manual* contains detailed solutions to all of the end-of chapter problems, problems, and cumulative review exercises.

- **Answers to Active Learning Questions** from the end-of-chapter questions, written by Donald J. DeCoste.

- ***Instructor's Guide for Introductory Chemistry in the Laboratory*** by James F. Hall includes general notes about each experiment, estimated completion time, materials required, and answers to both pre- and post-laboratory questions. Annotations in the AIE indicate where experiments from this manual are relevant to chapter content. The lab manual has been updated and revised for this edition.

- **Sample Chapters** from the *Student Solutions Manual* and *Study Guide*.

- **ExamView®** testing software, with all the test items from the Online Test Bank in electronic format. The electronic test bank by Steven S. Zumdahl and Donald J. DeCoste provides over 1600 multiple-choice, true-false, short-answer, matching, and completion questions. Approximately 200 questions from the previous edition have been made into algorithms, which enable you to create even more customized tests.

Acknowledgments

This book represents the collaborative efforts of many talented and dedicated people to whom we are greatly indebted. Charles Hartford, Publisher, was extremely supportive of the revision. Charlie asked good questions and provided helpful and creative ideas. We also wish to thank Cathy Brooks, Content Project Manager, who has an eye for detail and an uncanny ability to do everything at once and all of it well. We appreciate the efforts of Alyssa White, Development Editor, who, along with her other tasks, was instrumental in making sure the art was appealing and correct. We are grateful to have worked with Sharon Donahue, Photo Researcher, who once again displayed her remarkable ability for finding outstanding photos.

Jim Hall of the University of Massachusetts, Lowell contributed in many different ways to the success of this project. He has been a tremendous help with the end-of-chapter questions and problems and the cumulative review exercises, along with writing the *Solutions Guides, Introductory Chemistry in the Laboratory,* and the *Instructor's Guide for Introductory Chemistry in the Laboratory.*

We especially appreciate the efforts of Gretchen Adams of the University of Illinois for her work on revising the PowerPoint® media component, Richard Triplett of Des Moines Area Community College for reviewing the ancillaries, and Linda Bush for revising the test bank.

Thanks to others who provided valuable assistance on this revision: Stephanie VanCamp, Assistant Editor for the ancillaries; Rebecca Berardy-Schwartz, Technology Project Manager; Jon Olaffson, Editorial Assistant; Nicole Hamm, Marketing Manager; Megan Greiner, Project Manager (Graphic World); Jill Haber and Cate Barr, Art Directors; Betty Litt, Copyeditor; and David Shinn, who checked the textbook and solutions for accuracy.

Our sincerest appreciation goes to all of the reviewers whose feedback and suggestions contributed to the success of this project.

Angela Bickford
Northwest Missouri State University

Simon Bott
University of Houston

Jabe Breland
St. Petersburg College

Frank Calvagna
Rock Valley College

Jing-Yi Chin
Suffolk County Community College

Carl David
University of Connecticut

Cory DiCarlo
Grand Valley State University

Cathie Keenan
Chaffey College

Pamela Kimbrough
Crafton Hills College

1

Chemistry: An Introduction

● Chemistry deals with the natural world. *(Dr. John Brackenbury/Science Photo Library/Photo Researchers, Inc.)*

Did you ever see a fireworks display on July Fourth and wonder how it's possible to produce those beautiful, intricate designs in the air? Have you read about dinosaurs—how they ruled the earth for millions of years and then suddenly disappeared? Although the extinction happened 65 million years ago and may seem unimportant, could the same thing happen to us? Have you ever wondered why an ice cube (pure water) floats in a glass of water (also pure water)? Did you know that the "lead" in your pencil is made of the same substance (carbon) as the diamond in an engagement ring? Did you ever wonder how a corn plant or a palm tree grows seemingly by magic, or why leaves turn beautiful colors in autumn? Do you know how the battery works to start your car or run your calculator? Surely some of these things and many others in the world around you have intrigued you. The fact is that we can explain all of these things in convincing ways using the models of chemistry and the related physical and life sciences.

PhotoDisc/Getty Images

Fireworks are a beautiful illustration of chemistry in action.

1.1 Chemistry: An Introduction

OBJECTIVE: To understand the importance of learning chemistry.

Although chemistry might seem to have little to do with dinosaurs, knowledge of chemistry was the tool that enabled paleontologist Luis W. Alvarez and his coworkers from the University of California at Berkeley to "crack the case" of the disappearing dinosaurs. The key was the relatively high level of iridium found in the sediment that represents the boundary between the earth's Cretaceous (K) and Tertiary (T) periods—the time when the dinosaurs disappeared virtually overnight (on the geological scale). The Berkeley researchers knew that meteorites also have unusually high iridium content (relative to the earth's composition), which led them to suggest that a large meteorite impacted the earth 65 million years ago, causing the climatic changes that wiped out the dinosaurs.

A knowledge of chemistry is useful to almost everyone—chemistry occurs all around us all of the time, and an understanding of chemistry is useful to doctors, lawyers, mechanics, business people, firefighters, and poets among others. Chemistry is important—there is no doubt about that. It lies at the heart of our efforts to produce new materials that make our lives safer and easier, to produce new sources of energy that are abundant and nonpolluting, and to understand and control the many diseases that threaten us and our food supplies. Even if your future career does not require the daily use of chemical principles, your life will be greatly influenced by chemistry.

A strong case can be made that the use of chemistry has greatly enriched all of our lives. However, it is important to understand that the principles of chemistry are inherently neither good nor bad—it's what we do with this knowledge that really matters. Although humans are clever, resourceful, and concerned about others, they also can be greedy, selfish, and ignorant. In addition, we tend to be shortsighted; we concentrate too much on the present and do not think enough about the long-range implications of our actions. This type of thinking has already caused us a great deal of trouble—severe environmental damage has occurred on many fronts. We cannot place all the responsibility on the chemical companies, because everyone has contributed to these problems. However, it is less important to lay blame than to figure out how to solve these problems. An important part of the answer must rely on chemistry.

One of the "hottest" fields in the chemical sciences is environmental chemistry—an area that involves studying our environmental ills and finding creative ways to address them. For example, meet Bart Eklund, who works in the atmospheric chemistry field for Radian Corporation in Austin, Texas. Bart's interest in a career in environmental science was fostered by two environmental chemistry courses and two ecology courses he took as an undergraduate. His original plan to gain several years of industrial experience and then to return to school for a graduate degree changed when he discovered that professional advancement with a B.S. degree was possible in the environmental research field. The multidisciplinary nature of environmental problems has allowed Bart to pursue his interest in several fields at the same time. You might say that he specializes in being a generalist.

The environmental consulting field appeals to Bart for a number of reasons: the chance to define and solve a number of research problems; the simultaneous work on a number of diverse projects; the mix of desk, field, and laboratory work; the travel; and the opportunity to perform rewarding work that has a positive effect on people's lives.

Among his career highlights are the following:

Bart Eklund checking air quality at a hazardous waste site.

- Spending a winter month doing air sampling in the Grand Tetons, where he also met his wife and learned to ski;

- Driving sampling pipes by hand into the rocky ground of Death Valley Monument in California;

- Working regularly with experts in their fields and with people who enjoy what they do;

- Doing vigorous work in 100 °F weather while wearing a rubberized suit, double gloves, and a respirator; and

- Getting to work in and see Alaska, Yosemite Park, Niagara Falls, Hong Kong, the People's Republic of China, Mesa Verde, New York City, and dozens of other interesting places.

Bart Eklund's career demonstrates how chemists are helping to solve our environmental problems. It is how we use our chemical knowledge that makes all the difference.

An example that shows how technical knowledge can be a "double-edged sword" is the case of chlorofluorocarbons (CFCs). When the compound CCl_2F_2 (originally called Freon-12) was first synthesized, it was hailed as a near-miracle substance. Because of its noncorrosive nature and its unusual ability to resist decomposition, Freon-12 was rapidly applied in refrigeration and air-conditioning systems, cleaning applications, the blowing of foams used for insulation and packing materials, and many other ways. For years everything seemed fine—the CFCs actually replaced more dangerous materials, such as the ammonia formerly used in refrigeration systems. The CFCs were definitely viewed as "good guys." But then a problem was discovered—the ozone in the upper atmosphere that protects us from the high-energy radiation of the sun began to decline. What was happening to cause the destruction of the vital ozone?

Much to everyone's amazement, the culprits turned out to be the seemingly beneficial CFCs. Inevitably, large quantities of CFCs had leaked into the atmosphere but nobody was very worried about this development because these compounds seemed totally benign. In fact, the great stability of the CFCs (a tremendous advantage for their various applications) was in the end a great disadvantage when they were released into the environment. Professor F. S. Rowland and his colleagues at the University of California at Irvine demonstrated that the CFCs eventually drifted to high altitudes in the atmosphere, where the energy of the sun stripped off chlorine atoms. These chlorine atoms in turn promoted the decomposition of the ozone in the upper atmosphere. (We will discuss this in more detail in Chapter 13.) Thus a substance that possessed many advantages in earthbound applications turned against us in the atmosphere. Who could have guessed it would turn out this way?

The good news is that the U.S. chemical industry is leading the way to find environmentally safe alternatives to CFCs, and the levels of CFCs in the atmosphere are already dropping.

The saga of the CFCs demonstrates that we can respond relatively quickly to a serious environmental problem if we decide to do so. Also, it is important to understand that chemical manufacturers have a new attitude about the environment—they are now among the leaders in finding ways to address our environmental ills. The industries that apply the chemical sciences are now determined to be part of the solution rather than part of the problem.

As you can see, learning chemistry is both interesting and important. A chemistry course can do more than simply help you learn the principles of chemistry, however. A major by-product of your study of chemistry is that you will become a better problem solver. One reason chemistry has the reputation of being "tough" is that it often deals with rather complicated systems that require some effort to figure out. Although this might at first seem like a disadvantage, you can turn it to your advantage if you have the right attitude. Recruiters for companies of all types maintain that one of the first things they look for in a prospective employee is the ability to solve problems. We will spend a good deal of time solving various types of problems in this book by using a systematic, logical approach that will serve you well in solving any kind of problem in any field. Keep this broader goal in mind as you learn to solve the specific problems connected with chemistry.

Although learning chemistry is often not easy, it's never impossible. In fact, anyone who is interested, patient, and willing to work can learn

A chemist in the laboratory.

Dr. Ruth—Cotton Hero

Ruth Benerito, the inventor of easy-care cotton.

AP Photo/Ric Risberg

Dr. Ruth Rogan Benerito may have saved the cotton industry in the United States. In the 1960s, synthetic fibers posed a serious competitive threat to cotton, primarily because of wrinkling. Synthetic fibers such as polyester can be formulated to be highly resistant to wrinkles both in the laundering process and in wearing. On the other hand, 1960s' cotton fabrics wrinkled easily—white cotton shirts had to be ironed to look good. This requirement put cotton at a serious disadvantage and endangered an industry very important to the economic health of the South.

During the 1960s Ruth Benerito worked as a scientist for the Department of Agriculture, where she was instrumental in developing the

chemical treatment of cotton to make it wrinkle resistant. In so doing she enabled cotton to remain a preeminent fiber in the market—a place it continues to hold today. She was honored with the Lemelson–MIT Lifetime Achievement Award for Inventions in 2002 when she was 86 years old.

Dr. Benerito, who holds 55 patents, including the one for wrinkle-free cotton awarded in 1969, began her career when women were not expected to enter scientific fields. However, her mother, who was an artist, adamantly encouraged her to be anything she wanted to be.

Dr. Benerito graduated from high school at 14 and attended Newcomb College, the women's college associated with Tulane University. She majored in chemistry with minors in physics and math. At that time she was one of only two women allowed to take the physical chemistry course at Tulane. She earned her B.S. degree in 1935 at age 19 and subsequently earned a master's degree at Tulane and a Ph.D. at the University of Chicago.

In 1953 Dr. Benerito began working in the Agriculture Department's Southern Regional Research Center in New Orleans, where she mainly worked on cotton and cotton-related products. She also invented a special method for intravenous feeding in long-term medical patients.

Since her retirement in 1986, she has continued to tutor science students to keep busy. Everyone who knows Dr. Benerito describes her as a class act.

the fundamentals of chemistry. In this book we will try very hard to help you understand what chemistry is and how it works and to point out how chemistry applies to the things going on in your life.

Our sincere hope is that this text will motivate you to learn chemistry, make its concepts understandable to you, and demonstrate how interesting and vital the study of chemistry is.

1.2 What Is Chemistry?

OBJECTIVE: To define chemistry.

> Chemical and physical changes will be discussed in Chapter 3.

Chemistry can be defined as *the science that deals with the materials of the universe and the changes that these materials undergo.* Chemists are involved in activities as diverse as examining the fundamental particles of matter, looking for molecules in space, synthesizing and formulating new materials of all types, using bacteria to produce such chemicals as insulin, and inventing new diagnostic methods for early detection of disease.

Chemistry is often called the central science—and with good reason. Most of the phenomena that occur in the world around us involve chemical changes, changes where one or more substances become different substances. Here are some examples of chemical changes:

Wood burns in air, forming water, carbon dioxide, and other substances.

A plant grows by assembling simple substances into more complex substances.

The steel in a car rusts.

Eggs, flour, sugar, and baking powder are mixed and baked to yield a cake.

The definition of the term *chemistry* is learned and stored in the brain.

Emissions from a power plant lead to the formation of acid rain.

As we proceed, you will see how the concepts of chemistry allow us to understand the nature of these and other changes and thus help us manipulate natural materials to our benefit.

The launch of the space shuttle gives clear indications that chemical reactions are occurring.

1.3 Solving Problems Using a Scientific Approach

OBJECTIVE: To understand scientific thinking.

One of the most important things we do in everyday life is solve problems. In fact, most of the decisions you make each day can be described as solving problems.

It's 8:30 A.M. on Friday. Which is the best way to drive to school to avoid traffic congestion?

You have two tests on Monday. Should you divide your study time equally or allot more time to one than to the other?

Your car stalls at a busy intersection and your little brother is with you. What should you do next?

These are everyday problems of the type we all face. What process do we use to solve them? You may not have thought about it before, but there are several steps that almost everyone uses to solve problems:

1. Recognize the problem and state it clearly. Some information becomes known, or something happens that requires action. In science we call this step *making an observation*.

2. Propose *possible* solutions to the problem or *possible* explanations for the observation. In scientific language, suggesting such a possibility is called *formulating a hypothesis*.

A Mystifying Problem

To illustrate how science helps us solve problems, consider a true story about two people, David and Susan (not their real names). Several years ago David and Susan were healthy 40-year-olds living in California, where David was serving in the Air Force. Gradually Susan became quite ill, showing flu-like symptoms including nausea and severe muscle pains. Even her personality changed: she became uncharacteristically grumpy. She seemed like a totally different person from the healthy, happy woman of a few months earlier. Following her doctor's orders, she rested and drank a lot of fluids, including large quantities of coffee and orange juice from her favorite mug, part of a 200-piece set of pottery dishes recently purchased in Italy. However, she just got sicker, developing extreme abdominal cramps and severe anemia.

During this time David also became ill and exhibited symptoms much like Susan's: weight loss, excruciating pain in his back and arms, and uncharacteristic fits of temper. The disease became so debilitating that he retired early from the Air Force and the couple moved to Seattle. For a short time their health improved, but after they unpacked all their belongings (including those pottery dishes), their health began to deteriorate again. Susan's body became so sensitive that she could not tolerate the weight of a blanket. She was near death. What was wrong? The doctors didn't know, but one suggested she might have porphyria, a rare blood disease.

Desperate, David began to search the medical literature himself. One day while he was reading about porphyria, a phrase jumped off the page: "Lead poisoning can sometimes be confused with porphyria." Could the problem be lead poisoning?

We have described a very serious problem with life-or-death implications. What should David do next? Overlooking for a moment the obvious response of calling the couple's doctor immediately to discuss the possibility of lead poisoning, could David solve the problem via scientific thinking? Let's use the three steps described in Section 1.3 to attack the problem one part at a time. This is important: usually we solve complex problems by breaking them down into manageable parts. We can then assemble the solution to the overall problem from the answers we have found "piecemeal."

In this case there are many parts to the overall problem:

What is the disease?

Where is it coming from?

Can it be cured?

Let's attack "What is the disease?" first.

Observation: David and Susan are ill with the symptoms described. Is the disease lead poisoning?

Hypothesis: The disease is lead poisoning.

Experiment: If the disease is lead poisoning, the symptoms must match those known to characterize lead poisoning. Look up the symptoms of lead poisoning. David did this and found that they matched the couple's symptoms almost exactly.

This discovery points to lead poisoning as the source of their problem, but David needed more evidence.

Observation: Lead poisoning results from high levels of lead in the bloodstream.

Hypothesis: The couple have high levels of lead in their blood.

Experiment: Perform a blood analysis. Susan arranged for such an analysis, and the results showed high lead levels for both David and Susan.

3. Decide which of the solutions is the best or decide whether the explanation proposed is reasonable. To do this we search our memory for any pertinent information or we seek new information. In science we call searching for new information *performing an experiment.*

Ken O'Donoghue

Italian pottery.

This confirms that lead poisoning is probably the cause of the trouble, but the overall problem is still not solved. David and Susan are likely to die unless they find out where the lead is coming from.

Observation: There is lead in the couple's blood.

Hypothesis: The lead is in their food or drink when they buy it.

Experiment: Find out whether anyone else who shopped at the same store was getting sick (no one was). Also note that moving to a new area did not solve the problem.

Observation: The food they buy is free of lead.

Hypothesis: The dishes they use are the source of the lead poisoning.

Experiment: Find out whether their dishes contain lead. David and Susan learned that lead compounds are often used to put a shiny finish on pottery objects. And laboratory analysis of their Italian pottery dishes showed that lead was present in the glaze.

Observation: Lead is present in their dishes, so the dishes are a possible source of their lead poisoning.

Hypothesis: The lead is leaching into their food.

Experiment: Place a beverage, such as orange juice, in one of the cups and then analyze the beverage for lead. The results showed high levels of lead in drinks that had been in contact with the pottery cups.

After many applications of the scientific method, the problem is solved. We can summarize the answer to the problem (David and Susan's illness) as follows: the Italian pottery they used for everyday dishes contained a lead glaze that contaminated their food and drink with lead. This lead accumulated in their bodies to the point where it interfered seriously with normal functions and produced severe symptoms. This overall explanation, which summarizes the hypotheses that agree with the experimental results, is called a *theory* in science. This explanation accounts for the results of all the experiments performed.*

We could continue to use the scientific method to study other aspects of this problem, such as

What types of food or drink leach the most lead from the dishes?

Do all pottery dishes with lead glazes produce lead poisoning?

As we answer questions using the scientific method, other questions naturally arise. By repeating the three steps over and over, we can come to understand a given phenomenon thoroughly.

*"David" and "Susan" recovered from their lead poisoning and are now publicizing the dangers of using lead-glazed pottery. This happy outcome is the answer to the third part of their overall problem, "Can the disease be cured?" They simply stopped eating from that pottery!

As we will discover in the next section, scientists use these same procedures to study what happens in the world around us. The important point here is that scientific thinking can help you in all parts of your life. It's worthwhile to learn how to think scientifically—whether you want to be a scientist, an auto mechanic, a doctor, a politician, or a poet!

The Scientific Method

OBJECTIVE: To describe the method scientists use to study nature.

In the last section we began to see how the methods of science are used to solve problems. In this section we will further examine this approach.

Science is a framework for gaining and organizing knowledge. Science is not simply a set of facts but also a plan of action—a *procedure* for processing and understanding certain types of information. Although scientific thinking is useful in all aspects of life, in this text we will use it to understand how the natural world operates. The process that lies at the center of scientific inquiry is called the **scientific method.** As we saw in the previous section, it consists of the following steps:

Steps in the Scientific Method

1. *State the problem and collect data (make observations)*. Observations may be *qualitative* (the sky is blue; water is a liquid) or *quantitative* (water boils at 100 °C; a certain chemistry book weighs 4.5 pounds). A qualitative observation does not involve a number. A quantitative observation is called a **measurement** and does involve a number (and a unit, such as pounds or inches). We will discuss measurements in detail in Chapter 2.
2. *Formulate hypotheses*. A hypothesis is a *possible* explanation for the observation.
3. *Perform experiments*. An experiment is something we do to test the hypothesis. We gather new information that allows us to decide whether the hypothesis is supported by the new information we have learned from the experiment. Experiments always produce new observations, and this brings us back to the beginning of the process again.

Quantitative observations involve a number. Qualitative ones do not.

To explain the behavior of a given part of nature, we repeat these steps many times. Gradually we accumulate the knowledge necessary to understand what is going on.

Once we have a set of hypotheses that agrees with our various observations, we assemble them into a theory that is often called a *model*. A **theory** (model) is a set of tested hypotheses that gives an overall explanation of some part of nature (see Figure 1.1).

It is important to distinguish between observations and theories. An observation is something that is witnessed and can be recorded. A theory is an *interpretation*—a possible explanation of *why* nature behaves in a particular way. Theories inevitably change as more information becomes available. For example, the motions of the sun and stars have remained virtually the same over the thousands of years during which humans have been observing them, but our explanations—our theories—have changed greatly since ancient times.

The point is that we don't stop asking questions just because we have devised a theory that seems to account satisfactorily for some aspect of natural behavior. We continue doing experiments to refine our theories. We generally do this by using the theory to make a prediction and then doing an experiment (making a new observation) to see whether the results bear out this prediction.

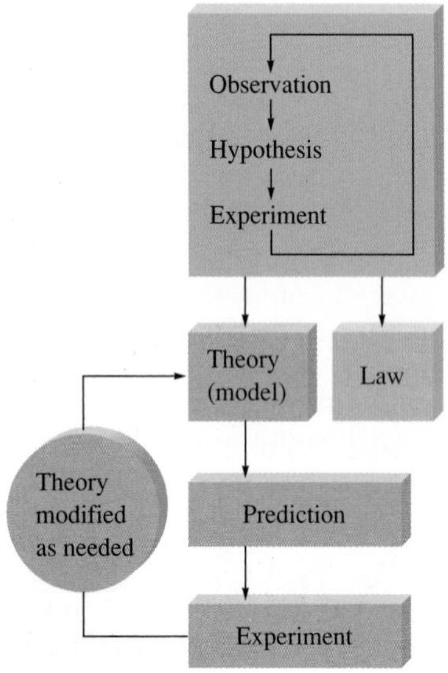

Figure 1.1

The various parts of the scientific method.

Always remember that theories (models) are human inventions. They represent our attempts to explain observed natural behavior in terms of our human experiences. We must continue to do experiments and refine our theories to be consistent with new knowledge if we hope to approach a more nearly complete understanding of nature.

As we observe nature, we often see that the same observation applies to many different systems. For example, studies of innumerable chemical changes have shown that the total mass of the materials involved is the same before and after the change. We often formulate such generally observed behavior into a statement called a **natural law.** The observation that the total mass of materials is not affected by a chemical change in those materials is called the law of conservation of mass.

You must recognize the difference between a law and a theory. A law is a summary of observed (measurable) behavior, whereas a theory is an explanation of behavior. *A law tells what happens; a theory (model) is our attempt to explain why it happens.*

In this section, we have described the scientific method (which is summarized in Figure 1.1) as it might ideally be applied. However, it is important to remember that science does not always progress smoothly and efficiently. Scientists are human. They have prejudices; they misinterpret data; they can become emotionally attached to their theories and thus lose objectivity; and they play politics. Science is affected by profit motives, budgets, fads, wars, and religious beliefs. Galileo, for example, was forced to recant his astronomical observations in the face of strong religious resistance. Lavoisier, the father of modern chemistry, was beheaded because of his political affiliations. And great progress in the chemistry of nitrogen fertilizers resulted from the desire to produce explosives to fight wars. The progress of science is often slowed more by the frailties of humans and their institutions than by the limitations of scientific measuring devices. The scientific method is only as effective as the humans using it. It does not automatically lead to progress.

> Law: A summary of observed behavior.

> Theory: An explanation of behavior.

1.5 Learning Chemistry

OBJECTIVE: To develop successful strategies for learning chemistry.

Chemistry courses have a universal reputation for being difficult. There are some good reasons for this. For one thing, the language of chemistry is unfamiliar in the beginning; many terms and definitions need to be memorized. As with any language, *you must know the vocabulary* before you can communicate effectively. We will try to help you by pointing out those things that need to be memorized.

But memorization is only the beginning. Don't stop there or your experience with chemistry will be frustrating. Be willing to do some thinking, and learn to trust yourself to figure things out. To solve a typical chemistry problem, you must sort through the given information and decide what is really crucial.

It is important to realize that chemical systems tend to be complicated—there are typically many components—and we must make approximations in describing them. Therefore, trial and error play a major role in solving chemical problems. In tackling a complicated system, a practicing chemist really does not expect to be right the first time he or she analyzes the problem. The usual practice is to make several simplifying assumptions and then give it a try. If the answer obtained doesn't make sense, the chemist adjusts the assumptions, using feedback from the first attempt, and tries

Chemistry: An Important Component of Your Education

What is the purpose of education? Because you are spending considerable time, energy, and money to pursue an education, this is an important question.

Some people seem to equate education with the storage of facts in the brain. These people apparently believe that education simply means memorizing the answers to all of life's present and future problems. Although this is clearly unreasonable, many students seem to behave as though this were their guiding principle. These students want to memorize lists of facts and to reproduce them on tests. They regard as unfair any exam questions that require some original thought or some processing of information. Indeed, it might be tempting to reduce education to a simple filling up with facts, because that approach can produce short-term satisfaction for both student and teacher. And of course, storing facts in the brain *is* important. You cannot function without knowing that red means stop, electricity is hazardous, ice is slippery, and so on.

However, mere recall of abstract information, without the ability to process it, makes you little better than a talking encyclopedia. Former students always seem to bring the same message

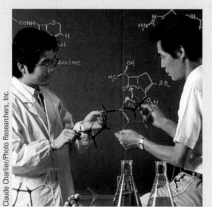

Students pondering the structure of a molecule.

when they return to campus. The characteristics that are most important to their success are a knowledge of the fundamentals of their fields, the ability to recognize and solve problems, and the ability to communicate effectively. They also emphasize the importance of a high level of motivation.

How does studying chemistry help you achieve these characteristics? The fact that chemical systems are complicated is really a blessing, though one that is well disguised. Studying chemistry will not by itself make you a good problem solver, but it can help you develop a positive, aggressive attitude toward problem solving and can help boost your confidence. Learning to "think like a chemist" can be valuable to anyone in any field. In fact, the chemical industry is heavily populated at all levels and in all areas by chemists and chemical engineers. People who were trained as chemical professionals often excel not only in chemical research and production but also in the areas of personnel, marketing, sales, development, finance, and management. The point is that much of what you learn in this course can be applied to any field of endeavor. So be careful not to take too narrow a view of this course. Try to look beyond short-term frustration to long-term benefits. It may not be easy to learn to be a good problem solver, but it's well worth the effort.

again. The point is this: in dealing with chemical systems, do not expect to understand immediately everything that is going on. In fact, it is typical (even for an experienced chemist) *not* to understand at first. Make an attempt to solve the problem and then analyze the feedback. *It is no disaster to make a mistake as long as you learn from it.*

The only way to develop your confidence as a problem solver is to practice solving problems. To help you, this book contains examples worked out in detail. Follow these through carefully, making sure you understand each step. These examples are usually followed by a similar exercise (called a self-check exercise) that you should try on your own (detailed solutions of the self-check exercises are given at the end of each chapter). Use the self-check exercises to test whether you are understanding the material as you go along.

There are questions and problems at the end of each chapter. The questions review the basic concepts of the chapter and give you an opportunity to check whether you properly understand the vocabulary introduced. Some of the problems are really just exercises that are very similar to examples done in the chapter. If you understand the material in the chapter, you should be able to do these exercises in a straightforward way. Other problems require more creativity. These contain a knowledge gap—some unfamiliar territory that you must cross—and call for thought and patience on your part. For this course to be really useful to you, it is important to go beyond the questions and exercises. Life offers us many exercises, routine events that we deal with rather automatically, but the real challenges in life are true problems. This course can help you become a more creative problem solver.

As you do homework, be sure to use the problems correctly. If you cannot do a particular problem, do not immediately look at the solution. Review the relevant material in the text and then try the problem again. Don't be afraid to struggle with a problem. Looking at the solution as soon as you get stuck short-circuits the learning process.

Learning chemistry takes time. Use all the resources available to you and study on a regular basis. Don't expect too much of yourself too soon. You may not understand everything at first, and you may not be able to do many of the problems the first time you try them. This is normal. It doesn't mean you can't learn chemistry. Just remember to keep working and to keep learning from your mistakes, and you will make steady progress.

CHAPTER **1** REVIEW

Key Terms

chemistry (1.2)
scientific method (1.4)
theory (1.4)
natural law (1.4)

F directs you to the *Chemistry in Focus* feature in the chapter
VP indicates visual problems
WL interactive versions of these problems are assignable in OWL

Active Learning Questions

These questions are designed to be considered by groups of students in class. Often these questions work well for introducing a particular topic in class.

1. Discuss how a hypothesis can become a theory. Can a theory become a law? Explain.

2. Make five qualitative and five quantitative observations about the room in which you now sit.

3. List as many chemical reactions you can think of that are part of your everyday life. Explain.

4. Differentiate between a "theory" and a "scientific theory."

5. Describe three situations when you used the scientific method (outside of school) in the past month.

6. Scientific models do not describe reality. They are simplifications and therefore incorrect at some level. So why are models useful?

7. Theories should inspire questions. Discuss a scientific theory you know and the questions it brings up.

8. Describe how you would set up an experiment to test the relationship between completion of assigned homework and the final grade you receive in the course.

9. If all scientists use the scientific method to try to arrive at a better understanding of the world, why do so many debates arise among scientists?

10. As stated in the text, there is no one scientific method. However, making observations, formulating hypotheses, and performing experiments are generally

components of "doing science." Read the following passage, and list any observations, hypotheses, and experiments. Support your answer.

> Joyce and Frank are eating raisins and drinking ginger ale. Frank accidentally drops a raisin into his ginger ale. They both notice that the raisin falls to the bottom of the glass. Soon, the raisin rises to the surface of the ginger ale, and then sinks. Within a couple of minutes, it rises and sinks again. Joyce asks, "I wonder why that happened?" Frank says, "I don't know, but let's see if it works in water." Joyce fills a glass with water and drops the raisin into the glass. After a few minutes, Frank says, "No, it doesn't go up and down in the water." Joyce closely observes the raisins in the two glasses and states, "Look, there are bubbles on the raisins in the ginger ale but not on the raisins in the water." Frank says, "It must be the bubbles that make the raisin rise." Joyce asks, "OK, but then why do they sink again?"

11. In Section 1.3 the statement is made that it is worthwhile for scientists, auto mechanics, doctors, politicians, and poets to take a scientific approach to their professions. Discuss how each of these people could use a scientific approach in his or her profession.

VP 12. As part of a science project, you study traffic patterns in your city at an intersection in the middle of downtown. You set up a device that counts the cars passing through this intersection for a 24-hour period during a weekday. The graph of hourly traffic looks like this.

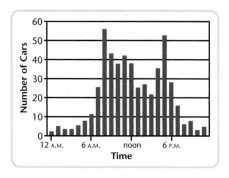

a. At what time(s) does the highest number of cars pass through the intersection?
b. At what time(s) does the lowest number of cars pass through the intersection?
c. Briefly describe the trend in numbers of cars over the course of the day.
d. Provide a hypothesis explaining the trend in numbers of cars over the course of the day.
e. Provide a possible experiment that could test your hypothesis.

VP 13. Confronted with the box shown in the diagram, you wish to discover something about its internal workings. You have no tools and cannot open the box. You pull on rope B, and it moves rather freely. When you pull on rope A, rope C appears to be pulled slightly into the box. When you pull on rope C, rope A almost disappears into the box.*

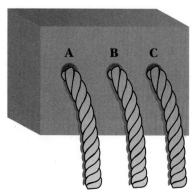

*From Yoder, Suydam, and Snavely, *Chemistry* (New York: Harcourt Brace Jovanovich, 1975), pp. 9–11.

a. Based on these observations, construct a model for the interior mechanism of the box.
b. What further experiments could you do to refine your model?

Questions and Problems

1.1 Chemistry: An Introduction

QUESTIONS

1. Chemistry is an intimidating academic subject for many students. You are not alone if you are afraid of not doing well in this course! Why do you suppose the study of chemistry is so intimidating for many students? What about having to take a chemistry course bothers you? Make a list of your concerns and bring them to class for discussion with your fellow students and your instructor.

2. The first paragraphs in this chapter ask you if you have ever wondered how and why various things in our everyday lives happen the way they do. For your next class meeting, make a list of five similar chemistry-related things for discussion with your instructor and the other students in your class.

3. This section presents several ways our day-to-day lives have been enriched by chemistry. List three materials or processes involving chemistry that you feel have contributed to such an enrichment and explain your choices.

F 4. The "Chemistry in Focus" segment titled *Dr. Ruth—Cotton Hero* discusses the enormous contribution of Dr. Ruth Rogan Benerito to the survival of the cotton fabric industry in the United States. In the discussion, it was mentioned that Dr. Benerito became a chemist when women were not expected to be interested in, or good at, scientific subjects. Has this attitude changed? Among your own friends, approximately how many of your female friends are studying a science? How many plan to pursue a career in science? Discuss.

All even-numbered Questions and Problems have answers in the back of this book and solutions in the Solutions Guide.

1.2 What Is Chemistry?

QUESTIONS

5. This textbook provides a specific definition of chemistry: the study of the materials of which the universe is made and the transformations that these materials undergo. Obviously, such a general definition has to be very broad and nonspecific. From your point of view at this time, how would *you* define chemistry? In your mind, what are "chemicals"? What do "chemists" do?

6. We use chemical reactions in our everyday lives, too, not just in the science laboratory. Give at least five examples of chemical transformations that you use in your daily activities. Indicate what the "chemical" is in each of your examples and how you recognize that a chemical change has taken place.

1.3 Solving Problems Using a Scientific Approach

QUESTIONS

F 7. Read the "Chemistry in Focus" segment *A Mystifying Problem* and discuss how David and Susan analyzed the situation, arriving at the theory that the lead glaze on the pottery was responsible for their symptoms.

8. Being a scientist is very much like being a detective. Detectives such as Sherlock Holmes or Miss Marple perform a very systematic analysis of a crime to solve it, much like a scientist does when addressing a scientific investigation. What are the steps that scientists (or detectives) use to solve problems?

1.4 The Scientific Method

QUESTIONS

9. Why does a scientist make repeated *observations* of phenomena? Is an observation the same as a *theory*? Why (or why not)? Is a *hypothesis* the same as a *theory*? When does a set of hypotheses *become* a theory?

10. Observations may be either qualitative or quantitative. Quantitative observations are usually referred to as *measurements*. List five examples of *qualitative observations* you might make around your home or school. List five examples of *measurements* you might make in everyday life.

11. Several words are used in this section that students sometimes may find hard to distinguish. Write your own definitions of the following terms, and bring them to class for discussion with your instructor and fellow students: *theory, experiment, natural law, hypothesis.*

12. Although, in general, science has advanced our standard of living tremendously, there is sometimes a "dark side" to science. Give an example of the misuse of science and explain how this has had an adverse effect on our lives.

13. Although science *should* lead to solutions to problems that are completely independent of outside forces, very often in history scientific investigations have been influenced by prejudice, profit motives, fads, wars, religious beliefs, and other forces. Your textbook mentions the case of Galileo having to change his theories about astronomy based on intervention by religious authorities. Can you give three additional examples of how scientific investigations have been similarly influenced by nonscientific forces?

1.5 Learning Chemistry

QUESTIONS

14. Although reviewing your lecture notes and reading your textbook are important, why does the study of chemistry depend so much on problem solving? Can you learn to solve problems yourself just by looking at the solved examples in your textbook or study guide? Discuss.

15. Why is the ability to solve problems important in the study of chemistry? Why is it that the *method* used to attack a problem is as important as the answer to the problem itself?

16. Students approaching the study of chemistry must learn certain basic facts (such as the names and symbols of the most common elements), but it is much more important that they learn to think critically and to go beyond the specific examples discussed in class or in the textbook. Explain how learning to do this might be helpful in any career, even one far removed from chemistry.

F 17. The "Chemistry in Focus" segment *Chemistry: An Important Component of Your Education* discusses how studying chemistry can be beneficial not only in your chemistry courses but in your studies in general. What are some characteristics of a good student, and how does studying chemistry help achieve these characteristics?

All even-numbered Questions and Problems have answers in the back of this book and solutions in the Solutions Guide.

2

Measurements and Calculations

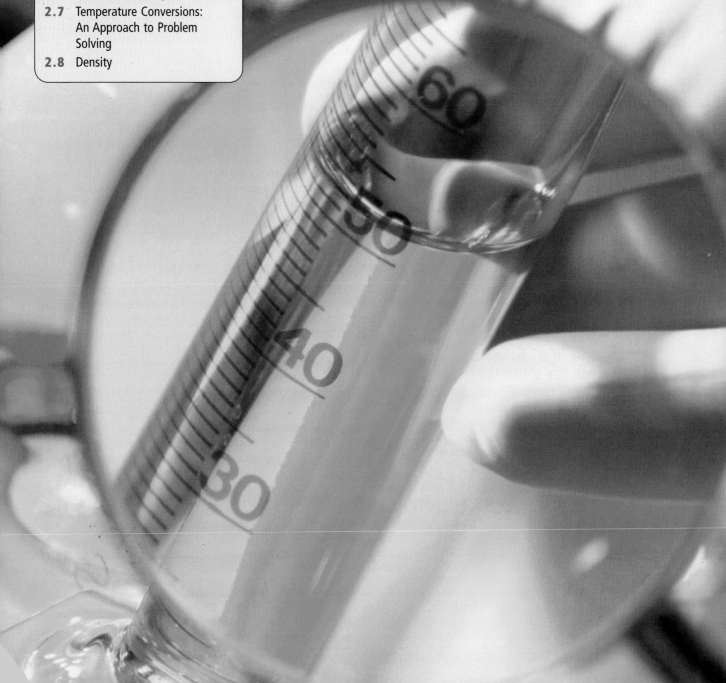

● An enlarged view of a graduated cylinder
(Masterfile)

OWL Sign in to OWL at **www.cengage.com/owl** to view tutoritals and simulations, develop problem-solving skills, and complete online homework assigned by your professor.

As we pointed out in Chapter 1, making observations is a key part of the scientific process. Sometimes observations are *qualitative* ("the substance is a yellow solid") and sometimes they are *quantitative* ("the substance weighs 4.3 grams"). A quantitative observation is called a **measurement.** Measurements are very important in our daily lives. For example, we pay for gasoline by the gallon, so the gas pump must accurately measure the gas delivered to our fuel tank. The efficiency of the modern automobile engine depends on various measurements, including the amount of oxygen in the exhaust gases, the temperature of the coolant, and the pressure of the lubricating oil. In addition, cars with traction control systems have devices to measure and compare the rates of rotation of all four wheels. As we will see in the "Chemistry in Focus" discussion in this chapter, measuring devices have become very sophisticated in dealing with our fast-moving and complicated society.

As we will discuss in this chapter, a measurement always consists of two parts: a number and a unit. Both parts are necessary to make the measurement meaningful. For example, suppose a friend tells you that she saw a bug 5 long. This statement is meaningless as it stands. Five what? If it's 5 millimeters, the bug is quite small. If it's 5 centimeters, the bug is quite large. If it's 5 meters, run for cover!

The point is that for a measurement to be meaningful, it must consist of both a number and a unit that tells us the scale being used.

In this chapter we will consider the characteristics of measurements and the calculations that involve measurements.

A gas pump measures the amount of gasoline delivered.

2.1 Scientific Notation

OBJECTIVE: To show how very large or very small numbers can be expressed as the product of a number between 1 and 10 and a power of 10.

A measurement must always consist of a number *and* a unit.

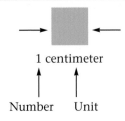

1 centimeter

Number   Unit

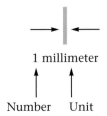

1 millimeter

Number   Unit

The numbers associated with scientific measurements are often very large or very small. For example, the distance from the earth to the sun is approximately 93,000,000 (93 million) miles. Written out, this number is rather bulky. Scientific notation is a method for making very large or very small numbers more compact and easier to write.

To see how this is done, consider the number 125, which can be written as the product

$$125 = 1.25 \times 100$$

Because $100 = 10 \times 10 = 10^2$, we can write

$$125 = 1.25 \times 100 = 1.25 \times 10^2$$

Similarly, the number 1700 can be written

$$1700 = 1.7 \times 1000$$

and because $1000 = 10 \times 10 \times 10 = 10^3$, we can write

$$1700 = 1.7 \times 1000 = 1.7 \times 10^3$$

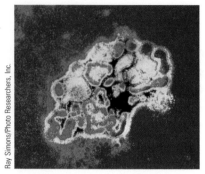

When describing very small distances, such as the diameter of a swine flu virus (shown here magnified 16,537 times), it is convenient to use scientific notation.

Scientific notation simply expresses a number as *a product of a number between 1 and 10 and the appropriate power of 10.* For example, the number 93,000,000 can be expressed as

$$93{,}000{,}000 = 9.3 \times 10{,}000{,}000 = 9.3 \times 10^7$$

Number   Appropriate
between   power of 10
1 and 10 $(10{,}000{,}000 = 10^7)$

The easiest way to determine the appropriate power of 10 for scientific notation is to start with the number being represented and count the number of places the decimal point must be moved to obtain a number between 1 and 10. For example, for the number

$$9\ \underset{7}{\overset{\frown}{3}}\ \underset{6}{\overset{\frown}{0}}\ \underset{5}{\overset{\frown}{0}}\ \underset{4}{\overset{\frown}{0}}\ \underset{3}{\overset{\frown}{0}}\ \underset{2}{\overset{\frown}{0}}\ \underset{1}{\overset{\frown}{0}}$$

we must move the decimal point seven places to the left to get 9.3 (a number between 1 and 10). To compensate for every move of the decimal point to the left, we must multiply by 10. That is, each time we move the decimal point to the left, we make the number smaller by one power of 10. So for each move of the decimal point to the left, we must multiply by 10 to restore the number to its original magnitude. Thus moving the decimal point seven places to the left means we must multiply 9.3 by 10 seven times, which equals 10^7:

$$93{,}000{,}000 = 9.3 \times 10^7$$

We moved the decimal point seven
places to the left, so we need
10^7 to compensate.

> **MATH SKILL BUILDER**
> Keep one digit to the left of the decimal point.

> **MATH SKILL BUILDER**
> Moving the decimal point to the left requires a positive exponent.

Remember: whenever the decimal point is moved to the *left,* the exponent of 10 is *positive.*

We can represent numbers smaller than 1 by using the same convention, but in this case the power of 10 is negative. For example, for the number 0.010 we must move the decimal point two places to the right to obtain a number between 1 and 10:

$$0\ .\ \underset{1}{\overset{\smile}{0}}\ \underset{2}{\overset{\smile}{1}}\ 0$$

> **MATH SKILL BUILDER**
> Moving the decimal point to the right requires a negative exponent.

This requires an exponent of -2, so $0.010 = 1.0 \times 10^{-2}$. Remember: whenever the decimal point is moved to the *right,* the exponent of 10 is *negative.*

Next consider the number 0.000167. In this case we must move the decimal point four places to the right to obtain 1.67 (a number between 1 and 10):

$$0\ .\ \underset{1}{\overset{\smile}{0}}\ \underset{2}{\overset{\smile}{0}}\ \underset{3}{\overset{\smile}{0}}\ \underset{4}{\overset{\smile}{1}}\ 6\ 7$$

> **MATH SKILL BUILDER**
> Read the Appendix if you need a further discussion of exponents and scientific notation.

Moving the decimal point four places to the right requires an exponent of -4. Therefore,

$$0.000167 = 1.67 \times 10^{-4}$$

We moved the decimal
point four places to the right.

We summarize these procedures below.

> ### Using Scientific Notation
>
> - Any number can be represented as the product of a number between 1 and 10 and a power of 10 (either positive or negative).
> - The power of 10 depends on the number of places the decimal point is moved and in which direction. The *number of places* the decimal point is moved determines the *power of 10*. The *direction* of the move determines whether the power of 10 is *positive* or *negative.* If the decimal point is moved to the left, the power of 10 is positive; if the decimal point is moved to the right, the power of 10 is negative.

MATH SKILL BUILDER
$100 = 1.0 \times 10^2$
$0.010 = 1.0 \times 10^{-2}$

MATH SKILL BUILDER
Left Is Positive; remember LIP.

EXAMPLE 2.1 | **Scientific Notation: Powers of 10 (Positive)**

MATH SKILL BUILDER
A number that is greater than 1 will always have a positive exponent when written in scientific notation.

Represent the following numbers in scientific notation.

a. 238,000

b. 1,500,000

SOLUTION

a. First we move the decimal point until we have a number between 1 and 10, in this case 2.38.

2 3 8 0 0 0
  5 4 3 2 1   The decimal point was moved five places to the left.

Because we moved the decimal point five places to the left, the power of 10 is positive 5. Thus $238,000 = 2.38 \times 10^5$.

b. 1 5 0 0 0 0
  6 5 4 3 2 1   The decimal point was moved six places to the left, so the power of 10 is 6.

Thus $1,500,000 = 1.5 \times 10^6$. ■

EXAMPLE 2.2 | **Scientific Notation: Powers of 10 (Negative)**

MATH SKILL BUILDER
A number that is less than 1 will always have a negative exponent when written in scientific notation.

Represent the following numbers in scientific notation.

a. 0.00043

b. 0.089

SOLUTION

a. First we move the decimal point until we have a number between 1 and 10, in this case 4.3.

0 . 0 0 0 4 3
    1 2 3 4   The decimal point was moved four places to the right.

Because we moved the decimal point four places to the right, the power of 10 is negative 4. Thus $0.00043 = 4.3 \times 10^{-4}$.

b. 0.089

1 2

The power of 10 is negative 2 because the decimal point was moved two places to the right.

Thus $0.089 = 8.9 \times 10^{-2}$.

Self-Check   EXERCISE 2.1   Write the numbers 357 and 0.0055 in scientific notation. If you are having difficulty with scientific notation at this point, reread the Appendix.

See Problems 2.5 through 2.14. ■

2.2 Units

OBJECTIVE: To learn the English, metric, and SI systems of measurement.

The **units** part of a measurement tells us what *scale* or *standard* is being used to represent the results of the measurement. From the earliest days of civilization, trade has required common units. For example, if a farmer from one region wanted to trade some of his grain for the gold of a miner who lived in another region, the two people had to have common standards (units) for measuring the amount of the grain and the weight of the gold.

The need for common units also applies to scientists, who measure quantities such as mass, length, time, and temperature. If every scientist had her or his own personal set of units, complete chaos would result. Unfortunately, although standard systems of units did arise, different systems were adopted in different parts of the world. The two most widely used systems are the **English system** used in the United States and the **metric system** used in most of the rest of the industrialized world.

The metric system has long been preferred for most scientific work. In 1960 an international agreement set up a comprehensive system of units called the **International System** (*le Système Internationale* in French), or **SI.** The SI units are based on the metric system and units derived from the metric system. The most important fundamental SI units are listed in Table 2.1. Later in this chapter we will discuss how to manipulate some of these units.

Because the fundamental units are not always a convenient size, the SI system uses prefixes to change the size of the unit. The most commonly used prefixes are listed in Table 2.2. Although the fundamental unit for length is the meter (m), we can also use the decimeter (dm), which represents one-tenth (0.1) of a meter; the centimeter (cm), which represents one one-hundredth (0.01) of a meter; the millimeter (mm), which represents one one-thousandth (0.001) of a meter; and so on. For example, it's much more convenient to specify the diameter of a certain contact lens as 1.0 cm than as 1.0×10^{-2} m.

Table 2.1	Some Fundamental SI Units	
Physical Quantity	**Name of Unit**	**Abbreviation**
mass	kilogram	kg
length	meter	m
time	second	s
temperature	kelvin	K

Critical Units!

How important are conversions from one unit to another? If you ask the National Aeronautics and Space Administration (NASA), very important! In 1999 NASA lost a $125 million Mars Climate Orbiter because of a failure to convert from English to metric units.

The problem arose because two teams working on the Mars mission were using different sets of units. NASA's scientists at the Jet Propulsion Laboratory in Pasadena, California, assumed that the thrust data for the rockets on the Orbiter they received from Lockheed Martin Astronautics in Denver, which built the spacecraft, were in metric units. In reality, the units were English. As a result the Orbiter dipped 100 kilometers lower into the Mars atmosphere than planned and the friction from the atmosphere caused the craft to burn up.

NASA's mistake refueled the controversy over whether Congress should require the United States to switch to the metric system. About 95% of the world now uses the metric system, and the United States is slowly switching from English to metric. For example, the automobile industry has adopted metric fasteners and we buy our soda in two-liter bottles.

Units can be very important. In fact, they can mean the difference between life and death on some occasions. In 1983, for example, a Canadian jetliner almost ran out of fuel when someone pumped 22,300 pounds of fuel into the aircraft instead of 22,300 kilograms. Remember to watch your units!

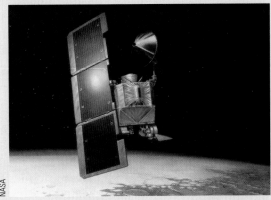

Artist's conception of the lost Mars Climate Orbiter.

Table 2.2	The Commonly Used Prefixes in the Metric System		
Prefix	Symbol	Meaning	Power of 10 for Scientific Notation
mega	M	1,000,000	10^6
kilo	k	1000	10^3
deci	d	0.1	10^{-1}
centi	c	0.01	10^{-2}
milli	m	0.001	10^{-3}
micro	μ	0.000001	10^{-6}
nano	n	0.000000001	10^{-9}

Measurements consist of both a number and a unit, and both are crucial. Just as you would not report a measurement without a numerical value, you would not report a measurement without a unit. You already use units in your daily life, whether you tell somebody, "Let's meet in one hour" (hour is the unit), or you and your friends order two pizzas for dinner (pizza is the unit).

2.3 Measurements of Length, Volume, and Mass

OBJECTIVE: To understand the metric system for measuring length, volume, and mass.

The fundamental SI unit of length is the **meter,** which is a little longer than a yard (1 meter = 39.37 inches). In the metric system fractions of a meter or multiples of a meter can be expressed by powers of 10, as summarized in Table 2.3.

The English and metric systems are compared on the ruler shown in Figure 2.1. Note that

$$1 \text{ inch} = 2.54 \text{ centimeters}$$

Other English–metric equivalences are given in Section 2.6.

Volume is the amount of three-dimensional space occupied by a substance. The fundamental unit of volume in the SI system is based on the volume of a cube that measures 1 meter in each of the three directions. That is, each edge of the cube is 1 meter in length. The volume of this cube is

$$1 \text{ m} \times 1 \text{ m} \times 1 \text{ m} = (1 \text{ m})^3 = 1 \text{ m}^3$$

or, in words, one cubic meter.

In Figure 2.2 this cube is divided into 1000 smaller cubes. Each of these small cubes represents a volume of 1 dm^3, which is commonly called the **liter** (rhymes with "meter" and is slightly larger than a quart) and abbreviated L.

The meter was originally defined, in the eighteenth century, as one ten-millionth of the distance from the equator to the North Pole and then, in the late nineteenth century, as the distance between two parallel marks on a special metal bar stored in a vault in Paris. More recently, for accuracy and convenience, a definition expressed in terms of light waves has been adopted.

Table 2.3	The Metric System for Measuring Length	
Unit	Symbol	Meter Equivalent
kilometer	km	1000 m or 10^3 m
meter	m	1 m
decimeter	dm	0.1 m or 10^{-1} m
centimeter	cm	0.01 m or 10^{-2} m
millimeter	mm	0.001 m or 10^{-3} m
micrometer	μm	0.000001 m or 10^{-6} m
nanometer	nm	0.000000001 m or 10^{-9} m

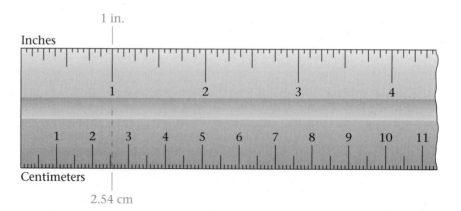

Figure 2.1

Comparison of English and metric units for length on a ruler.

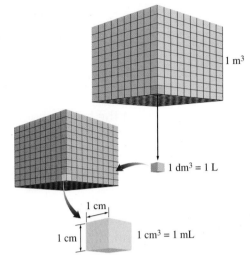

Figure 2.2

The largest drawing represents a cube that has sides 1 m in length and a volume of 1 m³. The middle-size cube has sides 1 dm in length and a volume of 1 dm³, or 1 L. The smallest cube has sides 1 cm in length and a volume of 1 cm³, or 1 mL.

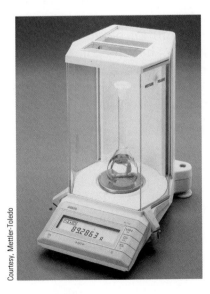

Figure 2.3

A 100-mL graduated cylinder.

The cube with a volume of 1 dm³ (1 liter) can in turn be broken into 1000 smaller cubes, each representing a volume of 1 cm³. This means that each liter contains 1000 cm³. One cubic centimeter is called a **milliliter** (abbreviated mL), a unit of volume used very commonly in chemistry. This relationship is summarized in Table 2.4.

The *graduated cylinder* (see Figure 2.3), commonly used in chemical laboratories for measuring the volumes of liquids, is marked off in convenient units of volume (usually milliliters). The graduated cylinder is filled to the desired volume with the liquid, which then can be poured out.

Another important measurable quantity is **mass,** which can be defined as the quantity of matter present in an object. The fundamental SI unit of mass is the **kilogram.** Because the metric system, which existed before the SI system, used the gram as the fundamental unit, the prefixes for the various mass units are based on the **gram,** as shown in Table 2.5.

In the laboratory we determine the mass of an object by using a balance. A balance compares the mass of the object to a set of standard masses ("weights"). For example, the mass of an object can be determined by using a single-pan balance (Figure 2.4).

To help you get a feeling for the common units of length, volume, and mass, some familiar objects are described in Table 2.6.

Figure 2.4

An electronic analytical balance used in chemistry labs.

Table 2.4	The Relationship of the Liter and Milliliter	
Unit	Symbol	Equivalence
liter	L	$1 \text{ L} = 1000 \text{ mL}$
milliliter	mL	$\frac{1}{1000} \text{ L} = 10^{-3} \text{ L} = 1 \text{ mL}$

Table 2.5	The Most Commonly Used Metric Units for Mass	
Unit	Symbol	Gram Equivalent
kilogram	kg	$1000 \text{ g} = 10^3 \text{ g} = 1 \text{ kg}$
gram	g	1 g
milligram	mg	$0.001 \text{ g} = 10^{-3} \text{ g} = 1 \text{ mg}$

Measurement: Past, Present, and Future

Measurement lies at the heart of doing science. We obtain the data for formulating laws and testing theories by doing measurements. Measurements also have very practical importance; they tell us if our drinking water is safe, whether we are anemic, and the exact amount of gasoline we put in our cars at the filling station.

Although the fundamental measuring devices we consider in this chapter are still widely used, new measuring techniques are being developed every day to meet the challenges of our increasingly sophisticated world. For example, engines in modern automobiles have oxygen sensors that analyze the oxygen content in the exhaust gases. This information is sent to the computer that controls the engine functions so that instantaneous adjustments can be made in spark timing and air–fuel mixtures to provide efficient power with minimum air pollution.

As another example, consider airline safety: How do we rapidly, conveniently, and accurately determine whether a given piece of baggage contains an explosive device? A thorough hand-search of each piece of luggage is out of the question. Scientists are now developing a screening procedure that bombards the luggage with high-

Ben Osborne/Stone/Getty Images

A pollution control officer measuring the oxygen content of river water.

energy particles that cause any substance present to emit radiation characteristic of that substance. This radiation is monitored to identify luggage with unusually large quantities of nitrogen, because most chemical explosives are based on compounds containing nitrogen.

Scientists are also examining the natural world to find supersensitive detectors because many organisms are sensitive to tiny amounts of chemicals in their environments—recall, for example, the sensitive noses of bloodhounds. One of these natural measuring devices uses the sensory hairs from Hawaiian red swimming crabs, which are connected to electrical analyzers and used to detect hormones down to levels of 10^{-8} g/L. Likewise, tissues from pineapple cores can be used to detect tiny amounts of hydrogen peroxide.

These types of advances in measuring devices have led to an unexpected problem: detecting all kinds of substances in our food and drinking water scares us. Although these substances were always there, we didn't worry so much when we couldn't detect them. Now that we know they are present what should we do about them? How can we assess whether these trace substances are harmful or benign? Risk assessment has become much more complicated as our sophistication in taking measurements has increased.

Table 2.6	Some Examples of Commonly Used Units
length	A dime is 1 mm thick.
	A quarter is 2.5 cm in diameter.
	The average height of an adult man is 1.8 m.
mass	A nickel has a mass of about 5 g.
	A 120-lb woman has a mass of about 55 kg.
volume	A 12-oz can of soda has a volume of about 360 mL.
	A half gallon of milk is equal to about 2 L of milk.

Uncertainty in Measurement

OBJECTIVES: To understand how uncertainty in a measurement arises. • To learn to indicate a measurement's uncertainty by using significant figures.

When you measure the amount of something by counting, the measurement is exact. For example, if you asked your friend to buy four apples from the store and she came back with three or five apples, you would be surprised. However, measurements are not always exact. For example, whenever a measurement is made with a device such as a ruler or a graduated cylinder, an estimate is required. We can illustrate this by measuring the pin shown in Figure 2.5a. We can see from the ruler that the pin is a little longer than 2.8 cm and a little shorter than 2.9 cm. Because there are no graduations on the ruler between 2.8 and 2.9, we must estimate the pin's length between 2.8 and 2.9 cm. We do this by *imagining* that the distance between 2.8 and 2.9 is broken into 10 equal divisions (Figure 2.5b) and estimating to which division the end of the pin reaches. The end of the pin appears to come about halfway between 2.8 and 2.9, which corresponds to 5 of our 10 imaginary divisions. So we estimate the pin's length as 2.85 cm. The result of our measurement is that the pin is approximately 2.85 cm in length, but we had to rely on a visual estimate, so it might actually be 2.84 or 2.86 cm.

Because the last number is based on a visual estimate, it may be different when another person makes the same measurement. For example, if five different people measured the pin, the results might be

A student performing a titration in the laboratory.

Person	Result of Measurement
1	2.85 cm
2	2.84 cm
3	2.86 cm
4	2.85 cm
5	2.86 cm

Note that the first two digits in each measurement are the same regardless of who made the measurement; these are called the *certain* numbers of the measurement. However, the third digit is estimated and can vary; it is called an *uncertain* number. When one is making a measurement, the custom is to record all of the certain numbers plus the *first* uncertain number. It would not make any sense to try to measure the pin to the third decimal place (thousandths of a centimeter), because this ruler requires an estimate of even the second decimal place (hundredths of a centimeter).

It is very important to realize that *a measurement always has some degree of uncertainty.* The uncertainty of a measurement depends on the

> Every measurement has some degree of uncertainty.

Andrew Lambert/Leslie Garland Picture Library/Alamy Images

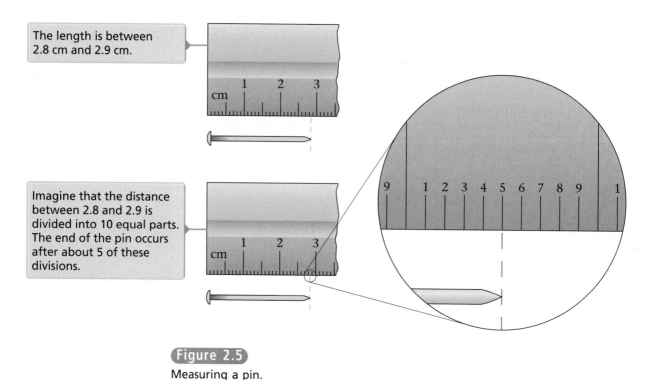

The length is between 2.8 cm and 2.9 cm.

Imagine that the distance between 2.8 and 2.9 is divided into 10 equal parts. The end of the pin occurs after about 5 of these divisions.

Figure 2.5

Measuring a pin.

measuring device. For example, if the ruler in Figure 2.5 had marks indicating hundredths of a centimeter, the uncertainty in the measurement of the pin would occur in the thousandths place rather than the hundredths place, but some uncertainty would still exist.

The numbers recorded in a measurement (all the certain numbers plus the first uncertain number) are called **significant figures.** The number of significant figures for a given measurement is determined by the inherent uncertainty of the measuring device. For example, the ruler used to measure the pin can give results only to hundredths of a centimeter. Thus, when we record the significant figures for a measurement, we automatically give information about the uncertainty in a measurement. The uncertainty in the last number (the estimated number) is usually assumed to be ± 1 unless otherwise indicated. For example, the measurement 1.86 kilograms can be interpreted as 1.86 ± 0.01 kilograms, where the symbol $\pm$ means plus or minus. That is, it could be 1.86 kg − 0.01 kg = 1.85 kg or 1.86 kg + 0.01 kg = 1.87 kg.

2.5 Significant Figures

OBJECTIVE: To learn to determine the number of significant figures in a calculated result.

We have seen that any measurement involves an estimate and thus is uncertain to some extent. We signify the degree of certainty for a particular measurement by the number of significant figures we record.

Because doing chemistry requires many types of calculations, we must consider what happens when we do arithmetic with numbers that contain uncertainties. It is important that we know the degree of uncertainty in the final result. Although we will not discuss the process here, mathematicians have studied how uncertainty accumulates and have designed a set of rules to determine how many significant figures the result of a calculation should have. You should follow these rules whenever you carry out a calculation. The first thing we need to do is learn how to count the significant figures in a given number. To do this we use the following rules:

Rules for Counting Significant Figures

1. *Nonzero integers.* Nonzero integers *always* count as significant figures. For example, the number 1457 has four nonzero integers, all of which count as significant figures.
2. *Zeros.* There are three classes of zeros:
   a. *Leading zeros* are zeros that *precede* all of the nonzero digits. They *never* count as significant figures. For example, in the number 0.0025, the three zeros simply indicate the position of the decimal point. The number has only two significant figures, the 2 and the 5.
   b. *Captive zeros* are zeros that fall *between* nonzero digits. They *always* count as significant figures. For example, the number 1.008 has four significant figures.
   c. *Trailing zeros* are zeros at the *right end* of the number. They are significant only if the number is written with a decimal point. The number one hundred written as 100 has only one significant figure, but written as 100., it has three significant figures.
3. *Exact numbers.* Often calculations involve numbers that were not obtained using measuring devices but were determined by counting: 10 experiments, 3 apples, 8 molecules. Such numbers are called *exact numbers.* They can be assumed to have an unlimited number of significant figures. Exact numbers can also arise from definitions. For example, 1 inch is defined as *exactly* 2.54 centimeters. Thus in the statement 1 in. = 2.54 cm, neither 2.54 nor 1 limits the number of significant figures when it is used in a calculation.

MATH SKILL BUILDER
Leading zeros are never significant figures.

MATH SKILL BUILDER
Captive zeros are always significant figures.

MATH SKILL BUILDER
Trailing zeros are sometimes significant figures.

MATH SKILL BUILDER
Exact numbers never limit the number of significant figures in a calculation.

MATH SKILL BUILDER
Significant figures are easily indicated by scientific notation.

Rules for counting significant figures also apply to numbers written in scientific notation. For example, the number 100. can also be written as 1.00×10^2, and both versions have three significant figures. Scientific notation offers two major advantages: the number of significant figures can be indicated easily, and fewer zeros are needed to write a very large or a very small number. For example, the number 0.000060 is much more conveniently represented as 6.0×10^{-5}, and the number has two significant figures, written in either form.

EXAMPLE 2.3 | Counting Significant Figures

Give the number of significant figures for each of the following measurements.

a. A sample of orange juice contains 0.0108 g of vitamin C.

b. A forensic chemist in a crime lab weighs a single hair and records its mass as 0.0050060 g.

c. The distance between two points was found to be 5.030×10^3 ft.

d. In yesterday's bicycle race, 110 riders started but only 60 finished.

SOLUTION

a. The number contains three significant figures. The zeros to the left of the 1 are leading zeros and are not significant, but the remaining zero (a captive zero) is significant.

b. The number contains five significant figures. The leading zeros (to the left of the 5) are not significant. The captive zeros between the 5 and the 6 are significant, and the trailing zero to the right of the 6 is significant because the number contains a decimal point.

c. This number has four significant figures. Both zeros in 5.030 are significant.

d. Both numbers are exact (they were obtained by counting the riders). Thus these numbers have an unlimited number of significant figures.

Self-Check   EXERCISE 2.2   Give the number of significant figures for each of the following measurements.

a. 0.00100 m

b. 2.0800×10^2 L

c. 480 Corvettes

See Problems 2.33 and 2.34. ∎

▶ Rounding Off Numbers

When you perform a calculation on your calculator, the number of digits displayed is usually greater than the number of significant figures that the result should possess. So you must "round off" the number (reduce it to fewer digits). The rules for **rounding off** follow.

> These rules reflect the way calculators round off.

Rules for Rounding Off

1. If the digit to be removed
   a. is less than 5, the preceding digit stays the same. For example, 1.33 rounds to 1.3.
   b. is equal to or greater than 5, the preceding digit is increased by 1. For example, 1.36 rounds to 1.4, and 3.15 rounds to 3.2.
2. In a series of calculations, carry the extra digits through to the final result and *then* round off.* This means that you should carry all of the digits that show on your calculator until you arrive at the final number (the answer) and then round off, using the procedures in Rule 1.

We need to make one more point about rounding off to the correct number of significant figures. Suppose the number 4.348 needs to be

---

*This practice will not be followed in the worked-out examples in this text, because we want to show the correct number of significant figures in each step of the example.

rounded to two significant figures. In doing this, we look *only* at the *first number* to the right of the 3:

4.348
↑
Look at this
number to round off
to two significant figures.

The number is rounded to 4.3 because 4 is less than 5. It is incorrect to round sequentially. For example, do *not* round the 4 to 5 to give 4.35 and then round the 3 to 4 to give 4.4.

When rounding off, *use only the first number to the right of the last significant figure.*

▶ Determining Significant Figures in Calculations

Next we will learn how to determine the correct number of significant figures in the result of a calculation. To do this we will use the following rules.

Rules for Using Significant Figures in Calculations

1. For *multiplication* or *division*, the number of significant figures in the result is the same as that in the measurement with the *smallest number* of significant figures. We say this measurement is *limiting*, because it limits the number of significant figures in the result. For example, consider this calculation:

$$4.56 \times 1.4 = 6.384 \boxed{\text{Round off}} \Rightarrow 6.4$$

Three significant figures   Limiting (two significant figures)   Two significant figures

Because 1.4 has only two significant figures, it limits the result to two significant figures. Thus the product is correctly written as 6.4, which has two significant figures. Consider another example. In the division $\dfrac{8.315}{298}$,

how many significant figures should appear in the answer? Because 8.315 has four significant figures, the number 298 (with three significant figures) limits the result. The calculation is correctly represented as

Four significant figures

$$\frac{8.315}{298} = 0.0279027 \boxed{\text{Round off}} \Rightarrow 2.79 \times 10^{-2}$$

Limiting (three significant figures)   Result shown on calculator   Three significant figures

(continued)

2. For *addition* or *subtraction,* the limiting term is the one with the smallest number of decimal places. For example, consider the following sum:

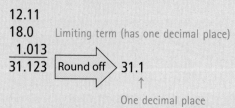

$$
\begin{array}{r}
12.11 \\
18.0 \quad \text{Limiting term (has one decimal place)} \\
\underline{1.013} \\
31.123 \quad \boxed{\text{Round off}} \Rightarrow 31.1 \\
\uparrow \\
\text{One decimal place}
\end{array}
$$

Why is the answer limited by the term with the smallest number of decimal places? Recall that the last digit reported in a measurement is actually an uncertain number. Although 18, 18.0, and 18.00 are treated as the same quantities by your calculator, they are different to a scientist. The problem above can be thought of as follows:

$$
\begin{array}{r}
12.11? \text{ mL} \\
18.0?? \text{ mL} \\
\underline{1.013 \text{ mL}} \\
31.1?? \text{ mL}
\end{array}
$$

Because the term 18.0 is reported only to the tenths place, our answer must be reported this way as well.

The correct result is 31.1 (it is limited to one decimal place because 18.0 has only one decimal place). Consider another example:

$$
\begin{array}{r}
0.6875 \\
\underline{-0.1} \quad \text{Limiting term (one decimal place)} \\
0.5875 \\
\boxed{\text{Round off}} \Rightarrow 0.6
\end{array}
$$

Note that *for multiplication and division, significant figures are counted. For addition and subtraction, the decimal places are counted.*

Now we will put together the things you have learned about significant figures by considering some mathematical operations in the following examples.

EXAMPLE 2.4 | Counting Significant Figures in Calculations

Without performing the calculations, tell how many significant figures each answer should contain.

a. $\begin{array}{r} 5.19 \\ 1.9 \\ \underline{+0.842} \end{array}$ b. $1081 - 7.25$ c. 2.3×3.14

d. the total cost of 3 boxes of candy at \$2.50 a box

SOLUTION

a. The answer will have one digit after the decimal place. The limiting number is 1.9, which has one decimal place, so the answer has two significant figures.

b. The answer will have no digits after the decimal point. The number 1081 has no digits to the right of the decimal point and limits the result, so the answer has four significant figures.

c. The answer will have two significant figures because the number 2.3 has only two significant figures (3.14 has three).

d. The answer will have three significant figures. The limiting factor is 2.50 because 3 (boxes of candy) is an exact number. ■

EXAMPLE 2.5 | Calculations Using Significant Figures

Carry out the following mathematical operations and give each result to the correct number of significant figures.

a. 5.18×0.0208

b. $(3.60 \times 10^{-3}) \times (8.123) \div 4.3$

c. $21 + 13.8 + 130.36$

d. $116.8 - 0.33$

e. $(1.33 \times 2.8) + 8.41$

SOLUTION

Limiting terms   Round to this digit.
↓

a. $5.18 \times 0.0208 = 0.107744 \Longrightarrow 0.108$

The answer should contain three significant figures because each number being multiplied has three significant figures (Rule 1). The 7 is rounded to 8 because the following digit is greater than 5.

Round to this digit.
↓

b. $\dfrac{(3.60 \times 10^{-3})(8.123)}{4.3} = 6.8006 \times 10^{-3} \Longrightarrow 6.8 \times 10^{-3}$

↑
Limiting term

MATH SKILL BUILDER
When we multiply and divide in a problem, perform all calculations before rounding the answer to the correct number of significant figures.

Because 4.3 has the least number of significant figures (two), the result should have two significant figures (Rule 1).

c.
$$\begin{array}{r} 21 \\ 13.8 \\ +130.36 \\ \hline 165.16 \end{array} \Longrightarrow 165$$

In this case 21 is limiting (there are no digits after the decimal point). Thus the answer must have no digits after the decimal point, in accordance with the rule for addition (Rule 2).

MATH SKILL BUILDER
When we multiply (or divide) and then add (or subtract) in a problem, round the first answer from the first operation (in this case, multiplication) before performing the next operation (in this case, addition). We need to know the correct number of decimal places.

d.
$$\begin{array}{r} 116.8 \\ - \;\; 0.33 \\ \hline 116.47 \end{array} \Longrightarrow 116.5$$

Because 116.8 has only one decimal place, the answer must have only one decimal place (Rule 2). The 4 is rounded up to 5 because the digit to the right (7) is greater than 5.

e. $1.33 \times 2.8 = 3.724 \Longrightarrow 3.7$

$$\begin{array}{r} 3.7 \leftarrow \text{Limiting term} \\ + \; 8.41 \\ \hline 12.11 \end{array} \Longrightarrow 12.1$$

Note that in this case we multiplied and then rounded the result to the correct number of significant figures before we performed the addition so that we would know the correct number of decimal places.

Self-Check EXERCISE 2.3

Give the answer for each calculation to the correct number of significant figures.

a. 12.6×0.53

b. $(12.6 \times 0.53) - 4.59$

c. $(25.36 - 4.15) \div 2.317$

See Problems 2.47 through 2.52. ■

2.6 Problem Solving and Dimensional Analysis

OBJECTIVE: To learn how dimensional analysis can be used to solve various types of problems.

Suppose that the boss at the store where you work on weekends asks you to pick up 2 dozen doughnuts on the way to work. However, you find that the doughnut shop sells by the doughnut. How many doughnuts do you need?

This "problem" is an example of something you encounter all the time: converting from one unit of measurement to another. Examples of this occur in cooking (The recipe calls for 3 cups of cream, which is sold in pints. How many pints do I buy?); traveling (The purse costs 250 pesos. How much is that in dollars?); sports (A recent Tour de France bicycle race was 3215 kilometers long. How many miles is that?); and many other areas.

How do we convert from one unit of measurement to another? Let's explore this process by using the doughnut problem.

$$\text{2 dozen doughnuts} = \text{? individual doughnuts}$$

where ? represents a number you don't know yet. The essential information you must have is the definition of a dozen:

$$\text{1 dozen} = 12$$

You can use this information to make the needed conversion as follows:

$$\text{2 dozen doughnuts} \times \frac{12}{\text{1 dozen}} = 24 \text{ doughnuts}$$

You need to buy 24 doughnuts.

Note two important things about this process.

MATH SKILL BUILDER
Since 1 dozen = 12, when we multiply by $\frac{12}{\text{1 dozen}}$, we are multiplying by 1. The unit "dozen" cancels.

1. The factor $\frac{12}{\text{1 dozen}}$ is a conversion factor based on the definition of the term *dozen*. This conversion factor is a ratio of the two parts of the definition of a dozen given above.

2. The unit "dozen" itself cancels.

Now let's generalize a bit. To change from one unit to another we will use a conversion factor.

$$\text{Unit}_1 \times \text{conversion factor} = \text{Unit}_2$$

The **conversion factor** is a ratio of the two parts of the statement that relates the two units. We will see this in more detail on the following pages.

Earlier in this chapter we considered a pin that measured 2.85 cm in length. What is the length of the pin in inches? We can represent this problem as

$$2.85 \text{ cm} \rightarrow \text{? in.}$$

The question mark stands for the number we want to find. To solve this problem, we must know the relationship between inches and centimeters. In Table 2.7, which gives several equivalents between the English and metric systems, we find the relationship

$$2.54 \text{ cm} = 1 \text{ in.}$$

Table 2.7	English–Metric and English–English Equivalents	
Length	1 m = 1.094 yd	
	2.54 cm = 1 in.	
	1 mi = 5280. ft	
	1 mi = 1760. yd	
Mass	1 kg = 2.205 lb	
	453.6 g = 1 lb	
Volume	1 L = 1.06 qt	
	1 ft^3 = 28.32 L	

This is called an **equivalence statement.** In other words, 2.54 cm and 1 in. stand for *exactly the same distance.* (See Figure 2.1.) The respective numbers are different because they refer to different *scales (units)* of distance.

The equivalence statement 2.54 cm = 1 in. can lead to either of two conversion factors:

$$\frac{2.54 \text{ cm}}{1 \text{ in.}} \quad \text{or} \quad \frac{1 \text{ in.}}{2.54 \text{ cm}}$$

Note that these *conversion factors* are *ratios of the two parts of the equivalence statement* that relates the two units. Which of the two possible conversion factors do we need? Recall our problem:

$$2.85 \text{ cm} = ? \text{ in.}$$

That is, we want to convert from units of centimeters to inches:

$$2.85 \text{ cm} \times \text{conversion factor} = ? \text{ in.}$$

We choose a conversion factor that cancels the units we want to discard and leaves the units we want in the result. Thus we do the conversion as follows:

MATH SKILL BUILDER
Units cancel just as numbers do.

$$2.85 \text{ cm} \times \frac{1 \text{ in.}}{2.54 \text{ cm}} = \frac{2.85 \text{ in.}}{2.54} = 1.12 \text{ in.}$$

Note two important facts about this conversion:

1. The centimeter units cancel to give inches for the result. This is exactly what we had wanted to accomplish. Using the other conversion factor $\left(2.85 \text{ cm} \times \dfrac{2.54 \text{ cm}}{1 \text{ in.}} \right)$ would not work because the units would not cancel to give inches in the result.

MATH SKILL BUILDER
When you finish a calculation, always check to make sure that the answer makes sense.

2. As the units changed from centimeters to inches, the number changed from 2.85 to 1.12. Thus 2.85 cm has exactly the same value (is the same length) as 1.12 in. Notice that in this conversion, the number decreased from 2.85 to 1.12. This makes sense because the inch is a larger unit of length than the centimeter is. That is, it takes fewer inches to make the same length in centimeters.

The result in the foregoing conversion has three significant figures as required. Caution: Noting that the term 1 appears in the conversion, you might think that because this number appears to have only one significant figure, the result should have only one significant figure. That is, the answer should be given as 1 in. rather than 1.12 in. However, in the equivalence statement 1 in. = 2.54 cm, the 1 is an exact number (by definition). In other words, exactly 1 in. equals 2.54 cm. Therefore, the 1 does not limit the number of significant digits in the result.

MATH SKILL BUILDER
When exact numbers are used in a calculation, they never limit the number of significant digits.

We have seen how to convert from centimeters to inches. What about the reverse conversion? For example, if a pencil is 7.00 in. long, what is its length in centimeters? In this case, the conversion we want to make is

$$7.00 \text{ in.} \rightarrow ? \text{ cm}$$

What conversion factor do we need to make this conversion?

Remember that two conversion factors can be derived from each equivalence statement. In this case, the equivalence statement 2.54 cm = 1 in. gives

$$\frac{2.54 \text{ cm}}{1 \text{ in.}} \quad \text{or} \quad \frac{1 \text{ in.}}{2.54 \text{ cm}}$$

Again, we choose which factor to use by looking at the *direction* of the required change. For us to change from inches to centimeters, the inches must cancel. Thus the factor

$$\frac{2.54 \text{ cm}}{1 \text{ in.}}$$

is used, and the conversion is done as follows:

$$7.00 \text{ in.} \times \frac{2.54 \text{ cm}}{1 \text{ in.}} = (7.00)(2.54) \text{ cm} = 17.8 \text{ cm}$$

> Consider the direction of the required change in order to select the correct conversion factor.

Here the inch units cancel, leaving centimeters as required.

Note that in this conversion, the number increased (from 7.00 to 17.8). This makes sense because the centimeter is a smaller unit of length than the inch. That is, it takes more centimeters to make the same length in inches. *Always take a moment to think about whether your answer makes sense.* This will help you avoid errors.

Changing from one unit to another via conversion factors (based on the equivalence statements between the units) is often called **dimensional analysis.** We will use this method throughout our study of chemistry.

We can now state some general steps for doing conversions by dimensional analysis.

Converting from One Unit to Another

Step 1 To convert from one unit to another, use the equivalence statement that relates the two units. The conversion factor needed is a ratio of the two parts of the equivalence statement.

Step 2 Choose the appropriate conversion factor by looking at the direction of the required change (make sure the unwanted units cancel).

Step 3 Multiply the quantity to be converted by the conversion factor to give the quantity with the desired units.

Step 4 Check that you have the correct number of significant figures.

Step 5 Ask whether your answer makes sense.

We will now illustrate this procedure in Example 2.6.

EXAMPLE 2.6 | Conversion Factors: One-Step Problems

An Italian bicycle has its frame size given as 62 cm. What is the frame size in inches?

SOLUTION

We can represent the problem as

$$62 \text{ cm} = ? \text{ in.}$$

In this problem we want to convert from centimeters to inches.

$$62 \text{ cm} \times \text{conversion factor} = ? \text{ in.}$$

Step 1 To convert from centimeters to inches, we need the equivalence statement 1 in. = 2.54 cm. This leads to two conversion factors:

$$\frac{1 \text{ in.}}{2.54 \text{ cm}} \quad \text{and} \quad \frac{2.54 \text{ cm}}{1 \text{ in.}}$$

Step 2 In this case, the direction we want is

$$\text{Centimeters} \rightarrow \text{inches}$$

so we need the conversion factor $\dfrac{1 \text{ in.}}{2.54 \text{ cm}}$. We know this is the one we want because using it will make the units of centimeters cancel, leaving units of inches.

Step 3 The conversion is carried out as follows:

$$62 \text{ cm} \times \frac{1 \text{ in.}}{2.54 \text{ cm}} = 24 \text{ in.}$$

Step 4 The result is limited to two significant figures by the number 62. The centimeters cancel, leaving inches as required.

Step 5 Note that the number decreased in this conversion. This makes sense; the inch is a larger unit of length than the centimeter.

Self-Check **EXERCISE 2.4** Wine is often bottled in 0.750-L containers. Using the appropriate equivalence statement from Table 2.7, calculate the volume of such a wine bottle in quarts.

See Problems 2.59 and 2.60. ∎

Next we will consider a conversion that requires several steps.

EXAMPLE 2.7 | **Conversion Factors: Multiple-Step Problems**

The length of the marathon race is approximately 26.2 mi. What is this distance in kilometers?

SOLUTION

The problem before us can be represented as follows:

$$26.2 \text{ mi} = ? \text{ km}$$

We could accomplish this conversion in several different ways, but because Table 2.7 gives the equivalence statements 1 mi = 1760 yd and 1 m = 1.094 yd, we will proceed as follows:

$$\text{Miles} \rightarrow \text{yards} \rightarrow \text{meters} \rightarrow \text{kilometers}$$

This process will be carried out one conversion at a time to make sure everything is clear.

MILES → YARDS: We convert from miles to yards using the conversion factor $\dfrac{1760 \text{ yd}}{1 \text{ mi}}$.

$$26.2 \text{ mi} \times \frac{1760 \text{ yd}}{1 \text{ mi}} = 46{,}112 \text{ yd}$$

Result shown on calculator

$$46{,}112 \text{ yd} \quad \boxed{\text{Round off}} \Rightarrow \quad 46{,}100 \text{ yd} = 4.61 \times 10^4 \text{ yd}$$

YARDS → METERS: The conversion factor used to convert yards to meters is $\dfrac{1 \text{ m}}{1.094 \text{ yd}}$.

$$4.61 \times 10^4 \text{ yd} \times \frac{1 \text{ m}}{1.094 \text{ yd}} = 4.213894 \times 10^4 \text{ m}$$

Result shown on calculator

4.213894×10^4 m　Round off ⟩ 4.21×10^4 m

METERS → KILOMETERS: Because 1000 m = 1 km, or 10^3 m = 1 km, we convert from meters to kilometers as follows:

$$4.21 \times 10^4 \text{ m} \times \frac{1 \text{ km}}{10^3 \text{ m}} = 4.21 \times 10^1 \text{ km}$$
$$= 42.1 \text{ km}$$

Thus the marathon (26.2 mi) is 42.1 km.

Once you feel comfortable with the conversion process, you can combine the steps. For the above conversion, the combined expression is

miles → yards → meters → kilometers

$$26.2 \text{ mi} \times \frac{1760 \text{ yd}}{1 \text{ mi}} \times \frac{1 \text{ m}}{1.094 \text{ yd}} \times \frac{1 \text{ km}}{10^3 \text{ m}} = 42.1 \text{ km}$$

Note that the units cancel to give the required kilometers and that the result has three significant figures.

MATH SKILL BUILDER
Remember that we are rounding off at the end of each step to show the correct number of significant figures. However, in doing a multi-step calculation, *you* should retain the extra numbers that show on your calculator and round off only at the end of the calculation.

Self-Check **EXERCISE 2.5** Racing cars at the Indianapolis Motor Speedway now routinely travel around the track at an average speed of 225 mi/h. What is this speed in kilometers per hour?

See Problems 2.65 and 2.66. ■

Units provide a very valuable check on the validity of your solution. Always use them.

Recap: Whenever you work problems, remember the following points:

1. Always include the units (a measurement always has two parts: a number *and* a unit).
2. Cancel units as you carry out the calculations.
3. Check that your final answer has the correct units. If it doesn't, you have done something wrong.
4. Check that your final answer has the correct number of significant figures.
5. Think about whether your answer makes sense.

2.7 Temperature Conversions: An Approach to Problem Solving

OBJECTIVES: To learn the three temperature scales. • To learn to convert from one scale to another. • To continue to develop problem-solving skills.

When the doctor tells you your temperature is 102 degrees and the weatherperson on TV says it will be 75 degrees tomorrow, they are using the **Fahrenheit scale.** Water boils at 212 °F and freezes at 32 °F, and normal body temperature is 98.6 °F (where °F signifies "Fahrenheit degrees"). This temperature scale is widely used in the United States and Great Britain, and it is the scale employed in most of the engineering sciences. Another temperature scale, used in Canada and Europe and in the physical and life sciences in most countries, is the **Celsius scale.** In keeping with the metric system, which is based on powers of 10, the freezing and boiling points of water on the Celsius scale are assigned as 0 °C and 100 °C, respectively. On both the Fahrenheit and the Celsius scales, the unit of temperature is called a degree, and the symbol for it is followed by the capital letter representing the scale on which the units are measured: °C or °F.

Still another temperature scale used in the sciences is the **absolute** or **Kelvin scale.** On this scale water freezes at 273 K and boils at 373 K. On the Kelvin scale, the unit of temperature is called a kelvin and is symbolized by K. Thus, on the three scales, the boiling point of water is stated as 212 Fahrenheit degrees (212 °F), 100 Celsius degrees (100 °C), and 373 kelvins (373 K).

> Although 373 K is often stated as 373 degrees Kelvin, it is more correct to say 373 kelvins.

The three temperature scales are compared in Figures 2.6 and 2.7. There are several important facts you should note.

1. The size of each temperature unit (each degree) is the same for the Celsius and Kelvin scales. This follows from the fact that the *difference* between the boiling and freezing points of water is 100 units on both of these scales.

2. The Fahrenheit degree is smaller than the Celsius and Kelvin units. Note that on the Fahrenheit scale there are 180 Fahrenheit degrees between the boiling and freezing points of water, as compared with 100 units on the other two scales.

3. The zero points are different on all three scales.

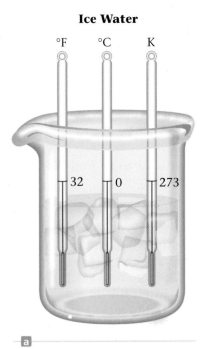

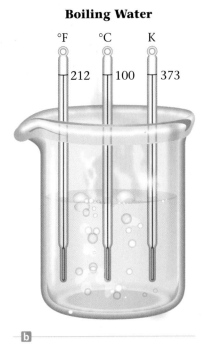

Figure 2.6

Thermometers based on the three temperature scales in a ice water and b boiling water.

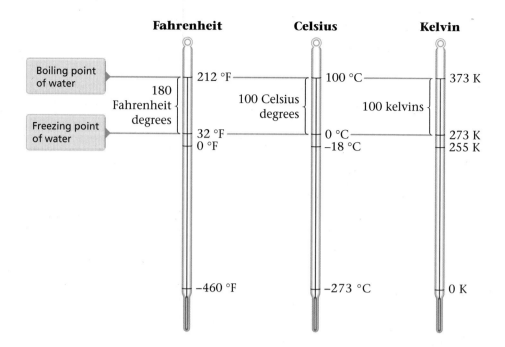

Figure 2.7
The three major temperature scales.

In your study of chemistry, you will sometimes need to convert from one temperature scale to another. We will consider in some detail how this is done. In addition to learning how to change temperature scales, you should also use this section as an opportunity to further develop your skills in problem solving.

▶ Converting Between the Kelvin and Celsius Scales

It is relatively simple to convert between the Celsius and Kelvin scales because the temperature unit is the same size; only the zero points are different. Because 0 °C corresponds to 273 K, converting from Celsius to Kelvin requires that we add 273 to the Celsius temperature. We will illustrate this procedure in Example 2.8.

EXAMPLE 2.8 | Temperature Conversion: Celsius to Kelvin

Boiling points will be discussed further in Chapter 14.

The boiling point of water at the top of Mt. Everest is 70. °C. Convert this temperature to the Kelvin scale. (The decimal point after the temperature reading indicates that the trailing zero is significant.)

SOLUTION

This problem asks us to find 70. °C in units of kelvins. We can represent this problem simply as

$$70. \ °C = ? \ K$$

In solving problems, it is often helpful to draw a diagram that depicts what the words are telling you.

In doing problems, it is often helpful to draw a diagram in which we try to represent the words in the problem with a picture. This problem can be diagramed as shown in Figure 2.8a.

In this picture we have shown what we want to find: "What temperature (in kelvins) is the same as 70. °C?" We also know from Figure 2.7 that 0 °C represents the same temperature as 273 K. How many degrees above 0 °C is 70. °C? The answer, of course, is 70. Thus we must add 70. to 0 °C to reach 70. °C. Because degrees are the *same size* on both the Celsius scale

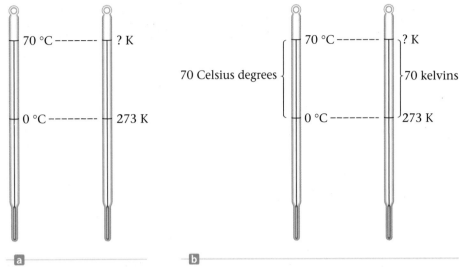

a	b
We know 0 °C = 273 K. We want to know 70. °C = ? K.	*There are 70 degrees on the Celsius scale between 0 °C and 70. °C. Because units on these scales are the same size, there are also 70 kelvins in this same distance on the Kelvin scale.*

Figure 2.8

Converting 70. °C to units measured on the Kelvin scale.

and the Kelvin scale (see Figure 2.8b), we must also add 70. to 273 K (same temperature as 0 °C) to reach ? K. That is,

$$? K = 273 + 70. = 343 K$$

Thus 70. °C corresponds to 343 K.

Note that to convert from the Celsius to the Kelvin scale, we simply add the temperature in °C to 273. That is,

$$T_{°C} \quad + \quad 273 \quad = \quad T_K$$

Temperature in Celsius degrees — Temperature in kelvins

Using this formula to solve the present problem gives

$$70. + 273 = 343$$

(with units of kelvins, K), which is the correct answer. ■

We can summarize what we learned in Example 2.8 as follows: to convert from the Celsius to the Kelvin scale, we can use the formula

$$T_{°C} \quad + \quad 273 \quad = \quad T_K$$

Temperature in Celsius degrees — Temperature in kelvins

EXAMPLE 2.9   **Temperature Conversion: Kelvin to Celsius**

Liquid nitrogen boils at 77 K. What is the boiling point of nitrogen on the Celsius scale?

SOLUTION

The problem to be solved here is 77 K = ? °C. Let's explore this question by examining the picture on the following page representing the two

Tiny Thermometers

Can you imagine a thermometer that has a diameter equal to one one-hundredth of a human hair? Such a device has actually been produced by scientists Yihica Gao and Yoshio Bando of the National Institute for Materials Science in Tsukuba, Japan. The thermometer they constructed is so tiny that it must be read using a powerful electron microscope.

It turns out that the tiny thermometers were produced by accident. The Japanese scientists were actually trying to make tiny (nanoscale) gallium nitride wires. However, when they examined the results of their experiment, they discovered tiny tubes of carbon atoms that were filled with elemental gallium. Because gallium is a liquid over an unusually large temperature range, it makes a perfect working liquid for a thermometer. Just as in mercury thermometers, which have mostly been phased out because of the toxicity of mercury, the gallium expands as the temperature increases. Therefore, gallium moves up the tube as the temperature increases.

These minuscule thermometers are not useful in the normal macroscopic world—they can't even be seen with the naked eye. However, they should be valuable for monitoring temperatures from 50 °C to 500 °C in materials in the nanoscale world.

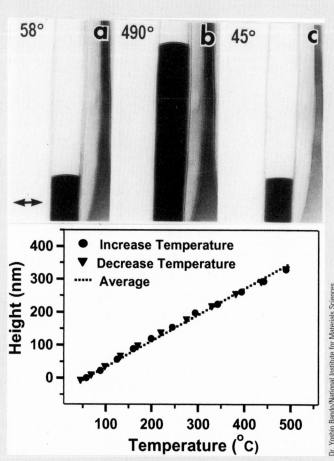

Liquid gallium expands within a carbon nanotube as the temperature increases (left to right).

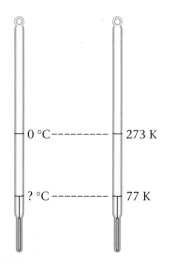

temperature scales. One key point is to recognize that 0 °C = 273 K. Also note that the difference between 273 K and 77 K is 196 kelvins (273 − 77 = 196). That is, 77 K is 196 kelvins below 273 K. The degree size is the same on these two temperature scales, so 77 K must correspond to 196 Celsius degrees below zero or −196 °C. Thus 77 K = ? °C = −196 °C.

We can also solve this problem by using the formula

$$T_{°C} + 273 = T_K$$

However, in this case we want to solve for the Celsius temperature, $T_{°C}$. That is, we want to isolate $T_{°C}$ on one side of the equals sign. To do this we use an important general principle: doing *the same thing on both sides of the equals sign* preserves the equality. In other words, it's always okay to perform the same operation on both sides of the equals sign.

To isolate $T_{°C}$ we need to subtract 273 from both sides:

$$T_{°C} + 273 - 273 = T_K - 273$$

↑ ↑

Sum is zero

to give

$$T_{°C} = T_K - 273$$

Using this equation to solve the problem, we have

$$T_{°C} = T_K - 273 = 77 - 273 = -196$$

So, as before, we have shown that

$$77 \text{ K} = -196 \text{ °C}$$

Self-Check   EXERCISE 2.6   Which temperature is colder, 172 K or −75 °C?

See Problems 2.73 and 2.74. ■

In summary, because the Kelvin and Celsius scales have the same size unit, to switch from one scale to the other we must simply account for the different zero points. We must add 273 to the Celsius temperature to obtain the temperature on the Kelvin scale:

$$T_K = T_{°C} + 273$$

To convert from the Kelvin scale to the Celsius scale, we must subtract 273 from the Kelvin temperature:

$$T_{°C} = T_K - 273$$

▶ Converting Between the Fahrenheit and Celsius Scales

The conversion between the Fahrenheit and Celsius temperature scales requires two adjustments:

1. For the different size units

2. For the different zero points

To see how to adjust for the different unit sizes, consider the diagram in Figure 2.9. Note that because 212 °F = 100 °C and 32 °F = 0 °C,

$$212 - 32 = 180 \text{ Fahrenheit degrees} = 100 - 0 = 100 \text{ Celsius degrees}$$

Thus

$$180. \text{ Fahrenheit degrees} = 100. \text{ Celsius degrees}$$

MATH SKILL BUILDER
Remember, it's okay to do the same thing to both sides of the equation.

Dividing both sides of this equation by 100. gives

$$\frac{180.}{100.} \text{ Fahrenheit degrees} = \frac{1\cancel{00}.}{1\cancel{00}.} \text{ Celsius degrees}$$

or

$$1.80 \text{ Fahrenheit degrees} = 1.00 \text{ Celsius degree}$$

The factor 1.80 is used to convert from one degree size to the other.

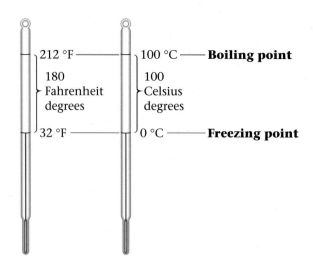

Figure 2.9

Comparison of the Celsius and Fahrenheit scales.

Next we have to account for the fact that 0 °C is *not* the same as 0 °F. In fact, 32 °F = 0 °C. Although we will not show how to derive it, the equation to convert a temperature in Celsius degrees to the Fahrenheit scale is

$$T_{°F} = 1.80(T_{°C}) + 32$$

Temperature   Temperature
in °F   in °C

In this equation the term $1.80(T_{°C})$ adjusts for the difference in degree size between the two scales. The 32 in the equation accounts for the different zero points. We will now show how to use this equation.

EXAMPLE 2.10   **Temperature Conversion: Celsius to Fahrenheit**

On a summer day the temperature in the laboratory, as measured on a lab thermometer, is 28 °C. Express this temperature on the Fahrenheit scale.

SOLUTION

This problem can be represented as 28 °C = ? °F. We will solve it using the formula

$$T_{°F} = 1.80 (T_{°C}) + 32$$

In this case,

$$T_{°C}$$
$$\downarrow$$
$$T_{°F} = ? \ °F = 1.80(28) + 32 = 50.4 + 32$$

Rounds
off to 50

$$= 50. + 32 = 82$$

Note that 28 °C is approximately equal to 82 °F. Because the numbers are just reversed, this is an easy reference point to remember for the two scales.

Thus 28 °C = 82 °F. ∎

EXAMPLE 2.11 | Temperature Conversion: Celsius to Fahrenheit

Express the temperature $-40.\,°C$ on the Fahrenheit scale.

SOLUTION

We can express this problem as $-40.\,°C = ?\,°F$. To solve it we will use the formula

$$T_{°F} = 1.80\,(T_{°C}) + 32$$

In this case,

$$
\overset{\displaystyle T_{°C}}{\underset{\displaystyle \downarrow}{}}
$$
$$T_{°F} = ?\,°F = 1.80(-40.) + 32$$
$$= -72 + 32 = -40$$

So $-40\,°C = -40\,°F$. This is a very interesting result and is another useful reference point.

Self-Check   **EXERCISE 2.7**   Hot tubs are often maintained at $41\,°C$. What is this temperature in Fahrenheit degrees?

See Problems 2.75 through 2.78. ∎

To convert from Celsius to Fahrenheit, we have used the equation

$$T_{°F} = 1.80\,(T_{°C}) + 32$$

To convert a Fahrenheit temperature to Celsius, we need to rearrange this equation to isolate Celsius degrees ($T_{°C}$). Remember, we can always do the same operation to both sides of the equation. First subtract 32 from each side:

$$T_{°F} - 32 = 1.80\,(T_{°C}) + 32 \underset{\underset{\text{Sum is zero}}{\uparrow \qquad \uparrow}}{} 32$$

to give

$$T_{°F} - 32 = 1.80(T_{°C})$$

Next divide both sides by 1.80

$$\frac{T_{°F} - 32}{1.80} = \frac{\cancel{1.80}(T_{°C})}{\cancel{1.80}}$$

to give

$$\frac{T_{°F} - 32}{1.80} = T_{°C}$$

or

$$T_{°C} = \frac{\overset{\text{Temperature in °F}}{T_{°F}} - 32}{\underset{\text{Temperature in °C}}{1.80}}$$

$$T_{°C} = \frac{T_{°F} - 32}{1.80}$$

EXAMPLE 2.12 | **Temperature Conversion: Fahrenheit to Celsius**

One of the body's responses to an infection or injury is to elevate its temperature. A certain flu victim has a body temperature of 101 °F. What is this temperature on the Celsius scale?

SOLUTION

The problem is 101 °F = ? °C. Using the formula

$$T_{°C} = \frac{T_{°F} - 32}{1.80}$$

yields

$$T_{°C} = ? °C = \frac{\overset{T_{°F}}{101} - 32}{1.80} = \frac{69}{1.80} = 38$$

That is, 101 °F = 38 °C.

Self-Check EXERCISE 2.8   An antifreeze solution in a car's radiator boils at 239 °F. What is this temperature on the Celsius scale?

See Problems 2.75 through 2.78. ∎

In doing temperature conversions, you will need the following formulas.

Temperature Conversion Formulas

- Celsius to Kelvin $T_K = T_{°C} + 273$
- Kelvin to Celsius $T_{°C} = T_K - 273$
- Celsius to Fahrenheit $T_{°F} = 1.80(T_{°C}) + 32$
- Fahrenheit to Celsius $T_{°C} = \dfrac{T_{°F} - 32}{1.80}$

2.8 Density

OBJECTIVE: To define density and its units.

Lead has a greater density than feathers.

When you were in elementary school, you may have been embarrassed by your answer to the question "Which is heavier, a pound of lead or a pound of feathers?" If you said lead, you were undoubtedly thinking about density, not mass. **Density** can be defined as the amount of matter present *in a given volume* of substance. That is, density is mass per unit volume, the ratio of the mass of an object to its volume:

$$\text{Density} = \frac{\text{mass}}{\text{volume}}$$

It takes a much bigger volume to make a pound of feathers than to make a pound of lead. This is because lead has a much greater mass per unit volume—a greater density.

The density of a liquid can be determined easily by weighing a known volume of the substance as illustrated in Example 2.13.

EXAMPLE 2.13 | Calculating Density

Suppose a student finds that 23.50 mL of a certain liquid weighs 35.062 g. What is the density of this liquid?

SOLUTION

We can calculate the density of this liquid simply by applying the definition

$$\text{Density} = \frac{\text{mass}}{\text{volume}} = \frac{35.062 \text{ g}}{23.50 \text{ mL}} = 1.492 \text{ g/mL}$$

This result could also be expressed as 1.492 g/cm³ because 1 mL = 1 cm³. ∎

The volume of a solid object is often determined indirectly by submerging it in water and measuring the volume of water displaced. In fact, this is the most accurate method for measuring a person's percent body fat. The person is submerged momentarily in a tank of water, and the increase in volume is measured (see Figure 2.10). It is possible to calculate the body density by using the person's weight (mass) and the volume of the person's body determined by submersion. Fat, muscle, and bone have different densities (fat is less dense than muscle tissue, for example), so the fraction of the person's body that is fat can be calculated. The more muscle and the less fat a person has, the higher his or her body density. For example, a muscular person weighing 150 lb has a smaller body volume (and thus a higher density) than a fat person weighing 150 lb.

EXAMPLE 2.14 | Determining Density

The most common units for density are g/mL = g/cm³.

At a local pawn shop a student finds a medallion that the shop owner insists is pure platinum. However, the student suspects that the medallion may actually be silver and thus much less valuable. The student buys the medallion only after the shop owner agrees to refund the price if the medallion is

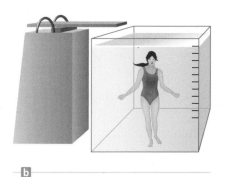

Figure 2.10

Tank of water

Person submerged in the tank, raising the level of the water

returned within two days. The student, a chemistry major, then takes the medallion to her lab and measures its density as follows. She first weighs the medallion and finds its mass to be 55.64 g. She then places some water in a graduated cylinder and reads the volume as 75.2 mL. Next she drops the medallion into the cylinder and reads the new volume as 77.8 mL. Is the medallion platinum (density = 21.4 g/cm³) or silver (density = 10.5 g/cm³)?

SOLUTION

The densities of platinum and silver differ so much that the measured density of the medallion will show which metal is present. Because by definition

$$\text{Density} = \frac{\text{mass}}{\text{volume}}$$

to calculate the density of the medallion, we need its mass and its volume. The mass of the medallion is 55.64 g. The volume of the medallion can be obtained by taking the difference between the volume readings of the water in the graduated cylinder before and after the medallion was added.

$$\text{Volume of medallion} = 77.8 \text{ mL} - 75.2 \text{ mL} = 2.6 \text{ mL}$$

The volume appeared to increase by 2.6 mL when the medallion was added, so 2.6 mL represents the volume of the medallion. Now we can use the measured mass and volume of the medallion to determine its density:

$$\text{Density of medallion} = \frac{\text{mass}}{\text{volume}} = \frac{55.64 \text{ g}}{2.6 \text{ mL}} = 21 \text{ g/mL}$$

or

$$= 21 \text{ g/cm}^3$$

The medallion is really platinum.

Self-Check   **EXERCISE 2.9**   A student wants to identify the main component in a commercial liquid cleaner. He finds that 35.8 mL of the cleaner weighs 28.1 g. Of the following possibilities, which is the main component of the cleaner?

Substance	Density, g/cm³
chloroform	1.483
diethyl ether	0.714
isopropyl alcohol	0.785
toluene	0.867

See Problems 2.89 and 2.90. ■

EXAMPLE 2.15 | **Using Density in Calculations**

Mercury has a density of 13.6 g/mL. What volume of mercury must be taken to obtain 225 g of the metal?

SOLUTION

To solve this problem, start with the definition of density,

$$\text{Density} = \frac{\text{mass}}{\text{volume}}$$

and then rearrange this equation to isolate the required quantity. In this case we want to find the volume. Remember that we maintain an equality

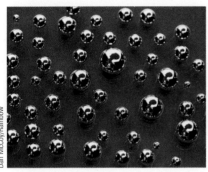

Spherical droplets of mercury, a very dense liquid.

when we do the same thing to both sides. For example, if we multiply *both sides* of the density definition by volume,

$$\text{Volume} \times \text{density} = \frac{\text{mass}}{\cancel{\text{volume}}} \times \cancel{\text{volume}}$$

volume cancels on the right, leaving

$$\text{Volume} \times \text{density} = \text{mass}$$

We want the volume, so we now divide both sides by density,

$$\frac{\text{Volume} \times \cancel{\text{density}}}{\cancel{\text{density}}} = \frac{\text{mass}}{\text{density}}$$

to give

$$\text{Volume} = \frac{\text{mass}}{\text{density}}$$

Now we can solve the problem by substituting the given numbers:

$$\text{Volume} = \frac{225 \text{ g}}{13.6 \text{ g/mL}} = 16.5 \text{ mL}$$

We must take 16.5 mL of mercury to obtain an amount that has a mass of 225 g. ■

The densities of various common substances are given in Table 2.8. Besides being a tool for the identification of substances, density has many other uses. For example, the liquid in your car's lead storage battery (a solution of sulfuric acid) changes density because the sulfuric acid is consumed as the battery discharges. In a fully charged battery, the density of the solution is about 1.30 g/cm³. When the density falls below 1.20 g/cm³, the battery has to be recharged. Density measurement is also used to determine the amount of antifreeze, and thus the level of protection against freezing, in the cooling system of a car. Water and antifreeze have different densities, so the measured density of the mixture tells us how much of each is present. The device used to test the density of the solution—a hydrometer—is shown in Figure 2.11.

Figure 2.11

A hydrometer being used to determine the density of the antifreeze solution in a car's radiator.

Table 2.8	Densities of Various Common Substances at 20 °C	
Substance	Physical State	Density (g/cm³)
oxygen	gas	0.00133*
hydrogen	gas	0.000084*
ethanol	liquid	0.785
benzene	liquid	0.880
water	liquid	1.000
magnesium	solid	1.74
salt (sodium chloride)	solid	2.16
aluminum	solid	2.70
iron	solid	7.87
copper	solid	8.96
silver	solid	10.5
lead	solid	11.34
mercury	liquid	13.6
gold	solid	19.32

*At 1 atmosphere pressure

In certain situations, the term *specific gravity* is used to describe the density of a liquid. **Specific gravity** is defined as the ratio of the density of a given liquid to the density of water at 4 °C. Because it is a ratio of densities, specific gravity has no units.

CHAPTER 2 REVIEW

Key Terms

measurement (p. 15)
scientific notation (2.1)
units (2.2)
English system (2.2)
metric system (2.2)
SI units (2.2)
volume (2.3)
mass (2.3)
significant figures (2.4)
rounding off (2.5)

conversion factor (2.6)
equivalence statement (2.6)
dimensional analysis (2.6)
Fahrenheit scale (2.7)
Celsius scale (2.7)
Kelvin (absolute) scale (2.7)
density (2.8)
specific gravity (2.8)

F   directs you to the *Chemistry in Focus* feature in the chapter
VP indicates visual problems
OWL interactive versions of these problems are assignable in OWL.

Active Learning Questions

These questions are designed to be considered by groups of students in class. Often these questions work well for introducing a particular topic in class.

1. a. There are 365 days/year, 24 hours/day, 12 months/year, and 60 minutes/hour. How many minutes are there in one month?
   b. There are 24 hours/day, 60 minutes/hour, 7 days/week, and 4 weeks/month. How many minutes are there in one month?
   c. Why are these answers different? Which (if either) is more correct and why?

2. You go to a convenience store to buy candy and find the owner to be rather odd. He allows you to buy pieces only in multiples of four, and to buy four, you need $0.23. He allows you only to use 3 pennies and 2 dimes. You have a bunch of pennies and dimes, and instead of counting them, you decide to weigh them. You have 636.3 g of pennies, and each penny weighs an average of 3.03 g. Each dime weighs an average of 2.29 g. Each piece of candy weighs an average of 10.23 g.

   a. How many pennies do you have?
   b. How many dimes do you need to buy as much candy as possible?
   c. How much would all of your dimes weigh?
   d. How many pieces of candy could you buy (based on the number of dimes from part b)?
   e. How much would this candy weigh?
   f. How many pieces of candy could you buy with twice as many dimes?

3. When a marble is dropped into a beaker of water, it sinks to the bottom. Which of the following is the best explanation?

   a. The surface area of the marble is not large enough for the marble to be held up by the surface tension of the water.
   b. The mass of the marble is greater than that of the water.

Summary

1. A quantitative observation is called a measurement and always consists of a number and a unit.

2. We can conveniently express very large or very small numbers using scientific notation, which represents the number as a number between 1 and 10 multiplied by 10 raised to a power.

3. Units give a scale on which to represent the results of a measurement. The three systems discussed are the English, metric, and SI systems. The metric and SI systems use prefixes (Table 2.2) to change the size of the units.

4. The mass of an object represents the quantity of matter in that object.

5. All measurements have a degree of uncertainty, which is reflected in the number of significant figures used to express them. Various rules are used to round off to the correct number of significant figures in a calculated result.

6. We can convert from one system of units to another by a method called dimensional analysis, in which conversion factors are used.

7. Temperature can be measured on three different scales: Fahrenheit, Celsius, and Kelvin. We can readily convert among these scales.

8. Density is the amount of matter present in a given volume (mass per unit volume). That is,

$$\text{Density} = \frac{\text{mass}}{\text{volume}}$$

c. The marble weighs more than an equivalent volume of the water.

d. The force from dropping the marble breaks the surface tension of the water.

e. The marble has greater mass and volume than the water.

Explain each choice. That is, for choices you did not pick, explain why you feel they are wrong, and justify the choice you did pick.

4. Consider water in each graduated cylinder as shown:

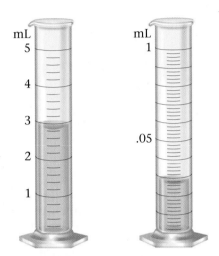

You add both samples of water to a beaker. How would you write the number describing the total volume? What limits the precision of this number?

5. What is the numerical value of a conversion factor? Why must this be true?

6. For each of the following numbers, indicate which zeros are significant and explain. Do not merely cite the rule that applies, but explain the rule.

   a. 10.020   b. 0.002050   c. 190   d. 270

7. Consider the addition of "15.4" to "28." What would a mathematician say the answer is? What would a scientist say? Justify the scientist's answer, not merely citing the rule, but explaining it.

8. Consider multiplying "26.2" by "16.43." What would a mathematician say the answer is? What would a scientist say? Justify the scientist's answer, not merely citing the rule, but explaining it.

9. In lab you report a measured volume of 128.7 mL of water. Using significant figures as a measure of the error, what range of answers does your reported volume imply? Explain.

10. Sketch two pieces of glassware: one that can measure volume to the thousandths place, and one that can measure volume only to the ones place.

11. Oil floats on water but is "thicker" than water. Why do you think this fact is true?

12. Show how converting numbers to scientific notation can help you decide which digits are significant.

13. You are driving 65 mph and take your eyes off the road "just for a second." How many feet do you travel in this time?

14. You have a 1.0-cm³ sample of lead and a 1.0-cm³ sample of glass. You drop each in a separate beaker of water. How do the volumes of water that are displaced by the samples compare? Explain.

VP 15. The beakers shown below have different precisions.

a. Label the amount of water in each of the three beakers to the correct number of significant figures.

b. Is it possible for each of the three beakers to contain the exact same amount of water? If no, why not? If yes, did you report the volumes as the same in part a? Explain.

c. Suppose you pour the water from these three beakers into one container. What should be the volume in the container reported to the correct number of significant figures?

16. True or False? For any mathematical operation performed on two measurements, the number of significant figures in the answer is the same as the least number of significant figures in either of the measurements. Explain your answer.

17. Complete the following and explain each in your own words: leading zeros are (never/sometimes/always) significant; captive zeros are (never/sometimes/always) significant; and trailing zeros are (never/sometimes/always) significant.

For any statement with an answer of "sometimes," give examples of when the zero is significant and when it is not, and explain.

VP 18. For each of the following figures, a through d, decide which block is more dense: the orange block, the blue block, or it cannot be determined. Explain your answers.

 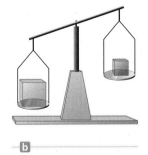

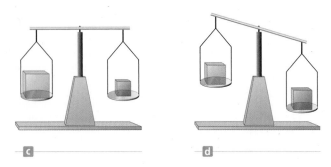

VP 19. For the pin shown below, why is the third digit determined for the length of the pin uncertain? Considering that the third digit is uncertain, explain why the length of the pin is indicated as 2.85 cm rather than, for example, 2.83 or 2.87 cm.

VP 20. Why can the length of the pin shown below not be recorded as 2.850 cm?

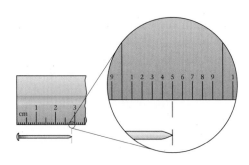

VP 21. Use the figure below to answer the following questions.

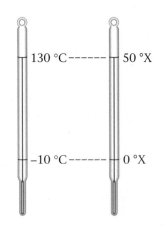

a. Derive the relationship between °C and °X.
b. If the temperature outside is 22.0 °C, what is the temperature in units of °X?
c. Convert 58.0 °X to units of °C, K, and °F.

Questions and Problems

2.1 Scientific Notation

QUESTIONS

1. A _____ represents a quantitative observation.

2. Although your textbook lists the rules for converting an ordinary number to scientific notation, oftentimes students remember such rules better if they put them into their own words. Pretend you are helping your 12-year-old niece with her math homework, and write a paragraph explaining to her how to convert the ordinary number 2421 to scientific notation.

3. When a large or small number is written in standard scientific notation, the number is expressed as the product of a *number* between 1 and 10, multiplied by the appropriate *power* of 10. For each of the following numbers, indicate what number between 1 and 10 would be appropriate when expressing the numbers in standard scientific notation.

   a. 9651   c. 93,241
   b. 0.003521   d. 0.000001002

4. When a large or small number is written in standard scientific notation, the number is expressed as the product of a *number* between 1 and 10, multiplied by the appropriate *power* of 10. For each of the following numbers, indicate what power of 10 would be appropriate when expressing the numbers in standard scientific notation.

   a. 82,350
   b. 0.009375
   c. 251
   d. 0.0000000000000000000000000000009109

PROBLEMS

5. Will the power of 10 have a *positive* or a *negative* exponent when each of the following numbers is rewritten in standard scientific notation?

   a. 42,751   c. 0.002045
   b. 1253   d. 0.1089

6. Will the power of 10 have a *positive, negative,* or *zero* exponent when each of the following numbers is rewritten in standard scientific notation?

   a. 0.9091   c. 9091
   b. 9.091   d. 0.00000009091

7. Express each of the following numbers in *standard* scientific notation.

   a. 0.5012
   b. 5,012,000
   c. 0.000005012
   d. 5.012
   e. 5012
   f. 0.005012

8. Rewrite each of the following as an "ordinary" decimal number.

    a. 2.789×10^3
    b. 2.789×10^{-3}
    c. 9.3×10^7
    d. 4.289×10^1
    e. 9.999×10^4
    f. 9.999×10^{-5}

9. By how many places must the decimal point be moved, and in which direction, to convert each of the following to "ordinary" decimal numbers?

    a. 4.311×10^6 d. 4.995×10^0
    b. 7.895×10^{-5} e. 2.331×10^{18}
    c. 8.712×10^1 f. 1.997×10^{-16}

10. By how many places must the decimal point be moved, and in which direction, to convert each of the following to standard scientific notation?

    a. 5993   d. 62.357
    b. −72.14   e. 0.01014
    c. 0.00008291   f. 324.9

11. Write each of the following numbers in *standard* scientific notation.

    a. 97,820   d. 0.0003914
    b. 42.14×10^3 e. 927.1
    c. 0.08214×10^{-3} f. $4.781 \times 10^2 \times 10^{-3}$

12. Write each of the following numbers as "ordinary" decimal numbers.

    a. 6.244×10^3 d. 1.771×10^{-4}
    b. 9.117×10^{-2} e. 5.451×10^2
    c. 8.299×10^1 f. 2.934×10^{-5}

13. Write each of the following numbers in *standard* scientific notation.

    a. 1/1033   e. 1/3,093,000
    b. $1/10^5$ f. $1/10^{-4}$
    c. $1/10^{-7}$ g. $1/10^9$
    d. 1/0.0002   h. 1/0.000015

14. Write each of the following numbers in *standard* scientific notation.

    a. 1/0.00032   e. $(10^5)(10^4)(10^{-4})/(10^{-2})$
    b. $10^3/10^{-3}$ f. $43.2/(4.32 \times 10^{-5})$
    c. $10^3/10^3$ g. $(4.32 \times 10^{-5})/432$
    d. 1/55,000   h. $1/(10^5)(10^{-6})$

2.2 Units

QUESTIONS

15. What are the fundamental units of mass, length, and temperature in the metric system?

16. Give several examples of how *prefixes* are used in the metric system to indicate quantities that are multiples or divisions of the fundamental units of the metric system.

2.3 Measurements of Length, Volume, and Mass

QUESTIONS

Students often have trouble relating measurements in the metric system to the English system they have grown up with. Give the approximate English system equivalents for each of the following metric system descriptions in Exercises 17–20.

17. My new kitchen floor will require 25 square meters of linoleum.

18. My recipe for chili requires a 125-g can of tomato paste.

19. The gas tank in my new car holds 48 liters.

20. I need some 2.5-cm-long nails to hang up this picture.

21. The road sign I just passed says "New York City 100 km," which is about _____ mi.

22. Which contains more soda, a 2-liter bottle or a 2-quart bottle?

23. The tablecloth on my dining room table is 2 m long, which is _____ cm or about _____ in.

24. Who is taller, a man who is 1.62 m tall or a woman who is 5 ft 6 in. tall?

25. The fundamental SI unit of length is the meter. However, we often deal with larger or smaller lengths or distances for which multiples or fractions of the fundamental unit are more useful. For each of the following situations, suggest what fraction or multiple of the meter might be the most appropriate measurement.

    a. the distance between Chicago and Saint Louis
    b. the size of your bedroom
    c. the dimensions of this textbook
    d. the thickness of a hair

26. Which metric unit of length or distance is most comparable in scale to each of the following English system units for making measurements?

    a. an inch
    b. a yard
    c. a mile

27. The unit of volume in the metric system is the liter, which consists of 1000 milliliters. How many liters or milliliters is each of the following common English system measurements approximately equivalent to?

    a. a gallon of gasoline
    b. a pint of milk
    c. a cup of water

28. Which metric system unit is most appropriate for measuring the distance between two cities?

    a. meters   c. centimeters
    b. millimeters   d. kilometers

All even-numbered Questions and Problems have answers in the back of this book and solutions in the Solutions Guide.

2.4 Uncertainty in Measurement

QUESTIONS

29. If you were to measure the width of this page using a ruler, and you used the ruler to the limits of precision permitted by the scale on the ruler, the last digit you would write down for the measurement would be *uncertain* no matter how careful you were. Explain.

30. What does it mean to say that every measurement we make with a measuring device contains some measure of *uncertainty?*

31. For the pin shown in Figure 2.5, why is the third figure determined for the length of the pin uncertain? Considering that the third figure is uncertain, explain why the length of the pin is indicated as 2.85 cm rather than, for example, 2.83 or 2.87 cm.

32. Why can the length of the pin shown in Figure 2.5 not be recorded as 2.850 cm?

2.5 Significant Figures

QUESTIONS

33. Indicate the number of significant figures in each of the following:

    a. 250.   b. 250   c. 2.5×10^2 d. 250.0

34. Indicate the number of significant figures implied in each of the following statements:

    a. One inch is equivalent to 2.54 cm.
    b. My chemistry instructor gave us 24 homework problems to solve this week!
    c. My monthly car payment is $249.75.
    d. It's about 2500 mi from California to Hawaii.

Rounding Off Numbers

QUESTIONS

35. When we round off a number, if the number to the right of the digit to be rounded is greater than 5, then we should _____ .

36. In a multiple-step calculation, is it better to round off the numbers to the correct number of significant figures in each step of the calculation or to round off only the final answer? Explain.

37. Round off each of the following numbers to three significant digits, and express the result in standard scientific notation.

    a. 254,931   c. 47.85×10^3
    b. 0.00025615   d. 0.08214×10^5

38. Round off each of the following numbers to three significant digits, and express the result in standard scientific notation.

    a. 0.004175×10^{-3}
    b. 38,652
    c. 0.0000000000000000000000000000009109
    d. 5.455×10^6

39. Round off each of the following numbers to the indicated number of significant digits and write the answer in standard scientific notation.

    a. 4341×10^2 to three significant digits
    b. 93.441×10^3 to three significant digits
    c. 0.99155×10^2 to four significant digits
    d. 9.3265 to four significant digits

40. Round off each of the following numbers to the indicated number of significant digits and write the answer in standard scientific notation.

    a. 0.0008751 to two significant digits
    b. 93,745 to four significant digits
    c. 0.89724 to three significant digits
    d. 9.995×10^2 to three significant digits

Determining Significant Figures in Calculations

QUESTIONS

41. Consider the calculation indicated below:

$$\frac{2.21 \times 0.072333 \times 0.15}{4.995}$$

    Explain why the answer to this calculation should be reported to only two significant digits.

42. Suppose a group of objects were to be weighed separately on a scale and then the individual masses *added together* to determine the total mass of the group of objects. What would determine how many significant digits should appear in the reported total mass? Give an example of such a calculation.

43. When the calculation $(2.31)(4.9795 \times 10^3)/(1.9971 \times 10^4)$ is performed, how many significant digits should be reported for the answer? You should *not* need to perform the calculation.

44. Try this with your calculator: Enter $2 \div 3$ and press the = sign. What does your calculator say is the answer? What would be wrong with that answer if the 2 and 3 were experimentally determined numbers?

45. When the sum $4.9965 + 2.11 + 3.887$ is calculated, to how many decimal places should the answer be reported? You should *not* need to perform the calculation.

46. How many digits after the decimal point should be reported when the calculation $(10,434 - 9.3344)$ is performed?

PROBLEMS

Note: See the Appendix for help in doing mathematical operations with numbers that contain exponents.

47. Evaluate each of the following mathematical expressions, and express the answer to the correct number of significant digits.

    a. $44.2124 + 0.81 + 7.335$
    b. $9.7789 + 3.3315 - 2.21$
    c. $0.8891 + 0.225 + 4.14$
    d. $(7.223 + 9.14 + 3.7795)/3.1$

48. Evaluate each of the following mathematical expressions, and express the answer to the correct number of significant digits.

a. $(4.771 + 2.3)/3.1$
b. $5.02 \times 10^2 + 4.1 \times 10^2$
c. $1.091 \times 10^3 + 2.21 \times 10^2 + 1.14 \times 10^1$
d. $(2.7991 \times 10^{-6})/(4.22 \times 10^6)$

49. *Without actually performing the calculations indicated,* tell to how many significant digits the answer to the calculation should be expressed.

a. $(0.196)(0.08215)(295)/(1.1)$
b. $(4.215 + 3.991 + 2.442)/(0.22)$
c. $(7.881)(4.224)(0.00033)/(2.997)$
d. $(6.219 + 2.03)/(3.1159)$

50. *Without actually performing the calculations indicated,* tell to how many significant digits the answer to the calculation should be expressed.

a. $\dfrac{(9.7871)(2)}{(0.00182)(43.21)}$
b. $(67.41 + 0.32 + 1.98)/(18.225)$
c. $(2.001 \times 10^{-3})(4.7 \times 10^{-6})(68.224 \times 10^{-2})$
d. $(72.15)(63.9)[1.98 + 4.8981]$

51. How many significant digits should be used to report the answer to each of the following calculations? Do not perform the calculations.

a. $(2.7518 + 9.01 + 3.3349)/(2.1)$
b. $(2.7751 \times 1.95)/(.98)$
c. $12.0078/3.014$
d. $(0.997 + 4.011 + 3.876)/(1.86 \times 10^{-3})$

52. Evaluate each of the following and write the answer to the appropriate number of significant figures.

a. $(2.0944 + 0.0003233 + 12.22)/(7.001)$
b. $(1.42 \times 10^2 + 1.021 \times 10^3)/(3.1 \times 10^{-1})$
c. $(9.762 \times 10^{-3})/(1.43 \times 10^2 + 4.51 \times 10^1)$
d. $(6.1982 \times 10^{-4})^2$

2.6 Problem Solving and Dimensional Analysis

QUESTIONS

53. A _____ represents a ratio based on an equivalence statement between two measurements.

54. How many significant figures are understood for the numbers in the following definition: 1 mi = 5280 ft?

55. Given that 1 mi = 1760 yd, determine what conversion factor is appropriate to convert 1849 yd to miles; to convert 2.781 mi to yards.

56. Given that 1 in. = 2.54 cm exactly, indicate what conversion factor is appropriate to convert 12.3 in. to centimeters; to convert 63.52 cm to inches.

For Exercises 57 and 58, apples cost $0.79 per pound.

57. What conversion factor is appropriate to express the cost of 5.3 lb of apples?

58. What conversion factor could be used to determine how many pounds of apples could be bought for $2.00?

PROBLEMS

Note: Appropriate equivalence statements for various units are found inside the back cover of this book.

59. Perform each of the following conversions, being sure to set up the appropriate conversion factor in each case.

a. 12.5 in. to centimeters
b. 12.5 cm to inches
c. 2513 ft to miles
d. 4.53 ft to meters
e. 6.52 min to seconds
f. 52.3 cm to meters
g. 4.21 m to yards
h. 8.02 oz to pounds

60. Perform each of the following conversions, being sure to set up the appropriate conversion factor in each case.

a. 4.21 ft to inches
b. 37.3 in. to feet
c. 45.2 cm to millimeters
d. 761.2 mm to centimeters
e. 1.25 L to quarts
f. 4.21 qt to pints
g. 6.21 kg to pounds
h. 1.75 lb to ounces

61. Perform each of the following conversions, being sure to set up the appropriate conversion factor in each case.

a. 1.75 mi to kilometers
b. 2.63 gal to quarts
c. 4.675 calories to joules
d. 756.2 mm Hg to atmospheres
e. 36.3 atomic mass units to kilograms
f. 46.2 in. to centimeters
g. 2.75 qt to fluid ounces
h. 3.51 yd to meters

62. Perform each of the following conversions, being sure to set up the appropriate conversion factor in each case.

a. 104.971 kilopascals to atmospheres
b. 6.25 pt to quarts
c. 18.0 oz to kilograms
d. 4.213 joules to calories
e. 1.632 mi to feet
f. 4.52 qt to pints
g. 9.25 oz to grams
h. 56.2 fluid ounces to quarts

63. 12.01 g of carbon contains 6.02×10^{23} carbon atoms. What is the mass in grams of 1.89×10^{25} carbon atoms?

64. Los Angeles and Honolulu are 2558 mi apart. What is this distance in kilometers?

65. The United States has high-speed trains running between Boston and New York capable of speeds up to 160 mi/h. Are these trains faster or slower than the fastest trains in the United Kingdom, which reach speeds of 225 km/h?

66. The radius of an atom is on the order of 10^{-10} m. What is this radius in centimeters? in inches? in nanometers?

All even-numbered Questions and Problems have answers in the back of this book and solutions in the *Solutions Guide*.

2.7 Temperature Conversions

QUESTIONS

67. The temperature scale used in everyday life in most of the world except the United States is the _____ scale.

68. The _____ point of water is at 32° on the Fahrenheit temperature scale.

69. The normal boiling point of water is _____ °F, or _____ °C.

70. The freezing point of water is _____ K.

71. On both the Celsius and Kelvin temperature scales, there are _____ degrees between the normal freezing and boiling points of water.

72. On which temperature scale (°F, °C, or K) does 1 degree represent the smallest change in temperature?

PROBLEMS

73. Make the following temperature conversions:

    a. 44.2 °C to kelvins   c. −20 °C to kelvins
    b. 891 K to °C   d. 273.1 K to °C

74. Make the following temperature conversions:

    a. −78.1 °C to kelvins   c. 489 K to °C
    b. 775 K to °C   d. 24.3 °C to kelvins

75. Convert the following Fahrenheit temperatures to Celsius degrees.

    a. a chilly morning in early autumn, 45 °F
    b. a hot, dry day in the Arizona desert, 115 °F
    c. the temperature in winter when my car won't start, −10 °F
    d. the surface of a star, 10,000 °F

76. Convert the following Celsius temperatures to Fahrenheit degrees.

    a. the boiling temperature of ethyl alcohol, 78.1 °C
    b. a hot day at the beach on a Greek isle, 40. °C
    c. the lowest possible temperature, −273 °C
    d. the body temperature of a person with hypothermia, 32 °C

Ⓕ 77. The "Chemistry in Focus" segment *Tiny Thermometers* states that the temperature range for the carbon nanotube gallium thermometers is 50 °C to 500 °C.

    a. What properties of gallium make it useful in a thermometer?
    b. Determine the useful temperature range for the gallium thermometer in Fahrenheit units.

78. Perform the indicated temperature conversions.

    a. 275 K to °C
    b. 82 °F to °C
    c. −21 °C to °F
    d. −40 °F to °C (Notice anything unusual about your answer?)

2.8 Density

QUESTIONS

79. What does the *density* of a substance represent?

80. The most common units for density are _____ .

81. A kilogram of lead occupies a much smaller volume than a kilogram of water, because _____ has a much higher density.

82. If a solid block of glass, with a volume of exactly 100 in.^{3}, is placed in a basin of water that is full to the brim, then _____ of water will overflow from the basin.

83. Is the density of a gaseous substance likely to be larger or smaller than the density of a liquid or solid substance at the same temperature? Why?

84. What property of density makes it useful as an aid in identifying substances?

85. Referring to Table 2.8, which substance listed is most dense? Which substance is least dense? For the two substances you have identified, for which one would a 1.00-g sample occupy the larger volume?

86. Referring to Table 2.8, determine whether copper, silver, lead, or mercury is the least dense.

PROBLEMS

87. For the masses and volumes indicated, calculate the density in grams per cubic centimeter.

    a. mass = 452.1 g; volume = 292 cm^3
    b. mass = 0.14 lb; volume = 125 mL
    c. mass = 1.01 kg; volume = 1000 cm^3
    d. mass = 225 mg; volume = 2.51 mL

88. For the masses and volumes indicated, calculate the density in grams per cubic centimeter.

    a. mass = 122.4 g; volume = 5.5 cm^3
    b. mass = 19,302 g; volume = 0.57 m^3
    c. mass = 0.0175 kg; volume = 18.2 mL
    d. mass = 2.49 g; volume = 0.12 m^3

89. The element bromine at room temperature is a liquid with a density of 3.12 g/mL. Calculate the mass of 125 mL of bromine. What volume does 85.0 g of bromine occupy?

90. Isopropyl alcohol (rubbing alcohol) has a density of 0.785 g/mL. What is the mass of 3.75 L of isopropyl alcohol? What volume would 125 g of isopropyl alcohol occupy?

91. If 1000. mL of linseed oil has a mass of 929 g, calculate the density of linseed oil.

92. A material will float on the surface of a liquid if the material has a density less than that of the liquid. Given that the density of water is approximately 1.0 g/mL under many conditions, will a block of material having a volume of 1.2×10^4 in.^{3} and weighing 3.5 lb float or sink when placed in a reservoir of water?

All even-numbered Questions and Problems have answers in the back of this book and solutions in the Solutions Guide.

93. Iron has a density of 7.87 g/cm^3. If 52.4 g of iron is added to 75.0 mL of water in a graduated cylinder, to what volume reading will the water level in the cylinder rise?

94. The density of pure silver is 10.5 g/cm^3 at 20 °C. If 5.25 g of pure silver pellets is added to a graduated cylinder containing 11.2 mL of water, to what volume level will the water in the cylinder rise?

95. Use the information in Table 2.8 to calculate the volume of 50.0 g of each of the following substances.

    a. sodium chloride   c. benzene
    b. mercury   d. silver

96. Use the information in Table 2.8 to calculate the mass of 50.0 cm^3 of each of the following substances.

    a. gold   c. lead
    b. iron   d. aluminum

Additional Problems

97. Indicate the number of significant digits in the answer when each of the following expressions is evaluated (you do *not* have to evaluate the expression).

    a. $(6.25)/(74.1143)$
    b. $(1.45)(0.08431)(6.022 \times 10^{23})$
    c. $(4.75512)(9.74441)/(3.14)$

98. Express each of the following as an "ordinary" decimal number.

    a. 3.011×10^{23} e. 4.32002×10^{-4}
    b. 5.091×10^{9} f. 3.001×10^{-2}
    c. 7.2×10^{2} g. 2.9901×10^{-7}
    d. 1.234×10^{5} h. 4.2×10^{-1}

99. Write each of the following numbers in standard scientific notation, rounding off the numbers to three significant digits.

    a. 424.6174   c. 26,755   e. 72.5654
    b. 0.00078145 d. 0.0006535

100. Which unit of length in the metric system would be most appropriate in size for measuring each of the following items?

    a. the dimensions of this page
    b. the size of the room in which you are sitting
    c. the distance from New York to London
    d. the diameter of a baseball
    e. the diameter of a common pin

101. Make the following conversions.

    a. 1.25 in. to feet and to centimeters
    b. 2.12 qt to gallons and to liters
    c. 2640 ft to miles and to kilometers
    d. 1.254 kg lead to its volume in cubic centimeters
    e. 250. mL ethanol to its mass in grams
    f. 3.5 $in.^3$ of mercury to its volume in milliliters and its mass in kilograms

102. On the planet Xgnu, the most common units of length are the blim (for long distances) and the kryll (for shorter distances). Because the Xgnuese have 14 fingers, perhaps it is not surprising that 1400 kryll = 1 blim.

    a. Two cities on Xgnu are 36.2 blim apart. What is this distance in kryll?
    b. The average Xgnuese is 170 kryll tall. What is this height in blims?
    c. This book is presently being used at Xgnu University. The area of the cover of this book is 72.5 square krylls. What is its area in square blims?

103. You pass a road sign saying "New York 110 km." If you drive at a constant speed of 100. km/h, how long should it take you to reach New York?

104. At the mall, you decide to try on a pair of French jeans. Naturally, the waist size of the jeans is given in centimeters. What does a waist measurement of 52 cm correspond to in inches?

105. Suppose your car is rated at 45 mi/gal for highway use and 38 mi/gal for city driving. If you wanted to write your friend in Spain about your car's mileage, what ratings in kilometers per liter would you report?

106. You are in Paris, and you want to buy some peaches for lunch. The sign in the fruit stand indicates that peaches cost 2.45 euros per kilogram. Given that 1 euro is equivalent to approximately $1.20, calculate what a pound of peaches will cost in dollars.

107. For a pharmacist dispensing pills or capsules, it is often easier to weigh the medication to be dispensed rather than to count the individual pills. If a single antibiotic capsule weighs 0.65 g, and a pharmacist weighs out 15.6 g of capsules, how many capsules have been dispensed?

108. On the planet Xgnu, the natives have 14 fingers. On the official Xgnuese temperature scale (°X), the boiling point of water (under an atmospheric pressure similar to earth's) is 140 °X, whereas water freezes at 14 °X. Derive the relationship between °X and °C.

109. For a material to float on the surface of water, the material must have a density less than that of water (1.0 g/mL) and must not react with the water or dissolve in it. A spherical ball has a radius of 0.50 cm and weighs 2.0 g. Will this ball float or sink when placed in water? (*Note:* Volume of a sphere $= \frac{4}{3}\pi r^3$.)

110. A gas cylinder having a volume of 10.5 L contains 36.8 g of gas. What is the density of the gas?

111. Using Table 2.8, calculate the volume of 25.0 g of each of the following:

    a. hydrogen gas (at 1 atmosphere pressure)
    b. mercury
    c. lead
    d. water

112. Ethanol and benzene dissolve in each other. When 100. mL of ethanol is dissolved in 1.00 L of benzene, what is the mass of the mixture? (See Table 2.8.)

113. When 2891 is written in scientific notation, the exponent indicating the power of 10 is _____ .

114. For each of the following numbers, if the number is rewritten in scientific notation, will the exponent of the power of 10 be positive, negative, or zero?

    a. $1/10^3$ d. 7.21
    b. 0.00045   e. 1/3
    c. 52,550

115. For each of the following numbers, if the number is rewritten in scientific notation, will the exponent of the power of 10 be positive, negative, or zero?

    a. 4,915,442   c. 0.001
    b. 1/1000   d. 3.75

116. For each of the following numbers, by how many places does the decimal point have to be moved to express the number in standard scientific notation? In each case, is the exponent positive or negative?

    a. 102   e. 398,000
    b. 0.00000000003489   f. 1
    c. 2500   g. 0.3489
    d. 0.00003489   h. 0.0000003489

117. For each of the following numbers, by how many places must the decimal point be moved to express the number in standard scientific notation? In each case, will the exponent be positive, negative, or zero?

    a. 55,651   d. 883,541
    b. 0.000008991   e. 0.09814
    c. 2.04

118. For each of the following numbers, by how many places must the decimal point be moved to express the number in standard scientific notation? In each case, will the exponent be positive, negative, or zero?

    a. 72.471   d. 6519
    b. 0.008941   e. 0.000000008715
    c. 9.9914

119. Express each of the following numbers in scientific (exponential) notation.

    a. 529   e. 0.0003442
    b. 240,000,000   f. 0.000000000902
    c. 301,000,000,000,000,000   g. 0.043
    d. 78,444   h. 0.0821

120. Express each of the following as an "ordinary" decimal number.

    a. 2.98×10^{-5} g. 9.87×10^7
    b. 4.358×10^9 h. 3.7899×10^2
    c. 1.9928×10^{-6} i. 1.093×10^{-1}
    d. 6.02×10^{23} j. 2.9004×10^0
    e. 1.01×10^{-1} k. 3.9×10^{-4}
    f. 7.87×10^{-3} l. 1.904×10^{-8}

121. Write each of the following numbers in *standard* scientific notation.

    a. 102.3×10^{-5} e. 5993.3×10^3
    b. 32.03×10^{-3} f. 2054×10^{-1}
    c. 59933×10^2 g. $32,000,000 \times 10^{-6}$
    d. 599.33×10^4 h. 59.933×10^5

122. Write each of the following numbers in *standard* scientific notation. See the Appendix if you need help multiplying or dividing numbers with exponents.

    a. $1/10^2$ e. $(10^6)^{1/2}$
    b. $1/10^{-2}$ f. $(10^6)(10^4)/(10^2)$
    c. $55/10^3$ g. $1/0.0034$
    d. $(3.1 \times 10^6)/10^{-3}$ h. $3.453/10^{-4}$

123. The fundamental unit of length or distance in the metric system is the _____ .

124. The SI unit of temperature is the _____ .

125. Which distance is farther, 100 km or 50 mi?

126. The unit of volume corresponding to 1/1000 of a liter is referred to as 1 milliliter, or 1 cubic _____ .

127. The volume 0.250 L could also be expressed as _____ mL.

128. The distance 10.5 cm could also be expressed as _____ m.

129. Would an automobile moving at a constant speed of 100 km/h violate a 65-mph speed limit?

130. Which weighs more, 100 g of water or 1 kg of water?

131. Which weighs more, 4.25 g of gold or 425 mg of gold?

132. The length 100 mm can also be expressed as _____ cm.

133. When a measurement is made, the certain numbers plus the first uncertain number are called the _____ of the measurement.

134. In the measurement of the length of the pin indicated in Figure 2.5, what are the *certain* numbers in the measurement shown?

135. Indicate the number of significant figures in each of the following:

    a. This book contains over 500 pages.
    b. A mile is just over 5000 ft.
    c. A liter is equivalent to 1.059 qt.
    d. The population of the United States is approaching 250 million.
    e. A kilogram is 1000 g.
    f. The Boeing 747 cruises at around 600 mph.

136. Round off each of the following numbers to three significant digits.

    a. 0.00042557   c. 5,991,556
    b. 4.0235×10^{-5} d. 399.85
    e. 0.0059998

137. Round off each of the following numbers to the indicated number of significant digits.

    a. 0.75555 to four digits   c. 17.005 to four digits
    b. 292.5 to three digits   d. 432.965 to five digits

138. Evaluate each of the following, and write the answer to the appropriate number of significant figures.

    a. $149.2 + 0.034 + 2000.34$
    b. $1.0322 \times 10^3 + 4.34 \times 10^3$

c. $4.03 \times 10^{-2} - 2.044 \times 10^{-3}$
d. $2.094 \times 10^5 - 1.073 \times 10^6$

139. Evaluate each of the following, and write the answer to the appropriate number of significant figures.

a. $(0.0432)(2.909)(4.43 \times 10^8)$
b. $(0.8922)/[(0.00932)(4.03 \times 10^2)]$
c. $(3.923 \times 10^2)(2.94)(4.093 \times 10^{-3})$
d. $(4.9211)(0.04434)/[(0.000934)(2.892 \times 10^{-7})]$

140. Evaluate each of the following, and write the answer to the appropriate number of significant figures.

a. $(2.9932 \times 10^4)[2.4443 \times 10^2 + 1.0032 \times 10^1]$
b. $[2.34 \times 10^2 + 2.443 \times 10^{-1}]/(0.0323)$
c. $(4.38 \times 10^{-3})^2$
d. $(5.9938 \times 10^{-6})^{1/2}$

141. Given that 1 L = 1000 cm^3, determine what conversion factor is appropriate to convert 350 cm^3 to liters; to convert 0.200 L to cubic centimeters.

142. Given that 12 months = 1 year, determine what conversion factor is appropriate to convert 72 months to years; to convert 3.5 years to months.

143. Perform each of the following conversions, being sure to set up clearly the appropriate conversion factor in each case.

a. 8.43 cm to millimeters
b. 2.41×10^2 cm to meters
c. 294.5 nm to centimeters
d. 404.5 m to kilometers
e. 1.445×10^4 m to kilometers
f. 42.2 mm to centimeters
g. 235.3 m to millimeters
h. 903.3 nm to micrometers

144. Perform each of the following conversions, being sure to set up clearly the appropriate conversion factor(s) in each case.

a. 908 oz to kilograms
b. 12.8 L to gallons
c. 125 mL to quarts
d. 2.89 gal to milliliters
e. 4.48 lb to grams
f. 550 mL to quarts

145. The mean distance from the earth to the sun is 9.3×10^7 mi. What is this distance in kilometers? in centimeters?

146. Given that one gross = 144 items, how many pencils are contained in 6 gross?

147. Convert the following temperatures to kelvins.

a. 0 °C
b. 25 °C
c. 37 °C
d. 100 °C
e. −175 °C
f. 212 °C

148. Carry out the indicated temperature conversions.

a. 175 °F to kelvins
b. 255 K to Celsius degrees
c. −45 °F to Celsius degrees
d. 125 °C to Fahrenheit degrees

149. For the masses and volumes indicated, calculate the density in grams per cubic centimeter.

a. mass = 234 g; volume = 2.2 cm^3
b. mass = 2.34 kg; volume = 2.2 m^3
c. mass = 1.2 lb; volume = 2.1 ft^3
d. mass = 4.3 ton; volume = 54.2 yd^3

150. A sample of a liquid solvent has a density of 0.915 g/mL. What is the mass of 85.5 mL of the liquid?

151. An organic solvent has a density of 1.31 g/mL. What volume is occupied by 50.0 g of the liquid?

152. A solid metal sphere has a volume of 4.2 ft^3. The mass of the sphere is 155 lb. Find the density of the metal sphere in grams per cubic centimeter.

153. A sample containing 33.42 g of metal pellets is poured into a graduated cylinder initially containing 12.7 mL of water, causing the water level in the cylinder to rise to 21.6 mL. Calculate the density of the metal.

154. Convert the following temperatures to Fahrenheit degrees.

a. −5 °C
b. 273 K
c. −196 °C
d. 0 K
e. 86 °C
f. −273 °C

155. For each of the following descriptions, identify the power of 10 being indicated by the *prefix* in the measurement.

a. The sign on the interstate highway says to tune my AM radio to 540 *kilo*hertz for traffic information.
b. My new digital camera has a two-*giga*byte flash memory card.
c. The shirt I bought for my dad on my European vacation shows the sleeve length in *centi*meters.
d. My brother's camcorder records on 8-*milli*meter tape cassettes.

F 156. The "Chemistry in Focus" segment *Critical Units!* discusses the importance of unit conversions. Read the segment and make the proper unit conversions to answer the following questions.

a. The Mars Climate Orbiter burned up because it dipped lower in the Mars atmosphere than planned. How many miles lower than planned did it dip?
b. A Canadian jetliner almost ran out of fuel because someone pumped less fuel into the aircraft than was thought. How many more pounds of fuel should have been pumped into the aircraft?

F 157. Read the "Chemistry in Focus" segment *Measurement: Past, Present, and Future* and answer the following questions.

a. Give three examples of how developing sophisticated measuring devices is useful in our society.
b. Explain how advances in measurement abilities can be a problem.

F 158. The "Chemistry in Focus" segment *Measurement: Past, Present, and Future* states that hormones can be detected to a level of 10^{-8} g/L. Convert this level to units of pounds per gallon.

All even-numbered Questions and Problems have answers in the back of this book and solutions in the Solutions Guide.

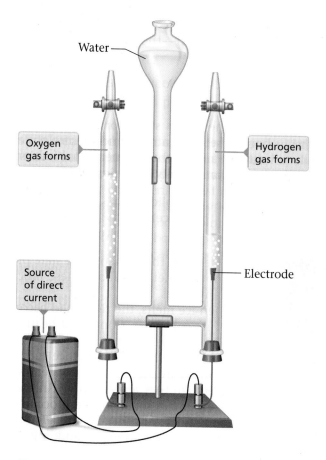

Water

Oxygen gas forms

Hydrogen gas forms

Source of direct current

Electrode

Figure 3.3

Electrolysis, the decomposition of water by an electric current, is a chemical process.

The most important thing about all these changes is that the water molecules are still intact. The motions of individual molecules and the distances between them change, but *H_2O molecules are still present*. These changes of state are **physical changes** because they do not affect the composition of the substance. In each state we still have water (H_2O), not some other substance.

Now suppose we run an electric current through water as illustrated in Figure 3.3. Something very different happens. The water disappears and is replaced by two new gaseous substances, hydrogen and oxygen. An electric current actually causes the water molecules to come apart—the water *decomposes* to hydrogen and oxygen. We can represent this process as follows:

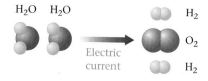

H_2O H_2O H_2

O_2

Electric current H_2

This is a **chemical change** because water (consisting of H_2O molecules) has changed into different substances: hydrogen (containing H_2 molecules) and oxygen (containing O_2 molecules). Thus in this process, the H_2O molecules have been replaced by O_2 and H_2 molecules. Let us summarize:

Coffee is a solu___
variable compo___
strong or weak___

Physical and Chemical Changes

1. A *physical change* involves a change in one or more physical properties, but no change in the fundamental components that make up the substance. The most common physical changes are changes of state: solid ⇔ liquid ⇔ gas.
2. A *chemical change* involves a change in the fundamental components of the substance; a given substance changes into a different substance or substances. Chemical changes are called **reactions**: silver tarnishes by reacting with substances in the air; a plant forms a leaf by combining various substances from the air and soil; and so on.

EXAMPLE 3.2 | Identifying Physical and Chemical Changes

Classify each of the following as a physical or a chemical change.

a. Iron metal is melted.

b. Iron combines with oxygen to form rust.

c. Wood burns in air.

d. A rock is broken into small pieces.

SOLUTION

a. Melted iron is just liquid iron and could cool again to the solid state. This is a physical change.

b. When iron combines with oxygen, it forms a different substance (rust) that contains iron and oxygen. This is a chemical change because a different substance forms.

c. Wood burns to form different substances (as we will see later, they include carbon dioxide and water). After the fire, the wood is no longer in its original form. This is a chemical change.

d. When the rock is broken up, all the smaller pieces have the same composition as the whole rock. Each new piece differs from the original only in size and shape. This is a physical change.

Oxygen combines with the chemicals in wood to produce flames. Is a physical or chemical change taking place?

Jim Pickerell/Stock Connection

Self-Check **EXERCISE 3.2** Classify each of the following as a chemical change, a physical change, or a combination of the two.

a. Milk turns sour.

b. Wax is melted over a flame and then catches fire and burns.

See Problems 3.17 and 3.18. ■

3.3 Elements and Compounds

OBJECTIVE: To understand the definitions of elements and compounds.

Element: a substance that cannot be broken down into other substances by chemical methods.

As we examine the chemical changes of matter, we encounter a series of fundamental substances called **elements.** Elements cannot be broken down into other substances by chemical means. Examples of elements are iron,

Self-Check

The separation
sometimes occ
environment a
benefit (see pl

Although we sa
separate mixtur
substances, it is
impossible to s
into totally pure
matter how har
impurities (com
original mixture
of the "pure su

A solution is a l
mixture.

Figure 3.4

When table salt is
homogeneous mi

F   directs you to the *Chemistry in Focus* feature in the chapter

VP   indicates visual problems

OWL   interactive versions of these problems are assignable in OWL.

Summary

1. Matter can exist in three states—solid, liquid, and gas—and can be described in terms of its physical and chemical properties. Chemical properties describe a substance's ability to undergo a change to a different substance. Physical properties are the characteristics a substance exhibits as long as no chemical change occurs.

2. A physical change involves a change in one or more physical properties, but no change in composition. A chemical change transforms a substance into a new substance or substances.

3. A mixture has variable composition. A homogeneous mixture has the same properties throughout; a heterogeneous mixture does not. A pure substance always has the same composition. We can physically separate mixtures of pure substances by distillation and filtration.

4. Pure substances are of two types: elements, which cannot be broken down chemically into simpler substances, and compounds, which can be broken down chemically into elements.

Active Learning Questions

These questions are designed to be considered by groups of students in class. Often these questions work well for introducing a particular topic in class.

1. When water boils, you can see bubbles rising to the surface of the water. Of what are these bubbles made?

   a. air
   b. hydrogen and oxygen gas
   c. oxygen gas
   d. water vapor
   e. carbon dioxide gas

2. If you place a glass rod over a burning candle, the glass turns black. What is happening to each of the following (physical change, chemical change, both, or neither) as the candle burns? Explain.

   a. the wax
   b. the wick
   c. the glass rod

3. The boiling of water is a

   a. physical change because the water disappears.
   b. physical change because the gaseous water is chemically the same as the liquid.
   c. chemical change because heat is needed for the process to occur.
   d. chemical change because hydrogen and oxygen gases are formed from water.
   e. chemical and physical change.

   Explain your answer.

---

4. Is there a difference between a homogeneous mixture of hydrogen and oxygen in a 2:1 ratio and a sample of water vapor? Explain.

5. Sketch a magnified view (showing atoms and/or molecules) of each of the following and explain why the specified type of mixture is

   a. a heterogeneous mixture of two different compounds
   b. a homogeneous mixture of an element and a compound

6. Are all physical changes accompanied by chemical changes? Are all chemical changes accompanied by physical changes? Explain.

7. Why would a chemist find fault with the phrase "pure orange juice"?

8. Are separations of mixtures physical or chemical changes? Explain.

9. Explain the terms *element, atom,* and *compound.* Provide an example and microscopic drawing of each.

10. Mixtures can be classified as either homogeneous or heterogeneous. Compounds cannot be classified in this way. Why not? In your answer, explain what is meant by heterogeneous and homogeneous.

11. Provide microscopic drawings down to the atoms for Figure 3.10 in your text.

12. Look at Table 2.8 in your text. How do the densities of gases, liquids, and solids compare to each other? Use microscopic pictures to explain why this is true.

VP 13. Label each of the following as an atomic element, a molecular element, or a compound.

VP 14. Match each description below with the following microscopic pictures. More than one picture may fit each description. A picture may be used more than once or not used at all.

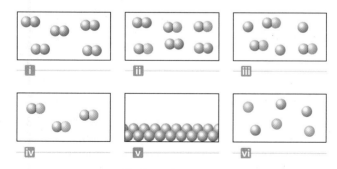

   a. a gaseous compound
   b. a mixture of two gaseous elements
   c. a solid element
   d. a mixture of gaseous element and a gaseous compound

Questions and Problems

3.1 Matter

QUESTIONS

1. What are the two characteristic properties of *matter?*

2. What is the chief factor that determines the *physical state* of a sample of matter?

3. Of the three states of matter, _____ and _____ are not very compressible.

4. Gases and _____ take on the shape of the container in which they are located.

5. Compare and contrast the ease with which molecules are able to move relative to each other in the three states of matter.

6. Matter in the _____ state has no shape and fills completely whatever container holds it.

7. What similarities are there between the liquid and gaseous states of matter? What differences are there between these two states?

8. A sample of matter that is "rigid" has (stronger/ weaker) forces among the particles in the sample than does a sample that is not rigid.

9. Consider three 10-g samples of water: one as ice, one as liquid, and one as vapor. How do the volumes of these three samples compare with one another? How is this difference in volume related to the physical state involved?

10. In a sample of a gaseous substance, more than 99% of the overall volume of the sample is empty space. How is this fact reflected in the properties of a gaseous substance, compared with the properties of a liquid or solid substance?

3.2 Physical and Chemical Properties and Changes

QUESTIONS

11. Elemental bromine is a dense, dark-red, pungent-smelling liquid. Are these characteristics of elemental bromine physical or chemical properties?

12. Elemental bromine reacts vigorously with elemental sodium metal to form a white solid. Does this characteristic of elemental bromine represent a physical or a chemical property?

(For Exercises 13–14) Magnesium metal is very malleable, and is able to be pounded and stretched into long, thin, narrow "ribbons" that are often used in the introductory chemistry lab as a source of the metal. If a strip of magnesium ribbon is ignited in a Bunsen burner flame, the magnesium burns brightly and produces a quantity of white magnesium oxide powder.

13. From the information given above, indicate one *chemical* property of magnesium metal.

14. From the information given above, indicate one *physical* property of magnesium metal.

15. Choose a chemical substance with which you are familiar, and give an example of a *chemical change* that might take place to the substance.

16. Which of the following does *not* represent a physical property/change?

   a. Elemental sulfur boils at 445 °C.
   b. Elemental sulfur is yellow in its most common form.
   c. Elemental sulfur burns with a dark blue flame in the air to form a gaseous material.
   d. Elemental sulfur is rigid and hard.

17. Classify each of the following as a *physical* or *chemical* change or property.

   a. Oven cleaners contain sodium hydroxide, which converts the grease/oil spatters inside the oven to water-soluble materials, which can be washed away.
   b. A rubber band stretches when you pull on it.
   c. A cast-iron frying pan will rust if it is not dried after washing.
   d. Concentrated hydrochloric acid has a choking, pungent odor.
   e. Concentrated hydrochloric acid will burn a hole in cotton jeans because the acid breaks down the cellulose fibers in cotton.
   f. Copper compounds often form beautiful blue crystals when a solution of a given copper compound is evaporated slowly.
   g. Copper metal combines with substances in the air to form a green "patina" that protects the copper from further reaction.
   h. Bread turns brown when you heat it in a toaster.
   i. When you use the perfume your boyfriend gave you for your birthday, the liquid of the perfume evaporates quickly from your skin.
   j. If you leave your steak on the gas grill too long, the steak will turn black and char.
   k. Hydrogen peroxide fizzes when it is applied to a cut or scrape.

18. Classify each of the following as a *physical* or *chemical* change or property.

   a. A fireplace poker glows red when you heat it in the fire.
   b. A marshmallow turns black when toasted too long in a campfire.
   c. Hydrogen peroxide dental strips will make your teeth whiter.
   d. If you wash your jeans with chlorine bleach, they will fade.
   e. If you spill some nail polish remover on your skin, it will evaporate quickly.
   f. When making ice cream at home, salt is added to lower the temperature of the ice being used to freeze the mixture.
   g. A hair clog in your bathroom sink drain can be cleared with drain cleaner.

All even-numbered Questions and Problems have answers in the back of this book and solutions in the Solutions Guide.

h. The perfume your boyfriend gave you for your birthday smells like flowers.

i. Mothballs pass directly into the gaseous state in your closet without first melting.

j. A log of wood is chopped up with an axe into smaller pieces of wood.

k. A log of wood is burned in a fireplace.

3.3 Elements and Compounds

QUESTIONS

19. Although some elements are found in an isolated state, most elements are found combined as _____ with other elements.

20. What is a *compound?* What are compounds composed of? What is true about the composition of a compound, no matter where we happen to find the compound?

21. Certain elements have special affinities for other elements. This causes them to bind together in special ways to form _____ .

22. _____ can be broken down into the component elements by chemical changes.

23. The composition of a given pure compound is always _____ no matter what the source of the compound.

24. How do the properties of a compound, in general, compare to the properties of the elements that constitute it? Give an example of a common compound and the elements of which it is composed to illustrate your answer.

3.4 Mixtures and Pure Substances

QUESTIONS

25. If iron filings are placed with excess powdered sulfur in a beaker, the iron filings are still attracted by a magnet and could be separated from the sulfur with the magnet. Would this combination of iron and sulfur represent a *mixture* or a *pure substance?*

26. If the combination of iron filings and sulfur in Question 25 is heated strongly, the iron reacts with the sulfur to form a solid that is no longer attracted by the magnet. Would this still represent a "mixture?" Why or why not?

27. What does it mean to say that a solution is a *homogeneous mixture?*

28. Give three examples of heterogeneous *mixtures* and three examples of *solutions* that you might use in everyday life.

29. Classify the following as *mixtures* or *pure substances.*

    a. the vegetable soup you had for lunch
    b. the fertilizer your dad spreads on the front lawn in the spring
    c. the salt you sprinkle on your French fries
    d. the hydrogen peroxide you cleaned a cut finger with

30. Classify the following as *mixtures* or *pure substances.*

    a. the sugar you just put into your coffee while studying
    b. the perfume you dab on before you go on a date
    c. the black pepper you grind onto your salad at dinner
    d. the distilled water you use in your iron so it won't get clogged

31. Classify the following mixtures as *heterogeneous* or *homogeneous.*

    a. soil
    b. mayonnaise
    c. Italian salad dressing
    d. the wood from which the desk you are studying on is made
    e. sand at the beach

F 32. Read the "Chemistry in Focus" segment *Concrete—An Ancient Material Made New* and classify concrete as an element, a mixture, or a compound. Defend your answer.

3.5 Separation of Mixtures

QUESTIONS

33. Describe how the process of *distillation* could be used to separate a solution into its component substances. Give an example.

34. Describe how the process of *filtration* could be used to separate a mixture into its components. Give an example.

35. In a common laboratory experiment in general chemistry, students are asked to determine the relative amounts of benzoic acid and charcoal in a solid mixture. Benzoic acid is relatively soluble in hot water, but charcoal is not. Devise a method for separating the two components of this mixture.

36. During a filtration or distillation experiment, we separate a mixture into its individual components. Do the chemical identities of the components of the mixture change during such a process? Explain.

Additional Problems

37. If powdered elemental zinc and powdered elemental sulfur are poured into a metal beaker and then heated strongly, a very vigorous chemical reaction takes place, and the _____ zinc sulfide is formed.

38. Pure substance X is melted, and the liquid is placed in an electrolysis apparatus such as that shown in Figure 3.3. When an electric current is passed through the liquid, a brown solid forms in one chamber and a white solid forms in the other chamber. Is substance X a compound or an element?

39. If a piece of hard white blackboard chalk is heated strongly in a flame, the mass of the piece of chalk will decrease, and eventually the chalk will crumble into a fine white dust. Does this change suggest that the chalk is composed of an element or a compound?

40. During a very cold winter, the temperature may remain below freezing for extended periods. However, fallen snow can still disappear, even though it cannot melt. This is possible because a solid can vaporize directly, without passing through the liquid state. Is this process (sublimation) a physical or a chemical change?

41. Discuss the similarities and differences between a liquid and a gas.

42. In gaseous substances, the individual molecules are relatively (close/far apart) and are moving freely, rapidly, and randomly.

43. The fact that solutions of potassium chromate are bright yellow is an example of a _____ property.

44. The fact that the substance copper(II) sulfate pentahydrate combines with ammonia in solution to form a new compound is an example of a _____ property.

(For Exercises 45–46) Solutions containing nickel(II) ion are usually bright green in color. When potassium hydroxide is added to such a nickel(II) solution, a pale-green fluffy solid forms and settles out of the solution.

45. The fact that a reaction takes place when potassium hydroxide is added to a solution of nickel(II) ions is an example of a _____ property.

46. The fact that a solution of nickel(II) ion is bright green is an example of a _____ property.

47. The processes of melting and evaporation involve changes in the _____ of a substance.

48. _____ is the process of making a chemical reaction take place by passage of an electric current through a substance or solution.

49. Classify each of the following as a *physical* or *chemical* change or property.

   a. Milk curdles if a few drops of lemon juice are added to it.
   b. Butter turns rancid if it is left exposed at room temperature.
   c. Salad dressing separates into layers after standing.
   d. Milk of magnesia neutralizes stomach acid.
   e. The steel in a car has rust spots.
   f. A person is asphyxiated by breathing carbon monoxide.
   g. Sulfuric acid spilled on a laboratory notebook page causes the paper to char and disintegrate.
   h. Sweat cools the body as the sweat evaporates from the skin.
   i. Aspirin reduces fever.
   j. Oil feels slippery.
   k. Alcohol burns, forming carbon dioxide and water.

50. Classify the following mixtures as *homogeneous* or *heterogeneous*.

   a. the freshman class at your school
   b. salsa
   c. mashed potatoes
   d. cream of tomato soup
   e. cream of mushroom soup

51. Classify the following mixtures as *homogeneous* or *heterogeneous*.

   a. potting soil   d. window glass
   b. white wine   e. granite
   c. your sock drawer

52. Mixtures can be heterogeneous or homogeneous. Give two examples of each type. Explain why you classified each example as you did.

53. Give three examples each of *heterogeneous* mixtures and *homogeneous* mixtures.

54. The fact that water freezes at 0 °C is an example of a _phys_ property, whereas the fact that water can be broken down by electricity into hydrogen gas and oxygen gas is a _____ property.

55. Choose an element or compound with which you are familiar in everyday life. Give two *physical* properties and two *chemical* properties of your choice of element or compound.

56. Oxygen forms molecules in which there are two oxygen atoms, O_2. Phosphorus forms molecules in which there are four phosphorus atoms, P_4. Does this mean that O_2 and P_4 are "compounds" because they contain multiple atoms? O_2 and P_4 react with each other to form diphosphorus pentoxide, P_2O_5. Is P_2O_5 a "compound"? Why (or why not)?

57. Give an example of each of the following:

   a. a heterogeneous mixture
   b. a homogeneous mixture
   c. an element
   d. a compound
   e. a physical property or change
   f. a chemical property or change
   g. a solution

58. Distillation and filtration are important methods for separating the components of mixtures. Suppose we had a mixture of sand, salt, and water. Describe how filtration and distillation could be used sequentially to separate this mixture into the three separate components.

59. Sketch the apparatus commonly used for simple distillation in the laboratory and identify each component.

60. The properties of a compound are often very different from the properties of the elements making up the compound. Water is an excellent example of this idea. Discuss.

All even-numbered Questions and Problems have answers in the back of this book and solutions in the Solutions Guide.

QUESTIONS

1. In the exercises for Chapter 1 of this text, you were asked to give your *own* definition of what chemistry represents. After having completed a few more chapters in this book, has your definition changed? Do you have a better appreciation for what chemists do? Explain.

2. Early on in this text, some aspects of the best way to go about learning chemistry were presented. In *beginning* your study of chemistry, you may initially have approached studying chemistry as you would any of your other academic subjects (taking notes in class, reading the text, memorizing facts, and so on). Discuss why the ability to sort through and analyze facts and the ability to propose and solve problems are so much more important in learning chemistry.

3. You have learned the basic way in which scientists analyze problems, propose models to explain the systems under consideration, and then experiment to test their models. Suppose you have a sample of a liquid material. You are not sure whether the liquid is a pure *compound* (for example, water or alcohol) or a *solution*. How could you apply the scientific method to study the liquid and to determine which type of material the liquid is?

4. Many college students would not choose to take a chemistry course if it were not required for their major. Do you have a better appreciation of *why* chemistry is a required course for your own particular major or career choice? Discuss.

5. In Chapter 2 of this text, you were introduced to the International System (SI) of measurements. What are the basic units of this system for mass, distance, time, and temperature? What are some of the prefixes used to indicate common multiples and subdivisions of these basic units? Give three examples of the *use* of such prefixes, and explain why the prefix is appropriate to the quantity or measurement being indicated.

6. Most people think of science as being a specific, exact discipline, with a "correct" answer for every problem. Yet you were introduced to the concept of *uncertainty* in scientific measurements. What is meant by "uncertainty"? How does uncertainty creep into measurements? How is uncertainty *indicated* in scientific measurements? Can uncertainty ever be completely eliminated in experiments? Explain.

7. After studying a few chapters of this text, and perhaps having done a few lab experiments and taken a few quizzes in chemistry, you are probably sick of hearing the term *significant figures*. Most chemistry teachers make a big deal about significant figures. Why is reporting the correct number of significant figures so important in science? Summarize the rules for deciding whether a figure in a calculation is "significant." Summarize the rules for rounding off numbers. Summarize the rules for doing arithmetic with the correct number of significant figures.

8. This chemistry course may have been the first time you have encountered the method of *dimensional analysis* in problem solving. Explain what are meant by a *conversion factor* and an *equivalence statement*. Give an everyday example of how you might use dimensional analysis to solve a simple problem.

9. You have learned about several temperature scales so far in this text. Describe the Fahrenheit, Celsius, and Kelvin temperature scales. How are these scales defined? Why were they defined this way? Which of these temperature scales is the most fundamental? Why?

10. What is *matter?* What is matter composed of? What are some of the different types of matter? How do these types of matter differ and how are they the same?

11. It is important to be able to distinguish between the *physical* and the *chemical* properties of chemical substances. Choose a chemical substance you are familiar with, then use the Internet or a handbook of chemical information to list three physical properties and three chemical properties of the substance.

12. What is an *element* and what is a *compound?* Give examples of each. What does it mean to say that a compound has a *constant composition?* Would samples of a particular compound here and in another part of the world have the same composition and properties?

13. What is a mixture? What is a solution? How do mixtures differ from pure substances? What are some of the techniques by which mixtures can be resolved into their components?

PROBLEMS

14. For each of the following, make the indicated conversion.

    a. 0.0008917 to standard scientific notation
    b. 2.795×10^{-4} to ordinary decimal notation
    c. 4.913×10^3 to ordinary decimal notation
    d. 85,100,000 to standard scientific notation
    e. $5.751 \times 10^5 \times 2.119 \times 10^{-4}$ to standard scientific notation.
    f. $\dfrac{2.791 \times 10^{-5}}{8.219 \times 10^3}$

15. For each of the following, make the indicated conversion, showing explicitly the conversion factor(s) you used.

    a. 493.2 g to kilograms
    b. 493.2 g to pounds
    c. 9.312 mi to kilometers
    d. 9.312 mi to feet

e. 4.219 m to feet

f. 4.219 m to centimeters

g. 429.2 mL to liters

h. 2.934 L to quarts

16. Without performing the actual calculations, determine to how many significant figures the results of the following calculations should be reported.

a. $\dfrac{(2.991)(4.3785)(1.97)}{(2.1)}$

b. $\dfrac{(5.2)}{(1.9311 + 0.4297)}$

c. $1.782 + 0.00035 + 2.11$

d. $(6.521)(5.338 + 2.11)$

e. $9 - 0.000017$

f. $(4.2005 + 2.7)(7.99118)$

g. $(5.12941 \times 10^4)(4.91 \times 10^{-3})(0.15)$

h. $97.215 + 42.1 - 56.3498$

17. Chapter 2 introduced the Kelvin and Celsius temperature scales and related them to the Fahrenheit temperature scale commonly used in the United States.

a. How is the size of the temperature unit (degree) related between the Kelvin and Celsius scale?

b. How does the size of the temperature unit (degree) on the Fahrenheit scale compare to the temperature unit on the Celsius scale?

c. What is the normal freezing point of water on each of the three temperature scales?

d. Convert 27.5 °C to kelvins and to Fahrenheit degrees.

e. Convert 298.1 K to Celsius degrees and to Fahrenheit degrees.

f. Convert 98.6 °F to kelvins and to Celsius degrees.

18. a. Given that 100. mL of ethyl alcohol weighs 78.5 g, calculate the density of ethyl alcohol.

b. What volume would 1.59 kg of ethyl alcohol occupy?

c. What is the mass of 1.35 L of ethyl alcohol?

d. Pure aluminum metal has a density of 2.70 g/cm^3. Calculate the volume of 25.2 g of pure aluminum.

e What will a rectangular block of pure aluminum having dimensions of 12.0 cm $\times$ 2.5 cm $\times$ 2.5 cm weigh?

19. Which of the following represent physical properties or changes, and which represent chemical properties or changes?

a. You curl your hair with a curling iron.

b. You curl your hair by getting a "permanent wave" at the hair salon.

c. Ice on your sidewalk melts when you put salt on it.

d. A glass of water evaporates overnight when it is left on the bedside table.

e. Your steak chars if the skillet is too hot.

f. Alcohol feels cool when it is spilled on the skin.

g. Alcohol ignites when a flame is brought near it.

h. Baking powder causes biscuits to rise.

4

Chemical Foundations: Elements, Atoms, and Ions

● Gold leafing on the ceiling of the Library of Congress in Washington, D.C. *(John Zoiner)*

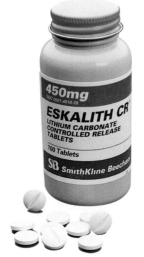

© Cengage Learning

Lithium is administered in the
form of lithium carbonate pills.

The Granger Collection, New York

Robert Boyle at 62 years of age.

The chemical elements are very important to each of us in our daily lives. Although certain elements are present in our bodies in tiny amounts, they can have a profound impact on our health and behavior. As we will see in this chapter, lithium can be a miracle treatment for someone with bipolar disorder, and our cobalt levels can have a remarkable impact on whether we behave violently.

Since ancient times, humans have used chemical changes to their advantage. The processing of ores to produce metals for ornaments and tools and the use of embalming fluids are two applications of chemistry that were used before 1000 B.C.

The Greeks were the first to try to explain why chemical changes occur. By about 400 B.C. they had proposed that all matter was composed of four fundamental substances: fire, earth, water, and air.

The next 2000 years of chemical history were dominated by alchemy. Some alchemists were mystics and fakes who were obsessed with the idea of turning cheap metals into gold. However, many alchemists were sincere scientists, and this period saw important events: the elements mercury, sulfur, and antimony were discovered, and alchemists learned how to prepare acids.

The first scientist to recognize the importance of careful measurements was the Irishman Robert Boyle (1627–1691). Boyle is best known for his pioneering work on the properties of gases, but his most important contribution to science was probably his insistence that science should be firmly grounded in experiments. For example, Boyle held no preconceived notions about how many elements there might be. His definition of the term *element* was based on experiments: a substance was an element unless it could be broken down into two or more simpler substances. For example, air could not be an element as the Greeks believed, because it could be broken down into many pure substances.

As Boyle's experimental definition of an element became generally accepted, the list of known elements grew, and the Greek system of four elements died. But although Boyle was an excellent scientist, he was not always right. For some reason he ignored his own definition of an element and clung to the alchemists' views that metals were not true elements and that a way would be found eventually to change one metal into another.

4.1 The Elements

OBJECTIVES: To learn about the relative abundances of the elements. • To learn the names of some elements.

In studying the materials of the earth (and other parts of the universe), scientists have found that all matter can be broken down chemically into about 100 different elements. At first it might seem amazing that the millions of known substances are composed of so few fundamental elements. Fortunately for those trying to understand and systematize it, nature often uses a relatively small number of fundamental units to assemble even extremely complex materials. For example, proteins, a group of substances that serve the human body in almost uncountable ways, are all made by linking together a few fundamental units to form huge molecules. A nonchemical example is the English language, where hundreds of thousands of words are constructed from only 26 letters. If you take apart the thousands of words in an English dictionary, you will find only these 26 fundamental components. In much the same way, when we take apart all of the substances in the world around us, we find only about 100 fundamental building blocks—the elements. Compounds are made by combining atoms of the various elements, just as words are constructed from the 26 letters of the alphabet. And just as you had to learn the letters of the alphabet before you learned to read and write, you need to learn the names and symbols of the chemical elements before you can read and write chemistry.

Presently about 116 different elements are known,* 88 of which occur naturally. (The rest have been made in laboratories.) The elements vary tremendously in abundance. In fact, only 9 elements account for most of the compounds found in the earth's crust. In Table 4.1, the elements are listed in order of their abundance (mass percent) in the earth's crust, oceans, and atmosphere. Note that nearly half of the mass is accounted for by oxygen alone. Also note that the 9 most abundant elements account for over 98% of the total mass.

Oxygen, in addition to accounting for about 20% of the earth's atmosphere (where it occurs as O_2 molecules), is found in virtually all the rocks, sand, and soil on the earth's crust. In these latter materials, oxygen is not present as O_2 molecules but exists in compounds that usually contain silicon and aluminum atoms. The familiar substances of the geological world, such as rocks and sand, contain large groups of silicon and oxygen atoms bound together to form huge clusters.

The list of elements found in living matter is very different from the list of elements found in the earth's crust. Table 4.2 shows the distribution of elements in the human body. Oxygen, carbon, hydrogen, and nitrogen form the basis for all biologically important molecules. Some elements found in the body (called trace elements) are crucial for life, even though they are present in relatively small amounts. For example, chromium helps the body use sugars to provide energy.

Footprints in the sand of the Namib Desert in Namibia.

Table 4.1	Distribution (Mass Percent) of the 18 Most Abundant Elements in the Earth's Crust, Oceans, and Atmosphere		
Element	Mass Percent	Element	Mass Percent
oxygen	49.2	titanium	0.58
silicon	25.7	chlorine	0.19
aluminum	7.50	phosphorus	0.11
iron	4.71	manganese	0.09
calcium	3.39	carbon	0.08
sodium	2.63	sulfur	0.06
potassium	2.40	barium	0.04
magnesium	1.93	nitrogen	0.03
hydrogen	0.87	fluorine	0.03
		all others	0.49

*This number changes as new elements are made in particle accelerators.

Table 4-2 Abundance of Elements in the Human Body

Major Elements	Mass Percent	Trace Elements (in alphabetical order)
oxygen	65.0	arsenic
carbon	18.0	chromium
hydrogen	10.0	cobalt
nitrogen	3.0	copper
calcium	1.4	fluorine
phosphorus	1.0	iodine
magnesium	0.50	manganese
potassium	0.34	molybdenum
sulfur	0.26	nickel
sodium	0.14	selenium
chlorine	0.14	silicon
iron	0.004	vanadium
zinc	0.003	

One more general comment is important at this point. As we have seen, elements are fundamental to understanding chemistry. However, students are often confused by the many different ways that chemists use the term *element*. Sometimes when we say *element*, we mean a single atom of that element. We might call this the microscopic form of an element. Other times when we use the term *element*, we mean a sample of the element large enough to weigh on a balance. Such a sample contains many, many atoms of the element, and we might call this the macroscopic form of the element. There is yet a further complication. As we will see in more detail in Section 4.9 the macroscopic forms of several elements contain molecules rather than individual atoms as the fundamental components. For example, chemists know that oxygen gas consists of molecules with two oxygen atoms connected together (represented as O—O or more commonly as O_2). Thus when we refer to the element oxygen we might mean a single atom of oxygen, a single O_2 molecule, or a macroscopic sample containing many O_2 molecules. Finally, we often use the term *element* in a generic fashion. When we say the human body contains the element sodium or lithium, we do not mean that free elemental sodium or lithium is present. Rather, we mean that atoms of these elements are present in some form. In this text we will try to make clear what we mean when we use the term *element* in a particular case.

4.2 Symbols for the Elements

OBJECTIVE: To learn the symbols of some elements.

The names of the chemical elements have come from many sources. Often an element's name is derived from a Greek, Latin, or German word that describes some property of the element. For example, gold was originally called *aurum*, a Latin word meaning "shining dawn," and lead was known as *plumbum*, which means "heavy." The names for chlorine and iodine come

CHEMISTRY *IN* FOCUS

Trace Elements: Small but Crucial

We all know that certain chemical elements, such as calcium, carbon, nitrogen, phosphorus, and iron, are essential for humans to live. However, many other elements that are present in tiny amounts in the human body are also essential to life. Examples are chromium, cobalt, iodine, manganese, and copper. Chromium assists in the metabolism of sugars, cobalt is present in vitamin B_{12}, iodine is necessary for the proper functioning of the thyroid gland, manganese appears to play a role in maintaining the proper calcium levels in bones, and copper is involved in the production of red blood cells.

It is becoming clear that certain trace elements are very important in determining human behavior. For example, lithium (administered as lithium carbonate) has been a miracle drug for some people afflicted with bipolar disorder, a disease that produces oscillatory behavior between inappropriate "highs" and the blackest of depressions. Although its exact function remains unknown, lithium seems to moderate the levels of neurotransmitters (compounds that are essential to nerve function), thus relieving some of the extreme emotions in sufferers of bipolar disorder.

In addition, a chemist named William Walsh has done some very interesting studies on the inmates of Stateville Prison in Illinois. By analyzing the trace elements in the hair of prisoners, he has found intriguing relationships between the behavior of the inmates and their trace element profile. For example, Walsh found an inverse relationship between the level of cobalt in the prisoner's body and the degree of violence in his behavior.

Besides the levels of trace elements in our bodies, the various substances in the water, the food we consume, and the air we breathe also are of great importance to our health. For example, many scientists are concerned about our exposure to aluminum, through aluminum compounds used in water purification, baked goods and cheese (sodium aluminum phosphate acts as a leavening agent and also is added to cheese to make it softer and easier to melt), and the aluminum that dissolves from our cookware and utensils. The effects of exposure to low levels of aluminum on humans are not presently clear, but there are some indications that we should limit our intake of this element.

Another example of low-level exposure to an element is the fluoride placed in many water supplies and toothpastes to control tooth decay by making tooth enamel more resistant to dissolving. However, the exposure of large numbers of people to fluoride is quite controversial—many people think it is harmful.

The chemistry of trace elements is fascinating and important. Keep your eye on the news for further developments.

---

from Greek words describing their colors, and the name for bromine comes from a Greek word meaning "stench." In addition, it is very common for an element to be named for the place where it was discovered. You can guess where the elements francium, germanium, californium,* and americium* were first found. Some of the heaviest elements are named after famous scientists—for example, einsteinium* and nobelium.*

We often use abbreviations to simplify the written word. For example, it is much easier to put MA on an envelope than to write out Massachusetts, and we often write USA instead of United States of America. Likewise, chemists have invented a set of abbreviations or **element symbols** for the chemical elements. These symbols usually consist of the first letter or the

*These elements are made artificially. They do not occur naturally.

first two letters of the element names. The first letter is always capitalized, and the second is not. Examples include

fluorine	F	neon	Ne
oxygen	O	silicon	Si
carbon	C		

Sometimes, however, the two letters used are not the first two letters in the name. For example,

zinc	Zn	cadmium	Cd
chlorine	Cl	platinum	Pt

The symbols for some other elements are based on the original Latin or Greek name.

Current Name	Original Name	Symbol
gold	aurum	Au
lead	plumbum	Pb
sodium	natrium	Na
iron	ferrum	Fe

A list of the most common elements and their symbols is given in Table 4.3. You can also see the elements represented on a table in the inside front cover of this text. We will explain the form of this table (which is called the periodic table) in later chapters.

In the symbol for an element, only the first letter is capitalized.

Walter Urie/West Light/Corbis

Various forms of the element gold.

Table 4.3   The Names and Symbols of the Most Common Elements

Element	Symbol	Element	Symbol
aluminum	Al	lithium	Li
antimony (stibium)*	Sb	magnesium	Mg
argon	Ar	manganese	Mn
arsenic	As	mercury (hydrargyrum)	Hg
barium	Ba	neon	Ne
bismuth	Bi	nickel	Ni
boron	B	nitrogen	N
bromine	Br	oxygen	O
cadmium	Cd	phosphorus	P
calcium	Ca	platinum	Pt
carbon	C	potassium (kalium)	K
chlorine	Cl	radium	Ra
chromium	Cr	silicon	Si
cobalt	Co	silver (argentium)	Ag
copper (cuprum)	Cu	sodium (natrium)	Na
fluorine	F	strontium	Sr
gold (aurum)	Au	sulfur	S
helium	He	tin (stannum)	Sn
hydrogen	H	titanium	Ti
iodine	I	tungsten (wolfram)	W
iron (ferrum)	Fe	uranium	U
lead (plumbum)	Pb	zinc	Zn

*Where appropriate, the original name is shown in parentheses so that you can see where some of the symbols came from.

4.3 Dalton's Atomic Theory

OBJECTIVES: To learn about Dalton's theory of atoms. • To understand and illustrate the law of constant composition.

Figure 4.1

John Dalton (1766–1844) was an English scientist who made his living as a teacher in Manchester. Although Dalton is best known for his atomic theory, he made contributions in many other areas, including meteorology (he recorded daily weather conditions for 46 years, producing a total of 200,000 data entries). A rather shy man, Dalton was colorblind to red (a special handicap for a chemist) and suffered from lead poisoning contracted from drinking stout (strong beer or ale) that had been drawn through lead pipes.

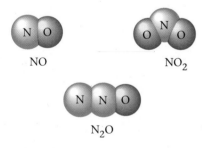

Figure 4.2

Dalton pictured compounds as collections of atoms. Here NO, NO_2, and N_2O are represented. Note that the number of atoms of each type in a molecule is given by a subscript, except that the number 1 is always assumed and never written.

As scientists of the eighteenth century studied the nature of materials, several things became clear:

1. Most natural materials are mixtures of pure substances.

2. Pure substances are either elements or combinations of elements called compounds.

3. A given compound always contains the same proportions (by mass) of the elements. For example, water *always* contains 8 g of oxygen for every 1 g of hydrogen, and carbon dioxide *always* contains 2.7 g of oxygen for every 1 g of carbon. This principle became known as the **law of constant composition.** It means that a given compound always has the same composition, regardless of where it comes from.

John Dalton (Figure 4.1), an English scientist and teacher, was aware of these observations, and in about 1808 he offered an explanation for them that became known as **Dalton's atomic theory.** The main ideas of this theory (model) can be stated as follows:

Dalton's Atomic Theory

1. Elements are made of tiny particles called **atoms.**
2. All atoms of a given element are identical.
3. The atoms of a given element are different from those of any other element.
4. Atoms of one element can combine with atoms of other elements to form compounds. A given compound always has the same relative numbers and types of atoms.
5. Atoms are indivisible in chemical processes. That is, atoms are not created or destroyed in chemical reactions. A chemical reaction simply changes the way the atoms are grouped together.

Dalton's model successfully explained important observations such as the law of constant composition. This law makes sense because if a compound always contains the same relative numbers of atoms, it will always contain the same proportions by mass of the various elements.

Like most new ideas, Dalton's model was not accepted immediately. However, Dalton was convinced he was right and *used his model to predict* how a given pair of elements might combine to form more than one compound. For example, nitrogen and oxygen might form a compound containing one atom of nitrogen and one atom of oxygen (written NO), a compound containing two atoms of nitrogen and one atom of oxygen (written N_2O), a compound containing one atom of nitrogen and two atoms of oxygen (written NO_2), and so on (Figure 4.2). When the existence of these substances was verified, it was a triumph for Dalton's model. Because Dalton was able to predict correctly the formation of multiple compounds between two elements, his atomic theory became widely accepted.

No Laughing Matter

Sometimes solving one problem leads to another. One such example involves the catalytic converters now required on all automobiles sold around much of the world. The purpose of these converters is to remove harmful pollutants such as CO and NO_2 from automobile exhausts. The good news is that these devices are quite effective and have led to much cleaner air in congested areas. The bad news is that these devices produce significant amounts of nitrous oxide, N_2O, commonly known as laughing gas because when inhaled it produces relaxation and mild inebriation. It was long used by dentists to make their patients more tolerant of some painful dental procedures.

The problem with N_2O is not that it is an air pollutant but that it is a "greenhouse gas." Certain molecules, such as CO_2, CH_4, N_2O, and others,

strongly absorb infrared light ("heat radiation"), which causes the earth's atmosphere to retain more of its heat energy. Human activities have significantly increased the concentrations of these gases in the atmosphere. Mounting evidence suggests that the earth is warming as a result, leading to possible dramatic climatic changes.

A recent study by the Environmental Protection Agency (EPA) indicates that N_2O now accounts for over 7% of the greenhouse gases in the atmosphere and that automobiles equipped with catalytic converters produce nearly half of this N_2O. Ironically, N_2O is not regulated, because the Clean Air Act of 1970 was written to control smog—not greenhouse gases. The United States and other industrialized nations are now negotiating to find ways to control global warming, but no agreement is in place.

The N_2O situation illustrates just how complex environmental issues are. Clean may not necessarily be "green."

4.4 Formulas of Compounds

OBJECTIVE: To learn how a formula describes a compound's composition.

A **compound** is a distinct substance that is composed of the atoms of two or more elements and always contains exactly the same relative masses of those elements. In light of Dalton's atomic theory, this simply means that a compound always contains the same relative *numbers* of atoms of each element. For example, water always contains two hydrogen atoms for each oxygen atom.

> Here, *relative* refers to ratios.

The types of atoms and the number of each type in each unit (molecule) of a given compound are conveniently expressed by a **chemical formula.** In a chemical formula the atoms are indicated by the element symbols, and the number of each type of atom is indicated by a subscript, a number that appears to the right of and below the symbol for the element. The formula for water is written H_2O, indicating that each molecule of water contains two atoms of hydrogen and one atom of oxygen (the subscript 1 is always understood and not written). Following are some general rules for writing formulas:

Rules for Writing Formulas

1. Each atom present is represented by its element symbol.
2. The number of each type of atom is indicated by a subscript written to the right of the element symbol.
3. When only one atom of a given type is present, the subscript 1 is not written.

EXAMPLE 4.1 | Writing Formulas of Compounds

Write the formula for each of the following compounds, listing the elements in the order given.

a. Each molecule of a compound that has been implicated in the formation of acid rain contains one atom of sulfur and three atoms of oxygen.

b. Each molecule of a certain compound contains two atoms of nitrogen and five atoms of oxygen.

c. Each molecule of glucose, a type of sugar, contains six atoms of carbon, twelve atoms of hydrogen, and six atoms of oxygen.

SOLUTION

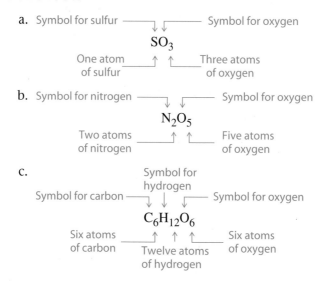

a. Symbol for sulfur ———↓ ↓——— Symbol for oxygen
$$SO_3$$
One atom ——↑ ↑—— Three atoms
of sulfur   of oxygen

b. Symbol for nitrogen ———↓ ↓——— Symbol for oxygen
$$N_2O_5$$
Two atoms ——↑ ↑—— Five atoms
of nitrogen   of oxygen

c.   Symbol for hydrogen
Symbol for carbon ——↓ ↓ ↓—— Symbol for oxygen
$$C_6H_{12}O_6$$
Six atoms ——↑ ↑ ↑—— Six atoms
of carbon   Twelve atoms   of oxygen
            of hydrogen

Self-Check   EXERCISE 4.1   Write the formula for each of the following compounds, listing the elements in the order given.

a. A molecule contains four phosphorus atoms and ten oxygen atoms.

b. A molecule contains one uranium atom and six fluorine atoms.

c. A molecule contains one aluminum atom and three chlorine atoms.

See Problems 4.19 and 4.20. ■

4.5 The Structure of the Atom

OBJECTIVES: To learn about the internal parts of an atom. • To understand Rutherford's experiment to characterize the atom's structure.

Dalton's atomic theory, proposed in about 1808, provided such a convincing explanation for the composition of compounds that it became generally accepted. Scientists came to believe that *elements consist of atoms* and that *compounds are a specific collection of atoms* bound together in some way. But what is an atom like? It might be a tiny ball of matter that is the same throughout with no internal structure—like a ball bearing. Or the atom

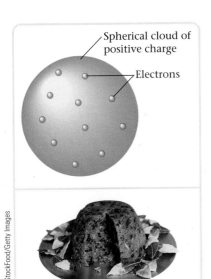

Spherical cloud of positive charge

Electrons

StockFood/Getty Images

Figure 4.3

One of the early models of the atom was the plum pudding model, in which the electrons were pictured as embedded in a positively charged spherical cloud, much as raisins are distributed in an old-fashioned plum pudding.

Some historians credit J. J. Thomson for the plum pudding model.

might be composed of parts—it might be made up of a number of subatomic particles. But if the atom contains parts, there should be some way to break up the atom into its components.

Many scientists pondered the nature of the atom during the 1800s, but it was not until almost 1900 that convincing evidence became available that the atom has a number of different parts.

A physicist in England named J. J. Thomson showed in the late 1890s that the atoms of any element can be made to emit tiny negative particles. (He knew the particles had a negative charge because he could show that they were repelled by the negative part of an electric field.) Thus he concluded that all types of atoms must contain these negative particles, which are now called **electrons.**

On the basis of his results, Thomson wondered what an atom must be like. Although he knew that atoms contain these tiny negative particles, he also knew that whole atoms are not negatively *or* positively charged. Thus he concluded that the atom must also contain positive particles that balance exactly the negative charge carried by the electrons, giving the atom a zero overall charge.

Another scientist pondering the structure of the atom was William Thomson (better known as Lord Kelvin and no relation to J. J. Thomson). Lord Kelvin got the idea (which might have occurred to him during dinner) that the atom might be something like plum pudding (a pudding with raisins randomly distributed throughout). Kelvin reasoned that the atom might be thought of as a uniform "pudding" of positive charge with enough negative electrons scattered within to counterbalance that positive charge (see Figure 4.3). Thus the plum pudding model of the atom came into being.

If you had taken this course in 1910, the plum pudding model would have been the only picture of the atom described. However, our ideas about the atom were changed dramatically in 1911 by a physicist named Ernest Rutherford (Figure 4.4), who learned physics in J. J. Thomson's laboratory in the late 1890s. By 1911 Rutherford had become a distinguished scientist with many important discoveries to his credit. One of his main areas of interest involved alpha particles (α particles), positively charged particles with a mass approximately 7500 times that of an electron. In studying the flight of these particles through air, Rutherford found that some of the α particles were deflected by something in the air. Puzzled by this, he designed an experiment that involved directing α particles toward a thin metal foil. Surrounding the foil was a detector coated with a substance that produced tiny

Figure 4.4

Ernest Rutherford (1871–1937) was born on a farm in New Zealand. In 1895 he placed second in a scholarship competition to attend Cambridge University but was awarded the scholarship when the winner decided to stay home and get married. Rutherford was an intense, hard-driving person who became a master at designing just the right experiment to test a given idea. He was awarded the Nobel Prize in chemistry in 1908.

Corbis-Bettmann

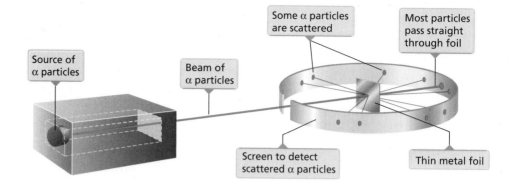

Figure 4.5
Rutherford's experiment on α-particle bombardment of metal foil.

flashes wherever it was hit by an α particle (Figure 4.5). The results of the experiment were very different from those Rutherford anticipated. Although most of the α particles passed straight through the foil, some of the particles were deflected at large angles, as shown in Figure 4.5, and some were reflected backward.

This outcome was a great surprise to Rutherford. (He described this result as comparable to shooting a gun at a piece of paper and having the bullet bounce back.) Rutherford knew that if the plum pudding model of the atom was correct, the massive α particles would crash through the thin foil like cannonballs through paper (as shown in Figure 4.6a). So he expected the α particles to travel through the foil experiencing, at most, very minor deflections of their paths.

Rutherford concluded from these results that the plum pudding model for the atom could not be correct. The large deflections of the α particles could be caused only by a center of concentrated positive charge that would repel the positively charged α particles, as illustrated in Figure 4.6b. Most of the α particles passed directly through the foil because the atom is mostly open space. The deflected α particles were those that had a "close encounter" with the positive center of the atom, and the few reflected α particles were those that scored a "direct hit" on the positive center. In Rutherford's mind these results could be explained only in terms of a **nuclear atom**—an atom with a dense center of positive charge (the **nucleus**) around which tiny electrons moved in a space that was otherwise empty.

He concluded that the nucleus must have a positive charge to balance the negative charge of the electrons and that it must be small and dense.

One of Rutherford's coworkers in this experiment was an undergraduate named Ernest Marsden who, like Rutherford, was from New Zealand.

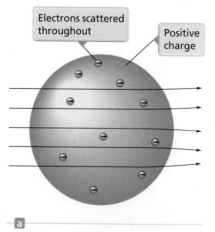

The results that the metal foil experiment would have yielded if the plum pudding model had been correct.

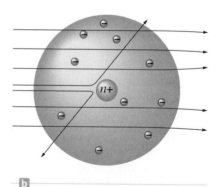

Actual results of Rutherford's experiment.

Figure 4.6

What was it made of? By 1919 Rutherford concluded that the nucleus of an atom contained what he called protons. A **proton** has the same magnitude (size) of charge as the electron, but its charge is *positive*. We say that the proton has a charge of 1+ and the electron a charge of 1−.

Rutherford reasoned that the hydrogen atom has a single proton at its center and one electron moving through space at a relatively large distance from the proton (the hydrogen nucleus). He also reasoned that other atoms must have nuclei (the plural of *nucleus*) composed of many protons bound together somehow. In addition, Rutherford and a coworker, James Chadwick, were able to show in 1932 that most nuclei also contain a neutral particle that they named the **neutron.** A neutron is slightly more massive than a proton but has no charge.

> If the atom were expanded to the size of a huge stadium, the nucleus would be only about as big as a fly at the center.

4.6 Introduction to the Modern Concept of Atomic Structure

OBJECTIVE: To understand some important features of subatomic particles.

> In this model the atom is called a nuclear atom because the positive charge is localized in a small, compact structure (the nucleus) and not spread out uniformly, as in the plum pudding view.

> The *chemistry* of an atom arises from its electrons.

In the years since Thomson and Rutherford, a great deal has been learned about atomic structure. The simplest view of the atom is that it consists of a tiny nucleus (about 10^{-13} cm in diameter) and electrons that move about the nucleus at an average distance of about 10^{-8} cm from it (Figure 4.7). To visualize how small the nucleus is compared with the size of the atom, consider that if the nucleus were the size of a grape, the electrons would be about one *mile* away on average. The nucleus contains protons, which have a positive charge equal in magnitude to the electron's negative charge, and neutrons, which have almost the same mass as a proton but no charge. The neutrons' function in the nucleus is not obvious. They may help hold the protons (which repel each other) together to form the nucleus, but we will not be concerned with that here. The relative masses and charges of the electron, proton, and neutron are shown in Table 4.4.

An important question arises at this point: *"If all atoms are composed of these same components, why do different atoms have different chemical properties?"* The answer lies in the number and arrangement of the electrons. The space in which the electrons move accounts for most of the atomic volume. The electrons are the parts of atoms that "intermingle" when atoms combine to form molecules. Therefore, the number of electrons a given atom possesses greatly affects the way it can interact with other atoms. As a result, atoms of different elements, which have different numbers of electrons, show different chemical behavior. Although the atoms of different elements also differ in their numbers of protons, it is the number of electrons that really determines chemical behavior. We will discuss how this happens in later chapters.

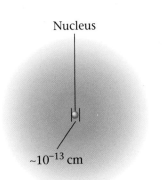

Nucleus

~10^{-13} cm

~10^{-8} cm

Figure 4.7

A nuclear atom viewed in cross section. (The symbol ~ means approximately.) This drawing does not show the actual scale. The nucleus is actually *much* smaller compared with the size of an atom.

Table 4.4	The Mass and Charge of the Electron, Proton, and Neutron	
Particle	Relative Mass*	Relative Charge
electron	1	1−
proton	1836	1+
neutron	1839	none

*The electron is arbitrarily assigned a mass of 1 for comparison.

4.7 Isotopes

OBJECTIVES: To learn about the terms isotope, atomic number, and mass number. • To understand the use of the symbol $^A_Z X$ to describe a given atom.

We have seen that an atom has a nucleus with a positive charge due to its protons and has electrons in the space surrounding the nucleus at relatively large distances from it.

As an example, consider a sodium atom, which has 11 protons in its nucleus. Because an atom has no overall charge, the number of electrons must equal the number of protons. Therefore, a sodium atom has 11 electrons in the space around its nucleus. It is *always* true that a sodium atom has 11 protons and 11 electrons. However, each sodium atom also has neutrons in its nucleus, and different types of sodium atoms exist that have different numbers of neutrons.

When Dalton stated his atomic theory in the early 1800s, he assumed all of the atoms of a given element were identical. This idea persisted for over a hundred years, until James Chadwick discovered that the nuclei of most atoms contain neutrons as well as protons. (This is a good example of how a theory changes as new observations are made.) After the discovery of the neutron, Dalton's statement that all atoms of a given element are identical had to be changed to "All atoms of the same element contain the same number of protons and electrons, but atoms of a given element may have different numbers of neutrons."

To illustrate this idea, consider the sodium atoms represented in Figure 4.8. These atoms are **isotopes,** or *atoms with the same number of protons but different numbers of neutrons.* The number of protons in a nucleus is called the atom's **atomic number.** The *sum* of the number of neutrons and the number of protons in a given nucleus is called the atom's **mass number.** To specify which of the isotopes of an element we are talking about, we use the symbol

$$^A_Z X$$

where

$\quad$ X = the symbol of the element
$\quad$ A = the mass number (number of protons and neutrons)
$\quad$ Z = the atomic number (number of protons)

> All atoms of the same element have the same number of protons (the element's atomic number) and the same number of electrons.

> In a free atom, the positive and negative charges always balance to yield a net zero charge.

> Atomic number: the number of protons. Mass number: the sum of protons and neutrons.

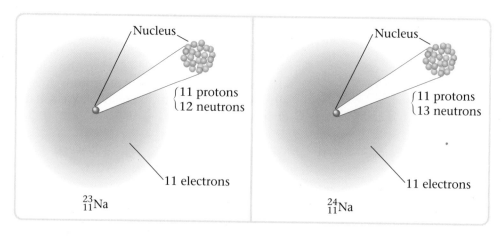

Figure 4.8

Two isotopes of sodium. Both have 11 protons and 11 electrons, but they differ in the number of neutrons in their nuclei.

"Whair" Do You Live?

Picture a person who has been the victim of a crime in a large city in the eastern United States. The person has been hit in the head and, as a result, has total amnesia. The person's ID has been stolen, but the authorities suspect he may not be from the local area. Is there any way to find out where the person might be from? The answer is yes. Recent research indicates that the relative amounts of the isotopes of hydrogen and oxygen in a person's hair indicate in which part of the United States a person lives.

Support for this idea has come from a recent study by James Ehleringer, a chemist at the University of Utah in Salt Lake City. Noting that the concentrations of hydrogen-2 (deuterium) and oxygen-18 in drinking water vary significantly from region to region in the United States (see accompanying illustration), Ehleringer and his colleagues collected hair samples from barbershops in 65 cities and 18 states. Their analyses showed that 86% of the variations in the hydrogen and oxygen isotopes in the hair samples result from the isotopic composition of the local water. Based on their results, the group was able to develop estimates of the isotopic signature of peoples' hair from various regions of the country. Although this method cannot be used to pinpoint a person's place of residence, it can give a general region. This method might be helpful for the amnesia victim described above by showing where to look for his family. His picture could be shown on TV in the region indicated by analysis of his hair. Another possible use of this technique is identifying the country of origin of victims of a natural disaster in a tourist region with visitors from all over the world. In fact, a similar technique was used to specify the countries of origin of the victims of the tsunami that devastated southern Asia in December 2004.

An interesting verification of this technique occurred when the researchers examined a strand of hair from a person who had recently moved from Beijing, China, to Salt Lake City. Analysis of various parts of the hair showed a distinct change in isotopic distribution corresponding to his change of residence. Thus the isotopes of elements can provide useful information in unexpected ways.

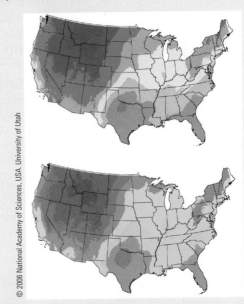

© 2006 National Academy of Sciences, USA. University of Utah

Maps of predicted concentrations of hydrogen-2 (top) and oxygen-18 (bottom). Red represents the highest concentration, and blue represents the lowest concentration of each isotope.

For example, the symbol for one particular type of sodium atom is written

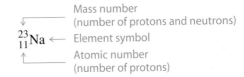

The particular atom represented here is called sodium-23, because it has a mass number of 23. Let's specify the number of each type of subatomic particle. From the atomic number 11 we know that the nucleus contains

11 protons. And because the number of electrons is equal to the number of protons, we know that this atom contains 11 electrons. How many neutrons are present? We can calculate the number of neutrons from the definition of the mass number

$$\text{Mass number} = \text{number of protons} + \text{number of neutrons}$$

or, in symbols,

$$A = Z + \text{number of neutrons}$$

We can isolate (solve for) the number of neutrons by subtracting Z from both sides of the equation

$$A - Z = Z - Z + \text{number of neutrons}$$
$$A - Z = \text{number of neutrons}$$

This is a general result. You can always determine the number of neutrons present in a given atom by subtracting the atomic number from the mass number. In this case ($^{23}_{11}\text{Na}$), we know that $A = 23$ and $Z = 11$. Thus

$$A - Z = 23 - 11 = 12 = \text{number of neutrons}$$

In summary, sodium-23 has 11 electrons, 11 protons, and 12 neutrons.

EXAMPLE 4.2 | **Interpreting Symbols for Isotopes**

In nature, elements are usually found as a mixture of isotopes. Three isotopes of elemental carbon are $^{12}_{6}\text{C}$ (carbon-12), $^{13}_{6}\text{C}$ (carbon-13), and $^{14}_{6}\text{C}$ (carbon-14). Determine the number of each of the three types of subatomic particles in each of these carbon atoms.

SOLUTION

The number of protons and electrons is the same in each of the isotopes and is given by the atomic number of carbon, 6. The number of neutrons can be determined by subtracting the atomic number (Z) from the mass number (A):

$$A - Z = \text{number of neutrons}$$

The numbers of neutrons in the three isotopes of carbon are

$$^{12}_{6}\text{C: number of neutrons} = A - Z = 12 - 6 = 6$$
$$^{13}_{6}\text{C: number of neutrons} = 13 - 6 = 7$$
$$^{14}_{6}\text{C: number of neutrons} = 14 - 6 = 8$$

In summary,

Symbol	Number of Protons	Number of Electrons	Number of Neutrons
$^{12}_{6}\text{C}$	6	6	6
$^{13}_{6}\text{C}$	6	6	7
$^{14}_{6}\text{C}$	6	6	8

Self-Check   **EXERCISE 4.2**   Give the number of protons, neutrons, and electrons in the atom symbolized by $^{90}_{38}\text{Sr}$. Strontium-90 occurs in fallout from nuclear testing. It can accumulate in bone marrow and may cause leukemia and bone cancer.

See Problems 4.39 and 4.42. ■

Isotope Tales

The atoms of a given element typically consist of several isotopes—atoms with the same number of protons but different numbers of neutrons. It turns out that the ratio of isotopes found in nature can be very useful in natural detective work. One reason is that the ratio of isotopes of elements found in living animals and humans reflects their diets. For example, African elephants that feed on grasses have a different $^{13}C/^{12}C$ ratio in their tissues than elephants that primarily eat tree leaves. This difference arises because grasses have a different growth pattern than leaves do, resulting in different amounts of ^{13}C and ^{12}C being incorporated from the CO_2 in the air. Because leaf-eating and grass-eating elephants live in different areas of Africa, the observed differences in the $^{13}C/^{12}C$ isotope ratios in elephant ivory samples have enabled authorities to identify the sources of illegal samples of ivory.

Another case of isotope detective work involves the tomb of King Midas, who ruled the kingdom Phyrgia in the eighth century B.C. Analysis of nitrogen isotopes in the king's decayed casket has revealed details about the king's diet. Scientists have learned that the $^{15}N/^{14}N$ ratios of carnivores are higher than those of herbivores, which in turn are higher than those of plants. It turns out that the organism responsible for decay of the king's wooden casket has an unusually large requirement for nitrogen. The source of this nitrogen was the body of the dead king. Because the decayed wood under his now-decomposed body showed a high $^{15}N/^{14}N$ ratio, researchers feel sure that the king's diet was rich in meat.

A third case of historical isotope detective work concerns the Pueblo ancestor people (commonly called the Anasazi), who lived in what is now northwestern New Mexico between A.D. 900 and 1150. The center of their civilization, Chaco Canyon, was a thriving cultural center boasting dwellings made of hand-hewn sandstone and more than 200,000 logs. The sources of the logs have always been controversial. Many theories have been advanced concerning the distances over which the logs were hauled. Recent research by Nathan B. English, a geochemist at the University of Arizona in Tucson, has used the distribution of strontium isotopes in the wood to identify the probable sources of the logs. This effort has enabled scientists to understand more clearly the Anasazi building practices.

Ancient Anasazi Indian cliff dwellings.

Paul Chesley/National Geographic/Getty images

These stories illustrate how isotopes can serve as valuable sources of biologic and historical information.

Self-Check **EXERCISE 4.3** Give the number of protons, neutrons, and electrons in the atom symbolized by $^{201}_{80}Hg$.

See Problems 4.39 and 4.42. ∎

EXAMPLE 4.3 | Writing Symbols for Isotopes

Write the symbol for the magnesium atom (atomic number 12) with a mass number of 24. How many electrons and how many neutrons does this atom have?

Magnesium burns in air to give a bright white flame.

SOLUTION

The atomic number 12 means the atom has 12 protons. The element magnesium is symbolized by Mg. The atom is represented as

$$^{24}_{12}\text{Mg}$$

and is called magnesium-24. Because the atom has 12 protons, it must also have 12 electrons. The mass number gives the total number of protons and neutrons, which means that this atom has 12 neutrons ($24 - 12 = 12$). ■

EXAMPLE 4.4 | Calculating Mass Number

Write the symbol for the silver atom ($Z = 47$) that has 61 neutrons.

SOLUTION

The element symbol is ^A_ZAg, where we know that $Z = 47$. We can find A from its definition, $A = Z +$ number of neutrons. In this case,

$$A = 47 + 61 = 108$$

The complete symbol for this atom is $^{108}_{47}\text{Ag}$.

Self-Check | **EXERCISE 4.4** Give the symbol for the phosphorus atom ($Z = 15$) that contains 17 neutrons.

See Problem 4.42. ■

4.8 Introduction to the Periodic Table

OBJECTIVES: To learn about various features of the periodic table. • To learn some of the properties of metals, nonmetals, and metalloids.

In any room where chemistry is taught or practiced, you are almost certain to find a chart called the **periodic table** hanging on the wall. This chart shows all of the known elements and gives a good deal of information about each. As our study of chemistry progresses, the usefulness of the periodic table will become more obvious. This section will simply introduce it.

A simple version of the periodic table is shown in Figure 4.9. Note that each box of this table contains a number written over one, two, or three letters. The letters are the symbols for the elements. The number shown above each symbol is the atomic number (the number of protons and also the number of electrons) for that element. For example, carbon (C) has atomic number 6:

6
C

Figure 4.9

The periodic table.

Lead (Pb) has atomic number 82:

82
Pb

Notice that elements 112 through 115 and 118 have unusual three-letter designations beginning with U. These are abbreviations for the systematic names of the atomic numbers of these elements. "Regular" names for these elements will be chosen eventually by the scientific community.

Note that the elements are listed on the periodic table in order of increasing atomic number. They are also arranged in specific horizontal rows and vertical columns. The elements were first arranged in this way in 1869 by Dmitri Mendeleev, a Russian scientist. Mendeleev arranged the elements in this way because of similarities in the chemical properties of various "families" of elements. For example, fluorine and chlorine are reactive gases that form similar compounds. It was also known that sodium and potassium behave very similarly. Thus the name *periodic table* refers to the fact that as we increase the atomic numbers, every so often an element occurs with

Mendeleev actually arranged the elements in order of increasing atomic mass rather than atomic number.

properties similar to those of an earlier (lower-atomic-number) element. For example, the elements

| 9 |
| F |
| 17 |
| Cl |
| 35 |
| Br |
| 53 |
| I |
| 85 |
| At |

all show similar chemical behavior and so are listed vertically, as a "family" of elements.

Throughout the text, we will highlight the location of various elements by presenting a small version of the periodic table.

These families of elements with similar chemical properties that lie in the same vertical column on the periodic table are called **groups.** Groups are often referred to by the number over the column (see Figure 4.9). Note that the group numbers are accompanied by the letter A on the periodic table in Figure 4.9 and the one inside the front cover of the text. For simplicity we will delete the A's when we refer to groups in the text. Many of the groups have special names. For example, the first column of elements (Group 1) has the name **alkali metals.** The Group 2 elements are called the **alkaline earth metals,** the Group 7 elements are the **halogens,** and the elements in Group 8 are called the **noble gases.** A large collection of elements that spans many vertical columns consists of the **transition metals.**

There's another convention recommended by the International Union of Pure and Applied Chemistry for group designations that uses numbers 1 through 18 and includes the transition metals (see Fig. 4.9). Do not confuse that system with the one used in this text, where only the representative elements have group numbers (1 through 8).

Most of the elements are **metals.** Metals have the following characteristic physical properties:

Physical Properties of Metals

1. Efficient conduction of heat and electricity
2. Malleability (they can be hammered into thin sheets)
3. Ductility (they can be pulled into wires)
4. A lustrous (shiny) appearance

Nonmetals sometimes have one or more metallic properties. For example, solid iodine is lustrous, and graphite (a form of pure carbon) conducts electricity.

For example, copper is a typical metal. It is lustrous (although it tarnishes readily); it is an excellent conductor of electricity (it is widely used in electrical wires); and it is readily formed into various shapes, such as pipes for water systems. Copper is one of the transition metals—the metals shown in the center of the periodic table. Iron, aluminum, and gold are other familiar elements that have metallic properties. All of the elements shown to the left of and below the heavy "stair-step" black line in Figure 4.9 are classified as metals, except for hydrogen (Figure 4.10).

The relatively small number of elements that appear in the upper-right corner of the periodic table (to the right of the heavy line in Figures 4.9 and 4.10) are called **nonmetals.** Nonmetals generally lack those properties that characterize metals and show much more variation in their properties than metals do. Whereas almost all metals are solids at normal temperatures,

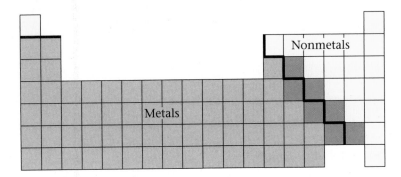

Figure 4.10

The elements classified as metals and as nonmetals.

many nonmetals (such as nitrogen, oxygen, chlorine, and neon) are gaseous and one (bromine) is a liquid. Several nonmetals (such as carbon, phosphorus, and sulfur) are also solids.

The elements that lie close to the "stair-step" line as shown in blue in Figure 4.10 often show a mixture of metallic and nonmetallic properties. These elements, which are called **metalloids** or **semimetals,** include silicon, germanium, arsenic, antimony, and tellurium.

As we continue our study of chemistry, we will see that the periodic table is a valuable tool for organizing accumulated knowledge and that it helps us predict the properties we expect a given element to exhibit. We will also develop a model for atomic structure that will explain why there are groups of elements with similar chemical properties.

EXAMPLE 4.5 | Interpreting the Periodic Table

Indonesian men carrying chunks of elemental sulfur in baskets.

For each of the following elements, use the periodic table in the front of the book to give the symbol and atomic number and to specify whether the element is a metal or a nonmetal. Also give the named family to which the element belongs (if any).

    a. iodine   b. magnesium   c. gold   d. lithium

SOLUTION

    a. Iodine (symbol I) is element 53 (its atomic number is 53). Iodine lies to the right of the stair-step line in Figure 4.10 and thus is a nonmetal. Iodine is a member of Group 7, the family of halogens.

    b. Magnesium (symbol Mg) is element 12 (atomic number 12). Magnesium is a metal and is a member of the alkaline earth metal family (Group 2).

    c. Gold (symbol Au) is element 79 (atomic number 79). Gold is a metal and is not a member of a named vertical family. It is classed as a transition metal.

    d. Lithium (symbol Li) is element 3 (atomic number 3). Lithium is a metal in the alkali metal family (Group 1).

Self-Check EXERCISE 4.5   Give the symbol and atomic number for each of the following elements. Also indicate whether each element is a metal or a nonmetal and whether it is a member of a named family.

    a. argon   b. chlorine   c. barium   d. cesium

See Problems 4.53 and 4.54. ■

Putting the Brakes on Arsenic

The toxicity of arsenic is well known. Indeed, arsenic has often been the poison of choice in classic plays and films—rent *Arsenic and Old Lace* sometime. Contrary to its treatment in the aforementioned movie, arsenic poisoning is a serious, contemporary problem. For example, the World Health Organization estimates that 77 million people in Bangladesh are at risk from drinking water that contains large amounts of naturally occurring arsenic. Recently, the Environmental Protection Agency announced more stringent standards for arsenic in U.S. public drinking water supplies. Studies show that prolonged exposure to arsenic can lead to a higher risk of bladder, lung, and skin cancers as well as other ailments, although the levels of arsenic that induce these symptoms remain in dispute in the scientific community.

Cleaning up arsenic-contaminated soil and water poses a significant problem. One approach is to find plants that will leach arsenic from the soil. Such a plant, the brake fern, recently has been shown to have a voracious appetite for arsenic. Research led by Lenna Ma, a chemist at the University of Florida in Gainesville, has shown that the brake fern accumulates arsenic at a rate 200 times that of the average plant. The arsenic, which becomes concentrated in fronds that grow up to 5 feet long, can be easily harvested and hauled away. Researchers are now investigating the best way to dispose of the plants so the arsenic can be isolated. The fern (*Pteris vittata*) looks promising for putting the brakes on arsenic pollution.

Lenna Ma and Pteris vittata—*called the brake fern.*

Tara Piasio/IFAS/University of Florida

4.9 Natural States of the Elements

OBJECTIVE: To learn the natures of the common elements.

As we have noted, the matter around us consists mainly of mixtures. Most often these mixtures contain compounds, in which atoms from different elements are bound together. Most elements are quite reactive: their atoms tend to combine with those of other elements to form compounds. Thus we do not often find elements in nature in pure form—uncombined with other elements. However, there are notable exceptions. The gold nuggets found at Sutter's Mill in California that launched the Gold Rush in 1849 are virtually pure elemental gold. And platinum and silver are often found in nearly pure form.

Gold, silver, and platinum are members of a class of metals called *noble metals* because they are relatively unreactive. (The term *noble* implies a class set apart.)

Other elements that appear in nature in the uncombined state are the elements in Group 8: helium, neon, argon, krypton, xenon, and radon. Because the atoms of these elements do not combine readily with those of other elements, we call them the *noble gases*. For example, helium gas is found in uncombined form in underground deposits with natural gas.

> A gold nugget weighing 13 lb, 7 oz, which came to be called Tom's Baby, was found by Tom Grove near Breckenridge, Colorado, on July 23, 1887.

Recall that a molecule is a collection of atoms that behaves as a unit. Molecules are always electrically neutral (zero charge).

When we take a sample of air (the mixture of gases that constitute the earth's atmosphere) and separate it into its components, we find several pure elements present. One of these is argon. Argon gas consists of a collection of separate argon atoms, as shown in Figure 4.11.

Air also contains nitrogen gas and oxygen gas. When we examine these two gases, however, we find that they do not contain single atoms, as argon does, but instead contain **diatomic molecules:** molecules made up of *two atoms,* as represented in Figure 4.12. In fact, any sample of elemental oxygen gas at normal temperatures contains O_2 molecules. Likewise, nitrogen gas contains N_2 molecules.

Hydrogen is another element that forms diatomic molecules. Though virtually all of the hydrogen found on earth is present in compounds with other elements (such as with oxygen in water), when hydrogen is prepared as a free element it contains diatomic H_2 molecules. For example, an electric current can be used to decompose water (see Figure 4.13 and Figure 3.3 on p. 60) into elemental hydrogen and oxygen containing H_2 and O_2 molecules, respectively.

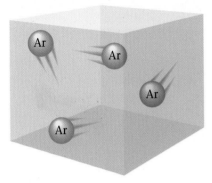

Figure 4.11

Argon gas consists of a collection of separate argon atoms.

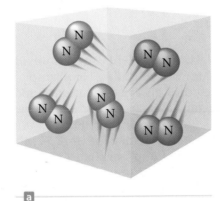

a

Nitrogen gas contains N—N (N_2) molecules.

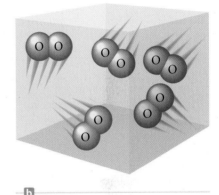

b

Oxygen gas contains O—O (O_2) molecules.

Figure 4.12

Gaseous nitrogen and oxygen contain diatomic (two-atom) molecules.

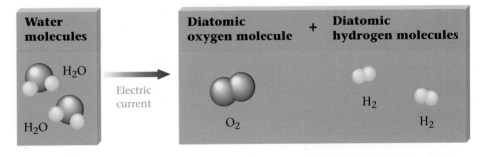

Figure 4.13

The decomposition of two water molecules (H_2O) to form two hydrogen molecules (H_2) and one oxygen molecule (O_2). Note that only the grouping of the atoms changes in this process; no atoms are created or destroyed. There must be the same number of H atoms and O atoms before and after the process. Thus the decomposition of two H_2O molecules (containing four H atoms and two O atoms) yields one O_2 molecule (containing two O atoms) and two H_2 molecules (containing a total of four H atoms).

a

b

Figure 4.14

Sodium chloride (common table salt) can be decomposed to its elements.

Sodium metal (on the left) and chlorine gas.

> The only elemental hydrogen found naturally on earth occurs in the exhaust gases of volcanoes.

Several other elements, in addition to hydrogen, nitrogen, and oxygen, exist as diatomic molecules. For example, when sodium chloride is melted and subjected to an electric current, chlorine gas is produced (along with sodium metal). This chemical change is represented in Figure 4.14. Chlorine gas is a pale green gas that contains Cl_2 molecules.

Chlorine is a member of Group 7, the halogen family. All the elemental forms of the Group 7 elements contain diatomic molecules. Fluorine is a pale yellow gas containing F_2 molecules. Bromine is a brown liquid made up of Br_2 molecules. Iodine is a lustrous, purple solid that contains I_2 molecules.

Table 4.5 lists the elements that contain diatomic molecules in their pure, elemental forms.

So far we have seen that several elements are gaseous in their elemental forms at normal temperatures ($\sim$25 °C). The noble gases (the Group 8 elements) contain individual atoms, whereas several other gaseous elements contain diatomic molecules (H_2, N_2, O_2, F_2, and Cl_2).

Only two elements are liquids in their elemental forms at 25 °C: the nonmetal bromine (containing Br_2 molecules) and the metal mercury. The metals gallium and cesium almost qualify in this category; they are solids at 25 °C, but both melt at $\sim$30 °C.

> $\sim$ means "approximately."

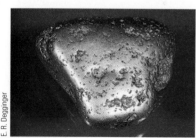

Platinum is a noble metal used in jewelry and in many industrial processes.

Table 4.5	Elements That Exist as Diatomic Molecules in Their Elemental Forms	
Element Present	Elemental State at 25 °C	Molecule
hydrogen	colorless gas	H_2
nitrogen	colorless gas	N_2
oxygen	pale blue gas	O_2
fluorine	pale yellow gas	F_2
chlorine	pale green gas	Cl_2
bromine	reddish brown liquid	Br_2
iodine	lustrous, dark purple solid	I_2

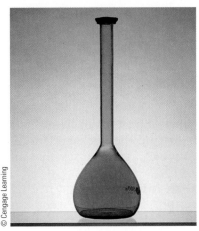

© Cengage Learning

Liquid bromine in a flask with bromine vapor.

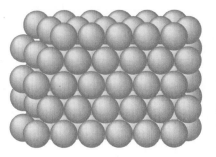

Frank Cox

Figure 4.15

In solid metals, the spherical atoms are packed closely together.

Steve Hamblin/Alamy

Cut diamond, held over coal.

The other elements are solids in their elemental forms at 25 °C. For metals these solids contain large numbers of atoms packed together much like marbles in a jar (see Figure 4.15).

The structures of solid nonmetallic elements are more varied than those of metals. In fact, different forms of the same element often occur. For example, solid carbon occurs in three forms. Different forms of a given element are called *allotropes*. The three allotropes of carbon are the familiar diamond and graphite forms plus a form that has only recently been discovered called *buckminsterfullerene*. These elemental forms have very different properties because of their different structures (see Figure 4.16). Diamond is the hardest natural substance known and is often used for industrial cutting tools. Diamonds are also valued as gemstones. Graphite, by contrast, is a rather soft material useful for writing (pencil "lead" is really graphite) and (in the form of a powder) for lubricating locks. The rather odd name given to buckminsterfullerene comes from the structure of the C_{60} molecules that form this allotrope. The soccer-ball-like structure contains five- and six-member rings reminiscent of the structure of geodesic domes suggested by the late industrial designer Buckminster Fuller. Other "fullerenes" containing molecules with more than 60 carbon atoms have also been discovered, leading to a new area of chemistry.

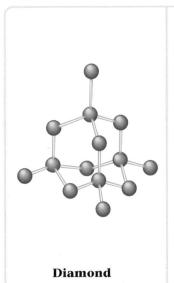

Diamond

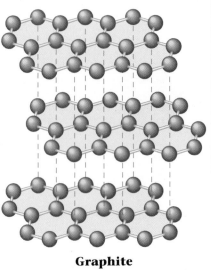

Graphite

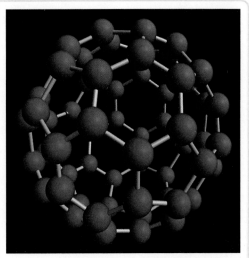

Buckminsterfullerene

Figure 4.16

The three solid elemental forms of carbon (allotropes): diamond, graphite, and buckminsterfullerene. The representations of diamond and graphite are fragments of much larger structures that extend in all directions from the parts shown here. Buckminsterfullerene contains C_{60} molecules, one of which is shown.

4.10 Ions

OBJECTIVES: To understand the formation of ions from their parent atoms, and learn to name them. • To learn how the periodic table can help predict which ion a given element forms.

go Chemistry Module 2: Predicting Ion Charges covers concepts in this section.

We have seen that an atom has a certain number of protons in its nucleus and an equal number of electrons in the space around the nucleus. This results in an exact balance of positive and negative charges. We say that an atom is a neutral entity—it has *zero net charge*.

We can produce a charged entity, called an **ion,** by taking a neutral atom and adding or removing one or more electrons. For example, a sodium atom ($Z = 11$) has eleven protons in its nucleus and eleven electrons outside its nucleus.

11 electrons
(11–)

11+

Neutral sodium
atom (Na)

An ion has a net positive or negative charge.

If one of the electrons is lost, there will be eleven positive charges but only ten negative charges. This gives an ion with a net positive one (1+) charge: $(11+) + (10-) = 1+$. We can represent this process as follows:

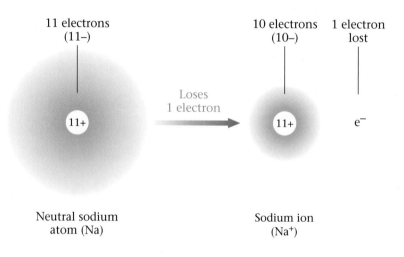

11 electrons
(11–)

11+

Neutral sodium
atom (Na)

Loses
1 electron

10 electrons
(10–)

11+

Sodium ion
(Na⁺)

1 electron
lost

e⁻

or, in shorthand form, as

$$Na \rightarrow Na^+ + e^-$$

where Na represents the neutral sodium atom, Na^+ represents the 1+ ion formed, and e^- represents an electron.

A positive ion, called a **cation** (pronounced *cat' eye on*), is produced when one or more electrons are *lost* from a neutral atom. We have seen that sodium loses one electron to become a 1+ cation. Some atoms lose more than one electron. For example, a magnesium atom typically loses two electrons to form a 2+ cation:

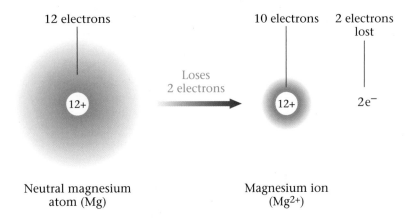

12 electrons   10 electrons   2 electrons lost

Loses 2 electrons

12+   12+ $2e^-$

Neutral magnesium   Magnesium ion
atom (Mg)   (Mg^{2+})

We usually represent this process as follows:

$$Mg \rightarrow Mg^{2+} + 2e^-$$

Aluminum forms a 3+ cation by losing three electrons:

13 electrons   10 electrons   3 electrons lost

Loses 3 electrons

13+   13+ $3e^-$

Neutral aluminum   Aluminum ion
atom (Al)   (Al^{3+})

> Note the size decreases dramatically when an atom loses one or more electrons to form a positive ion.

or

$$Al \rightarrow Al^{3+} + 3e^-$$

A cation is named using the name of the parent atom. Thus Na$^+$ is called the sodium ion (or sodium cation), Mg^{2+} is called the magnesium ion (or magnesium cation), and Al^{3+} is called the aluminum ion (or aluminum cation).

When electrons are *gained* by a neutral atom, an ion with a negative charge is formed. A negatively charged ion is called an **anion** (pronounced *an' ion*). An atom that gains one extra electron forms an anion with a

1− charge. An example of an atom that forms a 1− anion is the chlorine atom, which has seventeen protons and seventeen electrons:

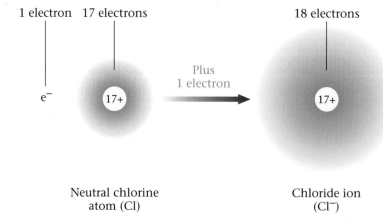

1 electron   17 electrons

18 electrons

Plus
1 electron

e^-

17+

17+

Neutral chlorine
atom (Cl)

Chloride ion
(Cl⁻)

Note the size increases dramatically when an atom gains one or more electrons to form a negative ion.

or

$$Cl + e^- \rightarrow Cl^-$$

Note that the anion formed by chlorine has eighteen electrons but only seventeen protons, so the net charge is $(18-) + (17+) = 1-$. Unlike a cation, which is named for the parent atom, an anion is named by taking the root name of the atom and changing the ending. For example, the Cl⁻ anion produced from the Cl (chlorine) atom is called the *chloride* ion (or chloride anion). Notice that the word *chloride* is obtained from the root of the atom name (*chlor-*) plus the suffix *-ide*. Other atoms that add one electron to form 1− ions include

The name of an anion is obtained by adding *-ide* to the root of the atom name.

fluorine	$F + e^- \rightarrow F^-$	(*fluor*ide ion)
bromine	$Br + e^- \rightarrow Br^-$	(*brom*ide ion)
iodine	$I + e^- \rightarrow I^-$	(*iod*ide ion)

Note that the name of each of these anions is obtained by adding *-ide* to the root of the atom name.

Some atoms can add two electrons to form 2− anions. Examples include

| oxygen | $O + 2e^- \rightarrow O^{2-}$ | (*ox*ide ion) |
| sulfur | $S + 2e^- \rightarrow S^{2-}$ | (*sulf*ide ion) |

Note that the names for these anions are derived in the same way as those for the 1− anions.

It is important to recognize that ions are always formed by removing electrons from an atom (to form cations) or adding electrons to an atom (to form anions). *Ions are never formed by changing the number of protons in an atom's nucleus.*

It is essential to understand that isolated atoms do not form ions on their own. Most commonly, ions are formed when metallic elements combine with nonmetallic elements. As we will discuss in detail in Chapter 7, when metals and nonmetals react, the metal atoms tend to lose one or more electrons, which are in turn gained by the atoms of the nonmetal. Thus reactions between metals and nonmetals tend to form compounds that contain metal cations and nonmetal anions. We will have more to say about these compounds in Section 4.11.

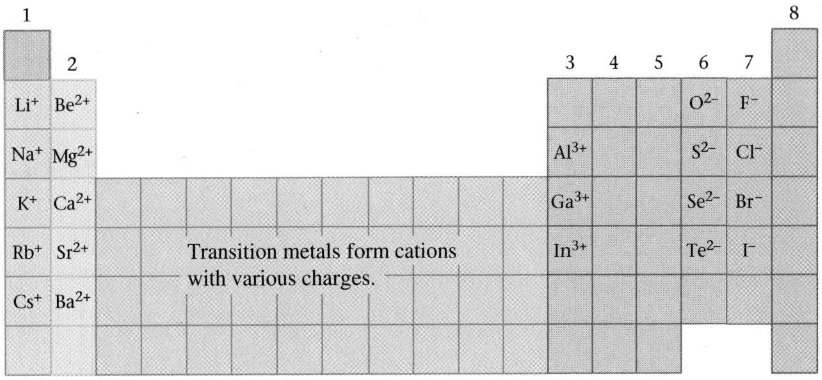

Figure 4.17

The ions formed by selected members of Groups 1, 2, 3, 6, and 7.

▶ Ion Charges and the Periodic Table

We find the periodic table very useful when we want to know what type of ion is formed by a given atom. Figure 4.17 shows the types of ions formed by atoms in several of the groups on the periodic table. Note that the Group 1 metals all form 1+ ions (M^+), the Group 2 metals all form 2+ ions (M^{2+}), and the Group 3 metals form 3+ ions (M^{3+}). Thus for Groups 1 through 3 the charges of the cations formed are identical to the group numbers.

> For Groups 1, 2, and 3, the charges of the cations equal the group numbers.

In contrast to the Group 1, 2, and 3 metals, most of the many *transition metals* form cations with various positive charges. For these elements there is no easy way to predict the charge of the cation that will be formed.

Note that metals always form positive ions. This tendency to lose electrons is a fundamental characteristic of metals. Nonmetals, on the other hand, form negative ions by gaining electrons. Note that the Group 7 atoms all gain one electron to form 1− ions and that all the nonmetals in Group 6 gain two electrons to form 2− ions.

At this point you should memorize the relationships between the group number and the type of ion formed, as shown in Figure 4.17. You will understand why these relationships exist after we further discuss the theory of the atom in Chapter 11.

4.11 Compounds That Contain Ions

OBJECTIVE: To learn how ions combine to form neutral compounds.

Chemists have good reasons to believe that many chemical compounds contain ions. For instance, consider some of the properties of common table salt, sodium chloride (NaCl). It must be heated to about 800 °C to melt and to almost 1500 °C to boil (compare to water, which boils at 100 °C). As a solid, salt will not conduct an electric current, but when melted it is a very good conductor. Pure water does not conduct electricity (does not allow an electric current to flow), but when salt is dissolved in water, the resulting solution readily conducts electricity (see Figure 4.18).

> Melting means that the solid, where the ions are locked into place, is changed to a liquid, where the ions can move.

Chemists have come to realize that we can best explain these properties of sodium chloride (NaCl) by picturing it as containing Na^+ ions and Cl^- ions packed together as shown in Figure 4.19. Because the positive and negative charges attract each other very strongly, it must be heated to a very high temperature (800 °C) before it melts.

To explore further the significance of the electrical conductivity results, we need to discuss briefly the nature of electric currents. An electric current

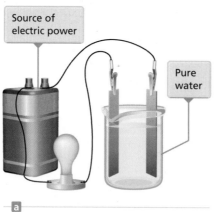 

Figure 4.18

a Pure water does not conduct a current, so the circuit is not complete and the bulb does not light.

b Water containing dissolved salt conducts electricity and the bulb lights.

A substance containing ions that can move can conduct an electric current.

Dissolving NaCl causes the ions to be randomly dispersed in the water, allowing them to move freely. Dissolving is not the same as melting, but both processes free the ions to move.

An ionic compound cannot contain only anions or only cations, because the net charge of a compound must be zero.

can travel along a metal wire because *electrons are free to move* through the wire; the moving electrons carry the current. In ionic substances the ions carry the current. Thus substances that contain ions can conduct an electric current *only if the ions can move*—the current travels by the movement of the charged ions. In solid NaCl the ions are tightly held and cannot move, but when the solid is melted and changed to a liquid, the structure is disrupted and the ions can move. As a result, an electric current can travel through the melted salt.

The same reasoning applies to NaCl dissolved in water. When the solid dissolves, the ions are dispersed throughout the water and can move around in the water, allowing it to conduct a current.

Thus, we recognize substances that contain ions by their characteristic properties. They often have very high melting points, and they conduct an electric current when melted or when dissolved in water.

Many substances contain ions. In fact, whenever a compound forms between a metal and a nonmetal, it can be expected to contain ions. We call these substances **ionic compounds.**

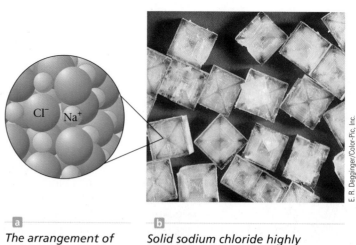

a The arrangement of sodium ions (Na^+) and chloride ions (Cl^-) in the ionic compound sodium chloride.

b Solid sodium chloride highly magnified.

Figure 4.19

E. R. Degginger/Color-Pic, Inc.

One fact very important to remember is that *a chemical compound must have a net charge of zero*. This means that if a compound contains ions, then

1. Both positive ions (cations) and negative ions (anions) must be present.

2. The numbers of cations and anions must be such that the net charge is zero.

For example, note that the formula for sodium chloride is written NaCl, indicating one of each type of these elements. This makes sense because sodium chloride contains Na^+ ions and Cl^- ions. Each sodium ion has a 1+ charge and each chloride ion has a 1− charge, so they must occur in equal numbers to give a net charge of zero.

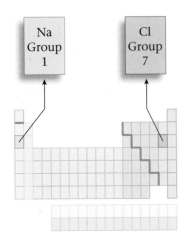

$$Na^+ \qquad Cl^- \qquad \rightarrow \qquad NaCl$$

Charge: 1+   Charge: 1−   Net charge: 0

And for *any* ionic compound,

$$\frac{\text{Total charge}}{\text{of cations}} + \frac{\text{Total charge}}{\text{of anions}} = \frac{\text{Zero}}{\text{net charge}}$$

Consider an ionic compound that contains the ions Mg^{2+} and Cl^-. What combination of these ions will give a net charge of zero? To balance the 2+ charge on Mg^{2+}, we will need two Cl^- ions to give a net charge of zero.

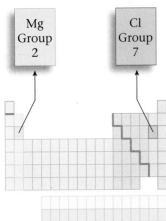

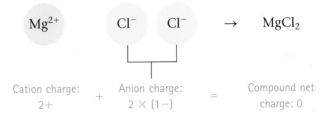

$$Mg^{2+} \qquad Cl^- \qquad Cl^- \qquad \rightarrow \qquad MgCl_2$$

Cation charge: Anion charge: Compound net
2+   +   2 × (1−)   =   charge: 0

This means that the formula of the compound must be $MgCl_2$. Remember that subscripts are used to give the relative numbers of atoms (or ions).

Now consider an ionic compound that contains the ions Ba^{2+} and O^{2-}. What is the correct formula? These ions have charges of the same size (but opposite sign), so they must occur in equal numbers to give a net charge of zero. The formula of the compound is BaO, because (2+) + (2−) = 0.

Similarly, the formula of a compound that contains the ions Li^+ and N^{3-} is Li_3N, because three Li^+ cations are needed to balance the charge of the N^{3-} anion.

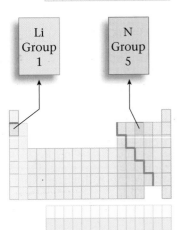

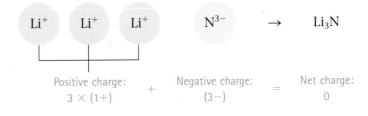

$$Li^+ \qquad Li^+ \qquad Li^+ \qquad N^{3-} \qquad \rightarrow \qquad Li_3N$$

Positive charge: Negative charge: Net charge:
3 × (1+)   +   (3−)   =   0

EXAMPLE 4.6 | Writing Formulas for Ionic Compounds

The pairs of ions contained in several ionic compounds are listed below. Give the formula for each compound.

a. Ca^{2+} and Cl^- b. Na^+ and S^{2-} c. Ca^{2+} and P^{3-}

> The subscript 1 in a formula is not written.

SOLUTION

a. Ca^{2+} has a 2+ charge, so two Cl^- ions (each with the charge 1−) will be needed.

$$\text{where} \quad 2+ \quad + \quad 2(1-) \quad = 0$$

The formula is $CaCl_2$.

b. In this case S^{2-}, with its 2− charge, requires two Na^+ ions to produce a zero net charge.

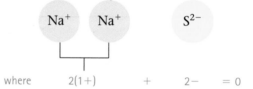

$$\text{where} \quad 2(1+) \quad + \quad 2- \quad = 0$$

The formula is Na_2S.

c. We have the ions Ca^{2+} (charge 2+) and P^{3-} (charge 3−). We must figure out how many of each are needed to balance exactly the positive and negative charges. Let's try two Ca^{2+} and one P^{3-}.

$$Ca^{2+} \quad Ca^{2+} \quad P^{3-}$$

The resulting net charge is 2(2+) + (3−) = (4+) + (3−) = 1−. This doesn't work because the net charge is not zero. We can obtain the same total positive and total negative charges by having three Ca^{2+} ions and two P^{3-} ions.

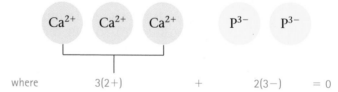

$$\text{where} \quad 3(2+) \quad + \quad 2(3-) \quad = 0$$

Thus the formula must be Ca_3P_2.

Self-Check | **EXERCISE 4.6**   Give the formulas for the compounds that contain the following pairs of ions.

a. K^+ and I^- b. Mg^{2+} and N^{3-} c. Al^{3+} and O^{2-}

See Problems 4.83 and 4.84. ■

CHAPTER 4 REVIEW

Key Terms

element symbols (4.2)

law of constant
  composition (4.3)

Dalton's atomic
  theory (4.3)

atom (4.3)

compound (4.4)

chemical formula (4.4)

electron (4.5)

nuclear atom (4.5)

nucleus (4.5)

proton (4.5)

neutron (4.5)

isotopes (4.7)

atomic number, Z (4.7)

mass number, A (4.7)

periodic table (4.8)

groups (4.8)

alkali metals (4.8)

alkaline earth metals (4.8)

halogens (4.8)

noble gases (4.8)

transition metals (4.8)

metals (4.8)

nonmetals (4.8)

metalloids
  (semimetals) (4.8)

diatomic molecule (4.9)

ion (4.10)

cation (4.10)

anion (4.10)

ionic compound (4.11)

F directs you to the *Chemistry in Focus* feature in the chapter

VP indicates visual problems

OWL interactive versions of these problems are assignable in OWL

Summary

1. Of the more than 100 different elements now known, only 9 account for about 98% of the total mass of the earth's crust, oceans, and atmosphere. In the human body, oxygen, carbon, hydrogen, and nitrogen are the most abundant elements.

2. Elements are represented by symbols that usually consist of the first one or two letters of the element's name. Sometimes, however, the symbol is taken from the element's original Latin or Greek name.

3. The law of constant composition states that a given compound always contains the same proportions by mass of the elements of which it is composed.

4. Dalton accounted for this law with his atomic theory. He postulated that all elements are composed of atoms; that all atoms of a given element are identical, but that atoms of different elements are different; that chemical compounds are formed when atoms combine; and that atoms are not created or destroyed in chemical reactions.

5. A compound can be represented by a chemical formula that uses the symbol for each type of atom and gives the number of each type of atom that appears in a molecule of the compound.

6. Atoms consist of a nucleus containing protons and neutrons, surrounded by electrons that occupy a large volume relative to the size of the nucleus. Electrons have a relatively small mass (1/1836 of the proton mass) and a negative charge. Protons have a positive charge equal in magnitude (but opposite in sign) to that of the electron. A neutron has a slightly greater mass than the proton but no charge.

7. Isotopes are atoms with the same number of protons but different numbers of neutrons.

8. The periodic table displays the elements in rows and columns in order of increasing atomic number. Elements that have similar chemical properties fall into vertical columns called groups. Most of the elements are metals. These occur on the left-hand side of the periodic table; the nonmetals appear on the right-hand side.

9. Each chemical element is composed of a given type of atom. These elements may exist as individual atoms or as groups of like atoms. For example, the noble gases contain single, separated atoms. However, elements such as oxygen, nitrogen, and chlorine exist as diatomic (two-atom) molecules.

10. When an atom loses one or more electrons, it forms a positive ion called a cation. This behavior is characteristic of metals. When an atom gains one or more electrons, it becomes a negatively charged ion called an anion. This behavior is characteristic of nonmetals. Oppositely charged ions form ionic compounds. A compound is always neutral overall—it has zero net charge.

11. The elements in Groups 1 and 2 on the periodic table form 1+ and 2+ cations, respectively. Group 7 atoms can gain one electron to form 1− ions. Group 6 atoms form 2− ions.

Active Learning Questions

These questions are designed to be considered by groups of students in class. Often these questions work well for introducing a particular topic in class.

1. Knowing the number of protons in the atom of a neutral element enables you to determine which of the following?

   a. the number of neutrons in the atom of the neutral element
   b. the number of electrons in the atom of the neutral element
   c. the name of the element
   d. two of the above
   e. none of the above

   Explain.

2. The average mass of a carbon atom is 12.011. Assuming you could pick up one carbon atom, what is the chance that you would randomly get one with a mass of 12.011?

   a. 0%
   b. 0.011%
   c. about 12%
   d. 12.011%
   e. greater than 50%
   f. none of the above

   Explain.

3. How is an ion formed?

   a. by either adding or subtracting protons from the atom
   b. by either adding or subtracting neutrons from the atom
   c. by either adding or subtracting electrons from the atom
   d. all of the above
   e. two of the above

   Explain.

4. The formula of water, H_2O, suggests which of the following?

   a. There is twice as much mass of hydrogen as oxygen in each molecule.
   b. There are two hydrogen atoms and one oxygen atom per water molecule.
   c. There is twice as much mass of oxygen as hydrogen in each molecule.
   d. There are two oxygen atoms and one hydrogen atom per water molecule.
   e. Two of the above.

   Explain.

5. The vitamin niacin (nicotinic acid, $C_6H_5NO_2$) can be isolated from a variety of natural sources, such as liver, yeast, milk, and whole grain. It also can be synthesized from commercially available materials. Which source of nicotinic acid, from a nutritional view, is best for use in a multivitamin tablet? Why?

6. One of the best indications of a useful theory is that it raises more questions for further experimentation than it originally answered. How does this apply to Dalton's atomic theory? Give examples.

7. Dalton assumed that all atoms of the same element are identical in all their properties. Explain why this assumption is not valid.

8. How does Dalton's atomic theory account for the law of constant composition?

9. Which of the following is true about the state of an individual atom?

   a. An individual atom should be considered to be a solid.
   b. An individual atom should be considered to be a liquid.
   c. An individual atom should be considered to be a gas.
   d. The state of the atom depends on which element it is.

   e. An individual atom cannot be considered to be a solid, liquid, or gas.

   For choices you did not pick, explain what you feel is wrong with them, and justify the choice you did pick.

10. These questions concern the work of J. J. Thomson:

    a. From Thomson's work, which particles do you think he would feel are most important in the formation of compounds (chemical changes) and why?
    b. Of the remaining two subatomic particles, which do you place second in importance for forming compounds and why?
    c. Come up with three models that explain Thomson's findings and evaluate them. To be complete you should include Thomson's findings.

11. Heat is applied to an ice cube until only steam is present. Draw a sketch of this process, assuming you can see it at an extremely high level of magnification. What happens to the size of the molecules? What happens to the total mass of the sample?

12. What makes a carbon atom different from a nitrogen atom? How are they alike?

13. Hundreds of years ago, alchemists tried to turn lead into gold. Is this possible? If not, why not? If yes, how would you do it?

14. Chlorine has two prominent isotopes, ^{37}Cl and ^{35}Cl. Which is more abundant? How do you know?

15. Differentiate between an atomic element and a molecular element. Provide an example and microscopic drawing of each.

16. Science often develops by using the known theories and expanding, refining, and perhaps changing these theories. As discussed in Section 4.5, Rutherford used Thompson's ideas when thinking about his model of the atom. What if Rutherford had not known about Thompson's work? How might Rutherford's model of the atom have been different?

17. Rutherford was surprised when some of the α-particles bounced back. He was surprised because he was thinking of Thompson's model of the atom. What if Rutherford believed atoms were as Dalton envisioned them? What do you suppose Rutherford would have expected, and what would have surprised him?

18. It is good practice to actively read the textbook and to try to verify claims that are made when you can. The following claim is made in your textbook: " . . . if the nucleus were the size of a grape, the electrons would be about one mile away on average."

    Provide mathematical support for this statement.

19. Why is the term "sodium chloride molecule" incorrect but the term "carbon dioxide molecule" is correct?

20. Both atomic elements and molecular elements exist. Are there such entities as atomic compounds and molecular compounds? If so, provide an example and microscopic drawing. If not, explain why not.

21. Now that you have gone through Chapter 4, go back to Section 4.3 and review Dalton's Atomic Theory. Which of the premises are no longer accepted? Explain your answer.

VP 22. Write the formula for each of the following substances, listing the elements in the order given.

a.

List the phosphorus atom first.

b. a molecule containing two boron atoms and six hydrogen atoms

c. a compound containing one calcium atom for every two chlorine atoms

d.

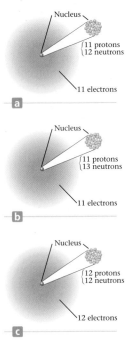

List the carbon atom first.

e. a compound containing two iron atoms for every three oxygen atoms

f. a molecule containing three hydrogen atoms, one phosphorus atom, and four oxygen atoms

VP 23. Use the following figures to identify the element or ion. Write the symbol for each, using the $_Z^A X$ format.

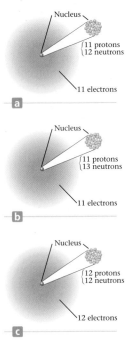

a —————

b —————

c —————

Questions and Problems

4.1 The Elements

QUESTIONS

1. What were the four fundamental substances postulated by the Greeks?

2. Who was the first scientist generally accredited with putting the study of chemistry on a firm experimental basis?

3. In addition to his important work on the properties of gases, what other valuable contributions did Robert Boyle make to the development of the study of chemistry?

4. How many elements are presently known? How many of these elements occur naturally, and how many are synthesized artificially? What are the most common elements present on the earth?

5. What are the five most abundant elements (by mass) in the earth's crust, oceans, and atmosphere?

F 6. Read the "Chemistry in Focus" segment *Trace Elements: Small but Crucial,* and answer the following questions.

a. What is meant by the term *trace element?*

b. Name two essential trace elements in the body and list their function(s).

4.2 Symbols for the Elements

Note: Refer to the tables on the inside front cover when appropriate.

QUESTIONS

7. The letters *C, S,* and *T* have been very popular when naming the elements, and there are ten or more elements whose names begin with each of these letters. Without looking in your textbook, see if you can list the symbol and name of five elements for each letter.

8. The symbols for most elements are based on the first few letters of the respective element's common English name. In some cases, however, the symbol seems to have nothing to do with the element's common name. Give three examples of elements whose symbols are not directly derived from the element's common English name.

9. Find the symbol in Column 2 for each name in Column 1.

Column 1	Column 2
a. helium	1. Si
b. sodium	2. So
c. silver	3. S
d. sulfur	4. He
e. bromine	5. C
f. potassium	6. Co
g. neon	7. Ba
h. barium	8. Br
i. cobalt	9. K
j. carbon	10. Po
	11. Na
	12. Ag
	13. Ne
	14. Ca

All even-numbered Questions and Problems have answers in the back of this book and solutions in the Solutions Guide.

10. Find the name in Column 2 that corresponds to each symbol in Column 1.

Column 1	Column 2
a. Si	1. sulfur
b. O	2. copper
c. Fe	3. molybdenum
d. W	4. strontium
e. Ni	5. platinum
f. Zn	6. oxygen
g. Mo	7. protactinium
h. Pt	8. iron
i. Sr	9. silicon
j. Cu	10. nitrogen
	11. nickel
	12. tungsten
	13. zinc
	14. gold

11. Use the periodic table inside the front cover of this book to find the symbol or name for each of the following elements.

Symbol	Name
Co	_____
_____	rubidium
Rn	_____
_____	radium
U	_____

12. Use the periodic table inside the front cover of this book to find the symbol or name for each of the following elements.

Symbol	Name
Zr	_____
_____	cesium
Se	_____
_____	gold
Ce	_____

13. For each of the following chemical symbols, give the name of the corresponding element.

a. K   e. N
b. Ge   g. Ne
c. P   f. Na
d. C   h. I

14. Several chemical elements have English names beginning with the letters B, N, P, or S. For each letter, list the English *names* for two elements whose names begin with that letter, and give the symbols for the elements you choose (the symbols do not necessarily need to begin with the same letters).

4.3 Dalton's Atomic Theory

QUESTIONS

🅕 15. The "Chemistry in Focus" segment *No Laughing Matter* ends with the statement "Clean may not necessarily be 'green.'" Read this segment and explain the statement.

16. Correct each of the following misstatements from Dalton's atomic theory.

a. Elements are made of tiny particles called molecules.
b. All atoms of a given element are very similar.
c. The atoms of a given element may be the same as those of another element.
d. A given compound may vary in the relative number and types of atoms depending on the source of the compound.
e. A chemical reaction may involve the gain or loss of atoms as it takes place.

4.4 Formulas of Compounds

QUESTIONS

17. What is a compound?

18. A given compound always contains the same relative masses of its constituent elements. How is this related to the relative numbers of each kind of atom present?

19. Based on the following word descriptions, write the formula for each of the indicated substances.

a. a compound whose molecules each contain six carbon atoms and six hydrogen atoms
b. an aluminum compound in which there are three chlorine atoms for each aluminum atom
c. a compound in which there are two sodium atoms for every sulfur atom
d. a compound whose molecules each contain two nitrogen atoms and four oxygen atoms
e. a compound in which there is an equal number of sodium, hydrogen, and carbon atoms but there are three times as many oxygen atoms as atoms of the other three elements
f. a compound that has equal numbers of potassium and iodide atoms

20. Based on the following word descriptions, write the formula for each of the indicated substances.

a. a compound whose molecules contain twice as many oxygen atoms as carbon atoms
b. a compound whose molecules contain an equal number of carbon and oxygen atoms
c. a compound in which there is an equal number of calcium and carbon atoms but there are three times as many atoms of oxygen as of the other two elements
d. a compound whose molecules contain twice as many hydrogen atoms as sulfur atoms and four times as many oxygen atoms as sulfur atoms
e. a compound in which there are twice as many chlorine atoms as barium atoms
f. a compound in which there are three sulfur atoms for every two aluminum atoms

4.5 The Structure of the Atom

QUESTIONS

21. Scientists J. J. Thomson and William Thomson (Lord Kelvin) made numerous contributions to our understanding of the atom's structure.

    a. Which subatomic particle did J. J. Thomson discover, and what did this lead him to postulate about the nature of the atom?

    b. William Thomson postulated what became known as the "plum pudding" model of the atom's structure. What did this model suggest?

22. Indicate whether each of the following statements is true or false. If false, correct the statement so that it becomes true.

    a. Rutherford's bombardment experiments with metal foil suggested that the alpha particles were being deflected by coming near a large, negatively charged atomic nucleus.

    b. The proton and the electron have similar masses but opposite electrical charges.

    c. Most atoms also contain neutrons, which are slightly heavier than protons but carry no charge.

4.6 Introduction to the Modern Concept of Atomic Structure

QUESTIONS

23. Where are neutrons found in an atom? Are neutrons positively charged, negatively charged, or electrically uncharged?

24. What two common types of particles are found in the nucleus of the atom? What are the relative charges of these particles? What are the relative masses of these particles?

25. Do the proton and the neutron have exactly the same mass? How do the masses of the proton and the neutron compare to the mass of the electron? Which particles make the greatest contribution to the mass of an atom? Which particles make the greatest contribution to the chemical properties of an atom?

26. The proton and the (electron/neutron) have almost equal masses. The proton and the (electron/neutron) have charges that are equal in magnitude but opposite in nature.

27. An average atomic nucleus has a diameter of about _____ m.

28. Which particles in an atom are most responsible for the chemical properties of the atom? Where are these particles located in the atom?

4.7 Isotopes

QUESTIONS

29. Explain what we mean when we say that a particular element consists of several *isotopes*.

30. Imagine you are talking to a friend who has never taken any science courses. Explain to your friend what are meant by the *atomic number* and *mass number* of a nucleus.

31. For an isolated atom, why do we expect the number of electrons present in the atom to be the *same* as the number of protons in the nucleus of the atom?

32. Why do we not necessarily expect the number of neutrons in the nucleus of an atom to be the same as the number of protons?

33. Dalton's original atomic theory proposed that all atoms of a given element are *identical*. Did this turn out to be true after further experimentation was carried out? Explain.

34. Are all atoms of the same element identical? If not, how can they differ?

35. For each of the following elements, use the periodic table on the inside cover of this book to write the element's atomic number, symbol, or name.

Atomic Number	Symbol	Name
8	_____	_____
_____	Cu	_____
78	_____	_____
_____	_____	phosphorus
17	_____	_____
_____	Sn	_____
_____	_____	zinc

36. For each of the following elements, use the periodic table on the inside cover of this book to write the element's atomic number, symbol, or name.

Atomic Number	Symbol	Name
14	Si	_____
_____	Xe	xenon
79	_____	gold
56	_____	barium
_____	I	iodine
_____	Sn	tin
48	_____	cadmium

37. Write the atomic symbol ($_Z^A X$) for each of the isotopes described below.

    a. the isotope of carbon with 7 neutrons
    b. the isotope of carbon with 6 neutrons
    c. $Z = 6$, number of neutrons = 8
    d. atomic number 5, mass number 11
    e. number of protons = 5, number of neutrons = 5
    f. the isotope of boron with mass number 10

38. Write the atomic symbol ($_Z^A X$) for each of the isotopes described below.

    a. $Z = 26$, $A = 54$
    b. the isotope of iron with 30 neutrons
    c. number of protons-26, number of neutrons-31
    d. the isotope of nitrogen with 7 neutrons
    e. $Z = 7$, $A = 15$
    f. atomic number 7, number of neutrons-8

39. How many protons and neutrons are contained in the nucleus of each of the following atoms? Assuming each atom is uncharged, how many electrons are present?

   a. $^{130}_{56}Ba$ c. $^{46}_{22}Ti$ e. $^{6}_{3}Li$
   b. $^{136}_{56}Ba$ d. $^{48}_{22}Ti$ f. $^{7}_{3}Li$

F 40. Read the "Chemistry in Focus" segment "Whair" Do You Live? How can isotopes be used to identify the general region of a person's place of residence?

F 41. Read the "Chemistry in Focus" segment Isotope Tales. Define the term isotope, and explain how isotopes can be used to answer scientific and historical questions.

42. Complete the following table.

Name	Symbol	Atomic Number	Mass Number	Number of Neutrons
_____	$^{17}_{8}O$	_____	_____	_____
_____	_____	8	_____	9
_____	_____	10	20	_____
iron	_____	_____	56	_____
_____	$^{244}_{94}Pu$	_____	_____	_____
_____	$^{202}_{80}Hg$	_____	_____	_____
cobalt	_____	_____	59	_____
_____	_____	28	56	_____
_____	$^{19}_{9}F$	_____	_____	_____
chromium	_____	_____	_____	26

4.8 Introduction to the Periodic Table

QUESTIONS

43. True or false? The elements are arranged in the periodic table in order of increasing mass.

44. In which direction on the periodic table, horizontal or vertical, are elements with similar chemical properties aligned? What are families of elements with similar chemical properties called?

45. List the characteristic physical properties that distinguish the metallic elements from the nonmetallic elements.

46. Where are the metallic elements found on the periodic table? Are there more metallic elements or nonmetallic elements?

47. Most, but not all, metallic elements are solids under ordinary laboratory conditions. Which metallic elements are not solids?

48. List five nonmetallic elements that exist as gaseous substances under ordinary conditions. Do any metallic elements ordinarily occur as gases?

49. Under ordinary conditions, only a few pure elements occur as liquids. Give an example of a metallic and a nonmetallic element that ordinarily occur as liquids.

50. What is a metalloid? Where are the metalloids found on the periodic table?

51. Write the number and name (if any) of the group (family) to which each of the following elements belongs.

   a. cesium   e. strontium
   b. Ra   f. Xe
   c. Rn   g. Rb
   d. chlorine

52. Without looking at your textbook or the periodic table, name three elements in each of the following groups (families).

   a. halogens
   b. alkali metals
   c. alkaline earth metals
   d. noble/inert gases

53. For each of the following elements, use the tables on the inside cover of this book to give the chemical symbol, atomic number, and group number of each element, and to specify whether each element is a metal, nonmetal, or metalloid.

   a. strontium   c. silicon   e. sulfur
   b. iodine   d. cesium

F 54. The "Chemistry in Focus" segment Putting the Brakes on Arsenic discusses the dangers of arsenic and a possible help against arsenic pollution. Is arsenic a metal, a nonmetal, or a metalloid? What other elements are in the same group on the periodic table as arsenic?

4.9 Natural States of the Elements

QUESTIONS

55. Most substances are composed of _____ rather than elemental substances.

56. Are most of the chemical elements found in nature in the elemental form or combined in compounds? Why?

57. The noble gas present in relatively large concentrations in the atmosphere is _____ .

58. Why are the elements of Group 8 referred to as the noble or inert gas elements?

59. Molecules of nitrogen gas and oxygen gas are said to be _____ , which means they consist of pairs of atoms.

60. Give three examples of gaseous elements that exist as diatomic molecules. Give three examples of gaseous elements that exist as monatomic species.

61. A simple way to generate elemental hydrogen gas is to pass _____ through water.

62. If sodium chloride (table salt) is melted and then subjected to an electric current, elemental _____ gas is produced, along with sodium metal.

All even-numbered Questions and Problems have answers in the back of this book and solutions in the Solutions Guide.

63. Most of the elements are solids at room temperature. Give three examples of elements that are *liquids* at room temperature, and three examples of elements that are *gases* at room temperature.

64. The two most common elemental forms of carbon are graphite and _____ .

4.10 Ions

QUESTIONS

65. An isolated atom has a net charge of _____ .

66. Ions are produced when an atom gains or loses _____ .

67. A simple ion with a 3+ charge (for example, Al^{3+}) results when an atom (gains/loses) _____ electrons.

68. An ion that has three more protons in the nucleus than there are electrons outside the nucleus will have a charge of _____ .

69. Positive ions are called _____ , whereas negative ions are called _____ .

70. Simple negative ions formed from single atoms are given names that end in _____ .

71. Based on their location in the periodic table, give the symbols for three elements that would be expected to form positive ions in their reactions.

72. The tendency to *gain* electrons is a fundamental property of the _____ elements.

73. How many electrons are present in each of the following ions?

    a. Ba^{2+} c. Mn^{2+} e. Cs^+
    b. P^{3-} d. Mg^{2+} f. Pb^{2+}

74. How many electrons are present in each of the following ions?

    a. Se^{2-} c. Cr^{3+} e. Bi^{3+}
    b. Br^- d. Rb^+ f. Cu^{2+}

75. For the following processes that show the formation of ions, use the periodic table to indicate the number of electrons and protons present in both the *ion* and the *neutral atom* from which the ion is made.

    a. $Ca \rightarrow Ca^{2+} + 2e^-$
    b. $P + 3e^- \rightarrow P^{3-}$
    c. $Br + e^- \rightarrow Br^-$
    d. $Fe \rightarrow Fe^{3+} + 3e^-$
    e. $Al \rightarrow Al^{3+} + 3e^-$
    f. $N + 3e^- \rightarrow N^{3-}$

76. For the following ions, indicate whether electrons must be *gained* or *lost* from the parent neutral atom, and *how many* electrons must be gained or lost.

    a. O^{2-} c. Cr^{3+} e. Rb^+
    b. P^{3-} d. Sn^{2+} f. Pb^{2+}

77. For each of the following atomic numbers, use the periodic table to write the formula (including the charge) for the simple *ion* that the element is most likely to form.

    a. 53   c. 55   e. 9
    b. 38   d. 88   f. 13

78. On the basis of the element's location in the periodic table, indicate what simple ion each of the following elements is most likely to form.

    a. P   c. At   e. Cs
    b. Ra   d. Rn   f. Se

4.11 Compounds That Contain Ions

QUESTIONS

79. List some properties of a substance that would lead you to believe it consists of ions. How do these properties differ from those of nonionic compounds?

80. Why does a solution of sodium chloride in water conduct an electric current, whereas a solution of sugar in water does not?

81. Why does an ionic compound conduct an electric current when the compound is melted but not when it is in the solid state?

82. Why must the total number of positive charges in an ionic compound equal the total number of negative charges?

83. For each of the following positive ions, use the concept that a chemical compound must have a net charge of zero to predict the formula of the simple compounds that the positive ions would form with the Cl^-, S^{2-}, and N^{3-} ions.

    a. K^+ c. Al^{3+} e. Li^+
    b. Mg^{2+} d. Ca^{2+}

84. For each of the following negative ions, use the concept that a chemical compound must have a net charge of zero to predict the formula of the simple compounds that the negative ions would form with the Cs^+, Ba^{2+}, and Al^{3+} ions.

    a. I^- c. P^{3-} e. H^-
    b. O^{2-} d. Se^{2-}

Additional Problems

85. For each of the following elements, give the chemical symbol and atomic number.

    a. astatine   e. lead
    b. xenon   f. selenium
    c. radium   g. argon
    d. strontium   h. cesium

86. Give the group number (if any) in the periodic table for the elements listed in problem 85. If the group has a family name, give that name.

All even-numbered Questions and Problems have answers in the back of this book and solutions in the Solutions Guide.

87. List the names, symbols, and atomic numbers of the top four elements in Groups 1, 2, 6, and 7.

88. List the names, symbols, and atomic numbers of the top four elements in Groups 3, 5, and 8.

89. What is the difference between the atomic number and the mass number of an element? Can atoms of two different elements have the same atomic number? Could they have the same mass number? Why or why not?

90. Which subatomic particles contribute most to the atom's mass? Which subatomic particles determine the atom's chemical properties?

91. Is it possible for the same two elements to form more than one compound? Is this consistent with Dalton's atomic theory? Give an example.

92. Carbohydrates, a class of compounds containing the elements carbon, hydrogen, and oxygen, were originally thought to contain one water molecule (H_2O) for each carbon atom present. The carbohydrate glucose contains six carbon atoms. Write a general formula showing the relative numbers of each type of atom present in glucose.

93. When iron rusts in moist air, the product is typically a mixture of two iron–oxygen compounds. In one compound, there is an equal number of iron and oxygen atoms. In the other compound, there are three oxygen atoms for every two iron atoms. Write the formulas for the two iron oxides.

94. How many protons and neutrons are contained in the nucleus of each of the following atoms? For an atom of the element, how many electrons are present?

    a. $^{63}_{29}Cu$ b. $^{80}_{35}Br$ c. $^{24}_{12}Mg$

95. Though the common isotope of aluminum has a mass number of 27, isotopes of aluminum have been isolated (or prepared in nuclear reactors) with mass numbers of 24, 25, 26, 28, 29, and 30. How many neutrons are present in each of these isotopes? Why are they all considered aluminum atoms, even though they differ greatly in mass? Write the atomic symbol for each isotope.

96. The principal goal of alchemists was to convert cheaper, more common metals into gold. Considering that gold had no particular practical uses (for example, it was too soft to be used for weapons), why do you think early civilizations placed such emphasis on the value of gold?

97. How did Robert Boyle define an element?

98. Give the chemical symbol for each of the following elements.

    a. iodine   d. iron
    b. silicon   e. copper
    c. tungsten   f. cobalt

99. Give the chemical symbol for each of the following elements.

    a. barium   d. lead
    b. potassium   e. platinum
    c. cesium   f. gold

100. Give the chemical symbol for each of the following elements.

    a. bromine   d. vanadium
    b. bismuth   e. fluorine
    c. mercury   f. calcium

101. Give the chemical symbol for each of the following elements.

    a. silver   d. antimony
    b. aluminum   e. tin
    c. cadmium   f. arsenic

102. For each of the following chemical symbols, give the name of the corresponding element.

    a. Os   e. U
    b. Zr   f. Mn
    c. Rb   g. Ni
    d. Rn   h. Br

103. For each of the following chemical symbols, give the name of the corresponding element.

    a. Te   e. Cs
    b. Pd   f. Bi
    c. Zn   g. F
    d. Si   h. Ti

104. Write the simplest formula for each of the following substances, listing the elements in the order given.

    a. a molecule containing one carbon atom and two oxygen atoms
    b. a compound containing one aluminum atom for every three chlorine atoms
    c. perchloric acid, which contains one hydrogen atom, one chlorine atom, and four oxygen atoms
    d. a molecule containing one sulfur atom and six chlorine atoms

105. For each of the following atomic numbers, write the name and chemical symbol of the corresponding element. (Refer to Figure 4.11.)

    a. 7   e. 22
    b. 10   f. 18
    c. 11   g. 36
    d. 28   h. 54

106. Write the atomic symbol ($^A_Z X$) for each of the isotopes described below.

    a. $Z = 6$, number of neutrons = 7
    b. the isotope of carbon with a mass number of 13
    c. $Z = 6$, $A = 13$
    d. $Z = 19$, $A = 44$
    e. the isotope of calcium with a mass number of 41
    f. the isotope with 19 protons and 16 neutrons

107. How many protons and neutrons are contained in the nucleus of each of the following atoms? In an atom of each element, how many electrons are present?

a. $_{22}^{41}Ti$ d. $_{36}^{86}Kr$

b. $_{30}^{64}Zn$ e. $_{33}^{75}As$

c. $_{32}^{76}Ge$ f. $_{19}^{41}K$

108. Complete the following table.

Symbol	Protons	Neutrons	Mass Number
$_{20}^{41}Ca$	___	___	___
___	25	30	___
___	47	___	109
$_{21}^{45}Sc$	___	___	___

109. For each of the following elements, use the table on the inside front cover of the book to give the chemical symbol and atomic number and to specify whether the element is a metal or a nonmetal. Also give the named family to which the element belongs (if any).

a. carbon

b. selenium

c. radon

d. beryllium

5

Nomenclature

● Clouds over tufa towers in Mono Lake, California. *(Fred Hirschmann/Science Faction)*

When chemistry was an infant science, there was no system for naming compounds. Names such as sugar of lead, blue vitriol, quicklime, Epsom salts, milk of magnesia, gypsum, and laughing gas were coined by early chemists. Such names are called *common names.* As our knowledge of chemistry grew, it became clear that using common names for compounds was not practical. More than four million chemical compounds are currently known. Memorizing common names for all these compounds would be impossible.

The solution, of course, is a *system* for naming compounds in which the name tells something about the composition of the compound. After learning the system, you should be able to name a compound when you are given its formula. And, conversely, you should be able to construct a compound's formula, given its name. In the next few sections we will specify the most important rules for naming compounds other than organic compounds (those based on chains of carbon atoms).

An artist using plaster of Paris, a gypsum plaster.

Bob Daemmrich/The Image Works

5.1 Naming Compounds

OBJECTIVE: To understand why it is necessary to have a system for naming compounds.

We will begin by discussing the system for naming **binary compounds**—compounds composed of two elements. We can divide binary compounds into two broad classes:

1. Compounds that contain a metal and a nonmetal

2. Compounds that contain two nonmetals

We will describe how to name compounds in each of these classes in the next several sections. Then, in succeeding sections, we will describe the systems used for naming more complex compounds.

Sugar of Lead

In ancient Roman society it was common to boil wine in a lead-lined vessel, driving off much of the water to produce a very sweet, viscous syrup called *sapa*. This syrup was commonly used as a sweetener for many types of food and drink.

We now realize that a major component of this syrup was lead acetate, $Pb(C_2H_3O_2)_2$. This compound has a very sweet taste—hence its original name, sugar of lead.

Many historians believe that the fall of the Roman Empire was due at least in part to lead poisoning, which causes lethargy and mental malfunctions. One major source of this lead was the sapa syrup. In addition, the Romans' highly advanced plumbing system employed lead water pipes, which allowed lead to be leached into their drinking water.

Sadly, this story is more relevant to today's society than you might think. Lead-based solder was widely used for many years to connect the copper pipes in water systems in homes and commercial buildings. There is evidence that dangerous amounts of lead can be leached from these soldered joints into drinking water. In fact, large quantities of lead have been found in the water that some drinking fountains and water coolers dispense. In response to these problems, the U.S. Congress has passed a law banning lead from the solder used in plumbing systems for drinking water.

Art Resource, NY

An ancient painting showing Romans drinking wine.

5.2 Naming Binary Compounds That Contain a Metal and a Nonmetal (Types I and II)

OBJECTIVE: To learn to name binary compounds of a metal and a nonmetal.

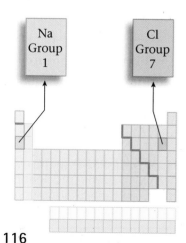

As we saw in Section 4.11, when a metal such as sodium combines with a nonmetal such as chlorine, the resulting compound contains ions. The metal loses one or more electrons to become a cation, and the nonmetal gains one or more electrons to form an anion. The resulting substance is called a **binary ionic compound.** Binary ionic compounds contain a positive ion (cation), which is always written first in the formula, and a negative ion (anion). *To name these compounds we simply name the ions.*

In this section we will consider binary ionic compounds of two types based on the cations they contain. Certain metal atoms form only one cation. For example, the Na atom always forms Na^+, *never* Na^{2+} or Na^{3+}. Likewise, Cs always forms Cs^+, Ca always forms Ca^{2+}, and Al always forms Al^{3+}. We will call compounds that contain this type of metal atom Type I binary compounds and the cations they contain Type I cations. Examples of Type I cations are Na^+, Ca^{2+}, Cs^+, and Al^{3+}.

go Chemistry **Module 3: Names to Formulas of Ionic Compounds** covers concepts in this section.

go Chemistry **Module 4: The Mole** covers concepts in this section.

go Chemistry **Module 5: Predicting the Water Solubility of Common Ionic Compounds** covers concepts in this section.

go Chemistry **Module 6: Writing Net Ionic Equations** covers concepts in this section.

Table 5.1	Common Simple Cations and Anions		
Cation	Name	Anion	Name*
H^+	hydrogen	H^-	hydride
Li^+	lithium	F^-	fluoride
Na^+	sodium	Cl^-	chloride
K^+	potassium	Br^-	bromide
Cs^+	cesium	I^-	iodide
Be^{2+}	beryllium	O^{2-}	oxide
Mg^{2+}	magnesium	S^{2-}	sulfide
Ca^{2+}	calcium		
Ba^{2+}	barium		
Al^{3+}	aluminum		
Ag^+	silver		
Zn^{2+}	zinc		

*The root is given in color.

Other metal atoms can form two or more cations. For example, Cr can form Cr^{2+} and Cr^{3+} and Cu can form Cu^+ and Cu^{2+}. We will call such ions Type II cations and their compounds Type II binary compounds.

In summary:

Type I compounds: The metal present forms only one type of cation.

Type II compounds: The metal present can form two (or more) cations that have different charges.

Some common cations and anions and their names are listed in Table 5.1. You should memorize these. They are an essential part of your chemical vocabulary.

▶ Type I Binary Ionic Compounds

The following rules apply for Type I ionic compounds:

Rules for Naming Type I Ionic Compounds

A simple cation has the same name as its parent element.

1. The cation is always named first and the anion second.
2. A simple cation (obtained from a single atom) takes its name from the name of the element. For example, Na^+ is called sodium in the names of compounds containing this ion.
3. A simple anion (obtained from a single atom) is named by taking the first part of the element name (the root) and adding *-ide*. Thus the Cl^- ion is called chloride.

We will illustrate these rules by naming a few compounds. For example, the compound NaI is called sodium iodide. It contains Na^+ (the sodium cation, named for the parent metal) and I^- (iodide: the root of *iodine* plus *-ide*). Similarly, the compound CaO is called calcium oxide because it contains Ca^{2+} (the calcium cation) and O^{2-} (the oxide anion).

The rules for naming binary compounds are also illustrated by the following examples:

Compound	Ions Present	Name
NaCl	Na^+, Cl^-	sodium chloride
KI	K^+, I^-	potassium iodide
CaS	Ca^{2+}, S^{2-}	calcium sulfide
CsBr	Cs^+, Br^-	cesium bromide
MgO	Mg^{2+}, O^{2-}	magnesium oxide

It is important to note that in the *formulas* of ionic compounds, simple ions are represented by the element symbol: Cl means Cl^-, Na means Na^+, and so on. However, when *individual ions* are shown, the charge is always included. Thus the formula of potassium bromide is written KBr, but when the potassium and bromide ions are shown individually, they are written K^+ and Br^-.

EXAMPLE 5.1 | Naming Type I Binary Compounds

Name each binary compound.

a. CsF   b. $AlCl_3$ c. MgI_2

SOLUTION

We will name these compounds by systematically following the rules given above.

a. CsF

Step 1   Identify the cation and anion. Cs is in Group 1, so we know it will form the 1+ ion Cs^+. Because F is in Group 7, it forms the 1− ion F^-.

Step 2   Name the cation. Cs^+ is simply called cesium, the same as the element name.

Step 3   Name the anion. F^- is called fluoride: we use the root name of the element plus *-ide*.

Step 4   Name the compound by combining the names of the individual ions. The name for CsF is cesium fluoride. (Remember that the name of the cation is always given first.)

b.

Compound	Ions Present	Ion Names	Comments
$AlCl_3$ → Cation	Al^{3+}	aluminum	Al (Group 3) always forms Al^{3+}.
$AlCl_3$ → Anion	Cl^-	chloride	Cl (Group 7) always forms Cl^-.

The name of $AlCl_3$ is aluminum chloride.

c.

Compound	Ions Present	Ion Names	Comments
MgI_2 → Cation	Mg^{2+}	magnesium	Mg (Group 2) always forms Mg^{2+}.
MgI_2 → Anion	I^-	iodide	I (Group 7) gains one electron to form I^-.

The name of MgI_2 is magnesium iodide.

Self-Check **EXERCISE 5.1**   Name the following compounds.

a. Rb_2O b. SrI_2 c. K_2S

See Problems 5.9 and 5.10. ■

Example 5.1 reminds us of three things:

1. Compounds formed from metals and nonmetals are ionic.

2. In an ionic compound the cation is always named first.

3. The *net* charge on an ionic compound is always zero. Thus, in CsF, one of each type of ion (Cs^+ and F^-) is required: $(1+) + (1-) = 0$ charge. In $AlCl_3$, however, three Cl^- ions are needed to balance the charge of Al^{3+}: $(3+) + 3(1-) = 0$ charge. In MgI_2, two I^- ions are needed for each Mg^{2+} ion: $(2+) + 2(1-) = 0$ charge.

▶ Type II Binary Ionic Compounds

> Type II binary ionic compounds contain a metal that can form more than one type of cation.

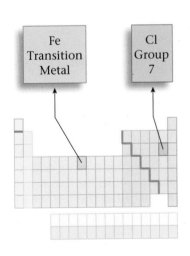

So far we have considered binary ionic compounds (Type I) containing metals that always give the same cation. For example, sodium always forms the Na^+ ion, calcium always forms the Ca^{2+} ion, and aluminum always forms the Al^{3+} ion. As we said in the previous section, we can predict with certainty that each Group 1 metal will give a 1+ cation and each Group 2 metal will give a 2+ cation. Aluminum always forms Al^{3+}.

However, there are many metals that can form more than one type of cation. For example, lead (Pb) can form Pb^{2+} or Pb^{4+} in ionic compounds. Also, iron (Fe) can produce Fe^{2+} or Fe^{3+}, chromium (Cr) can produce Cr^{2+} or Cr^{3+}, gold (Au) can produce Au^+ or Au^{3+}, and so on. This means that if we saw the name gold chloride, we wouldn't know whether it referred to the compound AuCl (containing Au^+ and Cl^-) or the compound $AuCl_3$ (containing Au^{3+} and three Cl^- ions). Therefore, we need a way of specifying which cation is present in compounds containing metals that can form more than one type of cation.

Chemists have decided to deal with this situation by using a Roman numeral to specify the charge on the cation. To see how this works, consider the compound $FeCl_2$. Iron can form Fe^{2+} or Fe^{3+}, so we must first decide which of these cations is present. We can determine the charge on the iron cation, because we know it must just balance the charge on the two 1− anions (the chloride ions). Thus if we represent the charges as

$$(?+) + 2\ (1-) = 0$$

| Charge on iron cation | Charge on Cl^- | Net charge |

we know that ? must represent 2 because

$$(2+) + 2(1-) = 0$$

> $FeCl_3$ must contain Fe^{3+} to balance the charge of three Cl^- ions.

The compound $FeCl_2$, then, contains one Fe^{2+} ion and two Cl^- ions. We call this compound iron(II) chloride, where the II tells the charge of the iron cation. That is, Fe^{2+} is called iron(II). Likewise, Fe^{3+} is called iron(III). And $FeCl_3$, which contains one Fe^{3+} ion and three Cl^- ions, is called iron(III) chloride. Remember that the Roman numeral tells the *charge* on the ion, not the number of ions present in the compound.

Copper(II) sulfate crystals.

Table 5.2	Common Type II Cations	
Ion	Systematic Name	Older Name
Fe^{3+}	iron(III)	ferric
Fe^{2+}	iron(II)	ferrous
Cu^{2+}	copper(II)	cupric
Cu^{+}	copper(I)	cuprous
Co^{3+}	cobalt(III)	cobaltic
Co^{2+}	cobalt(II)	cobaltous
Sn^{4+}	tin(IV)	stannic
Sn^{2+}	tin(II)	stannous
Pb^{4+}	lead(IV)	plumbic
Pb^{2+}	lead(II)	plumbous
Hg^{2+}	mercury(II)	mercuric
Hg_2^{2+}★	mercury(I)	mercurous

*Mercury(I) ions always occur bound together in pairs to form Hg_2^{2+}.

Note that in the preceding examples the Roman numeral for the cation turned out to be the same as the subscript needed for the anion (to balance the charge). This is often not the case. For example, consider the compound PbO_2. Since the oxide ion is O^{2-}, for PbO_2 we have

$$\underset{\substack{\uparrow \\ \text{Charge on} \\ \text{lead ion}}}{(?+)} + \underset{\substack{\uparrow \\ (4-) \\ \text{Charge on} \\ \text{two } O^{2-} \text{ ions}}}{2\,(2-)} = \underset{\substack{\uparrow \\ \text{Net} \\ \text{charge}}}{0}$$

Thus the charge on the lead ion must be 4+ to balance the 4− charge of the two oxide ions. The name of PbO_2 is therefore lead(IV) oxide, where the IV indicates the presence of the Pb^{4+} cation.

There is another system for naming ionic compounds containing metals that form two cations. *The ion with the higher charge has a name ending in -ic, and the one with the lower charge has a name ending in -ous.* In this system, for example, Fe^{3+} is called the ferric ion, and Fe^{2+} is called the ferrous ion. The names for $FeCl_3$ and $FeCl_2$, in this system, are ferric chloride and ferrous chloride, respectively. Table 5.2 gives both names for many Type II cations. We will use the system of Roman numerals exclusively in this text; the other system is falling into disuse.

To help distinguish between Type I and Type II cations, remember that Group 1 and 2 metals are always Type I. On the other hand, transition metals are almost always Type II.

Rules for Naming Type II Ionic Compounds

1. The cation is always named first and the anion second.
2. Because the cation can assume more than one charge, the charge is specified by a Roman numeral in parentheses.

EXAMPLE 5.2 | **Naming Type II Binary Compounds**

Give the systematic name of each of the following compounds.

   a. $CuCl$ b. HgO c. Fe_2O_3 d. MnO_2 e. $PbCl_4$

SOLUTION

All these compounds include a metal that can form more than one type of cation; thus we must first determine the charge on each cation. We do this by recognizing that a compound must be electrically neutral; that is, the positive and negative charges must balance exactly. We will use the known charge on the anion to determine the charge of the cation.

   a. In $CuCl$ we recognize the anion as Cl^-. To determine the charge on the copper cation, we invoke the principle of charge balance.

$$\underset{\substack{\uparrow \\ \text{Charge} \\ \text{on copper} \\ \text{ion}}}{\textcircled{?+}} \quad + \quad \underset{\substack{\uparrow \\ \text{Charge} \\ \text{on } Cl^-}}{\textcircled{1-}} \quad = \quad \underset{\substack{\uparrow \\ \text{Net charge} \\ \text{(must be zero)}}}{0}$$

In this case, ?+ must be 1+ because $(1+) + (1-) = 0$. Thus the copper cation must be Cu^+. Now we can name the compound by using the regular steps.

Compound	Ions Present	Ion Names	Comments
$\overset{\text{Cation}}{\longrightarrow}$ $CuCl$ $\underset{\text{Anion}}{\longrightarrow}$	Cu^+ Cl^-	copper(I) chloride	Copper forms other cations (it is a transition metal), so we must include the I to specify its charge.

The name of $CuCl$ is copper(I) chloride.

   b. In HgO we recognize the O^{2-} anion. To yield zero net charge, the cation must be Hg^{2+}.

Compound	Ions Present	Ion Names	Comments
$\overset{\text{Cation}}{\longrightarrow}$ HgO $\underset{\text{Anion}}{\longrightarrow}$	Hg^{2+} O^{2-}	mercury(II) oxide	The II is necessary to specify the charge.

The name of HgO is mercury(II) oxide.

   c. Because Fe_2O_3 contains three O^{2-} anions, the charge on the iron cation must be 3+.

$$\underset{\substack{\uparrow \\ Fe^{3+}}}{2(3+)} + \underset{\substack{\uparrow \\ O^{2-}}}{3(2-)} = \underset{\substack{\uparrow \\ \text{Net charge}}}{0}$$

Compound	Ions Present	Ion Names	Comments
$\overset{\text{Cation}}{\longrightarrow}$ Fe_2O_3 $\underset{\text{Anion}}{\longrightarrow}$	Fe^{3+} O^{2-}	iron(III) oxide	Iron is a transition metal and requires a III to specify the charge on the cation.

The name of Fe_2O_3 is iron(III) oxide.

d. MnO_2 contains two O^{2-} anions, so the charge on the manganese cation is 4+.

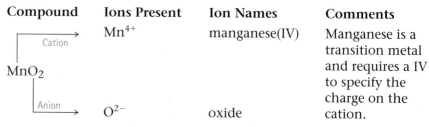

$$(4+) + 2(2-) = 0$$

Mn⁴⁺   O²⁻   Net charge

Compound	Ions Present	Ion Names	Comments
MnO_2 Cation → Mn^{4+}	Mn^{4+}	manganese(IV)	Manganese is a transition metal and requires a IV to specify the charge on the cation.
Anion → O^{2-}	O^{2-}	oxide	

The name of MnO_2 is manganese(IV) oxide.

e.   Because $PbCl_4$ contains four Cl^- anions, the charge on the lead cation is 4+.

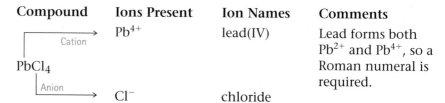

$$(4+) + 4(1-) = 0$$

Pb⁴⁺   Cl⁻   Net charge

Compound	Ions Present	Ion Names	Comments
$PbCl_4$ Cation → Pb^{4+}	Pb^{4+}	lead(IV)	Lead forms both Pb^{2+} and Pb^{4+}, so a Roman numeral is required.
Anion → Cl^-	Cl^-	chloride	

The name for $PbCl_4$ is lead(IV) chloride. ■

> Sometimes transition metals form only one ion, such as silver, which forms Ag^+; zinc, which forms Zn^{2+}; and cadmium, which forms Cd^{2+}. In these cases, chemists do not use a Roman numeral, although it is not "wrong" to do so.

The use of a Roman numeral in a systematic name for a compound is required only in cases where more than one ionic compound forms between a given pair of elements. This occurs most often for compounds that contain transition metals, which frequently form more than one cation. *Metals that form only one cation do not need to be identified by a Roman numeral.* Common metals that do not require Roman numerals are the Group 1 elements, which form only 1+ ions; the Group 2 elements, which form only 2+ ions; and such Group 3 metals as aluminum and gallium, which form only 3+ ions.

As shown in Example 5.2, when a metal ion that forms more than one type of cation is present, the charge on the metal ion must be determined by balancing the positive and negative charges of the compound. To do this, you must be able to recognize the common anions and you must know their charges (see Table 5.1).

EXAMPLE 5.3   **Naming Binary Ionic Compounds: Summary**

Give the systematic name of each of the following compounds.

   a. $CoBr_2$

   b. $CaCl_2$

   c. Al_2O_3

   d. $CrCl_3$

SOLUTION

	Compound	Ions and Names	Compound Name	Comments
a.	CoBr$_2$	Co^{2+} cobalt(II) Br$^-$ bromide	cobalt(II) bromide	Cobalt is a transition metal; the name of the compound must have a Roman numeral. The two Br$^-$ ions must be balanced by a Co^{2+} cation.
b.	CaCl$_2$	Ca^{2+} calcium Cl$^-$ chloride	calcium chloride	Calcium, a Group 2 metal, forms only the Ca^{2+} ion. A Roman numeral is not necessary.
c.	Al$_2$O$_3$	Al^{3+} aluminum O^{2-} oxide	aluminum oxide	Aluminum forms only Al^{3+}. A Roman numeral is not necessary.
d.	CrCl$_3$	Cr^{3+} chromium(III) Cl$^-$ chloride	chromium(III) chloride	Chromium is a transition metal. The name of the compound must have a Roman numeral. CrCl$_3$ contains Cr^{3+}.

Self-Check   **EXERCISE 5.2**   Give the names of the following compounds.

a. PbBr$_2$ and PbBr$_4$ b. FeS and Fe$_2$S$_3$ c. AlBr$_3$ d. Na$_2$S   e. CoCl$_3$

See Problems 5.9, 5.10, and 5.13 through 5.16. ■

The following flow chart is useful when you are naming binary ionic compounds:

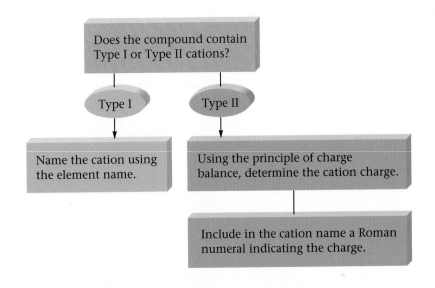

5.3

OBJECTIVE: **Naming Binary Compounds That Contain Only Nonmetals (Type III)**

To learn how to name binary compounds containing only nonmetals.

Table 5.3 Prefixes Used to Indicate Numbers in Chemical Names

Prefix	Number Indicated
mono-	1
di-	2
tri-	3
tetra-	4
penta-	5
hexa-	6
hepta-	7
octa-	8

Binary compounds that contain only nonmetals are named in accordance with a system similar in some ways to the rules for naming binary ionic compounds, but there are important differences. *Type III binary compounds contain only nonmetals.* The following rules cover the naming of these compounds.

Rules for Naming Type III Binary Compounds

1. The first element in the formula is named first, and the full element name is used.
2. The second element is named as though it were an anion.
3. Prefixes are used to denote the numbers of atoms present. These prefixes are given in Table 5.3.
4. The prefix *mono-* is never used for naming the first element. For example, CO is called carbon monoxide, *not* monocarbon monoxide.

We will illustrate the application of these rules in Example 5.4.

EXAMPLE 5.4 | Naming Type III Binary Compounds

Name the following binary compounds, which contain two nonmetals (Type III).

a. BF_3 b. NO   c. N_2O_5

SOLUTION

a. BF_3

Rule 1   Name the first element, using the full element name: boron.

Rule 2   Name the second element as though it were an anion: fluoride.

Rules 3 and 4   Use prefixes to denote numbers of atoms. One boron atom: do not use *mono-* in first position. Three fluorine atoms: use the prefix *tri-*.

The name of BF_3 is boron trifluoride.

b.
Compound	Individual Names	Prefixes	Comments
NO	nitrogen	none	*Mono-* is not used
	oxide	*mono-*	for the first element.

The name for NO is nitrogen monoxide. Note that the second *o* in *mono-* has been dropped for easier pronunciation. The *common* name for NO, which is often used by chemists, is nitric oxide.

c.
Compound	Individual Names	Prefixes	Comments
N_2O_5	nitrogen	*di-*	two N atoms
	oxide	*penta-*	five O atoms

The name for N_2O_5 is dinitrogen pentoxide. The *a* in *penta-* has been dropped for easier pronunciation.

© Cengage Learning

A piece of copper metal about to be placed in nitric acid (*left*). Copper reacts with nitric acid to produce colorless NO, which immediately reacts with the oxygen in the air to form reddish-brown NO_2 gas and Cu^{2+} ions in solution (which produce the green color) (*right*).

Self-Check **EXERCISE 5.3**   Name the following compounds.

a. CCl_4 b. NO_2 c. IF_5 See Problems 5.17 and 5.18. ■

The previous examples illustrate that, to avoid awkward pronunciation, we often drop the final *o* or *a* of the prefix when the second element is oxygen. For example, N_2O_4 is called dinitrogen tetroxide, *not* dinitrogen tetr*a*oxide, and CO is called carbon monoxide, *not* carbon mon*o*oxide.

> Water and ammonia are always referred to by their common names.

Some compounds are always referred to by their common names. The two best examples are water and ammonia. The systematic names for H_2O and NH_3 are never used.

To make sure you understand the procedures for naming binary nonmetallic compounds (Type III), study Example 5.5 and then do Self-Check Exercise 5.4.

EXAMPLE 5.5 | Naming Type III Binary Compounds: Summary

Name each of the following compounds.

a. PCl_5 c. SF_6 d. SO_2
b. P_4O_6 d. SO_3 f. N_2O_3

SOLUTION

Compound	Name
a. PCl_5	phosphorus pentachloride
b. P_4O_6	tetraphosphorus hexoxide
c. SF_6	sulfur hexafluoride
d. SO_3	sulfur trioxide
e. SO_2	sulfur dioxide
f. N_2O_3	dinitrogen trioxide

Self-Check   **EXERCISE 5.4**   Name the following compounds.

> a. SiO_2 b. O_2F_2 c. XeF_6

See Problems 5.17 and 5.18. ■

5.4 Naming Binary Compounds: A Review

OBJECTIVE: To review the naming of Type I, Type II, and Type III binary compounds.

Because different rules apply for naming various types of binary compounds, we will now consider an overall strategy to use for these compounds. We have considered three types of binary compounds, and naming each of them requires different procedures.

> Type I: Ionic compounds with metals that always form a cation with the same charge
>
> Type II: Ionic compounds with metals (usually transition metals) that form cations with various charges
>
> Type III: Compounds that contain only nonmetals

In trying to determine which type of compound you are naming, use the periodic table to help identify metals and nonmetals and to determine which elements are transition metals.

The flow chart given in Figure 5.1 should help you as you name binary compounds of the various types.

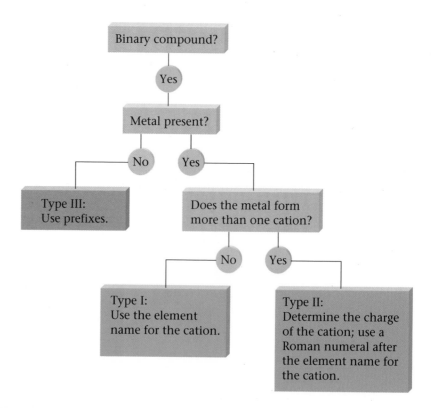

Figure 5.1

A flow chart for naming binary compounds.

Chemophilately

Philately is the study of postage stamps. Chemophilately, a term coined by the Israeli chemist Zvi Rappoport, refers to the study of stamps that have some sort of chemical connection. Collectors estimate that more than 2000 chemical-related stamps have been printed throughout the world. Relatively few of these stamps have been produced in the United States. One example is a 29¢ stamp honoring minerals that shows a copper nugget.

Courtesy, Daniel Rabinovich

Chemists also have been honored on U.S. postage stamps. One example is a 29¢ stamp printed in 1993 honoring Percy L. Julian, an African-American chemist who was the grandson of slaves. Julian is noted for his synthesis of steroids used to treat glaucoma and rheumatoid arthritis. As a holder of more than 100 patents, he was inducted into the National Inventors Hall of Fame in 1990.

Courtesy, Daniel Rabinovich

In 1983 the United States issued a stamp honoring Joseph Priestley, whose experiments led to the discovery of oxygen.

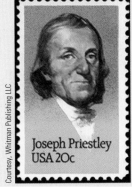

Courtesy, Whitman Publishing LLC

A stamp from 2005 pictures J. Willard Gibbs, a Yale professor who was instrumental in developing thermodynamics—the study of energy and its transformations.

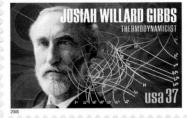

In 2008, a 41¢ stamp was issued that honors Linus C. Pauling, who pioneered the concept of the chemical bond. Pauling received two Nobel Prizes: one for his work on chemical bonds and the other for his work championing world peace. His stamp includes drawings of red blood cells to commemorate his work on the study of hemoglobin, which led to the classification of sickle cell anemia as a molecular disease.

Courtesy, Daniel Rabinovich

Postal chemistry also shows up in postmarks from places in the United States with chemical names. Examples include Radium, KS, Neon, KY, Boron, CA, Bromide, OK, and Telluride, CO.

Courtesy, Daniel Rabinovich

Chemophilately—further proof that chemistry is everywhere!

EXAMPLE 5.6   Naming Binary Compounds: Summary

Name the following binary compounds.

  a. CuO   c. B_2O_3 e. K_2S g. NH_3
  b. SrO   d. $TiCl_4$ f. OF_2

SOLUTION

a.

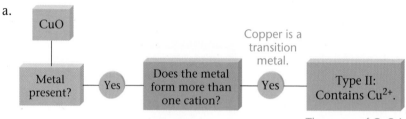

The name of CuO is copper(II) oxide.

b.

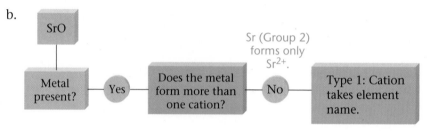

The name of SrO is strontium oxide.

c.

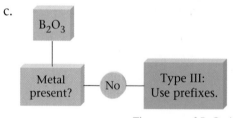

The name of B_2O_3 is diboron trioxide.

d.

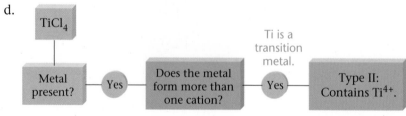

The name of $TiCl_4$ is titanium(IV) chloride.

e.

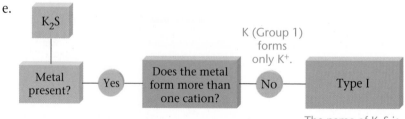

The name of K_2S is potassium sulfide.

f.

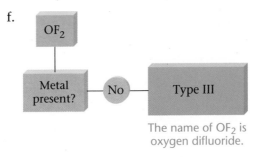

The name of OF$_2$ is oxygen difluoride.

g.

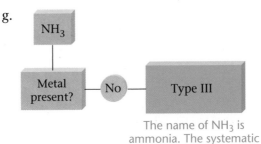

The name of NH$_3$ is ammonia. The systematic name is never used.

Self-Check **EXERCISE 5.5** Name the following binary compounds.

a. ClF$_3$ d. MnO$_2$

b. VF$_5$ e. MgO

c. CuCl   f. H$_2$O

See Problems 5.19 through 5.22. ■

5.5 Naming Compounds That Contain Polyatomic Ions

OBJECTIVE: To learn the names of common polyatomic ions and how to use them in naming compounds.

> Ionic compounds containing polyatomic ions are not binary compounds, because they contain more than two elements.

> The names and charges of polyatomic ions must be memorized. They are an important part of the vocabulary of chemistry.

A type of ionic compound that we have not yet considered is exemplified by ammonium nitrate, NH$_4$NO$_3$, which contains the **polyatomic ions** NH$_4^+$ and NO$_3^-$. As their name suggests, polyatomic ions are charged entities composed of several atoms bound together. Polyatomic ions are assigned special names that you *must memorize* to name the compounds containing them. The most important polyatomic ions and their names are listed in Table 5.4.

Note in Table 5.4 that several series of polyatomic anions exist that contain an atom of a given element and different numbers of oxygen atoms. These anions are called **oxyanions.** When there are two members in such a series, the name of the one with the smaller number of oxygen atoms ends in *-ite,* and the name of the one with the larger number ends in *-ate.* For example, SO$_3^{2-}$ is sulfite and SO$_4^{2-}$ is sulfate. When more than two oxyanions make up a series, *hypo-* (less than) and *per-* (more than) are used as prefixes to name the members of the series with the fewest and the most oxygen

Table 5.4   Names of Common Polyatomic Ions

Ion	Name	Ion	Name
NH_4^+	ammonium	CO_3^{2-}	carbonate
NO_2^-	nitrite	HCO_3^-	hydrogen carbonate (bicarbonate is a widely used common name)
NO_3^-	nitrate		
SO_3^{2-}	sulfite	ClO^-	hypochlorite
SO_4^{2-}	sulfate	ClO_2^-	chlorite
HSO_4^-	hydrogen sulfate (bisulfate is a widely used common name)	ClO_3^-	chlorate
		ClO_4^-	perchlorate
OH^-	hydroxide	$C_2H_3O_2^-$	acetate
CN^-	cyanide	MnO_4^-	permanganate
PO_4^{3-}	phosphate	$Cr_2O_7^{2-}$	dichromate
HPO_4^{2-}	hydrogen phosphate	CrO_4^{2-}	chromate
$H_2PO_4^-$	dihydrogen phosphate	O_2^{2-}	peroxide

atoms, respectively. The best example involves the oxyanions containing chlorine:

ClO^- *hypo*chlor*ite*

ClO_2^- chlor*ite*

ClO_3^- chlor*ate*

ClO_4^- *per*chlor*ate*

Naming ionic compounds that contain polyatomic ions is very similar to naming binary ionic compounds. For example, the compound NaOH is called sodium hydroxide, because it contains the Na^+ (sodium) cation and the OH^- (hydroxide) anion. To name these compounds, *you must learn to recognize the common polyatomic ions.* That is, you must learn the *composition* and *charge* of each of the ions in Table 5.4. Then when you see the formula $NH_4C_2H_3O_2$, you should immediately recognize its two "parts":

$$NH_4 \backslash C_2H_3O_2$$
$$\uparrow \qquad \uparrow$$
$$NH_4^+ \quad C_2H_3O_2^-$$

The correct name is ammonium acetate.

Remember that when a metal is present that forms more than one cation, a Roman numeral is required to specify the cation charge, just as in naming Type II binary ionic compounds. For example, the compound $FeSO_4$ is called iron(II) sulfate, because it contains Fe^{2+} (to balance the 2− charge on SO_4^{2-}). Note that to determine the charge on the iron cation, you must know that sulfate has a 2− charge.

EXAMPLE 5.7   Naming Compounds That Contain Polyatomic Ions

Give the systematic name of each of the following compounds.

a. Na_2SO_4 c. $Fe(NO_3)_3$ e. Na_2SO_3

b. KH_2PO_4 d. $Mn(OH)_2$ f. NH_4ClO_3

SOLUTION

Compound	Ions Present	Ion Names	Compound Name
a. Na_2SO_4	two Na^+ SO_4^{2-}	sodium sulfate	sodium sulfate
b. KH_2PO_4	K^+ $H_2PO_4^-$	potassium dihydrogen phosphate	potassium dihydrogen phosphate
c. $Fe(NO_3)_3$	Fe^{3+} three NO_3^-	iron(III) nitrate	iron(III) nitrate
d. $Mn(OH)_2$	Mn^{2+} two OH^-	manganese(II) hydroxide	manganese(II) hydroxide
e. Na_2SO_3	two Na^+ SO_3^{2-}	sodium sulfite	sodium sulfite
f. NH_4ClO_3	NH_4^+ ClO_3^-	ammonium chlorate	ammonium chlorate

---

Self-Check   **EXERCISE 5.6**   Name each of the following compounds.

a. $Ca(OH)_2$ d. $(NH_4)_2Cr_2O_7$ g. $Cu(NO_2)_2$

b. Na_3PO_4 e. $Co(ClO_4)_2$

c. $KMnO_4$ f. $KClO_3$

See Problems 5.35 and 5.36. ∎

Example 5.7 illustrates that when more than one polyatomic ion appears in a chemical formula, parentheses are used to enclose the ion and a subscript is written after the closing parenthesis. Other examples are $(NH_4)_2SO_4$ and $Fe_3(PO_4)_2$.

In naming chemical compounds, use the strategy summarized in Figure 5.2. If the compound being considered is binary, use the procedure summarized in Figure 5.1. If the compound has more than two elements, ask yourself whether it has any polyatomic ions. Use Table 5.4 to help you recognize these ions until you have committed them to memory. If a polyatomic ion is present, name the compound using procedures very similar to those for naming binary ionic compounds.

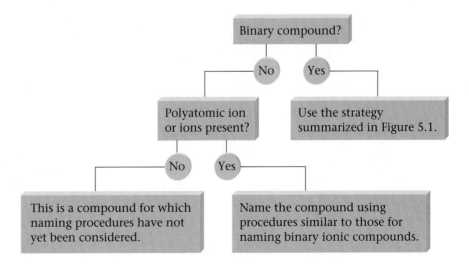

Figure 5.2

Overall strategy for naming chemical compounds.

EXAMPLE 5.8

Summary of Naming Binary Compounds and Compounds That Contain Polyatomic Ions

Name the following compounds.

    a. Na_2CO_3

    b. $FeBr_3$

    c. $CsClO_4$

    d. PCl_3

    e. $CuSO_4$

SOLUTION

Compound	Name	Comments
a. Na_2CO_3	sodium carbonate	Contains $2Na^+$ and CO_3^{2-}.
b. $FeBr_3$	iron(III) bromide	Contains Fe^{3+} and $3Br^-$.
c. $CsClO_4$	cesium perchlorate	Contains Cs^+ and ClO_4^-.
d. PCl_3	phosphorus trichloride	Type III binary compound (both P and Cl are non-metals).
e. $CuSO_4$	copper(II) sulfate	Contains Cu^{2+} and SO_4^{2-}.

Self-Check **EXERCISE 5.7** Name the following compounds.

    a. $NaHCO_3$

    b. $BaSO_4$

    c. $CsClO_4$

    d. BrF_5

    e. $NaBr$

    f. $KOCl$

    g. $Zn_3(PO_4)_2$

See Problems 5.29 through 5.36. ■

Although we have emphasized that a Roman numeral is required in the name of a compound that contains a transition metal ion, certain transition metals form only one ion. Common examples are zinc (forms only Zn^{2+}) and silver (forms only Ag^+). For these cases the Roman numeral is omitted from the name.

5.6 Naming Acids

OBJECTIVES: To learn how the anion composition determines the acid's name. • To learn names for common acids.

When dissolved in water, certain molecules produce H^+ ions (protons). These substances, which are called **acids,** were first recognized by the sour taste of their solutions. For example, citric acid is responsible for the tartness of lemons and limes. Acids will be discussed in detail later. Here we simply present the rules for naming acids.

    An acid can be viewed as a molecule with one or more H^+ ions attached to an anion. The rules for naming acids depend on whether the anion contains oxygen.

Rules for Naming Acids

1. If the *anion does not contain oxygen*, the acid is named with the prefix *hydro-* and the suffix *-ic* attached to the root name for the element. For example, when gaseous HCl (hydrogen chloride) is dissolved in water, it forms hydrochloric acid. Similarly, hydrogen cyanide (HCN) and dihydrogen sulfide (H_2S) dissolved in water are called hydrocyanic acid and hydrosulfuric acid, respectively.

2. When the *anion contains oxygen*, the acid name is formed from the root name of the central element of the anion or the anion name, with a suffix of *-ic* or *-ous*. When the anion name ends in *-ate*, the suffix *-ic* is used. For example,

Acid	Anion	Name
H_2SO_4	SO_4^{2-} (sulfate)	sulfuric acid
H_3PO_4	PO_4^{3-} (phosphate)	phosphoric acid
$HC_2H_3O_2$	$C_2H_3O_2^-$ (acetate)	acetic acid

When the anion name ends in *-ite*, the suffix *-ous* is used in the acid name. For example,

Acid	Anion	Name
H_2SO_3	SO_3^{2-} (sulfite)	sulfurous acid
HNO_2	NO_2^- (nitrite)	nitrous acid

Table 5.5 Names of Acids That Do Not Contain Oxygen

Acid	Name
HF	hydrofluoric acid
HCl	hydrochloric acid
HBr	hydrobromic acid
HI	hydroiodic acid
HCN	hydrocyanic acid
H_2S	hydrosulfuric acid

Table 5.6 Names of Some Oxygen-Containing Acids

Acid	Name
HNO_3	nitric acid
HNO_2	nitrous acid
H_2SO_4	sulfuric acid
H_2SO_3	sulfurous acid
H_3PO_4	phosphoric acid
$HC_2H_3O_2$	acetic acid

The application of Rule 2 can be seen in the names of the acids of the oxyanions of chlorine below.

Acid	Anion	Name
$HClO_4$	perchlor*ate*	perchlor*ic* acid
$HClO_3$	chlor*ate*	chlor*ic* acid
$HClO_2$	chlor*ite*	chlor*ous* acid
$HClO$	hypochlor*ite*	hypochlor*ous* acid

The rules for naming acids are given in schematic form in Figure 5.3. The names of the most important acids are given in Table 5.5 and Table 5.6. These should be memorized.

Figure 5.3

A flow chart for naming acids. The acid is considered as one or more H^+ ions attached to an anion.

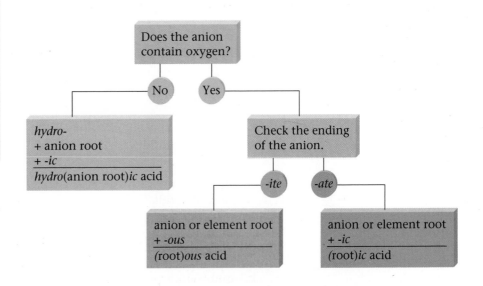

5.7 Writing Formulas from Names

OBJECTIVE: To learn to write the formula of a compound, given its name.

So far we have started with the chemical formula of a compound and decided on its systematic name. Being able to reverse the process is also important. Often a laboratory procedure describes a compound by name, but the label on the bottle in the lab shows only the formula of the chemical it contains. It is essential that you are able to get the formula of a compound from its name. In fact, you already know enough about compounds to do this. For example, given the name calcium hydroxide, you can write the formula as $Ca(OH)_2$ because you know that calcium forms only Ca^{2+} ions and that, since hydroxide is OH^-, two of these anions are required to give a neutral compound. Similarly, the name iron(II) oxide implies the formula FeO, because the Roman numeral II indicates the presence of the cation Fe^{2+} and the oxide ion is O^{2-}.

We emphasize at this point that it is essential to learn the name, composition, and charge of each of the common polyatomic anions (and the NH_4^+ cation). If you do not recognize these ions by formula and by name, you will not be able to write the compound's name given its formula or the compound's formula given its name. You must also learn the names of the common acids.

EXAMPLE 5.9   Writing Formulas from Names

Give the formula for each of the following compounds.

a. potassium hydroxide	e. calcium chloride
b. sodium carbonate	f. lead(IV) oxide
c. nitric acid	g. dinitrogen pentoxide
d. cobalt(III) nitrate	h. ammonium perchlorate

SOLUTION

Name	Formula	Comments
a. potassium hydroxide	KOH	Contains K^+ and OH^-.
b. sodium carbonate	Na_2CO_3	We need two Na^+ to balance CO_3^{2-}.
c. nitric acid	HNO_3	Common strong acid; memorize.
d. cobalt(III) nitrate	$Co(NO_3)_3$	Cobalt(III) means Co^{3+}; we need three NO_3^- to balance Co^{3+}.
e. calcium chloride	$CaCl_2$	We need two Cl^- to balance Ca^{2+}; Ca (Group 2) always forms Ca^{2+}.
f. lead(IV) oxide	PbO_2	Lead(IV) means Pb^{4+}; we need two O^{2-} to balance Pb^{4+}.
g. dinitrogen pentoxide	N_2O_5	*Di-* means two; *pent(a)-* means five.
h. ammonium perchlorate	NH_4ClO_4	Contains NH_4^+ and ClO_4^-.

Self-Check **EXERCISE 5.8** Write the formula for each of the following compounds.

   a. ammonium sulfate

   b. vanadium(V) fluoride

   c. disulfur dichloride

   d. rubidium peroxide

   e. aluminum oxide

See Problems 5.41 through 5.46. ■

CHAPTER 5 REVIEW

Key Terms

binary compound (5.1)
binary ionic
   compound (5.2)

polyatomic ion (5.5)
oxyanion (5.5)
acid (5.6)

F directs you to the *Chemistry in Focus* feature in the chapter
VP indicates visual problems
OWL interactive versions of these problems are assignable in OWL

Summary

1. Binary compounds can be named systematically by following a set of relatively simple rules. For compounds containing both a metal and a nonmetal, the metal is always named first, followed by a name derived from the root name for the nonmetal. For compounds containing a metal that can form more than one cation (Type II), we use a Roman numeral to specify the cation's charge. In binary compounds containing only nonmetals (Type III), prefixes are used to specify the numbers of atoms.

2. Polyatomic ions are charged entities composed of several atoms bound together. These have special names that must be memorized. Naming ionic compounds that contain polyatomic ions is very similar to naming binary ionic compounds.

3. The names of acids (molecules with one or more H^+ ions attached to an anion) depend on whether the anion contains oxygen.

Active Learning Questions

These questions are designed to be considered by groups of students in class. Often these questions work well for introducing a particular topic in class.

1. In some cases the Roman numeral in a name is the same as a subscript in the formula, and in some cases it is not. Provide an example (formula and name) for each of these cases. Explain why the Roman numeral is not necessarily the same as the subscript.

2. The formulas $CaCl_2$ and $CoCl_2$ look very similar. What is the name for each compound? Why do we name them differently?

3. The formulas MgO and CO look very similar. What is the name for each compound? Why do we name them differently?

4. Explain how to use the periodic table to determine that there are two chloride ions for every magnesium ion in magnesium chloride and one chloride ion for every sodium ion in sodium chloride. Then write the formulas for calcium oxide and potassium oxide and explain how you got them.

5. What is the general formula for an ionic compound formed by elements in the following groups? Explain your reasoning and provide an example for each (name and formula).

   a. Group 1 with group 7
   b. Group 2 with group 7
   c. Group 1 with group 6
   d. Group 2 with group 6

6. An element forms an ionic compound with chlorine, leading to a compound having the formula XCl_2. The ion of element X has mass number 89 and 36 electrons. Identify the element X, tell how many neutrons it has, and name the compound.

VP 7. Name each of the following compounds.

   a.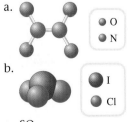

   b.

   O
   N

   I
   Cl

   c. SO_s
   d. P_2S_5

8. Why do we call $Ba(NO_3)_2$ barium nitrate but call $Fe(NO_3)_2$ iron(II) nitrate?

9. What is the difference between sulfuric acid and hydrosulfuric acid?

Questions and Problems

5.1 Naming Compounds

QUESTIONS

F 1. The "Chemistry in Focus" segment *Sugar of Lead* discusses $Pb(C_2H_3O_2)_2$, which originally was known as sugar of lead.

   a. Why was it called sugar of lead?
   b. What is the systematic name for $Pb(C_2H_3O_2)_2$?
   c. Why is it necessary to have a *system* for the naming of chemical compounds?

2. What is a *binary* chemical compound? What are the two major *types* of binary chemical compounds? Give three examples of each type of binary compound.

5.2 Naming Binary Compounds That Contain a Metal and a Nonmetal (Types I and II)

QUESTIONS

3. Cations are _____ ions, and anions are _____ ions.

4. In naming ionic compounds, we always name the _____ first.

5. In a simple binary ionic compound, which ion (cation/anion) has the same name as its parent element?

6. When we write the formula for an ionic compound, we are merely indicating the relative numbers of each type of ion in the compound, *not* the presence of "molecules" in the compound with that formula. Explain.

7. For a metallic element that forms two stable cations, the ending _____ is used to indicate the cation of lower charge and the ending _____ is used to indicate the cation of higher charge.

8. We indicate the charge of a metallic element that forms more than one cation by adding a _____ after the name of the cation.

9. Give the name of each of the following simple binary ionic compounds.

   a. NaBr   d. $SrBr_2$
   b. $MgCl_2$ e. AgI
   c. AlP   f. K_2S

10. Give the name of each of the following simple binary ionic compounds.

   a. LiCl   d. AlI_3
   b. BaF_2 e. MgS
   c. CaO   f. Rb_2O

11. In each of the following, identify which names are incorrect for the given formulas, and give the correct name.

   a. CaH_2, calcium hydride
   b. $PbCl_2$, lead(IV) chloride
   c. CrI_3, chromium(III) iodide
   d. Na_2S, disodium sulfide
   e. $CuBr_2$, cupric bromide

12. In each of the following, identify which names are incorrect for the given formulas, and give the correct name.

   a. $MnCl_2$, manganese(II) chloride
   b. Cu_2O, copper(II) oxide
   c. K_2O, potassium(I) oxide
   d. ZnS, zinc sulfide
   e. Rb_2S, rubidium(II) sulfide

13. Write the name of each of the following ionic substances, using the system that includes a Roman numeral to specify the charge of the cation.

   a. $SnCl_4$ d. Cr_2S_3
   b. Fe_2S_3 e. CuO
   c. PbO_2 f. Cu_2O

14. Write the name of each of the following ionic substances, using the system that includes a Roman numeral to specify the charge of the cation.

   a. $CuCl_2$ d. Hg_2O
   b. Cr_2O_3 e. $AuBr_3$
   c. $HgCl_2$ f. MnO_2

15. Write the name of each of the following ionic substances, using *–ous* or *–ic* endings to indicate the charge of the cation.

   a. CuCl   d. $MnCl_2$
   b. Fe_2O_3 e. TiO_2
   c. Hg_2Cl_2 f. PbO

16. Write the name of each of the following ionic substances, using *–ous* or *–ic* endings to indicate the charge of the cation.

   a. $CoCl_3$ d. $SnCl_4$
   b. $FeBr_2$ e. HgI_2
   c. PbO_2 f. FeS

5.3 Naming Binary Compounds That Contain Only Nonmetals (Type III)

QUESTIONS

17. Write the name of each of the following binary compounds of nonmetallic elements.

   a. KrF_2
   b. Se_2S_6
   c. AsH_3
   d. XeO_4
   e. BrF_3
   f. P_2S_5

All even-numbered Questions and Problems have answers in the back of this book and solutions in the Solutions Guide.

18. Write the name of each of the following binary compounds of nonmetallic elements.

    a. ClF_5 d. N_2O_3
    b. $XeCl_2$ e. I_2Cl_6
    c. SeO_2 f. CS_2

5.4 Naming Binary Compounds: A Review

QUESTIONS

19. Name each of the following binary compounds, using the periodic table to determine whether the compound is likely to be ionic (containing a metal and a nonmetal) or nonionic (containing only nonmetals).

    a. Fe_3P_2 d. $PbCl_4$
    b. $CaBr_2$ e. S_2F_{10}
    c. N_2O_5 f. Cu_2O

20. Name each of the following binary compounds, using the periodic table to determine whether the compound is likely to be ionic (containing a metal and a nonmetal) or nonionic (containing only nonmetals).

    a. PbS_2 d. SnF_4
    b. PbS e. Cl_2O_7
    c. SiO_2 f. Co_2S_3

21. Name each of the following binary compounds, using the periodic table to determine whether the compound is likely to be ionic (containing a metal and a nonmetal) or nonionic (containing only nonmetals).

    a. MgS d. $ClBr$
    b. $AlCl_3$ e. Li_2O
    c. PH_3 f. P_4O_{10}

22. Name each of the following binary compounds, using the periodic table to determine whether the compound is likely to be ionic (containing a metal and a nonmetal) or nonionic (containing only nonmetals).

    a. BaF_2 d. Rb_2O
    b. RaO e. As_2O_5
    c. N_2O f. Ca_3N_2

5.5 Naming Compounds That Contain Polyatomic Ions

QUESTIONS

23. What is a *polyatomic* ion? Give examples of five common polyatomic ions.

24. What is an *oxyanion?* List the series of oxyanions that chlorine and bromine form and give their names.

25. For the oxyanions of sulfur, the ending *-ite* is used for SO_3^{2-} to indicate that it contains _____ than does SO_4^{2-}.

26. In naming oxyanions, when there are more than two members in the series for a given element, what prefixes are used to indicate the oxyanions in the series with the *fewest* and the *most* oxygen atoms?

27. Complete the following list by filling in the missing names or formulas of the oxyanions of chlorine.

    ClO_4^- _____

    _____   hypochlorite

    ClO_3^- _____

    _____   chlorite

28. A series of oxyanions of iodine, comparable to the series for chlorine discussed in the text, also exists. Write the formulas and names for the oxyanions of iodine.

29. Write the formula for each of the following phosphorus-containing ions, including the overall charge of the ion.

    a. phosphide
    b. phosphate
    c. phosphite
    d. hydrogen phosphate

30. Write the formula for each of the following nitrogen-containing polyatomic ions, including the overall charge of the ion.

    a. nitrate
    b. nitrite
    c. ammonium
    d. cyanide

31. Chlorine occurs in several common polyatomic anions. List the formulas of as many such anions as you can, along with the names of the anions.

32. Carbon occurs in several common polyatomic anions. List the formulas of as many such anions as you can, along with the names of the anions.

33. Give the name of each of the following polyatomic ions.

    a. HCO_3^- d. OH^-
    b. $C_2H_3O_2^-$ e. NO_2^-
    c. CN^- f. HPO_4^{2-}

34. Give the name of each of the following polyatomic ions.

    a. NH_4^+ d. HSO_3^-
    b. $H_2PO_4^-$ e. ClO_4^-
    c. SO_4^{2-} f. IO_3^-

35. Name each of the following compounds, which contain polyatomic ions.

    a. NH_4NO_3 d. Na_2HPO_4
    b. $Ca(HCO_3)_2$ e. $KClO_4$
    c. $MgSO_4$ f. $Ba(C_2H_3O_2)_2$

36. Name each of the following compounds, which contain polyatomic ions.

    a. $NaMnO_4$ d. $Ca(ClO)_2$
    b. $AlPO_4$ e. $BaCO_3$
    c. $CrCO_3$ f. $CaCrO_4$

All even-numbered Questions and Problems have answers in the back of this book and solutions in the Solutions Guide.

5.6 Naming Acids

QUESTIONS

37. Give a simple definition of an *acid*.

38. Many acids contain the element _____ in addition to hydrogen.

39. Name each of the following acids.

    a. HCl   f. $HClO_3$
    b. H_2SO_4 g. HBr
    c. HNO_3 h. HF
    d. HI   i. $HC_2H_3O_2$
    e. HNO_2

40. Name each of the following acids.

    a. HOCl   e. $HBrO_4$
    b. H_2SO_3 f. H_2S
    c. $HBrO_3$ g. H_2Se
    d. HOI   h. H_3PO_3

5.7 Writing Formulas from Names

PROBLEMS

41. Write the formula for each of the following simple binary ionic compounds.

    a. cobalt(II) chloride
    b. cobaltic chloride
    c. sodium phosphide
    d. iron(II) oxide
    e. calcium hydride
    f. manganese(IV) oxide
    g. magnesium iodide
    h. copper(I) sulfide

42. Write the formula for each of the following simple binary ionic compounds.

    a. magnesium fluoride
    b. ferric iodide
    c. mercuric sulfide
    d. barium nitride
    e. plumbous chloride
    f. stannic fluoride
    g. silver oxide
    h. potassium selenide

43. Write the formula for each of the following binary compounds of nonmetallic elements.

    a. carbon disulfide
    b. water
    c. dinitrogen trioxide
    d. dichlorine heptoxide
    e. carbon dioxide
    f. ammonia
    g. xenon tetrafluoride

44. Write the formula for each of the following binary compounds of nonmetallic elements.

    a. dinitrogen oxide
    b. nitrogen dioxide
    c. dinitrogen tetraoxide (tetroxide)
    d. sulfur hexafluoride
    e. phosphorus tribromide
    f. carbon tetraiodide
    g. oxygen dichloride

45. Write the formula for each of the following compounds that contain polyatomic ions. Be sure to enclose the polyatomic ion in parentheses if more than one such ion is needed to balance the oppositely charged ion(s).

    a. ammonium nitrate
    b. magnesium acetate
    c. calcium peroxide
    d. potassium hydrogen sulfate
    e. iron(II) sulfate
    f. potassium hydrogen carbonate
    g. cobalt(II) sulfate
    h. lithium perchlorate

46. Write the formula for each of the following compounds that contain polyatomic ions. Be sure to enclose the polyatomic ion in parentheses if more than one such ion is needed to balance the oppositely charged ions.

    a. ammonium acetate
    b. ferrous hydroxide
    c. cobalt(III) carbonate
    d. barium dichromate
    e. lead(II) sulfate
    f. potassium dihydrogen phosphate
    g. lithium peroxide
    h. zinc chloride

47. Write the formula for each of the following acids.

    a. hydrosulfuric acid   e. chlorous acid
    b. perbromic acid   f. hydroselenic acid
    d. acetic acid   g. sulfurous acid
    d. hydrobromic acid   h. perchloric acid

48. Write the formula for each of the following acids.

    a. hydrocyanic acid   e. hypochlorous acid
    b. nitric acid   f. hydrobromic acid
    c. sulfuric acid   g. bromous acid
    d. phosphoric acid   h. hydrofluoric acid

49. Write the formula for each of the following substances.

    a. sodium peroxide
    b. calcium chlorate
    c. rubidium hydroxide
    d. zinc nitrate
    e. ammonium dichromate
    f. hydrosulfuric acid
    g. calcium bromide
    h. hypochlorous acid
    i. potassium sulfate
    j. nitric acid
    k. barium acetate
    l. lithium sulfite

All even-numbered Questions and Problems have answers in the back of this book and solutions in the Solutions Guide.

50. Write the formula for each of the following substances.

   a. calcium hydrogen sulfate
   b. zinc phosphate
   c. iron(III) perchlorate
   d. cobaltic hydroxide
   e. potassium chromate
   f. aluminum dihydrogen phosphate
   g. lithium bicarbonate
   h. manganese(II) acetate
   i. magnesium hydrogen phosphate
   j. cesium chlorite
   k. barium peroxide
   l. nickelous carbonate

Additional Problems

51. Iron forms both 2+ and 3+ cations. Write formulas for the oxide, sulfide, and chloride compound of each iron cation, and give the name of each compound in both the nomenclature method that uses Roman numerals to specify the charge of the cation and the -ous/-ic notation.

52. Before an electrocardiogram (ECG) is recorded for a cardiac patient, the ECG leads are usually coated with a moist paste containing sodium chloride. What property of an ionic substance such as NaCl is being made use of here?

53. Nitrogen and oxygen form numerous binary compounds, including NO, NO_2, N_2O_4, N_2O_5, and N_2O. Give the name of each of these oxides of nitrogen.

54. On some periodic tables, hydrogen is listed both as a member of Group 1 and as a member of Group 7. Write an equation showing the formation of H^+ ion and an equation showing the formation of H^- ion.

55. List the names and formulas of five common oxyacids.

56. Complete the following list by filling in the missing oxyanion or oxyacid for each pair.

   ClO_4^- _____

   _____ HIO_3

   ClO^- _____

   BrO_2^- _____

   _____ $HClO_2$

57. Name the following compounds.

   a. $Ca(C_2H_3O_2)_2$ e. $LiHCO_3$
   b. PCl_3 f. Cr_2S_3
   c. $Cu(MnO_4)_2$ g. $Ca(CN)_2$
   d. $Fe_2(CO_3)_3$

58. Name the following compounds.

   a. $AuBr_3$ e. NH_3
   b. $Co(CN)_3$ f. Ag_2SO_4
   c. $MgHPO_4$ g. $Be(OH)_2$
   d. B_2H_6

59. Name the following compounds.

   a. $HClO_3$ e. $HC_2H_3O_2$
   b. $CoCl_3$ f. $Fe(NO_3)_3$
   c. B_2O_3 g. $CuSO_4$
   d. H_2O

60. Name the following compounds.

   a. $(NH_4)_2CO_3$ e. MnO_2
   b. NH_4HCO_3 f. HIO_3
   c. $Ca_3(PO_4)_2$ g. KH
   d. H_2SO_3

61. Most metallic elements form *oxides*, and often the oxide is the most common compound of the element that is found in the earth's crust. Write the formulas for the oxides of the following metallic elements.

   a. potassium   e. zinc(II)
   b. magnesium   f. lead(II)
   c. iron(II)   g. aluminum
   d. iron(III)

62. Consider a hypothetical simple ion M^{4+}. Determine the formula of the compound this ion would form with each of the following anions.

   a. acetate   d. hydrogen phosphate
   b. permanganate   e. hydroxide
   c. oxide   f. nitrite

63. Consider a hypothetical element M, which is capable of forming stable simple cations that have charges of 1+, 2+, and 3+, respectively. Write the formulas of the compounds formed by the various M cations with each of the following anions.

   a. chromate   d. bromide
   b. dichromate   e. bicarbonate
   c. sulfide   f. hydrogen phosphate

64. Consider the hypothetical metallic element M, which is capable of forming stable simple cations that have charges of 1+, 2+, and 3+, respectively. Consider also the nonmetallic elements D, E, and F, which form anions that have charges of 1−, 2−, and 3−, respectively. Write the formulas of all possible compounds between metal M and nonmetals D, E, and F.

65. Complete Table 5.A (on page 140) by writing the names and formulas for the ionic compounds formed when the cations listed across the top combine with the anions shown in the left-hand column.

66. Complete Table 5.B (on page 140) by writing the formulas for the ionic compounds formed when the anions listed across the top combine with the cations shown in the left-hand column.

67. The noble metals gold, silver, and platinum are often used in fashioning jewelry because they are relatively _____ .

68. The noble gas _____ is frequently found in underground deposits of natural gas.

69. The elements of Group 7 (fluorine, chlorine, bromine, and iodine) consist of molecules containing _____ atom(s).

All even-numbered Questions and Problems have answers in the back of this book and solutions in the Solutions Guide.

Table 5.A

Ions	Fe^{2+}	Al^{3+}	Na^+	Ca^{2+}	NH_4^+	Fe^{3+}	Ni^{2+}	Hg_2^{2+}	Hg^{2+}
CO_3^{2-}									
BrO_3^-									
$C_2H_3O_2^-$									
OH^-									
HCO_3^-									
PO_4^{3-}									
SO_3^{2-}									
ClO_4^-									
SO_4^{2-}									
O^{2-}									
Cl^-									

Table 5.B

Ions	nitrate	sulfate	hydrogen sulfate	dihydrogen phosphate	oxide	chloride
calcium						
strontium						
ammonium						
aluminum						
iron(III)						
nickel(II)						
silver(I)						
gold(III)						
potassium						
mercury(II)						
barium						

70. Under what physical state at room temperature do each of the halogen elements exist?

71. When an atom gains two electrons, the ion formed has a charge of _____ .

72. An ion with one more electron than it has protons has a _____ charge.

73. An atom that has lost three electrons will have a charge of _____ .

74. An atom that has gained one electron has a charge of _____ .

75. For each of the negative ions listed in column 1, use the periodic table to find in column 2 the total number of electrons the ion contains. A given answer may be used more than once.

Column 1	Column 2
[1] Se^{2-}	[a] 18
[2] S^{2-}	[b] 35
[3] P^{3-}	[c] 52
[4] O^{2-}	[d] 34
[5] N^{3-}	[e] 36
[6] I^-	[f] 54
[7] F^-	[g] 10
[8] Cl^-	[h] 9
[9] Br^-	[i] 53
[10] At^-	[j] 86

76. For each of the following processes that show the formation of ions, complete the process by indicating the number of electrons that must be gained or lost to form the ion. Indicate the total number of electrons in the ion, and in the atom from which it was made.

a. $Al \rightarrow Al^{3+}$
b. $S \rightarrow S^{2-}$
c. $Cu \rightarrow Cu^+$
d. $F \rightarrow F^-$
e. $Zn \rightarrow Zn^{2+}$
f. $P \rightarrow P^{3-}$

77. For each of the following atomic numbers, use the periodic table to write the formula (including the charge) for the simple *ion* that the element is most likely to form.

a. 36   d. 81
b. 31   e. 35
c. 52   f. 87

78. For the following pairs of ions, use the principle of electrical neutrality to predict the formula of the binary compound that the ions are most likely to form.

a. Na^+ and S^{2-} e. Cu^{2+} and Br^-
b. K^+ and Cl^- f. Al^{3+} and I^-
c. Ba^{2+} and O^{2-} g. Al^{3+} and O^{2-}
d. Mg^{2+} and Se^{2-} h. Ca^{2+} and N^{3-}

79. Give the name of each of the following simple binary ionic compounds.
    a. BeO e. HCl
    b. MgI_2 f. LiF
    c. Na_2S g. Ag_2S
    d. Al_2O_3 h. CaH_2

80. In which of the following pairs is the name incorrect? Give the correct name for the formulas indicated.
    a. Ag_2O, disilver monoxide
    b. N_2O, dinitrogen monoxide
    c. Fe_2O_3, iron(II) oxide
    d. PbO_2, plumbous oxide
    e. $Cr_2(SO_4)_3$, chromium(III) sulfate

81. Write the name of each of the following ionic substances, using the system that includes a Roman numeral to specify the charge of the cation.
    a. $FeBr_2$ d. SnO_2
    b. CoS e. Hg_2Cl_2
    c. Co_2S_3 f. $HgCl_2$

82. Write the name of each of the following ionic substances, using –ous or –ic endings to indicate the charge of the cation.
    a. $SnCl_2$ d. PbS
    b. FeO e. Co_2S_3
    c. SnO_2 f. $CrCl_2$

83. Name each of the following binary compounds.
    a. XeF_6 d. N_2O_4
    b. OF_2 e. Cl_2O
    c. AsI_3 f. SF_6

84. Name each of the following compounds.
    a. $Fe(C_2H_3O_2)_3$ d. $SiBr_4$
    b. BrF e. $Cu(MnO_4)_2$
    c. K_2O_2 f. $CaCrO_4$

85. Which oxyanion of nitrogen contains a larger number of oxygen atoms, the nit*rate* ion or the nit*rite* ion?

86. Write the formula for each of the following carbon-containing polyatomic ions, including the overall charge of the ion.
    a. carbonate   c. acetate
    b. hydrogen carbonate   d. cyanide

87. Write the formula for each of the following chromium-containing ions, including the overall charge of the ion.
    a. chromous   c. chromic
    b. chromate   d. dichromate

88. Give the name of each of the following polyatomic anions.
    a. CO_3^{2-} d. PO_4^{3-}
    b. ClO_3^- e. ClO_4^-
    c. SO_4^{2-} f. MnO_4^-

89. Name each of the following compounds, which contain polyatomic ions.
    a. LiH_2PO_4 d. Na_2HPO_4
    b. $Cu(CN)_2$ e. $NaClO_2$
    c. $Pb(NO_3)_2$ f. $Co_2(SO_4)_3$

90. Choose any five simple cations and any five polyatomic anions, and write the formulas for all possible compounds between the cations and the anions. Give the name of each compound.

91. Write the formula for each of the following binary compounds of nonmetallic elements.
    a. sulfur dioxide
    b. dinitrogen monoxide
    c. xenon tetrafluoride
    d. tetraphosphorus decoxide
    e. phosphorus pentachloride
    f. sulfur hexafluoride
    g. nitrogen dioxide

92. Write the formula of each of the following ionic substances.
    a. sodium dihydrogen phosphate
    b. lithium perchlorate
    c. copper(II) hydrogen carbonate
    d. potassium acetate
    e. barium peroxide
    f. cesium sulfite

93. Write the formula for each of the following compounds, which contain polyatomic ions. Be sure to enclose the polyatomic ion in parentheses if more than one such ion is needed to balance the oppositely charged ion(s).
    a. silver(I) perchlorate (usually called silver perchlorate)
    b. cobalt(III) hydroxide
    c. sodium hypochlorite
    d. potassium dichromate
    e. ammonium nitrite
    f. ferric hydroxide
    g. ammonium hydrogen carbonate
    h. potassium perbromate

QUESTIONS

1. What is an element? Which elements are most abundant on the earth? Which elements are most abundant in the human body?

2. Without consulting any reference, write the name and symbol for as many elements as you can. How many could you name? How many symbols did you write correctly?

3. The symbols for the elements silver (Ag), gold (Au), and tungsten (W) seem to bear no relation to their English names. Explain and give three additional examples.

4. Without consulting your textbook or notes, state as many points as you can of Dalton's atomic theory. Explain in your own words each point of the theory.

5. What is a compound? What is meant by the *law of constant composition* for compounds and why is this law so important to our study of chemistry?

6. What is meant by a *nuclear atom?* Describe the points of Rutherford's model for the nuclear atom and how he tested this model. Based on his experiments, how did Rutherford envision the structure of the atom? How did Rutherford's model of the atom's structure differ from Kelvin's "plum pudding" model?

7. Consider the neutron, the proton, and the electron.

   a. Which is(are) found in the nucleus?
   b. Which has the largest relative mass?
   c. Which has the smallest relative mass?
   d. Which is negatively charged?
   e. Which is electrically neutral?

8. What are *isotopes?* To what do the *atomic number* and the *mass number* of an isotope refer? How are specific isotopes indicated symbolically (give an example and explain)? Do the isotopes of a given element have the same chemical and physical properties? Explain.

9. Complete the following table by giving the symbol, name, atomic number, and/or group(family) number as required.

Symbol	Name	Atomic Number	Group Number
Ca	————	————	————
I	————	————	————
————	cesium	————	————
————	————	16	————
————	arsenic	————	————
Sr	————	————	————
————	————	14	————
Rn	————	————	————
————	radium	————	————
Se	————	————	————

10. Are most elements found in nature in the elemental or the combined form? Why? Name several elements that are usually found in the elemental form.

11. What are *ions?* How are ions formed from atoms? Do isolated atoms form ions spontaneously? To what do the terms *cation* and *anion* refer? In terms of subatomic particles, how is an ion related to the atom from which it is formed? Does the nucleus of an atom change when the atom is converted into an ion? How can the periodic table be used to predict what ion an element's atoms will form?

12. What are some general physical properties of ionic compounds such as sodium chloride? How do we know that substances such as sodium chloride consist of positively and negatively charged particles? Since ionic compounds are made up of electrically charged particles, why doesn't such a compound have an overall electric charge? Can an ionic compound consist only of cations or anions (but not both)? Why not?

13. What principle do we use in writing the formula of an ionic compound such as NaCl or MgI_2? How do we know that *two* iodide ions are needed for each magnesium ion, whereas only one chloride ion is needed per sodium ion?

14. When writing the name of an ionic compound, which is named first, the anion or the cation? Give an example. What ending is added to the root name of an element to show that it is a simple anion in a Type I ionic compound? Give an example. What *two* systems are used to show the charge of the cation in a Type II ionic compound? Give examples of each system for the same compound. What general type of element is involved in Type II compounds?

15. Describe the system used to name Type III binary compounds (compounds of nonmetallic elements). Give several examples illustrating the method. How does this system differ from that used for ionic compounds? How is the system for Type III compounds similar to those for ionic compounds?

16. What is a *polyatomic* ion? Without consulting a reference, list the formulas and names of at least ten polyatomic ions. When writing the overall formula of an ionic compound involving polyatomic ions, why are parentheses used around the formula of a polyatomic ion when more than one such ion is present? Give an example.

17. What is an *oxyanion?* What special system is used in a series of related oxyanions that indicates the relative number of oxygen atoms in each ion? Give examples.

18. What is an *acid?* How are acids that do *not* contain oxygen named? Give several examples. Describe the naming system for the oxyacids. Give examples of a series of oxyacids illustrating this system.

PROBLEMS

19. Complete the following table by giving the symbol, name, atomic number, and/or group (family) number as required.

Symbol	Name	Atomic Number	Group Number
Al	_____	_____	_____
_____	radon	_____	_____
_____	sulfur	_____	_____
_____	_____	38	_____
Br	_____	_____	_____
_____	carbon	_____	_____
Ba	_____	_____	_____
_____	_____	88	_____
_____	_____	11	_____
K	_____	_____	_____
_____	germanium	_____	_____
_____	_____	17	_____

20. Your text indicates that the Group 1, Group 2, Group 7, and Group 8 elements all have "family" names (alkali metals, alkaline earth metals, halogens, and noble gases, respectively). Without looking at your textbook, name as many elements in each family as you can. What similarities are there among the members of a family? Why?

21. Using the periodic table on the inside cover of this book, for each of the following symbols, write the name of the element and its atomic number.

a. Mg   j. Co   s. Se
b. Ga   k. Cu   t. W
c. Sn   l. Ag   u. Ra
d. Sb   m. U   v. Rn
e. Sr   n. As   w. Ce
f. Si   o. At   x. Zr
g. Cs   p. Ar   y. Al
h. Ca   q. Zn   z. Pd
i. Cr   r. Mn

22. How many electrons, protons, and neutrons are found in isolated atoms having the following atomic symbols?

a. $^{17}_{8}O$ e. $^{4}_{2}He$
b. $^{235}_{92}U$ f. $^{119}_{50}Sn$
c. $^{37}_{17}Cl$ g. $^{124}_{54}Xe$
d. $^{3}_{1}H$ h. $^{64}_{30}Zn$

23. What simple ion does each of the following elements most commonly form?

a. Mg   f. Ba   j. Ca
b. F   g. Na   k. S
c. Ag   h. Br   l. Li
d. Al   i. K   m. Cl
e. O

24. For each of the following simple ions, indicate the number of protons and electrons the ion contains.

a. Mg^{2+} d. F^{-} g. Co^{3+} j. Rb^{+}
b. Fe^{2+} e. Ni^{2+} h. N^{3-} k. Se^{2-}
c. Fe^{3+} f. Zn^{2+} i. S^{2-} l. K^{+}

25. Using the ions indicated in Problem 24, write the formulas and give the names for all possible simple ionic compounds involving these ions.

26. Write the formula for each of the following binary ionic compounds.

a. copper(I) iodide
b. cobaltous chloride
c. silver sulfide
d. mercurous bromide
e. mercuric oxide
f. chromium(III) sulfide
g. plumbic oxide
h. potassium nitride
i. stannous fluoride
j. ferric oxide

27. Which of the following formula–name pairs are incorrect? Explain why for each case.

a. $Ag(NO_3)_2$ silver nitrate
b. Fe_2Cl ferrous chloride
c. NaH_2PO_4 sodium hydrogen phosphate
d. NH_4S ammonium sulfide
e. $KC_2H_3O_2$ potassium acetate
f. $Ca(ClO_4)_2$ calcium perchlorate
g. $K_2Cr_2O_7$ potassium dichromate
h. $BaOH$ barium hydroxide
i. Na_2O_2 sodium peroxide
j. $Ca(CO_3)_2$ calcium carbonate

28. Give the name of each of the following polyatomic ions.

a. NH_4^{+} e. NO_2^{-} h. ClO_4^{-}
b. SO_3^{2-} f. CN^{-} i. ClO^{-}
c. NO_3^{-} g. OH^{-} j. PO_4^{3-}
d. SO_4^{2-}

29. Using the negative polyatomic ions listed in Table 5.4, write formulas for each of their sodium and calcium compounds.

30. Give the name of each of the following compounds.

a. XeO_2 e. OF_2
b. ICl_5 f. P_2O_5
c. PCl_3 g. AsI_3
d. CO h. SO_3

31. Write formulas for each of the following compounds.

a. mercuric chloride   i. potassium nitride
b. iron(III) oxide   j. nitrogen dioxide
c. sulfurous acid   k. silver acetate
d. calcium hydride   l. acetic acid
e. potassium nitrate   m. platinum(IV) chloride
f. aluminum fluoride   n. ammonium sulfide
g. dinitrogen monoxide   o. cobalt(III) bromide
h. sulfuric acid   p. hydrofluoric acid

Table 6.1 Some Clues That a Chemical Reaction Has Occurred

1. The color changes.
2. A solid forms.
3. Bubbles form.
4. Heat and/or a flame is produced, or heat is absorbed.

visual signal. Steel changes from a smooth, shiny material to a reddish-brown, flaky substance when it rusts. Hair changes color when it is bleached. Solid nylon is formed when two particular liquid solutions are brought into contact. A blue flame appears when natural gas reacts with oxygen. Chemical reactions, then, often give *visual* clues: a color changes, a solid forms, bubbles are produced (see Figure 6.1), a flame occurs, and so on. However, reactions are not always visible. Sometimes the only signal that a reaction is occurring is a change in temperature as heat is produced or absorbed (see Figure 6.2).

Table 6.1 summarizes common clues to the occurrence of a chemical reaction, and Figure 6.3 gives some examples of reactions that show these clues.

Oxygen gas   Hydrogen gas

© Cengage Learning

Figure 6.1

Bubbles of hydrogen and oxygen gas form when an electric current is used to decompose water.

Spencer Grant/PhotoEdit

© Cengage Learning

a

An injured girl wearing a cold pack to help prevent swelling. The pack is activated by breaking an ampule; this initiates a chemical reaction that absorbs heat rapidly, lowering the temperature of the area to which the pack is applied.

b

A hot pack used to warm hands and feet in winter. When the package is opened, oxygen from the air penetrates a bag containing solid chemicals. The resulting reaction produces heat for several hours.

Figure 6.2

© Cengage Learning

a When colorless hydrochloric acid is added to a red solution of cobalt(II) nitrate, the solution turns blue, a sign that a chemical reaction has taken place.

b A solid forms when a solution of sodium dichromate is added to a solution of lead nitrate.

c Bubbles of hydrogen gas form when calcium metal reacts with water.

d Methane gas reacts with oxygen to produce a flame in a Bunsen burner.

Figure 6.3

6.2 Chemical Equations

OBJECTIVE: To learn to identify the characteristics of a chemical reaction and the information given by a chemical equation.

Chemists have learned that a chemical change always involves a rearrangement of the ways in which the atoms are grouped. For example, when the methane, CH_4, in natural gas combines with oxygen, O_2, in the air and burns, carbon dioxide, CO_2, and water, H_2O, are formed. A chemical change such as this is called a **chemical reaction.** We represent a chemical reaction by writing a **chemical equation** in which the chemicals present before the reaction (the **reactants**) are shown to the left of an arrow and the chemicals formed by the reaction (the **products**) are shown to the right of an arrow. The arrow indicates the direction of the change and is read as "yields" or "produces":

$$\text{Reactants} \rightarrow \text{Products}$$

For the reaction of methane with oxygen, we have

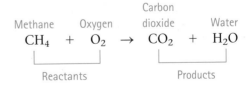

$$\underset{\text{Methane}}{CH_4} \ + \ \underset{\text{Oxygen}}{O_2} \ \rightarrow \ \underset{\text{Carbon dioxide}}{CO_2} \ + \ \underset{\text{Water}}{H_2O}$$

Reactants   Products

Note from this equation that the products contain the same atoms as the reactants but that the atoms are associated in different ways. That is, a *chemical reaction involves changing the ways the atoms are grouped.*

It is important to recognize that **in a chemical reaction, atoms are neither created nor destroyed.** *All atoms present in the reactants must be accounted for among the products.* In other words, there must be the same number of each type of atom on the product side as on the reactant side of the arrow. Making sure that the equation for a reaction obeys this rule is called **balancing the chemical equation** for a reaction.

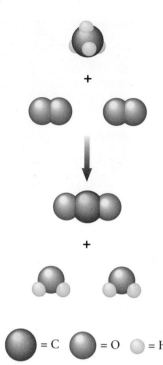

The reaction between methane and oxygen to give water and carbon dioxide. Note that there are four oxygen atoms in the products *and* in the reactants; none has been gained or lost in the reaction. Similarly, there are four hydrogen atoms and one carbon atom in the reactants *and* in the products. The reaction simply changes the way the atoms are grouped.

The equation that we have shown for the reaction between CH_4 and O_2 is not balanced. We can see that it is not balanced by taking the reactants and products apart.

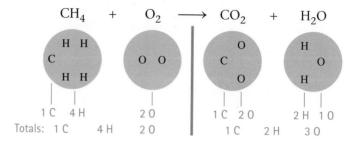

The reaction cannot happen this way because, as it stands, this equation states that one oxygen atom is created and two hydrogen atoms are destroyed. A reaction is only rearrangement of the way the atoms are grouped; atoms are not created or destroyed. The total number of each type of atom must be the same on both sides of the arrow. We can fix the imbalance in this equation by involving one more O_2 molecule on the left and by showing the production of one more H_2O molecule on the right.

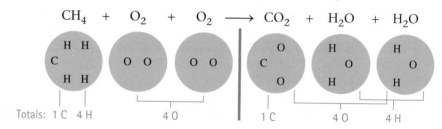

This *balanced chemical equation* shows the actual numbers of molecules involved in this reaction (see Figure 6.4).

When we write the balanced equation for a reaction, we group like molecules together. Thus

$$CH_4 + \boxed{O_2 + O_2} \longrightarrow CO_2 + \boxed{H_2O + H_2O}$$

is written

$$CH_4 + \boxed{2O_2} \longrightarrow CO_2 + \boxed{2H_2O}$$

The chemical equation for a reaction provides us with two important types of information:

1. The identities of the reactants and products
2. The relative numbers of each

▶ Physical States

Besides specifying the compounds involved in the reaction, we often indicate in the equation the *physical states* of the reactants and products by using the following symbols:

Symbol	State
(s)	solid
(l)	liquid
(g)	gas
(aq)	dissolved in water (in aqueous solution)

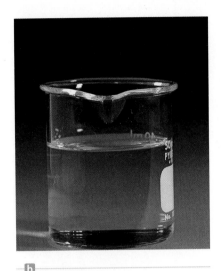

Richard Megna/Fundamental Photographs

a The reactant potassium metal (stored in mineral oil to prevent oxidation).

Figure 6.5

b The reactant water.

c The reaction of potassium with water. The flame occurs because hydrogen gas, $H_2(g)$, produced by the reaction burns in air [reacts with $O_2(g)$] at the high temperatures caused by the reaction.

For example, when solid potassium reacts with liquid water, the products are hydrogen gas and potassium hydroxide; the latter remains dissolved in the water. From this information about the reactants and products, we can write the equation for the reaction. Solid potassium is represented by $K(s)$; liquid water is written as $H_2O(l)$; hydrogen gas contains diatomic molecules and is represented as $H_2(g)$; potassium hydroxide dissolved in water is written as $KOH(aq)$. So the *unbalanced* equation for the reaction is

Solid potassium		Water		Hydrogen gas		Potassium hydroxide dissolved in water
$K(s)$	+	$H_2O(l)$	$\rightarrow$	$H_2(g)$	+	$KOH(aq)$

This reaction is shown in Figure 6.5.

The hydrogen gas produced in this reaction then reacts with the oxygen gas in the air, producing gaseous water and a flame. The *unbalanced* equation for this second reaction is

$$H_2(g) + O_2(g) \rightarrow H_2O(g)$$

Both of these reactions produce a great deal of heat. In Example 6.1 we will practice writing the unbalanced equations for reactions. Then, in the next section, we will discuss systematic procedures for balancing equations.

EXAMPLE 6.1

Chemical Equations: Recognizing Reactants and Products

Write the *unbalanced* chemical equation for each of the following reactions.

a. Solid mercury(II) oxide decomposes to produce liquid mercury metal and gaseous oxygen.

b. Solid carbon reacts with gaseous oxygen to form gaseous carbon dioxide.

c. Solid zinc is added to an aqueous solution containing dissolved hydrogen chloride to produce gaseous hydrogen that bubbles out of the solution and zinc chloride that remains dissolved in the water.

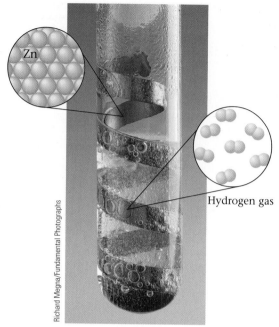

Richard Megna/Fundamental Photographs

Zinc metal reacts with hydrochloric acid to produce bubbles of hydrogen gas.

SOLUTION

a. In this case we have only one reactant, mercury(II) oxide. The name mercury(II) oxide means that the Hg^{2+} cation is present, so one O^{2-} ion is required for a zero net charge. Thus the formula is HgO, which is written HgO(s) in this case because it is given as a solid. The products are liquid mercury, written Hg(l), and gaseous oxygen, written $O_2(g)$. (Remember that oxygen exists as a diatomic molecule under normal conditions.) The unbalanced equation is

$$\underset{\text{Reactant}}{\text{HgO}(s)} \quad \rightarrow \quad \underset{\text{Products}}{\text{Hg}(l) \quad + \quad O_2(g)}$$

b. In this case, solid carbon, written C(s), reacts with oxygen gas, $O_2(g)$, to form gaseous carbon dioxide, which is written $CO_2(g)$. The equation (which happens to be balanced) is

$$\underset{\text{Reactants}}{C(s) \quad + \quad O_2(g)} \quad \rightarrow \quad \underset{\text{Product}}{CO_2(g)}$$

c. In this reaction solid zinc, Zn(s), is added to an aqueous solution of hydrogen chloride, which is written HCl(aq) and called hydrochloric acid. These are the reactants. The products of the reaction are gaseous hydrogen, $H_2(g)$, and aqueous zinc chloride. The name zinc chloride means that the Zn^{2+} ion is present, so two Cl^- ions are needed to achieve a zero net charge. Thus zinc chloride dissolved in water is written $ZnCl_2(aq)$. The unbalanced equation for the reaction is

> Because Zn forms only the Zn^{2+} ion, a Roman numeral is usually not used. Thus $ZnCl_2$ is commonly called zinc chloride.

$$\underset{\text{Reactants}}{Zn(s) \quad + \quad HCl(aq)} \quad \rightarrow \quad \underset{\text{Products}}{H_2(g) \quad + \quad ZnCl_2(aq)}$$

Self-Check **EXERCISE 6.1** Identify the reactants and products and write the *unbalanced* equation (including symbols for states) for each of the following chemical reactions.

a. Solid magnesium metal reacts with liquid water to form solid magnesium hydroxide and hydrogen gas.

b. Solid ammonium dichromate (review Table 5.4 if this compound is unfamiliar) decomposes to solid chromium(III) oxide, gaseous nitrogen, and gaseous water.

c. Gaseous ammonia reacts with gaseous oxygen to form gaseous nitrogen monoxide and gaseous water.

See Problems 6.13 through 6.34. ■

6.3 Balancing Chemical Equations

OBJECTIVE: To learn how to write a balanced equation for a chemical reaction.

As we saw in the previous section, an unbalanced chemical equation is not an accurate representation of the reaction that occurs. Whenever you see an equation for a reaction, you should ask yourself whether it is balanced. The principle that lies at the heart of the balancing process is that **atoms are conserved in a chemical reaction.** That is, atoms are neither created nor destroyed. They are just grouped differently. The same number of each type of atom is found among the reactants and among the products.

> Trial and error is often useful for solving problems. It's okay to make a few wrong turns before you get to the right answer.

Chemists determine the identity of the reactants and products of a reaction by experimental observation. For example, when methane (natural gas) is burned in the presence of sufficient oxygen gas, the products are always carbon dioxide and water. **The identities (formulas) of the compounds must never be changed in balancing a chemical equation.** In other words, the subscripts in a formula cannot be changed, nor can atoms be added to or subtracted from a formula.

Most chemical equations can be balanced by trial and error—that is, by inspection. Keep trying until you find the numbers of reactants and products that give the same number of each type of atom on both sides of the arrow. For example, consider the reaction of hydrogen gas and oxygen gas to form liquid water. First, we write the unbalanced equation from the description of the reaction.

$$H_2(g) + O_2(g) \rightarrow H_2O(l)$$

We can see that this equation is unbalanced by counting the atoms on both sides of the arrow.

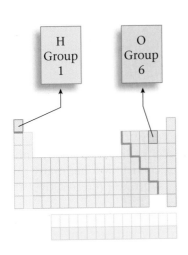

$$H_2(g) \quad + \quad O_2(g) \longrightarrow H_2O(l)$$

H H	O O	H
		O
		H
2 H	2 O	2 H, 1 O

Reactants	Products
2 H	2 H
2 O	1 O

We have one more oxygen atom in the reactants than in the product. Because we cannot create or destroy atoms and because we *cannot change the formulas* of the reactants or products, we must balance the equation by adding more molecules of reactants and/or products. In this case we need one more oxygen atom on the right, so we add another water molecule (which contains one O atom). Then we count all of the atoms again.

$$H_2(g) + O_2(g) \longrightarrow H_2O(l) + H_2O(l)$$

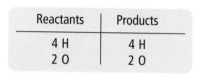

Reactants	Products
2 H	4 H
2 O	2 O

Totals: 2 H   2 O   4 H   2 O

We have balanced the oxygen atoms, but now the hydrogen atoms have become unbalanced. There are more hydrogen atoms on the right than on the left. We can solve this problem by adding another hydrogen molecule (H_2) to the reactant side.

$$H_2(g) + H_2(g) + O_2(g) \longrightarrow H_2O(l) + H_2O(l)$$

Reactants	Products
4 H	4 H
2 O	2 O

Totals: 4 H   2 O   4 H   2 O

The equation is now balanced. We have the same numbers of hydrogen and oxygen atoms represented on both sides of the arrow. Collecting like molecules, we write the balanced equation as

$$2H_2(g) + O_2(g) \rightarrow 2H_2O(l)$$

Consider next what happens if we multiply every part of this balanced equation by 2:

$$2 \times [2H_2(g) + O_2(g) \rightarrow 2H_2O(l)]$$

to give

$$4H_2(g) + 2O_2(g) \rightarrow 4H_2O(l)$$

This equation is balanced (count the atoms to verify this). In fact, we can multiply or divide *all parts* of the original balanced equation by any number to give a new balanced equation. Thus each chemical reaction has many possible balanced equations. Is one of the many possibilities preferred over the others? Yes.

The accepted convention is that the "best" balanced equation is the one with the *smallest integers (whole numbers)*. These integers are called the **coefficients** for the balanced equation. Therefore, for the reaction of hydrogen and oxygen to form water, the "correct" balanced equation is

$$2H_2(g) + O_2(g) \rightarrow 2H_2O(l)$$

The coefficients 2, 1 (never written), and 2, respectively, are the smallest *integers* that give a balanced equation for this reaction.

Next we will balance the equation for the reaction of liquid ethanol, C_2H_5OH, with oxygen gas to form gaseous carbon dioxide and water. This reaction, among many others, occurs in engines that burn a gasoline–ethanol mixture called gasohol.

The first step in obtaining the balanced equation for a reaction is always to identify the reactants and products from the description given for the reaction. In this case we are told that liquid ethanol, $C_2H_5OH(l)$, reacts

The Beetle That Shoots Straight

If someone said to you, "Name something that protects itself by spraying its enemies," your answer would almost certainly be "a skunk." Of course, you would be correct, but there is another correct answer—the bombardier beetle. When threatened, this beetle shoots a boiling stream of toxic chemicals at its enemy. How does this clever beetle accomplish this? Obviously, the boiling mixture cannot be stored inside the beetle's body all the time. Instead, when endangered, the beetle mixes chemicals that produce the hot spray. The chemicals involved are stored in two compartments. One compartment contains the chemicals hydrogen peroxide (H_2O_2) and methylhydroquinone ($C_7H_8O_2$). The key reaction is the decomposition of hydrogen peroxide to form oxygen gas and water:

$$2H_2O_2(aq) \rightarrow 2H_2O(l) + O_2(g)$$

Hydrogen peroxide also reacts with the hydroquinones to produce other compounds that become part of the toxic spray.

However, none of these reactions occurs very fast unless certain enzymes are present. (En-zymes are natural substances that speed up biologic reactions by means we will not discuss here.) When the beetle mixes the hydrogen peroxide and hydroquinones with the enzyme, the decomposition of H_2O_2 occurs rapidly, producing a hot mixture pressurized by the formation of oxygen gas. When the gas pressure becomes high enough, the hot spray is ejected in one long stream or in short bursts. The beetle has a highly accurate aim and can shoot several attackers with one batch of spray.

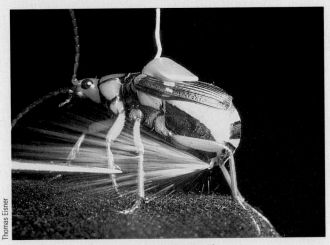

Thomas Eisner

A bombardier beetle defending itself.

with gaseous oxygen, $O_2(g)$, to produce gaseous carbon dioxide, $CO_2(g)$, and gaseous water, $H_2O(g)$. Therefore, the unbalanced equation is

$$\underset{\substack{\text{Liquid} \\ \text{ethanol}}}{C_2H_5OH(l)} + \underset{\substack{\text{Gaseous} \\ \text{oxygen}}}{O_2(g)} \rightarrow \underset{\substack{\text{Gaseous} \\ \text{carbon} \\ \text{dioxide}}}{CO_2(g)} + \underset{\substack{\text{Gaseous} \\ \text{water}}}{H_2O(g)}$$

> In balancing equations, start by looking at the most complicated molecule.

C_2H_5OH

H
C H
H O H
C H
H

2 C, 6 H, 1 O

When one molecule in an equation is more complicated (contains more elements) than the others, it is best to start with that molecule. The most complicated molecule here is C_2H_5OH, so we begin by considering the products that contain the atoms in C_2H_5OH. We start with carbon. The only product that contains carbon is CO_2. Because C_2H_5OH contains two carbon atoms, we place a 2 before the CO_2 to balance the carbon atoms.

$$C_2H_5OH(l) + O_2(g) \longrightarrow 2CO_2(g) + H_2O(g)$$

2 C atoms   2 C atoms

Remember, we cannot change the formula of any reactant or product when we balance an equation. We can only place coefficients in front of the formulas.

153

Next we consider hydrogen. The only product containing hydrogen is H_2O. C_2H_5OH contains six hydrogen atoms, so we need six hydrogen atoms on the right. Because each H_2O contains two hydrogen atoms, we need three H_2O molecules to yield six hydrogen atoms. So we place a 3 before the H_2O.

$$C_2H_5OH(l) + O_2(g) \longrightarrow 2CO_2(g) + 3H_2O(g)$$

$$\underset{6\,H}{\underset{(5+1)\,H}{\uparrow\;\uparrow}} \qquad\qquad \underset{6\,H}{\underset{(3\times2)\,H}{\uparrow\;\uparrow}}$$

Finally, we count the oxygen atoms. On the left we have three oxygen atoms (one in C_2H_5OH and two in O_2), and on the right we have seven oxygen atoms (four in $2CO_2$ and three in $3H_2O$). We can correct this imbalance if we have three O_2 molecules on the left. That is, we place a coefficient of 3 before the O_2 to produce the balanced equation.

$$C_2H_5OH(l) + 3O_2(g) \longrightarrow 2CO_2(g) + 3H_2O(g)$$

$$\underset{1\,O}{\uparrow}\qquad \underset{(3\times2)\,O}{\uparrow\;\uparrow}\qquad \underset{(2\times2)\,O}{\uparrow\;\uparrow}\qquad \underset{3\,O}{\uparrow}$$

$$\underbrace{\hspace{3cm}}_{7\,O} \qquad \underbrace{\hspace{3cm}}_{7\,O}$$

At this point you may have a question: why did we choose O_2 on the left when we balanced the oxygen atoms? Why not use C_2H_5OH, which has an oxygen atom? The answer is that if we had changed the coefficient in front of C_2H_5OH, we would have unbalanced the hydrogen and carbon atoms. Now we count all of the atoms as a check to make sure the equation is balanced.

$$C_2H_5OH(l) + 3O_2(g) \longrightarrow 2CO_2(g) + 3H_2O(g)$$

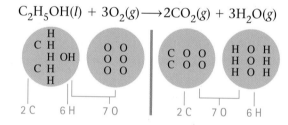

| Totals: | 2 C | 6 H | 7 O | | 2 C | 7 O | 6 H |

The equation is now balanced. We have the same numbers of all types of atoms on both sides of the arrow. Notice that these coefficients are the smallest integers that give a balanced equation.

The process of writing and balancing the equation for a chemical reaction consists of several steps:

How to Write and Balance Equations

Step 1 Read the description of the chemical reaction. What are the reactants, the products, and their states? Write the appropriate formulas.

Step 2 Write the *unbalanced* equation that summarizes the information from step 1.

Step 3 Balance the equation by inspection, starting with the most complicated molecule. Proceed element by element to determine what coefficients are necessary so that the same number of each type of atom appears on both the reactant side and the product side. Do not change the identities (formulas) of any of the reactants or products.

(continued)

Side tables:

O—C—O	H—O—H
O—C—O	H—O—H
	H—O—H
4 O atoms	3 O atoms

Reactants	Products
2 C	2 C
6 H	6 H
7 O	7 O

> **Step 4** Check to see that the coefficients used give the same number of each type of atom on both sides of the arrow. (Note that an "atom" may be present in an element, a compound, or an ion.) Also check to see that the coefficients used are the smallest integers that give the balanced equation. This can be done by determining whether all coefficients can be divided by the same integer to give a set of smaller *integer* coefficients.

EXAMPLE 6.2 | Balancing Chemical Equations I

For the following reaction, write the unbalanced equation and then balance the equation: solid potassium reacts with liquid water to form gaseous hydrogen and potassium hydroxide that dissolves in the water.

SOLUTION

Step 1   From the description given for the reaction, we know that the reactants are solid potassium, $K(s)$, and liquid water, $H_2O(l)$. The products are gaseous hydrogen, $H_2(g)$, and dissolved potassium hydroxide, $KOH(aq)$.

Step 2   The unbalanced equation for the reaction is

$$K(s) + H_2O(l) \rightarrow H_2(g) + KOH(aq)$$

Step 3   Although none of the reactants or products is very complicated, we will start with KOH because it contains the most elements (three). We will arbitrarily consider hydrogen first. Note that on the reactant side of the equation in step 2, there are two hydrogen atoms but on the product side there are three. If we place a coefficient of 2 in front of both H_2O and KOH, we now have four H atoms on each side.

$$K(s) + 2H_2O(l) \rightarrow H_2(g) + 2KOH(aq)$$

| 4 H | 2 H | 2 H |
| atoms | atoms | atoms |

Also note that the oxygen atoms balance.

$$K(s) + 2H_2O(l) \rightarrow H_2(g) + 2KOH(aq)$$

| 2 O | 2 O |
| atoms | atoms |

However, the K atoms do not balance; we have one on the left and two on the right. We can fix this easily by placing a coefficient of 2 in front of $K(s)$ to give the balanced equation:

$$2K(s) + 2H_2O(l) \rightarrow H_2(g) + 2KOH(aq)$$

Step 4

CHECK: There are 2 K, 4 H, and 2 O on both sides of the arrow, and the coefficients are the smallest integers that give a balanced equation. We know this because we cannot divide through by a given integer to give a set of smaller *integer* (whole-number) coefficients. For example, if we divide all of the coefficients by 2, we get

$$K(s) + H_2O(l) \rightarrow \tfrac{1}{2}H_2(g) + KOH(aq)$$

This is not acceptable because the coefficient for H_2 is not an integer. ∎

Reactants	Products
2 K	2 K
4 H	4 H
2 O	2 O

EXAMPLE 6.3 | Balancing Chemical Equations II

Under appropriate conditions at 1000 °C, ammonia gas reacts with oxygen gas to produce gaseous nitrogen monoxide (common name, nitric oxide) and gaseous water. Write the unbalanced and balanced equations for this reaction.

SOLUTION

Step 1   The reactants are gaseous ammonia, $NH_3(g)$, and gaseous oxygen, $O_2(g)$. The products are gaseous nitrogen monoxide, $NO(g)$, and gaseous water, $H_2O(g)$.

Reactants	Products
1 N	1 N
3 H	2 H
2 O	2 O

Step 2   The unbalanced equation for the reaction is

$$NH_3(g) + O_2(g) \rightarrow NO(g) + H_2O(g)$$

Step 3   In this equation there is no molecule that is obviously the most complicated. Three molecules contain two elements, so we arbitrarily start with NH_3. We arbitrarily begin by looking at hydrogen. A coefficient of 2 for NH_3 and a coefficient of 3 for H_2O give six atoms of hydrogen on both sides.

$$2NH_3(g) + O_2(g) \rightarrow NO(g) + 3H_2O(g)$$

6 H   6 H

We can balance the nitrogen by giving NO a coefficient of 2.

$$2NH_3(g) + O_2(g) \rightarrow 2NO(g) + 3H_2O(g)$$

2 N   2 N

$\frac{5}{2} = 2\frac{1}{2}$
O—O
O—O $2\frac{1}{2}\,O_2$
O+O   contains
                     5 O atoms

Finally, we note that there are two atoms of oxygen on the left and five on the right. The oxygen can be balanced with a coefficient of $\frac{5}{2}$ for O_2, because $\frac{5}{2} \times O_2$ gives five oxygen atoms.

$$2NH_3(g) + \tfrac{5}{2}O_2(g) \rightarrow 2NO(g) + 3H_2O(g)$$

5 O   2 O   3 O

However, the convention is to have integer (whole-number) coefficients, so we multiply the entire equation by 2.

$$2 \times [2NH_3(g) + \tfrac{5}{2}O_2(g) \rightarrow 2NO(g) + 3H_2O(g)]$$

or

$$2 \times 2NH_3(g) + 2 \times \tfrac{5}{2}O_2(g) \rightarrow 2 \times 2NO(g) + 2 \times 3H_2O(g)$$
$$4NH_3(g) + 5O_2(g) \rightarrow 4NO(g) + 6H_2O(g)$$

Reactants	Products
4 N	4 N
12 H	12 H
10 O	10 O

Step 4

CHECK: There are 4 N, 12 H, and 10 O atoms on both sides, so the equation is balanced. These coefficients are the smallest integers that give a balanced equation. That is, we cannot divide all coefficients by the same integer and obtain a smaller set of *integers*.

Self-Check EXERCISE 6.2   Propane, C_3H_8, a liquid at 25 °C under high pressure, is often used for gas grills and as a fuel in rural areas where there is no natural gas pipeline. When liquid propane is released from its storage tank, it changes to propane gas that reacts with oxygen gas (it "burns") to give gaseous carbon dioxide and gaseous water. Write and balance the equation for this reaction.

HINT: This description of a chemical process contains many words, some of which are crucial to solving the problem and some of which are not. First sort out the important information and use symbols to represent it.

See Problems 6.37 through 6.44. ■

EXAMPLE 6.4 Balancing Chemical Equations III

Decorations on glass are produced by etching with hydrofluoric acid.

Glass is sometimes decorated by etching patterns on its surface. Etching occurs when hydrofluoric acid (an aqueous solution of HF) reacts with the silicon dioxide in the glass to form gaseous silicon tetrafluoride and liquid water. Write and balance the equation for this reaction.

SOLUTION

Step 1 From the description of the reaction we can identify the reactants:

hydrofluoric acid	$HF(aq)$
solid silicon dioxide	$SiO_2(s)$

and the products:

gaseous silicon tetrafluoride	$SiF_4(g)$
liquid water	$H_2O(l)$

Step 2 The unbalanced equation is

$$SiO_2(s) + HF(aq) \rightarrow SiF_4(g) + H_2O(l)$$

Reactants	Products
1 Si	1 Si
1 H	2 H
1 F	4 F
2 O	1 O

Step 3 There is no clear choice here for the most complicated molecule. We arbitrarily start with the elements in SiF_4. The silicon is balanced (one atom on each side), but the fluorine is not. To balance the fluorine, we need a coefficient of 4 before the HF.

$$SiO_2(s) + 4HF(aq) \rightarrow SiF_4(g) + H_2O(l)$$

Reactants	Products
1 Si	1 Si
4 H	2 H
4 F	4 F
2 O	1 O

Hydrogen and oxygen are not balanced. Because we have four hydrogen atoms on the left and two on the right, we place a 2 before the H_2O:

$$SiO_2(s) + 4HF(aq) \rightarrow SiF_4(g) + 2H_2O(l)$$

This balances the hydrogen *and* the oxygen (two atoms on each side).

Reactants	Products
1 Si	1 Si
4 H	4 H
4 F	4 F
2 O	2 O

Step 4

CHECK: $SiO_2(s) + 4HF(aq) \quad \rightarrow \quad SiF_4(g) + 2H_2O(l)$

Totals: 1 Si, 2 O, 4 H, 4 F $\rightarrow$ 1 Si, 4 F, 4 H, 2 O

All atoms check, so the equation is balanced.

Self-Check **EXERCISE 6.3**   Give the balanced equation for each of the following reactions.

a. When solid ammonium nitrite is heated, it produces nitrogen gas and water vapor.

b. Gaseous nitrogen monoxide (common name, nitric oxide) decomposes to produce dinitrogen monoxide gas (common name, nitrous oxide) and nitrogen dioxide gas.

c. Liquid nitric acid decomposes to reddish-brown nitrogen dioxide gas, liquid water, and oxygen gas. (This is why bottles of nitric acid become yellow upon standing.)

If you are having trouble writing formulas from names, review the appropriate sections of Chapter 5. It is very important that you are able to do this.

See Problems 6.37 through 6.44. ■

CHAPTER 6 REVIEW

Key Terms

chemical reaction (6.2)
chemical equation (6.2)
reactant (6.2)
product (6.2)

balancing a chemical
equation (6.2)
coefficient (6.3)

 F   directs you to the *Chemistry in Focus* feature in the chapter

VP   indicates visual problems

OWL   interactive versions of these problems are assignable in OWL

Summary

1. Chemical reactions usually give some kind of visual signal—a color changes, a solid forms, bubbles form, heat and/or flame is produced.

2. A chemical equation represents a chemical reaction. Reactants are shown on the left side of an arrow and products on the right. In a chemical reaction, atoms are neither created nor destroyed; they are merely rearranged. A balanced chemical equation gives the relative numbers of reactant and product molecules.

3. A chemical equation for a reaction can be balanced by using a systematic approach. First identify the reactants and products and write the formulas. Next write the unbalanced equation. Then balance by trial and error, starting with the most complicated molecule(s). Finally, check to be sure the equation is balanced.

Active Learning Questions

These questions are designed to be considered by groups of students in class. Often these questions work well for introducing a particular topic in class.

1. The following are actual student responses to the question: Why is it necessary to balance chemical equations?

   a. The chemicals will not react until you have added the correct ratios.
   b. The correct products will not form unless the right amounts of reactants have been added.
   c. A certain number of products cannot form without a certain number of reactants.
   d. The balanced equation tells you how much reactant you need, and allows you to predict how much product you will make.
   e. A ratio must be established for the reaction to occur as written.

   Justify the best choice, and, for choices you did not pick, explain what is wrong with them.

2. What information do we get from a formula? From an equation?

3. Given the equation for the reaction: $N_2 + H_2 \rightarrow NH_3$, draw a molecular diagram that represents the reaction (make sure it is balanced).

4. What do the subscripts in a chemical formula represent? What do the coefficients in a balanced chemical equation represent?

5. Can the subscripts in a chemical formula be fractions? Explain.

6. Can the coefficients in a balanced chemical equation be fractions? Explain.

7. Changing the subscripts of chemicals can mathematically balance the equations. Why is this unacceptable?

8. Table 6.1 lists some clues that a chemical reaction has occurred. However, these events do not necessarily prove the existence of a chemical change. Give an example for each of the clues that is not a chemical reaction but a physical change.

9. Use molecular-level drawings to show the difference between physical and chemical changes.

10. It is stated in Section 6.3 of the text that to balance equations by inspection you start "with the most complicated molecule." What does this mean? Why is it best to do this?

11. Which of the following statements concerning balanced chemical equations are true? There may be more than one true statement.

    a. Atoms are neither created nor destroyed.

    b. The coefficients indicate the mass ratios of the substances used.

    c. The sum of the coefficients on the reactant side always equals the sum of the coefficients on the product side.

12. Consider the generic chemical equation $aA + bB \rightarrow cC + dD$ (where a, b, c, and d represent coefficients for the chemicals A, B, C, and D, respectively).

    a. How many possible values are there for "c"? Explain your answer.

    b. How many possible values are there for "c/d"? Explain your answer.

13. How is the balancing of chemical equations related to the law of conservation of mass?

14. Which of the following correctly describes the balanced chemical equation given below? There may be more than one true statement. If a statement is incorrect, explain why it is incorrect.

$$4Al + 3O_2 \rightarrow 2Al_2O_3$$

a. For every 4 atoms of aluminum that react with 6 atoms of oxygen, 2 molecules of aluminum oxide are produced.

b. For every 4 moles of aluminum that reacts with 3 moles of oxygen, 2 moles of aluminum (III) oxide is produced.

c. For every 4 grams of aluminum that reacts with 3 grams of oxygen, 2 grams of aluminum oxide is produced.

15. Which of the following correctly balances the chemical equation given below? There may be more than one correct balanced equation. If a balanced equation is incorrect, explain why it is incorrect.

$$CaO + C \rightarrow CaC_2 + CO_2$$

a. $CaO_2 + 3C \rightarrow CaC_2 + CO_2$

b. $2CaO + 5C \rightarrow 2CaC_2 + CO_2$

c. $CaO + 2\frac{1}{2}C \rightarrow CaC_2 + \frac{1}{2}CO_2$

d. $4CaO + 10C \rightarrow 4CaC_2 + 2CO_2$

VP 16. The reaction of an element X ($\triangle$) with element Y ($\bigcirc$) is represented in the following diagram. Which of the elements best describes this reaction?

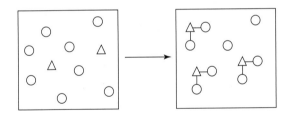

a. $3X + 8Y \rightarrow X_3Y_8$

b. $3X + 6Y \rightarrow X_3Y_6$

c. $X + 2Y \rightarrow XY_2$

d. $3X + 8Y \rightarrow 3XY_2 + 2Y$

Questions and Problems

6.1 Evidence for a Chemical Reaction

QUESTIONS

1. How do we *know* when a chemical reaction is taking place? Can you think of an example of how each of the five senses (sight, hearing, taste, touch, smell)

might be used in detecting when a chemical reaction has taken place?

2. These days many products are available to whiten teeth at home. Many of these products contain a peroxide that bleaches stains from the teeth. What evidence is there that the bleaching process is a chemical reaction?

3. Although these days many people have "self-cleaning" ovens, if your oven gets *really* dirty you may have to resort to one of the spray-on oven cleaner preparations sold in supermarkets. What evidence is there that such oven cleaners work by a chemical reaction?

4. Small cuts and abrasions on the skin are frequently cleaned using hydrogen peroxide solution. What evidence is there that treating a wound with hydrogen peroxide causes a chemical reaction to take place?

5. You have probably had the unpleasant experience of discovering that a flashlight battery has gotten old and begun to leak. Is there evidence that this change is due to a chemical reaction?

6. If you've ever left bread in a toaster too long, you know that the bread eventually burns and turns black. What evidence is there that this represents a chemical process?

6.2 Chemical Equations

QUESTIONS

7. What are the substances to the *left* of the arrow in a chemical equation called? To the *right* of the arrow? What does the arrow itself mean?

8. In an ordinary chemical reaction, _____ are neither created nor destroyed.

9. In a chemical reaction, the total number of atoms present after the reaction is complete is (larger than/smaller than/the same as) the total number of atoms present before the reaction began.

10. What does "balancing" an equation accomplish?

11. Why are the *physical states* of the reactants and products often indicated when writing a chemical equation?

12. When indicating the physical state of a reactant or product in a chemical equation, how do we indicate that a reactant is a solid? A liquid? A gaseous substance?

PROBLEMS

Note: In some of the following problems you will need to write a chemical formula from the name of the compound. Review Chapter 5 if you are having trouble.

13. A common experiment to determine the relative reactivity of metallic elements is to place a pure sample of one metal into an aqueous solution of a

compound of another metallic element. If the pure metal you are adding is more reactive than the metallic element in the compound, then the pure metal will *replace* the metallic element in the compound. For example, if you place a piece of pure zinc metal into a solution of copper(II) sulfate, the zinc will slowly dissolve to produce zinc sulfate solution, and the copper(II) ion of the copper(II) sulfate will be converted to metallic copper. Write the unbalanced equation for this process.

14. Hydrogen peroxide, H_2O_2, is often used to cleanse wounds. Hydrogen peroxide is ordinarily stable in dilute solution at room temperature, but its decomposition into water and oxygen gas is catalyzed by many enzymes and metal ions (the iron contained in blood, for example). Hydrogen peroxide is useful in the treatment of wounds because the oxygen gas produced both helps to clean the wound and suppresses the growth of anaerobic bacteria. Write the unbalanced equation for the decomposition of aqueous hydrogen peroxide into water and oxygen gas.

15. If a sample of pure hydrogen gas is ignited very carefully, the hydrogen burns gently, combining with the oxygen gas of the air to form water vapor. Write the unbalanced chemical equation for this reaction.

16. Liquid hydrazine, N_2H_4, has been used as a fuel for rockets. When the rocket is to be launched, a catalyst causes the liquid hydrazine to decompose quickly into elemental nitrogen and hydrogen gases. The rapid expansion of the product gases and the heat released by the reaction provide the thrust for the rocket. Write the unbalanced equation for the reaction of hydrazine to produce nitrogen and hydrogen gases.

17. If electricity of sufficient voltage is passed into a solution of potassium iodide in water, a reaction takes place in which elemental hydrogen gas and elemental iodine are produced, leaving a solution of potassium hydroxide. Write the unbalanced equation for this process.

18. Your family may have a "gas grill" for outdoor cooking. Gas grills typically use bottled propane gas (C_3H_8), which burns in air (oxygen) to produce carbon dioxide gas and water vapor. Write the unbalanced chemical equation for this process. Gas grills should never be used indoors, however, because if the supply of oxygen is restricted, the products of the reaction tend to be water vapor and toxic carbon monoxide, instead of nontoxic carbon dioxide. Write the unbalanced chemical equation for this process.

19. Elemental boron is produced in one industrial process by heating diboron trioxide with magnesium metal, also producing magnesium oxide as a by-product. Write the unbalanced chemical equation for this process.

20. Many over-the-counter antacid tablets are now formulated using calcium carbonate as the active ingredient, which enables such tablets to also be used as dietary calcium supplements. As an antacid for gastric hyperacidity, calcium carbonate reacts by combining with hydrochloric acid found in the stomach, producing a solution of calcium chloride, converting the stomach acid to water, and releasing carbon dioxide gas (which the person suffering from stomach problems may feel as a "burp"). Write the unbalanced chemical equation for this process.

21. Phosphorus trichloride is used in the manufacture of certain pesticides, and may be synthesized by direct combination of its constituent elements. Write the unbalanced chemical equation for this process.

22. Pure silicon, which is needed in the manufacturing of electronic components, may be prepared by heating silicon dioxide (sand) with carbon at high temperatures, releasing carbon monoxide gas. Write the unbalanced chemical equation for this process.

23. Nitrous oxide gas (systematic name: dinitrogen monoxide) is used by some dental practitioners as an anesthetic. Nitrous oxide (and water vapor as by-product) can be produced in small quantities in the laboratory by careful heating of ammonium nitrate. Write the unbalanced chemical equation for this reaction.

24. Although there are many processes by which pure metallic substances corrode, one simple process is the reaction of the metal with moisture (water) to produce the oxide of the metal and hydrogen gas. Write an unbalanced chemical equation showing the reaction of iron metal with water to produce solid iron(II) oxide and hydrogen gas.

25. Acetylene gas (C_2H_2) is often used by plumbers, welders, and glass blowers because it burns in oxygen with an intensely hot flame. The products of the combustion of acetylene are carbon dioxide and water vapor. Write the unbalanced chemical equation for this process.

26. The burning of high-sulfur fuels has been shown to cause the phenomenon of "acid rain." When a high-sulfur fuel is burned, the sulfur is converted to sulfur dioxide (SO_2) and sulfur trioxide (SO_3). When sulfur dioxide and sulfur trioxide gas dissolve in water in the atmosphere, sulfurous acid and sulfuric acid are produced, respectively. Write the unbalanced chemical equations for the reactions of sulfur dioxide and sulfur trioxide with water.

27. The Group 2 metals (Ba, Ca, Sr) can be produced in the elemental state by the reaction of their oxides with aluminum metal at high temperatures, also producing solid aluminum oxide as a by-product. Write the unbalanced chemical equations for the reactions of barium oxide, calcium oxide, and strontium oxide with aluminum.

28. There are fears that the protective ozone layer around the earth is being depleted. Ozone, O_3, is produced by the interaction of ordinary oxygen gas in the atmosphere with ultraviolet light and lightning discharges.

All even-numbered Questions and Problems have answers in the back of this book and solutions in the Solutions Guide.

The oxides of nitrogen (which are common in automobile exhaust gases), in particular, are known to decompose ozone. For example, gaseous nitric oxide (NO) reacts with ozone gas to produce nitrogen dioxide gas and oxygen gas. Write the unbalanced chemical equation for this process.

29. Carbon tetrachloride was widely used for many years as a solvent until its harmful properties became well established. Carbon tetrachloride may be prepared by the reaction of natural gas (methane, CH_4) and elemental chlorine gas in the presence of ultraviolet light. Write the unbalanced chemical equation for this process.

30. When elemental phosphorus, P_4, burns in oxygen gas, it produces an intensely bright light, a great deal of heat, and massive clouds of white solid phosphorus(V) oxide (P_2O_5) product. Given these properties, it is not surprising that phosphorus has been used to manufacture incendiary bombs for warfare. Write the unbalanced equation for the reaction of phosphorus with oxygen gas to produce phosphorus(V) oxide.

31. Calcium oxide is sometimes very challenging to store in the chemistry laboratory. This compound reacts with moisture in the air and is converted to calcium hydroxide. If a bottle of calcium oxide is left on the shelf too long, it gradually absorbs moisture from the humidity in the laboratory. Eventually the bottle cracks and spills the calcium hydroxide that has been produced. Write the unbalanced chemical equation for this process.

32. Although they were formerly called the inert gases, the heavier elements of Group 8 do form relatively stable compounds. For example, at high temperatures in the presence of an appropriate catalyst, xenon gas will combine directly with fluorine gas to produce solid xenon tetrafluoride. Write the unbalanced chemical equation for this process.

33. The element tin often occurs in nature as the oxide, SnO_2. To produce pure tin metal from this sort of tin ore, the ore usually is heated with coal (carbon). This produces pure molten tin, with the carbon being removed from the reaction system as the gaseous byproduct carbon monoxide. Write the unbalanced equation for this process.

34. Nitric acid, HNO_3, can be produced by reacting high-pressure ammonia gas with oxygen gas at around 750 °C in the presence of a platinum catalyst. Water is a by-product of the reaction. Write the unbalanced chemical equation for this process.

6.3 Balancing Chemical Equations

QUESTIONS

35. When balancing chemical equations, beginning students are often tempted to change the numbers *within* a formula (the subscripts) to balance the equation. Why is this never permitted? What effect does changing a subscript have?

F 36. The "Chemistry in Focus" segment *The Beetle That Shoots Straight* discusses the bombardier beetle and the chemical reaction of the decomposition of hydrogen peroxide.

$$H_2O_2(aq) \rightarrow H_2O(l) + O_2(g)$$

The balanced equation given in the segment is

$$2H_2O_2(aq) \rightarrow 2H_2O(l) + O_2(g)$$

Why can't we balance the equation in the following way?

$$H_2O_2(aq) \rightarrow H_2(g) + O_2(g)$$

Use molecular level pictures like those in Section 6.3 to support your answer.

PROBLEMS

37. Balance each of the following chemical equations.
   a. $FeCl_3(aq) + KOH(aq) \rightarrow Fe(OH)_3(s) + KCl(aq)$
   b. $Pb(C_2H_3O_2)_2(aq) + KI(aq) \rightarrow$
       $PbI_2(s) + KC_2H_3O_2(aq)$
   c. $P_4O_{10}(s) + H_2O(l) \rightarrow H_3PO_4(aq)$
   d. $Li_2O(s) + H_2O(l) \rightarrow LiOH(aq)$
   e. $MnO_2(s) + C(s) \rightarrow Mn(s) + CO_2(g)$
   f. $Sb(s) + Cl_2(g) \rightarrow SbCl_3(s)$
   g. $CH_4(g) + H_2O(g) \rightarrow CO(g) + H_2(g)$
   h. $FeS(s) + HCl(aq) \rightarrow FeCl_2(aq) + H_2S(g)$

38. Balance each of the following chemical equations.
   a. $Zn(s) + CuO(s) \rightarrow ZnO(s) + Cu(l)$
   b. $P_4(s) + F_2(g) \rightarrow PF_3(g)$
   c. $Xe(g) + F_2(g) \rightarrow XeF_4(s)$
   d. $NH_4Cl(g) + Mg(OH)_2(s) \rightarrow$
       $NH_3(g) + H_2O(g) + MgCl_2(s)$
   e. $SiO(s) + Cl_2(g) \rightarrow SiCl_4(l) + O_2(g)$
   f. $Cs_2O(s) + H_2O(l) \rightarrow CsOH(aq)$
   g. $N_2O_3(g) + H_2O(l) \rightarrow HNO_2(aq)$
   h. $Fe_2O_3(s) + H_2SO_4(l) \rightarrow Fe_2(SO_4)_3(s) + H_2O(g)$

39. Balance each of the following chemical equations.
   a. $K_2SO_4(aq) + BaCl_2(aq) \rightarrow BaSO_4(s) + KCl(aq)$
   b. $Fe(s) + H_2O(g) \rightarrow FeO(s) + H_2(g)$
   c. $NaOH(aq) + HClO_4(aq) \rightarrow NaClO_4(aq) + H_2O(l)$
   d. $Mg(s) + Mn_2O_3(s) \rightarrow MgO(s) + Mn(s)$
   e. $KOH(s) + KH_2PO_4(aq) \rightarrow K_3PO_4(aq) + H_2O(l)$
   f. $NO_2(g) + H_2O(l) + O_2(g) \rightarrow HNO_3(aq)$
   g. $BaO_2(s) + H_2O(l) \rightarrow Ba(OH)_2(aq) + O_2(g)$
   h. $NH_3(g) + O_2(g) \rightarrow NO(g) + H_2O(l)$

40. Balance each of the following chemical equations.
   a. $Na_2SO_4(aq) + CaCl_2(aq) \rightarrow CaSO_4(s) + NaCl(aq)$
   b. $Fe(s) + H_2O(g) \rightarrow Fe_3O_4(s) + H_2(g)$
   c. $Ca(OH)_2(aq) + HCl(aq) \rightarrow CaCl_2(aq) + H_2O(l)$
   d. $Br_2(g) + H_2O(l) + SO_2(g) \rightarrow HBr(aq) + H_2SO_4(aq)$
   e. $NaOH(s) + H_3PO_4(aq) \rightarrow Na_3PO_4(aq) + H_2O(l)$
   f. $NaNO_3(s) \rightarrow NaNO_2(s) + O_2(g)$
   g. $Na_2O_2(s) + H_2O(l) \rightarrow NaOH(aq) + O_2(g)$
   h. $Si(s) + S_8(s) \rightarrow Si_2S_4(s)$

All even-numbered Questions and Problems have answers in the back of this book and solutions in the Solutions Guide.

41. Balance each of the following chemical equations.

a. $Fe_3O_4(s) + H_2(g) \rightarrow Fe(l) + H_2O(g)$
b. $K_2SO_4(aq) + BaCl_2(aq) \rightarrow BaSO_4(s) + KCl(aq)$
c. $HCl(aq) + FeS(s) \rightarrow FeCl_2(aq) + H_2S(g)$
d. $Br_2(g) + H_2O(l) + SO_2(g) \rightarrow HBr(aq) + H_2SO_4(aq)$
e. $CS_2(l) + Cl_2(g) \rightarrow CCl_4(l) + S_2Cl_2(g)$
f. $Cl_2O_7(g) + Ca(OH)_2(aq) \rightarrow Ca(ClO_4)_2(aq) + H_2O(l)$
g. $PBr_3(l) + H_2O(l) \rightarrow H_3PO_3(aq) + HBr(g)$
h. $Ba(ClO_3)_2(s) \rightarrow BaCl_2(s) + O_2(s)$

42. Balance each of the following chemical equations.

a. $NaCl(s) + SO_2(g) + H_2O(g) + O_2(g) \rightarrow$
$Na_2SO_4(s) + HCl(g)$
b. $Br_2(l) + I_2(s) \rightarrow IBr_3(s)$
c. $Ca_3N_2(s) + H_2O(l) \rightarrow Ca(OH)_2(aq) + PH_3(g)$
d. $BF_3(g) + H_2O(g) \rightarrow B_2O_3(s) + HF(g)$
e. $SO_2(g) + Cl_2(g) \rightarrow SOCl_2(l) + Cl_2O(g)$
f. $Li_2O(s) + H_2O(l) \rightarrow LiOH(aq)$
g. $Mg(s) + CuO(s) \rightarrow MgO(s) + Cu(l)$
h. $Fe_3O_4(s) + H_2(g) \rightarrow Fe(l) + H_2O(g)$

43. Balance each of the following chemical equations.

a. $KO_2(s) + H_2O(l) \rightarrow KOH(aq) + O_2(g) + H_2O_2(aq)$
b. $Fe_2O_3(s) + HNO_3(aq) \rightarrow Fe(NO_3)_3(aq) + H_2O(l)$
c. $NH_3(g) + O_2(g) \rightarrow NO(g) + H_2O(g)$
d. $PCl_5(l) + H_2O(l) \rightarrow H_3PO_4(aq) + HCl(g)$
e. $C_2H_5OH(l) + O_2(g) \rightarrow CO_2(g) + H_2O(l)$
f. $CaO(s) + C(s) \rightarrow CaC_2(s) + CO_2(g)$
g. $MoS_2(s) + O_2(g) \rightarrow MoO_3(s) + SO_2(g)$
h. $FeCO_3(s) + H_2CO_3(aq) \rightarrow Fe(HCO_3)_2(aq)$

44. Balance each of the following chemical equations.

a. $Ba(NO_3)_2(aq) + Na_2CrO_4(aq) \rightarrow$
$BaCrO_4(s) + NaNO_3(aq)$
b. $PbCl_2(aq) + K_2SO_4(aq) \rightarrow PbSO_4(s) + KCl(aq)$
c. $C_2H_5OH(l) + O_2(g) \rightarrow CO_2(g) + H_2O(l)$
d. $CaC_2(s) + H_2O(l) \rightarrow Ca(OH)_2(s) + C_2H_2(g)$
e. $Sr(s) + HNO_3(aq) \rightarrow Sr(NO_3)_2(aq) + H_2(g)$
f. $BaO_2(s) + H_2SO_4(aq) \rightarrow BaSO_4(s) + H_2O_2(aq)$
g. $AsI_3(s) \rightarrow As(s) + I_2(s)$
h. $CuSO_4(aq) + KI(s) \rightarrow CuI(s) + I_2(s) + K_2SO_4(aq)$

Additional Problems

45. Acetylene gas, C_2H_2, is used in welding because it generates an extremely hot flame when it is combusted with oxygen. The heat generated is sufficient to melt the metals being welded together. Carbon dioxide gas and water vapor are the chemical products of this reaction. Write the unbalanced chemical equation for the reaction of acetylene with oxygen.

46. Sodium commonly forms the peroxide, Na_2O_2, when reacted with pure oxygen, rather than the simple oxide, Na_2O, as we might expect. Sodium peroxide is fairly reactive. If sodium peroxide is added to water, oxygen gas is evolved, leaving a solution of sodium hydroxide. Write unbalanced chemical equations for the reaction of sodium with oxygen to form sodium peroxide and for the reaction of sodium peroxide with water.

47. Crude gunpowders often contain a mixture of potassium nitrate and charcoal (carbon). When such a mixture is heated until reaction occurs, a solid residue of potassium carbonate is produced. The explosive force of the gunpowder comes from the fact that two gases are also produced (carbon monoxide and nitrogen), which increase in volume with great force and speed. Write the unbalanced chemical equation for the process.

48. The sugar sucrose, which is present in many fruits and vegetables, reacts in the presence of certain yeast enzymes to produce ethyl alcohol (ethanol) and carbon dioxide gas. Balance the following equation for this reaction of sucrose.

$$C_{12}H_{22}O_{11}(aq) + H_2O(l) \rightarrow C_2H_5OH(aq) + CO_2(g)$$

49. Methanol (methyl alcohol), CH_3OH, is a very important industrial chemical. Formerly, methanol was prepared by heating wood to high temperatures in the absence of air. The complex compounds present in wood are degraded by this process into a charcoal residue and a volatile portion that is rich in methanol. Today, methanol is instead synthesized from carbon monoxide and elemental hydrogen. Write the balanced chemical equation for this latter process.

50. The Hall process is an important method by which pure aluminum is prepared from its oxide (alumina, Al_2O_3) by indirect reaction with graphite (carbon). Balance the following equation, which is a simplified representation of this process.

$$Al_2O_3(s) + C(s) \rightarrow Al(s) + CO_2(g)$$

51. Iron oxide ores, commonly a mixture of FeO and Fe_2O_3, are given the general formula Fe_3O_4. They yield elemental iron when heated to a very high temperature with either carbon monoxide or elemental hydrogen. Balance the following equations for these processes.

$$Fe_3O_4(s) + H_2(g) \rightarrow Fe(s) + H_2O(g)$$
$$Fe_3O_4(s) + CO(g) \rightarrow Fe(s) + CO_2(g)$$

52. The elements of Group 1 all react with sulfur to form the metal sulfides. Write balanced chemical equations for the reactions of the Group 1 elements with sulfur.

53. When steel wool (iron) is heated in pure oxygen gas, the steel wool bursts into flame and a fine powder consisting of a mixture of iron oxides (FeO and Fe_2O_3) forms. Write *separate* unbalanced equations for the reaction of iron with oxygen to give each of these products.

54. One method of producing hydrogen peroxide is to add barium peroxide to water. A precipitate of barium oxide forms, which may then be filtered off to leave a solution of hydrogen peroxide. Write the balanced chemical equation for this process.

55. When elemental boron, B, is burned in oxygen gas, the product is diboron trioxide. If the diboron trioxide is then reacted with a measured quantity of water, it reacts with the water to form what is commonly known as boric acid, $B(OH)_3$. Write a balanced chemical equation for each of these processes.

56. A common experiment in introductory chemistry courses involves heating a weighed mixture of potassium chlorate, $KClO_3$, and potassium chloride. Potassium chlorate decomposes when heated, producing potassium chloride and evolving oxygen gas. By measuring the volume of oxygen gas produced in this experiment, students can calculate the relative percentage of $KClO_3$ and KCl in the original mixture. Write the balanced chemical equation for this process.

57. A common demonstration in chemistry courses involves adding a tiny speck of manganese(IV) oxide to a concentrated hydrogen peroxide, H_2O_2, solution. Hydrogen peroxide is unstable, and it decomposes quite spectacularly under these conditions to produce oxygen gas and steam (water vapor). Manganese(IV) oxide is a catalyst for the decomposition of hydrogen peroxide and is not consumed in the reaction. Write the balanced equation for the decomposition reaction of hydrogen peroxide.

58. The benches in many undergraduate chemistry laboratories are often covered by a film of white dust. This may be due to poor housekeeping, but the dust is usually ammonium chloride, produced by the gaseous reaction in the laboratory of hydrogen chloride and ammonia; most labs have aqueous solutions of these common reagents. Write the balanced chemical equation for the reaction of gaseous ammonia and hydrogen chloride to form solid ammonium chloride.

59. Glass is a mixture of several compounds, but a major constituent of most glass is calcium silicate, $CaSiO_3$. Glass can be etched by treatment with hydrogen fluoride: HF attacks the calcium silicate of the glass, producing gaseous and water-soluble products (which can be removed by washing the glass). For example, the volumetric glassware in chemistry laboratories is often graduated by using this process. Balance the following equation for the reaction of hydrogen fluoride with calcium silicate.

$$CaSiO_3(s) + HF(g) \rightarrow CaF_2(aq) + SiF_4(g) + H_2O(l)$$

60. Fish has a "fishy" taste and odor because of the presence of nitrogen compounds called amines in the protein of the fish. Amines such as methyl amine, CH_3NH_2, can be thought of as close relatives of ammonia, NH_3, in which a hydrogen atom of ammonia is replaced by a carbon-containing group. When fish is served, it is often accompanied by lemon (or vinegar in some countries), which reduces the fishy odor and taste. Is there evidence that the action of the lemon juice or vinegar represents a chemical reaction?

61. If you had a "sour stomach," you might try an over-the-counter antacid tablet to relieve the problem. Can you think of evidence that the action of such an antacid is a chemical reaction?

62. When iron wire is heated in the presence of sulfur, the iron soon begins to glow, and a chunky, blue-black mass of iron(II) sulfide is formed. Write the unbalanced chemical equation for this reaction.

63. When finely divided solid sodium is dropped into a flask containing chlorine gas, an explosion occurs and a fine powder of sodium chloride is deposited on the walls of the flask. Write the unbalanced chemical equation for this process.

64. If aqueous solutions of potassium chromate and barium chloride are mixed, a bright yellow solid (barium chromate) forms and settles out of the mixture, leaving potassium chloride in solution. Write a balanced chemical equation for this process.

65. When hydrogen sulfide, H_2S, gas is bubbled through a solution of lead(II) nitrate, $Pb(NO_3)_2$, a black precipitate of lead(II) sulfide, PbS, forms, and nitric acid, HNO_3, is produced. Write the unbalanced chemical equation for this reaction.

66. If an electric current is passed through aqueous solutions of sodium chloride, sodium bromide, and sodium iodide, the elemental halogens are produced at one electrode in each case, with hydrogen gas being evolved at the other electrode. If the liquid is then evaporated from the mixture, a residue of sodium hydroxide remains. Write balanced chemical equations for these electrolysis reactions.

67. When a strip of magnesium metal is heated in oxygen, it bursts into an intensely white flame and produces a finely powdered dust of magnesium oxide. Write the unbalanced chemical equation for this process.

68. When small amounts of acetylene gas are needed, a common process is to react calcium carbide with water. Acetylene gas is evolved rapidly from this combination even at room temperature, leaving a residue of calcium hydroxide. Write the balanced chemical equation for this process.

69. When solid red phosphorus, P_4, is burned in air, the phosphorus combines with oxygen, producing a choking cloud of tetraphosphorus decoxide. Write the unbalanced chemical equation for this reaction.

70. When copper(II) oxide is boiled in an aqueous solution of sulfuric acid, a strikingly blue solution of copper(II) sulfate forms along with additional water. Write the unbalanced chemical equation for this reaction.

71. When lead(II) sulfide is heated to high temperatures in a stream of pure oxygen gas, solid lead(II) oxide forms with the release of gaseous sulfur dioxide. Write the unbalanced chemical equation for this reaction.

72. When sodium sulfite is boiled with sulfur, the sulfite ions, SO_3^{2-}, are converted to thiosulfate ions, $S_2O_3^{2-}$, resulting in a solution of sodium thiosulfate, $Na_2S_2O_3$. Write the unbalanced chemical equation for this reaction.

All even-numbered Questions and Problems have answers in the back of this book and solutions in the Solutions Guide.

73. Balance each of the following chemical equations.

a. $Cl_2(g) + KBr(aq) \rightarrow Br_2(l) + KCl(aq)$
b. $Cr(s) + O_2(g) \rightarrow Cr_2O_3(s)$
c. $P_4(s) + H_2(g) \rightarrow PH_3(g)$
d. $Al(s) + H_2SO_4(aq) \rightarrow Al_2(SO_4)_3(aq) + H_2(g)$
e. $PCl_3(l) + H_2O(l) \rightarrow H_3PO_3(aq) + HCl(aq)$
f. $SO_2(g) + O_2(g) \rightarrow SO_3(g)$
g. $C_7H_{16}(l) + O_2(g) \rightarrow CO_2(g) + H_2O(g)$
h. $C_2H_6(g) + O_2(g) \rightarrow CO_2(g) + H_2O(g)$

74. Balance each of the following chemical equations.

a. $Cl_2(g) + KI(aq) \rightarrow KCl(aq) + I_2(s)$
b. $CaC_2(s) + H_2O(l) \rightarrow Ca(OH)_2(s) + C_2H_2(g)$
c. $NaCl(s) + H_2SO_4(l) \rightarrow Na_2SO_4(s) + HCl(g)$
d. $CaF_2(s) + H_2SO_4(l) \rightarrow CaSO_4(s) + HF(g)$
e. $K_2CO_3(s) \rightarrow K_2O(s) + CO_2(g)$
f. $BaO(s) + Al(s) \rightarrow Al_2O_3(s) + Ba(s)$
g. $Al(s) + F_2(g) \rightarrow AlF_3(s)$
h. $CS_2(g) + Cl_2(g) \rightarrow CCl_4(l) + S_2Cl_2(g)$

75. Balance each of the following chemical equations.

a. $SiCl_4(l) + Mg(s) \rightarrow Si(s) + MgCl_2(s)$
b. $NO(g) + Cl_2(g) \rightarrow NOCl(g)$

c. $MnO_2(s) + Al(s) \rightarrow Mn(s) + Al_2O_3(s)$
d. $Cr(s) + S_8(s) \rightarrow Cr_2S_3(s)$
e. $NH_3(g) + F_2(g) \rightarrow NH_4F(s) + NF_3(g)$
f. $Ag_2S(s) + H_2(g) \rightarrow Ag(s) + H_2S(g)$
g. $O_2(g) \rightarrow O_3(g)$
h. $Na_2SO_3(aq) + S_8(s) \rightarrow Na_2S_2O_3(aq)$

76. Balance each of the following chemical equations.

a. $Pb(NO_3)_2(aq) + K_2CrO_4(aq) \rightarrow$
$$PbCrO_4(s) + KNO_3(aq)$$
b. $BaCl_2(aq) + Na_2SO_4(aq) \rightarrow BaSO_4(s) + NaCl(aq)$
c. $CH_3OH(l) + O_2(g) \rightarrow CO_2(g) + H_2O(g)$
d. $Na_2CO_3(aq) + S(s) + SO_2(g) \rightarrow$
$$CO_2(g) + Na_2S_2O_3(aq)$$
e. $Cu(s) + H_2SO_4(aq) \rightarrow$
$$CuSO_4(aq) + SO_2(g) + H_2O(l)$$
f. $MnO_2(s) + HCl(aq) \rightarrow$
$$MnCl_2(aq) + Cl_2(g) + H_2O(l)$$
g. $As_2O_3(s) + KI(aq) + HCl(aq) \rightarrow$
$$AsI_3(s) + KCl(aq) + H_2O(l)$$
h. $Na_2S_2O_3(aq) + I_2(aq) \rightarrow Na_2S_4O_6(aq) + NaI(aq)$

7 Reactions in Aqueous Solutions

● Chlorine in water reacting with potassium bromide. *(Richard Megna/Fundamental Photographs)*

A burning match involves several chemical reactions.

The chemical reactions that are most important to us occur in water—in aqueous solutions. Virtually all of the chemical reactions that keep each of us alive and well take place in the aqueous medium present in our bodies. For example, the oxygen you breathe dissolves in your blood, where it associates with the hemoglobin in the red blood cells. While attached to the hemoglobin it is transported to your cells, where it reacts with fuel (from the food you eat) to provide energy for living. However, the reaction between oxygen and fuel is not direct—the cells are not tiny furnaces. Instead, electrons are transferred from the fuel to a series of molecules that pass them along (this is called the respiratory chain) until they eventually reach oxygen. Many other reactions are also crucial to our health and well-being. You will see numerous examples of these as you continue your study of chemistry.

In this chapter we will study some common types of reactions that take place in water, and we will become familiar with some of the driving forces that make these reactions occur. We will also learn how to predict the products for these reactions and how to write various equations to describe them.

7.1 Predicting Whether a Reaction Will Occur

OBJECTIVE: To learn about some of the factors that cause reactions to occur.

In this text we have already seen many chemical reactions. Now let's consider an important question: Why does a chemical reaction occur? What causes reactants to "want" to form products? As chemists have studied reactions, they have recognized several "tendencies" in reactants that drive them to form products. That is, there are several "driving forces" that pull reactants toward products—changes that tend to make reactions go in the direction of the arrow. The most common of these driving forces are

1. Formation of a solid
2. Formation of water
3. Transfer of electrons
4. Formation of a gas

When two or more chemicals are brought together, if any of these things can occur, a chemical change (a reaction) is likely to take place. Accordingly, when we are confronted with a set of reactants and want to predict whether a reaction will occur and what products might form, we will consider these driving forces. They will help us organize our thoughts as we encounter new reactions.

7.2 Reactions in Which a Solid Forms

OBJECTIVE: To learn to identify the solid that forms in a precipitation reaction.

One driving force for a chemical reaction is the formation of a solid, a process called **precipitation.** The solid that forms is called a **precipitate,** and the reaction is known as a **precipitation reaction.** For example,

when an aqueous (water) solution of potassium chromate, $K_2CrO_4(aq)$, which is yellow, is added to a colorless aqueous solution containing barium nitrate, $Ba(NO_3)_2(aq)$, a yellow solid forms (see Figure 7.1). The fact that a solid forms tells us that a reaction—a chemical change—has occurred. That is, we have a situation where

Reactants → Products

What is the equation that describes this chemical change? To write the equation, we must decipher the identities of the reactants and products. The reactants have already been described: $K_2CrO_4(aq)$ and $Ba(NO_3)_2(aq)$. Is there some way in which we can predict the identities of the products? What is the yellow solid? The best way to predict the identity of this solid is to first *consider what products are possible*. To do this we need to know what chemical species are present in the solution that results when the reactant solutions are mixed. First, let's think about the nature of each reactant in an aqueous solution.

Figure 7.1

The precipitation reaction that occurs when yellow potassium chromate, $K_2CrO_4(aq)$, is mixed with a colorless barium nitrate solution, $Ba(NO_3)_2(aq)$.

▶ What Happens When an Ionic Compound Dissolves in Water?

The designation $Ba(NO_3)_2(aq)$ means that barium nitrate (a white solid) has been dissolved in water. Note from its formula that barium nitrate contains the Ba^{2+} and NO_3^- ions. *In virtually every case when a solid containing ions dissolves in water, the ions separate* and move around independently. That is, $Ba(NO_3)_2(aq)$ does not contain $Ba(NO_3)_2$ units. Rather, it contains separated Ba^{2+} and NO_3^- ions. In the solution there are two NO_3^- ions for every Ba^{2+} ion. Chemists know that separated ions are present in this solution because it is an excellent conductor of electricity (see Figure 7.2). Pure water does not conduct an electric current. Ions must be present in water for a current to flow.

When each unit of a substance that dissolves in water produces separated ions, the substance is called a **strong electrolyte.** Barium nitrate is a strong electrolyte in water, because each $Ba(NO_3)_2$ unit produces the separated ions (Ba^{2+}, NO_3^-, NO_3^-).

Similarly, aqueous K_2CrO_4 also behaves as a strong electrolyte. Potassium chromate contains the K^+ and CrO_4^{2-} ions, so an aqueous solution of

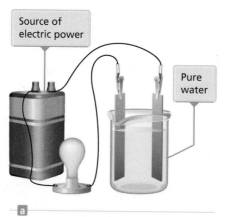

Pure water does not conduct an electric current. The lamp does not light.

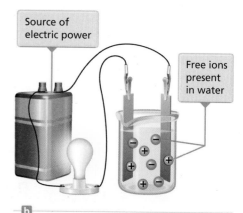

When an ionic compound is dissolved in water, current flows and the lamp lights. The result of this experiment is strong evidence that ionic compounds dissolved in water exist in the form of separated ions.

Figure 7.2

Electrical conductivity of aqueous solutions.

potassium chromate (which is prepared by dissolving solid K_2CrO_4 in water) contains these separated ions. That is, $K_2CrO_4(aq)$ does not contain K_2CrO_4 units but instead contains K^+ cations and CrO_4^{2-} anions, which move around independently. (There are two K^+ ions for each CrO_4^{2-} ion.)

The idea introduced here is very important: when ionic compounds dissolve, the *resulting solution contains the separated ions*. Therefore, we can represent the mixing of $K_2CrO_4(aq)$ and $Ba(NO_3)_2(aq)$ in two ways. We usually write these reactants as

$$K_2CrO_4(aq) + Ba(NO_3)_2(aq) \rightarrow Products$$

However, a more accurate representation of the situation is

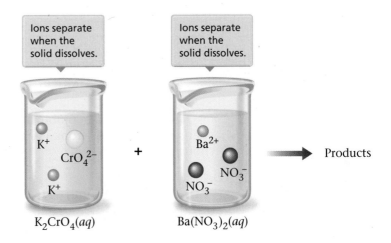

$$K_2CrO_4(aq) \qquad Ba(NO_3)_2(aq)$$

We can express this information in equation form as follows:

$$2K^+(aq) + CrO_4^{2-}(aq) + Ba^{2+}(aq) + 2NO_3^-(aq) \rightarrow Products$$

The ions in $K_2CrO_4 (aq)$

The ions in $Ba(NO_3)_2(aq)$

Thus the *mixed solution* contains four types of ions: K^+, CrO_4^{2-}, Ba^{2+}, and NO_3^-. Now that we know what the reactants are, we can make some educated guesses about the possible products.

▷ How to Decide What Products Form

Which of these ions combine to form the yellow solid observed when the original solutions are mixed? This is not an easy question to answer. Even an experienced chemist is not sure what will happen in a new reaction. The chemist tries to think of the various possibilities, considers the likelihood of each possibility, and then makes a prediction (an educated guess). Only after identifying each product experimentally can the chemist be sure what reaction actually has taken place. However, an educated guess is very useful because it indicates what kinds of products are most likely. It gives us a place to start. So the best way to proceed is first to think of the various possibilities and then to decide which of them is most likely.

What are the possible products of the reaction between $K_2CrO_4(aq)$ and $Ba(NO_3)_2(aq)$ or, more accurately, what reaction can occur among the ions K^+, CrO_4^{2-}, Ba^{2+}, and NO_3^-? We already know some things that will help us decide. We know that a *solid compound must have a zero net charge*. This means that the product of our reaction must contain *both anions and cations* (negative and positive ions). For example, K^+ and Ba^{2+} could not combine to form the solid because such a solid would have a positive charge. Similarly, CrO_4^{2-} and NO_3^- could not combine to form a solid because that solid would have a negative charge.

Something else that will help us is an observation that chemists have made by examining many compounds: *most ionic materials contain only two types of ions*—one type of cation and one type of anion. This idea is illustrated by the following compounds (among many others):

Compound	Cation	Anion
NaCl	Na^+	Cl^-
KOH	K^+	OH^-
Na_2SO_4	Na^+	SO_4^{2-}
NH_4Cl	NH_4^+	Cl^-
Na_2CO_3	Na^+	CO_3^{2-}

All the possible combinations of a cation and an anion to form uncharged compounds from among the ions K^+, CrO_4^{2-}, Ba^{2+}, and NO_3^- are shown below:

	NO_3^-	CrO_4^{2-}
K^+	KNO_3	K_2CrO_4
Ba^{2+}	$Ba(NO_3)_2$	$BaCrO_4$

So the compounds that *might* make up the solid are

K_2CrO_4	$BaCrO_4$
KNO_3	$Ba(NO_3)_2$

Which of these possibilities is most likely to represent the yellow solid? We know it's not K_2CrO_4 or $Ba(NO_3)_2$; these are the reactants. They were present (dissolved) in the separate solutions that were mixed initially. The only real possibilities are KNO_3 and $BaCrO_4$. To decide which of these is more likely to represent the yellow solid, we need more facts. An experienced chemist, for example, knows that KNO_3 is a white solid. On the other hand, the CrO_4^{2-} ion is yellow. Therefore, the yellow solid most likely is $BaCrO_4$.

We have determined that one product of the reaction between $K_2CrO_4(aq)$ and $Ba(NO_3)_2(aq)$ is $BaCrO_4(s)$, but what happened to the K^+ and NO_3^- ions? The answer is that these ions are left dissolved in the solution. That is, KNO_3 does not form a solid when the K^+ and NO_3^- ions are present in water. In other words, if we took the white solid $KNO_3(s)$ and put it in water, it would totally dissolve (the white solid would "disappear," yielding a colorless solution). So when we mix $K_2CrO_4(aq)$ and $Ba(NO_3)_2(aq)$, $BaCrO_4(s)$ forms but KNO_3 is left behind in solution [we write it as $KNO_3(aq)$]. (If we poured the mixture through a filter to remove the solid $BaCrO_4$ and then evaporated all of the water, we would obtain the white solid KNO_3.)

After all this thinking, we can finally write the unbalanced equation for the precipitation reaction:

$$K_2CrO_4(aq) + Ba(NO_3)_2(aq) \rightarrow BaCrO_4(s) + KNO_3(aq)$$

We can represent this reaction in pictures as follows:

Note that the K^+ and NO_3^- ions are not involved in the chemical change. They remain dispersed in the water before and after the reaction.

▶ Using Solubility Rules

In the example considered above we were finally able to identify the products of the reaction by using two types of chemical knowledge:

1. Knowledge of facts
2. Knowledge of concepts

For example, knowing the colors of the various compounds proved very helpful. This represents factual knowledge. Awareness of the concept that solids always have a net charge of zero was also essential. These two kinds of knowledge allowed us to make a good guess about the identity of the solid that formed. As you continue to study chemistry, you will see that a balance of factual and conceptual knowledge is always required. You must both *memorize* important facts and *understand* crucial concepts to succeed.

Solids must contain both anions and cations in the relative numbers necessary to produce zero net charge.

In the present case we are dealing with a reaction in which an ionic solid forms—that is, a process in which ions that are dissolved in water combine to give a solid. We know that for a solid to form, both positive and negative ions must be present in relative numbers that give zero net charge. However, oppositely charged ions in water do not always react to form a solid, as we have seen for K^+ and NO_3^-. In addition, Na^+ and Cl^- can coexist in water in very large numbers with no formation of solid NaCl. In other words, when solid NaCl (common salt) is placed in water, it dissolves—the white solid "disappears" as the Na^+ and Cl^- ions are dispersed throughout the water. (You probably have observed this phenomenon in preparing salt water to cook food.) The following two statements, then, are really saying the same thing.

1. Solid NaCl is very soluble in water.
2. Solid NaCl does not form when one solution containing Na^+ is mixed with another solution containing Cl^-.

To predict whether a given pair of dissolved ions will form a solid when mixed, we must know some facts about the solubilities of various types of ionic compounds. In this text we will use the term **soluble solid** to mean a solid that readily dissolves in water; the solid "disappears" as the ions are dispersed in the water. The terms **insoluble solid** and **slightly soluble solid** are taken to mean the same thing: a solid where such a tiny amount dissolves in water that it is undetectable with the naked eye. The solubility information about common solids that is summarized in Table 7.1 is based on observations of the behavior of many compounds. This is factual knowledge that you will need to predict what will happen in chemical reactions where a solid might form. This information is summarized in Figure 7.3.

Table 7.1 General Rules for Solubility of Ionic Compounds (Salts) in Water at 25 °C

1. Most nitrate (NO_3^-) salts are soluble.
2. Most salts of Na^+, K^+, and NH_4^+ are soluble.
3. Most chloride salts are soluble. Notable exceptions are $AgCl$, $PbCl_2$, and Hg_2Cl_2.
4. Most sulfate salts are soluble. Notable exceptions are $BaSO_4$, $PbSO_4$, and $CaSO_4$.
5. Most hydroxide compounds are only slightly soluble.* The important exceptions are $NaOH$ and KOH. $Ba(OH)_2$ and $Ca(OH)_2$ are only moderately soluble.
6. Most sulfide (S^{2-}), carbonate (CO_3^{2-}), and phosphate (PO_4^{3-}) salts are only slightly soluble.*

*The terms *insoluble* and *slightly soluble* really mean the same thing: such a tiny amount dissolves that it is not possible to detect it with the naked eye.

go Chemistry Module 5: Predicting the Water Solubility of Common Ionic Compounds covers concepts in this section.

Notice that in Table 7.1 and Figure 7.3 the term *salt* is used to mean *ionic compound*. Many chemists use the terms *salt* and *ionic compound* interchangeably. In Example 7.1, we will illustrate how to use the solubility rules to predict the products of reactions among ions.

EXAMPLE 7.1 | Identifying Precipitates in Reactions Where a Solid Forms

$AgNO_3$ is usually called silver nitrate rather than silver(I) nitrate because silver forms only Ag^+.

When an aqueous solution of silver nitrate is added to an aqueous solution of potassium chloride, a white solid forms. Identify the white solid and write the balanced equation for the reaction that occurs.

SOLUTION

First let's use the description of the reaction to represent what we know:

$$AgNO_3(aq) + KCl(aq) \rightarrow \text{White solid}$$

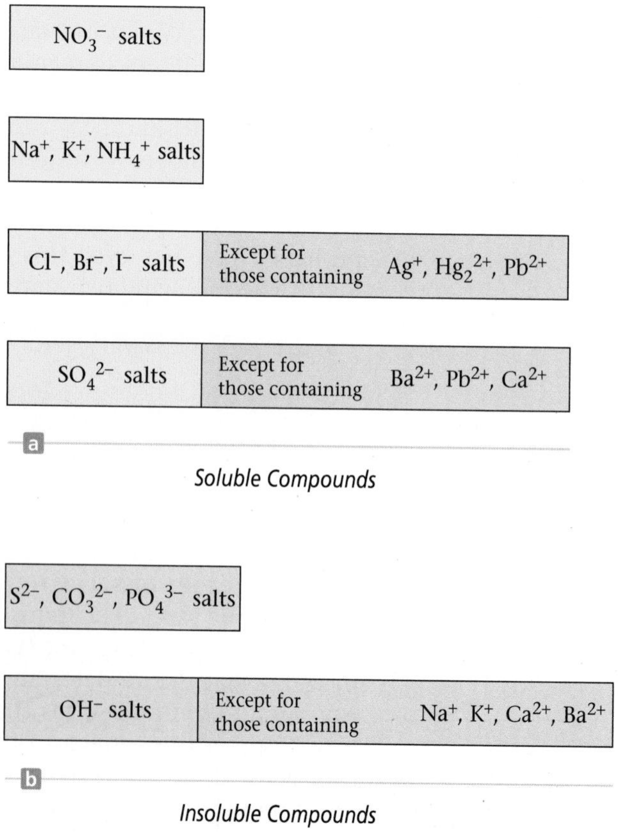

NO_3^- salts		
Na^+, K^+, NH_4^+ salts		
Cl^-, Br^-, I^- salts	Except for those containing	Ag^+, Hg_2^{2+}, Pb^{2+}
SO_4^{2-} salts	Except for those containing	Ba^{2+}, Pb^{2+}, Ca^{2+}

a

Soluble Compounds

S^{2-}, CO_3^{2-}, PO_4^{3-} salts		
OH^- salts	Except for those containing	Na^+, K^+, Ca^{2+}, Ba^{2+}

b

Insoluble Compounds

Figure 7.3

Solubilities of common compounds.

Remember, try to determine the essential facts from the words and represent these facts by symbols or diagrams. To answer the main question (What is the white solid?), we must establish what ions are present in the mixed solution. That is, we must know what the reactants are really like. Remember that *when ionic substances dissolve in water, the ions separate.* So we can write the equation

$$Ag^+(aq) + NO_3^-(aq) + K^+(aq) + Cl^-(aq) \rightarrow \text{Products}$$

Ions in
$AgNO_3(aq)$

Ions in
$KCl(aq)$

or using pictures

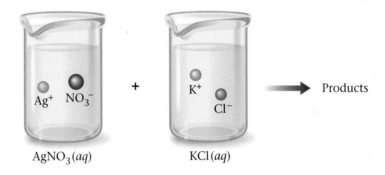

$AgNO_3(aq)$ $KCl(aq)$

to represent the ions present in the mixed solution before any reaction occurs. In summary:

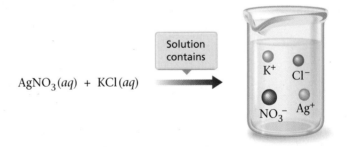

$AgNO_3(aq) + KCl(aq)$ Solution contains

	NO_3^-	Cl^-
Ag^+	$AgNO_3$	AgCl
K^+	KNO_3	KCl

Now we will consider what solid *might* form from this collection of ions. Because the solid must contain both positive and negative ions, the possible compounds that can be assembled from this collection of ions are

$AgNO_3$	AgCl
KNO_3	KCl

$AgNO_3$ and KCl are the substances already dissolved in the reactant solutions, so we know that they do not represent the white solid product. We are left with two possibilities:

AgCl

KNO_3

Figure 7.4

Precipitation of silver chloride occurs when solutions of silver nitrate and potassium chloride are mixed. The K^+ and NO_3^- ions remain in solution.

Another way to obtain these two possibilities is by *ion interchange*. This means that in the reaction of $AgNO_3(aq)$ and $KCl(aq)$, we take the cation from one reactant and combine it with the anion of the other reactant.

$$Ag^+ + NO_3^- + K^+ + Cl^- \rightarrow Products$$

Possible solid products

Ion interchange also leads to the following possible solids:

$$AgCl \text{ or } KNO_3$$

To decide whether $AgCl$ or KNO_3 is the white solid, we need the solubility rules (Table 7.1). Rule 2 states that most salts containing K^+ are soluble in water. Rule 1 says that most nitrate salts (those containing NO_3^-) are soluble. So the salt KNO_3 is water-soluble. That is, when K^+ and NO_3^- are mixed in water, a solid (KNO_3) does *not* form.

On the other hand, Rule 3 states that although most chloride salts (salts that contain Cl^-) are soluble, $AgCl$ is an exception. That is, $AgCl(s)$ is insoluble in water. Thus the white solid must be $AgCl$. Now we can write

$$AgNO_3(aq) + KCl(aq) \rightarrow AgCl(s) + ?$$

What is the other product?

To form $AgCl(s)$, we have used the Ag^+ and Cl^- ions:

$$Ag^+(aq) + NO_3^-(aq) + K^+(aq) + Cl^-(aq) \rightarrow AgCl(s)$$

This leaves the K^+ and NO_3^- ions. What do they do? Nothing. Because KNO_3 is very soluble in water (Rules 1 and 2), the K^+ and NO_3^- ions remain separate in the water; the KNO_3 remains dissolved and we represent it as $KNO_3(aq)$. We can now write the full equation:

$$AgNO_3(aq) + KCl(aq) \rightarrow AgCl(s) + KNO_3(aq)$$

Figure 7.4 shows the precipitation of $AgCl(s)$ that occurs when this reaction takes place. In graphic form, the reaction is

The following strategy is useful for predicting what will occur when two solutions containing dissolved salts are mixed.

How to Predict Precipitates When Solutions of Two Ionic Compounds Are Mixed

Step 1 Write the reactants as they actually exist before any reaction occurs. Remember that when a salt dissolves, its ions separate.

Step 2 Consider the various solids that could form. To do this, simply *exchange the anions* of the added salts.

Step 3 Use the solubility rules (Table 7.1) to decide whether a solid forms and, if so, to predict the identity of the solid.

EXAMPLE 7.2 | Using Solubility Rules to Predict the Products of Reactions

Using the solubility rules in Table 7.1, predict what will happen when the following solutions are mixed. Write the balanced equation for any reaction that occurs.

a. $KNO_3(aq)$ and $BaCl_2(aq)$

b. $Na_2SO_4(aq)$ and $Pb(NO_3)_2(aq)$

c. $KOH(aq)$ and $Fe(NO_3)_3(aq)$

SOLUTION (a)

Step 1 $KNO_3(aq)$ represents an aqueous solution obtained by dissolving solid KNO_3 in water to give the ions $K^+(aq)$ and $NO_3^-(aq)$. Likewise, $BaCl_2(aq)$ is a solution formed by dissolving solid $BaCl_2$ in water to produce $Ba^{2+}(aq)$ and $Cl^-(aq)$. When these two solutions are mixed, the following ions will be present:

$$K^+, \quad NO_3^-, \quad Ba^{2+}, \quad Cl^-$$

From $KNO_3(aq)$ From $BaCl_2(aq)$

Step 2 To get the possible products, we exchange the anions.

$$K^+ \quad NO_3^- \quad Ba^{2+} \quad Cl^-$$

This yields the possibilities KCl and $Ba(NO_3)_2$. These are the solids that *might* form. Notice that two NO_3^- ions are needed to balance the 2+ charge on Ba^{2+}.

Step 3 The rules listed in Table 7.1 indicate that both KCl and $Ba(NO_3)_2$ are soluble in water. So no precipitate forms when $KNO_3(aq)$ and $BaCl_2(aq)$ are mixed. All of the ions remain dissolved in the solution. This means that no reaction takes place. That is, no chemical change occurs.

SOLUTION (b)

Step 1 The following ions are present in the mixed solution before any reaction occurs:

$$Na^+, \quad SO_4^{2-}, \quad Pb^{2+}, \quad NO_3^-$$

From $Na_2SO_4(aq)$ From $Pb(NO_3)_2(aq)$

Step 2 Exchanging anions

$$Na^+ \quad SO_4^{2-} \quad Pb^{2+} \quad NO_3^-$$

yields the *possible* solid products $PbSO_4$ and $NaNO_3$.

Step 3 Using Table 7.1, we see that $NaNO_3$ is soluble in water (Rules 1 and 2) but that $PbSO_4$ is only slightly soluble (Rule 4). Thus, when these solutions are mixed, solid $PbSO_4$ forms. The balanced reaction is

$$Na_2SO_4(aq) + Pb(NO_3)_2\,(aq) \rightarrow PbSO_4(s) + 2NaNO_3(aq)$$

Remains dissolved

which can be represented as

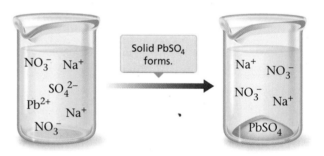

SOLUTION (c)

Step 1 The ions present in the mixed solution before any reaction occurs are

$$K^+, \quad OH^-, \quad Fe^{3+}, \quad NO_3^-$$

From $KOH(aq)$ From $Fe(NO_3)_3(aq)$

Step 2 Exchanging anions

$$K^+ \quad OH^- \quad Fe^{3+} \quad NO_3^-$$

yields the possible solid products KNO_3 and $Fe(OH)_3$.

Step 3 Rules 1 and 2 (Table 7.1) state that KNO_3 is soluble, whereas $Fe(OH)_3$ is only slightly soluble (Rule 5). Thus, when these solutions are mixed, solid $Fe(OH)_3$ forms. The balanced equation for the reaction is

$$3KOH(aq) + Fe(NO_3)_3(aq) \rightarrow Fe(OH)_3(s) + 3KNO_3(aq)$$

which can be represented as

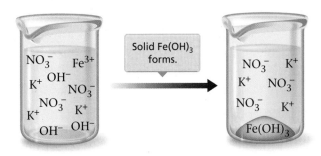

Self-Check   **EXERCISE 7.1**   Predict whether a solid will form when the following pairs of solutions are mixed. If so, identify the solid and write the balanced equation for the reaction.

    a. $Ba(NO_3)_2(aq)$ and $NaCl(aq)$

    b. $Na_2S(aq)$ and $Cu(NO_3)_2(aq)$

    c. $NH_4Cl(aq)$ and $Pb(NO_3)_2(aq)$

See Problems 7.17 and 7.18. ■

7.3 Describing Reactions in Aqueous Solutions

OBJECTIVE: To learn to describe reactions in solutions by writing molecular, complete ionic, and net ionic equations.

Much important chemistry, including virtually all of the reactions that make life possible, occurs in aqueous solutions. We will now consider the types of equations used to represent reactions that occur in water. For example, as we saw earlier, when we mix aqueous potassium chromate with aqueous barium nitrate, a reaction occurs to form solid barium chromate and dissolved potassium nitrate. One way to represent this reaction is by the equation

$$K_2CrO_4(aq) + Ba(NO_3)_2(aq) \rightarrow BaCrO_4(s) + 2KNO_3(aq)$$

This is called the **molecular equation** for the reaction; it shows the complete formulas of all reactants and products. However, although this equation shows the reactants and products of the reaction, it does not give a very clear picture of what actually occurs in solution. As we have seen, aqueous solutions of potassium chromate, barium nitrate, and potassium nitrate contain the individual ions, not molecules as is implied by the molecular equation. Thus the **complete ionic equation,**

Ions from K_2CrO_4 Ions from $Ba(NO_3)_2$

$$2K^+(aq) + CrO_4^{2-}(aq) + Ba^{2+}(aq) + 2NO_3^-(aq) \rightarrow$$
$$BaCrO_4(s) + 2K^+(aq) + 2NO_3^-(aq)$$

A strong electrolyte is a substance that completely breaks apart into ions when dissolved in water. The resulting solution readily conducts an electric current.

better represents the actual forms of the reactants and products in solution. *In a complete ionic equation, all substances that are strong electrolytes are represented as ions.* Notice that $BaCrO_4$ is not written as the separate ions, because it is present as a solid; it is not dissolved.

go Chemistry **Module 6: Writing Net Ionic Equations** covers concepts in this section.

The complete ionic equation reveals that only some of the ions participate in the reaction. Notice that the K^+ and NO_3^- ions are present in solution both before and after the reaction. Ions such as these, which do not participate directly in a reaction in solution, are called **spectator ions.** The ions that participate in this reaction are the Ba^{2+} and CrO_4^{2-} ions, which combine to form solid $BaCrO_4$:

$$Ba^{2+}(aq) + CrO_4^{2-}(aq) \rightarrow BaCrO_4(s)$$

> The net ionic equation includes only those components that undergo a change in the reaction.

This equation, called the **net ionic equation,** includes only those components that are directly involved in the reaction. Chemists usually write the net ionic equation for a reaction in solution, because it gives the actual forms of the reactants and products and includes only the species that undergo a change.

Types of Equations for Reactions in Aqueous Solutions

Three types of equations are used to describe reactions in solutions.

1. The *molecular equation* shows the overall reaction but not necessarily the actual forms of the reactants and products in solution.
2. The *complete ionic equation* represents all reactants and products that are strong electrolytes as ions. All reactants and products are included.
3. The *net ionic equation* includes only those components that undergo a change. Spectator ions are not included.

To make sure these ideas are clear, we will do another example. In Example 7.2 we considered the reaction between aqueous solutions of lead nitrate and sodium sulfate. The molecular equation for this reaction is

$$Pb(NO_3)_2(aq) + Na_2SO_4(aq) \rightarrow PbSO_4(s) + 2NaNO_3(aq)$$

Because any ionic compound that is dissolved in water is present as the separated ions, we can write the complete ionic equation as follows:

$$Pb^{2+}(aq) + 2NO_3^-(aq) + 2Na^+(aq) + SO_4^{2-}(aq) \rightarrow$$
$$PbSO_4(s) + 2Na^+(aq) + 2NO_3^-(aq)$$

The $PbSO_4$ is not written as separate ions because it is present as a solid. The ions that take part in the chemical change are the Pb^{2+} and the SO_4^{2-} ions, which combine to form solid $PbSO_4$. Thus the net ionic equation is

$$Pb^{2+}(aq) + SO_4^{2-}(aq) \rightarrow PbSO_4(s)$$

The Na^+ and NO_3^- ions do not undergo any chemical change; they are spectator ions.

EXAMPLE 7.3   Writing Equations for Reactions

For each of the following reactions, write the molecular equation, the complete ionic equation, and the net ionic equation.

> Because silver is present as Ag^+ in all of its common ionic compounds, we usually delete the (I) when naming silver compounds.

a. Aqueous sodium chloride is added to aqueous silver nitrate to form solid silver chloride plus aqueous sodium nitrate.

b. Aqueous potassium hydroxide is mixed with aqueous iron(III) nitrate to form solid iron(III) hydroxide and aqueous potassium nitrate.

SOLUTION

a. *Molecular equation:*

$$NaCl(aq) + AgNO_3(aq) \rightarrow AgCl(s) + NaNO_3(aq)$$

Complete ionic equation:

$$Na^+(aq) + Cl^-(aq) + Ag^+(aq) + NO_3^-(aq) \rightarrow$$
$$AgCl(s) + Na^+(aq) + NO_3^-(aq)$$

Net ionic equation:

$$Cl^-(aq) + Ag^+(aq) \rightarrow AgCl(s)$$

b. *Molecular equation:*

$$3KOH(aq) + Fe(NO_3)_3(aq) \rightarrow Fe(OH)_3(s) + 3KNO_3(aq)$$

Complete ionic equation:

$$3K^+(aq) + 3OH^-(aq) + Fe^{3+}(aq) + 3NO_3^-(aq) \rightarrow$$
$$Fe(OH)_3(s) + 3K^+(aq) + 3NO_3^-(aq)$$

Net ionic equation:

$$3OH^-(aq) + Fe^{3+}(aq) \rightarrow Fe(OH)_3(s)$$

Self-Check EXERCISE 7.2   For each of the following reactions, write the molecular equation, the complete ionic equation, and the net ionic equation.

a. Aqueous sodium sulfide is mixed with aqueous copper(II) nitrate to produce solid copper(II) sulfide and aqueous sodium nitrate.

b. Aqueous ammonium chloride and aqueous lead(II) nitrate react to form solid lead(II) chloride and aqueous ammonium nitrate.

See Problems 7.25 through 7.30. ■

7.4 Reactions That Form Water: Acids and Bases

OBJECTIVE: To learn the key characteristics of the reactions between strong acids and strong bases.

In this section we encounter two very important classes of compounds: acids and bases. Acids were first associated with the sour taste of citrus fruits. In fact, the word *acid* comes from the Latin word *acidus*, which means "sour." Vinegar tastes sour because it is a dilute solution of acetic acid; citric acid is responsible for the sour taste of a lemon. Bases, sometimes called *alkalis*, are characterized by their bitter taste and slippery feel, like wet soap. Most commercial preparations for unclogging drains are highly basic.

Don't taste chemicals!

Acids have been known for hundreds of years. For example, the *mineral acids* sulfuric acid, H_2SO_4, and nitric acid, HNO_3, so named because they were originally obtained by the treatment of minerals, were discovered around 1300. However, it was not until the late 1800s that the essential nature of acids was discovered by Svante Arrhenius, then a Swedish graduate student in physics.

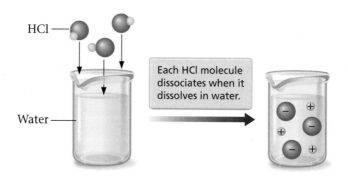

HCl

Water

Each HCl molecule dissociates when it dissolves in water.

Figure 7.5

When gaseous HCl is dissolved in water, each molecule dissociates to produce H^+ and Cl^- ions. That is, HCl behaves as a strong electrolyte.

The Nobel Prize in chemistry was awarded to Arrhenius in 1903 for his studies of solution conductivity.

Arrhenius, who was trying to discover why only certain solutions could conduct an electric current, found that conductivity arose from the presence of ions. In his studies of solutions, Arrhenius observed that when the substances HCl, HNO_3, and H_2SO_4 were dissolved in water, they behaved as strong electrolytes. He suggested that this was the result of ionization reactions in water.

$$HCl \xrightarrow{H_2O} H^+(aq) + Cl^-(aq)$$
$$HNO_3 \xrightarrow{H_2O} H^+(aq) + NO_3^-(aq)$$
$$H_2SO_4 \xrightarrow{H_2O} H^+(aq) + HSO_4^-(aq)$$

Arrhenius proposed that an **acid** is a substance that produces H^+ ions (protons) when it is dissolved in water.

Studies show that when HCl, HNO_3, and H_2SO_4 are placed in water, *virtually every molecule* dissociates to give ions. This means that when 100 molecules of HCl are dissolved in water, 100 H^+ ions and 100 Cl^- ions are produced. Virtually no HCl molecules exist in aqueous solution (see Figure 7.5). Because these substances are strong electrolytes that produce H^+ ions, they are called **strong acids.**

Arrhenius also found that *aqueous solutions that exhibit basic behavior always contain hydroxide ions.* He defined a **base** as a *substance that produces hydroxide ions (OH^-) in water.* The base most commonly used in the chemical laboratory is sodium hydroxide, NaOH, which contains Na^+ and OH^- ions and is very soluble in water. Sodium hydroxide, like all ionic substances, produces separated cations and anions when it is dissolved in water.

The Arrhenius definition of an acid: a substance that produces H^+ ions in aqueous solution.

$$NaOH(s) \xrightarrow{H_2O} Na^+(aq) + OH^-(aq)$$

Although dissolved sodium hydroxide is usually represented as NaOH(aq), you should remember that the solution really contains separated Na^+ and OH^- ions. In fact, for every 100 units of NaOH dissolved in water, 100 Na^+ and 100 OH^- ions are produced.

Potassium hydroxide (KOH) has properties markedly similar to those of sodium hydroxide. It is very soluble in water and produces separated ions.

$$KOH(s) \xrightarrow{H_2O} K^+(aq) + OH^-(aq)$$

Because these hydroxide compounds are strong electrolytes that contain OH^- ions, they are called **strong bases.**

When strong acids and strong bases (hydroxides) are mixed, the fundamental chemical change that always occurs is that *H^+ ions react with OH^- ions to form water.*

$$H^+(aq) + OH^-(aq) \rightarrow H_2O(l)$$

Water is a very stable compound, as evidenced by the abundance of it on the earth's surface. Therefore, when substances that can form water are

The marsh marigold is a beautiful but poisonous plant. Its toxicity results partly from the presence of erucic acid.

mixed, there is a strong tendency for the reaction to occur. In particular, the hydroxide ion OH^- has a high affinity for H^+ ions, because water is produced in the reaction between these ions.

Hydrochloric acid is an aqueous solution that contains dissolved hydrogen chloride. It is a strong electrolyte.

The tendency to form water is the second of the driving forces for reactions that we mentioned in Section 7.1. Any compound that produces OH^- ions in water reacts vigorously with any compound that can furnish H^+ ions to form H_2O. For example, the reaction between hydrochloric acid and aqueous sodium hydroxide is represented by the following molecular equation:

$$HCl(aq) + NaOH(aq) \rightarrow H_2O(l) + NaCl(aq)$$

Because HCl, NaOH, and NaCl exist as completely separated ions in water, the complete ionic equation for this reaction is

$$H^+(aq) + Cl^-(aq) + Na^+(aq) + OH^-(aq) \rightarrow H_2O(l) + Na^+(aq) + Cl^-(aq)$$

Notice that the Cl^- and Na^+ are spectator ions (they undergo no changes), so the net ionic equation is

$$H^+(aq) + OH^-(aq) \rightarrow H_2O(l)$$

Thus the only chemical change that occurs when these solutions are mixed is that water is formed from H^+ and OH^- ions.

EXAMPLE 7.4 | Writing Equations for Acid–Base Reactions

Nitric acid is a strong acid. Write the molecular, complete ionic, and net ionic equations for the reaction of aqueous nitric acid and aqueous potassium hydroxide.

SOLUTION

Molecular equation:

$$HNO_3(aq) + KOH(aq) \rightarrow H_2O(l) + KNO_3(aq)$$

Complete ionic equation:

$$H^+(aq) + NO_3^-(aq) + K^+(aq) + OH^-(aq) \rightarrow H_2O(l) + K^+(aq) + NO_3^-(aq)$$

Net ionic equation:

$$H^+(aq) + OH^-(aq) \rightarrow H_2O(l)$$

Note that K^+ and NO_3^- are spectator ions and that the formation of water is the driving force for this reaction. ∎

There are two important things to note as we examine the reaction of hydrochloric acid with aqueous sodium hydroxide and the reaction of nitric acid with aqueous potassium hydroxide.

1. The net ionic equation is the same in both cases; water is formed.

$$H^+(aq) + OH^-(aq) \rightarrow H_2O(l)$$

2. Besides water, which is *always a product* of the reaction of an acid with OH^-, the second product is an ionic compound, which might precipitate or remain dissolved, depending on its solubility.

$$HCl(aq) + NaOH(aq) \rightarrow H_2O(l) + NaCl(aq)$$

$$HNO_3(aq) + KOH(aq) \rightarrow H_2O(l) + KNO_3(aq)$$

> Dissolved ionic compounds

This ionic compound is called a **salt.** In the first case the salt is sodium chloride, and in the second case the salt is potassium nitrate. We can obtain these soluble salts in solid form (both are white solids) by evaporating the water.

We can represent this reaction in schematic form as follows:

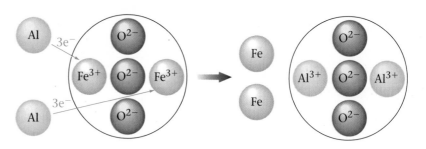

EXAMPLE 7.5 | **Identifying Electron Transfer in Oxidation–Reduction Reactions**

Figure 7.7

When powdered aluminum and iodine (shown in the foreground) are mixed (and a little water added), they react vigorously.

For each of the following reactions, show how electrons are gained and lost.

a. $2Al(s) + 3I_2(s) \rightarrow 2AlI_3(s)$ (This reaction is shown in Figure 7.7. Note the purple "smoke," which is excess I_2 being driven off by the heat.)

b. $2Cs(s) + F_2(g) \rightarrow 2CsF(s)$

SOLUTION

a. In AlI_3 the ions are Al^{3+} and I^- (aluminum always forms Al^{3+}, and iodine always forms I^-). In $Al(s)$ the aluminum is present as uncharged atoms. Thus aluminum goes from Al to Al^{3+} by losing three electrons ($Al \rightarrow Al^{3+} + 3e^-$). In I_2 each iodine atom is uncharged. Thus each iodine atom goes from I to I^- by gaining one electron ($I + e^- \rightarrow I^-$). A schematic for this reaction is

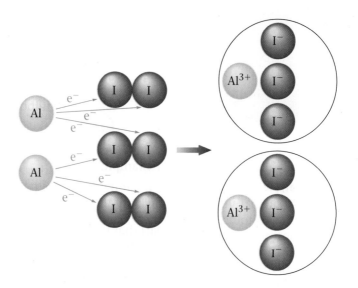

b. In CsF the ions present are Cs^+ and F^-. Cesium metal, $Cs(s)$, contains uncharged cesium atoms, and fluorine gas, $F_2(g)$, contains uncharged fluorine atoms. Thus in the reaction each cesium atom loses one electron ($Cs \rightarrow Cs^+ + e^-$) and each fluorine atom gains one electron ($F + e^- \rightarrow F^-$). The schematic for this reaction is

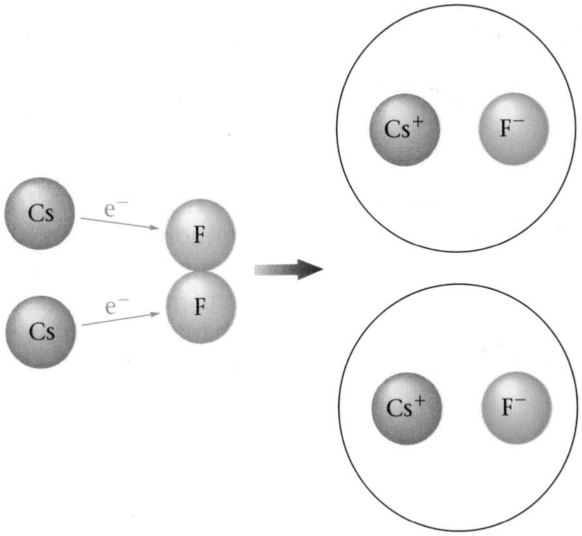

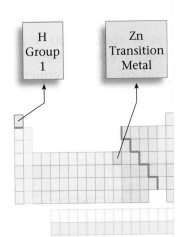

Self-Check   **EXERCISE 7.3**   For each reaction, show how electrons are gained and lost.

    a. $2Na(s) + Br_2(l) \rightarrow 2NaBr(s)$

    b. $2Ca(s) + O_2(g) \rightarrow 2CaO(s)$

See Problems 7.47 and 7.48. ■

So far we have emphasized electron transfer (oxidation–reduction) reactions that involve a metal and a nonmetal. Electron transfer reactions can also take place between two nonmetals. We will not discuss these re-actions in detail here. All we will say at this point is that one sure sign of an oxidation–reduction reaction between nonmetals is the presence of oxygen, $O_2(g)$, as a reactant or product. In fact, oxidation got its name from oxygen. Thus the reactions

$$CH_4(g) + 2O_2(g) \rightarrow CO_2(g) + 2H_2O(g)$$

and

$$2SO_2(g) + O_2(g) \rightarrow 2SO_3(g)$$

are electron transfer reactions, even though it is not obvious at this point.

We can summarize what we have learned about oxidation–reduction reactions as follows:

Characteristics of Oxidation–Reduction Reactions

1. When a metal reacts with a nonmetal, an ionic compound is formed. The ions are formed when the metal transfers one or more electrons to the nonmetal, the metal atom becoming a cation and the nonmetal atom becoming an anion. *Therefore, a metal–nonmetal reaction can always be assumed to be an oxidation–reduction reaction, which involves electron transfer.*

2. Two nonmetals can also undergo an oxidation–reduction reaction. At this point we can recognize these cases only by looking for O_2 as a reactant or product. When two nonmetals react, the compound formed is not ionic.

7.6

OBJECTIV

- Combustion of gasoline* (used to power cars and trucks)

$$2C_8H_{18}(l) + 25O_2(g) \rightarrow 16CO_2(g) + 18H_2O(g)$$

- Combustion of coal* (used to generate electricity)

$$C(s) + O_2(g) \rightarrow CO_2(g)$$

▶ Synthesis (Combination) Reactions

One of the most important activities in chemistry is the synthesis of new compounds. Each of our lives has been greatly affected by synthetic compounds such as plastic, polyester, and aspirin. When a given compound is formed from simpler materials, we call this a **synthesis** (or **combination**) **reaction.**

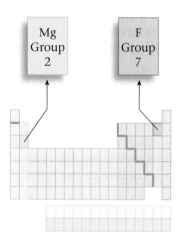

In many cases synthesis reactions start with elements, as shown by the following examples:

- Synthesis of water $2H_2(g) + O_2(g) \rightarrow 2H_2O(l)$
- Synthesis of carbon dioxide $C(s) + O_2(g) \rightarrow CO_2(g)$
- Synthesis of nitrogen monoxide $N_2(g) + O_2(g) \rightarrow 2NO(g)$

Notice that each of these reactions involves oxygen, so each can be classified as an oxidation–reduction reaction. The first two reactions are also commonly called combustion reactions because they produce flames. The reaction of hydrogen with oxygen to produce water, then, can be classified three ways: as an oxidation–reduction reaction, as a combustion reaction, and as a synthesis reaction.

There are also many synthesis reactions that do not involve oxygen:

- Synthesis of sodium chloride $2Na(s) + Cl_2(g) \rightarrow 2NaCl(s)$
- Synthesis of magnesium fluoride $Mg(s) + F_2(g) \rightarrow MgF_2(s)$

We have discussed the formation of sodium chloride before and have noted that it is an oxidation–reduction reaction; uncharged sodium atoms lose electrons to form Na^+ ions, and uncharged chlorine atoms gain electrons to form Cl^- ions. The synthesis of magnesium fluoride is also an oxidation–reduction reaction because Mg^{2+} and F^- ions are produced from the uncharged atoms.

We have seen that synthesis reactions in which the reactants are elements are oxidation–reduction reactions as well. In fact, we can think of these synthesis reactions as another subclass of the oxidation–reduction class of reactions.

▶ Decomposition Reactions

In many cases a compound can be broken down into simpler compounds or all the way to the component elements. This is usually accomplished by heating or by the application of an electric current. Such reactions are called **decomposition reactions.** We have discussed decomposition reactions before, including

- Decomposition of water

$$2H_2O(l) \xrightarrow{\text{Electric current}} 2H_2(g) + O_2(g)$$

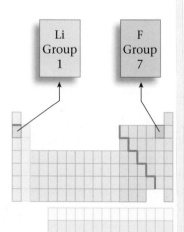

Michael Newman/PhotoEdit

Formation of the colorful plastics used in these zippers is an example of a synthetic reaction.

*This substance is really a complex mixture of compounds, but the reaction shown is representative of what takes place.

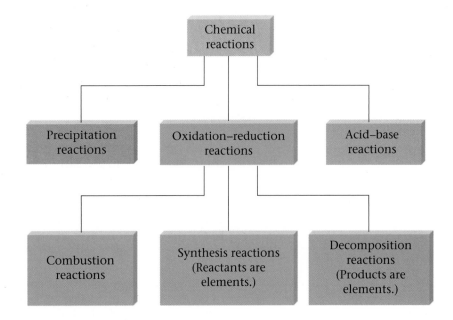

Figure 7.12

Summary of classes of reactions.

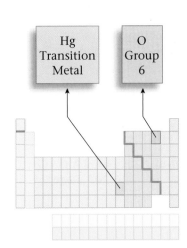

• Decomposition of mercury(II) oxide

$$2HgO(s) \xrightarrow{\text{Heat}} 2Hg(l) + O_2(g)$$

Because O_2 is involved in the first reaction, we recognize it as an oxidation–reduction reaction. In the second reaction, HgO, which contains Hg^{2+} and O^{2-} ions, is decomposed to the elements, which contain uncharged atoms. In this process each Hg^{2+} gains two electrons and each O^{2-} loses two electrons, so this is both a decomposition reaction and an oxidation–reduction reaction.

A decomposition reaction, in which a compound is broken down into its elements, is just the opposite of the synthesis (combination) reaction, in which elements combine to form the compound. For example, we have just discussed the synthesis of sodium chloride from its elements. Sodium chloride can be decomposed into its elements by melting it and passing an electric current through it:

$$2NaCl(l) \xrightarrow[\text{current}]{\text{Electric}} 2Na(l) + Cl_2(g)$$

There are other schemes for classifying reactions that we have not considered. However, we have covered many of the classifications that are commonly used by chemists as they pursue their science in laboratories and industrial plants.

It should be apparent that many important reactions can be classified as oxidation–reduction reactions. As shown in Figure 7.12, various types of reactions can be viewed as subclasses of the overall oxidation–reduction category.

EXAMPLE 7.6 | Classifying Reactions

Classify each of the following reactions in as many ways as possible.

a. $2K(s) + Cl_2(g) \rightarrow 2KCl(s)$

b. $Fe_2O_3(s) + 2Al(s) \rightarrow Al_2O_3(s) + 2Fe(s)$

c. $2Mg(s) + O_2(g) \rightarrow 2MgO(s)$

d. $HNO_3(aq) + NaOH(aq) \rightarrow H_2O(l) + NaNO_3(aq)$

e. $KBr(aq) + AgNO_3(aq) \rightarrow AgBr(s) + KNO_3(aq)$

f. $PbO_2(s) \rightarrow Pb(s) + O_2(g)$

SOLUTION

a. This is both a synthesis reaction (elements combine to form a compound) and an oxidation–reduction reaction (uncharged potassium and chlorine atoms are changed to K^+ and Cl^- ions in KCl).

b. This is an oxidation–reduction reaction. Iron is present in $Fe_2O_3(s)$ as Fe^{3+} ions and in elemental iron, $Fe(s)$, as uncharged atoms. So each Fe^{3+} must gain three electrons to form Fe. The reverse happens to aluminum, which is present initially as uncharged aluminum atoms, each of which loses three electrons to give Al^{3+} ions in Al_2O_3. Note that this reaction might also be called a single-replacement reaction because O is switched from Fe to Al.

c. This is both a synthesis reaction (elements combine to form a compound) and an oxidation–reduction reaction (each magnesium atom loses two electrons to give Mg^{2+} ions in MgO, and each oxygen atom gains two electrons to give O^{2-} in MgO).

d. This is an acid–base reaction. It might also be called a double-displacement reaction because NO_3^- and OH^- "switch partners."

e. This is a precipitation reaction that might also be called a double-displacement reaction in which the anions Br^- and NO_3^- are exchanged.

f. This is a decomposition reaction (a compound breaks down into elements). It also is an oxidation–reduction reaction, because the ions in PbO_2 (Pb^{4+} and O^{2-}) are changed to uncharged atoms in the elements $Pb(s)$ and $O_2(g)$. That is, electrons are transferred from O^{2-} to Pb^{4+} in the reaction.

Self-Check **EXERCISE 7.4**

Classify each of the following reactions in as many ways as possible.

a. $4NH_3(g) + 5O_2(g) \rightarrow 4NO(g) + 6H_2O(g)$

b. $S_8(s) + 8O_2(g) \rightarrow 8SO_2(g)$

c. $2Al(s) + 3Cl_2(g) \rightarrow 2AlCl_3(s)$

d. $2AlN(s) \rightarrow 2Al(s) + N_2(g)$

e. $BaCl_2(aq) + Na_2SO_4(aq) \rightarrow BaSO_4(s) + 2NaCl(aq)$

f. $2Cs(s) + Br_2(l) \rightarrow 2CsBr(s)$

g. $KOH(aq) + HCl(aq) \rightarrow H_2O(l) + KCl(aq)$

h. $2C_2H_2(g) + 5O_2(g) \rightarrow 4CO_2(g) + 2H_2O(l)$

See Problems 7.53 and 7.54. ■

Key Terms

precipitation (7.2)
precipitate (7.2)
precipitation
  reaction (7.2, 7.6)
strong electrolyte (7.2)
soluble solid (7.2)
insoluble (slightly
  soluble) solid (7.2)
molecular equation (7.3)
complete ionic
  equation (7.3)
spectator ions (7.3)
net ionic equation (7.3)
acid (7.4)
strong acid (7.4)
base (7.4)

strong base (7.4)
salt (7.4)
oxidation–reduction
  reaction (7.5, 7.6)
precipation reaction (7.6)
double-displacement
  reaction (7.6)
acid–base
  reaction (7.6)
combustion
  reaction (7.7)
synthesis (combination)
  reaction (7.7)
decomposition
  reaction (7.7)

Ⓕ directs you to the *Chemistry in Focus* feature in the chapter
🆅🅿 indicates visual problems
🅾WL interactive versions of these problems are assignable in OWL.

Summary

1. Four driving forces that favor chemical change (chemical reaction) are formation of a solid, formation of water, transfer of electrons, and formation of a gas.

2. A reaction where a solid forms is called a precipitation reaction. General rules on solubility help predict whether a solid—and what solid—will form when two solutions are mixed.

3. Three types of equations are used to describe reactions in solution: (1) the molecular equation, which shows the complete formulas of all reactants and products; (2) the complete ionic equation, in which all reactants and products that are strong electrolytes are shown as ions; and (3) the net ionic equation, which includes only those components of the solution that undergo a change. Spectator ions (those ions that remain unchanged in a reaction) are not included in a net ionic equation.

4. A strong acid is a compound in which virtually every molecule dissociates in water to give an H^+ ion and an anion. Similarly, a strong base is a metal hydroxide compound that is soluble in water, giving OH^- ions and cations. The products of the reaction of a strong acid and a strong base are water and a salt.

5. Reactions of metals and nonmetals involve a transfer of electrons and are called oxidation–reduction reactions. A reaction between a nonmetal and oxygen is also an oxidation–reduction reaction. Combustion reactions involve oxygen and are a subgroup of oxidation–reduction reactions.

6. When a given compound is formed from simpler materials, such as elements, the reaction is called a synthesis or combination reaction. The reverse process, which occurs when a compound is broken down into its component elements, is called a decomposition reaction. These reactions are also subgroups of oxidation–reduction reactions.

Active Learning Questions

These questions are designed to be considered by groups of students in class. Often these questions work well for introducing a particular topic in class.

1. Consider the mixing of aqueous solutions of lead(II) nitrate and sodium iodide to form a solid.
   a. Name the possible products, and determine the formulas of these possible products.
   b. What is the precipitate? How do you know?
   c. Must the subscript for an ion in a reactant stay the same as the subscript of that ion in a product? Explain your answer.

2. Assume a highly magnified view of a solution of HCl that allows you to "see" the HCl. Draw this magnified view. If you dropped in a piece of magnesium, the magnesium would disappear and hydrogen gas would be released. Represent this change using symbols for the elements, and write the balanced equation.

3. Why is the formation of a solid evidence of a chemical reaction? Use a molecular-level drawing in your explanation.

4. Sketch molecular-level drawings to differentiate between two soluble compounds: one that is a strong electrolyte, and one that is not an electrolyte.

5. Mixing an aqueous solution of potassium nitrate with an aqueous solution of sodium chloride does not result in a chemical reaction. Why?

6. Why is the formation of water evidence of a chemical reaction? Use a molecular-level drawing in your explanation.

7. Use the Arrhenius definition of acids and bases to write the net ionic equation for the reaction of an acid with a base.

8. Why is the transfer of electrons evidence of a chemical reaction? Use a molecular-level drawing in your explanation.

9. Why is the formation of a gas evidence of a chemical reaction? Use a molecular-level drawing in your explanation.

10. Label each of the following statements as true or false. Explain your answers, and provide an example for each that supports your answer.

    a. All nonelectrolytes are insoluble.
    b. All insoluble substances are nonelectrolytes.
    c. All strong electrolytes are soluble.
    d. All soluble substances are strong electrolytes.

11. Look at Figure 7.2 in the text. It is possible for a weak electrolyte solution to cause the bulb to glow brighter than a strong electrolyte. Explain how this is possible.

12. What is the purpose of spectator ions? If they are not present as part of the reaction, why are they present at all?

13. Which of the following **must** be an oxidation–reduction reaction? Explain your answer, and include an example oxidation–reduction reaction for all that apply.

    a. A metal reacts with a nonmetal.
    b. A precipitation reaction.
    c. An acid–base reaction.

14. If an element is a reactant or product in a chemical reaction, the reaction must be an oxidation–reduction reaction. Why is this true?

VP 15. Match each name below with the following microscopic pictures of that compound in aqueous solution.

a. barium nitrate   c. potassium carbonate
b. sodium chloride   d. magnesium sulfate

Which picture best represents $HNO_3(aq)$? Why aren't any of the pictures a good representation of $HC_2H_3O_2(aq)$?

VP 16. On the basis of the general solubility rules given in Table 7.1, predict the identity of the precipitate that forms when aqueous solutions of the following substances are mixed. If no precipitate is likely, indicate which rules apply.

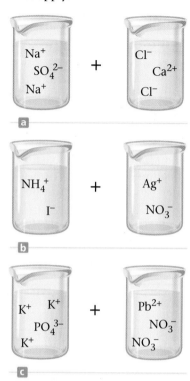

VP 17. Write the balanced formula and net ionic equation for the reaction that occurs when the contents of the two beakers are added together. What colors represent the spectator ions in each reaction?

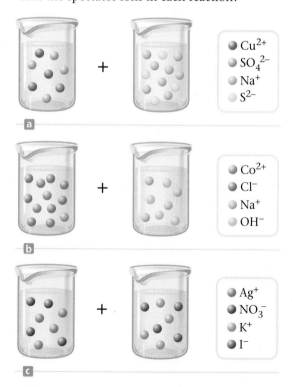

Questions and Problems

7.1 Predicting Whether a Reaction Will Occur

QUESTIONS

1. Why is water an important solvent? Although you have not yet studied water in detail, can you think of some properties of water that make it so important?

2. What is a "driving force"? What are some of the driving forces discussed in this section that tend to make reactions likely to occur? Can you think of any other possible driving forces?

7.2 Reactions in Which a Solid Forms

QUESTIONS

3. A reaction in aqueous solution that results in the formation of a *solid* is called a _____ reaction.

4. When writing the chemical equation for a reaction, how do you indicate that a given reactant is dissolved in water? How do you indicate that a precipitate has formed as a result of the reaction?

5. Describe briefly what happens when an ionic substance is dissolved in water.

6. When the ionic solute $MgCl_2$ is dissolved in water, what can you say about the number of chloride ions present in the solution compared to the number of magnesium ions in the solution?

7. What is meant by a *strong electrolyte?* Give two examples of substances that behave in solution as strong electrolytes.

8. How do chemists know that the ions behave independently of one another when an ionic solid is dissolved in water?

9. Suppose you are trying to help your friend understand the general solubility rules for ionic substances in water. Explain in general terms to your friend what the solubility rules mean, and give an example of how the rules could be applied in determining the identity of the precipitate in a reaction between solutions of two ionic compounds.

10. Using the general solubility rules given in Table 7.1, write the formulas and names of five ionic substances that would not be expected to be appreciably soluble in water. Indicate *why* each of the substances would not be expected to be soluble.

11. On the basis of the general solubility rules given in Table 7.1, predict which of the following substances are *not* likely to be soluble in water. Indicate which specific rule(s) led to your conclusion.

    a. PbS
    b. $Mg(OH)_2$
    c. Na_2SO_4
    d. $(NH_4)_2S$
    e. $BaCO_3$
    f. $AlPO_4$
    g. $PbCl_2$
    h. $CaSO_4$

12. On the basis of the general solubility rules given in Table 7.1, predict which of the following substances are likely to be appreciably soluble in water. Indicate which specific rule(s) led to your conclusion.

    a. $BaCl_2$
    b. $NH_4C_2H_3O_2$
    c. Na_2S
    d. $Fe(OH)_3$
    e. K_2CO_3
    f. $Au(NO_3)_3$
    g. $ZnSO_4$
    h. Fe_2S_3

13. On the basis of the general solubility rules given in Table 7.1, for each of the following compounds, explain why the compound would be expected to be appreciably soluble in water. Indicate which of the solubility rules covers each substance's particular situation.

    a. potassium sulfide
    b. cobalt(III) nitrate
    c. ammonium phosphate
    d. cesium sulfate
    e. strontium chloride

14. On the basis of the general solubility rules given in Table 7.1, for each of the following compounds, explain why the compound would *not* be expected to be appreciably soluble in water. Indicate which of the solubility rules covers each substance's particular situation.

    a. copper(II) sulfide   d. lead(II) chloride
    b. iron(III) carbonate   e. barium sulfate
    c. zinc phosphate

15. On the basis of the general solubility rules given in Table 7.1, predict the identity of the precipitate that forms when aqueous solutions of the following substances are mixed. If no precipitate is likely, indicate which rules apply.

    a. copper(II) chloride, $CuCl_2$, and ammonium sulfide, $(NH_4)_2S$
    b. barium nitrate, $Ba(NO_3)_2$, and potassium phosphate, K_3PO_4
    c. silver acetate, $AgC_2H_3O_2$, and calcium chloride, $CaCl_2$
    d. potassium carbonate, K_2CO_3, and cobalt(II) chloride, $CoCl_2$
    e. sulfuric acid, H_2SO_4, and calcium nitrate, $Ca(NO_3)_2$
    f. mercurous acetate, $Hg_2(C_2H_3O_2)_2$, and hydrochloric acid, HCl

16. On the basis of the general solubility rules given in Table 7.1, predict the identity of the precipitate that forms when aqueous solutions of the following substances are mixed. If no precipitate is likely, indicate which rules apply.

    a. sodium carbonate, Na_2CO_3, and manganese(II) chloride, $MnCl_2$
    b. potassium sulfate, K_2SO_4, and calcium acetate, $Ca(C_2H_3O_2)_2$
    c. hydrochloric acid, HCl, and mercurous acetate, $Hg_2(C_2H_3O_2)_2$
    d. sodium nitrate, $NaNO_3$, and lithium sulfate, Li_2SO_4
    e. potassium hydroxide, KOH, and nickel(II) chloride, $NiCl_2$
    f. sulfuric acid, H_2SO_4, and barium chloride, $BaCl_2$

All even-numbered Questions and Problems have answers in the back of this book and solutions in the Solutions Guide.

PROBLEMS

17. On the basis of the general solubility rules given in Table 7.1, write a balanced molecular equation for the precipitation reactions that take place when the following aqueous solutions are mixed. Underline the formula of the precipitate (solid) that forms. If no precipitation reaction is likely for the reactants given, explain why.

    a. ammonium chloride, NH_4Cl, and sulfuric acid, H_2SO_4

    b. potassium carbonate, K_2CO_3, and tin(IV) chloride, $SnCl_4$

    c. ammonium chloride, NH_4Cl, and lead(II) nitrate, $Pb(NO_3)_2$

    d. copper(II) sulfate, $CuSO_4$, and potassium hydroxide, KOH

    e. sodium phosphate, Na_3PO_4, and chromium(III) chloride, $CrCl_3$

    f. ammonium sulfide, $(NH_4)_2S$, and iron(III) chloride, $FeCl_3$

18. On the basis of the general solubility rules given in Table 7.1, write a balanced molecular equation for the precipitation reactions that take place when the following aqueous solutions are mixed. Underline the formula of the precipitate (solid) that forms. If no precipitation reaction is likely for the solutes given, so indicate.

    a. sodium carbonate, Na_2CO_3, and copper(II) sulfate, $CuSO_4$

    b. hydrochloric acid, HCl, and silver acetate, $AgC_2H_3O_2$

    c. barium chloride, $BaCl_2$, and calcium nitrate, $Ca(NO_3)_2$

    d. ammonium sulfide, $(NH_4)_2S$, and iron(III) chloride, $FeCl_3$

    e. sulfuric acid, H_2SO_4, and lead(II) nitrate, $Pb(NO_3)_2$

    f. potassium phosphate, K_3PO_4, and calcium chloride, $CaCl_2$

19. Balance each of the following equations that describe precipitation reactions.

    a. $Na_2SO_4(aq) + CaCl_2(aq) \rightarrow CaSO_4(s) + NaCl(aq)$

    b. $Co(C_2H_3O_2)_2(aq) + Na_2S(aq) \rightarrow$
                                   $CoS(s) + NaC_2H_3O_2(aq)$

    c. $KOH(aq) + NiCl_2(aq) \rightarrow Ni(OH)_2(s) + KCl(aq)$

20. Balance each of the following equations that describe precipitation reactions.

    a. $CaCl_2(aq) + AgNO_3(aq) \rightarrow Ca(NO_3)_2(aq) + AgCl(s)$

    b. $AgNO_3(aq) + K_2CrO_4(aq) \rightarrow Ag_2CrO_4(s) + KNO_3(aq)$

    c. $BaCl_2(aq) + K_2SO_4(aq) \rightarrow BaSO_4(s) + KCl(aq)$

21. For each of the following precipitation reactions, complete and balance the equation, indicating clearly which product is the precipitate. If no reaction would be expected, so indicate.

    a. $(NH_4)_2SO_4(aq) + Ba(NO_3)_2(aq) \rightarrow$

    b. $H_2S(aq) + NiSO_4(aq) \rightarrow$

    c. $FeCl_3(aq) + NaOH(aq) \rightarrow$

22. For each of the following precipitation reactions, complete and balance the equation, indicating clearly which product is the precipitate. If no reaction would be expected, so indicate.

    a. $Na_2CO_3(aq) + K_2SO_4(aq) \rightarrow$

    b. $CuCl_2(aq) + (NH_4)_2CO_3(aq) \rightarrow$

    c. $K_3PO_4(aq) + AlCl_3(aq) \rightarrow$

7.3 Describing Reactions in Aqueous Solutions

QUESTIONS

23. What is a net ionic equation? What species are shown in such an equation, and which species are not shown?

24. What are *spectator ions?* Write an example of an equation in which spectator ions are present and identify them.

PROBLEMS

25. Based on the general solubility rules given in Table 7.1, propose five combinations of aqueous ionic reagents that likely would form a precipitate when they are mixed. Write the balanced full molecular equation and the balanced net ionic equation for each of your choices.

26. Write balanced net ionic equations for the reactions that occur when the following aqueous solutions are mixed. If no reaction is likely to occur, so indicate.

    a. calcium nitrate and sulfuric acid

    b. nickel(II) nitrate and sodium hydroxide

    c. ammonium sulfide and iron(III) chloride

27. Many chromate (CrO_4^{2-}) salts are insoluble, and most have brilliant colors that have led to their being used as pigments. Write balanced net ionic equations for the reactions of Cu^{2+}, Co^{3+}, Ba^{2+}, and Fe^{3+} with chromate ion.

28. The procedures and principles of qualitative analysis are covered in many introductory chemistry laboratory courses. In qualitative analysis, students learn to analyze mixtures of the common positive and negative ions, separating and confirming the presence of the particular ions in the mixture. One of the first steps in such an analysis is to treat the mixture with hydrochloric acid, which precipitates and removes silver ion, lead(II) ion, and mercury(I) ion from the aqueous mixture as the insoluble chloride salts. Write balanced net ionic equations for the precipitation reactions of these three cations with chloride ion.

29. Many plants are poisonous because their stems and leaves contain oxalic acid, $H_2C_2O_4$, or sodium oxalate, $Na_2C_2O_4$; when ingested, these substances cause swelling of the respiratory tract and suffocation. A standard analysis for determining the amount of oxalate ion, $C_2O_4^{2-}$, in a sample is to precipitate this species as calcium oxalate, which is insoluble in water. Write the net ionic equation for the reaction between sodium oxalate and calcium chloride, $CaCl_2$, in aqueous solution.

All even-numbered Questions and Problems have answers in the back of this book and solutions in the Solutions Guide.

30. Another step in the qualitative analysis of cations (see Exercise 28) involves precipitating some of the metal ions as the insoluble sulfides (followed by subsequent treatment of the mixed sulfide precipitate to separate the individual ions). Write balanced net ionic equations for the reactions of Co(II), Co(III), Fe(II), and Fe(III) ions with sulfide ion, S^{2-}.

7.4 Reactions That Form Water: Acids and Bases

QUESTIONS

31. What is meant by a *strong acid?* Are the strong acids also strong *electrolytes?* Explain.

32. What is meant by a *strong base?* Are the strong bases also strong *electrolytes?* Explain.

33. The same net ionic process takes place when any strong acid reacts with any strong base. Write the equation for that process.

34. Write the formulas and names of three common strong acids and strong bases.

35. If 1000 NaOH units were dissolved in a sample of water, the NaOH would produce _____ Na^+ ions and _____ OH^- ions.

36. What is a *salt?* Give two balanced chemical equations showing how a salt is formed when an acid reacts with a base.

PROBLEMS

37. Write balanced equations showing how three of the common strong acids ionize to produce hydrogen ion.

38. In addition to the strong bases NaOH and KOH discussed in this chapter, the hydroxide compounds of other Group 1 elements behave as strong bases when dissolved in water. Write equations for RbOH and CsOH that show which ions form when they dissolve in water.

39. What salt would form when each of the following strong acid/strong base reactions takes place?

    a. $HCl(aq) + KOH(aq) \rightarrow$
    b. $RbOH(aq) + HNO_3(aq) \rightarrow$
    c. $HClO_4(aq) + NaOH(aq) \rightarrow$
    d. $HBr(aq) + CsOH(aq) \rightarrow$

40. Complete the following acid–base reactions by indicating the acid and base that must have reacted in each case to produce the indicated salt.

    a. _____ + _____ $\rightarrow K_2SO_4(aq) + 2H_2O(l)$
    b. _____ + _____ $\rightarrow NaNO_3(aq) + H_2O(l)$
    c. _____ + _____ $\rightarrow CaCl_2(aq) + 2H_2O(l)$
    d. _____ + _____ $\rightarrow Ba(ClO_4)_2(aq) + 2H_2O(l)$

7.5 Reactions of Metals with Nonmetals (Oxidation–Reduction)

QUESTIONS

41. What is an oxidation–reduction reaction? What is transferred during such a reaction?

42. Give an example of a simple chemical reaction that involves the *transfer of electrons* from a metallic element to a nonmetallic element.

43. What do we mean when we say that the transfer of electrons can be the "driving force" for a reaction? Give an example of a reaction where this happens.

44. If atoms of a metallic element (such as sodium) react with atoms of a nonmetallic element (such as sulfur), which element loses electrons and which element gains them?

45. If atoms of the metal calcium were to react with molecules of the nonmetal fluorine, F_2, how many electrons would each calcium atom lose? How many electrons would each fluorine atom gain? How many calcium atoms would be needed to react with one fluorine molecule? What charges would the resulting calcium and fluoride ions have?

46. If oxygen molecules, O_2, were to react with magnesium atoms, how many electrons would each magnesium atom lose? How many electrons would each oxygen atom gain? How many magnesium atoms would be needed to react with each oxygen molecule? What charges would the resulting magnesium and oxide ions have?

PROBLEMS

47. For the reaction $Mg(s) + Cl_2(g) \rightarrow MgCl_2(s)$, illustrate how electrons are gained and lost during the reaction.

48. For the reaction $2K(s) + S(g) \rightarrow K_2S(s)$, show how electrons are gained and lost by the atoms.

49. Balance each of the following oxidation–reduction reactions. For each, indicate which substance is being oxidized and which is being reduced.

    a. $Co(s) + Br_2(l) \rightarrow CoBr_3(s)$
    b. $Al(s) + H_2SO_4(aq) \rightarrow Al_2(SO_4)_3(aq) + H_2(g)$
    c. $Na(s) + H_2O(l) \rightarrow NaOH(aq) + H_2(g)$
    d. $Cu(s) + O_2(g) \rightarrow Cu_2O(s)$

50. Balance each of the following oxidation–reduction chemical reactions.

    a. $P_4(s) + O_2(g) \rightarrow P_4O_{10}(s)$
    b. $MgO(s) + C(s) \rightarrow Mg(s) + CO(g)$
    c. $Sr(s) + H_2O(l) \rightarrow Sr(OH)_2(aq) + H_2(g)$
    d. $Co(s) + HCl(aq) \rightarrow CoCl_2(aq) + H_2(g)$

7.6 Ways to Classify Reactions

QUESTIONS

51. a. Give two examples each of a single-displacement reaction and of a double-replacement reaction. How are the two reaction types similar, and how are they different?
    b. Give two examples each of a reaction in which formation of water is the driving force and in which formation of a gas is the driving force.

All even-numbered Questions and Problems have answers in the back of this book and solutions in the Solutions Guide.

(F) 52. The reaction between ammonium perchlorate and aluminum is discussed in the Chemistry in Focus segment *Oxidation–Reduction Reactions Launch the Space Shuttle*. The reaction is labeled as an oxidation–reduction reaction. Explain why this is an oxidation–reduction reaction and defend your answer.

53. Identify each of the following unbalanced reaction equations as belonging to one or more of the following categories: precipitation, acid–base, or oxidation–reduction.

a. $K_2SO_4(aq) + Ba(NO_3)_2(aq) \rightarrow BaSO_4(s) + KNO_3(aq)$
b. $HCl(aq) + Zn(s) \rightarrow H_2(g) + ZnCl_2(aq)$
c. $HCl(aq) + AgNO_3(aq) \rightarrow HNO_3(aq) + AgCl(s)$
d. $HCl(aq) + KOH(aq) \rightarrow H_2O(l) + KCl(aq)$
e. $Zn(s) + CuSO_4(aq) \rightarrow ZnSO_4(aq) + Cu(s)$
f. $NaH_2PO_4(aq) + NaOH(aq) \rightarrow Na_3PO_4(aq) + H_2O(l)$
g. $Ca(OH)_2(aq) + H_2SO_4(aq) \rightarrow CaSO_4(s) + H_2O(l)$
h. $ZnCl_2(aq) + Mg(s) \rightarrow Zn(s) + MgCl_2(aq)$
i. $BaCl_2(aq) + H_2SO_4(aq) \rightarrow BaSO_4(s) + HCl(aq)$

54. Identify each of the following unbalanced reaction equations as belonging to one or more of the following categories: precipitation, acid–base, or oxidation–reduction.

a. $H_2O_2(aq) \rightarrow H_2O(l) + O_2(g)$
b. $H_2SO_4(aq) + Zn(s) \rightarrow ZnSO_4(aq) + H_2(g)$
c. $H_2SO_4(aq) + NaOH(aq) \rightarrow Na_2SO_4(aq) + H_2O(l)$
d. $H_2SO_4(aq) + Ba(OH)_2(aq) \rightarrow BaSO_4(s) + H_2O(l)$
e. $AgNO_3(aq) + CuCl_2(aq) \rightarrow Cu(NO_3)_2(aq) + AgCl(s)$
f. $KOH(aq) + CuSO_4(aq) \rightarrow Cu(OH)_2(s) + K_2SO_4(aq)$
g. $Cl_2(g) + F_2(g) \rightarrow ClF(g)$
h. $NO(g) + O_2(g) \rightarrow NO_2(g)$
i. $Ca(OH)_2(s) + HNO_3(aq) \rightarrow Ca(NO_3)_2(aq) + H_2O(l)$

7.7 Other Ways to Classify Reactions

QUESTIONS

55. How do we define a *combustion* reaction? In addition to the chemical products, what other products do combustion reactions produce? Give two examples of balanced chemical equations for combustion reactions.

56. Reactions involving the combustion of fuel substances make up a subclass of _____ reactions.

57. What is a *synthesis* or *combination* reaction? Give an example. Can such reactions also be classified in other ways? Give an example of a synthesis reaction that is also a *combustion* reaction. Give an example of a synthesis reaction that is also an *oxidation–reduction* reaction, but that does not involve combustion.

58. What is a *decomposition* reaction? Give an example. Can such reactions also be classified in other ways?

PROBLEMS

59. Complete and balance each of the following combustion reactions.

a. $C_6H_6(l) + O_2(g) \rightarrow$
b. $C_5H_{12}(l) + O_2(g) \rightarrow$
c. $C_2H_6O(l) + O_2(g) \rightarrow$

60. Complete and balance each of the following combustion reactions.

a. $C_3H_8(g) + O_2(g) \rightarrow$
b. $C_2H_4(g) + O_2(g) \rightarrow$
c. $C_8H_{18}(l) + O_2(g) + H_2O(g) \rightarrow$

61. By now, you are familiar with enough chemical compounds to begin to write your own chemical reaction equations. Write two examples of what we mean by a *combustion* reaction.

62. By now, you are familiar with enough chemical compounds to begin to write your own chemical reaction equations. Write two examples each of what we mean by a *synthesis* reaction and by a *decomposition* reaction.

63. Balance each of the following equations that describe synthesis reactions.

a. $CaO(s) + H_2O(l) \rightarrow Ca(OH)_2(s)$
b. $Fe(s) + O_2(g) \rightarrow Fe_2O_3(s)$
c. $P_2O_5(s) + H_2O(l) \rightarrow H_3PO_4(aq)$

64. Balance each of the following equations that describe synthesis reactions.

a. $Fe(s) + S_8(s) \rightarrow FeS(s)$
b. $Co(s) + O_2(g) \rightarrow Co_2O_3(s)$
c. $Cl_2O_7(g) + H_2O(l) \rightarrow HClO_4(aq)$

65. Balance each of the following equations that describe decomposition reactions.

a. $CaSO_4(s) \rightarrow CaO(s) + SO_3(g)$
b. $Li_2CO_3(s) \rightarrow Li_2O(s) + CO_2(g)$
c. $LiHCO_3(s) \rightarrow Li_2CO_3(s) + H_2O(g) + CO_2(g)$
d. $C_6H_6(l) \rightarrow C(s) + H_2(g)$
e. $PBr_3(l) \rightarrow P_4(s) + Br_2(l)$

66. Balance each of the following equations that describe oxidation–reduction reactions.

a. $Al(s) + Br_2(l) \rightarrow AlBr_3(s)$
b. $Zn(s) + HClO_4(aq) \rightarrow Zn(ClO_4)_2(aq) + H_2(g)$
c. $Na(s) + P(s) \rightarrow Na_3P(s)$
d. $CH_4(g) + Cl_2(g) \rightarrow CCl_4(l) + HCl(g)$
e. $Cu(s) + AgNO_3(aq) \rightarrow Cu(NO_3)_2(aq) + Ag(s)$

Additional Problems

67. Distinguish between the *molecular* equation, the *complete ionic* equation, and the *net ionic* equation for a reaction in solution. Which type of equation most clearly shows the species that actually react with one another?

68. Using the general solubility rules given in Table 7.1, name three reactants that would form precipitates with each of the following ions in aqueous solution. Write the net ionic equation for each of your suggestions.

a. chloride ion   d. sulfate ion
b. calcium ion   e. mercury(I) ion, Hg_2^{2+}
c. iron(III) ion   f. silver ion

69. Without first writing a full molecular or ionic equation, write the net ionic equations for any precipitation reactions that occur when aqueous solutions of the following compounds are mixed. If no reaction occurs, so indicate.

   a. iron(III) nitrate and sodium carbonate
   b. mercurous nitrate and sodium chloride
   c. sodium nitrate and ruthenium nitrate
   d. copper(II) sulfate and sodium sulfide
   e. lithium chloride and lead(II) nitrate
   f. calcium nitrate and lithium carbonate
   g. gold(III) chloride and sodium hydroxide

70. Complete and balance each of the following molecular equations for strong acid/strong base reactions. Underline the formula of the *salt* produced in each reaction.

   a. $HNO_3(aq) + KOH(aq) \rightarrow$
   b. $H_2SO_4(aq) + Ba(OH)_2(aq) \rightarrow$
   c. $HClO_4(aq) + NaOH(aq) \rightarrow$
   d. $HCl(aq) + Ca(OH)_2(aq) \rightarrow$

71. For the cations listed in the left-hand column, give the formulas of the precipitates that would form with each of the anions in the right-hand column. If no precipitate is expected for a particular combination, so indicate.

Cations	Anions
Ag^+	$C_2H_3O_2^-$
Ba^{2+}	Cl^-
Ca^{2+}	CO_3^{2-}
Fe^{3+}	NO_3^-
Hg_2^{2+}	OH^-
Na^+	PO_4^{3-}
Ni^{2+}	S^{2-}
Pb^{2+}	SO_4^{2-}

72. On the basis of the general solubility rules given in Table 7.1, predict which of the following substances are likely to be soluble in water.

   a. potassium hexacyanoferrate(III), $K_3Fe(CN)_6$
   b. ammonium molybdate, $(NH_4)_2MoO_4$
   c. osmium(II) carbonate, $OsCO_3$
   d. gold(III) phosphate, $AuPO_4$
   e. sodium hexanitrocobaltate(III), $Na_3Co(NO_2)_6$
   f. barium carbonate, $BaCO_3$
   g. iron(III) chloride, $FeCl_3$

73. On the basis of the general solubility rules given in Table 7.1, predict the identity of the precipitate that forms when aqueous solutions of the following substances are mixed. If no precipitate is likely, indicate why (which rules apply).

   a. iron(III) chloride and sodium hydroxide
   b. nickel(II) nitrate and ammonium sulfide
   c. silver nitrate and potassium chloride
   d. sodium carbonate and barium nitrate
   e. potassium chloride and mercury(I) nitrate
   f. barium nitrate and sulfuric acid

74. On the basis of the general solubility rules given in Table 7.1, write a balanced molecular equation for the precipitation reactions that take place when the following aqueous solutions are mixed. Underline the formula of the precipitate (solid) that forms. If no precipitation reaction is likely for the reactants given, so indicate.

   a. silver nitrate and hydrochloric acid
   b. copper(II) sulfate and ammonium carbonate
   c. iron(II) sulfate and potassium carbonate
   d. silver nitrate and potassium nitrate
   e. lead(II) nitrate and lithium carbonate
   f. tin(IV) chloride and sodium hydroxide

75. For each of the following *un*balanced molecular equations, write the corresponding *balanced net ionic equation* for the reaction.

   a. $HCl(aq) + AgNO_3(aq) \rightarrow AgCl(s) + HNO_3(aq)$
   b. $CaCl_2(aq) + Na_3PO_4(aq) \rightarrow Ca_3(PO_4)_2(s) + NaCl(aq)$
   c. $Pb(NO_3)_2(aq) + BaCl_2(aq) \rightarrow$
   $$PbCl_2(s) + Ba(NO_3)_2(aq)$$
   d. $FeCl_3(aq) + NaOH(aq) \rightarrow Fe(OH)_3(s) + NaCl(aq)$

76. Most sulfide compounds of the transition metals are insoluble in water. Many of these metal sulfides have striking and characteristic colors by which we can identify them. Therefore, in the analysis of mixtures of metal ions, it is very common to precipitate the metal ions by using dihydrogen sulfide (commonly called hydrogen sulfide), H_2S. Suppose you had a mixture of Fe^{2+}, Cr^{3+}, and Ni^{2+}. Write net ionic equations for the precipitation of these metal ions by the use of H_2S.

77. What strong acid and what strong base would react in aqueous solution to produce the following salts?

   a. potassium perchlorate, $KClO_4$
   b. cesium nitrate, $CsNO_3$
   c. potassium chloride, KCl
   d. sodium sulfate, Na_2SO_4

78. Using the general solubility rules given in Table 7.1, name three reactants that would form precipitates with each of the following ions in aqueous solutions. Write the balanced molecular equation for each of your suggested reactants.

   a. sulfide ion   c. hydroxide ion
   b. carbonate ion   d. phosphate ion

79. For the reaction $16Fe(s) + 3S_8(s) \rightarrow 8Fe_2S_3(s)$, show how electrons are gained and lost by the atoms.

80. Balance the equation for each of the following oxidation–reduction chemical reactions.

   a. $Na(s) + O_2(g) \rightarrow Na_2O_2(s)$
   b. $Fe(s) + H_2SO_4(aq) \rightarrow FeSO_4(aq) + H_2(g)$
   c. $Al_2O_3(s) \rightarrow Al(s) + O_2(g)$
   d. $Fe(s) + Br_2(l) \rightarrow FeBr_3(s)$
   e. $Zn(s) + HNO_3(aq) \rightarrow Zn(NO_3)_2(aq) + H_2(g)$

81. Identify each of the following unbalanced reaction equations as belonging to one or more of the following categories: precipitation, acid–base, or oxidation–reduction.

   a. $Fe(s) + H_2SO_4(aq) \rightarrow Fe_3(SO_4)_2(aq) + H_2(g)$

b. $HClO_4(aq) + RbOH(aq) \rightarrow RbClO_4(aq) + H_2O(l)$
c. $Ca(s) + O_2(g) \rightarrow CaO(s)$
d. $H_2SO_4(aq) + NaOH(aq) \rightarrow Na_2SO_4(aq) + H_2O(l)$
e. $Pb(NO_3)_2(aq) + Na_2CO_3(aq) \rightarrow$
$$PbCO_3(s) + NaNO_3(aq)$$
f. $K_2SO_4(aq) + CaCl_2(aq) \rightarrow KCl(aq) + CaSO_4(s)$
g. $HNO_3(aq) + KOH(aq) \rightarrow KNO_3(aq) + H_2O(l)$
h. $Ni(C_2H_3O_2)_2(aq) + Na_2S(aq) \rightarrow$
$$NiS(s) + NaC_2H_3O_2(aq)$$
i. $Ni(s) + Cl_2(g) \rightarrow NiCl_2(s)$

82. Complete and balance each of the following equations that describe combustion reactions.

a. $C_4H_{10}(l) + O_2(g) \rightarrow$
b. $C_4H_{10}O(l) + O_2(g) \rightarrow$
c. $C_4H_{10}O_2(l) + O_2(g) \rightarrow$

83. Balance each of the following equations that describe synthesis reactions.

a. $FeO(s) + O_2(g) \rightarrow Fe_2O_3(s)$
b. $CO(g) + O_2(g) \rightarrow CO_2(g)$
c. $H_2(g) + Cl_2(g) \rightarrow HCl(g)$
d. $K(s) + S_8(s) \rightarrow K_2S(s)$
e. $Na(s) + N_2(g) \rightarrow Na_3N(s)$

84. Balance each of the following equations that describe decomposition reactions.

a. $NaHCO_3(s) \rightarrow Na_2CO_3(s) + H_2O(g) + CO_2(g)$
b. $NaClO_3(s) \rightarrow NaCl(s) + O_2(g)$
c. $HgO(s) \rightarrow Hg(l) + O_2(g)$
d. $C_{12}H_{22}O_{11}(s) \rightarrow C(s) + H_2O(g)$
e. $H_2O_2(l) \rightarrow H_2O(l) + O_2(g)$

85. Write a balanced oxidation–reduction equation for the reaction of each of the metals in the left-hand column with each of the nonmetals in the right-hand column.

Ba	O_2
K	S
Mg	Cl_2
Rb	N_2
Ca	Br_2
Li	

86. Sulfuric acid, H_2SO_4, oxidizes many metallic elements. One of the effects of acid rain is that it produces sulfuric acid in the atmosphere, which then reacts with metals used in construction. Write balanced oxidation–reduction equations for the reaction of sulfuric acid with Fe, Zn, Mg, Co, and Ni.

87. Although the metals of Group 2 of the periodic table are not nearly as reactive as those of Group 1, many of the Group 2 metals will combine with common nonmetals, especially at elevated temperatures. Write balanced chemical equations for the reactions of Mg, Ca, Sr, and Ba with Cl_2, Br_2, and O_2.

88. For each of the following metals, how many electrons will the metal atoms lose when the metal reacts with a nonmetal?

a. sodium   d. barium
b. potassium   e. aluminum
c. magnesium

89. For each of the following nonmetals, how many electrons will each atom of the nonmetal gain in reacting with a metal?

a. oxygen   d. chlorine
b. fluorine   e. sulfur
c. nitrogen

90. There is much overlapping of the classification schemes for reactions discussed in this chapter. Give an example of a reaction that is, at the same time, an oxidation–reduction reaction, a combustion reaction, and a synthesis reaction.

91. Classify the reactions represented by the following unbalanced equations by as many methods as possible. Balance the equations.

a. $I_4O_9(s) \rightarrow I_2O_6(s) + I_2(s) + O_2(g)$
b. $Mg(s) + AgNO_3(aq) \rightarrow Mg(NO_3)_2(aq) + Ag(s)$
c. $SiCl_4(l) + Mg(s) \rightarrow MgCl_2(s) + Si(s)$
d. $CuCl_2(aq) + AgNO_3(aq) \rightarrow Cu(NO_3)_2(aq) + AgCl(s)$
e. $Al(s) + Br_2(l) \rightarrow AlBr_3(s)$

92. Classify the reactions represented by the following unbalanced equations by as many methods as possible. Balance the equations.

a. $C_3H_8O(l) + O_2(g) \rightarrow CO_2(g) + H_2O(g)$
b. $HCl(aq) + AgC_2H_3O_2(aq) \rightarrow AgCl(s) + HC_2H_3O_2(aq)$
c. $HCl(aq) + Al(OH)_3(s) \rightarrow AlCl_3(aq) + H_2O(l)$
d. $H_2O_2(aq) \rightarrow H_2O(l) + O_2(g)$
e. $N_2H_4(l) + O_2(g) \rightarrow N_2(g) + H_2O(g)$

93. Corrosion of metals costs us billions of dollars annually, slowly destroying cars, bridges, and buildings. Corrosion of a metal involves the oxidation of the metal by the oxygen in the air, typically in the presence of moisture. Write a balanced equation for the reaction of each of the following metals with O_2: Zn, Al, Fe, Cr, and Ni.

94. Elemental chlorine, Cl_2, is very reactive, combining with most metallic substances. Write a balanced equation for the reaction of each of the following metals with Cl_2: Na, Al, Zn, Ca, and Fe.

95. Give a balanced molecular chemical equation to illustrate each of the following types of reactions.

a. a synthesis (combination) reaction
b. a precipitation reaction
c. a double-displacement reaction
d. an acid–base reaction
e. an oxidation–reduction reaction
f. a combustion reaction

QUESTIONS

1. What kind of *visual* evidence indicates that a chemical reaction has occurred? Give an example of each type of evidence you have mentioned. Do *all* reactions produce visual evidence that they have taken place?

2. What, in general terms, does a chemical equation indicate? What are the substances indicated to the left of the arrow called in a chemical equation? To the right of the arrow?

3. What does it mean to "balance" an equation? Why is it so important that equations be balanced? What does it mean to say that atoms must be *conserved* in a balanced chemical equation? How are the physical states of reactants and products indicated when writing chemical equations?

4. When balancing a chemical equation, why is it *not* permissible to adjust the subscripts in the formulas of the reactants and products? What would changing the subscripts within a formula do? What do the *coefficients* in a balanced chemical equation represent? Why is it acceptable to adjust a substance's coefficient but not permissible to adjust the subscripts within the substance's formula?

5. What is meant by the *driving force* for a reaction? Give some examples of driving forces that make reactants tend to form products. Write a balanced chemical equation illustrating each type of driving force you have named.

6. Explain to your friend what chemists mean by a *precipitation* reaction. What is the driving force in a precipitation reaction? Using the information provided about solubility in these chapters, write balanced molecular and net ionic equations for five examples of precipitation reactions.

7. Define the term *strong electrolyte*. What types of substances tend to be strong electrolytes? What does a solution of a strong electrolyte contain? Give a way to determine if a substance is a strong electrolyte.

8. Summarize the simple solubility rules for ionic compounds. How do we use these rules in determining the identity of the solid formed in a precipitation reaction? Give examples including balanced complete and net ionic equations.

9. In general terms, what are the *spectator ions* in a precipitation reaction? Why are the spectator ions not included in writing the net ionic equation for a precipitation reaction? Does this mean that the spectator ions do not have to be present in the solution?

10. Describe some physical and chemical properties of *acids* and *bases*. What is meant by a *strong* acid or base? Are strong acids and bases also strong electrolytes? Give several examples of strong acids and strong bases.

11. What is a *salt?* How are salts formed by acid–base reactions? Write chemical equations showing the formation of three different salts. What other product is formed when an aqueous acid reacts with an aqueous base? Write the net ionic equation for the formation of this substance.

12. What do we call reactions in which electrons are transferred between atoms or ions? What do we call a *loss* of electrons by an atom or ion? What is it called when an atom or ion *gains* electrons? Can we have a process in which electrons are lost by one species without there also being a process in which the electrons are gained by another species? Why? Give three examples of equations in which there is a transfer of electrons between a metallic element and a nonmetallic element. In your examples, identify which species loses electrons and which species gains electrons.

13. What is a *combustion* reaction? Are combustion reactions a unique type of reaction, or are they a special case of a more general type of reaction? Write an equation that illustrates a combustion reaction.

14. Give an example of a *synthesis* reaction and of a *decomposition* reaction. Are synthesis and decomposition reactions always also oxidation–reduction reactions? Explain.

15. List and define all the ways of classifying chemical reactions that have been discussed in the text. Give a balanced chemical equation as an example of each type of reaction, and show clearly how your example fits the definition you have given.

PROBLEMS

16. The element carbon undergoes many inorganic reactions, as well as being the basis for the field of organic chemistry. Write balanced chemical equations for the reactions of carbon described below.

   a. Carbon burns in an excess of oxygen (for example, in the air) to produce carbon dioxide.
   b. If the supply of oxygen is limited, carbon will still burn, but will produce carbon monoxide rather than carbon dioxide.
   c. If molten lithium metal is treated with carbon, lithium carbide, Li_2C_2, is produced.
   d. Iron(II) oxide reacts with carbon above temperatures of about 700 °C to produce carbon monoxide gas and molten elemental iron.
   e. Carbon reacts with fluorine gas at high temperatures to make carbon tetrafluoride.

17. Balance each of the following chemical equations.

   a. $Na_2SO_4(aq) + BaCl_2(aq) \rightarrow BaSO_4(s) + NaCl(aq)$
   b. $Zn(s) + H_2O(g) \rightarrow ZnO(s) + H_2(g)$
   c. $NaOH(aq) + H_3PO_4(aq) \rightarrow Na_3PO_4(aq) + H_2O(l)$
   d. $Al(s) + Mn_2O_3(s) \rightarrow Al_2O_3(s) + Mn(s)$
   e. $C_7H_6O_2(s) + O_2(g) \rightarrow CO_2(g) + H_2O(g)$

Plastic That Talks and Listens!

Imagine a plastic so "smart" that it can be used to sense a baby's breath, measure the force of a karate punch, sense the presence of a person 100 ft away, or make a balloon that sings. There is a plastic film capable of doing all these things. It's called **polyvinylidene difluoride (PVDF),** which has the structure

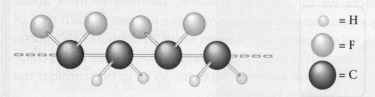

⊙	= H
◯	= F
●	= C

When this polymer is processed in a particular way, it becomes piezoelectric and pyroelectric. A *piezoelectric* substance produces an electric current when it is physically deformed or, alternatively, undergoes a deformation when a current is applied. A *pyroelectric* material is one that develops an electrical potential in response to a change in its temperature.

Because PVDF is piezoelectric, it can be used to construct a paper-thin microphone; it responds to sound by producing a current proportional to the deformation caused by the sound

waves. A ribbon of PVDF plastic one-quarter of an inch wide could be strung along a hallway and used to listen to all the conversations going on as people walk through. On the other hand, electric pulses can be applied to the PVDF film to produce a speaker. A strip of PVDF film glued to the inside of a balloon can play any song stored on a microchip attached to the film—hence a balloon that can sing happy birthday at a party. The PVDF film also can be used to construct a sleep apnea monitor, which, when placed beside the mouth of a sleeping infant, will set off an alarm if the breathing stops, thus helping to prevent sudden infant death syndrome (SIDS). The same type of film is used by the U.S. Olympic karate team to measure the force of kicks and punches as the team trains. Also, gluing two strips of film together gives a material that curls in response to a current, creating an artificial muscle. In addition, because the PVDF film is pyroelectric, it responds to the infrared (heat) radiation emitted by a human as far away as 100 ft, making it useful for burglar alarm systems. Making the PVDF polymer piezoelectric and pyroelectric requires some very special processing, which makes it costly ($10 per square foot), but this seems a small price to pay for its near-magical properties.

Can we count these nonidentical beans by weighing? Yes. The key piece of information we need is the *average mass* of the jelly beans. Let's compute the average mass for our 10-bean sample.

$$\text{Average mass} = \frac{\text{total mass of beans}}{\text{number of beans}}$$

$$= \frac{5.1\text{ g} + 5.2\text{ g} + 5.0\text{ g} + 4.8\text{ g} + 4.9\text{ g} + 5.0\text{ g} + 5.0\text{ g} + 5.1\text{ g} + 4.9\text{ g} + 5.0\text{ g}}{10}$$

$$= \frac{50.0}{10} = 5.0\text{ g}$$

The average mass of a jelly bean is 5.0 g. Thus, to count out 1000 beans, we need to weigh out 5000 g of beans. This sample of beans, in which the beans have an average mass of 5.0 g, can be treated exactly like a sample where all of the beans are identical. Objects do not need to have identical masses to be counted by weighing. We simply need to know the average mass of the objects. For purposes of counting, the objects *behave as though they were all identical,* as though they each actually had the average mass.

Suppose a customer comes into the store and says, "I want to buy a bag of candy for each of my kids. One of them likes jelly beans and the other one likes mints. Please put a scoopful of jelly beans in a bag and a scoopful of mints in another bag." Then the customer recognizes a problem. "Wait! My kids will fight unless I bring home exactly the same number of candies for each one. Both bags must have the same number of pieces because they'll definitely count them and compare. But I'm really in a hurry, so we don't have time to count them here. Is there a simple way you can be sure the bags will contain the same number of candies?"

You need to solve this problem quickly. Suppose you know the average masses of the two kinds of candy:

$$\text{Jelly beans:}\quad \text{average mass} = 5\text{ g}$$
$$\text{Mints:}\quad \text{average mass} = 15\text{ g}$$

You fill the scoop with jelly beans and dump them onto the scale, which reads 500 g. Now the key question: What mass of mints do you need to give the same number of mints as there are jelly beans in 500 g of jelly beans? Comparing the average masses of the jelly beans (5 g) and mints (15 g), you realize that each mint has three times the mass of each jelly bean:

$$\frac{15\text{ g}}{5\text{ g}} = 3$$

This means that you must weigh out an amount of mints that is three times the mass of the jelly beans:

$$3 \times 500\text{ g} = 1500\text{ g}$$

You weigh out 1500 g of mints and put them in a bag. The customer leaves with your assurance that both the bag containing 500 g of jelly beans and the bag containing 1500 g of mints contain the same number of candies.

In solving this problem, you have discovered a principle that is very important in chemistry: two samples containing different types of components, A and B, both *contain the same number of components if the ratio of the sample masses is the same as the ratio of the masses of the individual components* of A and B.

Let's illustrate this rather intimidating statement by using the example we just discussed. The individual components have the masses 5 g (jelly beans) and 15 g (mints). Consider several cases.

- Each sample contains 1 component:

$$\text{Mass of mint} = 15\text{ g}$$
$$\text{Mass of jelly bean} = 5\text{ g}$$

- Each sample contains 10 components:

$$10\text{ mints} \times \frac{15\text{ g}}{\text{mint}} = 150\text{ g of mints}$$
$$10\text{ jelly beans} \times \frac{5\text{ g}}{\text{jelly bean}} = 50\text{ g of jelly beans}$$

- Each sample contains 100 components:

$$100\text{ mints} \times \frac{15\text{ g}}{\text{mint}} = 1500\text{ g of mints}$$
$$100\text{ jelly beans} \times \frac{5\text{ g}}{\text{jelly bean}} = 500\text{ g of jelly beans}$$

Note in each case that the ratio of the masses is always 3 to 1:

$$\frac{1500}{500} = \frac{150}{50} = \frac{15}{5} = \frac{3}{1}$$

This is the ratio of the masses of the individual components:

$$\frac{\text{Mass of mint}}{\text{Mass of jelly bean}} = \frac{15}{5} = \frac{3}{1}$$

Any two samples, one of mints and one of jelly beans, that have a *mass ratio* of 15/5 = 3/1 will contain the same number of components. And these same ideas apply also to atoms, as we will see in the next section.

8.2 Atomic Masses: Counting Atoms by Weighing

OBJECTIVE: To understand atomic mass and its experimental determination.

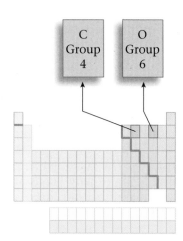

In Chapter 6 we considered the balanced equation for the reaction of solid carbon and gaseous oxygen to form gaseous carbon dioxide:

$$C(s) + O_2(g) \rightarrow CO_2(g)$$

Now suppose you have a small pile of solid carbon and want to know how many oxygen molecules are required to convert all of this carbon into carbon dioxide. The balanced equation tells us that one oxygen molecule is required for each carbon atom.

$$C(s) \quad + \quad O_2(g) \quad \rightarrow \quad CO_2(g)$$

1 atom reacts with 1 molecule to yield 1 molecule

To determine the number of oxygen molecules required, we must know how many carbon atoms are present in the pile of carbon. But individual atoms are far too small to see. We must learn to count atoms by weighing samples containing large numbers of them.

In the last section we saw that we can easily count things like jelly beans and mints by weighing. Exactly the same principles can be applied to counting atoms.

Because atoms are so tiny, the normal units of mass—the gram and the kilogram—are much too large to be convenient. For example, the mass of a single carbon atom is 1.99×10^{-23} g. To avoid using terms like 10^{-23} when describing the mass of an atom, scientists have defined a much smaller unit of mass called the **atomic mass unit,** which is abbreviated **amu.** In terms of grams,

$$1 \text{ amu} = 1.66 \times 10^{-24} \text{ g}$$

Now let's return to our problem of counting carbon atoms. To count carbon atoms by weighing, we need to know the mass of individual atoms, just as we needed to know the mass of the individual jelly beans. Recall from Chapter 4 that the atoms of a given element exist as isotopes. The isotopes of carbon are $^{12}_{6}C$, $^{13}_{6}C$, and $^{14}_{6}C$. Any sample of carbon contains a mixture of these isotopes, always in the same proportions. Each of these isotopes has a slightly different mass. Therefore, just as with the nonidentical jelly beans, we need to use an average mass for the carbon atoms. The **average atomic mass** for carbon atoms is 12.01 amu. This means that any sample of carbon from nature *can be treated as though it were composed of identical carbon atoms*, each with a mass of 12.01 amu. Now that we know the average mass of the carbon atom, we can count carbon atoms by weighing samples of natural carbon. For example, what mass of natural carbon must we take to have 1000 carbon atoms present? Because 12.01 amu is the average mass,

$$\text{Mass of 1000 natural carbon atoms} = (1000 \ \cancel{\text{atoms}}) \left(12.01 \ \frac{\text{amu}}{\cancel{\text{atom}}} \right)$$
$$= 12{,}010 \ \text{amu} = 12.01 \times 10^3 \ \text{amu}$$

Now let's assume that when we weigh the pile of natural carbon mentioned earlier, the result is 3.00×10^{20} amu. How many carbon atoms are present in this sample? We know that an average carbon atom has the mass 12.01 amu, so we can compute the number of carbon atoms by using the equivalence statement

$$1 \text{ carbon atom} = 12.01 \text{ amu}$$

to construct the appropriate conversion factor,

$$\frac{1 \text{ carbon atom}}{12.01 \text{ amu}}$$

The calculation is carried out as follows:

$$3.00 \times 10^{20} \ \cancel{\text{amu}} \times \frac{1 \text{ carbon atom}}{12.01 \ \cancel{\text{amu}}} = 2.50 \times 10^{19} \text{ carbon atoms}$$

The principles we have just discussed for carbon apply to all the other elements as well. All the elements as found in nature typically consist of a mixture of various isotopes. So to count the atoms in a sample of a given element by weighing, we must know the mass of the sample and the average mass for that element. Some average masses for common elements are listed in Table 8.1.

Table 8.1 Average Atomic Mass Values for Some Common Elements

Element	Average Atomic Mass (amu)
Hydrogen	1.008
Carbon	12.01
Nitrogen	14.01
Oxygen	16.00
Sodium	22.99
Aluminum	26.98

EXAMPLE 8.1 Calculating Mass Using Atomic Mass Units (amu)

Calculate the mass, in amu, of a sample of aluminum that contains 75 atoms.

SOLUTION

To solve this problem we use the average mass for an aluminum atom: 26.98 amu. We set up the equivalence statement:

$$1 \text{ Al atom} = 26.98 \text{ amu}$$

It gives the conversion factor we need:

$$75 \ \cancel{\text{Al atoms}} \times \frac{26.98 \text{ amu}}{1 \ \cancel{\text{Al atom}}} = 2024 \text{ amu}$$

Self-Check **EXERCISE 8.1** Calculate the mass of a sample that contains 23 nitrogen atoms.

See Problems 8.5 and 8.8. ∎

The opposite calculation can also be carried out. That is, if we know the mass of a sample, we can determine the number of atoms present. This procedure is illustrated in Example 8.2.

EXAMPLE 8.2   Calculating the Number of Atoms from the Mass

Calculate the number of sodium atoms present in a sample that has a mass of 1172.49 amu.

SOLUTION

We can solve this problem by using the average atomic mass for sodium (see Table 8.1) of 22.99 amu. The appropriate equivalence statement is

$$1 \text{ Na atom} = 22.99 \text{ amu}$$

which gives the conversion factor we need:

$$1172.49 \text{ amu} \times \frac{1 \text{ Na atom}}{22.99 \text{ amu}} = 51.00 \text{ Na atoms}$$

Self-Check   EXERCISE 8.2   Calculate the number of oxygen atoms in a sample that has a mass of 288 amu.

See Problems 8.6 and 8.7. ■

To summarize, we have seen that we can count atoms by weighing if we know the average atomic mass for that type of atom. This is one of the fundamental operations in chemistry, as we will see in the next section.

The average atomic mass for each element is listed in tables found inside the front cover of this book. Chemists often call these values the *atomic weights* for the elements, although this terminology is passing out of use.

8.3   The Mole

OBJECTIVES: To understand the mole concept and Avogadro's number. • To learn to convert among moles, mass, and number of atoms in a given sample.

In the previous section we used atomic mass units for mass, but these are extremely small units. In the laboratory a much larger unit, the gram, is the convenient unit for mass. In this section we will learn to count atoms in samples with masses given in grams.

Let's assume we have a sample of aluminum that has a mass of 26.98 g. What mass of copper contains exactly the same number of atoms as this sample of aluminum?

26.98 g aluminum	←——————→ Contains the same number of atoms	? grams copper

To answer this question, we need to know the average atomic masses for aluminum (26.98 amu) and copper (63.55 amu). Which atom has the greater atomic mass, aluminum or copper? The answer is copper. If we have 26.98 g of aluminum, do we need more or less than 26.98 g of copper to have the same number of copper atoms as aluminum atoms? We need more than 26.98 g of copper because each copper atom has a greater mass than each aluminum atom. Therefore, a given number of copper atoms will weigh more than an equal number of aluminum atoms. How much copper do we need? Because the average masses of aluminum and copper atoms are 26.98 amu and 63.55 amu, respectively, 26.98 g of aluminum and 63.55 g of copper

Lead bar
207.2 g

Silver bars
107.9 g

Pile of copper
63.55 g

Figure 8.1

All these samples of pure elements contain the *same number* (a mole) of atoms: 6.022×10^{23} atoms.

Figure 8.2

One-mole samples of iron (nails), iodine crystals, liquid mercury, and powdered sulfur.

This definition of the mole is slightly different from the SI definition but is used because it is easier to understand at this point.

Avogadro's number (to four significant figures) is 6.022×10^{23}. One mole of *anything* is 6.022×10^{23} units of that substance.

contain exactly the same number of atoms. So we need 63.55 g of copper. As we saw in the first section when we were discussing candy, *samples in which the ratio of the masses is the same as the ratio of the masses of the individual atoms always contain the same number of atoms*. In the case just considered, the ratios are

$$\frac{26.98 \text{ g}}{63.55 \text{ g}} = \frac{26.98 \text{ amu}}{63.55 \text{ amu}}$$

Ratio of sample masses   Ratio of atomic masses

Therefore, 26.98 g of aluminum contains the same number of aluminum atoms as 63.55 g of copper contains copper atoms.

Now compare carbon (average atomic mass, 12.01 amu) and helium (average atomic mass, 4.003 amu). A sample of 12.01 g of carbon contains the same number of atoms as 4.003 g of helium. In fact, if we weigh out samples of all the elements such that each sample has a mass equal to that element's average atomic mass in grams, these samples all contain the same number of atoms (Figure 8.1). This number (the number of atoms present in all of these samples) assumes special importance in chemistry. It is called the mole, the unit all chemists use in describing numbers of atoms. The **mole** (abbreviated mol) can be defined as *the number equal to the number of carbon atoms in 12.01 grams of carbon*. Techniques for counting atoms very precisely have been used to determine this number to be 6.022×10^{23}. This number is called **Avogadro's number**. *One mole of something consists of 6.022×10^{23} units of that substance.* Just as a dozen eggs is 12 eggs, a mole of eggs is 6.022×10^{23} eggs. And a mole of water contains 6.022×10^{23} H_2O molecules.

The magnitude of the number 6.022×10^{23} is very difficult to imagine. To give you some idea, 1 mole of seconds represents a span of time 4 million times as long as the earth has already existed! One mole of marbles is enough to cover the entire earth to a depth of 50 miles! However, because atoms are so tiny, a mole of atoms or molecules is a perfectly manageable quantity to use in a reaction (Figure 8.2).

How do we use the mole in chemical calculations? Recall that Avogadro's number is defined such that a 12.01-g sample of carbon contains 6.022×10^{23} atoms. By the same token, because the average atomic mass of hydrogen is 1.008 amu (Table 8.1), 1.008 g of hydrogen contains 6.022×10^{23} hydrogen atoms. Similarly, 26.98 g of aluminum contains 6.022×10^{23} aluminum atoms. The point is that a sample of *any* element that weighs a number of grams equal to the average atomic mass of that element contains 6.022×10^{23} atoms (1 mol) of that element.

Table 8.2 shows the masses of several elements that contain 1 mole of atoms.

Table 8.2	Comparison of 1-Mol Samples of Various Elements	
Element	Number of Atoms Present	Mass of Sample (g)
Aluminum	6.022×10^{23}	26.98
Gold	6.022×10^{23}	196.97
Iron	6.022×10^{23}	55.85
Sulfur	6.022×10^{23}	32.07
Boron	6.022×10^{23}	10.81
Xenon	6.022×10^{23}	131.3

The mass of 1 mole of an element is equal to its average atomic mass in grams.

In summary, *a sample of an element with a mass equal to that element's average atomic mass expressed in grams contains 1 mole of atoms.*

To do chemical calculations, you *must* understand what the mole means and how to determine the number of moles in a given mass of a substance. However, before we do any calculations, let's be sure that the process of counting by weighing is clear. Consider the following "bag" of H atoms (symbolized by dots), which contains 1 mole (6.022×10^{23}) of H atoms and has a mass of 1.008 g. Assume the bag itself has no mass.

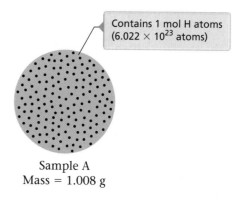

Contains 1 mol H atoms (6.022×10^{23} atoms)

Sample A
Mass = 1.008 g

Now consider another "bag" of hydrogen atoms in which the number of hydrogen atoms is unknown.

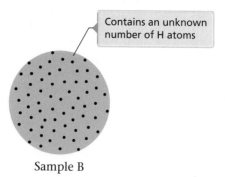

Contains an unknown number of H atoms

Sample B

A 1-mol sample of graphite (a form of carbon) weighs 12.01 g

We want to find out how many H atoms are present in sample ("bag") B. How can we do that? We can do it by weighing the sample. We find the mass of sample B to be 0.500 g.

How does this measured mass help us determine the number of atoms in sample B? We know that 1 mole of H atoms has a mass of 1.008 g. Sample B has a mass of 0.500 g, which is approximately half the mass of a mole of H atoms.

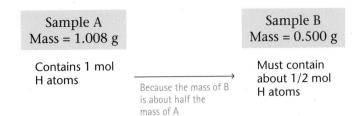

Sample A Mass = 1.008 g		Sample B Mass = 0.500 g
Contains 1 mol H atoms	Because the mass of B is about half the mass of A	Must contain about 1/2 mol H atoms

We carry out the actual calculation by using the equivalence statement

$$1 \text{ mol H atoms} = 1.008 \text{ g H}$$

to construct the conversion factor we need:

$$0.500 \text{ g H} \times \frac{1 \text{ mol H}}{1.008 \text{ g H}} = 0.496 \text{ mol H in sample B}$$

MATH SKILL BUILDER

In demonstrating how to solve problems requiring more than one step, we will often break the problem into smaller steps and report the answer to each step in the correct number of significant figures. While it may not always affect the final answer, it is a better idea to wait until the final step to round your answer to the correct number of significant figures.

Let's summarize. We know the mass of 1 mole of H atoms, so we can determine the number of moles of H atoms in any other sample of pure hydrogen by weighing the sample and *comparing* its mass to 1.008 g (the mass of 1 mole of H atoms). We can follow this same process for any element, because we know the mass of 1 mol for each of the elements.

Also, because we know that 1 mol is 6.022×10^{23} units, once we know the *moles* of atoms present, we can easily determine the *number* of atoms present. In the case considered above, we have approximately 0.5 mole of H atoms in sample B. This means that about 1/2 of 6×10^{23}, or 3×10^{23}, H atoms is present. We carry out the actual calculation by using the equivalence statement

$$1 \text{ mol} = 6.022 \times 10^{23}$$

to determine the conversion factor we need:

$$0.496 \text{ mol H atoms} \times \frac{6.022 \times 10^{23} \text{ H atoms}}{1 \text{ mol H atoms}}$$
$$= 2.99 \times 10^{23} \text{ H atoms in sample B}$$

These procedures are illustrated in Example 8.3.

EXAMPLE 8.3 | Calculating Moles and Number of Atoms

Aluminum (Al), a metal with a high strength-to-weight ratio and a high resistance to corrosion, is often used for structures such as high-quality bicycle frames. Compute both the number of moles of atoms and the number of atoms in a 10.0-g sample of aluminum.

SOLUTION

In this case we want to change from mass to moles of atoms:

10.0 g Al	➡	? moles of Al atoms

The mass of 1 mole (6.022×10^{23} atoms) of aluminum is 26.98 g. The sample we are considering has a mass of 10.0 g. Its mass is less than 26.98 g, so this sample contains less than 1 mole of aluminum atoms. We calculate the number of moles of aluminum atoms in 10.0 g by using the equivalence statement

$$1 \text{ mol Al} = 26.98 \text{ g Al}$$

A bicycle with an aluminum frame.

© Cengage Learning

to construct the appropriate conversion factor:

$$10.0 \ \cancel{g \ Al} \times \frac{1 \ mol \ Al}{26.98 \ \cancel{g \ Al}} = 0.371 \ mol \ Al$$

Next we convert from moles of atoms to the number of atoms, using the equivalence statement

$$6.022 \times 10^{23} \ Al \ atoms = 1 \ mol \ Al \ atoms$$

We have

$$0.371 \ \cancel{mol \ Al} \times \frac{6.022 \times 10^{23} \ Al \ atoms}{1 \ \cancel{mol \ Al}} = 2.23 \times 10^{23} \ Al \ atoms$$

We can summarize this calculation as follows:

$$\boxed{10.0 \ g \ Al} \times \frac{1 \ mol}{26.98 \ g} \ \Rightarrow \ \boxed{0.371 \ mol \ Al}$$

$$\boxed{0.371 \ mol \ Al \ atoms} \times \frac{6.022 \times 10^{23} \ Al \ atoms}{mol} \ \Rightarrow \ \boxed{2.23 \times 10^{23} \ Al \ atoms}$$

■

EXAMPLE 8.4   **Calculating the Number of Atoms**

A silicon chip used in an integrated circuit of a microcomputer has a mass of 5.68 mg. How many silicon (Si) atoms are present in this chip? The average atomic mass for silicon is 28.09 amu.

SOLUTION

Our strategy for doing this problem is to convert from milligrams of silicon to grams of silicon, then to moles of silicon, and finally to atoms of silicon:

$$\boxed{\text{Milligrams of Si atoms}} \ \Rightarrow \ \boxed{\text{Grams of Si atoms}} \ \Rightarrow \ \boxed{\text{Moles of Si atoms}} \ \Rightarrow \ \boxed{\text{Number of Si atoms}}$$

where each arrow in the schematic represents a conversion factor. Because 1 g = 1000 mg, we have

$$5.68 \ \cancel{mg \ Si} \times \frac{1 \ g \ Si}{1000 \ \cancel{mg \ Si}} = 5.68 \times 10^{-3} \ g \ Si$$

Next, because the average mass of silicon is 28.09 amu, we know that 1 mole of Si atoms weighs 28.09 g. This leads to the equivalence statement

$$1 \ mol \ Si \ atoms = 28.09 \ g \ Si$$

Thus,

$$5.68 \times 10^{-3} \ \cancel{g \ Si} \times \frac{1 \ mol \ Si}{28.09 \ \cancel{g \ Si}} = 2.02 \times 10^{-4} \ mol \ Si$$

Using the definition of a mole (1 mol = 6.022×10^{23}), we have

$$2.02 \times 10^{-4} \ \cancel{mol \ Si} \times \frac{6.022 \times 10^{23} \ atoms}{1 \ \cancel{mol \ Si}} = 1.22 \times 10^{20} \ Si \ atoms$$

A silicon chip of the type used in electronic equipment.

We can summarize this calculation as follows:

$$5.68 \text{ mg Si} \quad \times \quad \frac{1 \text{ g}}{1000 \text{ mg}} \quad \Rightarrow \quad 5.68 \times 10^{-3} \text{ g Si}$$

$$5.68 \times 10^{-3} \text{ g Si} \quad \times \quad \frac{1 \text{ mol}}{28.09 \text{ g}} \quad \Rightarrow \quad 2.02 \times 10^{-4} \text{ mol Si}$$

$$2.02 \times 10^{-4} \text{ mol Si} \quad \times \quad \frac{6.022 \times 10^{23} \text{ Si atoms}}{\text{mol}} \quad \Rightarrow \quad 1.22 \times 10^{20} \text{ Si atoms}$$

PROBLEM SOLVING: DOES THE ANSWER MAKE SENSE?

When you finish a problem, always think about the "reasonableness" of your answers. In Example 8.4, 5.68 mg of silicon is clearly much less than 1 mole of silicon (which has a mass of 28.09 g), so the final answer of 1.22×10^{20} atoms (compared to 6.022×10^{23} atoms in a mole) at least lies in the right direction. That is, 1.22×10^{20} atoms is a smaller number than 6.022×10^{23}. Also, always include the units as you perform calculations and make sure the correct units are obtained at the end. Paying careful attention to units and making this type of general check can help you detect errors such as an inverted conversion factor or a number that was incorrectly entered into your calculator.

As you can see, the problems are getting more complicated to solve. In the next section we will discuss strategies that will help you become a better problem solver.

Self-Check **EXERCISE 8.3**

The values for the average masses of the atoms of the elements are listed inside the front cover of this book.

Chromium (Cr) is a metal that is added to steel to improve its resistance to corrosion (for example, to make stainless steel). Calculate both the number of moles in a sample of chromium containing 5.00×10^{20} atoms and the mass of the sample.

See Problems 8.19 through 8.24. ∎

8.4 Learning to Solve Problems

OBJECTIVE: To understand how to solve problems by asking and answering a series of questions.

Imagine today is the first day of your new job. The problem is that you don't know how to get there. However, as luck would have it, a friend does know the way and offers to drive you. What should you do while you sit in the passenger seat? If your goal is simply to get to work today, you might not pay attention to how to get there. However, you will need to get there on your own tomorrow, so you should pay attention to distances, signs, and turns. The difference between these two approaches is the difference between taking a passive role (going along for the ride) and an active role (learning how to do it yourself). In this section, we will emphasize that you should take an active role in reading the text, especially the solutions to the practice problems.

One of the great rewards of studying chemistry is that you become a good problem solver. Being able to solve complex problems is a talent that will serve you well in all walks of life. It is our purpose in this text to help you learn to solve problems in a flexible, creative way based on understanding the fundamental ideas of chemistry. We call this approach **conceptual problem**

solving. The ultimate goal is to be able to solve new problems (that is, problems you have not seen before) on your own. In this text, we will provide problems, but instead of giving solutions for you to memorize, we will explain how to think about the solutions to the problems. Although the answers to these problems are important, it is even more important that you understand the process—the thinking necessary to get to the answer. At first we will be solving the problem for you (we will be "driving"). However, it is important that you do not take a passive role. While studying the solution, it is crucial that you interact—think through the problem with us, that is, take an active role so that eventually you can "drive" by yourself. Do not skip the discussion and jump to the answer. Usually, the solution involves asking a series of questions. Make sure that you understand each step in the process.

Although actively studying our solutions to the problems is helpful, at some point you will need to know how to think about these problems on your own. If we help you too much as you solve the problems, you won't really learn effectively. If we always "drive," you won't interact as meaningfully with the material. Eventually you need to learn to drive by yourself. Because of this, we will provide more help on the earlier problems and less as we proceed in later chapters. The goal is for you to learn how to solve a problem because you understand the main concepts and ideas in the problem.

Consider, for example, that you now know how to get from home to work. Does this mean that you can drive from work to home? Not necessarily, as you probably know from experience. If you have only memorized the directions from home to work and do not understand fundamental principles such as "I traveled north to get to the workplace, so my house is south of the workplace," you may find yourself stranded. Part of conceptual problem solving is understanding these fundamental principles.

Of course, there are many more places to go than from home to work and back. In a more complicated example, suppose you know how to get from your house to work (and back) and from your house to the library (and back). Can you get from work to the library without having to go back home? Probably not, if you have only memorized directions and you do not have a "big picture" of where your house, your workplace, and the library are relative to one another. Getting this big picture—a real understanding of the situation—is the other part of conceptual problem solving.

In conceptual problem solving, we let the problem guide us as we solve it. We ask a series of questions as we proceed and use our knowledge of fundamental principles to answer these questions. Learning this approach requires some patience, but the reward is that you become an effective solver of any new problem that confronts you in daily life or in your work in any field.

To help us as we proceed to solve a problem, the following organizing principles will be useful to us.

1. First, we need to read the problem and decide on the final goal. Then we sort through the facts given, focusing on keywords and often drawing a diagram of the problem. In this part of the analysis, we need to state the problem as simply and as visually as possible. We can summarize this process as *"Where Are We Going?"*

2. We need to work backward from the final goal in order to decide where to start. For example, in a stoichiometry problem we always start with the chemical reaction. Then as we proceed, we ask a series of questions, such as "What are the reactants and products?," "What is the balanced equation?," and "What are the amounts of the reactants?" Our understanding of the fundamental principles of chemistry will enable us to answer each of these simple questions

and eventually will lead us to the final solution. We can summarize this process as *"How Do We Get There?"*

3. Once we get the solution of the problem, then we ask ourselves: "Does it make sense?" That is, does our answer seem reasonable? We call this the Reality Check. It always pays to check your answer.

Using a conceptual approach to problem solving will enable you to develop real confidence as a problem solver. You will no longer panic when you see a problem that is different in some ways from those you have solved in the past. Although you might be frustrated at times as you learn this method, we guarantee that it will pay dividends later and should make your experience with chemistry a positive one that will prepare you for any career you choose.

To summarize, a creative problem solver has an understanding of fundamental principles and a big picture of the situation. One of our major goals in this text is to help you become a creative problem solver. We will do this first by giving you lots of guidance on how to solve problems. We will "drive," but we hope you will be paying attention instead of just "going along for the ride." As we move forward, we will gradually shift more of the responsibility to you. As you gain confidence in letting the problem guide you, you will be amazed at how effective you can be at solving some really complex problems, just like the ones you will confront in real life.

▶ An Example of Conceptual Problem Solving

Let's look at how conceptual problem solving works in practice. Because we used a driving analogy before, let's consider a problem about driving.

> Estimate the amount of money you would spend on gasoline to drive from New York, New York, to Los Angeles, California.

Where Are We Going?

The first thing we need to do is state the problem in words or as a diagram so that we understand the problem.

In this case, we are trying to estimate how much money we will spend on gasoline. How are we going to do this? We need to understand what factors cause us to spend more or less money. This requires us to ask, *"What Information Do We Need?,"* and *"What Do We Know?"*

Consider two people traveling in separate cars. Why might one person spend more money on gasoline than does the other person? In other words, if you were told that the two people spent different amounts of money on gasoline for a trip, what are some reasons you could give? Consider this, and write down some ideas before you continue reading.

Three factors that are important in this case are

- The price of a gallon of gasoline

- The distance of the trip between New York and Los Angeles

- The average gas mileage of the car we are driving

What do we know, or what are we given in the problem? In this problem, we are not given any of these values but are asked to estimate the cost of gasoline. So we need to estimate the required information. For example, the distance between New York and Los Angeles is about 3000 miles. The cost of gasoline varies over time and location, but a reasonable estimate is $2.00 a gallon. Gas mileage also varies, but we will assume it is about 30 miles per gallon.

Now that we have the necessary information, we will solve the problem.

How Do We Get There?

To set up the solution, we need to understand how the information affects our answer. Let's consider the relationship between the three factors we identified and our final answer.

- Price of gasoline: directly related. The more a gallon of gasoline costs, the more we will spend in total.

- Distance: directly related. The farther we travel, the more we will spend on gasoline.

- Gas mileage: inversely related. The better our gas mileage (the higher the number), the less we will spend on gasoline.

It should make sense, then, that we multiply the distance and price (because they are directly related) and then divide by the gas mileage (because it is inversely related). We will use dimensional analysis as discussed in Chapter 2. First let's determine how much gasoline we will need for our trip.

$$3000 \text{ miles} \times \frac{1 \text{ gal}}{30 \text{ miles}} = 100 \text{ gallons of gasoline}$$

Notice how the distance is in the numerator and the gas mileage is in the denominator, just as we determined they each should be. So, we will need about 100 gallons of gasoline. How much will this much gasoline cost?

$$100 \text{ gallons} \times \frac{\$2.00}{1 \text{ gallon}} = \$200$$

Notice that the price of a gallon of gas is in the numerator, just as predicted. So, given our information, we estimate the total cost of gasoline to be $200. The final step is to consider if this answer is reasonable.

REALITY CHECK Does our answer make sense? This is always a good question to consider, and our answer will depend on our familiarity with the situation. Sometimes we may not have a good feel for what the answer should be, especially when we are learning a new concept. Other times we may have only a rough idea and may be able to claim that the answer seems reasonable, although we cannot say it is exactly right. This will usually be the case, and it is the case here if you are familiar with how much you spend on gasoline. For example, the price to fill up the tank for an average car (at $2.00 per gallon) is around $20 to $40. So, if our answer is under $100, we should be suspicious. An answer in the thousands of dollars is way too high. So, an answer in the hundreds of dollars seems reasonable.

8.5 Molar Mass

OBJECTIVES: To understand the definition of molar mass. • To learn to convert between moles and mass of a given sample of a chemical compound.

A chemical compound is, fundamentally, a collection of atoms. For example, methane (the major component of natural gas) consists of molecules each containing one carbon atom and four hydrogen atoms (CH_4). How can we calculate the mass of 1 mole of methane? That is, what is the mass of 6.022×10^{23} CH_4 molecules? Because each CH_4 molecule contains one carbon atom and four hydrogen atoms, 1 mole of CH_4 molecules consists of

Note that when we say 1 mole of methane, we mean 1 mole of methane molecules.

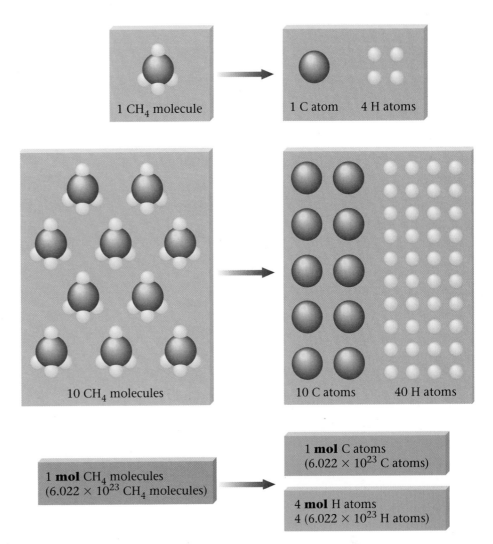

Figure 8.3

Various numbers of methane molecules showing their constituent atoms.

MATH SKILL BUILDER
Remember that the least number of decimal places limits the number of significant figures in addition.

1 mole of carbon atoms and 4 moles of hydrogen atoms (Figure 8.3). The mass of 1 mole of methane can be found by summing the masses of carbon and hydrogen present:

$$\text{Mass of 1 mol C} = 1 \times 12.01 \text{ g} = 12.01 \text{ g}$$
$$\text{Mass of 4 mol H} = 4 \times 1.008 \text{ g} = \underline{\ 4.032 \text{ g}}$$
$$\text{Mass of 1 mol CH}_4 \qquad\qquad\quad = 16.04 \text{ g}$$

A substance's molar mass (in grams) is the mass of 1 mole of that substance.

The quantity 16.04 g is called the molar mass for methane: the mass of 1 mole of CH_4 molecules. The **molar mass*** of any substance is the *mass (in grams) of 1 mole of the substance*. The molar mass is obtained by summing the masses of the component atoms.

EXAMPLE 8.5 | Calculating Molar Mass

Calculate the molar mass of sulfur dioxide, a gas produced when sulfur-containing fuels are burned. Unless "scrubbed" from the exhaust, sulfur dioxide can react with moisture in the atmosphere to produce acid rain.

---

*The term *molecular weight* was traditionally used instead of *molar mass*. The terms *molecular weight* and *molar mass* mean exactly the same thing. Because the term *molar mass* more accurately describes the concept, it will be used in this text.

SOLUTION

Where Are We Going?

We want to determine the molar mass of sulfur dioxide in units of g/mol.

What Do We Know?

- The formula for sulfur dioxide is SO_2, which means that 1 mole of SO_2 molecules contains 1 mole of sulfur atoms and 2 moles of oxygen atoms.

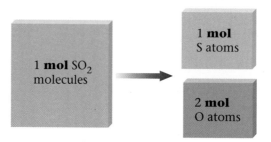

- We know the atomic masses of sulfur (32.07 g/mol) and oxygen (16.00 g/mol).

How Do We Get There?

We need to find the mass of 1 mole of SO_2 molecules, which is the molar mass of SO_2.

$$\begin{aligned}
\text{Mass of 1 mol S} &= 1 \times 32.07 = 32.07 \text{ g} \\
\text{Mass of 2 mol O} &= 2 \times 16.00 = \underline{32.00 \text{ g}} \\
\text{Mass of 1 mol } SO_2 & \qquad\qquad\quad = 64.07 \text{ g} = \text{molar mass}
\end{aligned}$$

The molar mass of SO_2 is 64.07 g. It represents the mass of 1 mole of SO_2 molecules.

REALITY CHECK   The answer is greater than the atomic masses of sulfur and oxygen. The units (g/mol) are correct, and the answer is reported to the correct number of significant figures (to two decimal places).

Self-Check **EXERCISE 8.4**   Polyvinyl chloride (called PVC), which is widely used for floor coverings ("vinyl") and for plastic pipes in plumbing systems, is made from a molecule with the formula C_2H_3Cl. Calculate the molar mass of this substance.

See Problems 8.27 through 8.30. ■

Some substances exist as a collection of ions rather than as separate molecules. For example, ordinary table salt, sodium chloride (NaCl), is composed of an array of Na^+ and Cl^- ions. There are no NaCl molecules present. In some books the term **formula weight** is used instead of molar mass for ionic compounds. However, in this book we will apply the term *molar mass* to both ionic and molecular substances.

To calculate the molar mass for sodium chloride, we must realize that 1 mole of NaCl contains 1 mole of Na^+ ions and 1 mole of Cl^- ions.

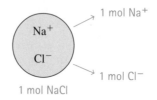

The mass of the electron is so small that Na^+ and Na have the same mass for our purposes, even though Na^+ has one electron fewer than Na. Also the mass of Cl virtually equals the mass of Cl^- even though it has one more electron than Cl.

Therefore, the molar mass (in grams) for sodium chloride represents the sum of the mass of 1 mole of sodium ions and the mass of 1 mole of chloride ions.

$$\begin{aligned} \text{Mass of 1 mol } Na^+ &= 22.99 \text{ g} \\ \text{Mass of 1 mol } Cl^- &= \underline{35.45 \text{ g}} \\ \text{Mass of 1 mol } NaCl &= 58.44 \text{ g} = \text{molar mass} \end{aligned}$$

The molar mass of NaCl is 58.44 g. It represents the mass of 1 mole of sodium chloride.

EXAMPLE 8.6   Calculating Mass from Moles

Calcium carbonate, $CaCO_3$ (also called calcite), is the principal mineral found in limestone, marble, chalk, pearls, and the shells of marine animals such as clams.

a. Calculate the molar mass of calcium carbonate.

b. A certain sample of calcium carbonate contains 4.86 mol. What is the mass in grams of this sample?

SOLUTION

a. Where Are We Going?

We want to determine the molar mass of calcium carbonate in units of g/mol.

What Do We Know?

- The formula for calcium carbonate is $CaCO_3$. One mole of $CaCO_3$ contains 1 mole of Ca, 1 mole of C, and 3 moles of O.

- We know the atomic masses of calcium (40.08 g/mol), carbon (12.01 g/mol), and oxygen 16.00 g/mol).

How Do We Get There?

Calcium carbonate is an ionic compound composed of Ca^{2+} and CO_3^{2-} ions. One mole of calcium carbonate contains 1 mole of Ca^{2+} and 1 mole of CO_3^{2-} ions. We calculate the molar mass by summing the masses of the components.

$$\begin{aligned} \text{Mass of 1 mol } Ca^{2+} &= 1 \times 40.08 \text{ g} = 40.08 \text{ g} \\ \text{Mass of 1 mol } CO_3^{2-} &\text{ (contains 1 mol C and 3 mol O):} \\ 1 \text{ mol C} &= 1 \times 12.01 \text{ g} = 12.01 \text{ g} \\ 3 \text{ mol O} &= 3 \times 16.00 \text{ g} = \underline{48.00 \text{ g}} \\ \text{Mass of 1 mol } CaCO_3 &= 100.09 \text{ g} = \text{molar mass} \end{aligned}$$

REALITY CHECK   The answer is greater than the atomic masses of calcium, carbon, and oxygen. The units (g/mol) are correct, and the answer is reported to the correct number of significant figures (to two decimal places).

b. Where Are We Going?

We want to determine the mass of 4.86 moles of $CaCO_3$.

What Do We Know?

- From part a, we know that the molar mass of $CaCO_3$ is 100.09 g/mol.

- We have 4.86 mol $CaCO_3$.

How Do We Get There?

We determine the mass of 4.86 moles of $CaCO_3$ by using the molar mass.

$$4.86 \ \text{mol} \ \cancel{CaCO_3} \times \frac{100.09 \ \text{g} \ CaCO_3}{1 \ \text{mol} \ \cancel{CaCO_3}} = 486 \ \text{g} \ CaCO_3$$

This can be diagrammed as follows:

$$\boxed{4.86 \ \text{mol} \ CaCO_3} \times \frac{100.09 \ \text{g}}{\text{mol}} \Rightarrow \boxed{486 \ \text{g} \ CaCO_3}$$

REALITY CHECK We have a bit less than 5 moles of $CaCO_3$, which has a molar mass of about 100 g/mol. We should expect an answer a bit less than 500 g, so our answer makes sense. The number of significant figures in our answer (486 g) is three, as required by the initial number of moles (4.86 mol).

Self-Check **EXERCISE 8.5**

For average atomic masses, look inside the front cover of this book.

Calculate the molar mass for sodium sulfate, Na_2SO_4. A sample of sodium sulfate with a mass of 300.0 g represents what number of moles of sodium sulfate?

See Problems 8.35 through 8.38. ∎

In summary, the molar mass of a substance can be obtained by summing the masses of the component atoms. The molar mass (in grams) represents the mass of 1 mole of the substance. Once we know the molar mass of a compound, we can compute the number of moles present in a sample of known mass. The reverse, of course, is also true as illustrated in Example 8.7.

EXAMPLE 8.7 | Calculating Moles from Mass

Juglone, a dye known for centuries, is produced from the husks of black walnuts. It is also a natural herbicide (weed killer) that kills off competitive plants around the black walnut tree but does not affect grass and other noncompetitive plants. The formula for juglone is $C_{10}H_6O_3$.

a. Calculate the molar mass of juglone.

b. A sample of 1.56 g of pure juglone was extracted from black walnut husks. How many moles of juglone does this sample represent?

SOLUTION

a. Where Are We Going?

We want to determine the molar mass of juglone in units of g/mol.

What Do We Know?

- The formula for juglone is $C_{10}H_6O_3$. One mole of juglone contains 10 moles of C, 6 moles of H, and 3 moles of O.

- We know the atomic masses of carbon (12.01 g/mol), hydrogen (1.008 g/mol), and oxygen (16.00 g/mol).

Black walnuts with and without their green hulls.

How Do We Get There?

The molar mass is obtained by summing the masses of the component atoms. In 1 mole of juglone there are 10 moles of carbon atoms, 6 moles of hydrogen atoms, and 3 moles of oxygen atoms.

MATH SKILL BUILDER
The 120.1 limits the sum to one decimal place.

$$
\begin{aligned}
\text{Mass of 10 mol C} &= 10 \times 12.01 \text{ g} = 120.1 \text{ g} \\
\text{Mass of 6 mol H} &= 6 \times 1.008 \text{ g} = 6.048 \text{ g} \\
\text{Mass of 3 mol O} &= 3 \times 16.00 \text{ g} = \underline{48.00 \text{ g}} \\
\text{Mass of 1 mol C}_{10}\text{H}_6\text{O}_3 &= 174.1 \text{ g} = \text{molar mass}
\end{aligned}
$$

REALITY CHECK   Ten moles of carbon would have a mass of about 120 g, and our answer is higher than this. The units (g/mol) are correct, and the answer is reported to the correct number of significant figures (to two decimal places).

b. Where Are We Going?

We want to determine the number of moles of juglone in a sample with mass of 1.56 g.

What Do We Know?

- From part a, we know that the molar mass of juglone is 174.1 g/mol.

- We have 1.56 g of juglone.

How Do We Get There?

The mass of 1 mole of this compound is 174.1 g, so 1.56 g is much less than a mole. We can determine the exact fraction of a mole by using the equivalence statement

$$1 \text{ mol} = 174.1 \text{ g juglone}$$

to derive the appropriate conversion factor:

$$1.56 \text{ g juglone} \times \frac{1 \text{ mol juglone}}{174.1 \text{ g juglone}} = 0.00896 \text{ mol juglone}$$
$$= 8.96 \times 10^{-3} \text{ mol juglone}$$

$$1.56 \text{ g juglone} \quad \times \frac{1 \text{ mol}}{174.1 \text{ g}} \quad \Rightarrow \quad 8.96 \times 10^{-3} \text{ mol juglone}$$

REALITY CHECK   The mass of 1 mole of juglone is 174.1 g, so 1.56 g is much less than 1 mole. Our answer has units of mol, and the number of significant figures in our answer is three, as required by the initial mass of 1.56 g. ∎

EXAMPLE 8.8   Calculating Number of Molecules

Isopentyl acetate, $C_7H_{14}O_2$, the compound responsible for the scent of bananas, can be produced commercially. Interestingly, bees release about 1 μg (1×10^{-6} g) of this compound when they sting. This attracts other bees, which then join the attack. How many moles and how many molecules of isopentyl acetate are released in a typical bee sting?

SOLUTION

Where Are We Going?

We want to determine the number of moles and the number of molecules of isopentyl acetate in a sample with mass of 1×10^{-6} g.

What Do We Know?

- The formula for isopentyl acetate is $C_7H_{14}O_2$.
- We know the atomic masses of carbon (12.01 g/mol), hydrogen (1.008 g/mol), and oxygen (16.00 g/mol).
- The mass of isopentyl acetate is 1×10^{-6} g.
- There are 6.022×10^{23} molecules in 1 mol.

How Do We Get There?

We are given a mass of isopentyl acetate and want the number of molecules, so we must first compute the molar mass.

$$7 \text{ mol C} \times 12.01 \frac{g}{\text{mol}} = 84.07 \text{ g C}$$

$$14 \text{ mol H} \times 1.008 \frac{g}{\text{mol}} = 14.11 \text{ g H}$$

$$2 \text{ mol O} \times 16.00 \frac{g}{\text{mol}} = \underline{32.00 \text{ g O}}$$

$$\text{Molar mass} = 130.18 \text{ g}$$

This means that 1 mole of isopentyl acetate (6.022×10^{23} molecules) has a mass of 130.18 g.

Next we determine the number of moles of isopentyl acetate in 1 μg, which is 1×10^{-6} g. To do this, we use the equivalence statement

$$1 \text{ mol isopentyl acetate} = 130.18 \text{ g isopentyl acetate}$$

which yields the conversion factor we need:

$$1 \times 10^{-6} \text{ g } C_7H_{14}O_2 \times \frac{1 \text{ mol } C_7H_{14}O_2}{130.18 \text{ g } C_7H_{14}O_2} = 8 \times 10^{-9} \text{ mol } C_7H_{14}O_2$$

Using the equivalence statement 1 mol = 6.022×10^{23} units, we can determine the number of molecules:

$$8 \times 10^{-9} \text{ mol } C_7H_{14}O_2 \times \frac{6.022 \times 10^{23} \text{ molecules}}{1 \text{ mol } C_7H_{14}O_2} = 5 \times 10^{15} \text{ molecules}$$

This very large number of molecules is released in each bee sting.

REALITY CHECK   The mass of isopentyl acetate released in each sting (1×10^{-6} g) is much less than the mass of 1 mole of $C_7H_{14}O_2$, so the number of moles should be less than 1 mol, and it is (8×10^{-9} mol). The number of molecules should be much less than 6.022×10^{23}, and it is (5×10^{15} molecules).

Our answers have the proper units, and the number of significant figures in our answer is one, as required by the initial mass.

(Self-Check)   **EXERCISE 8.6**   The substance Teflon, the slippery coating on many frying pans, is made from the C_2F_4 molecule. Calculate the number of C_2F_4 units present in 135 g of Teflon.

See Problems 8.39 and 8.40. ∎

8.6 Percent Composition of Compounds

OBJECTIVE: To learn to find the mass percent of an element in a given compound.

So far we have discussed the composition of compounds in terms of the numbers of constituent atoms. It is often useful to know a compound's composition in terms of the *masses* of its elements. We can obtain this information from the formula of the compound by comparing the mass of each element present in 1 mole of the compound to the total mass of 1 mole of the compound. The mass fraction for each element is calculated as follows:

MATH SKILL BUILDER

$$\text{Percent} = \frac{\text{Part}}{\text{Whole}} \times 100\%$$

$$\text{Mass fraction for a given element} = \frac{\text{mass of the element present in 1 mole of compound}}{\text{mass of 1 mole of compound}}$$

The mass fraction is converted to *mass percent* by multiplying by 100%.

We will illustrate this concept using the compound ethanol, an alcohol obtained by fermenting the sugar in grapes, corn, and other fruits and grains. Ethanol is often added to gasoline as an octane enhancer to form a fuel called gasohol. The added ethanol has the effect of increasing the octane of the gasoline and also lowering the carbon monoxide in automobile exhaust.

The formula for ethanol is written C_2H_5OH, although you might expect it to be written simply as C_2H_6O.

Note from its formula that each molecule of ethanol contains two carbon atoms, six hydrogen atoms, and one oxygen atom. This means that each mole of ethanol contains 2 moles of carbon atoms, 6 moles of hydrogen atoms, and 1 mole of oxygen atoms. We calculate the mass of each element present and the molar mass for ethanol as follows:

$$\text{Mass of C} = 2 \text{ mol} \times 12.01 \frac{g}{mol} = 24.02 \text{ g}$$

$$\text{Mass of H} = 6 \text{ mol} \times 1.008 \frac{g}{mol} = 6.048 \text{ g}$$

$$\text{Mass of O} = 1 \text{ mol} \times 16.00 \frac{g}{mol} = 16.00 \text{ g}$$

$$\text{Mass of 1 mol } C_2H_5OH = \overline{46.07 \text{ g}} = \text{molar mass}$$

The **mass percent** (sometimes called the weight percent) of carbon in ethanol can be computed by comparing the mass of carbon in 1 mole of ethanol with the total mass of 1 mole of ethanol and multiplying the result by 100%.

$$\text{Mass percent of C} = \frac{\text{mass of C in 1 mol } C_2H_5OH}{\text{mass of 1 mol } C_2H_5OH} \times 100\%$$

$$= \frac{24.02 \text{ g}}{46.07 \text{ g}} \times 100\% = 52.14\%$$

That is, ethanol contains 52.14% by mass of carbon. The mass percents of hydrogen and oxygen in ethanol are obtained in a similar manner.

$$\text{Mass percent of H} = \frac{\text{mass of H in 1 mol } C_2H_5OH}{\text{mass of 1 mol } C_2H_5OH} \times 100\%$$

$$= \frac{6.048 \text{ g}}{46.07 \text{ g}} \times 100\% = 13.13\%$$

MATH SKILL BUILDER
Sometimes, because of rounding-off effects, the sum of the mass percents in a compound is not exactly 100%.

$$\text{Mass percent of O} = \frac{\text{mass of O in 1 mol } C_2H_5OH}{\text{mass of 1 mol } C_2H_5OH} \times 100\%$$

$$= \frac{16.00 \text{ g}}{46.07 \text{ g}} \times 100\% = 34.73\%$$

The mass percents of all the elements in a compound add up to 100%, although rounding-off effects may produce a small deviation. Adding up the percentages is a good way to check the calculations. In this case, the sum of the mass percents is 52.14% + 13.13% + 34.73% = 100.00%.

EXAMPLE 8.9   **Calculating Mass Percent**

Carvone is a substance that occurs in two forms, both of which have the same molecular formula ($C_{10}H_{14}O$) and molar mass. One type of carvone gives caraway seeds their characteristic smell; the other is responsible for the smell of spearmint oil. Compute the mass percent of each element in carvone.

SOLUTION

Where Are We Going?

We want to determine the mass percent of each element in carvone.

What Do We Know?

- The formula for carvone is $C_{10}H_{14}O$.
- We know the atomic masses of carbon (12.01 g/mol), hydrogen (1.008 g/mol), and oxygen (16.00 g/mol).
- The mass of isopentyl acetate is 1×10^{-6} g.
- There are 6.022×10^{23} molecules in 1 mole.

What Do We Need To Know?

- The mass of each element (we'll use 1 mol carvone)
- Molar mass of carvone

How Do We Get There?

Because the formula for carvone is $C_{10}H_{14}O$, the masses of the various elements in 1 mole of carvone are

$$\text{Mass of C in 1 mol} = 10 \text{ mol} \times 12.01 \frac{g}{mol} = 120.1 \text{ g}$$

$$\text{Mass of H in 1 mol} = 14 \text{ mol} \times 1.008 \frac{g}{mol} = 14.11 \text{ g}$$

$$\text{Mass of O in 1 mol} = 1 \text{ mol} \times 16.00 \frac{g}{mol} = \underline{16.00 \text{ g}}$$

$$\text{Mass of 1 mol } C_{10}H_{14}O = 150.21 \text{ g}$$
$$\text{Molar mass} = 150.2 \text{ g}$$

(rounding to the correct number of significant figures)

MATH SKILL BUILDER
The 120.1 limits the sum to one decimal place.

Next we find the fraction of the total mass contributed by each element and convert it to a percentage.

$$\text{Mass percent of C} = \frac{120.1 \text{ g C}}{150.2 \text{ g } C_{10}H_{14}O} \times 100\% = 79.96\%$$

$$\text{Mass percent of H} = \frac{14.11 \text{ g H}}{150.2 \text{ g } C_{10}H_{14}O} \times 100\% = 9.394\%$$

$$\text{Mass percent of O} = \frac{16.00 \text{ g O}}{150.2 \text{ g } C_{10}H_{14}O} \times 100\% = 10.65\%$$

REALITY CHECK   Add the individual mass percent values—they should total 100% within a small range due to rounding off. In this case, the percentages add up to 100.00%.

Self-Check EXERCISE 8.7   Penicillin, an important antibiotic (antibacterial agent), was discovered accidentally by the Scottish bacteriologist Alexander Fleming in 1928, although he was never able to isolate it as a pure compound. This and similar antibiotics have saved millions of lives that would otherwise have been lost to infections. Penicillin, like many of the molecules produced by living systems, is a large molecule containing many atoms. One type of penicillin, penicillin F, has the formula $C_{14}H_{20}N_2SO_4$. Compute the mass percent of each element in this compound.

See Problems 8.45 through 8.50. ■

8.7   Formulas of Compounds

OBJECTIVE: To understand the meaning of empirical formulas of compounds.

Assume that you have mixed two solutions, and a solid product (a precipitate) forms. How can you find out what the solid is? What is its formula? There are several possible approaches you can take to answering these questions. For example, we saw in Chapter 7 that we can usually predict the identity of a precipitate formed when two solutions are mixed in a reaction of this type if we know some facts about the solubilities of ionic compounds.

However, although an experienced chemist can often predict the product expected in a chemical reaction, the only sure way to identify the product is to perform experiments. Usually we compare the physical properties of the product to the properties of known compounds.

Sometimes a chemical reaction gives a product that has never been obtained before. In such a case, a chemist determines what compound has been formed by determining which elements are present and how much of each. These data can be used to obtain the formula of the compound. In Section 8.6 we used the formula of the compound to determine the mass of each element present in a mole of the compound. To obtain the formula of an unknown compound, we do the opposite. That is, we use the measured masses of the elements present to determine the formula.

Recall that the formula of a compound represents the relative numbers of the various types of atoms present. For example, the molecular formula CO_2 tells us that for each carbon atom there are two oxygen atoms in each molecule of carbon dioxide. So to determine the formula of a substance we need to count the atoms. As we have seen in this chapter, we can do this by weighing. Suppose we know that a compound contains only the elements carbon, hydrogen, and oxygen, and we weigh out a 0.2015-g sample for analysis. Using methods we will not discuss here, we find that this 0.2015-g sample of compound contains 0.0806 g of carbon, 0.01353 g of hydrogen, and 0.1074 g of oxygen. We have just learned how to convert these masses to numbers of atoms by using the atomic mass of each element. We begin by converting to moles.

Carbon

$$(0.0806 \text{ g C}) \times \frac{1 \text{ mol C atoms}}{12.01 \text{ g C}} = 0.00671 \text{ mol C atoms}$$

Hydrogen

$$(0.01353 \text{ g H}) \times \frac{1 \text{ mol H atoms}}{1.008 \text{ g H}} = 0.01342 \text{ mol H atoms}$$

Oxygen

$$(0.1074 \text{ g O}) \times \frac{1 \text{ mol O atoms}}{16.00 \text{ g O}} = 0.006713 \text{ mol O atoms}$$

Let's review what we have established. We now know that 0.2015 g of the compound contains 0.00671 mole of C atoms, 0.01342 mole of H atoms, and 0.006713 mole of O atoms. Because 1 mol is 6.022×10^{23}, these quantities can be converted to actual numbers of atoms.

Carbon

$$(0.00671 \text{ mol C atoms}) \frac{(6.022 \times 10^{23} \text{ C atoms})}{1 \text{ mol C atoms}} = 4.04 \times 10^{21} \text{ C atoms}$$

Hydrogen

$$(0.01342 \text{ mol H atoms}) \frac{(6.022 \times 10^{23} \text{ H atoms})}{1 \text{ mol H atoms}} = 8.08 \times 10^{21} \text{ H atoms}$$

Oxygen

$$(0.006713 \text{ mol O atoms}) \frac{(6.022 \times 10^{23} \text{ O atoms})}{1 \text{ mol O atoms}} = 4.043 \times 10^{21} \text{ O atoms}$$

These are the numbers of the various types of atoms *in 0.2015 g of compound.* What do these numbers tell us about the formula of the compound? Note the following:

1. The compound contains the same number of C and O atoms.

2. There are twice as many H atoms as C atoms or O atoms.

We can represent this information by the formula CH_2O, which expresses the *relative* numbers of C, H, and O atoms present. Is this the true formula for the compound? In other words, is the compound made up of CH_2O molecules? It may be. However, it might also be made up of $C_2H_4O_2$ molecules, $C_3H_6O_3$ molecules, $C_4H_8O_4$ molecules, $C_5H_{10}O_5$ molecules, $C_6H_{12}O_6$ molecules, and so on. Note that each of these molecules has the required 1:2:1 ratio of carbon to hydrogen to oxygen atoms (the ratio shown by experiment to be present in the compound).

When we break a compound down into its separate elements and "count" the atoms present, we learn only the ratio of atoms—we get only the *relative* numbers of atoms. The formula of a compound that expresses the smallest whole-number ratio of the atoms present is called the **empirical formula** or *simplest formula.* A compound that contains the molecules $C_4H_8O_4$ has the same empirical formula as a compound that contains $C_6H_{12}O_6$ molecules. The empirical formula for both is CH_2O. The actual formula of a compound—the one that gives the composition of the molecules that are present—is called the **molecular formula.** The sugar called glucose is made of molecules with the molecular formula $C_6H_{12}O_6$ (Figure 8.4). Note from the molecular formula for glucose that the empirical formula is CH_2O. We can represent the molecular formula as a multiple (by 6) of the empirical formula:

$$C_6H_{12}O_6 = (CH_2O)_6$$

In the next section, we will explore in more detail how to calculate the empirical formula for a compound from the relative masses of the elements present. As we will see in Sections 8.8 and 8.9, we must know the molar mass of a compound to determine its molecular formula.

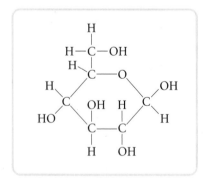

Figure 8.4

The glucose molecule. The molecular formula is $C_6H_{12}O_6$, as can be verified by counting the atoms. The empirical formula for glucose is CH_2O.

EXAMPLE 8.10 | Determining Empirical Formulas

In each case below, the molecular formula for a compound is given. Determine the empirical formula for each compound.

    a. C_6H_6. This is the molecular formula for benzene, a liquid commonly used in industry as a starting material for many important products.

    b. $C_{12}H_4Cl_4O_2$. This is the molecular formula for a substance commonly called dioxin, a powerful poison that sometimes occurs as a by-product in the production of other chemicals.

    c. $C_6H_{16}N_2$. This is the molecular formula for one of the reactants used to produce nylon.

SOLUTION

    a. $C_6H_6 = (CH)_6$; CH is the empirical formula. Each subscript in the empirical formula is multiplied by 6 to obtain the molecular formula.

    b. $C_{12}H_4Cl_4O_2$; $C_{12}H_4Cl_4O_2 = (C_6H_2Cl_2O)_2$; $C_6H_2Cl_2O$ is the empirical formula. Each subscript in the empirical formula is multiplied by 2 to obtain the molecular formula.

    c. $C_6H_{16}N_2 = (C_3H_8N)_2$; C_3H_8N is the empirical formula. Each subscript in the empirical formula is multiplied by 2 to obtain the molecular formula. ■

8.8 Calculation of Empirical Formulas

OBJECTIVE: To learn to calculate empirical formulas.

As we said in the previous section, one of the most important things we can learn about a new compound is its chemical formula. To calculate the empirical formula of a compound, we first determine the relative masses of the various elements that are present.

One way to do this is to measure the masses of elements that react to form the compound. For example, suppose we weigh out 0.2636 g of pure nickel metal into a crucible and heat this metal in the air so that the nickel can react with oxygen to form a nickel oxide compound. After the sample has cooled, we weigh it again and find its mass to be 0.3354 g. The gain in mass is due to the oxygen that reacts with the nickel to form the oxide. Therefore, the mass of oxygen present in the compound is the total mass of the product minus the mass of the nickel:

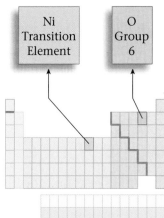

Total mass of nickel oxide	−	Mass of nickel originally present	=	Mass of oxygen that reacted with the nickel

or   0.3354 g   −   0.2636 g   =   0.0718 g

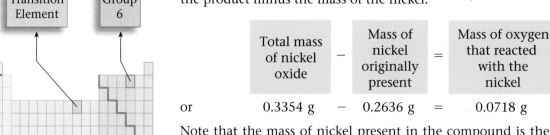

Note that the mass of nickel present in the compound is the nickel metal originally weighed out. So we know that the nickel oxide contains 0.2636 g of nickel and 0.0718 g of oxygen. What is the empirical formula of this compound?

To answer this question we must convert the masses to numbers of atoms, using atomic masses:

Four significant figures allowed.

$$0.2636 \text{ g Ni} \times \frac{1 \text{ mol Ni atoms}}{58.69 \text{ g Ni}} = 0.004491 \text{ mol Ni atoms}$$

Three significant figures allowed.

$$0.0718 \text{ g O} \times \frac{1 \text{ mol O atoms}}{16.00 \text{ g O}} = 0.00449 \text{ mol O atoms}$$

These mole quantities represent numbers of atoms (remember that a mole of atoms is 6.022×10^{23} atoms). It is clear from the moles of atoms that the compound contains an equal number of Ni and O atoms, so the formula is NiO. This is the *empirical formula;* it expresses the smallest whole-number (integer) ratio of atoms:

$$\frac{0.004491 \text{ mol Ni atoms}}{0.00449 \text{ mol O atoms}} = \frac{1 \text{ Ni}}{1 \text{ O}}$$

That is, this compound contains equal numbers of nickel atoms and oxygen atoms. We say the ratio of nickel atoms to oxygen atoms is 1:1 (1 to 1).

EXAMPLE 8.11 | Calculating Empirical Formulas

An oxide of aluminum is formed by the reaction of 4.151 g of aluminum with 3.692 g of oxygen. Calculate the empirical formula for this compound.

SOLUTION

Where Are We Going?

We want to determine the empirical formula for the aluminum oxide, Al_xO_y. That is, we want to solve for x and y.

What Do We Know?

- The compound contains 4.151 g of aluminum and 3.692 g of oxygen.

- We know the atomic masses of aluminum (26.98 g/mol), and oxygen (16.00 g/mol).

What Do We Need To Know?

- x and y represent moles of atoms in 1 mole of the compound, so we need to determine the relative number of moles of Al and O.

How Do We Get There?

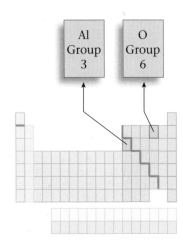

We need to know the relative numbers of each type of atom to write the formula, so we must convert these masses to moles of atoms to get the empirical formula. We carry out the conversion by using the atomic masses of the elements.

$$4.151 \text{ g Al} \times \frac{1 \text{ mol Al}}{26.98 \text{ g Al}} = 0.1539 \text{ mol Al atoms}$$

$$3.692 \text{ g O} \times \frac{1 \text{ mol O}}{16.00 \text{ g O}} = 0.2308 \text{ mol O atoms}$$

Because chemical formulas use only whole numbers, we next find the integer (whole-number) ratio of the atoms. To do this we start by dividing both numbers by the smallest of the two. This converts the smallest number to 1.

$$\frac{0.1539 \text{ mol Al}}{0.1539} = 1.000 \text{ mol Al atoms}$$

$$\frac{0.2308 \text{ mol O}}{0.1539} = 1.500 \text{ mol O atoms}$$

Note that dividing both numbers of moles of atoms by the *same* number does not change the *relative* numbers of oxygen and aluminum atoms. That is,

$$\frac{0.2308 \text{ mol O}}{0.1539 \text{ mol Al}} = \frac{1.500 \text{ mol O}}{1.000 \text{ mol Al}}$$

Thus we know that the compound contains 1.500 moles of O atoms for every 1.000 mole of Al atoms, or, in terms of individual atoms, we could say that the compound contains 1.500 O atoms for every 1.000 Al atom. However, because only *whole* atoms combine to form compounds, we must find a set of *whole numbers* to express the empirical formula. When we multiply both 1.000 and 1.500 by 2, we get the integers we need.

$$1.500 \text{ O} \times 2 = 3.000 = 3 \text{ O atoms}$$
$$1.000 \text{ Al} \times 2 = 2.000 = 2 \text{ Al atoms}$$

Therefore, this compound contains two Al atoms for every three O atoms, and the empirical formula is Al_2O_3. Note that the *ratio* of atoms in this compound is given by each of the following fractions:

$$\frac{0.2308 \text{ O}}{0.1539 \text{ Al}} = \frac{1.500 \text{ O}}{1.000 \text{ Al}} = \frac{\frac{3}{2} \text{O}}{1 \text{ Al}} = \frac{3 \text{ O}}{2 \text{ Al}}$$

The smallest whole-number ratio corresponds to the subscripts of the empirical formula, Al_2O_3.

REALITY CHECK   The values for x and y are whole numbers. ■

Sometimes the relative numbers of moles you get when you calculate an empirical formula will turn out to be nonintegers, as was the case in Example 8.11. When this happens, you must convert to the appropriate whole numbers. This is done by multiplying all the numbers by the same small integer, which can be found by trial and error. The multiplier needed is almost always between 1 and 6. We will now summarize what we have learned about calculating empirical formulas.

We might express these data as:

$Al_{1.000 \text{ mol}}O_{1.500 \text{ mol}}$

or

$Al_{2.000 \text{ mol}}O_{3.000 \text{ mol}}$

or

Al_2O_3

Steps for Determining the Empirical Formula of a Compound

Step 1 Obtain the mass of each element present (in grams).

Step 2 Determine the number of moles of each type of atom present.

Step 3 Divide the number of moles of each element by the smallest number of moles to convert the smallest number to 1. If all of the numbers so obtained are integers (whole numbers), these are the subscripts in the empirical formula. If one or more of these numbers are not integers, go on to step 4.

Step 4 Multiply the numbers you derived in step 3 by the smallest integer that will convert all of them to whole numbers. This set of whole numbers represents the subscripts in the empirical formula.

EXAMPLE 8.12	Calculating Empirical Formulas for Binary Compounds

When a 0.3546-g sample of vanadium metal is heated in air, it reacts with oxygen to achieve a final mass of 0.6330 g. Calculate the empirical formula of this vanadium oxide.

SOLUTION

Where Are We Going?

We want to determine the empirical formula for the vanadium oxide, V_xO_y. That is, we want to solve for x and y.

What Do We Know?

- The compound contains 0.3546 g of vanadium and has a total mass of 0.6330 g.

- We know the atomic masses of vanadium (50.94 g/mol) and oxygen (16.00 g/mol).

What Do We Need To Know?

- We need to know the mass of oxygen in the sample.

- x and y represent moles of atoms in 1 mole of the compound, so we need to determine the relative number of moles of V and O.

How Do We Get There?

Step 1   All the vanadium that was originally present will be found in the final compound, so we can calculate the mass of oxygen that reacted by taking the following difference:

$$\begin{array}{ccccc} \text{Total mass} & - & \text{Mass of} & = & \text{Mass of} \\ \text{of compound} & & \text{vanadium} & & \text{oxygen} \\ & & \text{in compound} & & \text{in compound} \\ 0.6330 \text{ g} & - & 0.3546 \text{ g} & = & 0.2784 \text{ g} \end{array}$$

Step 2   Using the atomic masses (50.94 for V and 16.00 for O), we obtain

$$0.3546 \text{ g V} \times \frac{1 \text{ mol V atoms}}{50.94 \text{ g V}} = 0.006961 \text{ mol V atoms}$$

$$0.2784 \text{ g O} \times \frac{1 \text{ mol O atoms}}{16.00 \text{ g O}} = 0.01740 \text{ mol O atoms}$$

Step 3   Then we divide both numbers of moles by the smaller, 0.006961.

$$\frac{0.006961 \text{ mol V atoms}}{0.006961} = 1.000 \text{ mol V atoms}$$

$$\frac{0.01740 \text{ mol O atoms}}{0.006961} = 2.500 \text{ mol O atoms}$$

Because one of these numbers (2.500) is not an integer, we go on to step 4.

MATH SKILL BUILDER
$V_{1.000}O_{2.500}$ becomes V_2O_5.

Step 4   We note that $2 \times 2.500 = 5.000$ and $2 \times 1.000 = 2.000$, so we multiply both numbers by 2 to get integers.

$$2 \times 1.000 \text{ V} = 2.000 \text{ V} = 2 \text{ V}$$
$$2 \times 2.500 \text{ O} = 5.000 \text{ O} = 5 \text{ O}$$

This compound contains 2 V atoms for every 5 O atoms, and the empirical formula is V_2O_5.

REALITY CHECK   The values for x and y are whole numbers.

Self-Check   **EXERCISE 8.8**   In a lab experiment it was observed that 0.6884 g of lead combines with 0.2356 g of chlorine to form a binary compound. Calculate the empirical formula of this compound.

See Problems 8.61, 8.63, 8.65, and 8.66. ■

The same procedures we have used for binary compounds also apply to compounds containing three or more elements, as Example 8.13 illustrates.

EXAMPLE 8.13 | Calculating Empirical Formulas for Compounds Containing Three or More Elements

A sample of lead arsenate, an insecticide used against the potato beetle, contains 1.3813 g of lead, 0.00672 g of hydrogen, 0.4995 g of arsenic, and 0.4267 g of oxygen. Calculate the empirical formula for lead arsenate.

SOLUTION

Where Are We Going?

We want to determine the empirical formula for lead arsenate, $Pb_aH_bAs_cO_d$. That is, we want to solve for a, b, c, and d.

What Do We Know?

- The compound contains 1.3813 g of Pb, 0.00672 g of H, 0.4995 g of As, and 0.4267 g of O.

- We know the atomic masses of lead (207.2 g/mol), hydrogen (1.008 g/mol), arsenic (74.92 g/mol), and oxygen (16.00 g/mol).

What Do We Need To Know?

- a, b, c, and d represent moles of atoms in 1 mole of the compound, so we need to determine the relative number of moles of Pb, H, As, and O.

How Do We Get There?

Step 1   The compound contains 1.3813 g Pb, 0.00672 g H, 0.4995 g As, and 0.4267 g O.

Step 2   We use the atomic masses of the elements present to calculate the moles of each.

$$1.3813 \text{ g Pb} \times \frac{1 \text{ mol Pb}}{207.2 \text{ g Pb}} = 0.006667 \text{ mol Pb}$$

$$0.00672 \text{ g H} \times \frac{1 \text{ mol H}}{1.008 \text{ g H}} = 0.00667 \text{ mol H}$$

$$0.4995 \text{ g As} \times \frac{1 \text{ mol As}}{74.92 \text{ g As}} = 0.006667 \text{ mol As}$$

$$0.4267 \text{ g O} \times \frac{1 \text{ mol O}}{16.00 \text{ g O}} = 0.02667 \text{ mol O}$$

Step 3 Now we divide by the smallest number of moles.

$$\frac{0.006667 \text{ mol Pb}}{0.006667} = 1.000 \text{ mol Pb}$$

$$\frac{0.00667 \text{ mol H}}{0.006667} = 1.00 \text{ mol H}$$

$$\frac{0.006667 \text{ mol As}}{0.006667} = 1.000 \text{ mol As}$$

$$\frac{0.02667 \text{ mol O}}{0.006667} = 4.000 \text{ mol O}$$

The numbers of moles are all whole numbers, so the empirical formula is $PbHAsO_4$.

REALITY CHECK   The values for *a*, *b*, *c*, and *d* are whole numbers.

___

Self-Check   EXERCISE 8.9   Sevin, the commercial name for an insecticide used to protect crops such as cotton, vegetables, and fruit, is made from carbamic acid. A chemist analyzing a sample of carbamic acid finds 0.8007 g of carbon, 0.9333 g of nitrogen, 0.2016 g of hydrogen, and 2.133 g of oxygen. Determine the empirical formula for carbamic acid.

See Problems 8.57 and 8.59. ■

When a compound is analyzed to determine the relative amounts of the elements present, the results are usually given in terms of percentages by masses of the various elements. In Section 8.6 we learned to calculate the percent composition of a compound from its formula. Now we will do the opposite. Given the percent composition, we will calculate the empirical formula.

MATH SKILL BUILDER
Percent by mass for a given element means the grams of that element in 100 g of the compound.

To understand this procedure, you must understand the meaning of *percent*. Remember that percent means parts of a given component per 100 parts of the total mixture. For example, if a given compound is 15% carbon (by mass), the compound contains 15 g of carbon per 100 g of compound.

Calculation of the empirical formula of a compound when one is given its percent composition is illustrated in Example 8.14.

EXAMPLE 8.14   Calculating Empirical Formulas from Percent Composition

Cisplatin, the common name for a platinum compound that is used to treat cancerous tumors, has the composition (mass percent) 65.02% platinum, 9.34% nitrogen, 2.02% hydrogen, and 23.63% chlorine. Calculate the empirical formula for cisplatin.

SOLUTION

Where Are We Going?

We want to determine the empirical formula for cisplatin, $Pt_aN_bH_cCl_d$. That is, we want to solve for *a*, *b*, *c*, and *d*.

What Do We Know?

- The compound has the composition (mass percent) 65.02% Pt, 9.34% N, 2.02% H, and 23.63% Cl.

- We know the atomic masses of platinum (195.1 g/mol), nitrogen (14.01 g/mol), hydrogen (1.008 g/mol), and chlorine (35.45 g/mol).

What Do We Need To Know?

- *a, b, c,* and *d* represent moles of atoms in 1 mole of the compound, so we need to determine the relative number of moles of Pt, N, H, and Cl.

- We have mass percent data, and to get to the number of moles we need to know the mass of each element (g) in the sample.

How Do We Get There?

Step 1   Determine how many grams of each element are present in 100 g of compound. Cisplatin is 65.02% platinum (by mass), which means there is 65.02 g of platinum (Pt) per 100.00 g of compound. Similarly, a 100.00-g sample of cisplatin contains 9.34 g of nitrogen (N), 2.02 g of hydrogen (H), and 26.63 g of chlorine (Cl).

If we have a 100.00-g sample of cisplatin, we have 65.02 g Pt, 9.34 g N, 2.02 g H, and 23.63 g Cl.

Step 2   Determine the number of moles of each type of atom. We use the atomic masses to calculate moles.

$$65.02 \text{ g Pt} \times \frac{1 \text{ mol Pt}}{195.1 \text{ g Pt}} = 0.3333 \text{ mol Pt}$$

$$9.34 \text{ g N} \times \frac{1 \text{ mol N}}{14.01 \text{ g N}} = 0.667 \text{ mol N}$$

$$2.02 \text{ g H} \times \frac{1 \text{ mol H}}{1.008 \text{ g H}} = 2.00 \text{ mol H}$$

$$23.63 \text{ g Cl} \times \frac{1 \text{ mol Cl}}{35.45 \text{ g Cl}} = 0.6666 \text{ mol Cl}$$

Step 3   Divide through by the smallest number of moles.

$$\frac{0.3333 \text{ mol Pt}}{0.3333} = 1.000 \text{ mol Pt}$$

$$\frac{0.667 \text{ mol N}}{0.3333} = 2.00 \text{ mol N}$$

$$\frac{2.00 \text{ mol H}}{0.3333} = 6.01 \text{ mol H}$$

$$\frac{0.6666 \text{ mol Cl}}{0.3333} = 2.000 \text{ mol Cl}$$

The empirical formula for cisplatin is $PtN_2H_6Cl_2$. Note that the number for hydrogen is slightly greater than 6 because of rounding-off effects.

REALITY CHECK   The values for *a, b, c,* and *d* are whole numbers.

Self-Check **EXERCISE 8.10**   The most common form of nylon (Nylon-6) is 63.68% carbon, 12.38% nitrogen, 9.80% hydrogen, and 14.14% oxygen. Calculate the empirical formula for Nylon-6.

See Problems 8.67 through 8.74. ∎

Note from Example 8.14 that once the percentages are converted to masses, this example is the same as earlier examples in which the masses were given directly.

8.9 Calculation of Molecular Formulas

OBJECTIVE: To learn to calculate the molecular formula of a compound, given its empirical formula and molar mass.

If we know the composition of a compound in terms of the masses (or mass percentages) of the elements present, we can calculate the empirical formula but not the molecular formula. For reasons that will become clear as we consider Example 8.15, to obtain the molecular formula we must know the molar mass. In this section we will consider compounds where both the percent composition and the molar mass are known.

EXAMPLE 8.15 | Calculating Molecular Formulas

A white powder is analyzed and found to have an empirical formula of P_2O_5. The compound has a molar mass of 283.88 g. What is the compound's molecular formula?

SOLUTION

Where Are We Going?

We want to determine the molecular formula (P_xO_y) for a compound. That is, we want to solve for x and y.

What Do We Know?

• The empirical formula of the compound is P_2O_5.

• The molar mass of the compound is 283.88 g/mol.

• We know the atomic masses of phosphorus (30.97 g/mol) and oxygen (16.00 g/mol).

• The molecular formula contains a whole number of empirical formula units. So, the molecular formula will be $P_{2x}O_{5y}$.

What Do We Need To Know?

• We need to know the empirical formula mass.

How Do We Get There?

To obtain the molecular formula, we must compare the empirical formula mass to the molar mass. The empirical formula mass for P_2O_5 is the mass of 1 mole of P_2O_5 units.

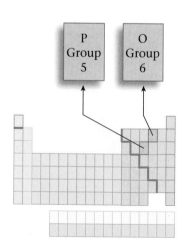

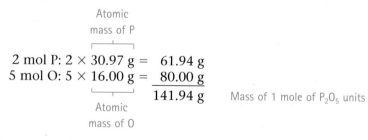

$$\begin{array}{ll} \text{2 mol P: } 2 \times 30.97 \text{ g} = & 61.94 \text{ g} \\ \text{5 mol O: } 5 \times 16.00 \text{ g} = & \underline{80.00 \text{ g}} \\ & 141.94 \text{ g} \end{array}$$

Mass of 1 mole of P_2O_5 units

Recall that the molecular formula contains a whole number of empirical formula units. That is,

Molecular formula = (empirical formula)$_n$

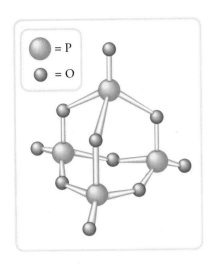

Figure 8.5

The structure of P_4O_{10} as a "ball-and-stick" model. This compound has a great affinity for water and is often used as a desiccant, or drying agent.

= P

= O

where n is a small whole number. Now, because

$$\text{Molecular formula} = n \times \text{empirical formula}$$

then

$$\text{Molar mass} = n \times \text{empirical formula mass}$$

Solving for n gives

$$n = \frac{\text{molar mass}}{\text{empirical formula mass}}$$

Thus, to determine the molecular formula, we first divide the molar mass by the empirical formula mass. This tells us how many empirical formula masses there are in one molar mass.

$$\frac{\text{Molar mass}}{\text{Empirical formula mass}} = \frac{283.88 \text{ g}}{141.94 \text{ g}} = 2$$

This result means that $n = 2$ for this compound, so the molecular formula consists of two empirical formula units, and the molecular formula is $(P_2O_5)_2$, or P_4O_{10}. The structure of this interesting compound is shown in Figure 8.5.

REALITY CHECK   The values for x and y are whole numbers. Also, the ratio of P:O in the molecular formula (4:10) is 2:5.

Self-Check EXERCISE 8.11   A compound used as an additive for gasoline to help prevent engine knock shows the following percent composition:

71.65% Cl   24.27% C   4.07% H

The molar mass is known to be 98.96 g. Determine the empirical formula and the molecular formula for this compound.

See Problems 8.81 and 8.82. ■

It is important to realize that the molecular formula is always an integer multiple of the empirical formula. For example, the sugar glucose (see Figure 8.4) has the empirical formula CH_2O and the molecular formula $C_6H_{12}O_6$. In this case there are six empirical formula units in each glucose molecule:

$$(CH_2O)_6 = C_6H_{12}O_6$$

In general, we can represent the molecular formula in terms of the empirical formula as follows:

$$(\text{Empirical formula})_n = \text{molecular formula}$$

where n is an integer. If $n = 1$, the molecular formula is the same as the empirical formula. For example, for carbon dioxide the empirical formula (CO_2) and the molecular formula (CO_2) are the same, so $n = 1$. On the other hand, for tetraphosphorus decoxide the empirical formula is P_2O_5 and the molecular formula is $P_4O_{10} = (P_2O_5)_2$. In this case $n = 2$.

Key Terms

atomic mass unit
(amu) (8.2)
average atomic mass (8.2)
mole (8.3)
Avogadro's number (8.3)

conceptual problem
solving (8.4)
molar mass (8.5)
mass percent (8.6)
empirical formula (8.7)
molecular formula (8.7)

tion of the compound. The molecular formula is the exact formula of the molecules present; it is always an integer multiple of the empirical formula. The diagram in the left column summarizes these different ways of expressing the same information.

Summary

1. We can count individual units by weighing if we know the average mass of the units. Thus, when we know the average mass of the atoms of an element as that element occurs in nature, we can calculate the number of atoms in any given sample of that element by weighing the sample.

2. A mole is a unit of measure equal to 6.022×10^{23}, which is called Avogadro's number. One mole of any substance contains 6.022×10^{23} units.

3. One mole of an element has a mass equal to the element's atomic mass expressed in grams. The molar mass of any compound is the mass (in grams) of 1 mole of the compound and is the sum of the masses of the component atoms.

4. Percent composition consists of the mass percent of each element in a compound:

$$\text{Mass percent} = \frac{\substack{\text{mass of a given element in} \\ \text{1 mole of compound}}}{\text{mass of 1 mole of compound}} \times 100\%$$

5. The empirical formula of a compound is the simplest whole-number ratio of the atoms present in the compound; it can be derived from the percent composi-

Active Learning Questions

These questions are designed to be considered by groups of students in class. Often these questions work well for introducing a particular topic in class.

1. In chemistry, what is meant by the term *mole?* What is the importance of the mole concept?

2. What is the difference between the empirical and molecular formulas of a compound? Can they ever be the same? Explain.

3. A substance A_2B is 60% A by mass. Calculate the percent B (by mass) for AB_2.

4. Give the formula for calcium phosphate and then answer the following questions:

   a. Calculate the percent composition of each of the elements in this compound.

   b. If you knew that there was 50.0 g of phosphorus in your sample, how many grams of calcium phosphate would you have? How many moles of calcium phosphate would this be? How many formula units of calcium phosphate?

5. How would you find the number of "chalk molecules" it takes to write your name on the board? Explain what you would need to do, and provide a sample calculation.

6. A 0.821-mol sample of a substance composed of diatomic molecules has a mass of 131.3 g. Identify this molecule.

7. How many molecules of water are there in a 10.0-g sample of water? How many hydrogen atoms are there in this sample?

8. What is the mass (in grams) of one molecule of ammonia?

9. Consider separate 100.0-g samples of each of the following: NH_3, N_2O, N_2H_4, HCN, HNO_3. Arrange these samples from largest mass of nitrogen to smallest mass of nitrogen and prove/explain your order.

10. A molecule has a mass of 4.65×10^{-23} g. Provide two possible chemical formulas for such a molecule.

11. Differentiate between the terms *atomic mass* and *molar mass*.

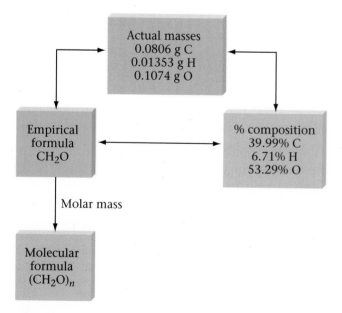

Actual masses
0.0806 g C
0.01353 g H
0.1074 g O

Empirical
formula
CH_2O

% composition
39.99% C
6.71% H
53.29% O

Molar mass

Molecular
formula
$(CH_2O)_n$

12. Consider Figure 4.19 in the text. Why is it that the formulas for ionic compound are always empirical formulas?

13. Why do we need to count atoms by weighing them?

14. The following claim is made in your text: 1 mole of marbles is enough to cover the entire earth to a depth of 50 miles.

    Provide mathematical support for this claim. Is it reasonably accurate?

15. Estimate the length of time it would take you to count to Avogadro's number. Provide mathematical support.

16. Suppose Avogadro's number was 1000 instead of 6.022×10^{23}. How, if at all, would this affect the relative masses on the periodic table? How, if at all, would this affect the absolute masses of the elements?

17. Estimate the number of atoms in your body and provide mathematical support. Because it is an estimate, it need not be exact, although you should choose your number wisely.

18. Consider separate equal mass samples of magnesium, zinc, and silver. Rank them from greatest to least number of atoms and support your answer.

19. You have a 20.0-g sample of silver metal. You are given 10.0 g of another metal and told that this sample contains twice the number of atoms as the sample of silver metal. Identify this metal.

20. How would you find the number of "ink molecules" it takes to write your name on a piece of paper with your pen? Explain what you would need to do, and provide a sample calculation.

21. True or false. The atom with the largest subscript in a formula is the atom with the largest percent by mass in the compound.

    If true, explain why with an example. If false, explain why and provide a counterexample. In either case, provide mathematical support.

VP 22. Which of the following compounds have the same empirical formulas?

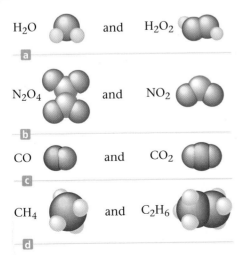

H_2O and H_2O_2

a

N_2O_4 and NO_2

b

CO   and CO_2

c

CH_4 and C_2H_6

d

VP 23. The percent by mass of nitrogen is 46.7% for a species containing only nitrogen and oxygen. Which of the following could be this species?

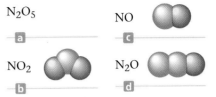

N_2O_5 NO

a   c

NO_2 N_2O

b   d

VP 24. Calculate the molar mass of the following substances.

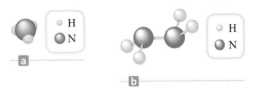

| ○ H |
| ● N |

a

| ○ H |
| ● N |

b

VP 25. Give the empirical formula for each of the compounds represented below.

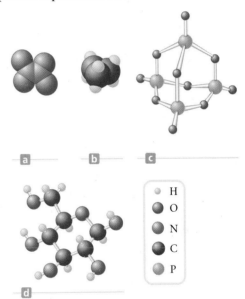

a   b   c

○	H
●	O
●	N
●	C
●	P

d

Questions and Problems*

8.1 Counting by Weighing

PROBLEMS

1. Merchants usually sell small nuts, washers, and bolts by weight (like jelly beans!) rather than by individually counting the items. Suppose a particular type of washer weighs 0.110 g on the average. What would 100 such washers weigh? How many washers would there be in 100. g of washers?

F 2. The Chemistry in Focus segment *Plastic That Talks and Listens!* discusses polyvinylidene difluoride (PVDF). What is the empirical formula of PVDF? Note: An empirical formula is the simplest whole-number ratio of atoms in a compound. This is discussed more fully in Sections 8.7 and 8.8 of your text.

*The element symbols and formulas are given in some problems but not in others to help you learn this necessary "vocabulary."

8.2 Atomic Masses: Counting Atoms by Weighing

QUESTIONS

3. Define the *amu*. What is one amu equivalent to in grams?

4. What do we mean by the *average* atomic mass of an element? What is "averaged" to arrive at this number?

PROBLEMS

5. Using the average atomic masses for each of the following elements (see the table inside the cover of this book), calculate the mass (in amu) of each of the following samples.

    a. 125 carbon atoms
    b. 5 million potassium atoms
    c. 1.04×10^{22} lithium atoms
    d. 1 atom of magnesium
    e. 3.011×10^{23} iodine atoms

6. Using the average atomic masses for each of the following elements (see the table inside the front cover of this book), calculate the number of atoms present in each of the following samples.

    a. 40.08 amu of calcium
    b. 919.5 amu of tungsten
    c. 549.4 amu of manganese
    d. 6345 amu of iodine
    e. 2072 amu of lead

7. What is the average atomic mass (in amu) of iron atoms? What would 299 iron atoms weigh? How many iron atoms are present in a sample of iron that has a mass of 5529.2 amu?

8. The atomic mass of tin is 118.7 amu. What would be the mass of 35 tin atoms? How many tin atoms are contained in a sample of tin that has a mass of 2967.5 amu?

8.3 The Mole

QUESTIONS

9. There are _____ iron atoms present in 55.85 g of iron.

10. There are 6.022×10^{23} aluminum atoms present in _____ g of aluminum.

PROBLEMS

11. Suppose you have a sample of sodium weighing 11.50 g. How many atoms of sodium are present in the sample? What mass of potassium would you need to have the same number of potassium atoms as there are sodium atoms in the sample of sodium?

12. Consider a sample of neon gas weighing 10.09 g. How many atoms of neon are present in the sample? What mass of helium gas would you need for the helium sample to contain the same number of atoms as the neon sample?

13. What mass of hydrogen contains the same number of atoms as 7.00 g of nitrogen?

14. What mass of cobalt contains the same number of atoms as 57.0 g of fluorine?

15. If an average sodium atom has a mass of 3.82×10^{-23} g, what is the mass of a magnesium atom in grams?

16. If an average aluminum atom has a mass of 4.48×10^{-23} g, what is the average mass of a carbon atom in grams?

17. Which has the smaller mass, 1 mole of He atoms or 4 moles of H atoms?

18. Which weighs less, 0.50 mole of neon atoms or 1.0 mole of boron atoms?

19. Use the average atomic masses given inside the front cover of this book to calculate the number of *moles* of the element present in each of the following samples.

    a. 4.95 g of neon
    b. 72.5 g of nickel
    c. 115 mg of silver
    d. 6.22 μg of uranium (μ is a standard abbreviation meaning "micro")
    e. 135 g of iodine

20. Use the average atomic masses given inside the front cover of this book to calculate the number of *moles* of the element present in each of the following samples.

    a. 66.50 g of fluorine atoms
    b. 401.2 mg of mercury
    c. 84.27 g of silicon
    d. 48.78 g of platinum
    e. 2431 g of magnesium
    f. 47.97 g of molybdenum

21. Use the average atomic masses given inside the front cover of this book to calculate the mass in grams of each of the following samples.

    a. 0.251 mole of lithium
    b. 1.51 moles of aluminum
    c. 8.75×10^{-2} moles of lead
    d. 125 moles of chromium
    e. 4.25×10^{3} moles of iron
    f. 0.000105 mole of magnesium

22. Use the average atomic masses given inside the front cover of this book to calculate the mass in grams of each of the following samples.

    a. 0.00552 mole of calcium
    b. 6.25 mmol of boron (1 mmol = $\frac{1}{1000}$ mole)
    c. 135 moles of aluminum
    d. 1.34×10^{-7} moles of barium
    e. 2.79 moles of phosphorus
    f. 0.0000997 mole of arsenic

23. Using the average atomic masses given inside the front cover of this book, calculate the number of *atoms* present in each of the following samples.

All even-numbered Questions and Problems have answers in the back of this book and solutions in the Solutions Guide.

a. 1.50 g of silver, Ag
b. 0.0015 mole of copper, Cu
c. 0.0015 g of copper, Cu
d. 2.00 kg of magnesium, Mg
e. 2.34 oz of calcium, Ca
f. 2.34 g of calcium, Ca
g. 2.34 moles of calcium, Ca

24. Using the average atomic masses given inside the front cover of this book, calculate the indicated quantities.

a. the mass in grams of 125 iron atoms
b. the mass in amu of 125 iron atoms
c. the number of moles of iron atoms in 125 g of iron
d. the mass in grams of 125 moles of iron
e. the number of iron atoms in 125 g of iron
f. the number of iron atoms in 125 moles of iron

8.5 Molar Mass

QUESTIONS

25. The _____ of a substance is the mass (in grams) of 1 mole of the substance.

26. Describe in your own words how the *molar mass* of a compound may be calculated.

PROBLEMS

27. Give the name and calculate the molar mass for each of the following substances.

a. H_3PO_4
b. Fe_2O_3
c. $NaClO_4$
d. $PbCl_2$
e. HBr
f. $Al(OH)_3$

28. Give the name and calculate the molar mass for each of the following substances.

a. $KHCO_3$
b. Hg_2Cl_2
c. H_2O_2
d. $BeCl_2$
e. $Al_2(SO_4)_3$
f. $KClO_3$

29. Write the formula and calculate the molar mass for each of the following substances.

a. barium chloride
b. aluminum nitrate
c. iron(II) chloride
d. sulfur dioxide
e. calcium acetate

30. Write the formula and calculate the molar mass for each of the following substances.

a. lithium perchlorate
b. sodium hydrogen sulfate
c. magnesium carbonate
d. aluminum bromide
e. chromium(III) sulfide

31. Calculate the number of *moles* of the indicated substance present in each of the following samples.

a. 21.4 mg of nitrogen dioxide
b. 1.56 g of copper(II) nitrate
c. 2.47 g of carbon disulfide
d. 5.04 g of aluminum sulfate
e. 2.99 g of lead(II) chloride
f. 62.4 g of calcium carbonate

32. Calculate the number of *moles* of the indicated substance present in each of the following samples.

a. 47.2 g of aluminum oxide
b. 1.34 kg of potassium bromide
c. 521 mg of germanium
d. 56.2 μg of uranium
e. 29.7 g of sodium acetate
f. 1.03 g of sulfur trioxide

33. Calculate the number of *moles* of the indicated substance in each of the following samples.

a. 41.5 g of $MgCl_2$
b. 135 mg of Li_2O
c. 1.21 kg of Cr
d. 62.5 g of H_2SO_4
e. 42.7 g of C_6H_6
f. 135 g of H_2O_2

34. Calculate the number of moles of the indicated substance present in each of the following samples.

a. 1.95×10^{-3} g of lithium carbonate
b. 4.23 kg of calcium chloride
c. 1.23 mg of strontium chloride
d. 4.75 g of calcium sulfate
e. 96.2 mg of nitrogen(IV) oxide
f. 12.7 g of mercury(I) chloride

35. Calculate the mass in grams of each of the following samples.

a. 1.25 moles of aluminum chloride
b. 3.35 moles of sodium hydrogen carbonate
c. 4.25 millimol of hydrogen bromide (1 millimol = ⅟₁₀₀₀ mole)
d. 1.31×10^{-3} moles of uranium
e. 0.00104 mole of carbon dioxide
f. 1.49×10^2 moles of iron

36. Calculate the mass in grams of each of the following samples.

a. 1.21 moles of hydrogen sulfide
b. 4.22×10^{-3} moles of lithium sulfide
c. 224 moles of ferric chloride
d. 7.29 mmol of sodium carbonate (1 mmol = ⅟₁₀₀₀ mole)
e. 8.14×10^3 moles of sodium acetate
f. 0.00793 mole of phosphine, PH_3

37. Calculate the mass in grams of each of the following samples.

a. 0.251 mole of ethyl alcohol, C_2H_6O
b. 1.26 moles of carbon dioxide
c. 9.31×10^{-4} moles of gold(III) chloride

d. 7.74 moles of sodium nitrate

e. 0.000357 mole of iron

38. Calculate the mass in grams of each of the following samples.

a. 0.994 mole of benzene, C_6H_6

b. 4.21 moles of calcium hydride

c. 1.79×10^{-4} moles of hydrogen peroxide, H_2O_2

d. 1.22 mmol of glucose, $C_6H_{12}O_6$ (1 mmol = $\frac{1}{1000}$ mole).

e. 10.6 moles of tin

f. 0.000301 mole of strontium fluoride

39. Calculate the number of *molecules* present in each of the following samples.

a. 4.75 mmol of phosphine, PH_3

b. 4.75 g of phosphine, PH_3

c. 1.25×10^{-2} g of lead(II) acetate, $Pb(CH_3CO_2)_2$

d. 1.25×10^{-2} moles of lead(II) acetate, $Pb(CH_3CO_2)_2$

e. a sample of benzene, C_6H_6, which contains a total of 5.40 moles of carbon

40. Calculate the number of *molecules* present in each of the following samples.

a. 6.37 moles of carbon monoxide

b. 6.37 g of carbon monoxide

c. 2.62×10^{-6} g of water

d. 2.62×10^{-6} moles of water

e. 5.23 g of benzene, C_6H_6

41. Calculate the number of *moles* of carbon atoms present in each of the following samples.

a. 1.271 g of ethanol, C_2H_5OH

b. 3.982 g of 1,4-dichlorobenzene, $C_6H_4Cl_2$

c. 0.4438 g of carbon suboxide, C_3O_2

d. 2.910 g of methylene chloride, CH_2Cl_2

42. Calculate the number of *moles* of sulfur atoms present in each of the following samples.

a. 2.01 g of sodium sulfate

b. 2.01 g of sodium sulfite

c. 2.01 g of sodium sulfide

d. 2.01 g of sodium thiosulfate, $Na_2S_2O_3$

8.6 Percent Composition of Compounds

QUESTIONS

43. The mass fraction of an element present in a compound can be obtained by comparing the mass of the particular element present in 1 mole of the compound to the _____ mass of the compound.

44. The mass percentage of a given element in a compound must always be (greater/less) than 100%.

PROBLEMS

45. Calculate the percent by mass of each element in the following compounds.

a. $HClO_3$ d. Ag_2S

b. UF_4 e. $NaHSO_3$

c. CaH_2 f. MnO_2

46. Calculate the percent by mass of each element in the following compounds.

a. ZnO d. H_2O_2

b. Na_2S e. CaH_2

c. $Mg(OH)_2$ f. K_2O

47. Calculate the percent by mass of the element listed *first* in the formulas for each of the following compounds.

a. methane, CH_4

b. sodium nitrate, $NaNO_3$

c. carbon monoxide, CO

d. nitrogen dioxide, NO_2

e. 1-octanol, $C_8H_{18}O$

f. calcium phosphate, $Ca_3(PO_4)_2$

g. 3-phenylphenol, $C_{12}H_{10}O$

h. aluminum acetate, $Al(C_2H_3O_2)_3$

48. Calculate the percent by mass of the element listed *first* in each of the following compounds.

a. barium peroxide, BaO_2

b. barium oxide, BaO

c. cobalt(II) bromide, $CoBr_2$

d. cobalt(III) bromide, $CoBr_3$

e. tin(II) chloride, $SnCl_2$

f. tin(IV) chloride, $SnCl_4$

g. lithium hydride, LiH

h. aluminum hydride, AlH_3

49. Calculate the percent by mass of the element listed *first* in the formulas for each of the following compounds.

a. adipic acid, $C_6H_{10}O_4$

b. ammonium nitrate, NH_4NO_3

c. caffeine, $C_8H_{10}N_4O_2$

d. chlorine dioxide, ClO_2

e. cyclohexanol, $C_6H_{11}OH$

f. dextrose, $C_6H_{12}O_6$

g. eicosane, $C_{20}H_{42}$

h. ethanol, C_2H_5OH

50. Calculate the percent by mass of the element listed *first* in each of the following compounds.

a. iodine monochloride, ICl

b. nitrogen(I) oxide, N_2O

c. nitrogen(II) oxide, NO

d. mercuric chloride, $HgCl_2$

e. mercurous chloride, Hg_2Cl_2

f. sulfur hexafluoride, SF_6

g. xenon difluoride, XeF_2

h. manganese(IV) oxide, MnO_2

51. For each of the following samples of ionic substances, calculate the number of moles and mass of the positive ions present in each sample.

a. 4.25 g of ammonium iodide, NH_4I

b. 6.31 moles of ammonium sulfide, $(NH_4)_2S$

c. 9.71 g of barium phosphide, Ba_3P_2

d. 7.63 moles of calcium phosphate, $Ca_3(PO_4)_2$

52. For each of the following ionic substances, calculate the percentage of the overall molar mass of the compound that is represented by the *negative* ions in the substance.

   a. ammonium sulfide
   b. calcium chloride
   c. barium oxide
   d. nickel(II) sulfate

8.7 Formulas of Compounds

QUESTIONS

53. What experimental evidence about a new compound must be known before its formula can be determined?

54. Explain to a friend who has not yet taken a chemistry course what is meant by the *empirical formula* of a compound.

55. Give the empirical formula that corresponds to each of the following molecular formulas.

   a. sodium peroxide, Na_2O_2
   b. terephthalic acid, $C_8H_6O_4$
   c. phenobarbital, $C_{12}H_{12}N_2O_3$
   d. 1,4-dichloro-2-butene, $C_4H_6Cl_2$

56. Which of the following pairs of compounds have the same *empirical* formula?

   a. acetylene, C_2H_2, and benzene, C_6H_6
   b. ethane, C_2H_6, and butane, C_4H_{10}
   c. nitrogen dioxide, NO_2, and dinitrogen tetroxide, N_2O_4
   d. diphenyl ether, $C_{12}H_{10}O$, and phenol, C_6H_5OH

8.8 Calculation of Empirical Formulas

PROBLEMS

57. A compound was analyzed and was found to contain the following percentages of the elements by mass: barium, 89.56%; oxygen, 10.44%. Determine the empirical formula of the compound.

58. A compound was analyzed and was found to contain the following percentages of the elements by mass: nitrogen, 11.64%; chlorine, 88.36%. Determine the empirical formula of the compound.

59. A 0.5998-g sample of a new compound has been analyzed and found to contain the following masses of elements: carbon, 0.2322 g; hydrogen, 0.05848 g; oxygen, 0.3091 g. Calculate the empirical formula of the compound.

60. A compound was analyzed and was found to contain the following percentages of the elements by mass: boron, 78.14%; hydrogen, 21.86%. Determine the empirical formula of the compound.

61. If a 1.271-g sample of aluminum metal is heated in a chlorine gas atmosphere, the mass of aluminum chloride produced is 6.280 g. Calculate the empirical formula of aluminum chloride.

62. A compound was analyzed and was found to contain the following percentages of the elements by mass: tin, 45.56%; chlorine, 54.43%. Determine the empirical formula of the compound.

63. When 3.269 g of zinc is heated in pure oxygen, the sample gains 0.800 g of oxygen in forming the oxide. Calculate the empirical formula of zinc oxide.

64. If cobalt metal is mixed with excess sulfur and heated strongly, a sulfide is produced that contains 55.06% cobalt by mass. Calculate the empirical formula of the sulfide.

65. If 1.25 g of aluminum metal is heated in an atmosphere of fluorine gas, 3.89 g of aluminum fluoride results. Determine the empirical formula of aluminum fluoride.

66. If 2.50 g of aluminum metal is heated in a stream of fluorine gas, it is found that 5.28 g of fluorine will combine with the aluminum. Determine the empirical formula of the compound that results.

67. A compound used in the nuclear industry has the following composition: uranium, 67.61%; fluorine, 32.39%. Determine the empirical formula of the compound.

68. A compound was analyzed and was found to contain the following percentages of the elements by mass: lithium, 46.46%; oxygen, 53.54%. Determine the empirical formula of the compound.

69. A compound has the following percentage composition by mass: copper, 33.88%; nitrogen, 14.94%; oxygen, 51.18%. Determine the empirical formula of the compound.

70. When lithium metal is heated strongly in an atmosphere of pure nitrogen, the product contains 59.78% Li and 40.22% N on a mass basis. Determine the empirical formula of the compound.

71. A compound has been analyzed and has been found to have the following composition: copper, 66.75%; phosphorus, 10.84%; oxygen, 22.41%. Determine the empirical formula of the compound.

72. A compound was analyzed and was found to contain the following percentages of the elements by mass: cobalt, 71.06%; oxygen, 28.94%. Determine the empirical formula of the compound.

73. When 1.00 mg of lithium metal is reacted with fluorine gas (F_2), the resulting fluoride salt has a mass of 3.73 mg. Calculate the empirical formula of lithium fluoride.

74. Phosphorus and chlorine form two binary compounds, in which the percentages of phosphorus are 22.55% and 14.87%, respectively. Calculate the empirical formulas of the two binary phosphorus–chlorine compounds.

All even-numbered Questions and Problems have answers in the back of this book and solutions in the Solutions Guide.

8.9 Calculation of Molecular Formulas

QUESTIONS

75. How does the *molecular* formula of a compound differ from the *empirical* formula? Can a compound's empirical and molecular formulas be the same? Explain.

76. What information do we need to determine the molecular formula of a compound if we know only the empirical formula?

PROBLEMS

77. A binary compound of boron and hydrogen has the following percentage composition: 78.14% boron, 21.86% hydrogen. If the molar mass of the compound is determined by experiment to be between 27 and 28 g, what are the empirical and molecular formulas of the compound?

78. A compound with empirical formula CH was found by experiment to have a molar mass of approximately 78 g. What is the molecular formula of the compound?

79. A compound with the empirical formula CH_2 was found to have a molar mass of approximately 84 g. What is the molecular formula of the compound?

80. A compound with empirical formula C_2H_5O was found in a separate experiment to have a molar mass of approximately 90 g. What is the molecular formula of the compound?

81. A compound having an approximate molar mass of 165–170 g has the following percentage composition by mass: carbon, 42.87%; hydrogen, 3.598%; oxygen, 28.55%; nitrogen, 25.00%. Determine the empirical and molecular formulas of the compound.

82. NO_2 (nitrogen dioxide) and N_2O_4 (dinitrogen tetroxide) have the same empirical formula, NO_2. Confirm this by calculating the percent by mass of each element present in the two compounds.

Additional Problems

83. Use the periodic table inside the front cover of this text to determine the atomic mass (per mole) or molar mass of each of the substances in column 1, and find that mass in column 2.

Column 1	Column 2
(1) molybdenum	(a)　33.99 g
(2) lanthanum	(b)　79.9 g
(3) carbon tetrabromide	(c)　95.94 g
(4) mercury(II) oxide	(d) 125.84 g
(5) titanium(IV) oxide	(e) 138.9 g
(6) manganese(II) chloride	(f) 143.1 g
(7) phosphine, PH_3	(g) 156.7 g
(8) tin(II) fluoride	(h) 216.6 g
(9) lead(II) sulfide	(i) 239.3 g
(10) copper(I) oxide	(j) 331.6 g

84. Complete the following table.

Mass of Sample	Moles of Sample	Atoms in Sample
5.00 g Al	_____	_____
_____	0.00250 mol Fe	_____
_____	_____	2.6×10^{24} atoms Cu
0.00250 g Mg	_____	_____
_____	2.7×10^{-3} mol Na	_____
_____	_____	1.00×10^{4} atoms U

85. Complete the following table.

Mass of Sample	Moles of Sample	Molecules in Sample	Atoms in Sample
4.24 g C_6H_6	_____	_____	_____
_____	0.224 mol H_2O	_____	_____
_____	_____	2.71×10^{22} molecules CO_2	_____
_____	1.26 mol HCl	_____	_____
_____	_____	4.21×10^{24} molecules H_2O	_____
0.297 g CH_3OH	_____	_____	_____

86. Consider a hypothetical compound composed of elements X, Y, and Z with the empirical formula X_2YZ_3. Given that the atomic masses of X, Y, and Z are 41.2, 57.7, and 63.9, respectively, calculate the percentage composition by mass of the compound. If the molecular formula of the compound is found by molar mass determination to be actually $X_4Y_2Z_6$, what is the percentage of each element present? Explain your results.

87. A binary compound of magnesium and nitrogen is analyzed, and 1.2791 g of the compound is found to contain 0.9240 g of magnesium. When a second sample of this compound is treated with water and heated, the nitrogen is driven off as ammonia, leaving a compound that contains 60.31% magnesium and 39.69% oxygen by mass. Calculate the empirical formulas of the two magnesium compounds.

88. When a 2.118-g sample of copper is heated in an atmosphere in which the amount of oxygen present is restricted, the sample gains 0.2666 g of oxygen in forming a reddish-brown oxide. However, when 2.118 g of copper is heated in a stream of pure oxygen, the sample gains 0.5332 g of oxygen. Calculate the empirical formulas of the two oxides of copper.

89. Hydrogen gas reacts with each of the halogen elements to form the hydrogen halides (HF, HCl, HBr, HI). Calculate the percent by mass of hydrogen in each of these compounds.

90. Calculate the number of atoms of each element present in each of the following samples.

a. 4.21 g of water
b. 6.81 g of carbon dioxide
c. 0.000221 g of benzene, C_6H_6
d. 2.26 moles of $C_{12}H_{22}O_{11}$

91. Calculate the mass in grams of each of the following samples.

 a. 10,000,000,000 nitrogen molecules
 b. 2.49×10^{20} carbon dioxide molecules
 c. 7.0983 moles of sodium chloride
 d. 9.012×10^{-6} moles of 1,2-dichloroethane, $C_2H_4Cl_2$

92. Calculate the mass of carbon in grams, the percent carbon by mass, and the number of individual carbon atoms present in each of the following samples.

 a. 7.819 g of carbon suboxide, C_3O_2
 b. 1.53×10^{21} molecules of carbon monoxide
 c. 0.200 mole of phenol, C_6H_6O

93. Find the item in column 2 that best explains or completes the statement or question in column 1.

 Column 1

 (1) 1 amu
 (2) 1008 amu
 (3) mass of the "average" atom of an element
 (4) number of carbon atoms in 12.01 g of carbon
 (5) 6.022×10^{23} molecules
 (6) total mass of all atoms in 1 mole of a compound
 (7) smallest whole-number ratio of atoms present in a molecule
 (8) formula showing actual number of atoms present in a molecule
 (9) product formed when any carbon-containing compound is burned in O_2
 (10) have the same empirical formulas, but different molecular formulas

 Column 2

 (a) 6.022×10^{23}
 (b) atomic mass
 (c) mass of 1000 hydrogen atoms
 (d) benzene, C_6H_6, and acetylene, C_2H_2
 (e) carbon dioxide
 (f) empirical formula
 (g) 1.66×10^{-24} g
 (h) molecular formula
 (i) molar mass
 (j) 1 mole

94. Calculate the number of grams of iron that contain the same number of atoms as 2.24 g of cobalt.

95. Calculate the number of grams of cobalt that contain the same number of atoms as 2.24 g of iron.

96. Calculate the number of grams of mercury that contain the same number of atoms as 5.00 g of tellurium.

97. Calculate the number of grams of lithium that contain the same number of atoms as 1.00 kg of zirconium.

98. Given that the molar mass of carbon tetrachloride, CCl_4, is 153.8 g, calculate the mass in grams of 1 molecule of CCl_4.

99. Calculate the mass in grams of hydrogen present in 2.500 g of each of the following compounds.

 a. benzene, C_6H_6
 b. calcium hydride, CaH_2
 c. ethyl alcohol, C_2H_5OH
 d. serine, $C_3H_7O_3N$

100. Calculate the mass in grams of nitrogen present in 5.000 g of each of the following compounds.

 a. glycine, $C_2H_5O_2N$
 b. magnesium nitride, Mg_3N_2
 c. calcium nitrate
 d. dinitrogen tetroxide

101. A strikingly beautiful copper compound with the common name "blue vitriol" has the following elemental composition: 25.45% Cu, 12.84% S, 4.036% H, 57.67% O. Determine the empirical formula of the compound.

102. A magnesium salt has the following elemental composition: 16.39% Mg, 18.89% N, 64.72% O. Determine the empirical formula of the salt.

103. The mass 1.66×10^{-24} g is equivalent to 1 _____.

104. Although exact isotopic masses are known with great precision for most elements, we use the *average* mass of an element's atoms in most chemical calculations. Explain.

105. Using the average atomic masses given in Table 8.1, calculate the number of atoms present in each of the following samples.

 a. 160,000 amu of oxygen
 b. 8139.81 amu of nitrogen
 c. 13,490 amu of aluminum
 d. 5040 amu of hydrogen
 e. 367,495.15 amu of sodium

106. If an average sodium atom weighs 22.99 amu, how many sodium atoms are contained in 1.98×10^{13} amu of sodium? What will 3.01×10^{23} sodium atoms weigh?

107. Using the average atomic masses given inside the front cover of this text, calculate how many *moles* of each element the following *masses* represent.

 a. 1.5 mg of chromium
 b. 2.0×10^{-3} g of strontium
 c. 4.84×10^4 g of boron
 d. 3.6×10^{-6} μg of californium
 e. 1.0 ton (2000 lb) of iron
 f. 20.4 g of barium
 g. 62.8 g of cobalt

108. Using the average atomic masses given inside the front cover of this text, calculate the *mass in grams* of each of the following samples.

 a. 5.0 moles of potassium
 b. 0.000305 mole of mercury
 c. 2.31×10^{-5} moles of manganese
 d. 10.5 moles of phosphorus
 e. 4.9×10^4 moles of iron
 f. 125 moles of lithium
 g. 0.01205 mole of fluorine

All even-numbered Questions and Problems have answers in the back of this book and solutions in the Solutions Guide.

109. Using the average atomic masses given inside the front cover of this text, calculate the number of *atoms* present in each of the following samples.

    a. 2.89 g of gold
    b. 0.000259 mole of platinum
    c. 0.000259 g of platinum
    d. 2.0 lb of magnesium
    e. 1.90 mL of liquid mercury (density = 13.6 g/mL)
    f. 4.30 moles of tungsten
    g. 4.30 g of tungsten

110. Calculate the molar mass for each of the following substances.

    a. ferrous sulfate
    b. mercuric iodide
    c. stannic oxide
    d. cobaltous chloride
    e. cupric nitrate

111. Calculate the molar mass for each of the following substances.

    a. adipic acid, $C_6H_{10}O_4$
    b. caffeine, $C_8H_{10}N_4O_2$
    c. eicosane, $C_{20}H_{42}$
    d. cyclohexanol, $C_6H_{11}OH$
    e. vinyl acetate, $C_4H_6O_2$
    f. dextrose, $C_6H_{12}O_6$

112. Calculate the number of *moles* of the indicated substance present in each of the following samples.

    a. 21.2 g of ammonium sulfide
    b. 44.3 g of calcium nitrate
    c. 4.35 g of dichlorine monoxide
    d. 1.0 lb of ferric chloride
    e. 1.0 kg of ferric chloride

113. Calculate the number of *moles* of the indicated substance present in each of the following samples.

    a. 1.28 g of iron(II) sulfate
    b. 5.14 mg of mercury(II) iodide
    c. 9.21 μg of tin(IV) oxide
    d. 1.26 lb of cobalt(II) chloride
    e. 4.25 g of copper(II) nitrate

114. Calculate the mass in grams of each of the following samples.

    a. 2.6×10^{-2} moles of copper(II) sulfate, $CuSO_4$
    b. 3.05×10^3 moles of tetrafluoroethylene, C_2F_4
    c. 7.83 mmol (1 mmol = 0.001 mol) of 1,4-pentadiene, C_5H_8
    d. 6.30 moles of bismuth trichloride, $BiCl_3$
    e. 12.2 moles of sucrose, $C_{12}H_{22}O_{11}$

115. Calculate the mass in grams of each of the following samples.

    a. 3.09 moles of ammonium carbonate
    b. 4.01×10^{-6} moles of sodium hydrogen carbonate
    c. 88.02 moles of carbon dioxide
    d. 1.29 mmol of silver nitrate
    e. 0.0024 mole of chromium(III) chloride

116. Calculate the number of *molecules* present in each of the following samples.

    a. 3.45 g of $C_6H_{12}O_6$
    b. 3.45 moles of $C_6H_{12}O_6$
    c. 25.0 g of ICl_5
    d. 1.00 g of B_2H_6
    e. 1.05 mmol of $Al(NO_3)_3$

117. Calculate the number of moles of hydrogen atoms present in each of the following samples.

    a. 2.71 g of ammonia
    b. 0.824 mole of water
    c. 6.25 mg of sulfuric acid
    d. 451 g of ammonium carbonate

118. Calculate the percent by mass of each element in the following compounds.

    a. calcium phosphate
    b. cadmium sulfate
    c. iron(III) sulfate
    d. manganese(II) chloride
    e. ammonium carbonate
    f. sodium hydrogen carbonate
    g. carbon dioxide
    h. silver(I) nitrate

119. Calculate the percent by mass of the element mentioned *first* in the formulas for each of the following compounds.

    a. sodium azide, NaN_3
    b. copper(II) sulfate, $CuSO_4$
    c. gold(III) chloride, $AuCl_3$
    d. silver nitrate, $AgNO_3$
    e. rubidium sulfate, Rb_2SO_4
    f. sodium chlorate, $NaClO_3$
    g. nitrogen triiodide, NI_3
    h. cesium bromide, $CsBr$

120. Calculate the percent by mass of the element mentioned *first* in the formulas for each of the following compounds.

    a. iron(II) sulfate
    b. silver(I) oxide
    c. strontium chloride
    d. vinyl acetate, $C_4H_6O_2$
    e. methanol, CH_3OH
    f. aluminum oxide
    g. potassium chlorite
    h. potassium chloride

121. A 1.2569-g sample of a new compound has been analyzed and found to contain the following masses of elements: carbon, 0.7238 g; hydrogen, 0.07088 g; nitrogen, 0.1407 g; oxygen, 0.3214 g. Calculate the empirical formula of the compound.

122. A 0.7221-g sample of a new compound has been analyzed and found to contain the following masses of elements: carbon, 0.2990 g; hydrogen, 0.05849 g; nitrogen, 0.2318 g; oxygen, 0.1328 g. Calculate the empirical formula of the compound.

All even-numbered Questions and Problems have answers in the back of this book and solutions in the Solutions Guide.

123. When 2.004 g of calcium is heated in pure nitrogen gas, the sample gains 0.4670 g of nitrogen. Calculate the empirical formula of the calcium nitride formed.

124. When 4.01 g of mercury is strongly heated in air, the resulting oxide weighs 4.33 g. Calculate the empirical formula of the oxide.

125. When 1.00 g of metallic chromium is heated with elemental chlorine gas, 3.045 g of a chromium chloride salt results. Calculate the empirical formula of the compound.

126. When barium metal is heated in chlorine gas, a binary compound forms that consists of 65.95% Ba and 34.05% Cl by mass. Calculate the empirical formula of the compound.

Your boss sends you to the store to get enough ingredients to make 50 sandwiches. How do you figure out how much of each ingredient to buy? Because you need enough to make 50 sandwiches, you multiply the preceding equation by 50.

$$50(2 \text{ slices bread}) + 50(3 \text{ slices meat}) + 50(1 \text{ slice cheese}) \rightarrow 50(1 \text{ sandwich})$$

That is

$$100 \text{ slices bread} + 150 \text{ slices meat} + 50 \text{ slices cheese} \rightarrow 50 \text{ sandwiches}$$

Notice that the numbers 100:150:50 correspond to the ratio 2:3:1, which represents the coefficients in the "balanced equation" of making a sandwich. If you were asked to make any number of sandwiches, it would be easy to use the original sandwich equation to determine how much of each ingredient you need.

The equation for a chemical reaction gives you the same type of information. It indicates the relative numbers of reactant and product molecules involved in the reaction. Using the equation permits us to determine the amounts of reactants needed to give a certain amount of product or to predict how much product we can make from a given quantity of reactants.

go Chemistry Module 7: Simple **Stoichiometry** covers concepts in this section.

To illustrate how this idea works with a chemistry example, consider the reaction between gaseous carbon monoxide and hydrogen to produce liquid methanol, $CH_3OH(l)$. The reactants and products are

$$\text{Unbalanced: } \underset{\text{Reactants}}{CO(g) + H_2(g)} \rightarrow \underset{\text{Product}}{CH_3OH(l)}$$

Because atoms are just rearranged (not created or destroyed) in a chemical reaction, we must always balance a chemical equation. That is, we must choose coefficients that give the same number of each type of atom on both sides. Using the smallest set of integers that satisfies this condition gives the balanced equation

$$\text{Balanced: } CO(g) + 2H_2(g) \rightarrow CH_3OH(l)$$

CHECK: Reactants: 1 C, 1 O, 4 H; Products: 1 C, 1 O, 4 H

Again, the coefficients in a balanced equation give the *relative* numbers of molecules. That is, we could multiply this balanced equation by any number and still have a balanced equation. For example, we could multiply by 12:

$$12[CO(g) + 2H_2(g) \rightarrow CH_3OH(l)]$$

to obtain

$$12CO(g) + 24H_2(g) \rightarrow 12CH_3OH(l)$$

This is still a balanced equation (check to be sure). Because 12 represents a dozen, we could even describe the reaction in terms of dozens:

$$1 \text{ dozen } CO(g) + 2 \text{ dozen } H_2(g) \rightarrow 1 \text{ dozen } CH_3OH(l)$$

We could also multiply the original equation by a very large number, such as 6.022×10^{23}:

$$6.022 \times 10^{23}[CO(g) + 2H_2(g) \rightarrow CH_3OH(l)]$$

which leads to the equation

$$6.022 \times 10^{23} \, CO(g) + 2(6.022 \times 10^{23}) \, H_2(g) \rightarrow 6.022 \times 10^{23} \, CH_3OH(l)$$

One mole is 6.022×10^{23} units.

Just as 12 is called a dozen, chemists call 6.022×10^{23} a *mole* (abbreviated mol). Our equation, then, can be written in terms of moles:

$$1 \text{ mol } CO(g) + 2 \text{ mol } H_2(g) \rightarrow 1 \text{ mol } CH_3OH(l)$$

Table 9.1	Information Conveyed by the Balanced Equation for the Production of Methanol			
$CO(g)$	+	$2H_2(g)$	$\rightarrow$	$CH_3OH(l)$
1 molecule CO	+	2 molecules H_2	$\rightarrow$	1 molecule CH_3OH
1 dozen CO molecules	+	2 dozen H_2 molecules	$\rightarrow$	1 dozen CH_3OH molecules
6.022×10^{23} CO molecules	+	$2(6.022 \times 10^{23})$ H_2 molecules	$\rightarrow$	6.022×10^{23} CH_3OH molecules
1 mol CO molecules	+	2 mol H_2 molecules	$\rightarrow$	1 mol CH_3OH molecules

Various ways of interpreting this balanced chemical equation are given in Table 9.1.

EXAMPLE 9.1 | Relating Moles to Molecules in Chemical Equations

Propane is often used as a fuel for outdoor grills.

Propane, C_3H_8, is a fuel commonly used for cooking on gas grills and for heating in rural areas where natural gas is unavailable. Propane reacts with oxygen gas to produce heat and the products carbon dioxide and water. This combustion reaction is represented by the unbalanced equation

$$C_3H_8(g) + O_2(g) \rightarrow CO_2(g) + H_2O(g)$$

Give the balanced equation for this reaction, and state the meaning of the equation in terms of numbers of molecules and moles of molecules.

SOLUTION

Using the techniques explained in Chapter 6, we can balance the equation.

$$C_3H_8(g) + 5O_2(g) \rightarrow 3CO_2(g) + 4H_2O(g)$$

CHECK: 3 C, 8 H, 10 O $\rightarrow$ 3 C, 8 H, 10 O

This equation can be interpreted in terms of molecules as follows:

1 molecule of C_3H_8 reacts with 5 molecules of O_2 to give

3 molecules of CO_2 plus 4 molecules of H_2O

or as follows in terms of moles (of molecules):

1 mol C_3H_8 reacts with 5 mol O_2 to give 3 mol

CO_2 plus 4 mol H_2O ■

9.2 Mole–Mole Relationships

OBJECTIVE: To learn to use a balanced equation to determine relationships between moles of reactants and moles of products.

Now that we have discussed the meaning of a balanced chemical equation in terms of moles of reactants and products, we can use an equation to predict the moles of products that a given number of moles of reactants will yield. For example, consider the decomposition of water to give hydrogen and oxygen, which is represented by the following balanced equation:

$$2H_2O(l) \rightarrow 2H_2(g) + O_2(g)$$

This equation tells us that 2 mol H_2O yields 2 mol H_2 and 1 mol O_2.

Now suppose that we have 4 mol water. If we decompose 4 mol water, how many moles of products do we get?

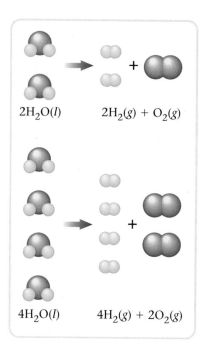

$2H_2O(l)$ $2H_2(g) + O_2(g)$

$4H_2O(l)$ $4H_2(g) + 2O_2(g)$

This equation with noninteger coefficients makes sense only if the equation means moles (of molecules) of the various reactants and products.

One way to answer this question is to multiply the entire equation by 2 (which will give us 4 mol H_2O).

$$2[2H_2O(l) \rightarrow 2H_2(g) + O_2(g)]$$
$$4H_2O(l) \rightarrow 4H_2(g) + 2O_2(g)$$

Now we can state that

4 mol H_2O yields 4 mol H_2 plus 2 mol O_2

which answers the question of how many moles of products we get with 4 mol H_2O.

Next, suppose we decompose 5.8 mol water. What numbers of moles of products are formed in this process? We could answer this question by rebalancing the chemical equation as follows: First, we divide *all coefficients* of the balanced equation

$$2H_2O(l) \rightarrow 2H_2(g) + O_2(g)$$

by 2, to give

$$H_2O(l) \rightarrow H_2(g) + \tfrac{1}{2}O_2(g)$$

Now, because we have 5.8 mol H_2O, we multiply this equation by 5.8.

$$5.8[H_2O(l) \rightarrow H_2(g) + \tfrac{1}{2}O_2(g)]$$

This gives

$$5.8H_2O(l) \rightarrow 5.8H_2(g) + 5.8\left(\tfrac{1}{2}\right)O_2(g)$$
$$5.8H_2O(l) \rightarrow 5.8H_2(g) + 2.9O_2(g)$$

(Verify that this is a balanced equation.) Now we can state that

5.8 mol H_2O yields 5.8 mol H_2 plus 2.9 mol O_2

This procedure of rebalancing the equation to obtain the number of moles involved in a particular situation always works, but it can be cumbersome. In Example 9.2 we will develop a more convenient procedure, which uses conversion factors, or **mole ratios,** based on the balanced chemical equation.

EXAMPLE 9.2   Determining Mole Ratios

What number of moles of O_2 will be produced by the decomposition of 5.8 moles of water?

SOLUTION

Where Are We Going?

We want to determine the number of moles of O_2 produced by the decomposition of 5.8 moles of H_2O.

What Do We Know?

- The balanced equation for the decomposition of water is

$$2H_2O \rightarrow 2H_2 + O_2$$

- We start with 5.8 mol H_2O.

How Do We Get There?

Our problem can be diagrammed as follows:

5.8 mol H_2O yields ▷   ? mol O_2

To answer this question, we need to know the relationship between moles of H_2O and moles of O_2 in the balanced equation (conventional form):

$$2H_2O(l) \rightarrow 2H_2(g) + O_2(g)$$

From this equation we can state that

$$\boxed{2 \text{ mol } H_2O} \xrightarrow{\text{yields}} \boxed{1 \text{ mol } O_2}$$

The statement 2 mol H_2O = 1 mol O_2 is obviously not true in a literal sense, but it correctly expresses the chemical equivalence between H_2O and O_2.

which can be represented by the following equivalence statement:

$$2 \text{ mol } H_2O = 1 \text{ mol } O_2$$

We now want to use this equivalence statement to obtain the conversion factor (mole ratio) that we need. Because we want to go from moles of H_2O to moles of O_2, we need the mole ratio

$$\frac{1 \text{ mol } O_2}{2 \text{ mol } H_2O}$$

MATH SKILL BUILDER
For a review of equivalence statements and dimensional analysis, see Section 2.6.

so that mol H_2O will cancel in the conversion from moles of H_2O to moles of O_2.

$$5.8 \text{ mol } H_2O \times \frac{1 \text{ mol } O_2}{2 \text{ mol } H_2O} = 2.9 \text{ mol } O_2$$

So if we decompose 5.8 mol H_2O, we will get 2.9 mol O_2.

REALITY CHECK   Note that this is the same answer we obtained earlier when we rebalanced the equation to give

$$5.8H_2O(l) \rightarrow 5.8H_2(g) + 2.9O_2(g) \blacksquare$$

We saw in Example 9.2 that to determine the moles of a product that can be formed from a specified number of moles of a reactant, we can use the balanced equation to obtain the appropriate mole ratio. We will now extend these ideas in Example 9.3.

EXAMPLE 9.3 | Using Mole Ratios in Calculations

Calculate the number of moles of oxygen required to react exactly with 4.30 moles of propane, C_3H_8, in the reaction described by the following balanced equation:

$$C_3H_8(g) + 5O_2(g) \rightarrow 3CO_2(g) + 4H_2O(g)$$

SOLUTION

Where Are We Going?

We want to determine the number of moles of O_2 required to react with 4.30 mol C_3H_8.

What Do We Know?

- The balanced equation for the reaction is

$$C_3H_8 + 5O_2 \rightarrow 3CO_2 + 4H_2O$$

- We start with 4.30 mol C_3H_8.

How Do We Get There?

In this case the problem can be stated as follows:

$$\boxed{4.30 \text{ mol } C_3H_8} \xrightarrow{\text{requires}} \boxed{? \text{ mol } O_2}$$

To solve this problem, we need to consider the relationship between the reactants C_3H_8 and O_2. Using the balanced equation, we find that

$$1 \text{ mol } C_3H_8 \text{ requires } 5 \text{ mol } O_2$$

which can be represented by the equivalence statement

$$1 \text{ mol } C_3H_8 = 5 \text{ mol } O_2$$

This leads to the required mole ratio

$$\frac{5 \text{ mol } O_2}{1 \text{ mol } C_3H_8}$$

for converting from moles of C_3H_8 to moles of O_2. We construct the conversion ratio this way so that mol C_3H_8 cancels:

$$4.30 \ \cancel{\text{mol } C_3H_8} \times \frac{5 \text{ mol } O_2}{1 \ \cancel{\text{mol } C_3H_8}} = 21.5 \text{ mol } O_2$$

We can now answer the original question:

$$4.30 \text{ mol } C_3H_8 \text{ requires } 21.5 \text{ mol } O_2$$

REALITY CHECK   According to the balanced equation, more O_2 is required (by mol) than C_3H_8 by a factor of 5. With about 4 mol C_3H_8, we would expect about 20 mol of O_2, which is close to our answer.

Self-Check   EXERCISE 9.1   Calculate the moles of CO_2 formed when 4.30 moles of C_3H_8 reacts with the required 21.5 moles of O_2.

HINT: Use the moles of C_3H_8, and obtain the mole ratio between C_3H_8 and CO_2 from the balanced equation.

See Problems 9.15 and 9.16. ∎

9.3 Mass Calculations

OBJECTIVE: To learn to relate masses of reactants and products in a chemical reaction.

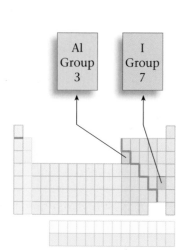

In the last section we saw how to use the balanced equation for a reaction to calculate the numbers of moles of reactants and products for a particular case. However, moles represent numbers of molecules, and we cannot count molecules directly. In chemistry we count by weighing. Therefore, in this section we will review the procedures for converting between moles and masses and will see how these procedures are applied to chemical calculations.

To develop these procedures we will consider the reaction between powdered aluminum metal and finely ground iodine to produce aluminum iodide. The balanced equation for this vigorous chemical reaction is

$$2Al(s) + 3I_2(s) \rightarrow 2AlI_3(s)$$

Suppose we have 35.0 g of aluminum. What mass of I_2 should we weigh out to react exactly with this amount of aluminum?

To answer this question, let's use the problem-solving strategy discussed in Chapter 8.

Aluminum (*left*) and iodine (*right*), shown at the top, react vigorously to form aluminum iodide. The purple cloud results from excess iodine vaporized by the heat of the reaction.

Where Are We Going?

We want to find the mass of iodine (I_2) that will react with 35.0 g of aluminum (Al). We know from the balanced equation that

$$\text{2 mol Al requires 3 mol } I_2$$

This can be written as the mole ratio

$$\frac{3 \text{ mol } I_2}{2 \text{ mol Al}}$$

We can use this ratio to calculate moles of I_2 needed from the moles of Al present. However, this leads us to two questions:

1. How many moles of Al are present?
2. How do we convert moles of I_2 to mass of I_2 as required by the problem?

We need to be able to convert from grams to moles and from moles to grams.

How Do We Get There?

The problem states that we have 35.0 g of aluminum, so we must convert from grams to moles of aluminum. This is something we already know how to do. Using the table of average atomic masses inside the front cover of this book, we find the atomic mass of aluminum to be 26.98. This means that 1 mole of aluminum has a mass of 26.98 g. We can use the equivalence statement

$$\text{1 mol Al} = 26.98 \text{ g}$$

to find the moles of Al in 35.0 g.

$$35.0 \text{ g Al} \times \frac{1 \text{ mol Al}}{26.98 \text{ g Al}} = 1.30 \text{ mol Al}$$

Now that we have moles of Al, we can find the moles of I_2 required.

$$1.30 \text{ mol Al} \times \frac{3 \text{ mol } I_2}{2 \text{ mol Al}} = 1.95 \text{ mol } I_2$$

We now know the *moles* of I_2 required to react with the 1.30 moles of Al (35.0 g). The next step is to convert 1.95 moles of I_2 to grams so we will know how much to weigh out. We do this by using the molar mass of I_2. The atomic mass of iodine is 126.9 g (for 1 mole of I atoms), so the molar mass of I_2 is

$$2 \times 126.9 \text{ g/mol} = 253.8 \text{ g/mol} = \text{mass of 1 mol } I_2$$

Now we convert the 1.95 moles of I_2 to grams of I_2.

$$1.95 \text{ mol } I_2 \times \frac{253.8 \text{ g } I_2}{\text{mol } I_2} = 495 \text{ g } I_2$$

We have solved the problem. We need to weigh out 495 g of iodine (contains I_2 molecules) to react exactly with the 35.0 g of aluminum. We will further develop procedures for dealing with masses of reactants and products in Example 9.4.

REALITY CHECK   We have determined that 495 g of I_2 is required to react with 35.0 g Al. Does this answer make sense? We know from the molar masses of Al and I_2 (26.98 g/mol and 253.8 g/mol) that the mass of 1 mol I_2 is almost 10 times as great as that of 1 mol Al. We also know that we need a greater number of moles of I_2 compared with Al (by a 3:2 ratio). So, we should expect to get a mass of I_2 that is well over 10 times as great as 35.0 g, and we did.

EXAMPLE 9.4 | **Using Mass–Mole Conversions with Mole Ratios**

Propane, C_3H_8, when used as a fuel, reacts with oxygen to produce carbon dioxide and water according to the following unbalanced equation:

$$C_3H_8(g) + O_2(g) \rightarrow CO_2(g) + H_2O(g)$$

What mass of oxygen will be required to react exactly with 96.1 g of propane?

SOLUTION

Where Are We Going?

We want to determine the mass of O_2 required to react exactly with 96.1 g C_3H_8.

What Do We Know?

- The unbalanced equation for the reaction is

$$C_3H_8 + O_2 \rightarrow CO_2 + H_2O.$$

- We start with 96.1 g mol C_3H_8.

- We know the atomic masses of carbon, hydrogen, and oxygen from the periodic table.

What Do We Need To Know?

- We need to know the balanced equation.

- We need the molar masses of O_2 and C_3H_8.

> Always balance the equation for the reaction first.

How Do We Get There?

To deal with the amounts of reactants and products, we first need the balanced equation for this reaction:

$$C_3H_8(g) + 5O_2(g) \rightarrow 3CO_2(g) + 4H_2O(g)$$

Our problem, in schematic form, is

> **MATH SKILL BUILDER**
> Remember that to show the correct significant figures in each step, we are rounding off after each calculation. In doing problems, you should carry extra numbers, rounding off only at the end.

| 96.1 g propane | requires | ? grams O_2 |

Using the ideas we developed when we discussed the aluminum–iodine reaction, we will proceed as follows:

1. We are given the number of grams of propane, so we must convert to moles of propane (C_3H_8).

2. Then we can use the coefficients in the balanced equation to determine the moles of oxygen (O_2) required.

3. Finally, we will use the molar mass of O_2 to calculate grams of oxygen.

We can sketch this strategy as follows:

$$C_3H_8(g) \quad + \quad 5O_2(g) \quad \rightarrow \quad 3CO_2(g) \quad + \quad 4H_2O(g)$$

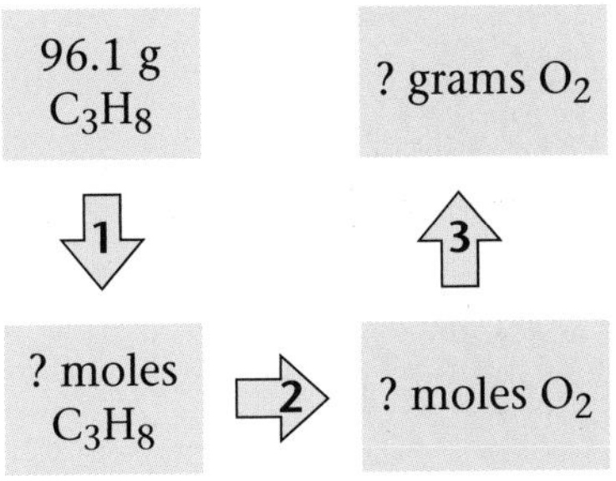

| 96.1 g C₃H₈ | | ? grams O₂ |

96.1 g
C_3H_8

? grams O_2

↓ 1

↑ 3

? moles
C_3H_8

⇒ 2

? moles O_2

1 Thus the first question we must answer is, *How many moles of propane are present in 96.1 g of propane?* The molar mass of propane is 44.09 g $(3 \times 12.01 + 8 \times 1.008)$. The moles of propane present can be calculated as follows:

$$96.1 \text{ g } C_3H_8 \times \frac{1 \text{ mol } C_3H_8}{44.09 \text{ g } C_3H_8} = 2.18 \text{ mol } C_3H_8$$

2 Next we recognize that each mole of propane reacts with 5 mol of oxygen. This gives us the equivalence statement

$$1 \text{ mol } C_3H_8 = 5 \text{ mol } O_2$$

from which we construct the mole ratio

$$\frac{5 \text{ mol } O_2}{1 \text{ mol } C_3H_8}$$

that we need to convert from moles of propane molecules to moles of oxygen molecules.

$$2.18 \text{ mol } C_3H_8 \times \frac{5 \text{ mol } O_2}{1 \text{ mol } C_3H_8} = 10.9 \text{ mol } O_2$$

Notice that the mole ratio is set up so that the moles of C_3H_8 cancel and the resulting units are moles of O_2.

3 Because the original question asked for the *mass* of oxygen needed to react with 96.1 g of propane, we must convert the 10.9 mol O_2 to grams, using the molar mass of O_2 $(32.00 = 2 \times 16.00)$.

$$10.9 \text{ mol } O_2 \times \frac{32.0 \text{ g } O_2}{1 \text{ mol } O_2} = 349 \text{ g } O_2$$

Therefore, 349 g of oxygen is required to burn 96.1 g of propane. We can summarize this problem by writing out a "conversion string" that shows how the problem was done.

$$96.1 \text{ g } C_3H_8 \times \frac{1 \text{ mol } C_3H_8}{44.09 \text{ g } C_3H_8} \times \frac{5 \text{ mol } O_2}{1 \text{ mol } C_3H_8} \times \frac{32.0 \text{ g } O_2}{1 \text{ mol } O_2} = 349 \text{ g } O_2$$

MATH SKILL BUILDER
Use units as a check to see that you have used the correct conversion factors (mole ratios).

This is a convenient way to make sure the final units are correct. The procedure we have followed is summarized below.

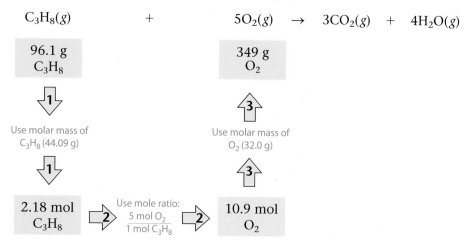

$$C_3H_8(g) \quad + \quad 5O_2(g) \quad \rightarrow \quad 3CO_2(g) \quad + \quad 4H_2O(g)$$

REALITY CHECK According to the balanced equation, more O_2 is required (by moles) than C_3H_8 by a factor of 5. Because the molar mass of C_3H_8 is not much greater than that of O_2, we should expect that a greater mass of oxygen is required, and our answer confirms this.

Self-Check **EXERCISE 9.2** What mass of carbon dioxide is produced when 96.1 g of propane reacts with sufficient oxygen?

See Problems 9.23 through 9.26. ∎

Self-Check **EXERCISE 9.3** Calculate the mass of water formed by the complete reaction of 96.1 g of propane with oxygen.

See Problems 9.23 through 9.26. ∎

So far in this chapter, we have spent considerable time "thinking through" the procedures for calculating the masses of reactants and products in chemical reactions. We can summarize these procedures in the following steps:

> ### Steps for Calculating the Masses of Reactants and Products in Chemical Reactions
>
> **Step 1** Balance the equation for the reaction.
>
> **Step 2** Convert the masses of reactants or products to moles.
>
> **Step 3** Use the balanced equation to set up the appropriate mole ratio(s).
>
> **Step 4** Use the mole ratio(s) to calculate the number of moles of the desired reactant or product.
>
> **Step 5** Convert from moles back to masses.

The process of using a chemical equation to calculate the relative masses of reactants and products involved in a reaction is called **stoichiometry** (pronounced stoi′ kē-ŏm′ i-trē). Chemists say that the balanced equation for a chemical reaction describes the stoichiometry of the reaction.

We will now consider a few more examples that involve chemical stoichiometry. Because real-world examples often involve very large or very small masses of chemicals that are most conveniently expressed by using scientific notation, we will deal with such a case in Example 9.5.

EXAMPLE 9.5 | Stoichiometric Calculations: Using Scientific Notation

For a review of writing formulas of ionic compounds, see Chapter 5.

Solid lithium hydroxide has been used in space vehicles to remove exhaled carbon dioxide from the living environment. The products are solid lithium carbonate and liquid water. What mass of gaseous carbon dioxide can 1.00×10^3 g of lithium hydroxide absorb?

SOLUTION

Where Are We Going?

We want to determine the mass of carbon dioxide absorbed by 1.00×10^3 g of lithium hydroxide.

What Do We Know?

- The names of the reactants and products.
- We start with 1.00×10^3 g of lithium hydroxide.
- We can obtain the atomic masses from the periodic table.

What Do We Need To Know?

- We need to know the balanced equation for the reaction, but we first have to write the formulas for the reactants and products.
- We need the molar masses of lithium hydroxide and carbon dioxide.

How Do We Get There?

Step 1 Using the description of the reaction, we can write the unbalanced equation

$$LiOH(s) + CO_2(g) \rightarrow Li_2CO_3(s) + H_2O(l)$$

The balanced equation is

$$2LiOH(s) + CO_2(g) \rightarrow Li_2CO_3(s) + H_2O(l)$$

Check this for yourself.

Step 2 We convert the given mass of LiOH to moles, using the molar mass of LiOH, which is 6.941 g + 16.00 g + 1.008 g = 23.95 g.

$$1.00 \times 10^3 \text{ g LiOH} \times \frac{1 \text{ mol LiOH}}{23.95 \text{ g LiOH}} = 41.8 \text{ mol LiOH}$$

Step 3 The appropriate mole ratio is

$$\frac{1 \text{ mol CO}_2}{2 \text{ mol LiOH}}$$

Astronaut Sidney M. Gutierrez changes the lithium hydroxide canisters on space shuttle *Columbia*.

Step 4   Using this mole ratio, we calculate the moles of CO_2 needed to react with the given mass of LiOH.

$$41.8 \ \text{mol LiOH} \times \frac{1 \ \text{mol } CO_2}{2 \ \text{mol LiOH}} = 20.9 \ \text{mol } CO_2$$

Step 5   We calculate the mass of CO_2 by using its molar mass (44.01 g).

$$20.9 \ \text{mol } CO_2 \times \frac{44.01 \ \text{g } CO_2}{1 \ \text{mol } CO_2} = 920. \ \text{g } CO_2 = 9.20 \times 10^2 \ \text{g } CO_2$$

Thus 1.00×10^3 g of LiOH(s) can absorb 920. g of $CO_2(g)$.
We can summarize this problem as follows:

$$2LiOH(s) \qquad + \qquad CO_2(g) \ \rightarrow \ Li_2CO_3(s) \ + \ H_2O(l)$$

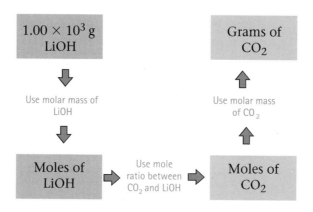

The conversion string is

$$1.00 \times 10^3 \ \text{g LiOH} \times \frac{1 \ \text{mol LiOH}}{23.95 \ \text{g LiOH}} \times \frac{1 \ \text{mol } CO_2}{2 \ \text{mol LiOH}} \times \frac{44.01 \ \text{g } CO_2}{1 \ \text{mol } CO_2}$$
$$= 9.19 \times 10^2 \ \text{g } CO_2$$

MATH SKILL BUILDER
Carrying extra significant figures and rounding off only at the end gives an answer of 919 g CO_2.

REALITY CHECK   According to the balanced equation, there is a 2:1 mole ratio of LiOH to CO_2. There is about a 1:2 molar mass ratio of LiOH:CO_2 (23.95:44.01). We should expect about the same mass of CO_2 as LiOH, and our answer confirms this (1000 g compared to 920 g).

Self-Check   **EXERCISE 9.4**   Hydrofluoric acid, an aqueous solution containing dissolved hydrogen fluoride, is used to etch glass by reacting with the silica, SiO_2, in the glass to produce gaseous silicon tetrafluoride and liquid water. The unbalanced equation is

$$HF(aq) + SiO_2(s) \rightarrow SiF_4(g) + H_2O(l)$$

a. Calculate the mass of hydrogen fluoride needed to react with 5.68 g of silica. *Hint:* Think carefully about this problem. What is the balanced equation for the reaction? What is given? What do you need to calculate? Sketch a map of the problem before you do the calculations.

b. Calculate the mass of water produced in the reaction described in part a.

See Problems 9.23 through 9.26. ■

EXAMPLE 9.6 | Stoichiometric Calculations: Comparing Two Reactions

Baking soda, $NaHCO_3$, is often used as an antacid. It neutralizes excess hydrochloric acid secreted by the stomach. The balanced equation for the reaction is

$$NaHCO_3(s) + HCl(aq) \rightarrow NaCl(aq) + H_2O(l) + CO_2(g)$$

Milk of magnesia, which is an aqueous suspension of magnesium hydroxide, $Mg(OH)_2$, is also used as an antacid. The balanced equation for the reaction is

$$Mg(OH)_2(s) + 2HCl(aq) \rightarrow 2H_2O(l) + MgCl_2(aq)$$

Which antacid can consume the most stomach acid, 1.00 g of $NaHCO_3$ or 1.00 g of $Mg(OH)_2$?

SOLUTION

Where Are We Going?

We want to compare the neutralizing power of two antacids, $NaHCO_3$ and $Mg(OH)_2$. In other words, how many moles of HCl will react with 1.00 g of each antacid?

What Do We Know?

- The balanced equations for the reactions.
- We start with 1.00 g each of $NaHCO_3$ and $Mg(OH)_2$.
- We can obtain atomic masses from the periodic table.

What Do We Need to Know?

- We need the molar masses of $NaHCO_3$ and $Mg(OH)_2$.

How Do We Get There?

The antacid that reacts with the larger number of moles of HCl is more effective because it will neutralize more moles of acid. A schematic for this procedure is

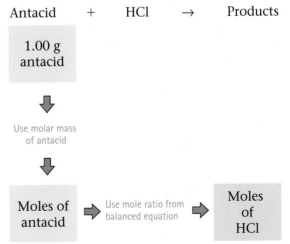

Notice that in this case we do not need to calculate how many grams of HCl react; we can answer the question with moles of HCl. We will now solve this problem for each antacid. Both of the equations are balanced, so we can proceed with the calculations.

Using the molar mass of $NaHCO_3$, which is 22.99 g + 1.008 g + 12.01 g + 3(16.00 g) = 84.01 g, we determine the moles of $NaHCO_3$ in 1.00 g of $NaHCO_3$.

Cars of the Future

There is a great deal of concern about how we are going to sustain our personal transportation system in the face of looming petroleum shortages (and the resultant high costs) and the challenges of global warming. The era of large gasoline-powered cars as the primary means of transportation in the United States seems to be drawing to a close. The fact that discoveries of petroleum are not keeping up with the rapidly increasing global demand for oil has caused skyrocketing prices. In addition, the combustion of gasoline produces carbon dioxide (about 1 lb of CO_2 per mile for many cars), which has been implicated in global warming.

So what will the car of the future in the United States be like? It seems that we are moving rapidly toward cars that have an electrical component as part of the power train. Hybrid cars, which use a small gasoline motor in conjunction with a powerful battery, have been quite successful. By supplementing the small gasoline engine, which would be inadequate by itself, with power from the battery, the typical

hybrid gets 40 to 50 miles per gallon of gasoline. In this type of hybrid car, both the battery and the engine are used to power the wheels of the car as needed.

Another type of system that involves both a gasoline engine and a battery is the so-called "plug-in hybrid." In this car, the battery is the sole source of power to the car's wheels. The gasoline engine is only used to charge the battery as needed. One example of this type of car is the Chevrolet Volt, which is slated for production in 2010. The Volt is being designed to run about 40 miles on each battery charge. The car would be plugged into a normal household electric outlet overnight to recharge the battery. For trips longer than 40 miles, the gasoline engine would turn on to charge the battery.

Another type of "electrical car" being tested is one powered by a hydrogen–oxygen fuel cell. An example of such a car is the Honda FCX Clarity. The Clarity stores hydrogen in a tank that holds 4.1 kg of H_2 at a pressure of 5000 lb per square inch. The H_2 is sent to a fuel cell, where it reacts with oxygen from the air supplied by an air compressor. About 200 of these cars are going to be tested in Southern Califor-

$$1.00 \text{ g NaHCO}_3 \times \frac{1 \text{ mol NaHCO}_3}{84.01 \text{ g NaHCO}_3} = 0.0119 \text{ mol NaHCO}_3$$
$$= 1.19 \times 10^{-2} \text{ mol NaHCO}_3$$

Next we determine the moles of HCl, using the mole ratio $\dfrac{1 \text{ mol HCl}}{1 \text{ mol NaHCO}_3}$.

$$1.19 \times 10^{-2} \text{ mol NaHCO}_3 \times \frac{1 \text{ mol HCl}}{1 \text{ mol NaHCO}_3} = 1.19 \times 10^{-2} \text{ mol HCl}$$

Thus 1.00 g of $NaHCO_3$ neutralizes 1.19×10^{-2} mol HCl. We need to compare this to the number of moles of HCl that 1.00 g of $Mg(OH)_2$ neutralizes.

Using the molar mass of $Mg(OH)_2$, which is 24.31 g + 2(16.00 g) + 2(1.008 g) = 58.33 g, we determine the moles of $Mg(OH)_2$ in 1.00 g of $Mg(OH)_2$.

$$1.00 \text{ g Mg(OH)}_2 \times \frac{1 \text{ mol Mg(OH)}_2}{58.33 \text{ g Mg(OH)}_2} = 0.0171 \text{ mol Mg(OH)}_2$$
$$= 1.71 \times 10^{-2} \text{ mol Mg(OH)}_2$$

nia in the next 3 years, leased to people who live near one of the three 24-hour public hydrogen stations. The Clarity gets about 72 miles per kilogram of hydrogen. One obvious advantage of a car powered by an H_2/O_2 fuel cell is that the combustion product is only H_2O. However, there is a catch (it seems there is always a catch). Currently, 95% of hydrogen produced is obtained by natural gas (CH_4), and CO_2 is a by-product of this process. Intense research is now being conducted to find economically feasible ways to produce H_2 from water.

It appears that our cars of the future will have an electrical drive component. Whether it will involve a conventional battery or a fuel cell will depend on technological developments and costs.

Even model cars are becoming "green." The H-racer from Horizon Fuel Cell Technologies uses a hydrogen–oxygen fuel cell.

The Honda FCX Clarity is powered by a hydrogen–oxygen fuel cell.

To determine the moles of HCl that react with this amount of $Mg(OH)_2$, we use the mole ratio $\dfrac{2 \text{ mol HCl}}{1 \text{ mol Mg(OH)}_2}$.

$$1.71 \times 10^{-2} \text{ mol Mg(OH)}_2 \times \frac{2 \text{ mol HCl}}{1 \text{ mol Mg(OH)}_2} = 3.42 \times 10^{-2} \text{ mol HCl}$$

Therefore, 1.00 g of $Mg(OH)_2$ neutralizes 3.42×10^{-2} mol HCl. We have already calculated that 1.00 g of $NaHCO_3$ neutralizes only 1.19×10^{-2} mol HCl. Therefore, $Mg(OH)_2$ is a more effective antacid than $NaHCO_3$ on a mass basis.

Self-Check **EXERCISE 9.5** In Example 9.6 we answered one of the questions we posed in the introduction to this chapter. Now let's see if you can answer the other question posed there. Determine what mass of carbon monoxide and what mass of hydrogen are required to form 6.0 kg of methanol by the reaction

$$CO(g) + 2H_2(g) \rightarrow CH_3OH(l)$$

See Problem 9.39. ■

The Concept of Limiting Reactants

OBJECTIVE: To understand what is meant by the term "limiting reactant."

Earlier in this chapter, we discussed making sandwiches. Recall that the sandwich-making process could be described as follows:

2 pieces bread + 3 slices meat + 1 slice cheese → 1 sandwich

In our earlier discussion, we always purchased the ingredients in the correct ratios so that we used all the components, with nothing left over.

Now assume that you came to work one day and found the following quantities of ingredients:

20 slices of bread
24 slices of meat
12 slices of cheese

How many sandwiches can you make? What will be left over?

To solve this problem, let's see how many sandwiches we can make with each component.

Bread: $20 \text{ slices bread} \times \dfrac{1 \text{ sandwich}}{2 \text{ slices of bread}} = 10 \text{ sandwiches}$

Meat: $24 \text{ slices meat} \times \dfrac{1 \text{ sandwich}}{3 \text{ slices of meat}} = 8 \text{ sandwiches}$

Cheese: $12 \text{ slices cheese} \times \dfrac{1 \text{ sandwich}}{1 \text{ slice of cheese}} = 12 \text{ sandwiches}$

How many sandwiches can you make? The answer is 8. When you run out of meat, you must stop making sandwiches. The meat is the limiting ingredient.

What do you have left over? Making 8 sandwiches requires 16 pieces of bread. You started with 20 pieces, so you have 4 pieces of bread left. You also used 8 pieces of cheese for the 8 sandwiches, so you have $12 - 8 = 4$ pieces of cheese left.

In this example, the ingredient present in the largest number (the meat) was actually the component that limited the number of sandwiches you could make. This situation arose because each sandwich required 3 slices of meat—more than the quantity required of any other ingredient.

You probably have been dealing with limiting-reactant problems for most of your life. For example, suppose a lemonade recipe calls for 1 cup of sugar for every 6 lemons. You have 12 lemons and 3 cups of sugar. Which ingredient is limiting, the lemons or the sugar?*

▶ ## A Closer Look

goChemistry **Module 8a: Stoichiometry and Limiting Reactants (Pt. 1)** covers concepts in this section.

When molecules react with each other to form products, considerations very similar to those involved in making sandwiches arise. We can illustrate these ideas with the reaction of $N_2(g)$ and $H_2(g)$ to form $NH_3(g)$:

$$N_2(g) + 3H_2(g) \rightarrow 2NH_3(g)$$

---

*The ratio of lemons to sugar that the recipe calls for is 6 lemons to 1 cup of sugar. We can calculate the number of lemons required to "react with" the 3 cups of sugar as follows:

$$3 \text{ cups sugar} \times \frac{6 \text{ lemons}}{1 \text{ cup sugar}} = 18 \text{ lemons}$$

Thus 18 lemons would be required to use up 3 cups of sugar. However, we have only 12 lemons, so the lemons are limiting.

Consider the following container of $N_2(g)$ and $H_2(g)$:

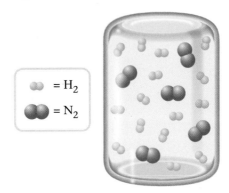

What will this container look like if the reaction between N_2 and H_2 proceeds to completion? To answer this question, you need to remember that each N_2 requires 3 H_2 molecules to form 2 NH_3. To make things more clear, we will circle groups of reactants:

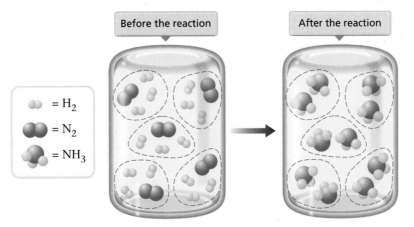

In this case, the mixture of N_2 and H_2 contained just the number of molecules needed to form NH_3 with nothing left over. That is, the ratio of the number of H_2 molecules to N_2 molecules was

$$\frac{15\ H_2}{5\ N_2} = \frac{3\ H_2}{1\ N_2}$$

This ratio exactly matches the numbers in the balanced equation

$$3H_2(g) + N_2(g) \rightarrow 2NH_3(g).$$

This type of mixture is called a *stoichiometric mixture*—one that contains the relative amounts of reactants that matches the numbers in the balanced equation. In this case, all reactants will be consumed to form products.

Now consider another container of $N_2(g)$ and $H_2(g)$:

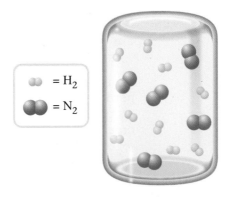

What will the container look like if the reaction between $N_2(g)$ and $H_2(g)$ proceeds to completion? Remember that each N_2 requires 3 H_2. Circling groups of reactants, we have

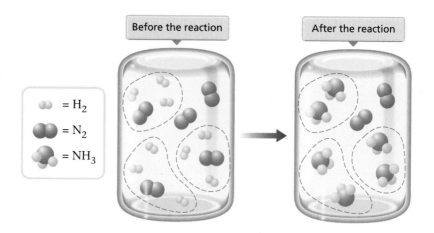

In this case, the hydrogen (H_2) is limiting. That is, the H_2 molecules are used up before all of the N_2 molecules are consumed. In this situation, the amount of hydrogen limits the amount of product (ammonia) that can form—hydrogen is the limiting reactant. Some N_2 molecules are left over in this case because the reaction runs out of H_2 molecules first.

> To determine how much product can be formed from a given mixture of reactants, we have to look for the reactant that is limiting—the one that runs out first and thus limits the amount of product that can form.

In some cases, the mixture of reactants might be stoichiometric—that is, all reactants run out at the same time. In general, however, you cannot assume that a given mixture of reactants is a stoichiometric mixture, so you must determine whether one of the reactants is limiting.

> The reactant that runs out first and thus limits the amounts of products that can form is called the **limiting reactant (limiting reagent).**

To this point, we have considered examples where the numbers of reactant molecules could be counted. In "real life" you can't count the molecules directly—you can't see them, and, even if you could, there would be far too many to count. Instead, you must count by weighing. We must therefore explore how to find the limiting reactant, given the masses of the reactants.

9.5 Calculations Involving a Limiting Reactant

OBJECTIVES: To learn to recognize the limiting reactant in a reaction. • To learn to use the limiting reactant to do stoichiometric calculations.

Manufacturers of cars, bicycles, and appliances order parts in the same proportion as they are used in their products. For example, auto manufacturers order four times as many wheels as engines and bicycle manufacturers order twice as many pedals as seats. Likewise, when chemicals are mixed together so that they can undergo a reaction, they are often mixed in stoichiometric quantities—that is, in exactly the correct amounts so that all

Farmer Rodney Donala looks out over his corn fields in front of his 30,000-gallon tank (at right) of anhydrous ammonia, a liquid fertilizer.

go Chemistry **Module 8b: Stoichiometry and Limiting Reactants (Pt. 2)** covers concepts in this section.

reactants "run out" (are used up) at the same time. To clarify this concept, we will consider the production of hydrogen for use in the manufacture of ammonia. Ammonia, a very important fertilizer itself and a starting material for other fertilizers, is made by combining nitrogen from the air with hydrogen. The hydrogen for this process is produced by the reaction of methane with water according to the balanced equation

$$CH_4(g) + H_2O(g) \rightarrow 3H_2(g) + CO(g)$$

Let's consider the question, *What mass of water is required to react exactly with 249 g of methane?* That is, how much water will just use up all of the 249 g of methane, leaving no methane or water remaining?

This problem requires the same strategies we developed in the previous section. Again, drawing a map of the problem is helpful.

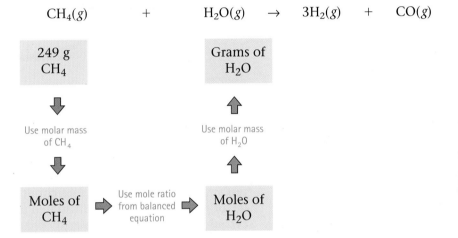

We first convert the mass of CH_4 to moles, using the molar mass of CH_4 (16.04 g/mol).

$$249 \text{ g } CH_4 \times \frac{1 \text{ mol } CH_4}{16.04 \text{ g } CH_4} = 15.5 \text{ mol } CH_4$$

Because in the balanced equation 1 mol CH_4 reacts with 1 mol H_2O, we have

$$15.5 \text{ mol } CH_4 \times \frac{1 \text{ mol } H_2O}{1 \text{ mol } CH_4} = 15.5 \text{ mol } H_2O$$

Therefore, 15.5 mol H_2O will react exactly with the given mass of CH_4. Converting 15.5 mol H_2O to grams of H_2O (molar mass = 18.02 g/mol) gives

$$15.5 \text{ mol } H_2O \times \frac{18.02 \text{ g } H_2O}{1 \text{ mol } H_2O} = 279 \text{ g } H_2O$$

This result means that if 249 g of methane is mixed with 279 g of water, both reactants will "run out" at the same time. The reactants have been mixed in stoichiometric quantities.

If, on the other hand, 249 g of methane is mixed with 300 g of water, the methane will be consumed before the water runs out. The water will be in *excess*. In this case, the quantity of products formed will be determined by the quantity of methane present. Once the methane is consumed, no more products can be formed, even though some water still remains. In this situation, the amount of methane *limits* the amount of products that can be formed. Recall from Section 9.4 that we call such a reactant the limiting reactant or the limiting reagent. In any stoichiometry problem where reactants

The reactant that is consumed first limits the amounts of products that can form.

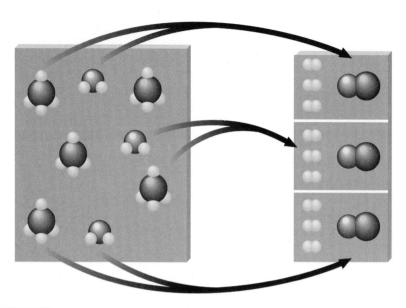

Figure 9.1

A mixture of 5CH$_4$ and 3H$_2$O molecules undergoes the reaction CH$_4$(g) + H$_2$O(g) → 3H$_2$(g) + CO(g). Note that the H$_2$O molecules are used up first, leaving two CH$_4$ molecules unreacted.

are not mixed in stoichiometric quantities, it is essential to determine which reactant is limiting to calculate correctly the amounts of products that will be formed. This concept is illustrated in Figure 9.1. Note from this figure that because there are fewer water molecules than CH$_4$ molecules, the water is consumed first. After the water molecules are gone, no more products can form. So in this case water is the limiting reactant.

EXAMPLE 9.7 | Stoichiometric Calculations: Identifying the Limiting Reactant

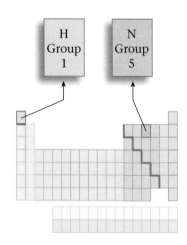

Suppose 25.0 kg (2.50 × 10^4 g) of nitrogen gas and 5.00 kg (5.00 × 10^3 g) of hydrogen gas are mixed and reacted to form ammonia. Calculate the mass of ammonia produced when this reaction is run to completion.

SOLUTION

Where Are We Going?

We want to determine the mass of ammonia produced given the masses of both reactants.

What Do We Know?

- The names of the reactants and products.
- We start with 2.50 × 10^4 g of nitrogen gas and 5.00 × 10^3 g of hydrogen gas.
- We can obtain the atomic masses from the periodic table.

What Do We Need To Know?

- We need to know the balanced equation for the reaction, but we first have to write the formulas for the reactants and products.
- We need the molar masses of nitrogen gas, hydrogen gas, and ammonia.
- We need to determine the limiting reactant.

How Do We Get There?

The unbalanced equation for this reaction is

$$N_2(g) + H_2(g) \rightarrow NH_3(g)$$

which leads to the balanced equation

$$N_2(g) + 3H_2(g) \rightarrow 2NH_3(g)$$

This problem is different from the others we have done so far in that we are mixing *specified amounts of two reactants* together. To know how much product forms, we must determine which reactant is consumed first. That is, we must determine which is the limiting reactant in this experiment. To do so we must add a step to our normal procedure. We can map this process as follows:

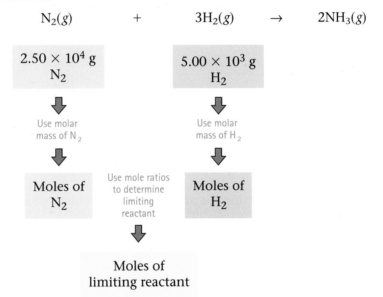

We will use the moles of the limiting reactant to calculate the moles and then the grams of the product.

We first calculate the moles of the two reactants present:

$$2.50 \times 10^4 \ \cancel{g \, N_2} \times \frac{1 \ mol \ N_2}{28.02 \ \cancel{g \, N_2}} = 8.92 \times 10^2 \ mol \ N_2$$

$$5.00 \times 10^3 \ \cancel{g \, H_2} \times \frac{1 \ mol \ H_2}{2.016 \ \cancel{g \, H_2}} = 2.48 \times 10^3 \ mol \ H_2$$

Now we must determine which reactant is limiting (will be consumed first). We have 8.92×10^2 moles of N_2. Let's determine *how many moles of H_2 are required to react with this much N_2.* Because 1 mole of N_2 reacts with 3 moles of H_2, the number of moles of H_2 we need to react completely with 8.92×10^2 moles of N_2 is determined as follows:

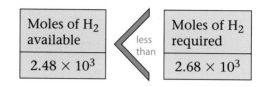

$$8.92 \times 10^2 \; \text{mol N}_2 \; \times \; \frac{3 \; \text{mol H}_2}{1 \; \text{mol N}_2} \; = \; 2.68 \times 10^3 \; \text{mol H}_2$$

Is N_2 or H_2 the limiting reactant? The answer comes from the comparison

Moles of H_2 available	*less than*	Moles of H_2 required
2.48×10^3		2.68×10^3

We see that 8.92×10^2 mol N_2 requires 2.68×10^3 mol H_2 to react completely. However, only 2.48×10^3 mol H_2 is present. This means that the hydrogen will be consumed before the nitrogen runs out, so hydrogen is the *limiting reactant* in this particular situation.

Note that in our effort to determine the limiting reactant, we could have started instead with the given amount of hydrogen and calculated the moles of nitrogen required.

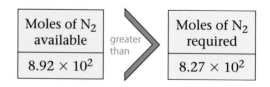

$$2.48 \times 10^3 \; \text{mol H}_2 \; \times \; \frac{1 \; \text{mol N}_2}{3 \; \text{mol H}_2} \; = \; 8.27 \times 10^2 \; \text{mol N}_2$$

Thus 2.48×10^3 mol H_2 requires 8.27×10^2 mol N_2. Because 8.92×10^2 mol N_2 is actually present, the nitrogen is in excess.

Moles of N_2 available	*greater than*	Moles of N_2 required
8.92×10^2		8.27×10^2

> Always check to see which, if any, reactant is limiting when you are given the amounts of two or more reactants.

If nitrogen is in excess, hydrogen will "run out" first; again we find that hydrogen limits the amount of ammonia formed.

Because the moles of H_2 present are limiting, we must use this quantity to determine the moles of NH_3 that can form.

$$2.48 \times 10^3 \; \text{mol H}_2 \times \frac{2 \; \text{mol NH}_3}{3 \; \text{mol H}_2} = 1.65 \times 10^3 \; \text{mol NH}_3$$

Next we convert moles of NH_3 to mass of NH_3.

$$1.65 \times 10^3 \; \text{mol NH}_3 \times \frac{17.03 \; \text{g NH}_3}{1 \; \text{mol NH}_3} = 2.81 \times 10^4 \; \text{g NH}_3 = 28.1 \; \text{kg NH}_3$$

Therefore, 25.0 kg of N_2 and 5.00 kg of H_2 can form 28.1 kg of NH_3.

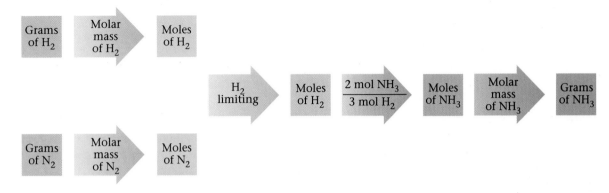

Figure 9.2

A map of the procedure used in Example 9.7.

REALITY CHECK   If neither reactant were limiting, we would expect an answer of 30.0 kg of NH_3 because mass is conserved (25.0 kg + 5.0 kg = 30.0 kg). Because one of the reactants (H_2 in this case) is limiting, the answer should be less than 30.0 kg, which it is. ∎

The strategy used in Example 9.7 is summarized in Figure 9.2.

The following list summarizes the steps to take in solving stoichiometry problems in which the amounts of two (or more) reactants are given.

Steps for Solving Stoichiometry Problems Involving Limiting Reactants

Step 1 Write and balance the equation for the reaction.

Step 2 Convert known masses of reactants to moles.

Step 3 Using the numbers of moles of reactants and the appropriate mole ratios, determine which reactant is limiting.

Step 4 Using the amount of the limiting reactant and the appropriate mole ratios, compute the number of moles of the desired product.

Step 5 Convert from moles of product to grams of product, using the molar mass (if this is required by the problem).

EXAMPLE 9.8

Stoichiometric Calculations: Reactions Involving the Masses of Two Reactants

Nitrogen gas can be prepared by passing gaseous ammonia over solid copper(II) oxide at high temperatures. The other products of the reaction are solid copper and water vapor. How many grams of N_2 are formed when 18.1 g of NH_3 is reacted with 90.4 g of CuO?

SOLUTION

Where Are We Going?

We want to determine the mass of nitrogen produced given the masses of both reactants.

Copper(II) oxide reacting with ammonia in a heated tube.

Ken O'Donoghue

What Do We Know?

- The names or formulas of the reactants and products.
- We start with 18.1 g of NH_3 and 90.4 g of CuO.
- We can obtain the atomic masses from the periodic table.

What Do We Need To Know?

- We need to know the balanced equation for the reaction, but we first have to write the formulas for the reactants and products.
- We need the molar masses of NH_3, CuO, and N_2.
- We need to determine the limiting reactant.

How Do We Get There?

Step 1   From the description of the problem, we obtain the following balanced equation:

$$2NH_3(g) + 3CuO(s) \rightarrow N_2(g) + 3Cu(s) + 3H_2O(g)$$

Step 2   Next, from the masses of reactants available we must compute the moles of NH_3 (molar mass = 17.03 g) and of CuO (molar mass = 79.55 g).

$$18.1 \text{ g } NH_3 \times \frac{1 \text{ mol } NH_3}{17.03 \text{ g } NH_3} = 1.06 \text{ mol } NH_3$$

$$90.4 \text{ g } CuO \times \frac{1 \text{ mol CuO}}{79.55 \text{ g } CuO} = 1.14 \text{ mol CuO}$$

Step 3   To determine which reactant is limiting, we use the mole ratio between CuO and NH_3.

$$1.06 \text{ mol } NH_3 \times \frac{3 \text{ mol CuO}}{2 \text{ mol } NH_3} = 1.59 \text{ mol CuO}$$

Then we compare how much CuO we have with how much of it we need.

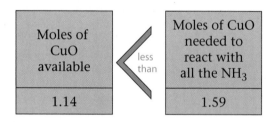

Moles of CuO available	less than	Moles of CuO needed to react with all the NH_3
1.14		1.59

Therefore, 1.59 mol CuO is required to react with 1.06 mol NH_3, but only 1.14 mol CuO is actually present. So the amount of CuO is limiting; CuO will run out before NH_3 does.

Step 4   CuO is the limiting reactant, so we must use the amount of CuO in calculating the amount of N_2 formed. Using the mole ratio between CuO and N_2 from the balanced equation, we have

$$1.14 \text{ mol CuO} \times \frac{1 \text{ mol } N_2}{3 \text{ mol CuO}} = 0.380 \text{ mol } N_2$$

Step 5   Using the molar mass of N_2 (28.02), we can now calculate the mass of N_2 produced.

$$0.380 \text{ mol } N_2 \times \frac{28.02 \text{ g } N_2}{1 \text{ mol } N_2} = 10.6 \text{ g } N_2$$

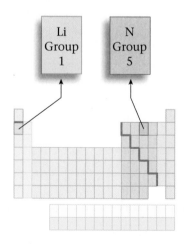

Self-Check **EXERCISE 9.6** Lithium nitride, an ionic compound containing the Li^+ and N^{3-} ions, is prepared by the reaction of lithium metal and nitrogen gas. Calculate the mass of lithium nitride formed from 56.0 g of nitrogen gas and 56.0 g of lithium in the unbalanced reaction

$$Li(s) + N_2(g) \rightarrow Li_3N(s)$$

See Problems 9.51 through 9.54. ■

9.6 Percent Yield

OBJECTIVE: To learn to calculate actual yield as a percentage of theoretical yield.

In the previous section we learned how to calculate the amount of products formed when specified amounts of reactants are mixed together. In doing these calculations, we used the fact that the amount of product is controlled by the limiting reactant. Products stop forming when one reactant runs out.

The amount of product calculated in this way is called the **theoretical yield** of that product. It is the amount of product predicted from the amounts of reactants used. For instance, in Example 9.8, 10.6 g of nitrogen represents the theoretical yield. This is the *maximum amount* of nitrogen that can be produced from the quantities of reactants used. Actually, however, the amount of product predicted (the theoretical yield) is seldom obtained. One reason for this is the presence of side reactions (other reactions that consume one or more of the reactants or products).

The *actual yield* of product, which is the amount of product *actually obtained,* is often compared to the theoretical yield. This comparison, usually expressed as a percentage, is called the **percent yield.**

Percent yield is important as an indicator of the efficiency of a particular reaction.

$$\frac{\text{Actual yield}}{\text{Theoretical yield}} \times 100\% = \text{percent yield}$$

For example, *if* the reaction considered in Example 9.8 *actually* gave 6.63 g of nitrogen instead of the *predicted* 10.6 g, the percent yield of nitrogen would be

$$\frac{6.63 \text{ g } N_2}{10.6 \text{ g } N_2} \times 100\% = 62.5\%$$

EXAMPLE 9.9 | Stoichiometric Calculations: Determining Percent Yield

In Section 9.1, we saw that methanol can be produced by the reaction between carbon monoxide and hydrogen. Let's consider this process again. Suppose 68.5 kg (6.85×10^4 g) of $CO(g)$ is reacted with 8.60 kg (8.60×10^3 g) of $H_2(g)$.

a. Calculate the theoretical yield of methanol.

b. If 3.57×10^4 g of CH_3OH is actually produced, what is the percent yield of methanol?

SOLUTION (a)

Where Are We Going?

We want to determine the theoretical yield of methanol and the percent yield given an actual yield.

What Do We Know?

- From Section 9.1 we know the balanced equation is

$$2H_2 + CO \rightarrow CH_3OH$$

- We start with 6.85×10^4 g of CO and 8.60×10^3 g of H_2.
- We can obtain the atomic masses from the periodic table.

What Do We Need To Know?

- We need the molar masses of H_2, CO, and CH_3OH.
- We need to determine the limiting reactant.

How Do We Get There?

Step 1 The balanced equation is

$$2H_2(g) + CO(g) \rightarrow CH_3OH(l)$$

Step 2 Next we calculate the moles of reactants.

$$6.85 \times 10^4 \text{ g CO} \times \frac{1 \text{ mol CO}}{28.01 \text{ g CO}} = 2.45 \times 10^3 \text{ mol CO}$$

$$8.60 \times 10^3 \text{ g H}_2 \times \frac{1 \text{ mol H}_2}{2.016 \text{ g H}_2} = 4.27 \times 10^3 \text{ mol H}_2$$

Step 3 Now we determine which reactant is limiting. Using the mole ratio between CO and H_2 from the balanced equation, we have

$$2.45 \times 10^3 \text{ mol CO} \times \frac{2 \text{ mol H}_2}{1 \text{ mol CO}} = 4.90 \times 10^3 \text{ mol H}_2$$

Moles of H_2 present		Moles of H_2 needed to react with all the CO
	less than	
4.27×10^3		4.90×10^3

We see that 2.45×10^3 mol CO requires 4.90×10^3 mol H_2. Because only 4.27×10^3 mol H_2 is actually present, *H_2 is limiting*.

Step 4 We must therefore use the amount of H_2 and the mole ratio between H_2 and CH_3OH to determine the maximum amount of methanol that can be produced in the reaction.

$$4.27 \times 10^3 \text{ mol H}_2 \times \frac{1 \text{ mol CH}_3\text{OH}}{2 \text{ mol H}_2} = 2.14 \times 10^3 \text{ mol CH}_3\text{OH}$$

This represents the theoretical yield in moles.

Step 5 Using the molar mass of CH_3OH (32.04 g), we can calculate the theoretical yield in grams.

$$2.14 \times 10^3 \text{ mol CH}_3\text{OH} \times \frac{32.04 \text{ g CH}_3\text{OH}}{1 \text{ mol CH}_3\text{OH}} = 6.86 \times 10^4 \text{ g CH}_3\text{OH}$$

So, from the amounts of reactants given, the maximum amount of CH_3OH that can be formed is 6.86×10^4 g. This is the *theoretical yield*.

SOLUTION (b)

The percent yield is

$$\frac{\text{Actual yield (grams)}}{\text{Theoretical yield (grams)}} \times 100\% = \frac{3.57 \times 10^4 \text{ g CH}_3\text{OH}}{6.86 \times 10^4 \text{ g CH}_3\text{OH}} \times 100\% = 52.0\%$$

Self-Check **EXERCISE 9.7** Titanium(IV) oxide is a white compound used as a coloring pigment. In fact, the page you are now reading is white because of the presence of this compound in the paper. Solid titanium(IV) oxide can be prepared by reacting gaseous titanium(IV) chloride with oxygen gas. A second product of this reaction is chlorine gas.

$$TiCl_4(g) + O_2(g) \rightarrow TiO_2(s) + Cl_2(g)$$

a. Suppose 6.71×10^3 g of titanium(IV) chloride is reacted with 2.45×10^3 g of oxygen. Calculate the maximum mass of titanium(IV) oxide that can form.

b. If the percent yield of TiO_2 is 75%, what mass is actually formed?

See Problems 9.63 and 9.64. ■

CHAPTER **9** REVIEW

Key Terms

mole ratio (9.2)
stoichiometry (9.3)
limiting reactant
  (limiting reagent) (9.4)

theoretical yield (9.6)
percent yield (9.6)

F directs you to the *Chemistry in Focus* feature in the chapter
VP indicates visual problems
⊙WL interactive versions of these problems are assignable in OWL.

Summary

1. A balanced equation relates the numbers of molecules of reactants and products. It can also be expressed in terms of the numbers of moles of reactants and products.

2. The process of using a chemical equation to calculate the relative amounts of reactants and products involved in the reaction is called doing stoichiometric calculations. To convert between moles of reactants and moles of products, we use mole ratios derived from the balanced equation.

3. Often reactants are not mixed in stoichiometric quantities (they do not "run out" at the same time). In that case, we must use the limiting reactant to calculate the amounts of products formed.

4. The actual yield of a reaction is usually less than its theoretical yield. The actual yield is often expressed as a percentage of the theoretical yield, which is called the percent yield.

Active Learning Questions

These questions are designed to be considered by groups of students in class. Often these questions work well for introducing a particular topic in class.

1. Relate Active Learning Question 2 from Chapter 2 to the concepts of chemical stoichiometry.

2. You are making cookies and are missing a key ingredient—eggs. You have plenty of the other ingredients, except that you have only 1.33 cups of butter and no eggs. You note that the recipe calls for 2 cups of butter and 3 eggs (plus the other ingredients) to make 6 dozen cookies. You telephone a friend and have him bring you some eggs.

a. How many eggs do you need?
b. If you use all the butter (and get enough eggs), how many cookies can you make?

Unfortunately, your friend hangs up before you tell him how many eggs you need. When he arrives, he has a surprise for you—to save time he has broken the eggs in a bowl for you. You ask him how many he brought, and he replies, "All of them, but I spilled some on the way over." You weigh the eggs and find that they weigh 62.1 g. Assuming that an average egg weighs 34.21 g:

c. How much butter is needed to react with all the eggs?
d. How many cookies can you make?
e. Which will you have left over, eggs or butter?
f. How much is left over?
g. Relate this question to the concepts of chemical stoichiometry.

VP 3. Nitrogen (N_2) and hydrogen (H_2) react to form ammonia (NH_3). Consider the mixture of N_2 () and H_2 ( ) in a closed container as illustrated below:

Assuming the reaction goes to completion, draw a representation of the product mixture. Explain how you arrived at this representation.

4. Which of the following equations best represents the reaction for Question 3?

a. $6N_2 + 6H_2 \rightarrow 4NH_3 + 4N_2$
b. $N_2 + H_2 \rightarrow NH_3$
c. $N + 3H \rightarrow NH_3$
d. $N_2 + 3H_2 \rightarrow 2NH_3$
e. $2N_2 + 6H_2 \rightarrow 4NH_3$

For choices you did not pick, explain what you feel is wrong with them, and justify the choice you did pick.

5. You know that chemical A reacts with chemical B. You react 10.0 g A with 10.0 g B. What information do you need to know to determine the amount of product that will be produced? Explain.

6. If 10.0 g of hydrogen gas is reacted with 10.0 g of oxygen gas according to the equation

$$2H_2 + O_2 \rightarrow 2H_2O$$

we should not expect to form 20.0 g of water. Why not? What mass of water can be produced with a complete reaction?

7. The limiting reactant in a reaction:

a. has the lowest coefficient in a balanced equation.
b. is the reactant for which you have the fewest number of moles.
c. has the lowest ratio: moles available/coefficient in the balanced equation.
d. has the lowest ratio: coefficient in the balanced equation/moles available.
d. None of the above.

For choices you did not pick, explain what you feel is wrong with them, and justify the choice you did pick.

8. Given the equation $3A + B \rightarrow C + D$, if 4 moles of A is reacted with 2 moles of B, which of the following is true?

a. The limiting reactant is the one with the higher molar mass.
b. A is the limiting reactant because you need 6 moles of A and have 4 moles.
c. B is the limiting reactant because you have fewer moles of B than moles of A.

d. B is the limiting reactant because three A molecules react with every one B molecule.
e. Neither reactant is limiting.

For choices you did not pick, explain what you feel is wrong with them, and justify the choice you did pick.

9. What happens to the weight of an iron bar when it rusts?

a. There is no change because mass is always conserved.
b. The weight increases.
c. The weight increases, but if the rust is scraped off, the bar has the original weight.
d. The weight decreases.

Justify your choice and, for choices you did not pick, explain what is wrong with them. Explain what it means for something to rust.

10. Consider the equation $2A + B \rightarrow A_2B$. If you mix 1.0 mole of A and 1.0 mole of B, how many moles of A_2B can be produced?

11. What is meant by the term *mole ratio*? Give an example of a mole ratio, and explain how it is used in solving a stoichiometry problem.

12. Which would produce a greater number of moles of product: a given amount of hydrogen gas reacting with an excess of oxygen gas to produce water, or the same amount of hydrogen gas reacting with an excess of nitrogen gas to make ammonia? Support your answer.

13. Consider a reaction represented by the following balanced equation

$$2A + 3B \rightarrow C + 4D$$

You find that it requires equal masses of A and B so that there are no reactants left over. Which of the following is true? Justify your choice.

a. The molar mass of A must be greater than the molar mass of B.
b. The molar mass of A must be less than the molar mass of B.
c. The molar mass of A must be the same as the molar mass of B.

14. Consider a chemical equation with two reactants forming one product. If you know the mass of each reactant, what else do you need to know to determine the mass of the product? Why isn't the mass necessarily the sum of the mass of the reactants? Provide a real example of such a reaction, and support your answer mathematically.

15. Consider the balanced chemical equation

$$A + 5B \rightarrow 3C + 4D$$

When equal masses of A and B are reacted, which is limiting, A or B? Justify your choice.

a. If the molar mass of A is greater than the molar mass of B, then A must be limiting.

b. If the molar mass of A is less than the molar mass of B, then A must be limiting.

c. If the molar mass of A is greater than the molar mass of B, then B must be limiting.

d. If the molar mass of A is less than the molar mass of B, then B must be limiting.

16. Which of the following reaction mixtures would produce the greatest amount of product, assuming all went to completion? Justify your choice.

Each involves the reaction symbolized by the equation

$$2H_2 + O_2 \rightarrow 2H_2O$$

a. 2 moles of H_2 and 2 moles of O_2.

b. 2 moles of H_2 and 3 moles of O_2.

c. 2 moles of H_2 and 1 mole of O_2.

d. 3 moles of H_2 and 1 mole of O_2.

e. Each would produce the same amount of product.

17. Baking powder is a mixture of cream of tartar ($KHC_4H_4O_6$) and baking soda ($NaHCO_3$). When it is placed in an oven at typical baking temperatures (as part of a cake, for example), it undergoes the following reaction (CO_2 makes the cake rise):

$$KHC_4H_4O_6(s) + NaHCO_3(s) \rightarrow$$
$$KNaC_4H_4O_6(s) + H_2O(g) + CO_2(g)$$

You decide to make a cake one day, and the recipe calls for baking powder. Unfortunately, you have no baking powder. You do have cream of tartar and baking soda, so you use stoichiometry to figure out how much of each to mix.

Of the following choices, which is the best way to make baking powder? The amounts given in the choices are in teaspoons (that is, you will use a teaspoon to measure the baking soda and cream of tartar). Justify your choice.

Assume a teaspoon of cream of tartar has the same mass as a teaspoon of baking soda.

a. Add equal amounts of baking soda and cream of tartar.

b. Add a bit more than twice as much cream of tartar as baking soda.

c. Add a bit more than twice as much baking soda as cream of tartar.

d. Add more cream of tartar than baking soda, but not quite twice as much.

e. Add more baking soda than cream of tartar, but not quite twice as much.

VP 18. You have seven closed containers each with equal masses of chlorine gas (Cl_2). You add 10.0 g of sodium to the first sample, 20.0 g of sodium to the second sample, and so on (adding 70.0 g of sodium to the seventh sample). Sodium and chloride react to form sodium chloride according to the equation

$$2Na(s) + Cl_2(g) \rightarrow 2NaCl(s)$$

After each reaction is complete, you collect and measure the amount of sodium chloride formed. A graph of your results is shown below.

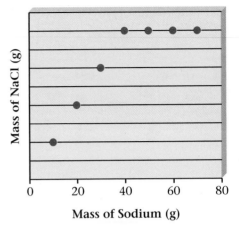

Answer the following questions:

a. Explain the shape of the graph.

b. Calculate the mass of NaCl formed when 20.0 g of sodium is used.

c. Calculate the mass of Cl_2 in each container.

d. Calculate the mass of NaCl formed when 50.0 g of sodium is used.

e. Identify the leftover reactant and determine its mass for parts b and d above.

VP 19. You have a chemical in a sealed glass container filled with air. The setup is sitting on a balance as shown below. The chemical is ignited by means of a magnifying glass focusing sunlight on the reactant. After the chemical has completely burned, which of the following is true? Explain your answer.

a. The balance will read less than 250.0 g.

b. The balance will read 250.0 g.

c. The balance will read greater than 250.0 g.

d. Cannot be determined without knowing the identity of the chemical.

VP 20. Consider an iron bar on a balance as shown.

As the iron bar rusts, which of the following is true? Explain your answer.

a. The balance will read less than 75.0 g.

b. The balance will read 75.0 g.

c. The balance will read greater than 75.0 g.

d. The balance will read greater than 75.0 g, but if the bar is removed, the rust scraped off, and the bar replaced, the balance will read 75.0 g.

VP 21. Consider the reaction between $NO(g)$ and $O_2(g)$ represented below.

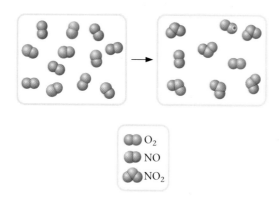

- O_2
- NO
- NO_2

What is the balanced equation for this reaction, and what is the limiting reactant?

Questions and Problems

9.1 Information Given by Chemical Equations

QUESTIONS

1. What do the coefficients of a balanced chemical equation tell us about the proportions in which atoms and molecules react on an individual (microscopic) basis?

2. What do the coefficients of a balanced chemical equation tell us about the proportions in which substances react on a macroscopic (mole) basis?

3. Although *mass* is a property of matter we can conveniently measure in the laboratory, the coefficients of a balanced chemical equation are *not* directly interpreted on the basis of mass. Explain why.

4. For the balanced chemical equation $H_2 + Br_2 \rightarrow 2HBr$, explain why we do *not* expect to produce 2 g of HBr if 1 g of H_2 is reacted with 1 g of Br_2.

PROBLEMS

5. For each of the following reactions, give the balanced equation for the reaction and state the meaning of the equation in terms of the numbers of *individual molecules* and in terms of *moles of molecules*.
   a. $PCl_3(l) + H_2O(l) \rightarrow H_3PO_3(aq) + HCl(g)$
   b. $XeF_2(g) + H_2O(l) \rightarrow Xe(g) + HF(g) + O_2(g)$
   c. $S(s) + HNO_3(aq) \rightarrow H_2SO_4(aq) + H_2O(l) + NO_2(g)$
   d. $NaHSO_3(s) \rightarrow Na_2SO_3(s) + SO_2(g) + H_2O(l)$

6. For each of the following reactions, balance the chemical equation and state the stoichiometric *meaning* of the equation in terms of the numbers of *individual molecules* reacting and in terms of *moles of molecules* reacting.
   a. $(NH_4)_2CO_3(s) \rightarrow NH_3(g) + CO_2(g) + H_2O(g)$
   b. $Mg(s) + P_4(s) \rightarrow Mg_3P_2(s)$
   c. $Si(s) + S_8(s) \rightarrow Si_2S_4(l)$
   d. $C_2H_5OH(l) + O_2(g) \rightarrow CO_2(g) + H_2O(g)$

9.2 Mole–Mole Relationships

QUESTIONS

7. Consider the reaction represented by the chemical equation

$$KOH(s) + SO_2(g) \rightarrow KHSO_3(s)$$

Since the coefficients of the balanced chemical equation are all equal to 1, we know that exactly 1 g of KOH will react with exactly 1 g of SO_2. True or false? Explain.

8. For the balanced chemical equation for the decomposition of hydrogen peroxide

$$2H_2O_2(aq) \rightarrow 2H_2O(l) + O_2(g)$$

explain why we know that decomposition of 2 g of hydrogen peroxide will *not* result in the production of 2 g of water and 1 g of oxygen gas.

9. Consider the balanced chemical equation

$$4Al(s) + 3O_2(g) \rightarrow 2Al_2O_3(s).$$

What mole ratio would you use to calculate how many moles of oxygen gas would be needed to react completely with a given number of moles of aluminum metal? What mole ratio would you use to calculate the number of moles of product that would be expected if a given number of moles of aluminum metal reacts completely?

10. Consider the balanced chemical equation

$$Fe_2O_3(s) + 3H_2SO_4(aq) \rightarrow Fe_2(SO_4)_3(s) + 3H_2O(l).$$

What mole ratio would you use to calculate the number of moles of sulfuric acid needed to react completely with a given number of moles of iron(III) oxide? What mole ratios would you use to calculate the number of moles of each product that would be produced if a given number of moles of $Fe_2O_3(s)$ reacts completely?

PROBLEMS

11. For each of the following balanced chemical equations, calculate how many *moles* of product(s) would be produced if 0.500 mole of the first reactant were to react completely.
   a. $CO_2(g) + 4H_2(g) \rightarrow CH_4(g) + 2H_2O(l)$
   b. $BaCl_2(aq) + 2AgNO_3(aq) \rightarrow 2AgCl(s) + Ba(NO_3)_2(aq)$
   c. $C_3H_8(g) + 5O_2(g) \rightarrow 4H_2O(l) + 3CO_2(g)$
   d. $3H_2SO_4(aq) + 2Fe(s) \rightarrow Fe_2(SO_4)_3(aq) + 3H_2(g)$

12. For each of the following balanced chemical equations, calculate how many *moles* of product(s) would be produced if 0.250 mole of the first reactant were to react completely.
   a. $4Bi(s) + 3O_2(g) \rightarrow 2Bi_2O_3(s)$
   b. $SnO_2(s) + 2H_2(g) \rightarrow Sn(s) + 2H_2O(g)$
   c. $SiCl_4(l) + 2H_2O(l) \rightarrow SiO_2(s) + 4HCl(g)$
   d. $2N_2(g) + 5O_2(g) + 2H_2O(l) \rightarrow 4HNO_3(aq)$

13. For each of the following balanced chemical equations, calculate how many *grams* of the product(s)

would be produced by complete reaction of 0.125 mole of the first reactant.

a. $AgNO_3(aq) + LiOH(aq) \rightarrow AgOH(s) + LiNO_3(aq)$
b. $Al_2(SO_4)_3(aq) + 3CaCl_2(aq) \rightarrow$
$$2AlCl_3(aq) + 3CaSO_4(s)$$
c. $CaCO_3(s) + 2HCl(aq) \rightarrow$
$$CaCl_2(aq) + CO_2(g) + H_2O(l)$$
d. $2C_4H_{10}(g) + 13O_2(g) \rightarrow 8CO_2(g) + 10H_2O(g)$

14. For each of the following balanced chemical equations, calculate how many *grams* of the product(s) would be produced by complete reaction of 0.750 mole of the first (or only) reactant.

a. $C_5H_{12}(l) + 8O_2(g) \rightarrow 5CO_2(g) + 6H_2O(l)$
b. $2CH_3OH(l) + 3O_2(g) \rightarrow 4H_2O(l) + 2CO_2(g)$
c. $Ba(OH)_2(aq) + H_3PO_4(aq) \rightarrow BaHPO_4(s) + 2H_2O(l)$
d. $C_6H_{12}O_6(aq) \rightarrow 2C_2H_5OH(aq) + 2CO_2(g)$

15. For each of the following *unbalanced* equations, indicate how many *moles* of the *second reactant* would be required to react exactly with *0.275 mol* of the *first reactant*. State clearly the mole ratio used for the conversion.

a. $Cl_2(g) + KI(aq) \rightarrow I_2(s) + KCl(aq)$
b. $Co(s) + P_4(s) \rightarrow Co_3P_2(s)$
c. $Zn(s) + HNO_3(aq) \rightarrow ZnNO_3(aq) + H_2(g)$
d. $C_5H_{12}(l) + O_2(g) \rightarrow CO_2(g) + H_2O(g)$

16. For each of the following *unbalanced* equations, indicate how many *moles* of the *first product* are produced if *0.625 mole* of the *second product* forms. State clearly the mole ratio used for each conversion.

a. $KO_2(s) + H_2O(l) \rightarrow O_2(g) + KOH(s)$
b. $SeO_2(g) + H_2Se(g) \rightarrow Se(s) + H_2O(g)$
c. $CH_3CH_2OH(l) + O_2(g) \rightarrow CH_3CHO(aq) + H_2O(l)$
d. $Fe_2O_3(s) + Al(s) \rightarrow Fe(l) + Al_2O_3(s)$

9.3 Mass Calculations

QUESTIONS

17. What quantity serves as the conversion factor between the mass of a sample and how many moles the sample contains?

18. What does it mean to say that the balanced chemical equation for a reaction describes the *stoichiometry* of the reaction?

PROBLEMS

19. Using the average atomic masses given inside the front cover of this book, calculate how many *moles* of each substance the following masses represent.

a. 4.15 g of silicon, Si
b. 2.72 mg of gold(III) chloride, $AuCl_3$
c. 1.05 kg of sulfur, S
d. 0.000901 g of iron(III) chloride, $FeCl_3$
e. 5.62×10^3 g of magnesium oxide, MgO

20. Using the average atomic masses given inside the front cover of this book, calculate how many *moles* of each substance the following masses represent.

a. 72.4 mg of argon, Ar
b. 52.7 g of carbon disulfide, CS_2
c. 784 kg of iron, Fe
d. 0.00104 g of calcium chloride, $CaCl_2$
e. 1.26×10^3 g of nickel(II) sulfide, NiS

21. Using the average atomic masses given inside the front cover of this book, calculate the *mass in grams* of each of the following samples.

a. 2.17 moles of germanium, Ge
b. 4.24 mmol of lead(II) chloride (1 mmol = 1/1000 mol)
c. 0.0971 mole of ammonia, NH_3
d. 4.26×10^3 moles of hexane, C_6H_{14}
e. 1.71 moles of iodine monochloride, ICl

22. Using the average atomic masses given inside the front cover of this book, calculate the *mass in grams* of each of the following samples.

a. 2.23 moles of propane, C_3H_8
b. 9.03 mmol of argon, Ar (1 mmol = 1/1000 mol)
c. 5.91×10^6 moles of silicon dioxide, SiO_2
d. 0.000104 mole of copper(II) chloride, $CuCl_2$
e. 0.000104 mole of copper(I) chloride, CuCl

23. For each of the following *unbalanced* equations, calculate how many *moles* of the second reactant would be required to react completely with 0.413 *moles* of the first reactant.

a. $Co(s) + F_2(g) \rightarrow CoF_3(s)$
b. $Al(s) + H_2SO_4(aq) \rightarrow Al_2(SO_4)_3(aq) + H_2(g)$
c. $K(s) + H_2O(l) \rightarrow KOH(aq) + H_2(g)$
d. $Cu(s) + O_2(g) \rightarrow Cu_2O(s)$

24. For each of the following *unbalanced* equations, calculate how many *moles* of the second reactant would be required to react completely with 0.557 *grams* of the first reactant.

a. $Al(s) + Br_2(l) \rightarrow AlBr_3(s)$
b. $Hg(s) + HClO_4(aq) \rightarrow Hg(ClO_4)_2(aq) + H_2(g)$
c. $K(s) + P(s) \rightarrow K_3P(s)$
d. $CH_4(g) + Cl_2(g) \rightarrow CCl_4(l) + HCl(g)$

25. For each of the following *unbalanced* equations, calculate how many *grams of each product* would be produced by complete reaction of 12.5 g of the reactant indicated in boldface. Indicate clearly the mole ratio used for the conversion.

a. $TiBr_4(g) + \mathbf{H_2}(g) \rightarrow Ti(s) + HBr(g)$
b. $\mathbf{SiH_4}(g) + NH_3(g) \rightarrow Si_3N_4(s) + H_2(g)$
c. $NO(g) + \mathbf{H_2}(g) \rightarrow N_2(g) + 2H_2O(l)$
d. $\mathbf{Cu_2S}(s) \rightarrow Cu(s) + S(g)$

26. For each of the following *balanced* equations, calculate how many *grams of each product* would be produced by complete reaction of 15.0 g of the reactant indicated in boldface.

a. $\mathbf{2BCl_3}(s) + 3H_2(g) \rightarrow 2B(s) + 6HCl(g)$
b. $\mathbf{2Cu_2S}(s) + 3O_2(g) \rightarrow 2Cu_2O(s) + 2SO_2(g)$
c. $2Cu_2O(s) + \mathbf{Cu_2S}(s) \rightarrow 6Cu(s) + SO_2(g)$
d. $CaCO_3(s) + \mathbf{SiO_2}(s) \rightarrow CaSiO_3(s) + CO_2(g)$

All even-numbered Questions and Problems have answers in the back of this book and solutions in the Solutions Guide.

27. "Smelling salts," which are used to revive someone who has fainted, typically contain ammonium carbonate, $(NH_4)_2CO_3$. Ammonium carbonate decomposes readily to form ammonia, carbon dioxide, and water. The strong odor of the ammonia usually restores consciousness in the person who has fainted. The unbalanced equation is

$$(NH_4)_2CO_3(s) \rightarrow NH_3(g) + CO_2(g) + H_2O(g)$$

Calculate the mass of ammonia gas that is produced if 1.25 g of ammonium carbonate decomposes completely.

28. Calcium carbide, CaC_2, can be produced in an electric furnace by strongly heating calcium oxide (lime) with carbon. The unbalanced equation is

$$CaO(s) + C(s) \rightarrow CaC_2(s) + CO(g)$$

Calcium carbide is useful because it reacts readily with water to form the flammable gas acetylene, C_2H_2, which is used extensively in the welding industry. The unbalanced equation is

$$CaC_2(s) + H_2O(l) \rightarrow C_2H_2(g) + Ca(OH)_2(s)$$

What mass of acetylene gas, C_2H_2, would be produced by complete reaction of 3.75 g of calcium carbide?

29. When elemental carbon is burned in the open atmosphere, with plenty of oxygen gas present, the product is carbon dioxide.

$$C(s) + O_2(g) \rightarrow CO_2(g)$$

However, when the amount of oxygen present during the burning of the carbon is restricted, carbon monoxide is more likely to result.

$$2C(s) + O_2(g) \rightarrow 2CO(g)$$

What mass of each product is expected when a 5.00-g sample of pure carbon is burned under each of these conditions?

30. If baking soda (sodium hydrogen carbonate) is heated strongly, the following reaction occurs:

$$2NaHCO_3(s) \rightarrow Na_2CO_3(s) + H_2O(g) + CO_2(g)$$

Calculate the mass of sodium carbonate that will remain if a 1.52-g sample of sodium hydrogen carbonate is heated.

31. Although we usually think of substances as "burning" only in oxygen gas, the process of rapid oxidation to produce a flame may also take place in other strongly oxidizing gases. For example, when iron is heated and placed in pure chlorine gas, the iron "burns" according to the following (unbalanced) reaction:

$$Fe(s) + Cl_2(g) \rightarrow FeCl_3(s)$$

How many milligrams of iron(III) chloride result when 15.5 mg of iron is reacted with an excess of chlorine gas?

32. When yeast is added to a solution of glucose or fructose, the sugars are said to undergo *fermentation* and ethyl alcohol is produced.

$$C_6H_{12}O_6(aq) \rightarrow 2C_2H_5OH(aq) + 2CO_2(g)$$

This is the reaction by which wines are produced from grape juice. Calculate the mass of ethyl alcohol, C_2H_5OH, produced when 5.25 g of glucose, $C_6H_{12}O_6$, undergoes this reaction.

33. Sulfurous acid is unstable in aqueous solution and gradually decomposes to water and sulfur dioxide gas (which explains the choking odor associated with sulfurous acid solutions).

$$H_2SO_3(aq) \rightarrow H_2O(l) + SO_2(g)$$

If 4.25 g of sulfurous acid undergoes this reaction, what mass of sulfur dioxide is released?

34. Small quantities of ammonia gas can be generated in the laboratory by heating an ammonium salt with a strong base. For example, ammonium chloride reacts with sodium hydroxide according to the following balanced equation:

$$NH_4Cl(s) + NaOH(s) \rightarrow NH_3(g) + NaCl(s) + H_2O(g)$$

What mass of ammonia gas is produced if 1.39 g of ammonium chloride reacts completely?

35. Elemental phosphorus burns in oxygen with an intensely hot flame, producing a brilliant light and clouds of the oxide product. These properties of the combustion of phosphorus have led to its being used in bombs and incendiary devices for warfare.

$$P_4(s) + 5O_2(g) \rightarrow 2P_2O_5(s)$$

If 4.95 g of phosphorus is burned, what mass of oxygen does it combine with?

36. Although we tend to make less use of mercury these days because of the environmental problems created by its improper disposal, mercury is still an important metal because of its unusual property of existing as a liquid at room temperature. One process by which mercury is produced industrially is through the heating of its common ore cinnabar (mercuric sulfide, HgS) with lime (calcium oxide, CaO).

$$4HgS(s) + 4CaO(s) \rightarrow 4Hg(l) + 3CaS(s) + CaSO_4(s)$$

What mass of mercury would be produced by complete reaction of 10.0 kg of HgS?

37. Ammonium nitrate has been used as a high explosive because it is unstable and decomposes into several gaseous substances. The rapid expansion of the gaseous substances produces the explosive force.

$$NH_4NO_3(s) \rightarrow N_2(g) + O_2(g) + H_2O(g)$$

Calculate the mass of each product gas if 1.25 g of ammonium nitrate reacts.

38. If common sugars are heated too strongly, they char as they decompose into carbon and water vapor. For example, if sucrose (table sugar) is heated, the reaction is

$$C_{12}H_{22}O_{11}(s) \rightarrow 12C(s) + 11H_2O(g)$$

What mass of carbon is produced if 1.19 g of sucrose decomposes completely?

All even-numbered Questions and Problems have answers in the back of this book and solutions in the Solutions Guide.

39. Thionyl chloride, $SOCl_2$, is used as a very powerful drying agent in many synthetic chemistry experiments in which the presence of even small amounts of water would be detrimental. The unbalanced chemical equation is

$$SOCl_2(l) + H_2O(l) \rightarrow SO_2(g) + HCl(g)$$

Calculate the mass of water consumed by complete reaction of 35.0 g of $SOCl_2$.

F 40. In the "Chemistry in Focus" segment *Cars of the Future,* the claim is made that the combustion of gasoline for some cars causes about 1 lb of CO_2 to be produced for each mile traveled.

Estimate the gas mileage of a car that produces about 1 lb of CO_2 per mile traveled. Assume gasoline has a density of 0.75 g/mL and is 100% octane (C_8H_{18}). While this last part is not true, it is close enough for an estimation. The reaction can be represented by the following *un*balanced chemical equation:

$$C_8H_{18} + O_2 \rightarrow CO_2 + H_2O$$

9.5 Calculations Involving a Limiting Reactant

QUESTIONS

41. Imagine you are chatting with a friend who has not yet taken a chemistry course. How would you explain the concept of *limiting reactant* to her? Your textbook uses the analogy of an automobile manufacturer ordering four wheels for each engine ordered as an example. Can you think of another analogy that might help your friend to understand the concept?

42. Explain how one determines which reactant in a process is the limiting reactant. Does this depend only on the masses of the reactant present? Is the mole ratio in which the reactants combine involved?

43. What is the *theoretical yield* for a reaction, and how does this quantity depend on the limiting reactant?

44. What does it mean to say a reactant is present "in excess" in a process? Can the *limiting reactant* be present in excess? Does the presence of an excess of a reactant affect the mass of products expected for a reaction?

PROBLEMS

45. For each of the following *unbalanced* reactions, suppose exactly 5.00 g of *each reactant* is taken. Determine which reactant is limiting, and also determine what mass of the excess reagent will remain after the limiting reactant is consumed.

a. $Na_2B_4O_7(s) + H_2SO_4(aq) + H_2O(l) \rightarrow$
$$H_3BO_3(s) + Na_2SO_4(aq)$$
b. $CaC_2(s) + H_2O(l) \rightarrow Ca(OH)_2(s) + C_2H_2(g)$
c. $NaCl(s) + H_2SO_4(l) \rightarrow HCl(g) + Na_2SO_4(s)$
d. $SiO_2(s) + C(s) \rightarrow Si(l) + CO(g)$

46. For each of the following *unbalanced* chemical equations, suppose that exactly 5.00 g of *each* reactant is taken. Determine which reactant is limiting, and calculate what mass of each product is expected (assuming that the limiting reactant is completely consumed).

a. $S(s) + H_2SO_4(aq) \rightarrow SO_2(g) + H_2O(l)$
b. $MnO_2(s) + H_2SO_4(l) \rightarrow Mn(SO_4)_2(s) + H_2O(l)$
c. $H_2S(g) + O_2(g) \rightarrow SO_2(g) + H_2O(l)$
d. $AgNO_3(aq) + Al(s) \rightarrow Ag(s) + Al(NO_3)_3(aq)$

47. For each of the following *unbalanced* chemical equations, suppose 10.0 g of *each* reactant is taken. Show by calculation which reactant is the limiting reagent. Calculate the mass of each product that is expected.

a. $C_3H_8(g) + O_2(g) \rightarrow CO_2(g) + H_2O(g)$
b. $Al(s) + Cl_2(g) \rightarrow AlCl_3(s)$
c. $NaOH(s) + CO_2(g) \rightarrow Na_2CO_3(s) + H_2O(l)$
d. $NaHCO_3(s) + HCl(aq) \rightarrow$
$$NaCl(aq) + H_2O(l) + CO_2(g)$$

48. For each of the following *unbalanced* chemical equations, suppose that exactly 1.00 g of *each* reactant is taken. Determine which reactant is limiting, and calculate what mass of the product in boldface is expected (assuming that the limiting reactant is completely consumed).

a. $CS_2(l) + O_2(g) \rightarrow \mathbf{CO_2}(g) + SO_2(g)$
b. $NH_3(g) + CO_2(g) \rightarrow CN_2H_4O(s) + \mathbf{H_2O}(g)$
c. $H_2(g) + MnO_2(s) \rightarrow MnO(s) + \mathbf{H_2O}(g)$
d. $I_2(l) + Cl_2(g) \rightarrow \mathbf{ICl}(g)$

49. For each of the following *unbalanced* chemical equations, suppose 1.00 g of *each* reactant is taken. Show by calculation which reactant is limiting. Calculate the mass of each product that is expected.

a. $UO_2(s) + HF(aq) \rightarrow UF_4(aq) + H_2O(l)$
b. $NaNO_3(aq) + H_2SO_4(aq) \rightarrow Na_2SO_4(aq) + HNO_3(aq)$
c. $Zn(s) + HCl(aq) \rightarrow ZnCl_2(aq) + H_2(g)$
d. $B(OH)_3(s) + CH_3OH(l) \rightarrow B(OCH_3)_3(s) + H_2O(l)$

50. For each of the following *unbalanced* chemical equations, suppose 10.0 mg of *each* reactant is taken. Show by calculation which reactant is limiting. Calculate the mass of each product that is expected.

a. $CO(g) + H_2(g) \rightarrow CH_3OH(l)$
b. $Al(s) + I_2(s) \rightarrow AlI_3(s)$
c. $Ca(OH)_2(aq) + HBr(aq) \rightarrow CaBr_2(aq) + H_2O(l)$
d. $Cr(s) + H_3PO_4(aq) \rightarrow CrPO_4(s) + H_2(g)$

51. Lead(II) carbonate, also called "white lead," was formerly used as a pigment in white paints. However, because of its toxicity, lead can no longer be used in paints intended for residential homes. Lead(II) carbonate is prepared industrially by reaction of aqueous lead(II) acetate with carbon dioxide gas. The unbalanced equation is

$$Pb(C_2H_3O_2)_2(aq) + H_2O(l) + CO_2(g) \rightarrow$$
$$PbCO_3(s) + HC_2H_3O_2(aq)$$

Suppose an aqueous solution containing 1.25 g of lead(II) acetate is treated with 5.95 g of carbon dioxide. Calculate the theoretical yield of lead carbonate.

All even-numbered Questions and Problems have answers in the back of this book and solutions in the Solutions Guide.

52. Copper(II) sulfate has been used extensively as a fungicide (kills fungus) and herbicide (kills plants). Copper(II) sulfate can be prepared in the laboratory by reaction of copper(II) oxide with sulfuric acid. The unbalanced equation is

$$CuO(s) + H_2SO_4(aq) \rightarrow CuSO_4(aq) + H_2O(l)$$

If 2.49 g of copper(II) oxide is treated with 5.05 g of pure sulfuric acid, which reactant would limit the quantity of copper(II) sulfate that could be produced?

53. Lead(II) oxide from an ore can be reduced to elemental lead by heating in a furnace with carbon.

$$PbO(s) + C(s) \rightarrow Pb(l) + CO(g)$$

Calculate the expected yield of lead if 50.0 kg of lead oxide is heated with 50.0 kg of carbon.

54. If steel wool (iron) is heated until it glows and is placed in a bottle containing pure oxygen, the iron reacts spectacularly to produce iron(III) oxide.

$$Fe(s) + O_2(g) \rightarrow Fe_2O_3(s)$$

If 1.25 g of iron is heated and placed in a bottle containing 0.0204 mole of oxygen gas, what mass of iron(III) oxide is produced?

55. A common method for determining how much chloride ion is present in a sample is to precipitate the chloride from an aqueous solution of the sample with silver nitrate solution and then to weigh the silver chloride that results. The balanced net ionic reaction is

$$Ag^+(aq) + Cl^-(aq) \rightarrow AgCl(s)$$

Suppose a 5.45-g sample of pure sodium chloride is dissolved in water and is then treated with a solution containing 1.15 g of silver nitrate. Will this quantity of silver nitrate be capable of precipitating *all* the chloride ion from the sodium chloride sample?

56. Although many sulfate salts are soluble in water, calcium sulfate is not (Table 7.1). Therefore, a solution of calcium chloride will react with sodium sulfate solution to produce a precipitate of calcium sulfate. The balanced equation is

$$CaCl_2(aq) + Na_2SO_4(aq) \rightarrow CaSO_4(s) + 2NaCl(aq)$$

If a solution containing 5.21 g of calcium chloride is combined with a solution containing 4.95 g of sodium sulfate, which is the limiting reactant? Which reactant is present in excess?

57. Hydrogen peroxide is used as a cleaning agent in the treatment of cuts and abrasions for several reasons. It is an oxidizing agent that can directly kill many microorganisms; it decomposes upon contact with blood, releasing elemental oxygen gas (which inhibits the growth of anaerobic microorganisms); and it foams upon contact with blood, which provides a cleansing action. In the laboratory, small quantities of hydrogen peroxide can be prepared by the action of an acid on an alkaline earth metal peroxide, such as barium peroxide.

$$BaO_2(s) + 2HCl(aq) \rightarrow H_2O_2(aq) + BaCl_2(aq)$$

What amount of hydrogen peroxide should result when 1.50 g of barium peroxide is treated with 25.0 mL of hydrochloric acid solution containing 0.0272 g of HCl per mL?

58. Silicon carbide, SiC, is one of the hardest materials known. Surpassed in hardness only by diamond, it is sometimes known commercially as carborundum. Silicon carbide is used primarily as an abrasive for sandpaper and is manufactured by heating common sand (silicon dioxide, SiO_2) with carbon in a furnace.

$$SiO_2(s) + C(s) \rightarrow CO(g) + SiC(s)$$

What mass of silicon carbide should result when 1.0 kg of pure sand is heated with an excess of carbon?

9.6 Percent Yield

QUESTIONS

59. Your text talks about several sorts of "yield" when experiments are performed in the laboratory. Students often confuse these terms. Define, compare, and contrast what are meant by *theoretical* yield, *actual* yield, and *percent* yield.

60. The text explains that one reason why the actual yield for a reaction may be less than the theoretical yield is side reactions. Suggest some other reasons why the percent yield for a reaction might not be 100%.

61. According to his prelaboratory theoretical yield calculations, a student's experiment should have produced 1.44 g of magnesium oxide. When he weighed his product after reaction, only 1.23 g of magnesium oxide was present. What is the student's percent yield?

62. Small quantities of oxygen gas can be generated in the laboratory by heating potassium chlorate.

$$2KClO_3(s) \rightarrow 2KCl(s) + 3O_2(g)$$

If 4.74 g of potassium chlorate is heated, what theoretical mass of oxygen gas should be produced? If only 1.51 g of oxygen is actually obtained, what is the percent yield?

PROBLEMS

63. The compound sodium thiosulfate pentahydrate, $Na_2S_2O_3 \cdot 5H_2O$, is important commercially to the photography business as "hypo," because it has the ability to dissolve unreacted silver salts from photographic film during development. Sodium thiosulfate pentahydrate can be produced by boiling elemental sulfur in an aqueous solution of sodium sulfite.

$$S_8(s) + Na_2SO_3(aq) + H_2O(l) \rightarrow Na_2S_2O_3 \cdot 5H_2O(s)$$
$$\text{(unbalanced)}$$

What is the theoretical yield of sodium thiosulfate pentahydrate when 3.25 g of sulfur is boiled with 13.1 g of sodium sulfite? Sodium thiosulfate pentahydrate is very soluble in water. What is the percent yield of the synthesis if a student doing this experiment is able to isolate (collect) only 5.26 g of the product?

64. Alkali metal hydroxides are sometimes used to "scrub" excess carbon dioxide from the air in closed spaces (such as submarines and spacecraft). For example, lithium hydroxide reacts with carbon dioxide according to the unbalanced chemical equation

$$LiOH(s) + CO_2(g) \rightarrow Li_2CO_3(s) + H_2O(g)$$

Suppose a lithium hydroxide canister contains 155 g of $LiOH(s)$. What mass of $CO_2(g)$ will the canister be able to absorb? If it is found that after 24 hours of use the canister has absorbed 102 g of carbon dioxide, what percentage of its capacity has been reached?

65. Although they were formerly called the inert gases, at least the heavier elements of Group 8 do form relatively stable compounds. For example, xenon combines directly with elemental fluorine at elevated temperatures in the presence of a nickel catalyst.

$$Xe(g) + 2F_2(g) \rightarrow XeF_4(s)$$

What is the theoretical mass of xenon tetrafluoride that should form when 130. g of xenon is reacted with 100. g of F_2? What is the percent yield if only 145 g of XeF_4 is actually isolated?

66. A common undergraduate laboratory analysis for the amount of sulfate ion in an unknown sample is to precipitate and weigh the sulfate ion as barium sulfate.

$$Ba^{2+}(aq) + SO_4^{2-}(aq) \rightarrow BaSO_4(s)$$

The precipitate produced, however, is very finely divided, and frequently some is lost during filtration before weighing. If a sample containing 1.12 g of sulfate ion is treated with 5.02 g of barium chloride, what is the theoretical yield of barium sulfate to be expected? If only 2.02 g of barium sulfate is actually collected, what is the percent yield?

Additional Problems

67. Natural waters often contain relatively high levels of calcium ion, Ca^{2+}, and hydrogen carbonate ion (bicarbonate), HCO_3^-, from the leaching of minerals into the water. When such water is used commercially or in the home, heating of the water leads to the formation of solid calcium carbonate, $CaCO_3$, which forms a deposit ("scale") on the interior of boilers, pipes, and other plumbing fixtures.

$$Ca(HCO_3)_2(aq) \rightarrow CaCO_3(s) + CO_2(g) + H_2O(l)$$

If a sample of well water contains 2.0×10^{-3} mg of $Ca(HCO_3)_2$ per milliliter, what mass of $CaCO_3$ scale would 1.0 mL of this water be capable of depositing?

68. One process for the commercial production of baking soda (sodium hydrogen carbonate) involves the following reaction, in which the carbon dioxide is used in its solid form ("dry ice") both to serve as a source of reactant and to cool the reaction system to a temperature low enough for the sodium hydrogen carbonate to precipitate:

$$NaCl(aq) + NH_3(aq) + H_2O(l) + CO_2(s) \rightarrow$$
$$NH_4Cl(aq) + NaHCO_3(s)$$

Because they are relatively cheap, sodium chloride and water are typically present in excess. What is the expected yield of $NaHCO_3$ when one performs such a synthesis using 10.0 g of ammonia and 15.0 g of dry ice, with an excess of NaCl and water?

69. A favorite demonstration among chemistry instructors, to show that the properties of a compound differ from those of its constituent elements, involves iron filings and powdered sulfur. If the instructor takes samples of iron and sulfur and just mixes them together, the two elements can be separated from one another with a magnet (iron is attracted to a magnet, sulfur is not). If the instructor then combines and *heats* the mixture of iron and sulfur, a reaction takes place and the elements combine to form iron(II) sulfide (which is not attracted by a magnet).

$$Fe(s) + S(s) \rightarrow FeS(s)$$

Suppose 5.25 g of iron filings is combined with 12.7 g of sulfur. What is the theoretical yield of iron(II) sulfide?

70. When the sugar glucose, $C_6H_{12}O_6$, is burned in air, carbon dioxide and water vapor are produced. Write the balanced chemical equation for this process, and calculate the theoretical yield of carbon dioxide when 1.00 g of glucose is burned completely.

71. When elemental copper is strongly heated with sulfur, a mixture of CuS and Cu_2S is produced, with CuS predominating.

$$Cu(s) + S(s) \rightarrow CuS(s)$$
$$2Cu(s) + S(s) \rightarrow Cu_2S(s)$$

What is the theoretical yield of CuS when 31.8 g of $Cu(s)$ is heated with 50.0 g of S? (Assume only CuS is produced in the reaction.) What is the percent yield of CuS if only 40.0 g of CuS can be isolated from the mixture?

72. Barium chloride solutions are used in chemical analysis for the quantitative precipitation of sulfate ion from solution.

$$Ba^{2+}(aq) + SO_4^{2-}(aq) \rightarrow BaSO_4(s)$$

Suppose a solution is known to contain on the order of 150 mg of sulfate ion. What mass of barium chloride should be added to guarantee precipitation of all the sulfate ion?

73. The traditional method of analysis for the amount of chloride ion present in a sample is to dissolve the

sample in water and then slowly to add a solution of silver nitrate. Silver chloride is very insoluble in water, and by adding a slight excess of silver nitrate, it is possible effectively to remove all chloride ion from the sample.

$$Ag^+(aq) + Cl^+(aq) \rightarrow AgCl(s)$$

Suppose a 1.054-g sample is known to contain 10.3% chloride ion by mass. What mass of silver nitrate must be used to completely precipitate the chloride ion from the sample? What mass of silver chloride will be obtained?

74. For each of the following reactions, give the balanced equation for the reaction and state the meaning of the equation in terms of numbers of *individual molecules* and in terms of *moles* of molecules.

a. $UO_2(s) + HF(aq) \rightarrow UF_4(aq) + H_2O(l)$
b. $NaC_2H_3O_2(aq) + H_2SO_4(aq) \rightarrow$
$$Na_2SO_4(aq) + HC_2H_3O_2(aq)$$
c. $Mg(s) + HCl(aq) \rightarrow MgCl_2(aq) + H_2(g)$
d. $B_2O_3(s) + H_2O(l) \rightarrow B(OH)_3(aq)$

75. True or false? For the reaction represented by the balanced chemical equation

$$Mg(OH)_2(aq) + 2HCl(aq) \rightarrow 2H_2O(l) + MgCl_2(aq)$$

for 0.40 mole of $Mg(OH)_2$, 0.20 mol of HCl will be needed.

76. Consider the balanced equation

$$C_3H_8(g) + 5O_2(g) \rightarrow 3CO_2(g) + 4H_2O(g)$$

What mole ratio enables you to calculate the number of moles of oxygen needed to react exactly with a given number of moles of $C_3H_8(g)$? What mole ratios enable you to calculate how many moles of each product form from a given number of moles of C_3H_8?

77. For each of the following balanced reactions, calculate how many *moles of each product* would be produced by complete conversion of *0.50 mole* of the reactant indicated in boldface. Indicate clearly the mole ratio used for the conversion.

a. $\mathbf{2H_2O_2}(l) \rightarrow 2H_2O(l) + O_2(g)$
b. $\mathbf{2KClO_3}(s) \rightarrow 2KCl(s) + 3O_2(g)$
c. $\mathbf{2Al}(s) + 6HCl(aq) \rightarrow 2AlCl_3(aq) + 3H_2(g)$
d. $\mathbf{C_3H_8}(g) + 5O_2(g) \rightarrow 3CO_2(g) + 4H_2O(g)$

78. For each of the following balanced equations, indicate how many *moles of the product* could be produced by complete reaction of *1.00 g* of the reactant indicated in boldface. Indicate clearly the mole ratio used for the conversion.

a. $\mathbf{NH_3}(g) + HCl(g) \rightarrow NH_4Cl(s)$
b. $\mathbf{CaO}(s) + CO_2(g) \rightarrow CaCO_3(s)$
c. $\mathbf{4Na}(s) + O_2(g) \rightarrow 2Na_2O(s)$
d. $\mathbf{2P}(s) + 3Cl_2(g) \rightarrow 2PCl_3(l)$

79. Using the average atomic masses given inside the front cover of the text, calculate how many *moles of* each substance the following masses represent.

a. 4.21 g of copper(II) sulfate
b. 7.94 g of barium nitrate
c. 1.24 mg of water
d. 9.79 g of tungsten
e. 1.45 lb of sulfur
f. 4.65 g of ethyl alcohol, C_2H_5OH
g. 12.01 g of carbon

80. Using the average atomic masses given inside the front cover of the text, calculate the *mass in grams* of each of the following samples.

a. 5.0 moles of nitric acid
b. 0.000305 mole of mercury
c. 2.31×10^{-5} mole of potassium chromate
d. 10.5 moles of aluminum chloride
e. 4.9×10^4 moles of sulfur hexafluoride
f. 125 moles of ammonia
g. 0.01205 mole of sodium peroxide

81. For each of the following *incomplete* and *unbalanced* equations, indicate how many *moles* of the *second reactant* would be required to react completely with *0.145 mol* of the *first reactant*.

a. $BaCl_2(aq) + H_2SO_4 \rightarrow$
b. $AgNO_3(aq) + NaCl(aq) \rightarrow$
c. $Pb(NO_3)_2(aq) + Na_2CO_3(aq) \rightarrow$
d. $C_3H_8(g) + O_2(g) \rightarrow$

82. One step in the commercial production of sulfuric acid, H_2SO_4, involves the conversion of sulfur dioxide, SO_2, into sulfur trioxide, SO_3.

$$2SO_2(g) + O_2(g) \rightarrow 2SO_3(g)$$

If 150 kg of SO_2 reacts completely, what mass of SO_3 should result?

83. Many metals occur naturally as sulfide compounds; examples include ZnS and CoS. Air pollution often accompanies the processing of these ores, because toxic sulfur dioxide is released as the ore is converted from the sulfide to the oxide by roasting (smelting). For example, consider the unbalanced equation for the roasting reaction for zinc:

$$ZnS(s) + O_2(g) \rightarrow ZnO(s) + SO_2(g)$$

How many kilograms of sulfur dioxide are produced when 1.0×10^2 kg of ZnS is roasted in excess oxygen by this process?

84. If sodium peroxide is added to water, elemental oxygen gas is generated:

$$Na_2O_2(s) + H_2O(l) \rightarrow NaOH(aq) + O_2(g)$$

Suppose 3.25 g of sodium peroxide is added to a large excess of water. What mass of oxygen gas will be produced?

85. When elemental copper is placed in a solution of silver nitrate, the following oxidation–reduction reaction takes place, forming elemental silver:

$$Cu(s) + 2AgNO_3(aq) \rightarrow Cu(NO_3)_2(aq) + 2Ag(s)$$

What mass of copper is required to remove all the silver from a silver nitrate solution containing 1.95 mg of silver nitrate?

86. When small quantities of elemental hydrogen gas are needed for laboratory work, the hydrogen is often generated by chemical reaction of a metal with acid. For example, zinc reacts with hydrochloric acid, releasing gaseous elemental hydrogen:

$$Zn(s) + 2HCl(aq) \rightarrow ZnCl_2(aq) + H_2(g)$$

What mass of hydrogen gas is produced when 2.50 g of zinc is reacted with excess aqueous hydrochloric acid?

87. The gaseous hydrocarbon acetylene, C_2H_2, is used in welders' torches because of the large amount of heat released when acetylene burns with oxygen.

$$2C_2H_2(g) + 5O_2(g) \rightarrow 4CO_2(g) + 2H_2O(g)$$

How many grams of oxygen gas are needed for the complete combustion of 150 g of acetylene?

88. For each of the following *unbalanced* chemical equations, suppose exactly 5.0 g of each reactant is taken. Determine which reactant is limiting, and calculate what mass of each product is expected, assuming that the limiting reactant is completely consumed.

a. $Na(s) + Br_2(l) \rightarrow NaBr(s)$
b. $Zn(s) + CuSO_4(aq) \rightarrow ZnSO_4(aq) + Cu(s)$
c. $NH_4Cl(aq) + NaOH(aq) \rightarrow$
$$NH_3(g) + H_2O(l) + NaCl(aq)$$
d. $Fe_2O_3(s) + CO(g) \rightarrow Fe(s) + CO_2(g)$

89. For each of the following *unbalanced* chemical equations, suppose 25.0 g of each reactant is taken. Show by calculation which reactant is limiting. Calculate the theoretical yield in grams of the product in boldface.

a. $C_2H_5OH(l) + O_2(g) \rightarrow \mathbf{CO_2}(g) + H_2O(l)$
b. $N_2(g) + O_2(g) \rightarrow \mathbf{NO}(g)$
c. $NaClO_2(aq) + Cl_2(g) \rightarrow ClO_2(g) + \mathbf{NaCl}(aq)$
d. $H_2(g) + N_2(g) \rightarrow \mathbf{NH_3}(g)$

90. Hydrazine, N_2H_4, emits a large quantity of energy when it reacts with oxygen, which has led to hydrazine's use as a fuel for rockets:

$$N_2H_4(l) + O_2(g) \rightarrow N_2(g) + 2H_2O(g)$$

How many moles of each of the gaseous products are produced when 20.0 g of pure hydrazine is ignited in the presence of 20.0 g of pure oxygen? How many grams of each product are produced?

91. Although elemental chlorine, Cl_2, is added to drinking water supplies primarily to kill microorganisms, another beneficial reaction that also takes place removes sulfides (which would impart unpleasant odors or tastes to the water). For example, the noxious-smelling gas hydrogen sulfide (its odor resembles that of rotten eggs) is removed from water by chlorine by the following reaction:

$$H_2S(aq) + Cl_2(aq) \rightarrow HCl(aq) + S_8(s) \quad \text{(unbalanced)}$$

What mass of sulfur is removed from the water when 50. L of water containing 1.5×10^{-5} g of H_2S per liter is treated with 1.0 g of $Cl_2(g)$?

92. Before going to lab, a student read in his lab manual that the percent yield for a difficult reaction to be studied was likely to be only 40.% of the theoretical yield. The student's prelab stoichiometric calculations predict that the theoretical yield should be 12.5 g. What is the student's actual yield likely to be?

EXAMPLE 10.3   Calculations Involving Specific Heat Capacity

a. What quantity of energy (in joules) is required to heat a piece of iron weighing 1.3 g from 25 °C to 46 °C?

b. What is the answer in calories?

SOLUTION

Where Are We Going?

We want to determine the amount of energy (units of joules and calories) to increase the temperature of 1.3 g, of iron from 25° C to 46° C.

What Do We Know?

- The mass of iron is 1.3 g, and the temperature is increased from 25° C to 46° C.

What Information Do We Need?

- We need the specific heat capacity of iron and the conversion factor between joules and calories.

How Do We Get There?

a. It is helpful to draw the following diagram to represent the problem.

| 1.3 g iron $T = 25\ °C$ | ⇨ ? joules | 1.3 g iron $T = 46\ °C$ |

From Table 10.1 we see that the specific heat capacity of iron is 0.45 J/g °C. That is, it takes 0.45 J to raise the temperature of a 1-g piece of iron by 1 °C.

| 1.0 g iron $T = 25\ °C$ | ⇨ 0.45 J | 1.0 g iron $T = 26\ °C$ |

In this case our sample is 1.3 g, so 1.3×0.45 J is required for *each* degree of temperature increase.

| 1.3 g iron $T = 25\ °C$ | ⇨ 1.3 × 0.45 J | 1.3 g iron $T = 26\ °C$ |

Because the temperature increase is 21 °C (46 °C − 25 °C = 21 °C), the total amount of energy required is

$$0.45\ \frac{J}{g\ °C} \times 1.3\ g \times 21\ °C = 12\ J$$

| 1.3 g iron $T = 25\ °C$ | ⇨ 21 × 1.3 × 0.45 J | 1.3 g iron $T = 46\ °C$ |

MATH SKILL BUILDER
The result you will get on your calculator is 0.45 × 1.3 × 21 = 12.285, which rounds off to 12.

Note that the final units are joules, as they should be.

b. To calculate this energy in calories, we can use the definition 1 cal = 4.184 J to construct the appropriate conversion factor. We want to change from joules to calories, so cal must be in the numerator and J in the denominator, where it cancels:

$$12\ \cancel{J} \times \frac{1\ cal}{4.184\ \cancel{J}} = 2.9\ cal$$

Remember that 1 in this case is an exact number by definition and therefore does not limit the number of significant figures (the number 12 is limiting here).

REALITY CHECK The units (joules and calories) are correct, and the answer is reported to the correct number of significant figures (two).

Self-Check EXERCISE 10.3 A 5.63-g sample of solid gold is heated from 21 °C to 32 °C. How much energy (in joules and calories) is required?

See Problems 10.31 through 10.36. ■

Note that in Example 10.3, to calculate the energy (heat) required, we took the product of the specific heat capacity, the sample size in grams, and the change in temperature in Celsius degrees.

$$\begin{array}{c}\text{Energy (heat)} \\ \text{required } (Q)\end{array} = \begin{array}{c}\text{Specific heat} \\ \text{capacity } (s)\end{array} \times \begin{array}{c}\text{Mass } (m) \text{ in} \\ \text{grams of} \\ \text{sample}\end{array} \times \begin{array}{c}\text{Change in} \\ \text{temperature} \\ (\Delta T) \text{ in °C}\end{array}$$

We can represent this by the following equation:

$$Q = s \times m \times \Delta T$$

MATH SKILL BUILDER
The symbol Δ (the Greek letter delta) is shorthand for "change in."

where

Q = energy (heat) required

s = specific heat capacity

m = mass of the sample in grams

ΔT = change in temperature in Celsius degrees

This equation always applies when a substance is being heated (or cooled) and no change of state occurs. Before you begin to use this equation, however, make sure you understand what it means.

EXAMPLE 10.4 | **Specific Heat Capacity Calculations: Using the Equation**

A 1.6-g sample of a metal that has the appearance of gold requires 5.8 J of energy to change its temperature from 23 °C to 41 °C. Is the metal pure gold?

SOLUTION

Where Are We Going?

We want to determine if a metal is gold.

What Do We Know?

- The mass of metal is 1.6 g, and 5.8 J of energy is required to increase the temperature from 23° C to 41° C.

What Information Do We Need?

- We need the specific heat capacity of gold.

Firewalking: Magic or Science?

For millennia people have been amazed at the ability of Eastern mystics to walk across beds of glowing coals without any apparent discomfort. Even in the United States, thousands of people have performed feats of firewalking as part of motivational seminars. How can this be possible? Do firewalkers have supernatural powers?

Actually, there are good scientific explanations of why firewalking is possible. First, human tissue is mainly composed of water, which has a relatively large specific heat capacity. This means that a large amount of energy must be transferred from the coals to change significantly the temperature of the feet. During the brief contact between feet and coals involved in firewalking, there is relatively little time for energy flow, so the feet do not reach a high enough temperature to cause damage.

Also, although the surface of the coals has a very high temperature, the red-hot layer is very thin. Therefore, the quantity of energy available to heat the feet is smaller than might be expected.

Thus, although firewalking is impressive, there are several scientific reasons why anyone with the proper training should be able to do it on a properly prepared bed of coals. (Don't try this on your own!)

A group of firewalkers in Japan.

AP Photo/Itsuo Inouye

How Do We Get There?

We can represent the data given in this problem by the following diagram:

1.6 g metal $T = 23\ °C$ ⇨ 5.8 J ⇨ 1.6 g metal $T = 41\ °C$

$$\Delta T = 41\ °C - 23\ °C = 18\ °C$$

Using the data given, we can calculate the value of the specific heat capacity for the metal and compare this value to the one for gold given in Table 10.1. We know that

$$Q = s \times m \times \Delta T$$

or, pictorially,

1.6 g metal $T = 23\ °C$ ⇨ $5.8\ J = ? \times 1.6 \times 18$ ⇨ 1.6 g metal $T = 41\ °C$

When we divide both sides of the equation

$$Q = s \times m \times \Delta T$$

by $m \times \Delta T$, we get

$$\frac{Q}{m \times \Delta T} = s$$

Thus, using the data given, we can calculate the value of s. In this case,

$\quad Q$ = energy (heat) required = 5.8 J

$\quad m$ = mass of the sample = 1.6 g

$\quad \Delta T$ = change in temperature = 18 °C (41 °C − 23 °C = 18 °C)

Thus

$$s = \frac{Q}{m \times \Delta T} = \frac{5.8 \text{ J}}{(1.6 \text{ g})(18 \text{ °C})} = 0.20 \text{ J/g °C}$$

MATH SKILL BUILDER
The result you will get on your calculator is 5.8/(1.6 × 18) = 0.2013889, which rounds off to 0.20.

From Table 10.1, the specific heat capacity for gold is 0.13 J/g °C. Thus the metal must not be pure gold.

Self-Check EXERCISE 10.4   A 2.8-g sample of pure metal requires 10.1 J of energy to change its temperature from 21 °C to 36 °C. What is this metal? (Use Table 10.1.)

See Problems 10.31 through 10.36. ■

Self-Check EXE

10.6   Thermochemistry (Enthalpy)

OBJECTIVE: To consider the heat (enthalpy) of chemical reactions.

We have seen that some reactions are exothermic (produce heat energy) and other reactions are endothermic (absorb heat energy). Chemists also like to know exactly how much energy is produced or absorbed by a given reaction. To make that process more convenient, we have invented a special energy function called **enthalpy,** which is designated by H. For a reaction occurring under conditions of constant pressure, the change in enthalpy (ΔH) is equal to the energy that flows as heat. That is,

$$\Delta H_p = \text{heat}$$

where the subscript "p" indicates that the process has occurred under conditions of constant pressure and Δ means "a change in." Thus the enthalpy change for a reaction (that occurs at constant pressure) is the same as the heat for that reaction.

EXAMPLE 10.5 | Enthalpy

When 1 mole of methane (CH_4) is burned at constant pressure, 890 kJ of energy is released as heat. Calculate ΔH for a process in which a 5.8-g sample of methane is burned at constant pressure.

SOLUTION

Where Are We Going?

We want to determine ΔH for the reaction of 5.8 g of methane (CH_4) with oxygen at constant pressure.

Which energy is easier to use to do work: the concentrated energy in the gasoline or the thermal energy spread from Chicago to Denver? Of course, the energy concentrated in the gasoline is more convenient to use.

This example illustrates a very important general principle: when we utilize energy to do work, we degrade its usefulness. In other words, when we use energy the *quality* of that energy (its ease of use) is lowered.

In summary,

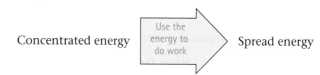

Concentrated energy | Use the energy to do work | Spread energy

You may have heard someone mention the "heat death" of the universe. Eventually (many eons from now), all energy will be spread evenly throughout the universe and everything will be at the same temperature. At this point it will no longer be possible to do any work. The universe will be "dead."

We don't have to worry about the heat death of the universe anytime soon, of course, but we do need to think about conserving "quality" energy supplies. The energy stored in petroleum molecules got there over millions of years through plants and simple animals absorbing energy from the sun and using this energy to construct molecules. As these organisms died and became buried, natural processes changed them into the petroleum deposits we now access for our supplies of gasoline and natural gas.

Petroleum is highly valuable because it furnishes a convenient, concentrated source of energy. Unfortunately, we are using this fuel at a much faster rate than natural processes can replace it, so we are looking for new sources of energy. The most logical energy source is the sun. *Solar energy* refers to using the sun's energy directly to do productive work in our society. We will discuss energy supplies in the next section.

10.9   Energy and Our World

OBJECTIVE: To consider the energy resources of our world.

Woody plants, coal, petroleum, and natural gas provide a vast resource of energy that originally came from the sun. By the process of photosynthesis, plants store energy that can be claimed by burning the plants themselves or the decay products that have been converted over millions of years to **fossil fuels.** Although the United States currently depends heavily on petroleum for energy, this dependency is a relatively recent phenomenon, as shown in Figure 10.7. In this section we discuss some sources of energy and their effects on the environment.

▶ **Petroleum and Natural Gas**

Although how they were produced is not completely understood, petroleum and natural gas were most likely formed from the remains of marine organisms that lived approximately 500 million years ago. **Petroleum** is a thick, dark liquid composed mostly of compounds called *hydrocarbons* that contain carbon and hydrogen. (Carbon is unique among elements in the extent to which it can bond to itself to form chains of various lengths.) Table 10.2 gives the formulas and names for several common hydrocarbons. **Natural**

Crystals of xenon the first reported compound contai gas element.

Argonne National Laboratory

EXA

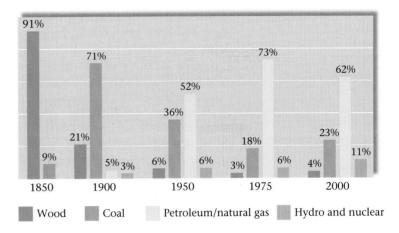

Figure 10.7

Energy sources used in the United States.

1850 1900 1950 1975 2000

■ Wood ■ Coal □ Petroleum/natural gas ■ Hydro and nuclear

gas, usually associated with petroleum deposits, consists mostly of methane, but it also contains significant amounts of ethane, propane, and butane.

The composition of petroleum varies somewhat, but it includes mostly hydrocarbons having chains that contain from 5 to more than 25 carbons. To be used efficiently, the petroleum must be separated into fractions by boiling. The lighter molecules (having the lowest boiling points) can be boiled off, leaving the heavier ones behind. The commercial uses of various petroleum fractions are shown in Table 10.3.

The petroleum era began when the demand for lamp oil during the Industrial Revolution outstripped the traditional sources: animal fats and whale oil. In response to this increased demand, Edwin Drake drilled the first oil well in 1859 at Titusville, Pennsylvania. The petroleum from this well was refined to produce *kerosene* (fraction C_{10}–C_{18}), which served as an excellent lamp oil. *Gasoline* (fraction C_5–C_{10}) had limited use and was often discarded. This situation soon changed. The development of the electric light decreased the need for kerosene, and the advent of the "horseless carriage" with its gasoline-powered engine signaled the birth of the gasoline age.

As gasoline became more important, new ways were sought to increase the yield of gasoline obtained from each barrel of petroleum. William Burton invented a process at Standard Oil of Indiana called *pyrolytic (high-temperature) cracking.* In this process, the heavier molecules of the kerosene fraction are heated to about 700 °C, causing them to break (crack) into the smaller molecules of hydrocarbons in the gasoline fraction. As cars became larger, more efficient internal combustion engines were designed. Because of the uneven burning of the gasoline then available, these engines "knocked,"

Table 10.2 Names and Formulas for Some Common Hydrocarbons	
Formula	Name
CH_4	Methane
C_2H_6	Ethane
C_3H_8	Propane
C_4H_{10}	Butane
C_5H_{12}	Pentane
C_6H_{14}	Hexane
C_7H_{16}	Heptane
C_8H_{18}	Octane

Table 10.3 Uses of the Various Petroleum Fractions	
Petroleum Fraction in Terms of Numbers of Carbon Atoms	Major Uses
C_5–C_{10}	Gasoline
C_{10}–C_{18}	Kerosene
	Jet fuel
C_{15}–C_{25}	Diesel fuel
	Heating oil
	Lubricating oil
$>C_{25}$	Asphalt

producing unwanted noise and even engine damage. Intensive research to find additives that would promote smoother burning produced tetraethyl lead, $(C_2H_5)_4Pb$, a very effective "antiknock" agent.

The addition of tetraethyl lead to gasoline became a common practice, and by 1960, gasoline contained as much as 3g of lead per gallon. As we have discovered so often in recent years, technological advances can produce environmental problems. To prevent air pollution from automobile exhaust, catalytic converters have been added to car exhaust systems. The effectiveness of these converters, however, is destroyed by lead. The use of leaded gasoline also greatly increased the amount of lead in the environment, where it can be ingested by animals and humans. For these reasons, the use of lead in gasoline has been phased out, requiring extensive (and expensive) modifications of engines and of the gasoline refining process.

▶ Coal

Coal was formed from the remains of plants that were buried and subjected to high pressure and heat over long periods of time. Plant materials have a high content of cellulose, a complex molecule whose empirical formula is CH_2O but whose molar mass is approximately 500,000 g/mol. After the plants and trees that grew on the earth at various times and places died and were buried, chemical changes gradually lowered the oxygen and hydrogen content of the cellulose molecules. Coal "matures" through four stages: lignite, subbituminous, bituminous, and anthracite. Each stage has a higher carbon-to-oxygen and carbon-to-hydrogen ratio; that is, the relative carbon content gradually increases. Typical elemental compositions of the various coals are given in Table 10.4. The energy available from the combustion of a given mass of coal increases as the carbon content increases. Anthracite is the most valuable coal, and lignite is the least valuable.

Coal is an important and plentiful fuel in the United States, currently furnishing approximately 20% of our energy. As the supply of petroleum decreases, the share of the energy supply from coal could eventually increase to as high as 30%. However, coal is expensive and dangerous to mine underground, and the strip mining of fertile farmland in the Midwest or of scenic land in the West causes obvious problems. In addition, the burning of coal, especially high-sulfur coal, yields air pollutants such as sulfur dioxide, which, in turn, can lead to acid rain. However, even if coal were pure carbon, the carbon dioxide produced when it was burned would still have significant effects on the earth's climate.

Roland Weinrauch/dpa/Corbis

Table 10.4	Element Composition of Various Types of Coal				
	Mass Percent of Each Element				
Type of Coal	C	H	O	N	S
Lignite	71	4	23	1	1
Subbituminous	77	5	16	1	1
Bituminous	80	6	8	1	5
Anthracite	92	3	3	1	1

▶ Effects of Carbon Dioxide on Climate

The earth receives a tremendous quantity of radiant energy from the sun, about 30% of which is reflected back into space by the earth's atmosphere. The remaining energy passes through the atmosphere to the earth's surface. Some of this energy is absorbed by plants for photosynthesis and some by the oceans to evaporate water, but most of it is absorbed by soil, rocks, and water, increasing the temperature of the earth's surface. This energy is, in turn, radiated from the heated surface mainly as *infrared radiation,* often called *heat radiation.*

The atmosphere, like window glass, is transparent to visible light but does not allow all the infrared radiation to pass back into space. Molecules in the atmosphere, principally H_2O and CO_2, strongly absorb infrared radiation and radiate it back toward the earth, as shown in Figure 10.8. A net amount of thermal energy is retained by the earth's atmosphere, causing the earth to be much warmer than it would be without its atmosphere. In a way, the atmosphere acts like the glass of a greenhouse, which is transparent to visible light but absorbs infrared radiation, thus raising the temperature inside the building. This **greenhouse effect** is seen even more spectacularly on Venus, where the dense atmosphere is thought to be responsible for the high surface temperature of that planet.

Thus the temperature of the earth's surface is controlled to a significant extent by the carbon dioxide and water content of the atmosphere. The effect of atmospheric moisture (humidity) is readily apparent in the Midwest, for example. In summer, when the humidity is high, the heat of the sun is retained well into the night, giving very high nighttime temperatures. In winter, the coldest temperatures always occur on clear nights, when the low humidity allows efficient radiation of energy back into space.

The atmosphere's water content is controlled by the water cycle (evaporation and precipitation), and the average has remained constant over the years. However, as fossil fuels have been used more extensively, the carbon dioxide concentration has increased—up about 20% from 1880 to the present. Projections indicate that the carbon dioxide content of the atmosphere

Figure 10.8

The earth's atmosphere is transparent to visible light from the sun. This visible light strikes the earth, and part of it is changed to infrared radiation. The infrared radiation from the earth's surface is strongly absorbed by CO_2, H_2O, and other molecules present in smaller amounts (for example, CH_4 and N_2O) in the atmosphere. In effect, the atmosphere traps some of the energy, acting like the glass in a greenhouse and keeping the earth warmer than it would otherwise be.

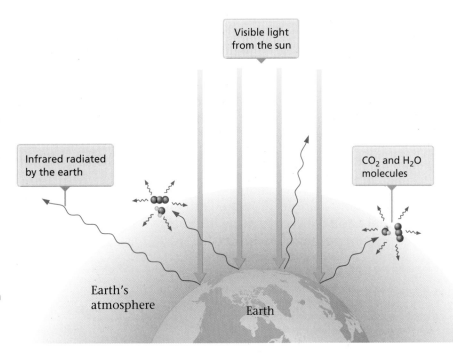

Seeing the Light

We are about to have a revolution in lighting. The incandescent light bulb developed by Thomas Edison in the late nineteenth century still dominates our lighting systems. However, this is about to change because Edison's light bulb is so inefficient: about 95% of the energy goes to heat instead of light. In the United States, 22% of total electricity production goes for lighting, for a cost of about $58 million. Globally, illumination consumes about 19% of electricity, and demand for lighting is expected to grow by 60% in the next 25 years. Given energy prices and the problems associated with global warming, we must find more efficient lighting devices.

In the short term, the answer appears to be compact fluorescent lights (CFLs). These bulbs, which have a screw-type base, draw only about 20% as much energy as incandescent bulbs for a comparable amount of light production. Although they cost four times as much, CFLs last ten times as long as incandescent bulbs. CFLs produce light from a type of compound called a phosphor that coats the inner walls of the bulb. The phosphor is mixed with a small amount of mercury (about 5 mg per bulb). When the bulb is turned on, a beam of electrons is produced. The electrons are absorbed by mercury atoms, which are caused to emit ultraviolet (UV) light. This UV light is absorbed by phosphor, which then emits visible light (a process called fluorescence). It is estimated that replacing all of the incandescent bulbs in our homes with CFLs would reduce our electrical demand in the United States by the equivalent of the power produced by 20 new 1000-MW nuclear power plants. This is a very significant savings.

Although the amount of mercury in each bulb is small (breaking a single CFL would not endanger a normal adult), recycling large numbers of CFLs does present potential pollution hazards. Research is now underway to find ways to alleviate this danger. For example, Professor Robert Hurt and his colleagues at Brown University have found that selenium prepared as tiny particles has a very high affinity for mercury and can be used in recycling operations to prevent dangerous occupational exposure to mercury.

Another type of lighting device that looks to be very valuable in the near future is the light-emitting diode (LED). An LED is a solid-state semiconductor designed to emit visible light when its electrons fall to lower energy levels. The tiny glowing light that indicates an audio system or television is on is an LED. In recent years, LEDs have been used in traffic lights, turn signals on cars, flashlights, and street lights. The use of LEDs for holiday lighting is rapidly increasing. It is estimated that LEDs eventually will reduce energy consumption for holiday lighting by 90%. The light production of LEDs per amount of energy consumed has increased dramatically in recent months, and the costs are decreasing steadily. Currently, LED lights are ten times more expensive than CFLs but last more than 15 years. Thus dramatic changes are occurring in the methods for lighting, and we all need to do our part to make our lives more energy efficient.

A compact fluorescent light bulb (CFL).

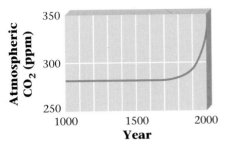

Figure 10.9

The atmospheric CO_2 concentration over the past 1000 years, based on ice core data and direct readings (since 1958). Note the dramatic increase in the past 100 years.

may be double in the twenty-first century what it was in 1880. This trend *could* increase the earth's average temperature by as much as 10 °C, causing dramatic changes in climate and greatly affecting the growth of food crops.

How well can we predict the long-term effects of carbon dioxide? Because weather has been studied for a period of time that is minuscule compared with the age of the earth, the factors that control the earth's climate in the long range are not clearly understood. For example, we do not understand what causes the earth's periodic ice ages. So it is difficult to estimate the effects of the increasing carbon dioxide levels.

In fact, the variation in the earth's average temperature over the past century is somewhat confusing. In the northern latitudes during the past century, the average temperature rose by 0.8 °C over a period of 60 years, then cooled by 0.5 °C during the next 25 years, and finally warmed by 0.2 °C in the succeeding 15 years. Such fluctuations do not match the steady increase in carbon dioxide. However, in southern latitudes and near the equator during the past century, the average temperature showed a steady rise totaling 0.4 °C. This figure is in reasonable agreement with the predicted effect of the increasing carbon dioxide concentration over that period. Another significant fact is that the last 10 years of the twentieth century have been the warmest decade on record.

Although the exact relationship between the carbon dioxide concentration in the atmosphere and the earth's temperature is not known at present, one thing is clear: The increase in the atmospheric concentration of carbon dioxide is quite dramatic (see Figure 10.9). We must consider the implications of this increase as we consider our future energy needs.

▶ New Energy Sources

As we search for the energy sources of the future, we need to consider economic, climatic, and supply factors. There are several potential energy sources: the sun (solar), nuclear processes (fission and fusion), biomass (plants), and synthetic fuels. Direct use of the sun's radiant energy to heat our homes and run our factories and transportation systems seems a sensible long-term goal. But what do we do now? Conservation of fossil fuels is one obvious step, but substitutes for fossil fuels also must be found. There is much research going on now to solve this problem.

10.10   Energy as a Driving Force

OBJECTIVE: To understand energy as a driving force for natural processes.

A major goal of science is to understand why things happen as they do. In particular, we are interested in the driving forces of nature. Why do things occur in a particular direction? For example, consider a log that has burned in a fireplace, producing ashes and heat energy. If you are sitting in front of the fireplace, you would be very surprised to see the ashes begin to absorb heat from the air and reconstruct themselves into the log. It just doesn't happen. That is, the process that always occurs is

$$\text{log} + O_2(g) \rightarrow CO_2(g) + H_2O(g) + \text{ashes} + \text{energy}$$

The reverse of this process

$$CO_2(g) + H_2O(g) + \text{ashes} + \text{energy} \rightarrow \text{log} + O_2(g)$$

never happens.

Consider another example. A gas is trapped in one end of a vessel as shown below.

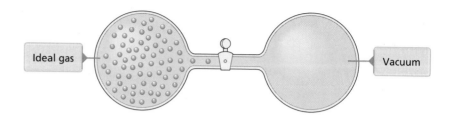

When the valve is opened, what always happens? The gas spreads evenly throughout the entire container.

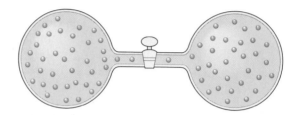

You would be very surprised to see the following process occur spontaneously:

So, why does this process

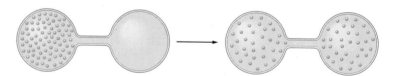

occur spontaneously but the reverse process

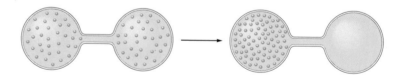

never occurs?

In many years of analyzing these and many other processes, scientists have discovered two very important driving forces:

- Energy spread
- Matter spread

Energy spread means that in a given process, concentrated energy is dispersed widely. This distribution happens every time an exothermic process occurs. For example, when a Bunsen burner burns, the energy stored in the fuel (natural gas—mostly methane) is dispersed into the surrounding air:

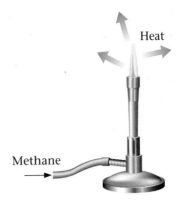

The energy that flows into the surroundings through heat increases the thermal motions of the molecules in the surroundings. In other words, this process increases the random motions of the molecules in the surroundings. *This always happens in every exothermic process.*

Matter spread means exactly what it says: the molecules of a substance are spread out and occupy a larger volume.

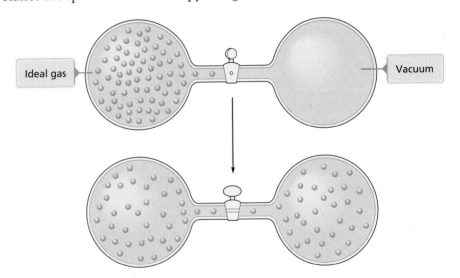

After looking at thousands of processes, scientists have concluded that these two factors are the important driving forces that cause events to occur. That is, processes are favored if they involve energy spread and matter spread.

Do these driving forces ever occur in opposition? Yes, they do—in many, many processes.

For example, consider ordinary table salt dissolving in water.

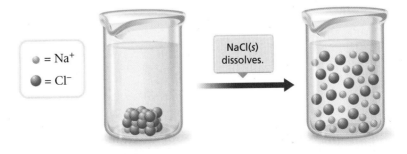

This process occurs spontaneously. You observe it every time you add salt to water to cook potatoes or pasta. Surprisingly, dissolving salt in water is *endothermic*. This process seems to go in the wrong direction—it involves energy concentration, not energy spread. Why does the salt dissolve? Because of matter spread. The Na^+ and Cl^- that are closely packed in the solid NaCl become spread around randomly in a much larger volume in the resulting solution. Salt dissolves in water because the favorable matter spread overcomes an unfavorable energy change.

▶ Entropy

Entropy is a function we have invented to keep track of the natural tendency for the components of the universe to become disordered—entropy (designated by the letter S) is a measure of disorder or randomness. As randomness increases, S increases. Which has lower entropy, solid water (ice) or gaseous water (steam)? Remember that ice contains closely packed, ordered H_2O molecules, and steam has widely dispersed, randomly moving H_2O molecules (see Figure 10.10). Thus ice has more order and a lower value of S.

What do you suppose happens to the disorder of the universe as energy spread and matter spread occur during a process?

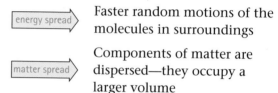

Faster random motions of the molecules in surroundings

Components of matter are dispersed—they occupy a larger volume

It seems clear that both energy spread and matter spread lead to greater entropy (greater disorder) in the universe. This idea leads to a very important conclusion that is summarized in the **second law of thermodynamics:**

The entropy of the universe is always increasing.

A **spontaneous process** is one that occurs in nature without outside intervention—it happens "on its own." The second law of thermodynamics

Solid (Ice)   **Gas** (Steam)

Figure 10.10

Comparing the entropies of ice and steam.

helps us to understand why certain processes are spontaneous and others are not. It also helps us to understand the conditions necessary for a process to be spontaneous. For example, at 1 atm (1 atmosphere of pressure), ice will spontaneously melt above a temperature of 0 °C but not below this temperature. A process is spontaneous only if the entropy of the universe increases as a result of the process. That is, all processes that occur in the universe lead to a net increase in the disorder of the universe. As the universe "runs," it is always heading toward more disorder. We are plunging slowly but inevitably toward total randomness—the heat death of the universe. But don't despair; it will not happen soon.

CHAPTER 10 REVIEW

Key Terms

energy (10.1)
potential energy (10.1)
kinetic energy (10.1)
law of conservation of
  energy (10.1)
work (10.1)
state function (10.1)
temperature (10.2)
heat (10.2)
system (10.3)
surroundings (10.3)
exothermic (10.3)
endothermic (10.3)
thermodynamics (10.4)
first law of thermo-
  dynamics (10.4)
internal energy (10.4)
calorie (10.5)

joule (10.5)
specific heat
  capacity (10.5)
enthalpy (10.6)
calorimeter (10.6)
Hess's law (10.7)
fossil fuels (10.9)
petroleum (10.9)
natural gas (10.9)
coal (10.9)
greenhouse effect (10.9)
energy spread (10.10)
matter spread (10.10)
entropy (10.10)
second law of thermo-
  dynamics (10.10)
spontaneous process
  (10.10)

F directs you to the *Chemistry in Focus* feature in the chapter
VP indicates visual problems
OWL interactive versions of these problems are assignable in OWL

Summary

1. One of the fundamental characteristics of energy is that it is conserved. Energy is changed in form but it is not produced or consumed in a process. Thermodynamics is the study of energy and its changes.

2. In a process some functions—called state functions—depend only on the beginning and final states of the system, not on the specific pathway followed. Energy is a state function. Other functions, such as heat and work, depend on the specific pathway followed and are not state functions.

3. The temperature of a substance indicates the vigor of the random motions of the components of that substance. The thermal energy of an object is the energy content of the object as produced by its random motions.

4. Heat is a flow of energy between two objects due to a temperature difference in the two objects. In an exothermic reaction, energy as heat flows out of the system into its surroundings. In an endothermic process, energy as heat flows from the surroundings into the system.

5. The internal energy of an object is the sum of the kinetic (due to motion) and potential (due to position) energies of the object. Internal energy can be changed by two types of energy flows, work (w) and heat (q): $\Delta E = q + w$.

6. A calorimeter is used to measure the heats of chemical reactions. The common units for heat are joules and calories.

7. The specific heat capacity of a substance (the energy required to change the temperature of one gram of the substance by one Celsius degree) is used to calculate temperature changes when a substance is heated.

8. The change in enthalpy for a process is equal to the heat for that process run at constant pressure.

9. Hess's law allows the calculation of the heat of a given reaction from known heats of related reactions.

10. Although energy is conserved in every process, the quality (usefulness) of the energy decreases with each use.

11. Our world has many sources of energy. The use of these sources affects the environment in various ways.

12. Natural processes occur in the direction that leads to an increase in the disorder (entropy) of the universe. The principal driving forces for processes are energy spread and matter spread.

Active Learning Questions

These questions are designed to be considered by groups of students in class. Often these questions work well for introducing a particular topic in class.

1. Look at Figure 10.1 in your text. Ball A has stopped moving. However, energy must be conserved. So what happened to the energy of ball A?

2. A friend of yours reads that the process of water freezing is exothermic. This friend tells you that this can't be true because exothermic implies "hot," and ice is cold. Is the process of water freezing exothermic? If so, explain this process so your friend can understand it. If not, explain why not.

3. You place hot metal into a beaker of cold water.

    a. Eventually what is true about the temperature of the metal compared to that of the water? Explain why this is true.
    b. Label this process as endothermic or exothermic if we consider the system to be

        i. the metal. Explain.
        ii. the water. Explain.

4. What does it mean when the heat for a process is reported with a negative sign?

5. You place 100.0 g of a hot metal in 100.0 g of cold water. Which substance (metal or water) undergoes a larger temperature change? Why is this?

6. Explain why aluminum cans make good storage containers for soft drinks. Styrofoam cups can be used to keep coffee hot and cola cold. How can this be?

7. In Section 10.7, two characteristics of enthalpy changes for reactions are listed. What are these characteristics? Explain why these characteristics are true.

8. What is the difference between *quality* and *quantity* of energy? Are both conserved? Is either conserved?

9. What is meant by the term *driving forces?* Why are *matter spread* and *energy spread* considered to be driving forces?

10. Give an example of a process in which *matter spread* is a driving force and an example of a process in which *energy spread* is a driving force, and explain each. These examples should be different from the ones given in the text.

11. Explain in your own words what is meant by the term *entropy*. Explain how both *matter spread* and *energy spread* are related to the concept of entropy.

12. Consider the processes

$$H_2O(g) \rightarrow H_2O(l)$$
$$H_2O(l) \rightarrow H_2O(g)$$

    a. Which process is favored by energy spread? Explain.
    b. Which process is favored by matter spread? Explain.
    c. How does temperature affect which process is favored? Explain.

13. What if energy was not conserved? How would this affect our lives?

14. The internal energy of a system is said to be the sum of the kinetic and potential energies of all the particles in the system. Section 10.1 discusses *potential energy* and *kinetic energy* in terms of a ball on a hill. Explain *potential energy* and *kinetic energy* for a chemical reaction.

15. Hydrogen gas and oxygen gas react violently to form water.

    a. Which is lower in energy: a mixture of hydrogen gases, or water? Explain.
    b. Sketch an energy-level diagram (like Figure 10.5) for this reaction and explain it.

16. Consider four 100.0-g samples of water, each in a separate beaker at 25.0 °C. Into each beaker you drop 10.0 g of a different metal that has been heated to 95.0 °C. Assuming no heat loss to the surroundings, which water sample will have the highest final temperature? Explain your answer.

    a. The water to which you have added aluminum (c = 0.89 J/g °C).
    b. The water to which you have added iron (c = 0.45 J/g °C).
    c. The water to which you have added copper (c = 0.20 J/g °C).
    d. The water to which you have added lead (c = 0.14 J/g °C).
    e. Because the masses of the metals are the same, the final temperatures would be the same.

17. For each of the following situations a–c, use the following choices i–iii to complete the statement "The final temperature of the water should be"

    i.   Between 50 °C and 90 °C
    ii. 50 °C
    iii. Between 10 °C and 50 °C

    a. A 100.0-g sample of water at 90 °C is added to a 100.0-g sample of water at 10 °C.
    b. A 100.0-g sample of water at 90 °C is added to a 500.0-g sample of water at 10 °C.
    c. You have a Styrofoam cup with 50.0 g of water at 10 °C. You add a 50.0-g iron ball at 90 °C to the water.

18. How is Hess's law a restatement of the first law of thermodynamics?

19. Does the entropy of the system increase or decrease for each of the following? Explain.

    a. the evaporation of alcohol
    b. the freezing of water
    c. dissolving NaCl in water

VP **20.** Predict the sign of $\Delta S°$ for each of the following changes.

a.

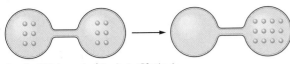

b. $AgCl(s) \rightarrow Ag^+(aq) + Cl^-(aq)$
c. $2H_2(g) + O_2 \rightarrow 2H_2O(l)$
d. $H_2O(l) \rightarrow H_2O(g)$

Questions and Problems

10.1 The Nature of Energy

QUESTIONS

1. _____ represents the ability to do work or to produce heat.

2. What is meant by *potential* energy? Give an example of an object or material that possesses potential energy.

3. What is the kinetic energy of a particle of mass m moving through space with velocity v?

4. Explain what we mean by the *law of conservation of energy*.

5. What is meant by a *state* function? Give an example.

6. In Figure 10.1, what kind of energy does ball A possess initially when at rest at the top of the hill? What kind of energies are involved as ball A moves down the hill? What kind of energy does ball A possess when it reaches the bottom of the hill and *stops* moving after hitting ball B? Where did the energy gained by ball B, allowing it to move up the hill, come from?

10.2 Temperature and Heat

QUESTIONS

7. Students often confuse what is meant by *heat* and *temperature*. Define each. How are the two concepts related?

8. If you spilled a cup of freshly brewed *hot* tea on yourself, you would be burned. If you spilled the same quantity of *iced* tea on yourself, you would not be burned. Explain.

9. What does the *thermal energy* of an object represent?

10. How are the *temperature* of an object and the *thermal energy* of an object related?

10.3 Exothermic and Endothermic Processes

QUESTIONS

11. In studying heat flows for chemical processes, what do we mean by the terms *system* and *surroundings*?

12. When a chemical system evolves energy, where does the energy go?

13. The combustion of methane, CH_4, is an exothermic process. Therefore, the products of this reaction must possess (higher/lower) total potential energy than do the reactants.

14. In any process, the energy gained by the surroundings must be _____ to the energy lost by the system.

10.4 Thermodynamics

QUESTIONS

15. What do we mean by *thermodynamics?* What is the *first law of thermodynamics?*

16. The _____ energy, E, of a system represents the sum of the kinetic and potential energies of all particles within the system.

17. Explain the meaning of each of the terms in the equation $\Delta E = q + w$.

18. If q for a process is a negative number, then the system is (gaining/losing) energy.

19. For an endothermic process, q will have a (positive/negative) sign.

20. If w for a process is a positive number, then the system must be (gaining/losing) energy from the surroundings.

10.5 Measuring Energy Changes

QUESTIONS

21. How is the *calorie* defined? How does a *Calorie* differ from a *calorie?* How is the *joule* related to the calorie?

22. Write the conversion factors that would be necessary to perform each of the following conversions:

a. an energy given in calories to its equivalent in joules

b. an energy given in joules to its equivalent in calories

c. an energy given in calories to its equivalent in kilocalories

d. an energy given in kilojoules to its equivalent in joules

PROBLEMS

23. If 8.40 kJ of heat is needed to raise the temperature of a sample of metal from 15 °C to 20 °C, how many kilojoules of heat will be required to raise the temperature of the same sample of metal from 25 °C to 40 °C?

24. If it takes 654 J of energy to warm a 5.51-g sample of water, how much energy would be required to warm 55.1 g of water by the same amount?

25. Convert the following numbers of calories or kilocalories into joules and kilojoules (Remember: *Kilo* means 1000.)

a. 75.2 kcal   c. 1.41×10^3 cal
b. 75.2 cal   d. 1.41 kcal

26. Convert the following numbers of calories into kilocalories. (Remember: *kilo* means 1000.)

a. 8254 cal   c. 8.231×10^3 cal
b. 41.5 cal   d. 752,900 cal

27. Convert the following numbers of kilojoules into kilocalories. (Remember: *kilo* means 1000.)

a. 652.1 kJ   c. 4.184 kJ
b. 1.00 kJ   d. 4.351×10^3 kJ

28. Convert the following numbers of joules into kilojoules. (Remember: *kilo* means 1000.)

a. 243,000 J   c. 0.251 J
b. 4.184 J   d. 450.3 J

29. Perform the indicated conversions.

a. 625.2 cal into kilojoules
b. 82.41 kJ into joules
c. 52.61 kcal into joules
d. 124.2 kJ into kilocalories

30. Perform the indicated conversions.

a. 91.74 kcal into calories
b. 1.781 kJ into calories
c. 4.318×10^3 J into kilocalories
d. 9.173×10^4 cal into kilojoules

31. If 69.5 kJ of heat is applied to a 1012-g block of metal, the temperature of the metal increases by 11.4 °C. Calculate the specific heat capacity of the metal in J/g °C.

32. What quantity of heat energy must have been applied to a block of aluminum weighing 42.7 g if the temperature of the block of aluminum increased by 15.2 °C? (See Table 10.1.)

33. If 125 J of heat energy is applied to a block of silver weighing 29.3 g, by how many degrees will the temperature of the silver increase? (See Table 10.1.)

34. If 100. J of heat energy is applied to a 25-g sample of mercury, by how many degrees will the temperature of the sample of mercury increase? (See Table 10.1.)

35. What quantity of heat is required to raise the temperature of 55.5 g of gold from 20 °C to 45 °C? (See Table 10.1.)

F 36. The "Chemistry in Focus" segment *Coffee: Hot and Quick(lime)* discusses self-heating cups of coffee using the chemical reaction between quicklime, CaO(*s*), and water. Is this reaction endothermic or exothermic?

F 37. The "Chemistry in Focus" segment *Nature Has Hot Plants* discusses thermogenic, or heat-producing, plants. For some plants, enough heat is generated to increase the temperature of the blossom by 15 °C. About how much heat is required to increase the temperature of 1 L of water by 15 °C?

F 38. In the "Chemistry in Focus" segment *Firewalking: Magic or Science?*, it is claimed that one reason people can walk on hot coals is that human tissue is mainly composed of water. Because of this, a large amount of heat must be transferred from the coals to change significantly the temperature of the feet. How much heat must be transferred to 100.0 g of water to change its temperature by 35 °C?

10.6 Thermochemistry (Enthalpy)

QUESTIONS

39. What do we mean by the *enthalpy change* for a reaction that occurs at constant pressure?

40. What is a *calorimeter*?

PROBLEMS

41. The enthalpy change for the reaction of hydrogen gas with fluorine gas to produce hydrogen fluoride is −542 kJ for the equation *as written*:

$$H_2(g) + F_2(g) \rightarrow 2HF(g) \quad \Delta H = -542 \text{ kJ}$$

a. What is the enthalpy change *per mole* of hydrogen fluoride produced?
b. Is the reaction exothermic or endothermic as written?
c. What would be the enthalpy change for the *reverse* of the given equation (that is, for the decomposition of HF into its constituent elements)?

42. For the reaction $S(s) + O_2(g) \rightarrow SO_2(g)$, $\Delta H = -296$ kJ per mole of SO_2 formed.

a. Calculate the quantity of heat released when 1.00 g of sulfur is burned in oxygen.
b. Calculate the quantity of heat released when 0.501 mole of sulfur is burned in air.
c. What quantity of energy is required to break up 1 mole of $SO_2(g)$ into its constituent elements?

10.7 Hess's Law

QUESTIONS

F 43. The "Chemistry in Focus" segment *Methane: An Important Energy Source* discusses methane as a fuel. Determine ΔH for methane in terms of kJ/mol.

44. When ethanol (grain alcohol, C_2H_5OH) is burned in oxygen, approximately 1360 kJ of heat energy is released per mole of ethanol.

$$C_2H_5OH(l) + 3O_2(g) \rightarrow 2CO_2(g) + 3H_2O(g)$$

a. What quantity of heat is released for each *gram* of ethanol burned?
b. What is ΔH for the reaction *as written*?
c. How much heat is released when sufficient ethanol is burned so as to produce 1 mole of water vapor?

PROBLEMS

45. Given the following hypothetical data:

$$X(g) + Y(g) \rightarrow XY(g) \text{ for which } \Delta H = a \text{ kJ}$$
$$X(g) + Z(g) \rightarrow XZ(g) \text{ for which } \Delta H = b \text{ kJ}$$

Calculate ΔH for the reaction

$$Y(g) + XZ(g) \rightarrow XY(g) + Z(g)$$

46. Given the following data:

$$C(s) + O_2(g) \rightarrow CO_2(g) \qquad \Delta H = -393 \text{ kJ}$$
$$2CO(g) + O_2(g) \rightarrow 2CO_2(g) \qquad \Delta H = -566 \text{ kJ}$$

Calculate ΔH for the reaction $2C(s) + O_2(g) \rightarrow CO(g)$.

47. Given the following data:

$$S(s) + \tfrac{3}{2}O_2(g) \rightarrow SO_3(g) \qquad \Delta H = -395.2 \text{ kJ}$$
$$2SO_2(g) + O_2(g) \rightarrow 2SO_3(g) \qquad \Delta H = -198.2 \text{ kJ}$$

Calculate ΔH for the reaction $S(s) + O_2(g) \rightarrow SO_2(g)$.

48. Given the following data:

$$2O_3(g) \rightarrow 3O_2(g) \qquad \Delta H = -427 \text{ kJ}$$
$$O_2(g) \rightarrow 2O(g) \qquad \Delta H = +495 \text{ kJ}$$
$$NO(g) + O_3(g) \rightarrow NO_2(g) + O_2(g) \qquad \Delta H = -199 \text{ kJ}$$

Calculate ΔH for the reaction

$$NO(g) + O(g) \rightarrow NO_2(g)$$

10.8 Quality Versus Quantity of Energy

QUESTIONS

49. Consider gasoline in your car's gas tank. What happens to the energy stored in the gasoline when you drive your car? Although the total energy in the universe remains constant, can the energy stored in the gasoline be reused once it is dispersed to the environment?

50. Although the total energy of the universe will remain constant, why will energy no longer be useful once everything in the universe is at the same temperature?

51. Why are petroleum products especially useful as sources of energy?

52. Why is the "quality" of energy decreasing in the universe?

10.9 Energy and Our World

QUESTIONS

53. Where did the energy stored in wood, coal, petroleum, and natural gas originally come from?

54. What does petroleum consist of? What are some "fractions" into which petroleum is refined? How are these fractions related to the sizes of the molecules involved?

55. What does natural gas consist of? Where is natural gas commonly found?

56. What was tetraethyl lead used for in the petroleum industry? Why is it no longer commonly used?

57. What are the four "stages" of coal formation? How do the four types of coal differ?

58. What is the "greenhouse effect"? Why is a certain level of greenhouse gases beneficial, but too high a level dangerous to life on earth? What is the most common greenhouse gas?

10.10 Energy as a Driving Force

QUESTIONS

59. What do chemists mean by a "driving force"?

60. What does it mean to say that "energy spread" and "matter spread" are driving forces in chemical reactions?

61. If a reaction occurs readily but has an endothermic heat of reaction, what must be the driving force for the reaction?

62. Does a double-displacement reaction such as

$$NaCl(aq) + AgNO_3(aq) \rightarrow AgCl(s) + NaNO_3(aq)$$

result in a matter spread or in a concentration of matter?

63. What do we mean by *entropy?* Why does the entropy of the universe increase during a spontaneous process?

64. A chunk of ice at room temperature melts, even though the process is endothermic. Why?

Additional Problems

65. Consider a sample of *steam* (water in the gaseous state) at 150 °C. Describe what happens to the molecules in the sample as the sample is slowly cooled until it liquefies and then solidifies.

66. Convert the following numbers of kilojoules into kilocalories. (Remember: *kilo* means 1000.)

a. 462.4 kJ c. 1.014 kJ
b. 18.28 kJ d. 190.5 kJ

67. Perform the indicated conversions.

a. 85.21 cal into joules
b. 672.1 J into calories
c. 8.921 kJ into joules
d. 556.3 cal into kilojoules

68. Calculate the amount of energy required (in calories) to heat 145 g of water from 22.3 °C to 75.0 °C.

69. It takes 1.25 kJ of energy to heat a certain sample of pure silver from 12.0 °C to 15.2 °C. Calculate the mass of the sample of silver.

70. What quantity of heat energy would have to be applied to a 25.1-g block of iron in order to raise the temperature of the iron sample by 17.5 °C? (See Table 10.1.)

71. The specific heat capacity of gold is 0.13 J/g °C. Calculate the specific heat capacity of gold in cal/g °C.

All even-numbered Questions and Problems have answers in the back of this book and solutions in the Solutions Guide.

72. Calculate the amount of energy required (in joules) to heat 2.5 kg of water from 18.5 °C to 55.0 °C.

73. If 10. J of heat is applied to 5.0-g samples of each of the substances listed in Table 10.1, which substance's temperature will increase the most? Which substance's temperature will increase the least?

74. A 50.0-g sample of water at 100. °C is poured into a 50.0-g sample of water at 25 °C. What will be the final temperature of the water?

75. A 25.0-g sample of pure iron at 85 °C is dropped into 75 g of water at 20. °C. What is the final temperature of the water–iron mixture?

76. If it takes 4.5 J of energy to warm 5.0 g of aluminum from 25 °C to a certain higher temperature, then it will take _____ J to warm 10. g of aluminum over the same temperature interval.

77. For each of the substances listed in Table 10.1, calculate the quantity of heat required to heat 150. g of the substance by 11.2 °C.

78. Suppose you had 10.0-g samples of each of the substances listed in Table 10.1 and that 1.00 kJ of heat is applied to each of these samples. By what amount would the temperature of each sample be raised?

79. Calculate ΔE for each of the following.

   a. $q = -47$ kJ, $w = +88$ kJ
   b. $q = +82$ kJ, $w = +47$ kJ
   c. $q = +47$ kJ, $w = 0$
   d. In which of these cases do the surroundings do work on the system?

80. Are the following processes exothermic or endothermic?

   a. the combustion of gasoline in a car engine
   b. water condensing on a cold pipe
   c. $CO_2(s) \rightarrow CO_2(g)$
   d. $F_2(g) \rightarrow 2F(g)$

81. The overall reaction in commercial heat packs can be represented as

$$4Fe(s) + 3O_2(g) \rightarrow 2Fe_2O_3(s) \qquad \Delta H = -1652 \text{ kJ}$$

   a. How much heat is released when 4.00 mol iron is reacted with excess O_2?
   b. How much heat is released when 1.00 mol Fe_2O_3 is produced?
   c. How much heat is released when 1.00 g iron is reacted with excess O_2?
   d. How much heat is released when 10.0 g Fe and 2.00 g O_2 are reacted?

82. Consider the following equations:

$$3A + 6B \rightarrow 3D \qquad \Delta H = -403 \text{ kJ/mol}$$
$$E + 2F \rightarrow A \qquad \Delta H = -105.2 \text{ kJ/mol}$$
$$C \rightarrow E + 3D \qquad \Delta H = +64.8 \text{ kJ/mol}$$

Suppose the first equation is reversed and multiplied by $\frac{1}{6}$, the second and third equations are divided by 2, and the three adjusted equations are added. What is the net reaction and what is the overall heat of this reaction?

83. It has been determined that the body can generate 5500 kJ of energy during one hour of strenuous exercise. Perspiration is the body's mechanism for eliminating this heat. How many grams and how many liters of water would have to be evaporated through perspiration to rid the body of the heat generated during two hours of exercise? (The heat of vaporization of water is 40.6 kJ/mol.)

84. One way to lose weight is to exercise! Walking briskly at 4.0 miles per hour for an hour consumes about 400 kcal of energy. How many hours would you have to walk at 4.0 miles per hour to lose one pound of body fat? One gram of body fat is equivalent to 7.7 kcal of energy. There are 454 g in 1 lb.

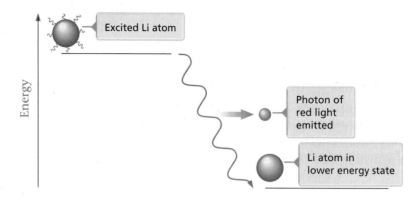

Figure 11.8

An excited lithium atom emitting a photon of red light to drop to a lower energy state.

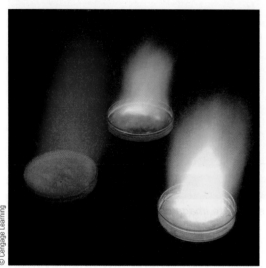

When salts containing Li⁺, Cu²⁺, and Na⁺ dissolved in methyl alcohol are set on fire, brilliant colors result: Li^+, red; Cu^{2+}, green; and Na^+, yellow.

Notice the brilliant colors that result. The solution containing Li^+ gives a beautiful, deep-red color, while the Cu^{2+} solution burns green. Notice that the Na^+ solution burns with a yellow–orange color, a color that should look familiar to you from the lights used in many parking lots. The color of these "sodium vapor lights" arises from the same source (the sodium atom) as the color of the burning solution containing Na^+ ions.

As we will see in more detail in the next section, the colors of these flames result from atoms in these solutions releasing energy by emitting visible light of specific wavelengths (that is, specific colors). The heat from the flame causes the atoms to absorb energy—we say that the atoms become *excited*. Some of this excess energy is then released in the form of light. The atom moves to a lower energy state as it emits a photon of light.

Lithium emits red light because its energy change corresponds to photons of red light (see Figure 11.8). Copper emits green light because it undergoes a different energy change than lithium; the energy change for copper corresponds to the energy of a photon of green light. Likewise, the energy change for sodium corresponds to a photon with a yellow–orange color.

To summarize, we have the following situation. When atoms receive energy from some source—they become excited—they can release this energy by emitting light. The emitted energy is carried away by a photon. Thus the energy of the photon corresponds exactly to the energy change experienced by the emitting atom. High-energy photons correspond to short-wavelength light and low-energy photons correspond to long-wavelength light. The photons of red light therefore carry less energy than the photons of blue light because red light has a longer wavelength than blue light does.

11.4   The Energy Levels of Hydrogen

OBJECTIVE: To understand how the emission spectrum of hydrogen demonstrates the quantized nature of energy.

An atom can lose energy by *emitting* a photon.

As we learned in the last section, an atom with excess energy is said to be in an *excited state*. An excited atom can release some or all of its excess energy by emitting a photon (a "particle" of electromagnetic radiation) and thus move to a lower energy state. The lowest possible energy state of an atom is called its *ground state*.

We can learn a great deal about the energy states of hydrogen atoms by observing the photons they emit. To understand the significance of this, you need to remember that the *different wavelengths of light carry different amounts*

Each photon of blue light carries a larger quantity of energy than a photon of red light.

A particular color (wavelength) of light carries a particular amount of energy per photon.

of energy per photon. Recall that a beam of red light has lower-energy photons than a beam of blue light.

When a hydrogen atom absorbs energy from some outside source, it uses this energy to enter an excited state. It can release this excess energy (go back to a lower state) by emitting a photon of light (Figure 11.9). We can picture this process in terms of the energy-level diagram shown in Figure 11.10. The important point here is that *the energy contained in the photon corresponds to the change in energy that the atom experiences* in going from the excited state to the lower state.

Consider the following experiment. Suppose we take a sample of H atoms and put a lot of energy into the system (as represented in Figure 11.9). When we study the photons of visible light emitted, we see only certain colors (Figure 11.11). That is, *only certain types of photons* are produced. We don't see all colors, which would add up to give "white light"; we see only selected colors. This is a very significant result. Let's discuss carefully what it means.

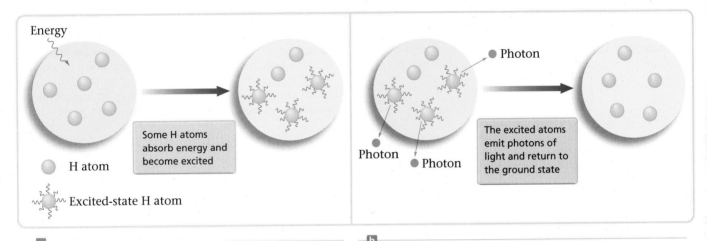

a *A sample of H atoms receives energy from an external source, which causes some of the atoms to become excited (to possess excess energy).*

b *The excited H atoms can release the excess energy by emitting photons. The energy of each emitted photon corresponds exactly to the energy lost by each excited atom.*

Figure 11.9

Figure 11.10

When an excited H atom returns to a lower energy level, it emits a photon that contains the energy released by the atom. Thus the energy of the photon corresponds to the difference in energy between the two states.

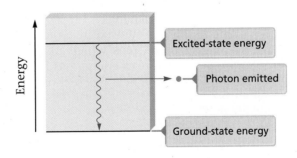

Figure 11.11

When excited hydrogen atoms return to lower energy states, they emit photons of certain energies, and thus certain colors. Shown here are the colors and wavelengths (in nanometers) of the photons in the visible region that are emitted by excited hydrogen atoms.

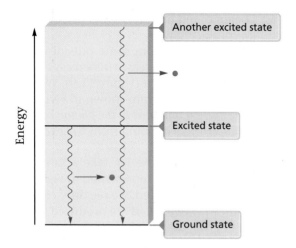

Figure 11.12

Hydrogen atoms have several excited-state energy levels. The color of the photon emitted depends on the energy change that produces it. A larger energy change may correspond to a blue photon, whereas a smaller change may produce a red photon.

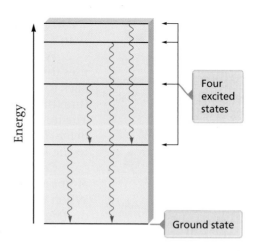

Figure 11.13

Each photon emitted by an excited hydrogen atom corresponds to a particular energy change in the hydrogen atom. In this diagram the horizontal lines represent discrete energy levels present in the hydrogen atom. A given H atom can exist in any of these energy states and can undergo energy changes to the ground state as well as to other excited states.

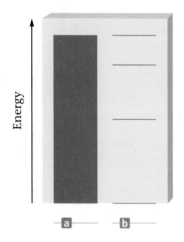

Figure 11.14

a Continuous energy levels. Any energy value is allowed.
b Discrete (quantized) energy levels. Only certain energy states are allowed.

Because only certain photons are emitted, we know that only certain energy changes are occurring (Figure 11.12). This means that the hydrogen atom must have *certain discrete energy levels* (Figure 11.13). Excited hydrogen atoms *always* emit photons with the same discrete colors (wavelengths)—those shown in Figure 11.11. They *never* emit photons with energies (colors) in between those shown. So we can conclude that all hydrogen atoms have the same set of discrete energy levels. We say the energy levels of hydrogen are **quantized.** That is, only *certain values are allowed.* Scientists have found that the energy levels of *all* atoms are quantized.

The quantized nature of the energy levels in atoms was a surprise when scientists discovered it. It had been assumed previously that an atom could exist at any energy level. That is, everyone had assumed that atoms could have a continuous set of energy levels rather than only certain discrete values (Figure 11.14). A useful analogy here is the contrast between the elevations allowed by a ramp, which vary continuously, and those allowed by a set of steps, which are discrete (Figure 11.15). The discovery of the quantized nature of energy has radically changed our view of the atom, as we will see in the next few sections.

Figure 11.15

The difference between continuous and quantized energy levels can be illustrated by comparing a flight of stairs with a ramp.

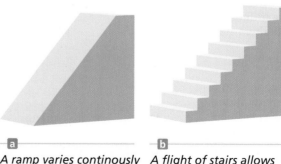

a *A ramp varies continuously in elevation.*

b *A flight of stairs allows only certain elevations; the elevations are quantized.*

11.5 The Bohr Model of the Atom

OBJECTIVE: To learn about Bohr's model of the hydrogen atom.

In 1911 at the age of twenty-five, Niels Bohr (Figure 11.16) received his Ph.D. in physics. He was convinced that the atom could be pictured as a small positive nucleus with electrons orbiting around it.

Over the next two years, Bohr constructed a model of the hydrogen atom with quantized energy levels that agreed with the hydrogen emission results we have just discussed. Bohr pictured the electron moving in circular orbits corresponding to the various allowed energy levels. He suggested that the electron could jump to a different orbit by absorbing or emitting a photon of light with exactly the correct energy content. Thus, in the Bohr atom, the energy levels in the hydrogen atom represented certain allowed circular orbits (Figure 11.17).

At first Bohr's model appeared very promising. It fit the hydrogen atom very well. However, when this model was applied to atoms other than hydrogen, it did not work. In fact, further experiments showed that the Bohr model is fundamentally incorrect. Although the Bohr model paved the way for later theories, it is important to realize that the current theory of atomic structure is not the same as the Bohr model. Electrons do *not* move around the nucleus in circular orbits like planets orbiting the sun. Surprisingly, as we shall see later in this chapter, we do not know exactly how the electrons move in an atom.

Figure 11.16

Niels Hendrik David Bohr (1885–1962) as a boy lived in the shadow of his younger brother Harald, who played on the 1908 Danish Olympic Soccer Team and later became a distinguished mathematician. In school, Bohr received his poorest marks in composition and struggled with writing during his entire life. In fact, he wrote so poorly that he was forced to dictate his Ph.D. thesis to his mother. He is one of the very few people who felt the need to write rough drafts of postcards. Nevertheless, Bohr was a brilliant physicist. After receiving his Ph.D. in Denmark, he constructed a quantum model for the hydrogen atom by the time he was 27. Even though his model later proved to be incorrect, Bohr remained a central figure in the drive to understand the atom. He was awarded the Nobel Prize in physics in 1922.

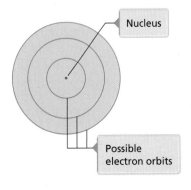

Figure 11.17

The Bohr model of the hydrogen atom represented the electron as restricted to certain circular orbits around the nucleus.

11.6 The Wave Mechanical Model of the Atom

OBJECTIVE: To understand how the electron's position is represented in the wave mechanical model.

By the mid-1920s it had become apparent that the Bohr model was incorrect. Scientists needed to pursue a totally new approach. Two young physicists, Louis Victor de Broglie from France and Erwin Schrödinger from Austria, suggested that because light seems to have both wave and particle characteristics (it behaves simultaneously as a wave and as a stream of particles), the electron might also exhibit both of these characteristics. Although everyone

Louis Victor de Broglie

had assumed that the electron was a tiny particle, these scientists said it might be useful to find out whether it could be described as a wave.

When Schrödinger carried out a mathematical analysis based on this idea, he found that it led to a new model for the hydrogen atom that seemed to apply equally well to other atoms—something Bohr's model failed to do. We will now explore a general picture of this model, which is called the **wave mechanical model** of the atom.

In the Bohr model, the electron was assumed to move in circular orbits. In the wave mechanical model, on the other hand, the electron states are described by orbitals. *Orbitals are nothing like orbits.* To approximate the idea of an orbital, picture a single male firefly in a room in the center of which an open vial of female sex-attractant hormones is suspended. The room is extremely dark and there is a camera in one corner with its shutter open. Every time the firefly "flashes," the camera records a pinpoint of light and thus the firefly's position in the room at that moment. The firefly senses the sex attractant, and as you can imagine, it spends a lot of time at or close to it. However, now and then the insect flies randomly around the room.

When the film is taken out of the camera and developed, the picture will probably look like Figure 11.18. Because a picture is brightest where the film has been exposed to the most light, the color intensity at any given point tells us how often the firefly visited a given point in the room. Notice that, as we might expect, the firefly spent the most time near the room's center.

Now suppose you are watching the firefly in the dark room. You see it flash at a given point far from the center of the room. Where do you expect to see it next? There is really no way to be sure. The firefly's flight path is not precisely predictable. However, if you had seen the time-exposure picture of the firefly's activities (Figure 11.18), you would have some idea where to look next. Your best chance would be to look more toward the center of the room. Figure 11.18 suggests there is the highest probability (the highest odds, the greatest likelihood) of finding the firefly at any particular moment near the center of the room. You *can't be sure* the firefly will fly toward the center of the room, but it *probably* will. So the time-exposure picture is a kind of "probability map" of the firefly's flight pattern.

According to the wave mechanical model, the electron in the hydrogen atom can be pictured as being something like this firefly. Schrödinger found that he could not precisely describe the electron's path. His mathematics enabled him only to predict the probabilities of finding the electron at given points in space around the nucleus. In its ground state the hydrogen electron has a probability map like that shown in Figure 11.19. The more intense the color at a particular point, the more probable that the electron will be found at that point at a given instant. The model gives *no information about when* the electron occupies a certain point in space or *how it moves.* In fact, we have good reasons to believe that we can *never know* the details of electron motion, no matter how sophisticated our models may become. But one thing we feel confident about is that the electron *does not* orbit the nucleus in circles as Bohr suggested.

Figure 11.18

A representation of the photo of the firefly experiment. Remember that a picture is brightest where the film has been exposed to the most light. Thus the intensity of the color reflects how often the firefly visited a given point in the room. Notice that the brightest area is in the center of the room near the source of the sex attractant.

Figure 11.19

The probability map, or orbital, that describes the hydrogen electron in its lowest possible energy state. The more intense the color of a given dot, the more likely it is that the electron will be found at that point. We have no information about when the electron will be at a particular point or about how it moves. Note that the probability of the electron's presence is highest closest to the positive nucleus (located at the center of this diagram), as might be expected.

11.7 The Hydrogen Orbitals

OBJECTIVE: To learn about the shapes of orbitals designated by *s*, *p*, and *d*.

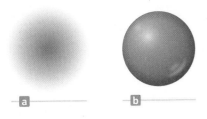

Figure 11.20

a The hydrogen 1*s* orbital.
b The size of the orbital is defined by a sphere that contains 90% of the total electron probability. That is, the electron can be found *inside* this sphere 90% of the time. The 1*s* orbital is often represented simply as a sphere. However, the most accurate picture of the orbital is the probability map represented in **a**.

The probability map for the hydrogen electron shown in Figure 11.19 is called an **orbital.** Although the probability of finding the electron decreases at greater distances from the nucleus, the probability of finding it even at great distances from the nucleus never becomes exactly zero. A useful analogy might be the lack of a sharp boundary between the earth's atmosphere and "outer space." The atmosphere fades away gradually, but there are always a few molecules present. Because the edge of an orbital is "fuzzy," an orbital does not have an exactly defined size. So chemists arbitrarily define its size as the sphere that contains 90% of the total electron probability (Figure 11.20b). This means that the electron spends 90% of the time inside this surface and 10% somewhere outside this surface. (Note that we are *not* saying the electron travels only on the *surface* of the sphere.) The orbital represented in Figure 11.20 is named the **1s orbital,** and it describes the hydrogen electron's lowest energy state (the ground state).

In Section 11.4 we saw that the hydrogen atom can absorb energy to transfer the electron to a higher energy state (an excited state). In terms of the obsolete Bohr model, this meant the electron was transferred to an orbit with a larger radius. In the wave mechanical model, these higher energy states correspond to different kinds of orbitals with different shapes.

At this point we need to stop and consider how the hydrogen atom is organized. Remember, we showed earlier that the hydrogen atom has discrete energy levels. We call these levels **principal energy levels** and label them with integers (Figure 11.21). Next we find that each of these levels is subdivided into **sublevels.** The following analogy should help you understand this. Picture an inverted triangle (Figure 11.22). We divide the principal levels into various numbers of sublevels. Principal level 1 consists of one sublevel, principal level 2 has two sublevels, principal level 3 has three sublevels, and principal level 4 has four sublevels.

Like our triangle, the principal energy levels in the hydrogen atom contain sublevels. As we will see presently, these sublevels contain spaces for the electron that we call orbitals. Principal energy level 1 consists of just one sublevel, or one type of orbital. The spherical shape of this orbital is shown in Figure 11.20. We label this orbital 1*s*. The number 1 is for the principal energy level, and *s* is a shorthand way to label a particular sublevel (type of orbital).

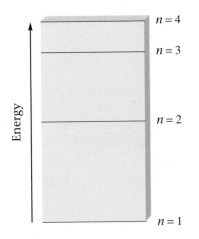

Figure 11.21

The first four principal energy levels in the hydrogen atom. Each level is assigned an integer, *n*.

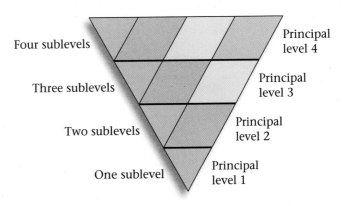

Figure 11.22

An illustration of how principal levels can be divided into sublevels.

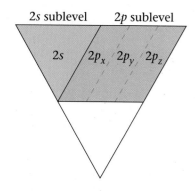

2s sublevel   2p sublevel

2s $2p_x$ $2p_y$ $2p_z$

Figure 11.23

Principal level 2 shown divided into the 2s and 2p sublevels.

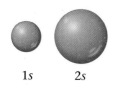

1s   2s

Figure 11.24

The relative sizes of the 1s and 2s orbitals of hydrogen.

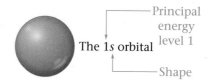

The 1s orbital — Principal energy level 1

— Shape

Principal energy level 2 has two sublevels. (Note the correspondence between the principal energy level number and the number of sublevels.) These sublevels are labeled 2s and 2p. The 2s sublevel consists of one orbital (called the 2s), and the 2p sublevel consists of three orbitals (called $2p_x$, $2p_y$, and $2p_z$). Let's return to the inverted triangle to illustrate this. Figure 11.23 shows principal level 2 divided into the sublevels 2s and 2p (which is subdivided into $2p_x$, $2p_y$, and $2p_z$). The orbitals have the shapes shown in Figures 11.24 and 11.25. The 2s orbital is spherical like the 1s orbital but larger in size (see Figure 11.24). The three 2p orbitals are not spherical but have two "lobes." These orbitals are shown in Figure 11.25 both as electron probability maps and as surfaces that contain 90% of the total electron probability. Notice that the label x, y, or z on a given 2p orbital tells along which axis the lobes of that orbital are directed.

What we have learned so far about the hydrogen atom is summarized in Figure 11.26. Principal energy level 1 has one sublevel, which contains the 1s orbital. Principal energy level 2 contains two sublevels, one of which contains the 2s orbital and one of which contains the 2p orbitals (three of them). Note that each orbital is designated by a symbol or label. We summarize the information given by this label in the following box.

Orbital Labels

1. The number tells the principal energy level.
2. The letter tells the shape. The letter *s* means a spherical orbital; the letter *p* means a two-lobed orbital. The *x, y,* or *z* subscript on a *p* orbital label tells along which of the coordinate axes the two lobes lie.

One important characteristic of orbitals is that as the level number increases, the average distance of the electron in that orbital from the nucleus also increases. That is, when the hydrogen electron is in the 1s orbital (the ground state), it spends most of its time much closer to the nucleus than when it occupies the 2s orbital (an excited state).

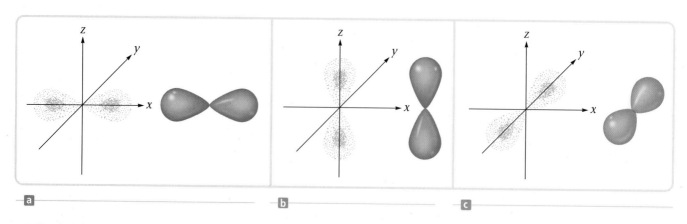

Figure 11.25

The three 2p orbitals: **a** $2p_x$ **b** $2p_z$ **c** $2p_y$. The x, y, or z label indicates along which axis the two lobes are directed. Each orbital is shown both as a probability map and as a surface that encloses 90% of the electron probability.

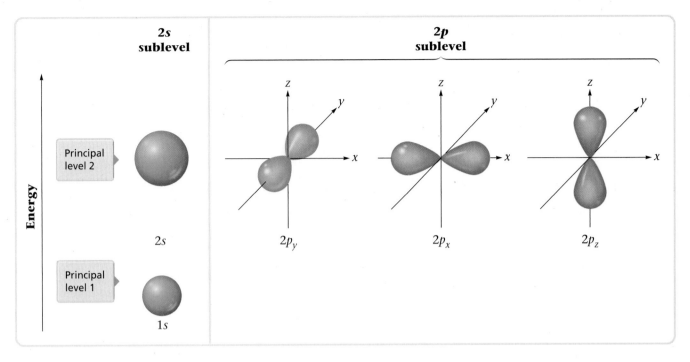

Figure 11.26

A diagram of principal energy levels 1 and 2 showing the shapes of orbitals that compose the sublevels.

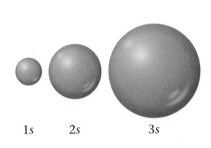

Figure 11.27

The relative sizes of the spherical 1s, 2s, and 3s orbitals of hydrogen.

You may be wondering at this point why hydrogen, which has only one electron, has more than one orbital. It is best to think of an orbital as a *potential space* for an electron. The hydrogen electron can occupy only a single orbital at a time, but the other orbitals are still available should the electron be transferred into one of them. For example, when a hydrogen atom is in its ground state (lowest possible energy state), the electron is in the 1s orbital. By adding the correct amount of energy (for example, a specific photon of light), we can excite the electron to the 2s orbital or to one of the 2p orbitals.

So far we have discussed only two of hydrogen's energy levels. There are many others. For example, level 3 has three sublevels (see Figure 11.22), which we label 3s, 3p, and 3d. The 3s sublevel contains a single 3s orbital, a spherical orbital larger than 1s and 2s (Figure 11.27). Sublevel 3p contains three orbitals: $3p_x$, $3p_y$, and $3p_z$, which are shaped like the 2p orbitals except that they are larger. The 3d sublevel contains five 3d orbitals with the shapes and labels shown in Figure 11.28. (You do not need to memorize the 3d orbital shapes and labels. They are shown for completeness.)

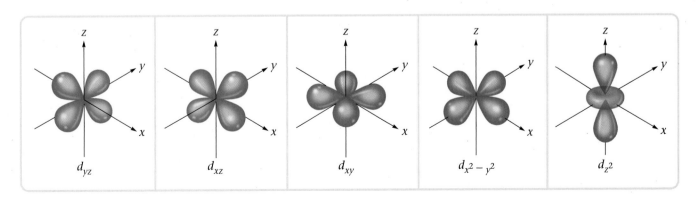

Figure 11.28

The shapes and labels of the five 3d orbitals.

Notice as you compare levels 1, 2, and 3 that a new type of orbital (sublevel) is added in each principal energy level. (Recall that the *p* orbitals are added in level 2 and the *d* orbitals in level 3.) This makes sense because in going farther out from the nucleus, there is more space available and thus room for more orbitals.

It might help you to understand that the number of orbitals increases with the principal energy level if you think of a theater in the round. Picture a round stage with circular rows of seats surrounding it. The farther from the stage a row of seats is, the more seats it contains because the circle is larger. Orbitals divide up the space around a nucleus somewhat like the seats in this circular theater. The greater the distance from the nucleus, the more space there is and the more orbitals we find.

The pattern of increasing numbers of orbitals continues with level 4. Level 4 has four sublevels labeled 4*s*, 4*p*, 4*d*, and 4*f*. The 4*s* sublevel has a single 4*s* orbital. The 4*p* sublevel contains three orbitals ($4p_x$, $4p_y$, and $4p_z$). The 4*d* sublevel has five 4*d* orbitals. The 4*f* sublevel has seven 4*f* orbitals.

The 4*s*, 4*p*, and 4*d* orbitals have the same shapes as the earlier *s*, *p*, and *d* orbitals, respectively, but are larger. We will not be concerned here with the shapes of the *f* orbitals.

11.8   The Wave Mechanical Model: Further Development

OBJECTIVES: To review the energy levels and orbitals of the wave mechanical model of the atom. • To learn about electron spin.

A model for the atom is of little use if it does not apply to all atoms. The Bohr model was discarded because it could be applied only to hydrogen. The wave mechanical model can be applied to all atoms in basically the same form as the one we have just used for hydrogen. In fact, the major triumph of this model is its ability to explain the periodic table of the elements. Recall that the elements on the periodic table are arranged in vertical groups, which contain elements that typically show similar chemical properties. The wave mechanical model of the atom allows us to explain, based on electron arrangements, why these similarities occur. We will see in due time how this is done.

Remember that an atom has as many electrons as it has protons to give it a zero overall charge. Therefore, all atoms beyond hydrogen have more than one electron. Before we can consider the atoms beyond hydrogen, we must describe one more property of electrons that determines how they can be arranged in an atom's orbitals. This property is spin. Each electron appears to be spinning as a top spins on its axis. Like the top, an electron can spin only in one of two directions. We often represent spin with an arrow: either ↑ or ↓. One arrow represents the electron spinning in the one direction, and the other represents the electron spinning in the opposite direction. For our purposes, what is most important about electron spin is that two electrons must have *opposite* spins to occupy the same orbital. That is, two electrons that have the same spin cannot occupy the same orbital. This leads to the **Pauli exclusion principle:** an atomic orbital can hold a maximum of two electrons, and those two electrons must have opposite spins.

Before we apply the wave mechanical model to atoms beyond hydrogen, we will summarize the model for convenient reference.

Principal Components of the Wave Mechanical Model of the Atom

1. Atoms have a series of energy levels called **principal energy levels,** which are designated by whole numbers symbolized by n; n can equal 1, 2, 3, 4, ... Level 1 corresponds to $n = 1$, level 2 corresponds to $n = 2$, and so on.
2. The energy of the level increases as the value of n increases.
3. Each principal energy level contains one or more *types* of orbitals, called **sublevels.**
4. The number of sublevels present in a given principal energy level equals n. For example, level 1 contains one sublevel ($1s$); level 2 contains two sublevels (two types of orbitals), the $2s$ orbital and the three $2p$ orbitals; and so on. These are summarized in the following table. The number of each type of orbital is shown in parentheses.

n	Sublevels (Types of Orbitals) Present
1	$1s(1)$
2	$2s(1)$ $2p(3)$
3	$3s(1)$ $3p(3)$ $3d(5)$
4	$4s(1)$ $4p(3)$ $4d(5)$ $4f(7)$

5. The n value is always used to label the orbitals of a given principal level and is followed by a letter that indicates the type (shape) of the orbital. For example, the designation $3p$ means an orbital in level 3 that has two lobes (a p orbital always has two lobes).
6. An orbital can be empty or it can contain one or two electrons, but never more than two. If two electrons occupy the same orbital, they must have opposite spins.
7. The shape of an orbital does not indicate the details of electron movement. It indicates the probability distribution for an electron residing in that orbital.

EXAMPLE 11.1   Understanding the Wave Mechanical Model of the Atom

Indicate whether each of the following statements about atomic structure is true or false.

a. An s orbital is always spherical in shape.

b. The $2s$ orbital is the same size as the $3s$ orbital.

c. The number of lobes on a p orbital increases as n increases. That is, a $3p$ orbital has more lobes than a $2p$ orbital.

d. Level 1 has one s orbital, level 2 has two s orbitals, level 3 has three s orbitals, and so on.

e. The electron path is indicated by the surface of the orbital.

SOLUTION

a. True. The size of the sphere increases as n increases, but the shape is always spherical.

b. False. The 3*s* orbital is larger (the electron is farther from the nucleus on average) than the 2*s* orbital.

c. False. A *p* orbital always has two lobes.

d. False. Each principal energy level has only one *s* orbital.

e. False. The electron is *somewhere inside* the orbital surface 90% of the time. The electron does not move around *on* this surface.

Self-Check EXERCISE 11.1 Define the following terms.

　　a. Bohr orbits

　　b. orbitals

　　c. orbital size

　　d. sublevel

See Problems 11.37 through 11.44. ■

11.9 Electron Arrangements in the First Eighteen Atoms on the Periodic Table

OBJECTIVES: To understand how the principal energy levels fill with electrons in atoms beyond hydrogen. • To learn about valence electrons and core electrons.

We will now describe the electron arrangements in atoms with $Z = 1$ to $Z = 18$ by placing electrons in the various orbitals in the principal energy levels, starting with $n = 1$, and then continuing with $n = 2$, $n = 3$, and so on. For the first eighteen elements, the individual sublevels fill in the following order: 1*s*, then 2*s*, then 2*p*, then 3*s*, then 3*p*.

The most attractive orbital to an electron in an atom is always the 1*s*, because in this orbital the negatively charged electron is closer to the positively charged nucleus than in any other orbital. That is, the 1*s* orbital involves the space around the nucleus that is closest to the nucleus. As *n* increases, the orbital becomes larger—the electron, on average, occupies space farther from the nucleus.

So in its ground state hydrogen has its lone electron in the 1*s* orbital. This is commonly represented in two ways. First, we say that hydrogen has the electron arrangement, or **electron configuration**, $1s^1$. This just means there is one electron in the 1*s* orbital. We can also represent this configuration by using an **orbital diagram**, also called a **box diagram**, in which orbitals are represented by boxes grouped by sublevel with small arrows indicating the electrons. For *hydrogen*, the electron configuration and box diagram are

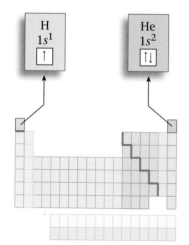

$$\text{H:} \qquad 1s^1 \qquad\qquad \overset{\displaystyle 1s}{\boxed{\uparrow}}$$

　　　　　　Configuration　　　Orbital diagram

The arrow represents an electron spinning in a particular direction. The next element is *helium*, $Z = 2$. It has two protons in its nucleus and so has two electrons. Because the 1*s* orbital is the most desirable, both electrons go there but with opposite spins. For helium, the electron configuration and box diagram are

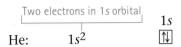

He: $1s^2$

The opposite electron spins are shown by the opposing arrows in the box.

Lithium ($Z = 3$) has three electrons, two of which go into the 1s orbital. That is, two electrons fill that orbital. The 1s orbital is the only orbital for $n = 1$, so the third electron must occupy an orbital with $n = 2$—in this case the 2s orbital. This gives a $1s^22s^1$ configuration. The electron configuration and box diagram are

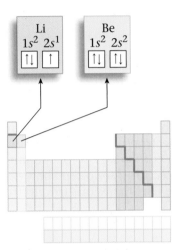

Li: $1s^22s^1$

The next element, *beryllium*, has four electrons, which occupy the 1s and 2s orbitals with opposite spins.

Be: $1s^22s^2$

Boron has five electrons, four of which occupy the 1s and 2s orbitals. The fifth electron goes into the second type of orbital with $n = 2$, one of the 2p orbitals.

B: $1s^22s^22p^1$

Because all the 2p orbitals have the same energy, it does not matter which 2p orbital the electron occupies.

Carbon, the next element, has six electrons: two electrons occupy the 1s orbital, two occupy the 2s orbital, and two occupy 2p orbitals. There are three 2p orbitals, so each of the mutually repulsive electrons occupies a different 2p orbital. For reasons we will not consider, in the separate 2p orbitals the electrons have the same spin.

The configuration for carbon could be written $1s^22s^22p^12p^1$ to indicate that the electrons occupy separate 2p orbitals. However, the configuration is usually given as $1s^22s^22p^2$, and it is understood that the electrons are in different 2p orbitals.

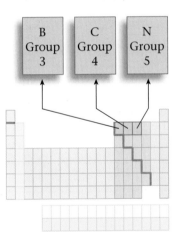

C: $1s^22s^22p^2$

Note the like spins for the unpaired electrons in the 2p orbitals.

The configuration for *nitrogen,* which has seven electrons, is $1s^22s^22p^3$. The three electrons in 2p orbitals occupy separate orbitals and have like spins.

N: $1s^22s^22p^3$

The configuration for *oxygen,* which has eight electrons, is $1s^22s^22p^4$. One of the 2p orbitals is now occupied by a pair of electrons with opposite spins, as required by the Pauli exclusion principle.

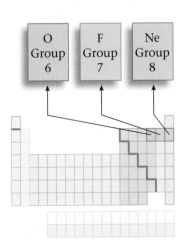

O: $1s^22s^22p^4$

H $1s^1$									He $1s^2$
Li $2s^1$	Be $2s^2$			B $2p^1$	C $2p^2$	N $2p^3$	O $2p^4$	F $2p^5$	Ne $2p^6$
Na $3s^1$	Mg $3s^2$			Al $3p^1$	Si $3p^2$	P $3p^3$	S $3p^4$	Cl $3p^5$	Ar $3p^6$

Figure 11.29

The electron configurations in the sublevel last occupied for the first eighteen elements.

The electron configurations and orbital diagrams for *fluorine* (nine electrons) and *neon* (ten electrons) are

F: $1s^2 2s^2 2p^5$

Ne: $1s^2 2s^2 2p^6$

With neon, the orbitals with $n = 1$ and $n = 2$ are completely filled.

For *sodium*, which has eleven electrons, the first ten electrons occupy the 1s, 2s, and 2p orbitals, and the eleventh electron must occupy the first orbital with $n = 3$, the 3s orbital. The electron configuration for sodium is $1s^2 2s^2 2p^6 3s^1$. To avoid writing the inner-level electrons, we often abbreviate the configuration $1s^2 2s^2 2p^6 3s^1$ as [Ne]$3s^1$, where [Ne] represents the electron configuration of neon, $1s^2 2s^2 2p^6$.

The orbital diagram for sodium is

The next element, *magnesium*, $Z = 12$, has the electron configuration $1s^2 2s^2 2p^6 3s^2$, or [Ne]$3s^2$.

The next six elements, *aluminum* through *argon,* have electron configurations obtained by filling the 3p orbitals one electron at a time. Figure 11.29 summarizes the electron configurations of the first eighteen elements by giving the number of electrons in the type of orbital (sublevel) occupied last.

EXAMPLE 11.2 | **Writing Orbital Diagrams**

Write the orbital diagram for magnesium.

SOLUTION

Magnesium ($Z = 12$) has twelve electrons that are placed successively in the 1s, 2s, 2p, and 3s orbitals to give the electron configuration $1s^2 2s^2 2p^6 3s^2$. The orbital diagram is

Only occupied orbitals are shown here.

Self-Check EXERCISE 11.2 Write the complete electron configuration and the orbital diagram for each of the elements aluminum through argon.

See Problems 11.49 through 11.54. ■

A Magnetic Moment

An anesthetized frog lies in the hollow core of an electromagnet. As the current in the coils of the magnet is increased, the frog magically rises and floats in midair (see photo). How can this happen? Is the electromagnet an antigravity machine? In fact, there is no magic going on here. This phenomenon demonstrates the magnetic properties of all matter. We know that iron magnets attract and repel each other depending on their relative orientations. Is a frog magnetic like a piece of iron? If a frog lands on a steel manhole cover, will it be trapped there by magnetic attractions? Of course not. The magnetism of the frog, as with most objects, shows up only in the presence of a strong inducing magnetic field. In other words, the powerful electromagnet surrounding the frog in the experiment described

above *induces* a magnetic field in the frog that opposes the inducing field. The opposing magnetic field in the frog repels the inducing field, and the frog lifts up until the magnetic force is balanced by the gravitational pull on its body. The frog then "floats" in air.

How can a frog be magnetic if it is not made of iron? It's the electrons. Frogs are composed of cells containing many kinds of molecules. Of course, these molecules are made of atoms—carbon atoms, nitrogen atoms, oxygen atoms, and other types. Each of these atoms contains electrons that are moving around the atomic nuclei. When these electrons sense a strong magnetic field, they respond by moving in a fashion that produces magnetic fields aligned to oppose the inducing field. This phenomenon is called *diamagnetism*.

All substances, animate and inanimate, because they are made of atoms, exhibit diamagnetism. Andre Geim and his colleagues at the University of Nijmegan, the Netherlands, have levitated frogs, grasshoppers, plants, and water droplets, among other objects. Geim says that, given a large enough electromagnet, even humans can be levitated. He notes, however, that constructing a magnet strong enough to float a human would be very expensive, and he sees no point in it. Geim does point out that inducing weightlessness with magnetic fields may be a good way to pretest experiments on weightlessness intended as research for future space flights—to see if the ideas fly as well as the objects.

A live frog levitated in a magnetic field.

Andrey K. Geim/High Field Magnet Laboratory/ University of Nijmegen

At this point it is useful to introduce the concept of **valence electrons**—that is, *the electrons in the outermost (highest) principal energy level of an atom.* For example, nitrogen, which has the electron configuration $1s^2 2s^2 2p^3$, has electrons in principal levels 1 and 2. Therefore, level 2 (which has 2*s* and 2*p* sublevels) is the valence level of nitrogen, and the 2*s* and 2*p* electrons are the valence electrons. For the sodium atom (electron configuration $1s^2 2s^2 2p^6 3s^1$, or $[Ne]3s^1$), the valence electron is the electron in the 3*s* orbital, because in this case principal energy level 3 is the outermost level that contains an electron. The valence electrons are the most important electrons to chemists because, being the outermost electrons, they are the ones involved when atoms attach to each other (form bonds), as we will see in the next chapter. The inner electrons, which are known as **core electrons,** are not involved in bonding atoms to each other.

Note in Figure 11.29 that a very important pattern is developing: except for helium, *the atoms of elements in the same group (vertical column of the periodic table) have the same number of electrons in a given type of orbital* (sublevel), except that the orbitals are in different principal energy levels. Remember that the elements were originally organized into groups on the periodic table on the basis of similarities in chemical properties. Now we understand the reason behind these groupings. Elements with the same valence electron arrangement show very similar chemical behavior.

11.10 Electron Configurations and the Periodic Table

OBJECTIVE: To learn about the electron configurations of atoms with Z greater than 18.

In the previous section we saw that we can describe the atoms beyond hydrogen by simply filling the atomic orbitals starting with level $n = 1$ and working outward in order. This works fine until we reach the element *potassium* ($Z = 19$), which is the next element after argon. Because the $3p$ orbitals are fully occupied in argon, we might expect the next electron to go into a $3d$ orbital (recall that for $n = 3$ the sublevels are $3s$, $3p$, and $3d$). However, experiments show that the chemical properties of potassium are very similar to those of lithium and sodium. Because we have learned to associate similar chemical properties with similar valence-electron arrangements, we predict that the valence-electron configuration for potassium is $4s^1$, resembling sodium ($3s^1$) and lithium ($2s^1$). That is, we expect the last electron in potassium to occupy the $4s$ orbital instead of one of the $3d$ orbitals. This means that principal energy level 4 begins to fill before level 3 has been completed. This conclusion is confirmed by many types of experiments. So the electron configuration of potassium is

$$K: 1s^2 2s^2 2p^6 3s^2 3p^6 4s^1, \text{ or } [Ar]4s^1$$

The next element is *calcium*, with an additional electron that also occupies the $4s$ orbital.

$$Ca: 1s^2 2s^2 2p^6 3s^2 3p^6 4s^2, \text{ or } [Ar]4s^2$$

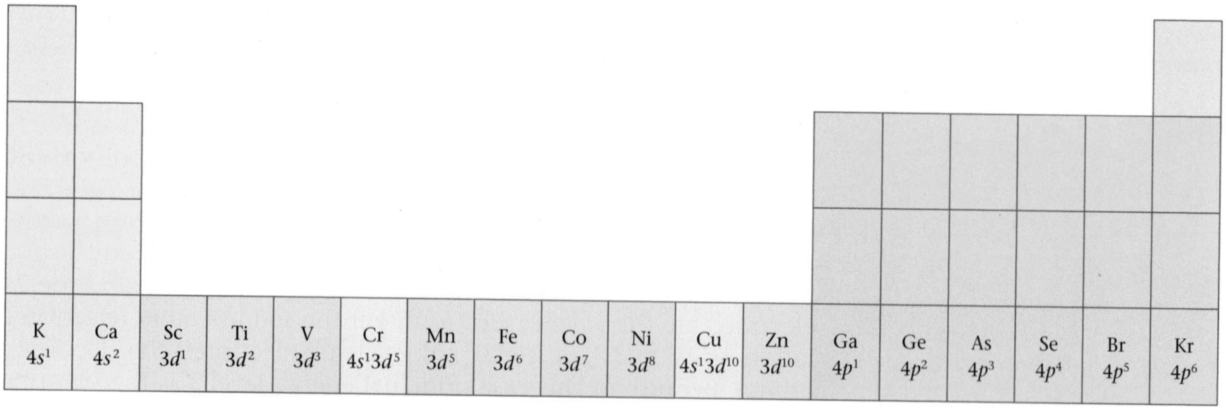

K	Ca	Sc	Ti	V	Cr	Mn	Fe	Co	Ni	Cu	Zn	Ga	Ge	As	Se	Br	Kr
$4s^1$	$4s^2$	$3d^1$	$3d^2$	$3d^3$	$4s^1 3d^5$	$3d^5$	$3d^6$	$3d^7$	$3d^8$	$4s^1 3d^{10}$	$3d^{10}$	$4p^1$	$4p^2$	$4p^3$	$4p^4$	$4p^5$	$4p^6$

Figure 11.30

Partial electron configurations for the elements potassium through krypton. The transition metals shown in green (scandium through zinc) have the general configuration $[Ar]4s^2 3d^n$, except for chromium and copper.

The Chemistry of Bohrium

One of the best uses of the periodic table is to predict the properties of newly discovered elements. For example, the artificially synthesized element bohrium (Z = 107) is found in the same family as manganese, technetium, and rhenium and is expected to show chemistry similar to these elements. The problem, of course, is that only a few atoms of bohrium (Bh) can be made at a time and the atoms exist for only a very short time (about 17 seconds). It's a real challenge to study the chemistry of an element under these conditions. However, a team of nuclear chemists led by Heinz W. Gaggeler of the University of Bern in Switzerland isolated six atoms of ^{267}Bh and prepared the compound BhO_3Cl. Analysis of the decay products of this compound helped define the thermochemical properties of BhO_3Cl and showed that bohrium seems to behave as might be predicted from its position in the periodic table.

The 4s orbital is now full.

After calcium the next electrons go into the 3d orbitals to complete principal energy level 3. The elements that correspond to filling the 3d orbitals are called transition metals. Then the 4p orbitals fill. Figure 11.30 gives partial electron configurations for the elements potassium through krypton.

Note from Figure 11.30 that all of the transition metals have the general configuration $[Ar]4s^23d^n$ except chromium ($4s^13d^5$) and copper ($4s^13d^{10}$). The reasons for these exceptions are complex and will not be discussed here.

Instead of continuing to consider the elements individually, we will now look at the overall relationship between the periodic table and orbital filling. Figure 11.31 shows which type of orbital is filling in each area of the periodic table. Note the points in the box below.

Orbital Filling

1. In a principal energy level that has d orbitals, the s orbital from the *next* level fills before the d orbitals in the current level. That is, the $(n + 1)s$ orbitals always fill before the nd orbitals. For example, the 5s orbitals fill for rubidium and strontium before the 4d orbitals fill for the second row of transition metals (yttrium through cadmium).
2. After lanthanum, which has the electron configuration $[Xe]6s^25d^1$, a group of fourteen elements called the **lanthanide series,** or the lanthanides, occurs. This series of elements corresponds to the filling of the seven 4f orbitals.
3. After actinium, which has the configuration $[Rn]7s^26d^1$, a group of fourteen elements called the **actinide series,** or the actinides, occurs. This series corresponds to the filling of the seven 5f orbitals.
4. Except for helium, the group numbers indicate the sum of electrons in the ns and np orbitals in the highest principal energy level that contains electrons (where n is the number that indicates a particular principal energy level). These electrons are the valence electrons, the electrons in the outermost principal energy level of a given atom.

343

Groups

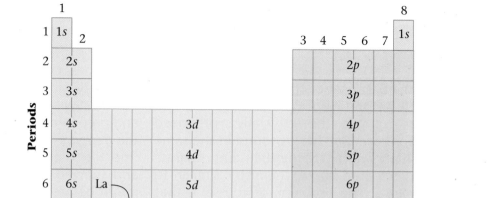

The orbitals being filled for elements in various parts of the periodic table. Note that in going along a horizontal row (a period), the $(n + 1)s$ orbital fills before the nd orbital. The group label indicates the number of valence electrons (the number of s plus the number of p electrons in the highest occupied principal energy level) for the elements in each group.

*After the $6s$ orbital is full, one electron goes into a $5d$ orbital. This corresponds to the element lanthanum ([Xe]$6s^2 5d^1$). After lanthanum, the $4f$ orbitals fill with electrons.

**After the $7s$ orbital is full, one electron goes into $6d$. This is actinium ([Rn]$7s^2 6d^1$). The $5f$ orbitals then fill.

To help you further understand the connection between orbital filling and the periodic table, Figure 11.32 shows the orbitals in the order in which they fill.

A periodic table is almost always available to you. If you understand the relationship between the electron configuration of an element and its position on the periodic table, you can figure out the expected electron configuration of any atom.

EXAMPLE 11.3 | Determining Electron Configurations

Using the periodic table inside the front cover of the text, give the electron configurations for sulfur (S), gallium (Ga), hafnium (Hf), and radium (Ra).

SOLUTION

Sulfur is element 16 and resides in Period 3, where the $3p$ orbitals are being filled (see Figure 11.33). Because sulfur is the fourth among the "$3p$ elements," it must have four $3p$ electrons. Sulfur's electron configuration is

$$\text{S: } 1s^2 2s^2 2p^6 3s^2 3p^4, \text{ or [Ne]}3s^2 3p^4$$

Gallium is element 31 in Period 4 just after the transition metals (see Figure 11.33). It is the first element in the "$4p$ series" and has a $4p^1$ arrangement. Gallium's electron configuration is

$$\text{Ga: } 1s^2 2s^2 2p^6 3s^2 3p^6 4s^2 3d^{10} 4p^1, \text{ or [Ar]}4s^2 3d^{10} 4p^1$$

Hafnium is element 72 and is found in Period 6, as shown in Figure 11.33. Note that it occurs just after the lanthanide series (see Figure 11.31).

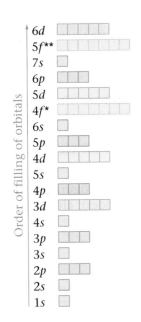

Figure 11.32

A box diagram showing the order in which orbitals fill to produce the atoms in the periodic table. Each box can hold two electrons.

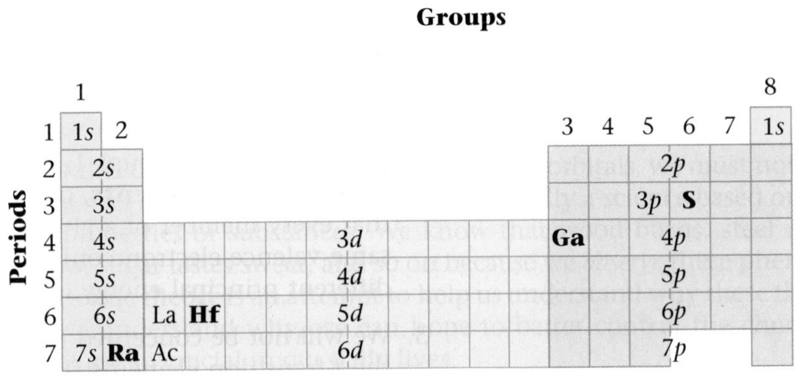

Groups

Figure 11.33

The positions of the elements considered in Example 11.3.

Thus the $4f$ orbitals are already filled. Hafnium is the second member of the $5d$ transition series and has two $5d$ electrons. Its electron configuration is

Hf: $1s^2 2s^2 2p^6 3s^2 3p^6 4s^2 3d^{10} 4p^6 5s^2 4d^{10} 5p^6 6s^2 4f^{14} 5d^2$, or $[Xe]6s^2 4f^{14} 5d^2$

Radium is element 88 and is in Period 7 (and Group 2), as shown in Figure 11.33. Thus radium has two electrons in the $7s$ orbital, and its electron configuration is

Ra: $1s^2 2s^2 2p^6 3s^2 3p^6 4s^2 3d^{10} 4p^6 5s^2 4d^{10} 5p^6 6s^2 4f^{14} 5d^{10} 6p^6 7s^2$, or $[Rn]7s^2$

Self-Check **EXERCISE 11.3**   Using the periodic table inside the front cover of the text, predict the electron configurations for fluorine, silicon, cesium, lead, and iodine. If you have trouble, use Figure 11.31.

See Problems 11.59 through 11.68. ■

▶ **Summary of the Wave Mechanical Model and Valence-Electron Configurations**

The concepts we have discussed in this chapter are very important. They allow us to make sense of a good deal of chemistry. When it was first observed that elements with similar properties occur periodically as the atomic number increases, chemists wondered why. Now we have an explanation. The wave mechanical model pictures the electrons in an atom as arranged in orbitals, with each orbital capable of holding two electrons. As we build up the atoms, the same types of orbitals recur in going from one principal energy level to another. This means that particular valence-electron configurations recur periodically. For reasons we will explore in the next chapter, elements with a particular type of valence configuration all show very similar chemical behavior. Thus groups of elements, such as the alkali metals, show similar chemistry because all the elements in that group have the same type of valence-electron arrangement. This concept, which explains so much chemistry, is the greatest contribution of the wave mechanical model to modern chemistry.

For reference, the valence-electron configurations for all the elements are shown on the periodic table in Figure 11.34. Note the following points:

1. The group labels for Groups 1, 2, 3, 4, 5, 6, 7, and 8 indicate the *total number* of valence electrons for the atoms in these groups. For

9. Ionization energy, the energy required to remove an electron from a gaseous atom, decreases going down a group and increases going from left to right across a period.

10. For the representative elements, atomic size increases going down a group but decreases going from left to right across a period.

Active Learning Questions

These questions are designed to be considered by groups of students in class. Often these questions work well for introducing a particular topic in class.

1. How does probability fit into the description of the atom?

2. What is meant by an *orbital?*

3. Account for the fact that the line that separates the metals from the nonmetals on the periodic table is diagonal downward to the right instead of horizontal or vertical.

4. Consider the following statements: "The ionization energy for the potassium atom is negative because when K loses an electron to become K^+, it achieves a noble gas electron configuration." Indicate everything that is correct in this statement. Indicate everything that is incorrect. Correct the mistaken information and explain the error.

5. In going across a row of the periodic table, protons and electrons are added and ionization energy generally increases. In going down a column of the periodic table, protons and electrons are also being added but ionization energy generally decreases. Explain.

6. Which is larger, the H $1s$ orbital or the Li $1s$ orbital? Why? Which has the larger radius, the H atom or the Li atom? Why?

7. True or false? The hydrogen atom has a $3s$ orbital. Explain.

8. Differentiate among the terms *energy level, sublevel,* and *orbital.*

9. Make sense of the fact that metals tend to lose electrons and nonmetals tend to gain electrons. Use the periodic table to support your answer.

10. Show how using the periodic table helps you find the expected electron configuration of any element.

For Questions 11–13, you will need to consider ionizations beyond the first ionization energy. For example, the second ionization energy is the energy to remove a second electron from an element.

11. Compare the first ionization energy of helium to its second ionization energy, remembering that both electrons come from the $1s$ orbital.

12. Which would you expect to have a larger second ionization energy, lithium or beryllium? Why?

13. The first four ionization energies for elements X and Y are shown below. The units are not kJ/mol.

	X	Y
first	170	200
second	350	400
third	1800	3500
fourth	2500	5000

Identify the elements X and Y. There may be more than one answer, so explain completely.

14. Explain what is meant by the term "excited state" as it applies to an electron. Is an electron in an excited state higher or lower in energy than an electron in the ground state? Is an electron in an excited state more or less stable than an electron in the ground state?

15. What does it mean when we say energy levels are *quantized?*

16. What evidence do we have that energy levels in an atom are quantized? State and explain the evidence.

17. Explain the hydrogen emission spectrum. Why is it significant that the color emitted is not white? How does the emission spectrum support the idea of quantized energy levels?

18. There are an infinite number of allowed transitions in the hydrogen atom. Why don't we see more lines in the emission spectrum for hydrogen?

19. You have learned that each orbital is allowed two electrons, and this pattern is evident on the periodic table. What if each orbital was allowed three electrons? How would this change the appearance of the periodic table? For example, what would be the atomic numbers of the noble gases?

20. Atom A has valence electrons that are lower in energy than the valence electrons of Atom B. Which atom has the higher ionization energy? Explain.

VP 21. Consider the following waves representing electromagnetic radiation:

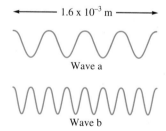

Questions and Problems

11.1 Rutherford's Atom

QUESTIONS

1. An atom has a small _____ charged core called the nucleus, with _____ charged electrons moving in the space around the nucleus.

All even-numbered Questions and Problems have answers in the back of this book and solutions in the Solutions Guide.

100. In the text (Sectio...
rent theories of ...
matter and all e...
like and wave-lik...
conditions, altho...
becomes appaten...
moving particles...
length (λ) observ...
velocity of that p...
tionship. It is

in which h is Plan...
represents the ma...
v represents the v...
second. Calculate...
each of the follo...
swers to explain v...
not ordinarily dis...
properties.

a. an electron mo...
b. a 150-g ball m...
c. a 75-kg person...

101. Light waves mo...
_____ meters p...

102. How do we know...
gen atom are not...
assumed?

103. How does the att...
on an electron ch...
of the electron?

104. Into how many su...
level of hydrogen...
orbitals that cons...
general shapes of...

105. A student writes t...
($Z = 6$) as $1s^3 2s^3$....
this configuration...

106. Write three orbit...
rect and explain...
$1p$ would be an in...
there is no p subs...

107. Why do we belie...
sublevel of nitrog...

108. Write the full ele...
each of the follov...

a. bromine, $Z = $...
b. xenon, $Z = 54$...

*Note that s is the abbrev...

All even-

2. What major conclusions did Rutherford draw about the atom based on his gold foil bombardment experiments? What questions were left unanswered by Rutherford's experiments?

11.2 Electromagnetic Radiation

QUESTIONS

3. What is _electromagnetic radiation?_ At what speed does electromagnetic radiation travel?

4. How are the different types of electromagnetic radiation similar? How do they differ?

5. What does the _wavelength_ of electromagnetic radiation represent? How is the wavelength of radiation related to the _energy_ of the photons of the radiation?

6. What do we mean by the _frequency_ of electromagnetic radiation? Is the frequency the same as the _speed_ of the electromagnetic radiation?

F 7. The "Chemistry in Focus" segment _Light as a Sex Attractant_ discusses fluorescence. In fluorescence, ultraviolet radiation is absorbed and intense white visible light is emitted. Is ultraviolet radiation a higher or a lower energy radiation than visible light?

F 8. The "Chemistry in Focus" segment _Atmospheric Effects_ discusses the greenhouse effect. How do the greenhouse gases CO_2, H_2O, and CH_4 have an effect on the temperature of the atmosphere?

11.3 Emission of Energy by Atoms

QUESTIONS

9. When lithium salts are heated in a flame, they emit red light. When copper salts are heated in a flame in the same manner, they emit green light. Why do we know that lithium salts will never emit green light, and copper salts will never emit red light?

10. The energy of a photon of visible light emitted by an excited atom is _____ the energy change that takes place within the atom itself.

11.4 The Energy Levels of Hydrogen

QUESTIONS

11. What does the _ground state_ of an atom represent?

12. When an atom in an excited state returns to its ground state, what happens to the excess energy of the atom?

13. How is the energy carried per photon of light related to the wavelength of the light? Does short-wavelength light carry more energy or less energy than long-wavelength light?

14. When an atom _____ energy from outside, the atom goes from a lower energy state to a higher energy state.

15. Describe briefly why the study of electromagnetic radiation has been important to our understanding of the arrangement of electrons in atoms.

16. What does it mean to say that the hydrogen atom has _discrete energy levels?_ How is this fact reflected in the radiation that excited hydrogen atoms emit?

17. Because a given element's atoms emit only certain photons of light, only certain _____ are occurring in those particular atoms.

18. How does the energy possessed by an emitted photon compare to the difference in energy levels that gave rise to the emission of the photon?

19. The energy levels of hydrogen (and other atoms) are said to be _____, which means that only certain energy values are allowed.

20. When a tube containing hydrogen atoms is energized by passing several thousand volts of electricity into the tube, the hydrogen emits light that, when passed through a prism, resolves into the "bright line" spectrum shown in Figure 11.11. Why do hydrogen atoms emit bright lines of specific wavelengths rather than a continuous spectrum?

11.5 The Bohr Model of the Atom

QUESTIONS

21. What are the essential points of Bohr's theory of the structure of the hydrogen atom?

22. According to Bohr, what happens to the electron when a hydrogen atom absorbs a photon of light of sufficient energy?

23. How does the Bohr theory account for the observed phenomenon of the emission of discrete wavelengths of light by excited atoms?

24. Why was Bohr's theory for the hydrogen atom initially accepted, and why was it ultimately discarded?

11.6 The Wave Mechanical Model of the Atom

QUESTIONS

25. What major assumption (that was analogous to what had already been demonstrated for electromagnetic radiation) did de Broglie and Schrödinger make about the motion of tiny particles?

26. Discuss briefly the difference between an orbit (as described by Bohr for hydrogen) and an orbital (as described by the more modern, wave mechanical picture of the atom).

27. Why was Schrödinger not able to describe exactly the pathway an electron takes as it moves through the space of an atom?

28. Section 11.6 uses a "firefly" analogy to illustrate how the wave mechanical model for the atom differs from Bohr's model. Explain this analogy.

All even-numbered Questions and Problems have answers in the back of this book and solutions in the Solutions Guide.

76. Why do the meta
izontal row) typ
energies than de
same period?

77. What are the *m*
found on the per

F 78. The "Chemistry
cusses some of th
ors of fireworks.
istence of quanti

PROBLEMS

79. In each of the f
least reactive?

a. Group 1
b. Group 7

80. In each of the fo
ment would be e
tion energy?

a. Cs, K, Li
b. Ba, Sr, Ca

81. Arrange the follo
creasing atomic s

a. Sn, Xe, Rb, Sr
b. Rn, He, Xe, Kr

82. In each of the f
which element h

a. Na, K, Rb
b. Na, Si, S

Additional Problems

83. Consider the b
shown in Figure
represents photo
the lowest energy

84. The speed at whi
through a vacuu

85. The portion of
tween wavelengt
nanometers is ca

86. A beam of light
stream of light pa

87. The lowest possi
the _____ state

88. The energy levels
_____, which r
ergy are allowed.

89. According to Bo
atom moved arc
called _____.

90. In the modern th
resents a region
probability of fin

12

Chemical Bonding

● The ionic structure of boron. *(Artem Oganov/Stony Brook University, New York)*

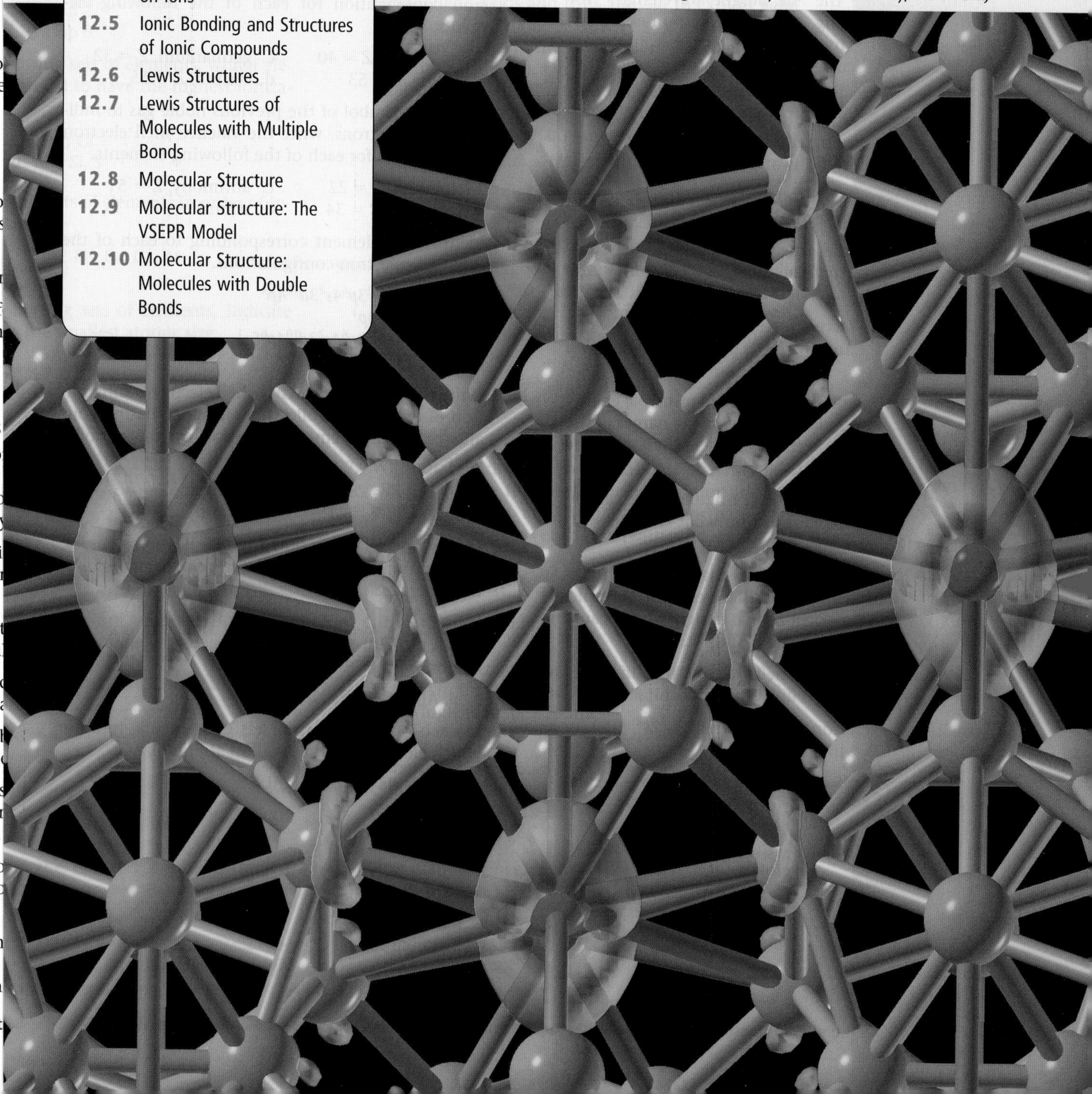

ⓦWL Sign in to OWL at **www.cengage.com/owl** to view tutorials and simulations, develop problem-solving skills, and complete online homework assigned by your professor.

go Chemistry Download mini-lecture videos for key concept review and exam prep from OWL or purchase them from **www.ichapters.com**

Diamond, composed of carbon atoms bonded together to produce one of the hardest materials known, makes a beautiful gemstone.

Tino Hammid

The world around us is composed almost entirely of compounds and mixtures of compounds. Rocks, coal, soil, petroleum, trees, and human beings are all complex mixtures of chemical compounds in which different kinds of atoms are bound together. Most of the pure elements found in the earth's crust also contain many atoms bound together. In a gold nugget each gold atom is bound to many other gold atoms, and in a diamond many carbon atoms are bonded very strongly to each other. Substances composed of unbound atoms do exist in nature, but they are very rare. (Examples include the argon atoms in the atmosphere and the helium atoms found in natural gas reserves.)

The manner in which atoms are bound together has a profound effect on the chemical and physical properties of substances. For example, both graphite and diamond are composed solely of carbon atoms. However, graphite is a soft, slippery material used as a lubricant in locks, and diamond is one of the hardest materials known, valuable both as a gemstone and in industrial cutting tools. Why do these materials, both composed solely of carbon atoms, have such different properties? The answer lies in the different ways in which the carbon atoms are bound to each other in these substances.

Molecular bonding and structure play the central role in determining the course of chemical reactions, many of which are vital to our survival. Most reactions in biological systems are very sensitive to the structures of the participating molecules; in fact, very subtle differences in shape sometimes serve to channel the chemical reaction one way rather than another. Molecules that act as drugs must have exactly the right structure to perform their functions correctly. Structure also plays a central role in our senses of smell and taste. Substances have a particular odor because they fit into the specially shaped receptors in our nasal passages. Taste is also dependent on molecular shape, as we discuss in the "Chemistry in Focus" on page 383.

To understand the behavior of natural materials, we must understand the nature of chemical bonding and the factors that control the structures of compounds. In this chapter, we will present various classes of compounds that illustrate the different types of bonds. We will then develop models to describe the structure and bonding that characterize the materials found in nature.

12.1 Types of Chemical Bonds

OBJECTIVES:
To learn about ionic and covalent bonds and explain how they are formed.
• To learn about the polar covalent bond.

A water molecule.

What is a chemical bond? Although there are several possible ways to answer this question, we will define a **bond** as a force that holds groups of two or more atoms together and makes them function as a unit. For example, in water the fundamental unit is the H—O—H molecule, which we describe as being held together by the two O—H bonds. We can obtain information about the strength of a bond by measuring the energy required to break the bond, the **bond energy.**

Atoms can interact with one another in several ways to form aggregates. We will consider specific examples to illustrate the various types of chemical bonds.

In Chapter 7 we saw that when solid sodium chloride is dissolved in water, the resulting solution conducts electricity, a fact that convinces chemists that sodium chloride is composed of Na^+ and Cl^- ions. Thus, when sodium and chlorine react to form sodium chloride, electrons are transferred from the sodium atoms to the chlorine atoms to form Na^+ and Cl^- ions, which then aggregate to form solid sodium chloride. The resulting solid sodium chloride is a very sturdy material; it has a melting point of approximately 800 °C. The strong bonding forces present in sodium chloride result from the attractions among the closely packed, oppositely charged ions. This is an example of **ionic bonding.** Ionic substances are formed when an atom that loses electrons relatively easily reacts with an atom that has a high affinity for electrons. In other words, an **ionic compound** results when a metal reacts with a nonmetal.

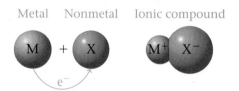

We have seen that a bonding force develops when two very different types of atoms react to form oppositely charged ions. But how does a bonding force develop between two identical atoms? Let's explore this situation by considering what happens when two hydrogen atoms are brought close together, as shown in Figure 12.1. When hydrogen atoms are close together, the two electrons are simultaneously attracted to both nuclei. Note in Figure 12.1b how the electron probability increases between the two nuclei indicating that the electrons are shared by the two nuclei.

The type of bonding we encounter in the hydrogen molecule and in many other molecules where *electrons are shared by nuclei* is called **covalent bonding.** Note that in the H_2 molecule the electrons reside primarily in the space between the two nuclei, where they are attracted simultaneously by both protons. Although we will not go into detail about it here, the increased attractive forces in this area lead to the formation of the H_2 molecule from

Figure 12.1

The formation of a bond between two hydrogen atoms.

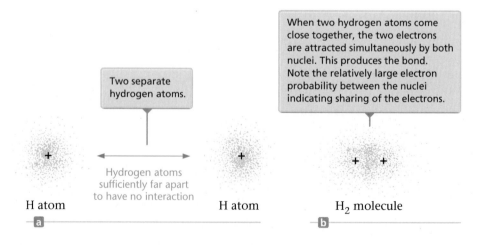

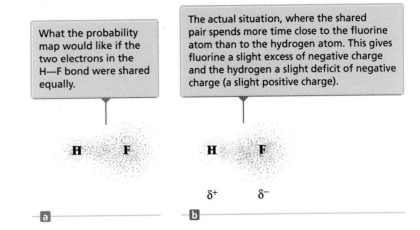

Figure 12.2

Probability representations of the electron sharing in HF.

Ionic and covalent bonds are the extreme bond types.

the two separated hydrogen atoms. When we say that a bond is formed between the hydrogen atoms, we mean that the H_2 molecule is more stable than two separated hydrogen atoms by a certain quantity of energy (the bond energy).

So far we have considered two extreme types of bonding. In ionic bonding, the participating atoms are so different that one or more electrons are transferred to form oppositely charged ions. The bonding results from the attractions among these ions. In covalent bonding, two identical atoms share electrons equally. The bonding results from the mutual attraction of the two nuclei for the shared electrons. Between these extremes are intermediate cases in which the atoms are not so different that electrons are completely transferred but are different enough so that unequal sharing of electrons results, forming what is called a **polar covalent bond.** The hydrogen fluoride (HF) molecule contains this type of bond, which produces the following charge distribution,

$$H{-}F$$
$$\delta^+ \quad \delta^-$$

where δ (delta) is used to indicate a partial or fractional charge.

The most logical explanation for the development of *bond polarity* (the partial positive and negative charges on the atoms in such molecules as HF) is that the electrons in the bonds are not shared equally. For example, we can account for the polarity of the HF molecule by assuming that the fluorine atom has a stronger attraction than the hydrogen atom for the shared electrons (Figure 12.2). Because bond polarity has important chemical implications, we find it useful to assign a number that indicates an atom's ability to attract shared electrons. In the next section we show how this is done.

12.2 Electronegativity

OBJECTIVE: To understand the nature of bonds and their relationship to electronegativity.

We saw in the previous section that when a metal and a nonmetal react, one or more electrons are transferred from the metal to the nonmetal to give ionic bonding. On the other hand, two identical atoms react to form a covalent bond in which electrons are shared equally. When *different* nonmetals react, a bond forms in which electrons are shared *unequally,* giving a polar

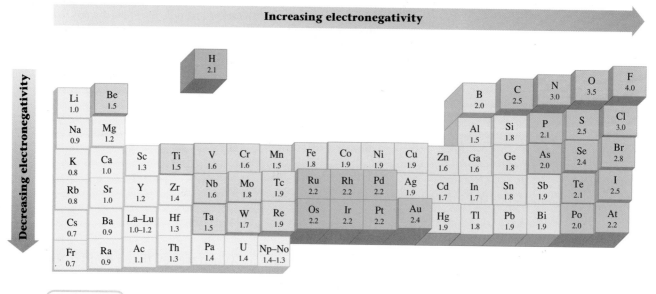

Figure 12.3

Electronegativity values for selected elements. Note that electronegativity generally increases across a period and decreases down a group. Note also that metals have relatively low electronegativity values and that nonmetals have relatively high values.

covalent bond. The unequal sharing of electrons between two atoms is described by a property called **electronegativity:** *the relative ability of an atom in a molecule to attract shared electrons to itself.*

Chemists determine electronegativity values for the elements (Figure 12.3) by measuring the polarities of the bonds between various atoms. Note that electronegativity generally increases going from left to right across a period and decreases going down a group for the representative elements. The range of electronegativity values is from 4.0 for fluorine to 0.7 for cesium and francium. Remember, the higher the atom's electronegativity value, the closer the shared electrons tend to be to that atom when it forms a bond.

The polarity of a bond depends on the *difference* between the electronegativity values of the atoms forming the bond. If the atoms have very similar electronegativities, the electrons are shared almost equally and the bond shows little polarity. If the atoms have very different electronegativity values, a very polar bond is formed. In extreme cases one or more electrons are actually transferred, forming ions and an ionic bond. For example, when an element from Group 1 (electronegativity values of about 0.8) reacts with an element from Group 7 (electronegativity values of about 3), ions are formed and an ionic substance results.

The relationship between electronegativity and bond type is shown in Table 12.1. The various types of bonds are summarized in Figure 12.4.

Table 12.1 The Relationship Between Electronegativity and Bond Type

Electronegativity Difference Between the Bonding Atoms	Bond Type	Covalent Character	Ionic Character
Zero	Covalent		
↓	↓	Decreases	Increases
Intermediate	Polar covalent		
↓	↓		
Large	Ionic		

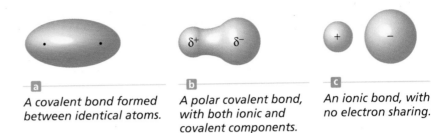

a	b	c
A covalent bond formed between identical atoms.	A polar covalent bond, with both ionic and covalent components.	An ionic bond, with no electron sharing.

Figure 12.4
The three possible types of bonds.

EXAMPLE 12.1 | **Using Electronegativity to Determine Bond Polarity**

Using the electronegativity values given in Figure 12.3, arrange the following bonds in order of increasing polarity: H—H, O—H, Cl—H, S—H, and F—H.

SOLUTION

The polarity of the bond increases as the difference in electronegativity increases. From the electronegativity values in Figure 12.3, the following variation in bond polarity is expected (the electronegativity value appears below each element).

Bond	Electronegativity Values	Difference in Electronegativity Values	Bond Type	Polarity
H—H	(2.1)(2.1)	2.1 − 2.1 = 0	Covalent	
S—H	(2.5)(2.1)	2.5 − 2.1 = 0.4	Polar covalent	
Cl—H	(3.0)(2.1)	3.0 − 2.1 = 0.9	Polar covalent	Increasing
O—H	(3.5)(2.1)	3.5 − 2.1 = 1.4	Polar covalent	
F—H	(4.0)(2.1)	4.0 − 2.1 = 1.9	Polar covalent	

Therefore, in order of increasing polarity, we have

$$\text{H—H} \quad \text{S—H} \quad \text{Cl—H} \quad \text{O—H} \quad \text{F—H}$$

Least polar   Most polar

Self-Check EXERCISE 12.1   For each of the following pairs of bonds, choose the bond that will be more polar.

     a. H—P, H—C

     b. O—F, O—I

     c. N—O, S—O

     d. N—H, Si—H

See Problems 12.17 through 12.20. ■

12.3 Bond Polarity and Dipole Moments

OBJECTIVE: To understand bond polarity and how it is related to molecular polarity.

We saw in Section 12.1 that hydrogen fluoride has a positive end and a negative end. A molecule such as HF that has a center of positive charge and a center of negative charge is said to have a **dipole moment.** The dipolar character of a molecule is often represented by an arrow. This arrow points toward the negative charge center, and its tail indicates the positive center of charge:

δ^+ δ^-

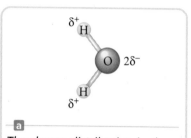

a

The charge distribution in the water molecule. The oxygen has a charge of $2\delta^-$ because it pulls δ^- of charge from each hydrogen atom ($\delta^- + \delta^- = 2\delta^-$).

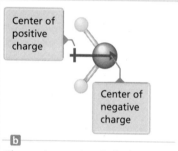

Center of positive charge

Center of negative charge

b

The water molecule behaves as if it had a positive end and a negative end, as indicated by the arrow.

Figure 12.5

Any diatomic (two-atom) molecule that has a polar bond has a dipole moment. Some polyatomic (more than two atoms) molecules also have dipole moments. For example, because the oxygen atom in the water molecule has a greater electronegativity than the hydrogen atoms, the electrons are not shared equally. This results in a charge distribution (Figure 12.5) that causes the molecule to behave as though it had two centers of charge—one positive and one negative. So the water molecule has a dipole moment.

The fact that the water molecule is polar (has a dipole moment) has a profound impact on its properties. In fact, it is not overly dramatic to state that the polarity of the water molecule is crucial to life as we know it on earth. Because water molecules are polar, they can surround and attract both positive and negative ions (Figure 12.6). These attractions allow ionic materials to dissolve in water. Also, the polarity of water molecules causes them to attract each other strongly (Figure 12.7). This means that much energy is required to change water from a liquid to a gas (the molecules must be separated from each other to undergo this change of state). Therefore, it is the polarity of the water molecule that causes water to remain a liquid at the temperatures on the earth's surface. If it were nonpolar, water would be a gas and the oceans would be empty.

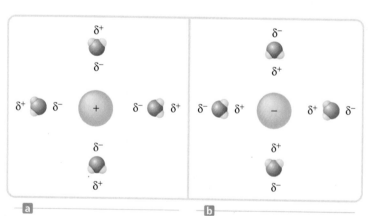

a

Polar water molecules are strongly attracted to positive ions by their negative ends.

b

They are also strongly attracted to negative ions by their positive ends.

Figure 12.6

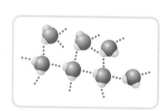

Figure 12.7

Polar water molecules are strongly attracted to each other.

Stable Electron Configurations and Charges on Ions

OBJECTIVES: To learn about stable electron configurations. • To learn to predict the formulas of ionic compounds.

We have seen many times that when a metal and a nonmetal react to form an ionic compound, the metal atom loses one or more electrons to the nonmetal. In Chapter 5, where binary ionic compounds were introduced, we saw that in these reactions, Group 1 metals always form 1+ cations, Group 2 metals always form 2+ cations, and aluminum in Group 3 always forms a 3+ cation. For the nonmetals, the Group 7 elements always form 1− anions, and the Group 6 elements always form 2− anions. This is further illustrated in Table 12.2.

Notice something very interesting about the ions in Table 12.2: they all have the electron configuration of neon, a noble gas. That is, sodium loses its one valence electron (the 3s) to form Na^+, which has an [Ne] electron configuration. Likewise, Mg loses its two valence electrons to form Mg^{2+}, which also has an [Ne] electron configuration. On the other hand, the nonmetal atoms gain just the number of electrons needed for them to achieve the noble gas electron configuration. The O atom gains two electrons and the F atom gains one electron to give O^{2-} and F^-, respectively, both of which have the [Ne] electron configuration. We can summarize these observations as follows:

Electron Configurations of Ions

1. Representative (main-group) metals form ions by losing enough electrons to achieve the configuration of the previous noble gas (that is, the noble gas that occurs before the metal in question on the periodic table). For example, note from the periodic table inside the front cover of the text that neon is the noble gas previous to sodium and magnesium. Similarly, helium is the noble gas previous to lithium and beryllium.

2. Nonmetals form ions by gaining enough electrons to achieve the configuration of the next noble gas (that is, the noble gas that follows the element in question on the periodic table). For example, note that neon is the noble gas that follows oxygen and fluorine, and argon is the noble gas that follows sulfur and chlorine.

Table 12.2 The Formation of Ions by Metals and Nonmetals

		Electron Configuration	
Group	Ion Formation	Atom	Ion
1	$Na \rightarrow Na^+ + e^-$	$[Ne]3s^1 \xrightarrow{\text{e}^- \text{ lost}}$	[Ne]
2	$Mg \rightarrow Mg^{2+} + 2e^-$	$[Ne]3s^2 \xrightarrow{\text{2e}^- \text{ lost}}$	[Ne]
3	$Al \rightarrow Al^{3+} + 3e^-$	$[Ne]3s^23p^1 \xrightarrow{\text{3e}^- \text{ lost}}$	[Ne]
6	$O + 2e^- \rightarrow O^{2-}$	$[He]2s^22p^4 + 2e^- \rightarrow [He]2s^22p^6 =$	[Ne]
7	$F + e^- \rightarrow F^-$	$[He]2s^22p^5 + e^- \rightarrow [He]2s^22p^6 =$	[Ne]

Atoms in stable compounds almost always have a noble gas electron configuration.

This brings us to an important general principle. In observing millions of stable compounds, chemists have learned that **in almost all stable chemical compounds of the representative elements, all of the atoms have achieved a noble gas electron configuration.** The importance of this observation cannot be overstated. It forms the basis for all of our fundamental ideas about why and how atoms bond to each other.

We have already seen this principle operating in the formation of ions (see Table 12.2). We can summarize this behavior as follows: when representative metals and nonmetals react, they transfer electrons in such a way that both the cation and the anion have noble gas electron configurations.

On the other hand, when nonmetals react with each other, they share electrons in ways that lead to a noble gas electron configuration for each atom in the resulting molecule. For example, oxygen ($[He]2s^22p^4$), which needs two more electrons to achieve an $[Ne]$ configuration, can get these electrons by combining with two H atoms (each of which has one electron),

$$O: \quad [He] \quad \overset{2s}{\boxed{\uparrow\downarrow}} \quad \overset{2p}{\boxed{\uparrow\downarrow|\uparrow|\uparrow}}$$
$$\overset{}{\text{H} \quad \text{H}}$$

to form water, H_2O. This fills the valence orbitals of oxygen.

In addition, each H shares two electrons with the oxygen atom,

$$\text{H} \overset{O}{\diagdown} \text{H}$$

which fills the H $1s$ orbital, giving it a $1s^2$ or $[He]$ electron configuration. We will have much more to say about covalent bonding in Section 12.6.

At this point let's summarize the ideas we have introduced so far.

Electron Configurations and Bonding

1. When a *nonmetal and a Group 1, 2, or 3 metal* react to form a binary ionic compound, the ions form in such a way that the valence-electron configuration of the *nonmetal* is *completed* to achieve the configuration of the *next* noble gas, and the valence orbitals of the *metal* are *emptied* to achieve the configuration of the *previous* noble gas. In this way both ions achieve noble gas electron configurations.

2. When *two nonmetals* react to form a covalent bond, they share electrons in a way that completes the valence-electron configurations of both atoms. That is, both nonmetals attain noble gas electron configurations by sharing electrons.

▶ Predicting Formulas of Ionic Compounds

Now that we know something about the electron configurations of atoms, we can explain *why* these various ions are formed.

To show how to predict what ions form when a metal reacts with a nonmetal, we will consider the formation of an ionic compound from calcium and oxygen. We can predict what compound will form by considering the valence electron configurations of the following two atoms:

$$Ca: \quad [Ar]4s^2$$
$$O: \quad [He]2s^22p^4$$

From Figure 12.3 we see that the electronegativity of oxygen (3.5) is much greater than that of calcium (1.0), giving a difference of 2.5. Because of this large difference, electrons are transferred from calcium to oxygen to form an oxygen anion and a calcium cation. How many electrons are transferred? We can base our prediction on the observation that noble gas configurations are the most stable. Note that oxygen needs two electrons to fill its valence orbitals ($2s$ and $2p$) and achieve the configuration of neon ($1s^2 2s^2 2p^6$), which is the next noble gas.

$$O + 2e^- \rightarrow O^{2-}$$
$$[He]2s^2 2p^4 + 2e^- \rightarrow [He]2s^2 2p^6, \text{ or } [Ne]$$

And by losing two electrons, calcium can achieve the configuration of argon (the previous noble gas).

$$Ca \rightarrow Ca^{2+} + 2e^-$$
$$[Ar]4s^2 \rightarrow [Ar] \quad + 2e^-$$

Two electrons are therefore transferred as follows:

$$Ca + O \rightarrow Ca^{2+} + O^{2-}$$
$$2e^-$$

To predict the formula of the ionic compound, we use the fact that chemical compounds are always electrically neutral—they have the same total quantities of positive and negative charges. In this case we must have equal numbers of Ca^{2+} and O^{2-} ions, and the empirical formula of the compound is CaO.

The same principles can be applied to many other cases. For example, consider the compound formed from aluminum and oxygen. Aluminum has the electron configuration $[Ne]3s^2 3p^1$. To achieve the neon configuration, aluminum must lose three electrons, forming the Al^{3+} ion.

$$Al \rightarrow Al^{3+} + 3e^-$$
$$[Ne]3s^2 3p^1 \rightarrow [Ne] + 3e^-$$

$3 \times (2-)$ balances $2 \times (3+)$.

Therefore, the ions will be Al^{3+} and O^{2-}. Because the compound must be electrically neutral, there will be three O^{2-} ions for every two Al^{3+} ions, and the compound has the empirical formula Al_2O_3.

Table 12.3 shows common elements that form ions with noble gas electron configurations in ionic compounds.

Notice that our discussion in this section refers to metals in Groups 1, 2, and 3 (the representative metals). The transition metals exhibit more complicated behavior (they form a variety of ions), which we will not be concerned with in this text.

Table 12.3 Common Ions with Noble Gas Configurations in Ionic Compounds

Group 1	Group 2	Group 3	Group 6	Group 7	Electron Configuration
Li^+	Be^{2+}				[He]
Na^+	Mg^{2+}	Al^{3+}	O^{2-}	F^-	[Ne]
K^+	Ca^{2+}		S^{2-}	Cl^-	[Ar]
Rb^+	Sr^{2+}		Se^{2-}	Br^-	[Kr]
Cs^+	Ba^{2+}		Te^{2-}	I^-	[Xe]

12.5 Ionic Bonding and Structures of Ionic Compounds

OBJECTIVES: To learn about ionic structures. • To understand factors governing ionic size.

When metals and nonmetals react, the resulting ionic compounds are very stable; large amounts of energy are required to "take them apart." For example, the melting point of sodium chloride is approximately 800 °C. The strong bonding in these ionic compounds results from the attractions among the oppositely charged cations and anions.

We write the formula of an ionic compound such as lithium fluoride simply as LiF, but this is really the empirical, or simplest, formula. The actual solid contains huge and equal numbers of Li^+ and F^- ions packed together in a way that maximizes the attractions of the oppositely charged ions. A representative part of the lithium fluoride structure is shown in Figure 12.8a. In this structure the larger F^- ions are packed together like hard spheres, and the much smaller Li^+ ions are interspersed regularly among the F^- ions. The structure shown in Figure 12.8b represents only a tiny part of the actual structure, which continues in all three dimensions with the same pattern as that shown.

> When spheres are packed together, they do not fill up all of the space. The spaces (holes) that are left can be occupied by smaller spheres.

The structures of virtually all binary ionic compounds can be explained by a model that involves packing the ions as though they were hard spheres. The larger spheres (usually the anions) are packed together, and the small ions occupy the interstices (spaces or holes) among them.

To understand the packing of ions it helps to realize that *a cation is always smaller than the parent atom, and an anion is always larger than the parent atom.* This makes sense because when a metal loses all of its valence electrons to form a cation, it gets much smaller. On the other hand, in forming an anion, a nonmetal gains enough electrons to achieve the next noble gas electron configuration and so becomes much larger. The relative sizes of the Group 1 and Group 7 atoms and their ions are shown in Figure 12.9.

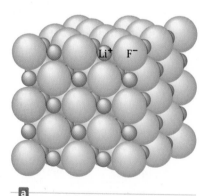

a This structure represents the ions as packed spheres.

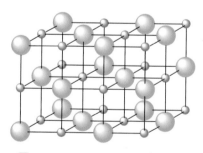

b This structure shows the positions (centers) of the ions. The spherical ions are packed in the way that maximizes the ionic attractions.

Figure 12.8
The structure of lithium fluoride.

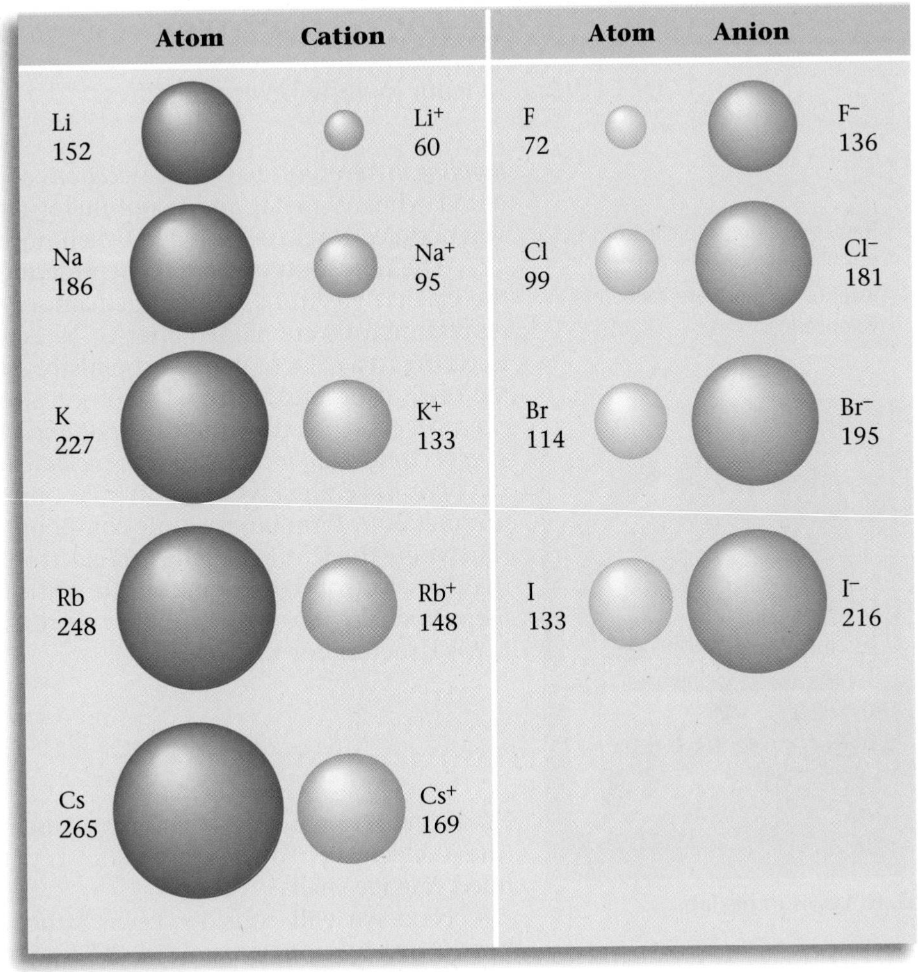

Atom	Cation		Atom	Anion
Li 152		Li⁺ 60	F 72	F⁻ 136
Na 186		Na⁺ 95	Cl 99	Cl⁻ 181
K 227		K⁺ 133	Br 114	Br⁻ 195
Rb 248		Rb⁺ 148	I 133	I⁻ 216
Cs 265		Cs⁺ 169		

Figure 12.9

Relative sizes of some ions and their parent atoms. Note that cations are smaller and anions are larger than their parent atoms. The sizes (radii) are given in units of picometers (1 pm = 10^{-12} m).

▶ Ionic Compounds Containing Polyatomic Ions

So far in this chapter we have discussed only binary ionic compounds, which contain ions derived from single atoms. However, many compounds contain polyatomic ions: charged species composed of several atoms. For example, ammonium nitrate contains the NH_4^+ and NO_3^- ions. These ions with their opposite charges attract each other in the same way as do the simple ions in binary ionic compounds. However, the *individual* polyatomic ions are held together by covalent bonds, with all of the atoms behaving as a unit. For example, in the ammonium ion, NH_4^+, there are four N—H covalent bonds. Likewise the nitrate ion, NO_3^-, contains three covalent N—O bonds. Thus, although ammonium nitrate is an ionic compound because it contains the NH_4^+ and NO_3^- ions, it also contains covalent bonds in the individual polyatomic ions. When ammonium nitrate is dissolved in water, it behaves as a strong electrolyte like the binary ionic compounds sodium chloride and potassium bromide. As we saw in Chapter 7, this occurs because when an ionic solid dissolves, the ions are freed to move independently and can conduct an electric current.

The common polyatomic ions, which are listed in Table 5.4, are all held together by covalent bonds.

12.6   Lewis Structures

OBJECTIVE: To learn to write Lewis structures.

Remember that the electrons in the highest principal energy level of an atom are called the valence electrons.

G. N. Lewis in his lab.

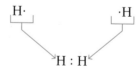 **Module 12: Drawing Lewis Electron Dot Structures** covers concepts in this section.

Bonding involves just the valence electrons of atoms. Valence electrons are transferred when a metal and a nonmetal react to form an ionic compound. Valence electrons are shared between nonmetals in covalent bonds.

The **Lewis structure** is a representation of a molecule that shows how the valence electrons are arranged among the atoms in the molecule. These representations are named after G. N. Lewis, who conceived the idea while lecturing to a class of general chemistry students in 1902. The rules for writing Lewis structures are based on observations of many molecules from which chemists have learned that the *most important requirement for the formation of a stable compound is that the atoms achieve noble gas electron configurations.*

We have already seen this rule operate in the reaction of metals and nonmetals to form binary ionic compounds. An example is the formation of KBr, where the K^+ ion has the [Ar] electron configuration and the Br^- ion has the [Kr] electron configuration. In writing Lewis structures, *we include only the valence electrons.* Using dots to represent valence electrons, we write the Lewis structure for KBr as follows:

$$K^+ \qquad\qquad [:\overset{..}{Br}:]^-$$

Noble gas configuration [Ar]   Noble gas configuration [Kr]

No dots are shown on the K^+ ion because it has lost its only valence electron (the 4s electron). The Br^- ion is shown with eight electrons because it has a filled valence shell.

Next we will consider Lewis structures for molecules with covalent bonds, involving nonmetals in the first and second periods. The principle of achieving a noble gas electron configuration applies to these elements as follows:

1. Hydrogen forms stable molecules where it shares two electrons. That is, it follows a **duet rule.** For example, when two hydrogen atoms, each with one electron, combine to form the H_2 molecule, we have

$$H \cdot \qquad\qquad \cdot H$$
$$H : H$$

By sharing electrons, each hydrogen in H_2 has, in effect, two electrons; that is, each hydrogen has a filled valence shell.

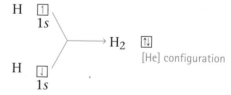

2. Helium does not form bonds because its valence orbital is already filled; it is a noble gas. Helium has the electron configuration $1s^2$ and can be represented by the Lewis structure

$$He:$$

[He] configuration

3. The second-row nonmetals carbon through fluorine form stable molecules when they are surrounded by enough electrons to fill the valence orbitals—that is, the one 2s and the three 2p orbitals. Eight electrons are required to fill these orbitals, so these elements typically obey the **octet rule;** they are surrounded by eight electrons. An example is the F_2 molecule, which has the following Lewis structure:

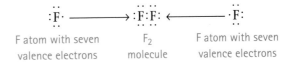

F atom with seven valence electrons F_2 molecule   F atom with seven valence electrons

Note that each fluorine atom in F_2 is, in effect, surrounded by eight valence electrons, two of which are shared with the other atom. This is a **bonding pair** of electrons, as we discussed earlier. Each fluorine atom also has three pairs of electrons that are not involved in bonding. These are called **lone pairs** or **unshared pairs.**

4. Neon does not form bonds because it already has an octet of valence electrons (it is a noble gas). The Lewis structure is

Note that only the valence electrons ($2s^2 2p^6$) of the neon atom are represented by the Lewis structure. The $1s^2$ electrons are core electrons and are not shown.

Next we want to develop some general procedures for writing Lewis structures for molecules. Remember that Lewis structures involve only the valence electrons of atoms, so before we proceed, we will review the relationship of an element's position on the periodic table to the number of valence electrons it has. Recall that the group number gives the total number of valence electrons. For example, all Group 6 elements have six valence electrons (valence configuration $ns^2 np^4$).

> Carbon, nitrogen, oxygen, and fluorine almost always obey the octet rule in stable molecules.

> Lewis structures show only valence electrons.

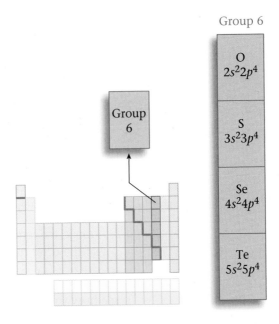

Similarly, all Group 7 elements have seven valence electrons (valence configuration ns^2np^5).

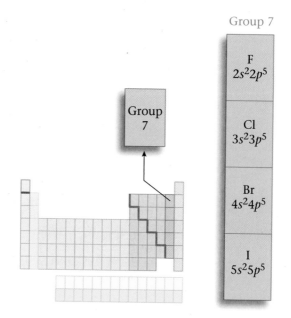

In writing the Lewis structure for a molecule, we need to keep the following things in mind:

1. We must include all the valence electrons from all atoms. The total number of electrons available is the sum of all the valence electrons from all the atoms in the molecule.

2. Atoms that are bonded to each other share one or more pairs of electrons.

3. The electrons are arranged so that each atom is surrounded by enough electrons to fill the valence orbitals of that atom. This means two electrons for hydrogen and eight electrons for second-row nonmetals.

The best way to make sure we arrive at the correct Lewis structure for a molecule is to use a systematic approach. We will use the approach summarized by the following rules.

Steps for Writing Lewis Structures

Step 1 Obtain the sum of the valence electrons from all of the atoms. Do not worry about keeping track of which electrons come from which atoms. It is the *total* number of valence electrons that is important.

Step 2 Use one pair of electrons to form a bond between each pair of bound atoms. For convenience, a line (instead of a pair of dots) is often used to indicate each pair of bonding electrons.

Step 3 Arrange the remaining electrons to satisfy the duet rule for hydrogen and the octet rule for each second-row element.

To see how these rules are applied, we will write the Lewis structures of several molecules.

To Bee or Not to Bee

One of the problems we face in modern society is how to detect illicit substances, such as drugs and explosives, in a convenient, accurate manner. Trained dogs are often used for this purpose because of their acute sense of smell. Now several researches are trying to determine whether insects, such as honeybees and wasps, can be even more effective chemical detectors. In fact, studies have shown that bees can be trained in just a few minutes to detect the smell of almost any chemical.

Scientists at Los Alamos National Laboratory in New Mexico are designing a portable device using bees that possibly could be used to sniff out drugs and bombs at airports, border crossings, and schools. They call their study the Stealthy Insect Sensor Project. The Los Alamos project is based on the idea that bees can be trained to associate the smell of a particular chemical with a sugary treat. Bees stick out their "tongues" when they detect a food source. By pairing a drop of sugar water with the scent of TNT (trinitrotoluene) or C-4 (composition 4) plastic explosive about six times, the bees can be trained to extend their proboscis at a whiff of the chemical alone. The bee bomb detector is about half the size of a shoe box and weighs 4 lb. Inside the box, bees are lined up in a row and strapped into straw-like tubes, then exposed to puffs of air as a camera monitors their reactions. The signals from the video camera are sent to a computer, which analyzes the bees' behavior and signals when the bees respond to the particular scent they have been trained to detect.

A project at the University of Georgia uses tiny parasitic wasps as a chemical detector. Wasps do not extend their tongues when they detect a scent. Instead, they communicate the discovery of a scent by body movements that the scientists call "dances." The device, called the Wasp Hound, contains a team of wasps in a hand-held ventilated cartridge that has a fan at one end to draw in air from outside. If the scent is one the wasps do not recognize, they continue flying randomly. However, if the scent is one the wasps have been conditioned to recognize, they cluster around the opening. A video camera paired with a computer analyzes their behavior and signals when a scent is detected.

The insect sensors are now undergoing field trials, which typically compare the effectiveness of insects to that of trained dogs. Initial results appear promising, but the effectiveness of these devices remains to be proved.

Los Alamos National Laboratory. Photo by Leroy Sanchez

A honeybee receives a fragrant reminder of its target scent each morning and responds by sticking out its proboscis.

EXAMPLE 12.2 Writing Lewis Structures: Simple Molecules

Write the Lewis structure of the water molecule.

SOLUTION

We will follow the steps listed on page 372.

Step 1 Find the sum of the *valence* electrons for H_2O.

$$\underset{\substack{\uparrow \\ H \\ \text{(Group 1)}}}{1} \quad + \quad \underset{\substack{\uparrow \\ H \\ \text{(Group 1)}}}{1} \quad + \quad \underset{\substack{\uparrow \\ O \\ \text{(Group 6)}}}{6} \quad = 8 \text{ valence electrons}$$

Step 2 Using a pair of electrons per bond, we draw in the two O—H bonds, using a line to indicate each pair of bonding electrons.

$$H—O—H$$

Note that

$$H—O—H \text{ represents } H : O : H$$

Step 3 We arrange the remaining electrons around the atoms to achieve a noble gas electron configuration for each atom. Four electrons have been used in forming the two bonds, so four electrons (8 – 4) remain to be distributed. Each hydrogen is satisfied with two electrons (duet rule), but oxygen needs eight electrons to have a noble gas electron configuration. So the remaining four electrons are added to oxygen as two lone pairs. Dots are used to represent the lone pairs.

$$H—\overset{..}{\underset{..}{O}}—H \quad \text{Lone pairs}$$

> $$H—\overset{..}{\underset{..}{O}}—H$$
>
> might also be drawn as
>
> $$H:\overset{..}{\underset{..}{O}}:H$$

This is the correct Lewis structure for the water molecule. Each hydrogen shares two electrons, and the oxygen has four electrons and shares four to give a total of eight.

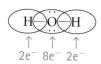

$$\underset{\substack{\uparrow \\ 2e^-}}{H} \underset{\substack{\uparrow \\ 8e^-}}{O} \underset{\substack{\uparrow \\ 2e^-}}{H}$$

Note that a line is used to represent a shared pair of electrons (bonding electrons) and dots are used to represent unshared pairs.

Self-Check EXERCISE 12.2   Write the Lewis structure for HCl.

See Problems 12.59 through 12.62. ∎

12.7 Lewis Structures of Molecules with Multiple Bonds

OBJECTIVE: To learn how to write Lewis structures for molecules with multiple bonds.

Now let's write the Lewis structure for carbon dioxide.

Step 1 Summing the valence electrons gives

$$\underset{\substack{\uparrow \\ C \\ \text{(Group 4)}}}{4} \quad + \quad \underset{\substack{\uparrow \\ O \\ \text{(Group 6)}}}{6} \quad + \quad \underset{\substack{\uparrow \\ O \\ \text{(Group 6)}}}{6} \quad = 16$$

Hiding Carbon Dioxide

As we discussed in Chapter 11 (see "Chemistry in Focus: Atmospheric Effects," page 326), global warming seems to be a reality. At the heart of this issue is the carbon dioxide produced by society's widespread use of fossil fuels. For example, in the United States, CO_2 makes up 81% of greenhouse gas emissions. Thirty percent of this CO_2 comes from coal-fired power plants used to produce electricity. One way to solve this problem would be to phase out coal-fired power plants. However, this outcome is not likely because the United States possesses so much coal (at least a 250-year supply) and coal is so cheap (about $0.03 per pound). Recognizing this fact, the U.S. government has instituted a research program to see if the CO_2 produced at power plants can be captured and sequestered (stored) underground in deep geological formations. The factors that need to be explored to determine whether sequestration is feasible are the capacities of underground storage sites and the chances that the sites will leak.

The injection of CO_2 into the earth's crust is already being undertaken by various oil companies. Since 1996, the Norwegian oil company Statoil has separated more than 1 million tons of CO_2 annually from natural gas and pumped it into a saltwater aquifer beneath the floor of the North Sea. In western Canada a group of oil companies has injected CO_2 from a North Dakota synthetic fuels plant into oil fields in an effort to increase oil recovery. The oil companies expect to store 22 million tons of CO_2 there and to produce 130 million barrels of oil over the next 20 years.

Sequestration of CO_2 has great potential as one method for decreasing the rate of global warming. Only time will tell whether it will work.

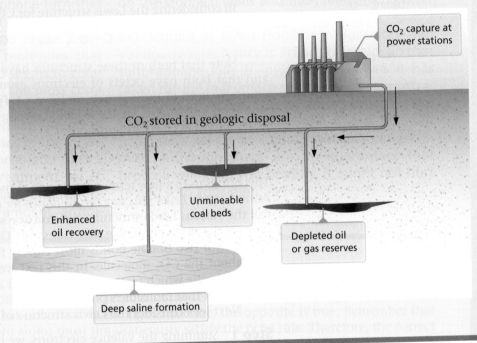

CO₂ capture at power stations

CO₂ stored in geologic disposal

Enhanced oil recovery

Unmineable coal beds

Depleted oil or gas reserves

Deep saline formation

$$O—C—O$$

represents

$$O:C:O$$

$$:\overset{..}{O}—C—\overset{..}{O}:$$

represents

$$:\overset{..}{O}:C:\overset{..}{O}:$$

Step 2 Form a bond between the carbon and each oxygen:

$$O—C—O$$

Step 3 Next, distribute the remaining electrons to achieve noble gas electron configurations on each atom. In this case twelve electrons $(16 - 4)$ remain after the bonds are drawn. The distribution of these electrons is determined by a trial-and-error process. We have six pairs of electrons to distribute. Suppose we try three pairs on each oxygen to give

$$:\overset{..}{O}—C—\overset{..}{O}:$$

Is this correct? To answer this question we need to check two things:

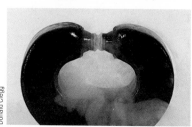

Donald Clegg

most molecules. However, with such a simple model, some exceptions are inevitable. Boron, for example, tends to form compounds in which the boron atom has fewer than eight electrons around it—that is, it does not have a complete octet. Boron trifluoride, BF_3, a gas at normal temperatures and pressures, reacts very energetically with molecules such as water and ammonia that have unshared electron pairs (lone pairs).

The violent reactivity of BF_3 with electron-rich molecules arises because the boron atom is electron-deficient. The Lewis structure that seems most consistent with the properties of BF_3 (twenty-four valence electrons) is

Note that in this structure the boron atom has only six electrons around it. The octet rule for boron could be satisfied by drawing a structure with a double bond between the boron and one of the fluorines. However, experiments indicate that each B—F bond is a single bond in accordance with the above Lewis structure. This structure is also consistent with the reactivity of BF_3 with electron-rich molecules. For example, BF_3 reacts vigorously with NH_3 to form H_3NBF_3.

Note that in the product H_3NBF_3, which is very stable, boron has an octet of electrons.

It is also characteristic of beryllium to form molecules where the beryllium atom is electron-deficient.

The compounds containing the elements carbon, nitrogen, oxygen, and fluorine are accurately described by Lewis structures in the vast majority of cases. However, there are a few exceptions. One important example is the oxygen molecule, O_2. The following Lewis structure that satisfies the octet rule can be drawn for O_2 (see Self-Check Exercise 12.4).

However, this structure does not agree with the *observed behavior* of oxygen. For example, the photos in Figure 12.10 show that when liquid oxygen is poured between the poles of a strong magnet, it "sticks" there until it boils away. This provides clear evidence that oxygen is paramagnetic—that is, it contains unpaired electrons. However, the above Lewis structure shows only pairs of electrons. That is, no unpaired electrons are shown. There is no simple Lewis structure that satisfactorily explains the paramagnetism of the O_2 molecule.

Any molecule that contains an odd number of electrons does not conform to our rules for Lewis structures. For example, NO and NO_2 have eleven and seventeen valence electrons, respectively, and conventional Lewis structures cannot be drawn for these cases.

Even though there are exceptions, most molecules can be described by Lewis structures in which all the atoms have noble gas electron configurations, and this is a very useful model for chemists.

Figure 12.10

When liquid oxygen is poured between the poles of a magnet, it "sticks" until it boils away. This shows that the O_2 molecule has unpaired electrons (is paramagnetic).

Paramagnetic substances have unpaired electrons and are drawn toward the space between a magnet's poles.

12.8 Molecular Structure

OBJECTIVE: To understand molecular structure and bond angles.

So far in this chapter we have considered the Lewis structures of molecules. These structures represent the arrangement of the *valence electrons* in a molecule. We use the word *structure* in another way when we talk about the **molecular structure** or **geometric structure** of a molecule. These terms refer to the three-dimensional arrangement of the *atoms* in a molecule. For example, the water molecule is known to have the molecular structure

$$O$$
$$H \quad H$$

which is often called "bent" or "V-shaped." To describe the structure more precisely, we often specify the **bond angle.** For the H_2O molecule the bond angle is about 105°.

$$O$$
$$H \quad H$$
$$\sim 105°$$

a

Computer graphic of a linear molecule containing three atoms

b

Computer graphic of a trigonal planar molecule

c

Computer graphic of a tetrahedral molecule

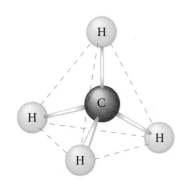

Figure 12.11

The tetrahedral molecular structure of methane. This representation is called a ball-and-stick model; the atoms are represented by balls and the bonds by sticks. The dashed lines show the outline of the tetrahedron.

On the other hand, some molecules exhibit a **linear structure** (all atoms in a line). An example is the CO_2 molecule.

$$O—C—O$$
$$180°$$

Note that a linear molecule has a 180° bond angle.

A third type of molecular structure is illustrated by BF_3, which is planar or flat (all four atoms in the same plane) with 120° bond angles.

$$F$$
$$120° \quad 120°$$
$$B$$
$$F \quad F$$
$$120°$$

The name usually given to this structure is **trigonal planar structure,** although triangular might seem to make more sense.

Another type of molecular structure is illustrated by methane, CH_4. This molecule has the molecular structure shown in Figure 12.11, which is called a **tetrahedral structure** or a **tetrahedron.** The dashed lines shown connecting the H atoms define the four identical triangular faces of the tetrahedron.

In the next section we will discuss these various molecular structures in more detail. In that section we will learn how to predict the molecular structure of a molecule by looking at the molecule's Lewis structure.

12.9 Molecular Structure: The VSEPR Model

OBJECTIVE: To learn to predict molecular geometry from the number of electron pairs.

The structures of molecules play a very important role in determining their properties. For example, as we see in the "Chemistry in Focus" on page 383, taste is directly related to molecular structure. Structure is particularly important for biological molecules; a slight change in the structure of a large biomolecule can completely destroy its usefulness to a cell and may even change the cell from a normal one to a cancerous one.

Many experimental methods now exist for determining the molecular structure of a molecule—that is, the three-dimensional arrangement of the atoms. These methods must be used when accurate information about the structure is required. However, it is often useful to be able to predict the *approximate* molecular structure of a molecule. In this section we consider a simple model that allows us to do this. This model, called the **valence shell electron pair repulsion (VSEPR) model,** is useful for predicting the molecular structures of molecules formed from nonmetals. The main idea of this model is that *the structure around a given atom is determined by minimizing repulsions between electron pairs.* This means that the bonding and nonbonding electron pairs (lone pairs) around a given atom are positioned *as far apart as possible.* To see how this model works, we will first consider the molecule $BeCl_2$, which has the following Lewis structure (it is an exception to the octet rule):

$$:\!\ddot{Cl}\!-\!Be\!-\!\ddot{Cl}\!:$$

Note that there are two pairs of electrons around the beryllium atom. What arrangement of these electron pairs allows them to be as far apart as possible to minimize the repulsions? The best arrangement places the pairs on opposite sides of the beryllium atom at 180° from each other.

$$\overset{}{-}\!Be\!\overset{}{-}$$
180°

This is the maximum possible separation for two electron pairs. Now that we have determined the optimal arrangement of the electron pairs around the central atom, we can specify the molecular structure of $BeCl_2$—that is, the positions of the atoms. Because each electron pair on beryllium is shared with a chlorine atom, the molecule has a **linear structure** with a 180° bond angle.

$$:\!\ddot{Cl}\!-\!Be\!-\!\ddot{Cl}\!:$$
180°

Whenever two pairs of electrons are present around an atom, they should always be placed at an angle of 180° to each other to give a linear arrangement.

Next let's consider BF_3, which has the following Lewis structure (it is another exception to the octet rule):

$$:\!\ddot{F}\!:$$
$$|$$
$$:\!\ddot{F}\!-\!B\!-\!\ddot{F}\!:$$

Taste—It's the Structure That Counts

Why do certain substances taste sweet, sour, bitter, or salty? Of course, it has to do with the taste buds on our tongues. But how do these taste buds work? For example, why does sugar taste sweet to us? The answer to this question remains elusive, but it does seem clear that sweet taste depends on how certain molecules fit the "sweet receptors" in our taste buds.

One of the mysteries of the sweet taste sensation is the wide variety of molecules that taste sweet. For example, the many types of sugars include glucose and sucrose (table sugar). The first artificial sweetener was probably the Romans' sapa (see "Chemistry in Focus: Sugar of Lead" in Chapter 5), made by boiling wine in lead vessels to produce a syrup that contained lead acetate, $Pb(C_2H_3O_2)_2$, called sugar of lead because of its sweet taste. Other widely used modern artificial sweeteners include saccharin, aspartame, sucralose, and steviol, whose structures are shown in the accompanying figure. The structure of steviol is shown in simplified form. Each vertex represents a carbon atom, and not all of the hydrogen atoms are shown. Note the great disparity of structures for these sweet-tasting molecules. It's certainly not obvious which structural features trigger a sweet sensation when these molecules interact with the taste buds.

The pioneers in relating structure to sweet taste were two chemists, Robert S. Shallenberger and Terry E. Acree of Cornell University, who almost thirty years ago suggested that all sweet-tasting substances must contain a common feature they called a glycophore. They postulated that a glycophore always contains an atom or group of atoms that have available electrons located near a hydrogen atom attached to a relatively elec-

tronegative atom. Murray Goodman, a chemist at the University of California at San Diego, expanded the definition of a glycophore to include a hydrophobic ("water-hating") region. Goodman finds that a "sweet molecule" tends to be L-shaped with positively and negatively charged regions on the upright of the L and a hydrophobic region on the base of the L. For a molecule to be sweet, the L must be planar. If the L is twisted in one direction, the molecule has a bitter taste. If the molecule is twisted in the other direction, the molecule is tasteless.

The latest model for the sweet-taste receptor, proposed by Piero Temussi of the University of Naples, postulates that there are four binding sites on the receptor that can be occupied independently. Small sweet-tasting molecules might bind to one of the sites, while a large molecule would bind to more than one site simultaneously.

So the search goes on for a better artificial sweetener. One thing's for sure; it all has to do with molecular structure.

Saccharin

Sucralose

Aspartame
(Nutra-Sweet™)

Steviol

Here the boron atom is surrounded by three pairs of electrons. What arrangement minimizes the repulsions among three pairs of electrons? Here the greatest distance between electron pairs is achieved by angles of 120°.

Because each of the electron pairs is shared with a fluorine atom, the mo-lec-ular structure is

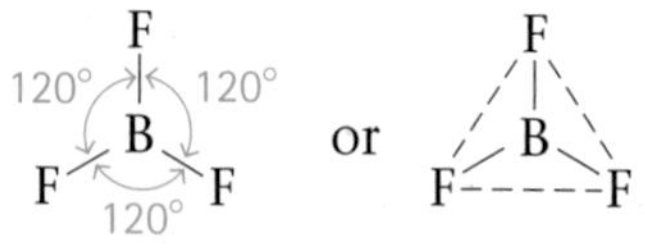

This is a planar (flat) molecule with a triangular arrangement of F atoms, commonly described as a trigonal planar structure. *Whenever three pairs of electrons are present around an atom, they should always be placed at the corners of a triangle (in a plane at angles of 120° to each other).*

Next let's consider the methane molecule, which has the Lewis structure

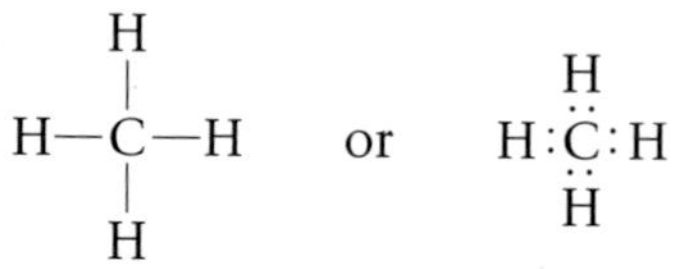

$$H—C—H \quad or \quad H:C:H$$

There are four pairs of electrons around the central carbon atom. What arrangement of these electron pairs best minimizes the repulsions? First we try a square planar arrangement:

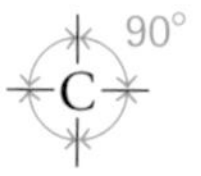

The carbon atom and the electron pairs are all in a plane represented by the surface of the paper, and the angles between the pairs are all 90°.

Is there another arrangement with angles greater than 90° that would put the electron pairs even farther away from each other? The answer is yes. We can get larger angles than 90° by using the following three-dimensional structure, which has angles of approximately 109.5°.

In this drawing the wedge indicates a position above the surface of the pa-per and the dashed lines indicate positions behind that surface. The solid line indicates a position on the surface of the page. The figure formed by connecting the lines is called a tetrahedron, so we call this arrangement of electron pairs the **tetrahedral arrangement.**

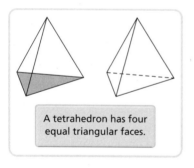

A tetrahedron has four equal triangular faces.

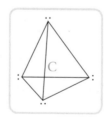

This is the maximum possible separation of four pairs around a given atom. *Whenever four pairs of electrons are present around an atom, they should always be placed at the corners of a tetrahedron (the tetrahedral arrangement).*

Now that we have the arrangement of electron pairs that gives the least repulsion, we can determine the positions of the atoms and thus the mo-lecular structure of CH_4. In methane each of the four electron pairs is shared

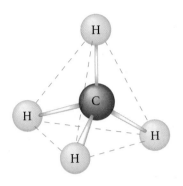

Figure 12.12

The molecular structure of methane. The tetrahedral arrangement of electron pairs produces a tetrahedral arrangement of hydrogen atoms.

between the carbon atom and a hydrogen atom. Thus the hydrogen atoms are placed as shown in Figure 12.12, and the molecule has a tetrahedral structure with the carbon atom at the center.

Recall that the main idea of the VSEPR model is to find the arrangement of electron pairs around the central atom that minimizes the repulsions. Then we can determine the *molecular structure* by knowing how the electron pairs are shared with the peripheral atoms. A systematic procedure for using the VSEPR model to predict the structure of a molecule is outlined below.

Steps for Predicting Molecular Structure Using the VSEPR Model

Step 1 Draw the Lewis structure for the molecule.

Step 2 Count the electron pairs and arrange them in the way that minimizes repulsion (that is, put the pairs as far apart as possible).

Step 3 Determine the positions of the atoms from the way the electron pairs are shared.

Step 4 Determine the name of the molecular structure from the positions of the atoms.

EXAMPLE 12.5   Predicting Molecular Structure Using the VSEPR Model, I

Ammonia, NH_3, is used as a fertilizer (injected into the soil) and as a household cleaner (in aqueous solution). Predict the structure of ammonia using the VSEPR model.

SOLUTION

Step 1   Draw the Lewis structure.

$$H-\overset{\cdot\cdot}{N}-H$$
$$|$$
$$H$$

Step 2   Count the pairs of electrons and arrange them to minimize repulsions. The NH_3 molecule has four pairs of electrons around the N atom: three bonding pairs and one nonbonding pair. From the discussion of the methane molecule, we know that the best arrangement of four electron pairs is the tetrahedral structure shown in Figure 12.13a.

Step 3   Determine the positions of the atoms. The three H atoms share electron pairs as shown in Figure 12.13b.

Step 4   Name the molecular structure. It is very important to recognize that the name of the molecular structure is always based on the *positions of the atoms. The placement of the electron pairs determines the structure, but the name is based on the positions of the atoms.* Thus it is incorrect to say that the NH_3 molecule is tetrahedral. It has a tetrahedral arrangement of electron pairs but *not* a tetrahedral arrangement of atoms. The molecular structure of ammonia is a **trigonal pyramid** (one side is different from the other three) rather than a tetrahedron. ■

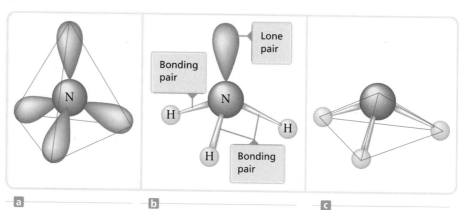

Figure 12.13

a The tetrahedral arrangement of electron pairs around the nitrogen atom in the ammonia molecule.

b Three of the electron pairs around nitrogen are shared with hydrogen atoms as shown, and one is a lone pair. Although the arrangement of electron pairs is tetrahedral, as in the methane molecule, the hydrogen atoms in the ammonia molecule occupy only three corners of the tetrahedron. A lone pair occupies the fourth corner.

c The NH₃ molecule has the trigonal pyramid structure (a pyramid with a triangle as a base).

EXAMPLE 12.6 | Predicting Molecular Structure Using the VSEPR Model, II

Describe the molecular structure of the water molecule.

SOLUTION

Step 1   The Lewis structure for water is

$$\text{H}—\overset{..}{\underset{..}{\text{O}}}—\text{H}$$

Step 2   There are four pairs of electrons: two bonding pairs and two nonbonding pairs. To minimize repulsions, these are best arranged in a tetrahedral structure as shown in Figure 12.14a.

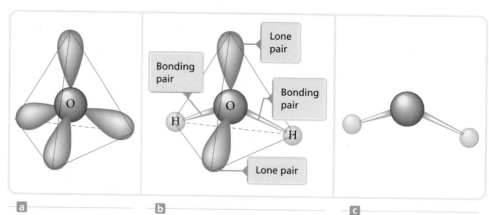

Figure 12.14

a The tetrahedral arrangement of the four electron pairs around oxygen in the water molecule.

b Two of the electron pairs are shared between oxygen and the hydrogen atoms, and two are lone pairs.

c The V-shaped molecular structure of the water molecule.

Step 3 Although H_2O has a tetrahedral arrangement of *electron pairs*, it is *not a tetrahedral molecule*. The *atoms* in the H_2O molecule form a V shape, as shown in Figure 12.14b and c.

Step 4 The molecular structure is called V-shaped or bent.

Self-Check **EXERCISE 12.5**   Predict the arrangement of electron pairs around the central atom. Then sketch and name the molecular structure for each of the following molecules or ions.

a. NH_4^+ d. H_2S

b. SO_4^{2-} e. ClO_3^-

c. NF_3 f. BeF_2

See Problems 12.81 through 12.84. ∎

The various molecules we have considered are summarized in Table 12.4 on the following page. Note the following general rules.

Rules for Predicting Molecular Structure Using the VSEPR Model

1. Two pairs of electrons on a central atom in a molecule are always placed 180° apart. This is a linear arrangement of pairs.
2. Three pairs of electrons on a central atom in a molecule are always placed 120° apart in the same plane as the central atom. This is a trigonal planar (triangular) arrangement of pairs.
3. Four pairs of electrons on a central atom in a molecule are always placed 109.5° apart. This is a tetrahedral arrangement of electron pairs.
4. When *every pair* of electrons on the central atom is *shared* with another atom, the molecular structure has the same name as the arrangement of electron pairs.

Number of Pairs	Name of Arrangement
2	linear
3	trigonal planar
4	tetrahedral

5. When one or more of the electron pairs around a central atom are unshared (lone pairs), the name for the molecular structure is *different* from that for the arrangement of electron pairs (see rows 4 and 5 in Table 12.4).

12.10 Molecular Structure: Molecules with Double Bonds

OBJECTIVE: To learn to apply the VSEPR model to molecules with double bonds.

Up to this point we have applied the VSEPR model only to molecules (and ions) that contain single bonds. In this section we will show that this model applies equally well to species with one or more double bonds. We will develop the procedures for dealing with molecules with double bonds by considering examples whose structures are known.

Table 12.4 Arrangements of Electron Pairs and the Resulting Molecular Structures for Two, Three, and Four Electron Pairs

Number of Electron Pairs	Bonds	Electron Pair Arrangement	Ball–and–Stick Model	Molecular Structure	Partial Lewis Structure	Ball–and–Stick Model
2	2	Linear	180°	Linear	A—B—A	Cl═Be═Cl
3	3	Trigonal planar (triangular)	120°	Trigonal planar (triangular)	A | B / A ⟍ A	F—B(F)(F)
4	4	Tetrahedral	109.5°	Tetrahedral	A | A—B—A | A	H—C(H)(H)(H)
4	3	Tetrahedral	109.5°	Trigonal pyramid	A—B̈—A | A	H—N(H)(H)
4	2	Tetrahedral	109.5°	Bent or V-shaped	A—B̈—A	H—O—H

First we will examine the structure of carbon dioxide, a substance that may be contributing to the warming of the earth. The carbon dioxide molecule has the Lewis structure

$$\ddot{O}=C=\ddot{O}$$

as discussed in Section 12.7. Carbon dioxide is known by experiment to be a linear molecule. That is, it has a 180° bond angle.

Recall from Section 12.9 that two electron pairs around a central atom can minimize their mutual repulsions by taking positions on opposite sides of the atom (at 180° from each other). This causes a molecule like BeCl$_2$, which has the Lewis structure

$$:\ddot{C}l—Be—\ddot{C}l:$$

to have a linear structure. Now recall that CO$_2$ has two double bonds and is known to be linear, so the double bonds must be at 180° from each other. Therefore, we conclude that each double bond in this molecule acts *effectively* as one repulsive unit. This conclusion makes sense if we think of a bond in terms of an electron density "cloud" between two atoms. For example, we can picture the single bonds in BeCl$_2$ as follows:

Minimotor Molecule

Our modern society is characterized by a continual quest for miniaturization. Our computers, cell phones, portable music players, calculators, and many other devices have been greatly downsized over the last several years. The ultimate in miniaturization—machines made of single molecules. Although this idea sounds like an impossible dream, recent advances place us on the doorstep of such devices. For example, Hermann E. Gaub and his coworkers at the Center for Nanoscience at Ludwig-Maximilians University in Munich have just reported a single molecule that can do simple work.

Gaub and his associates constructed a polymer about 75 nm long by hooking together many light-sensitive molecules called azobenzenes:

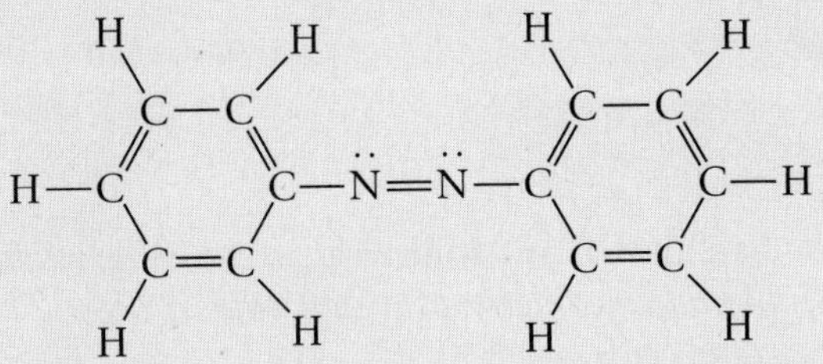

Azobenzene is ideal for this application because its bonds are sensitive to specific wavelengths of light. When azobenzene absorbs light of 420 nm, it becomes extended; light at 365 nm causes the molecule to contract.

To make their tiny machine, the German scientists attached one end of the azobenzene polymer to a tiny, bendable lever similar to the tip of an atomic-force microscope. The other end of the polymer was attached to a glass surface. Flashes of 365-nm light caused the molecule to contract, bending the lever down and storing mechanical energy. Pulses of 420-nm radiation then extended the molecule, causing the lever to rise and releasing the stored energy. Eventually, one can imagine having the lever operate some part of a nanoscale machine. It seems we are getting close to the ultimate in miniature machines.

The minimum repulsion between these two electron density clouds occurs when they are on opposite sides of the Be atom (180° angle between them).

Each double bond in CO_2 involves the sharing of four electrons between the carbon atom and an oxygen atom. Thus we might expect the bonding cloud to be "fatter" than for a single bond:

However, the repulsive effects of these two clouds produce the same result as for single bonds; the bonding clouds have minimum repulsions when they are positioned on opposite sides of the carbon. The bond angle is 180°, and so the molecule is linear:

In summary, examination of CO_2 leads us to the conclusion that in using the VSEPR model for molecules with double bonds, each double bond should be treated the same as a single bond. In other words, although a double bond involves four electrons, these electrons are restricted to the space between a given pair of atoms. Therefore, these four electrons do not function as two independent pairs but are "tied together" to form one effective repulsive unit.

We reach this same conclusion by considering the known structures of other molecules that contain double bonds. For example, consider the ozone molecule, which has eighteen valence electrons and exhibits two resonance structures:

$$:\ddot{O}-\ddot{O}=\ddot{O}: \longleftrightarrow :\ddot{O}=\ddot{O}-\ddot{O}:$$

The ozone molecule is known to have a bond angle close to 120°. Recall that 120° angles represent the minimum repulsion for three pairs of electrons.

This indicates that the double bond in the ozone molecule is behaving as one effective repulsive unit:

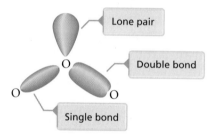

These and other examples lead us to the following rule: *When using the VSEPR model to predict the molecular geometry of a molecule, a double bond is counted the same as a single electron pair.*

Thus CO_2 has two "effective pairs" that lead to its linear structure, whereas O_3 has three "effective pairs" that lead to its bent structure with a 120° bond angle. Therefore, to use the VSEPR model for molecules (or ions) that have double bonds, we use the same steps as those given in Section 12.9, but we count any double bond the same as a single electron pair. Although we have not shown it here, triple bonds also count as one repulsive unit in applying the VSEPR model.

EXAMPLE 12.7 | Predicting Molecular Structure Using the VSEPR Model, III

Predict the structure of the nitrate ion.

SOLUTION

Step 1 The Lewis structures for NO_3^- are

$$\left[\begin{array}{c} :\ddot{O}: \\ \| \\ N \\ /\ \backslash \\ :\ddot{O}.\quad.\ddot{O}: \end{array}\right]^- \longleftrightarrow \left[\begin{array}{c} :\ddot{O}: \\ | \\ N \\ //\ \backslash \\ .\ddot{O}.\quad.\ddot{O}: \end{array}\right]^- \longleftrightarrow \left[\begin{array}{c} :\ddot{O}: \\ | \\ N \\ /\ \backslash\backslash \\ :\ddot{O}.\quad.\ddot{O}. \end{array}\right]^-$$

Step 2 In each resonance structure there are effectively three pairs of electrons: the two single bonds and the double bond (which counts as one pair).

These three "effective pairs" will require a trigonal planar arrangement (120° angles).

Step 3 The atoms are all in a plane, with the nitrogen at the center and the three oxygens at the corners of a triangle (trigonal planar arrangement).

Step 4 The NO_3^- ion has a trigonal planar structure. ■

CHAPTER 12 REVIEW

Key Terms

bond (12.1)
bond energy (12.1)
ionic bonding (12.1)
ionic compound (12.1)
covalent bonding (12.1)
polar covalent
   bond (12.1)
electronegativity (12.2)
dipole moment (12.3)
Lewis structure (12.6)
duet rule (12.6)
octet rule (12.6)
bonding pair (12.6)
lone (unshared)
   pair (12.6)
single bond (12.7)
double bond (12.7)

triple bond (12.7)
resonance (12.7)
resonance structure (12.7)
molecular (geometric)
   structure (12.8)
bond angle (12.8)
linear structure (12.8)
trigonal planar
   structure (12.8)
tetrahedral
   structure (12.8)
valence shell electron
   pair repulsion (VSEPR)
   model (12.9)
tetrahedral
   arrangement (12.9)
trigonal pyramid (12.9)

F directs you to the *Chemistry in Focus* feature in the chapter
VP indicates visual problems
OWL interactive versions of these problems are assignable in OWL

Summary

1. Chemical bonds hold groups of atoms together. They can be classified into several types. An ionic bond is formed when a transfer of electrons occurs to form ions; in a purely covalent bond, electrons are shared equally between identical atoms. Between these extremes lies the polar covalent bond, in which electrons are shared unequally between atoms with different electronegativities.

2. Electronegativity is defined as the relative ability of an atom in a molecule to attract the electrons shared in a bond. The difference in electronegativity values between the atoms involved in a bond determines the polarity of that bond.

3. In stable chemical compounds, the atoms tend to achieve a noble gas electron configuration. In the formation of a binary ionic compound involving representative elements, the valence-electron configuration of the nonmetal is completed: it achieves the configuration of the next noble gas. The valence or-

bitals of the metal are emptied to give the electron configuration of the previous noble gas. Two nonmetals share the valence electrons so that both atoms have completed valence-electron configurations (noble gas configurations).

4. Lewis structures are drawn to represent the arrangement of the valence electrons in a molecule. The rules for drawing Lewis structures are based on the observation that nonmetal atoms tend to achieve noble gas electron configurations by sharing electrons. This leads to a duet rule for hydrogen and to an octet rule for many other atoms.

5. Some molecules have more than one valid Lewis structure, a property called resonance. Although Lewis structures in which the atoms have noble gas electron configurations correctly describe most molecules, there are some notable exceptions, including O_2, NO, NO_2, and the molecules that contain Be and B.

6. The molecular structure of a molecule describes how the atoms are arranged in space.

7. The molecular structure of a molecule can be predicted by using the valence shell electron pair repulsion (VSEPR) model. This model bases its prediction on minimizing the repulsions among the electron pairs around an atom, which means arranging the electron pairs as far apart as possible.

Active Learning Questions

These questions are designed to be considered by groups of students in class. Often these questions work well for introducing a particular topic in class.

1. Using only the periodic table, predict the most stable ion for Na, Mg, Al, S, Cl, K, Ca, and Ga. Arrange these elements from largest to smallest radius and explain why the radius varies as it does.

2. Write the proper charges so that an alkali metal, a noble gas, and a halogen have the same electron configurations. What is the number of protons in each? The number of electrons in each? Arrange them from smallest to largest radii and explain your ordering rationale.

3. What is meant by a *chemical bond?*

4. Why do atoms form bonds with one another? What can make a molecule favored compared with the lone atoms?

5. How does a bond between Na and Cl differ from a bond between C and O? What about a bond between N and N?

6. In your own words, what is meant by the term *electronegativity?* What are the trends across and down the periodic table for electronegativity? Explain them, and describe how they are consistent with trends of ionization energy and atomic radii.

7. Explain the difference between ionic bonding and covalent bonding. How can we use the periodic table to help us determine the type of bonding between atoms?

8. True or false? In general, a larger atom has a smaller electronegativity. Explain.

9. Why is there an octet rule (and what does *octet* mean) in writing Lewis structures?

10. Does a Lewis structure tell which electrons came from which atoms? Explain.

11. If lithium and fluorine react, which has more attraction for an electron? Why?

12. In a bond between fluorine and iodine, which has more attraction for an electron? Why?

13. We use differences in electronegativity to account for certain properties of bond.
    What if all atoms had the same electronegativity values? How would bonding between atoms be affected? What are some differences we would notice?

14. Explain how you can use the periodic table to predict the formula of compounds.

15. Why do we only consider the valence electrons in drawing Lewis structures?

16. How do we determine the total number of valence electrons for an ion? Provide an example of an anion and a cation, and explain your answer.

17. What is the main idea in the valence shell electron pair repulsion (VSEPR) theory?

18. The molecules NH_3 and BF_3 have the same general formula (AB_3) but different shapes.
    a. Find the shape of each of the above molecules.
    b. Provide more examples of real molecules that have the same general formulas but different shapes.

19. How do we deal with multiple bonds in VSEPR theory?

20. In Section 12.10 of your text, the term "effective pairs" is used. What does this mean?

VP 21. Consider the ions Sc^{3+}, Cl^-, K^+, Ca^{2+}, and S^{2-}. Match these ions to the following pictures that represent the relative sizes of the ions.

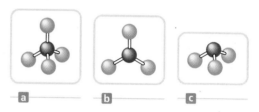

VP 22. Write the name of each of the following shapes of molecules.

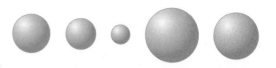

a   b   c

Questions and Problems

12.1 Types of Chemical Bonds

QUESTIONS

1. In general terms, what is a chemical *bond?*

2. What does the *bond energy* of a chemical bond represent?

3. A What sorts of elements react to form *ionic* compounds?

4. In general terms, what is a *covalent* bond?

5. Describe the type of bonding that exists in the $Cl_2(g)$ molecule. How does this type of bonding differ from that found in the $HCl(g)$ molecule? How is it similar?

6. Compare and contrast the bonding found in the $H_2(g)$ and $HF(g)$ molecules with that found in $NaF(s)$.

12.2 Electronegativity

QUESTIONS

7. The relative ability of an atom in a molecule to attract electrons to itself is called the atom's _____.

8. What does it mean to say that a bond is *polar?* Give two examples of molecules with *polar* bonds. Indicate in your examples the direction of the polarity.

9. A bond between atoms having a (small/large) difference in electronegativity will be ionic.

10. What factor determines the relative level of polarity of a polar covalent bond?

PROBLEMS

11. In each of the following groups, which element is the most electronegative? Which is the least electronegative?

    a. K, Na, H
    b. F, Br, Na
    c. B, N, F

12. In each of the following groups, which element is the most electronegative? Which is the least electronegative?

    a. Rb, Sr, I
    b. Ca, Mg, Sr
    c. Br, Ca, K

13. On the basis of the electronegativity values given in Figure 12.3, indicate whether each of the following bonds would be expected to be ionic, covalent, or polar covalent.

    a. O—O
    b. Al—O
    c. B—O

14. On the basis of the electronegativity values given in Figure 12.3, indicate whether each of the following bonds would be expected to be covalent, polar covalent, or ionic.

    a. K—Cl
    b. Br—Cl
    c. Cl—Cl

15. Which of the following molecules contain polar covalent bonds?

    a. water, H_2O
    b. carbon monoxide, CO
    c. fluorine, F_2
    d. nitrogen, N_2

16. Which of the following molecules contain polar covalent bonds?

    a. sulfur, S_8
    b. fluorine, F_2
    c. iodine monochloride, ICl
    d. hydrogen bromide, HBr

17. On the basis of the electronegativity values given in Figure 12.3, indicate which is the more polar bond in each of the following pairs.

    a. H—F or H—Cl
    b. H—Cl or H—I
    c. H—Br or H—Cl
    d. H—I or H—Br

18. On the basis of the electronegativity values given in Figure 12.3, indicate which is the more polar bond in each of the following pairs.

    a. O—Cl or O—Br   c. P—S or P—O
    b. N—O or N—F   d. H—O or H—N

19. Which bond in each of the following pairs has the greater ionic character?

    a. Na—F or Na—I   c. Li—Cl or Cs—Cl
    b. Ca—S or Ca—O   d. Mg—N or Mg—P

20. Which bond in each of the following pairs has less ionic character?

    a. Na—Cl or Ca—Cl   c. Fe—I or Fe—F
    b. Cs—Cl or Ba—Cl   d. Be—F or Ba—F

12.3 Bond Polarity and Dipole Moments

QUESTIONS

21. What is a *dipole moment?* Give four examples of molecules that possess dipole moments, and draw the direction of the dipole as shown in Section 12.3.

22. Why is the presence of a dipole moment in the water molecule so important? What are some properties of water that are determined by its polarity?

PROBLEMS

23. In each of the following diatomic molecules, which end of the molecule is negative relative to the other end?

    a. hydrogen chloride, HCl
    b. carbon monoxide, CO
    c. bromine monofluoride, BrF

24. In each of the following diatomic molecules, which end of the molecule is positive relative to the other end?

    a. hydrogen fluoride, HF
    b. chlorine monofluoride, ClF
    c. iodine monochloride, ICl

25. For each of the following bonds, draw a figure indicating the direction of the bond dipole, including which end of the bond is positive and which is negative.

    a. C—F   c. C—O
    b. Si—C   d. B—C

26. For each of the following bonds, draw a figure indicating the direction of the bond dipole, including which end of the bond is positive and which is negative.

    a. S—O   c. S—F
    b. S—N   d. S—Cl

27. For each of the following bonds, draw a figure indicating the direction of the bond dipole, including which end of the bond is positive and which is negative.

    a. Si—H   c. S—H
    b. P—H   d. Cl—H

28. For each of the following bonds, draw a figure indicating the direction of the bond dipole, including which end of the bond is positive and which is negative.

    a. H—C   c. N—S
    b. N—O   d. N—C

All even-numbered Questions and Problems have answers in the back of this book and solutions in the Solutions Guide.

12.4 Stable Electron Configurations and Charges on Ions

QUESTIONS

29. What does it mean when we say that in forming bonds, atoms try to achieve an electron configuration analogous to a noble gas?

30. The metallic elements lose electrons when reacting, and the resulting positive ions have an electron configuration analogous to the _____ noble gas element.

31. Nonmetals form negative ions by (losing/gaining) enough electrons to achieve the electron configuration of the next noble gas.

32. Explain how the atoms in *covalent* molecules achieve electron configurations similar to those of the noble gases. How does this differ from the situation in ionic compounds?

PROBLEMS

33. Which simple ion would each of the following elements be expected to form? What noble gas has an analogous electron configuration to each of the ions?

    a. chlorine, $Z = 17$
    b. strontium, $Z = 38$
    c. oxygen, $Z = 8$
    d. rubidium, $Z = 37$

34. Which simple ion would each of the following elements be expected to form? Which noble gas has an analogous electron configuration to each of the ions?

    a. bromine, $Z = 35$
    b. cesium, $Z = 55$
    c. phosphorus, $Z = 15$
    d. sulfur, $Z = 16$

35. For each of the following numbers of electrons, give the formula of a *positive ion* that would have that number of electrons, and write the complete electron configuration for each ion.

    a. 10 electrons   c. 18 electrons
    b. 2 electrons   d. 36 electrons

36. Give the formula of a *negative* ion that would have the same number of electrons as each of the following *positive* ions.

    a. Na^+ c. Al^{3+}
    b. Ca^{2+} d. Rb^+

37. On the basis of their electron configurations, predict the formula of the simple binary ionic compounds likely to form when the following pairs of elements react with each other.

    a. aluminum, Al, and sulfur, S
    b. radium, Ra, and oxygen, O
    c. calcium, Ca, and fluorine, F
    d. cesium, Cs, and nitrogen, N
    e. rubidium, Rb, and phosphorus, P

38. On the basis of their electron configurations, predict the formula of the simple binary ionic compound likely to form when the following pairs of elements react with each other.

    a. aluminum and bromine
    b. aluminum and oxygen
    c. aluminum and phosphorus
    d. aluminum and hydrogen

39. Name the noble gas atom that has the same electron configuration as each of the ions in the following compounds.

    a. barium sulfide, BaS
    b. strontium fluoride, SrF_2
    c. magnesium oxide, MgO
    d. aluminum sulfide, Al_2S_3

40. Atoms form ions so as to achieve electron configurations similar to those of the noble gases. For the following pairs of noble gas configurations, give the formulas of two simple ionic compounds that would have comparable electron configurations.

    a. [He] and [Ne]   c. [He] and [Ar]
    b. [Ne] and [Ne]   d. [Ne] and [Ar]

12.5 Ionic Bonding and Structures of Ionic Compounds

QUESTIONS

41. Is the formula we write for an ionic compound the *molecular* formula or the *empirical* formula? Why?

42. Describe in general terms the structure of ionic solids such as NaCl. How are the ions packed in the crystal?

43. Why are cations always smaller than the atoms from which they are formed?

44. Why are anions always larger than the atoms from which they are formed?

PROBLEMS

45. For each of the following pairs, indicate which species is smaller. Explain your reasoning in terms of the electron structure of each species.

    a. H or H^- c. Al or Al^{3+}
    b. N or N^{3-} d. F or Cl

46. For each of the following pairs, indicate which species is larger. Explain your reasoning in terms of the electron structure of each species.

    a. Li^+ or F^- c. Ca^{2+} or Ca
    b. Na^+ or Cl^- d. Cs^+ or I^-

47. For each of the following pairs, indicate which is smaller.

    a. Fe or Fe^{3+} b. Cl or Cl^- c. Al^{3+} or Na^+

48. For each of the following pairs, indicate which is larger.

    a. I or F   b. F or F^- c. Na^+ or F^-

All even-numbered Questions and Problems have answers in the back of this book and solutions in the Solutions Guide.

12.6 and 12.7 Lewis Structures

QUESTIONS

49. Why are the *valence* electrons of an atom the only electrons likely to be involved in bonding to other atoms?

50. Explain what the "duet" and "octet" rules are and how they are used to describe the arrangement of electrons in a molecule.

51. What type of structure must each atom in a compound usually exhibit for the compound to be stable?

52. When elements in the second and third periods occur in compounds, what number of electrons in the valence shell represents the most stable electron arrangement? Why?

PROBLEMS

53. How many electrons are involved when two atoms in a molecule are connected by a "double bond"? Write the Lewis structure of a molecule containing a double bond.

54. What does it mean when two atoms in a molecule are connected by a "triple bond"? Write the Lewis structure of a molecule containing a triple bond.

55. Write the simple Lewis structure for each of the following atoms.

a. I ($Z = 53$)
b. Al ($Z = 13$)
c. Xe ($Z = 54$)
d. Sr ($Z = 38$)

56. Write the simple Lewis structure for each of the following atoms.

a. Mg ($Z = 12$)
b. Br ($Z = 35$)
c. S ($Z = 16$)
d. Si ($Z = 14$)

57. Give the *total* number of valence electrons in each of the following molecules.

a. N_2O
b. B_2H_6
c. C_3H_8
d. NCl_3

58. Give the *total* number of valence electrons in each of the following molecules.

a. B_2O_3
b. CO_2
c. C_2H_6O
d. NO_2

59. Write a Lewis structure for each of the following simple molecules. Show all bonding valence electron pairs as lines and all nonbonding valence electron pairs as dots.

a. NBr_3
b. HF
c. CBr_4
d. C_2H_2

60. Write a Lewis structure for each of the following simple molecules. Show all bonding valence electron pairs as lines and all nonbonding valence electron pairs as dots.

a. H_2
b. Hcl
c. CF_4
d. C_2F_6

61. Write a Lewis structure for each of the following simple molecules. Show all bonding valence electron pairs as lines and all nonbonding valence electron pairs as dots.

a. C_2H_6
b. NF_3
c. C_4H_{10}
d. $SiCl_4$

62. Write a Lewis structure for each of the following molecules. Show all bonding valence electron pairs as lines and all nonbonding valence electron pairs as dots.

a. PCl_3
b. $CHCl_3$
c. $C_2H_4Cl_2$
d. N_2H_4

F 63. The "Chemistry in Focus" segment *Broccoli–Miracle Food?* discusses the health benefits of eating broccoli and gives a Lewis structure for sulforaphane, a chemical in broccoli. Draw possible resonance structures for sulforaphane.

F 64. The "Chemistry in Focus" segment *Hiding Carbon Dioxide* discusses attempts at sequestering (storing) underground CO_2 produced at power plants so as to diminish the greenhouse effect. Draw all resonance structures of the CO_2 molecule.

65. Write a Lewis structure for each of the following polyatomic ions. Show all bonding valence electron pairs as lines and all nonbonding valence electron pairs as dots. For those ions that exhibit resonance, draw the various possible resonance forms.

a. sulfate ion, SO_4^{2-}
b. phosphate ion, PO_4^{3-}
c. sulfite ion, SO_3^{2-}

66. Write a Lewis structure for each of the following polyatomic ions. Show all bonding valence electron pairs as lines and all nonbonding valence electron pairs as dots. For those ions that exhibit resonance, draw the various possible resonance forms.

a. chlorate ion, ClO_3^-
b. peroxide ion, O_2^{2-}
c. acetate ion, $C_2H_3O_2^-$

67. Write a Lewis structure for each of the following polyatomic ions. Show all bonding valence electron pairs as lines and all nonbonding valence electron pairs as dots. For those ions that exhibit resonance, draw the various possible resonance forms.

a. chlorite ion, ClO_2^-
b. perbromate ion, BrO_4^-
c. cyanide ion, CN^-

68. Write a Lewis structure for each of the following polyatomic ions. Show all bonding valence electron pairs as lines and all nonbonding valence electron pairs as dots. For those ions that exhibit resonance, draw the various possible resonance forms.

a. carbonate ion, CO_3^{2-}
b. ammonium ion, NH_4^+
c. hypochlorite ion, ClO^-

All even-numbered Questions and Problems have answers in the back of this book and solutions in the Solutions Guide.

12.8 Molecular Structure

QUESTIONS

69. What is the geometric structure of the water molecule? How many pairs of valence electrons are there on the oxygen atom in the water molecule? What is the approximate H—O—H bond angle in water?

70. What is the geometric structure of the ammonia molecule? How many pairs of electrons surround the nitrogen atom in NH_3? What is the approximate H—N—H bond angle in ammonia?

71. What is the geometric structure of the boron trifluoride molecule, BF_3? How many pairs of valence electrons are present on the boron atom in BF_3? What are the approximate F—B—F bond angles in BF_3?

72. What is the geometric structure of the SiF_4 molecule? How many pairs of valence electrons are present on the silicon atom of SiF_4? What are the approximate F—Si—F bond angles in SiF_4?

12.9 Molecular Structure: The VSEPR Model

QUESTIONS

73. Why is the geometric structure of a molecule important, especially for biological molecules?

74. What general principles determine the molecular structure (shape) of a molecule?

75. How is the structure around a given atom related to repulsion between valence electron pairs on the atom?

76. Why are all diatomic molecules *linear,* regardless of the number of valence electron pairs on the atoms involved?

77. Although the valence electron pairs in ammonia have a tetrahedral arrangement, the overall geometric structure of the ammonia molecule is *not* described as being tetrahedral. Explain.

78. Although both the BF_3 and NF_3 molecules contain the same number of atoms, the BF_3 molecule is flat, whereas the NF_3 molecule is trigonal pyramidal. Explain.

PROBLEMS

79. For the indicated atom in each of the following molecules or ions, give the number and arrangement of the electron pairs around that atom.

    a. As in AsO_4^{3-}
    b. Se in SeO_4^{2-}
    c. S in H_2S

80. For the indicated atom in each of the following molecules or ions, give the number and arrangement of the electron pairs around that atom.

    a. S in SO_3^{2-}
    b. S in HSO_3^-
    c. S in HS^-

81. Using the VSEPR theory, predict the molecular structure of each of the following molecules.

    a. NCl_3 b. H_2Se c. $SiCl_4$

82. Using the VSEPR theory, predict the molecular structure of each of the following molecules.

    a. NI_3 b. AsH_3 c. OF_2

83. Using the VSEPR theory, predict the molecular structure of each of the following polyatomic ions.

    a. sulfate ion, SO_4^{2-}
    b. phosphate ion, PO_4^{3-}
    c. ammonium ion, NH_4^+

84. Using the VSEPR theory, predict the molecular structure of each of the following polyatomic ions.

    a. dihydrogen phosphate ion, $H_2PO_4^-$
    b. perchlorate ion, ClO_4^-
    c. sulfite ion, SO_3^{2-}

85. For each of the following molecules or ions, indicate the bond angle expected between the central atom and any two adjacent hydrogen atoms.

    a. H_2O b. NH_3 c. NH_4^+ d. CH_4

86. For each of the following molecules or ions, indicate the bond angle expected between the central atom and any two adjacent chlorine atoms.

    a. Cl_2O b. NCl_3 c. CCl_4 d. C_2Cl_4

F 87. The "Chemistry in Focus" segment *Taste–It's the Structure That Counts* discusses artificial sweeteners. What are the expected bond angles around the nitrogen atom in aspartame?

F 88. The "Chemistry in Focus" segment *Minimotor Molecule* discusses a tiny polymer (75 nm long) made of azobenzenes that can do work. Consider the Lewis structure shown in this segment. What are the expected bond angles around the carbon atoms in the structure? What about the C—N—N bond angle?

Additional Problems

89. What is *resonance?* Give three examples of molecules or ions that exhibit resonance, and draw Lewis structures for each of the possible resonance forms.

90. When two atoms share two pairs of electrons, a(n) _____ bond is said to exist between them.

91. The geometric arrangement of electron pairs around a given atom is determined principally by the tendency to minimize _____ between the electron pairs.

92. In each case, which of the following pairs of bonded elements forms the more polar bond?

    a. S—F or S—Cl
    b. N—O or P—O
    c. C—H or Si—H

All even-numbered Questions and Problems have answers in the back of this book and solutions in the Solutions Guide.

93. In each case, which of the following pairs of bonded elements forms the more polar bond?

    a. Br—Cl or Br—F
    b. As—S or As—O
    c. Pb—C or Pb—Si

94. What do we mean by the *bond energy* of a chemical bond?

95. A(n) _____ chemical bond represents the equal sharing of a pair of electrons between two nuclei.

96. For each of the following pairs of elements, identify which element would be expected to be more electronegative. It should not be necessary to look at a table of actual electronegativity values.

    a. Be or Ba
    b. N or P
    c. F or Cl

97. On the basis of the electronegativity values given in Figure 12.3, indicate whether each of the following bonds would be expected to be ionic, covalent, or polar covalent.

    a. H—O   c. H—H
    b. O—O   d. H—Cl

98. Which of the following molecules contain polar covalent bonds?

    a. carbon monoxide, CO
    b. chlorine, Cl_2
    c. iodine monochloride, ICl
    d. phosphorus, P_4

99. On the basis of the electronegativity values given in Figure 12.3, indicate which is the more polar bond in each of the following pairs.

    a. N—P or N—O   c. N—S or N—C
    b. N—C or N—O   d. N—F or N—S

100. In each of the following molecules, which end of the molecule is negative relative to the other end?

    a. carbon monoxide, CO
    b. iodine monobromide, IBr
    c. hydrogen iodide, HI

101. For each of the following bonds, draw a figure indicating the direction of the bond dipole, including which end of the bond is positive and which is negative.

    a. N—Cl   c. N—S
    b. N—P   d. N—C

102. Write the electron configuration for each of the following atoms and for the simple ion that the element most commonly forms. In each case, indicate which noble gas has the same electron configuration as the ion.

    a. aluminum, $Z = 13$
    b. bromine, $Z = 35$
    c. calcium, $Z = 20$
    d. lithium, $Z = 3$
    e. fluorine, $Z = 9$

103. What simple ion does each of the following elements most commonly form?

    a. sodium   e. sulfur
    b. iodine   f. magnesium
    c. potassium   g. aluminum
    d. calcium   h. nitrogen

104. On the basis of their electron configurations, predict the formula of the simple binary ionic compound likely to form when the following pairs of elements react with each other.

    a. sodium, Na, and selenium, Se
    b. rubidium, Rb, and fluorine, F
    c. potassium, K, and tellurium, Te
    d. barium, Ba, and selenium, Se
    e. potassium, K, and astatine, At
    f. francium, Fr, and chlorine, Cl

105. Which noble gas has the same electron configuration as each of the ions in the following compounds?

    a. calcium bromide, $CaBr_2$
    b. aluminum selenide, Al_2Se_3
    c. strontium oxide, SrO
    d. potassium sulfide, K_2S

106. For each of the following pairs, indicate which is smaller.

    a. Rb^+ or Na^+ c. F^- or I^-
    b. Mg^{2+} or Al^{3+} d. Na^+ or K^+

107. Write the Lewis structure for each of the following atoms.

    a. He ($Z = 2$)
    b. Br ($Z = 35$)
    c. Sr ($Z = 38$)
    d. Ne ($Z = 10$)
    e. I ($Z = 53$)
    f. Ra ($Z = 88$)

108. What is the *total* number of *valence* electrons in each of the following molecules?

    a. HNO_3 c. H_3PO_4
    b. H_2SO_4 d. $HClO_4$

109. Write a Lewis structure for each of the following simple molecules. Show all bonding valence electron pairs as lines and all nonbonding valence electron pairs as dots.

    a. GeH_4 c. NI_3
    b. Icl   d. PF_3

110. Write a Lewis structure for each of the following simple molecules. Show all bonding valence electron pairs as lines and all nonbonding valence electron pairs as dots.

    a. N_2H_4 c. NCl_3
    b. C_2H_6 d. $SiCl_4$

111. Write a Lewis structure for each of the following simple molecules. Show all bonding valence electron pairs as lines and all nonbonding valence electron pairs as dots. For those molecules that exhibit

resonance, draw the various possible resonance forms.

a. SO_2
b. N_2O (N in center)
c. O_3

112. Write a Lewis structure for each of the following polyatomic ions. Show all bonding valence electron pairs as lines and all nonbonding valence electron pairs as dots. For those ions that exhibit resonance, draw the various possible resonance forms.

a. nitrate ion
b. carbonate ion
c. ammonium ion

113. Why is the molecular structure of H_2O nonlinear, whereas that of BeF_2 is linear, even though both molecules consist of three atoms?

114. For the indicated atom in each of the following molecules, give the number and the arrangement of the electron pairs around that atom.

a. C in CCl_4
b. Ge in GeH_4
c. B in BF_3

115. Using the VSEPR theory, predict the molecular structure of each of the following molecules.

a. Cl_2O
b. OF_2
c. $SiCl_4$

116. Using the VSEPR theory, predict the molecular structure of each of the following polyatomic ions.

a. chlorate ion
b. chlorite ion
c. perchlorate ion

117. For each of the following molecules, indicate the bond angle expected between the central atom and any two adjacent chlorine atoms.

a. Cl_2O c. $BeCl_2$
b. CCl_4 d. BCl_3

118. Using the VSEPR theory, predict the molecular structure of each of the following molecules or ions containing multiple bonds.

a. SO_2
b. SO_3
c. HCO_3^- (hydrogen is bonded to oxygen)
d. HCN

119. Using the VSEPR theory, predict the molecular structure of each of the following molecules or ions containing multiple bonds.

a. CO_3^{2-}
b. HNO_3 (hydrogen is bonded to oxygen)
c. NO_2^-
d. C_2H_2

120. Explain briefly how substances with ionic bonding differ in properties from substances with covalent bonding.

121. Explain the difference between a covalent bond formed between two atoms of the same element and a covalent bond formed between atoms of two different elements.

QUESTIONS

1. What is *potential* energy? What is *kinetic* energy? What do we mean by the *law of conservation of energy?* What do scientists mean by *work?* Explain what scientists mean by a *state function* and give an example of one.

2. What does *temperature* measure? Are the molecules in a beaker of warm water moving at the same speed as the molecules in a beaker of cold water? Explain. What is *heat?* Is *heat* the same as *temperature?*

3. When describing a reaction, a chemist might refer to the *system* and the *surroundings*. Explain each of these terms. If a reaction is *endothermic,* does heat travel from the surroundings into the system, or from the system into the surroundings? Suppose a reaction between ionic solutes is performed in aqueous solution, and the temperature of the solution increases. Is the reaction exothermic or endothermic? Explain.

4. What is the study of energy and energy changes called? What is the "first law" of thermodynamics and what does it mean? What do scientists mean by the *internal energy* of a system? Is the *internal energy* the same as *heat?*

5. How is the *calorie* defined? Is the *thermodynamic calorie* the same as the *Calorie* we are careful of when planning our diets? Although the calorie is our "working unit" of energy (based on its experimental definition), the SI unit of energy is the *joule.* How are joules and calories related? What does the *specific heat capacity* of a substance represent? What common substance has a relatively high specific heat capacity, which makes it useful for cooling purposes?

6. What is the *enthalpy* change for a process? Is enthalpy a state function? In what experimental apparatus are enthalpy changes measured?

7. Hess's law is often confusing to students. Imagine you are talking to a friend who has not taken any science courses. Using the reactions

    $P_4(s) + 6Cl_2(g) \rightarrow 4PCl_3(g)$ $\Delta H = -2.44 \times 10^3 \text{ kJ}$
    $4PCl_5(g) \rightarrow P_4(s) + 10Cl_2(g)$ $\Delta H = 3.43 \times 10^3 \text{ kJ}$

    Explain to your friend how Hess's law can be used to calculate the enthalpy change for the reaction

    $PCl_5(g) \rightarrow PCl_3(g) + Cl_2(g)$

8. The first law of thermodynamics indicates that the total energy content of the universe is constant. If this is true, why do we worry about "energy conservation"? What do we mean by the *quality* of energy, rather than the *quantity?* Give an example. Although the quantity of energy in the universe may be constant, is the *quality* of that energy changing?

9. What do *petroleum* and *natural gas* consist of? Indicate some petroleum "fractions" and explain what they are used for. What does it mean to "crack" petroleum and why is this done? What was tetraethyl lead used for, and why has its use been drastically reduced? What is the *greenhouse effect,* and why are scientists concerned about it?

10. What is a *driving force?* Name two common and important driving forces, and give an example of each. What is *entropy?* Although the total *energy* of the universe is constant, is the *entropy* of the universe constant? What is a spontaneous process?

11. Suppose we have separate 25-g samples of iron, silver, and gold. If 125 J of heat energy is applied separately to each of the three samples, show by calculation which sample will end up at the highest temperature.

12. Methane, CH_4, is the major component of natural gas. Methane burns in air, releasing approximately 890 kJ of heat energy per mole.

    $$CH_4(g) + 2O_2(g) \rightarrow CO_2(g) + 2H_2O(g)$$

    a. What quantity of heat is released if 0.521 mole of methane is burned?
    b. What quantity of heat is released if 1.25 g of methane is burned?
    c. What quantity of methane must have reacted if 1250 kJ of heat energy was released?

13. What is *electromagnetic radiation?* Give some examples of such radiation. Explain what the *wavelength* (λ) and *frequency* (ν) of electromagnetic radiation represent. Sketch a representation of a wave and indicate on your drawing one wavelength of the wave. At what speed does electromagnetic radiation move through space? How is this speed related to λ and ν?

14. Explain what it means for an atom to be in an *excited state* and what it means for an atom to be in its *ground state.* How does an excited atom *return* to its ground state? What is a *photon?* How is the wavelength (color) of light related to the energy of the photons being emitted by an atom? How is the energy of the photons being *emitted* by an atom related to the energy changes taking place *within* the atom?

15. Do atoms in excited states emit radiation randomly, at any wavelength? Why? What does it mean to say that the hydrogen atom has only certain *discrete energy levels* available? How do we know this? Why was the quantization of energy levels surprising to scientists when it was first discovered?

16. Describe Bohr's model of the hydrogen atom. How did Bohr envision the relationship between the electron and the nucleus of the hydrogen atom? How did Bohr's model explain the emission of only discrete wavelengths of light by excited hydrogen atoms? Why did Bohr's model not stand up as more experiments were performed using elements other than hydrogen?

17. Schrödinger and de Broglie suggested a "wave–particle duality" for small particles—that is, if electromagnetic radiation showed some particle-like properties, then perhaps small particles might exhibit some wave-like properties. Explain. How does the wave mechanical picture of the atom fundamentally differ from the Bohr model? How do wave mechanical *orbitals* differ from Bohr's *orbits*? What does it mean to say that an orbital represents a probability map for an electron?

18. Describe the general characteristics of the first (lowest-energy) hydrogen atomic orbital. How is this orbital designated symbolically? Does this orbital have a sharp "edge"? Does the orbital represent a surface upon which the electron travels at all times?

19. Use the wave mechanical picture of the hydrogen atom to describe what happens when the atom absorbs energy and moves to an "excited" state. What do the *principal energy levels* and their sublevels represent for a hydrogen atom? How do we designate specific principal energy levels and sublevels in hydrogen?

20. Describe the sublevels and orbitals that constitute the third and fourth principal energy levels of hydrogen. How is each of the orbitals designated and what are the general shapes of their probability maps?

21. Describe *electron spin*. How does electron spin affect the total number of electrons that can be accommodated in a given orbital? What does the *Pauli exclusion principle* tell us about electrons and their spins?

22. Summarize the postulates of the wave mechanical model of the atom.

23. List the *order* in which the orbitals are filled as the atoms beyond hydrogen are built up. How many electrons overall can be accommodated in the first and second principal energy levels? How many electrons can be placed in a given *s* subshell? In a given *p* subshell? In a specific *p* orbital? Why do we assign unpaired electrons in the 2*p* orbitals of carbon, nitrogen, and oxygen?

24. Which are the *valence* electrons in an atom? Choose three elements and write their electron configurations, circling the valence electrons in the configurations. Why are the valence electrons more important to an atom's chemical properties than are the core electrons or the nucleus?

25. Sketch the overall shape of the periodic table and indicate the general regions of the table that represent the various *s*, *p*, *d*, and *f* orbitals being filled. How is an element's position in the periodic table related to its chemical properties?

26. Using the general periodic table you developed in Question 25, show how the valence-electron configuration of most of the elements can be written just by knowing the relative *location* of the element on the table. Give specific examples.

27. What are the *representative elements?* In what region(s) of the periodic table are these elements found? In what general area of the periodic table are the *metallic* elements found? In what general area of the table are the *nonmetals* found? Where in the table are the *metalloids* located?

28. You have learned how the properties of the elements vary *systematically,* corresponding to the electron structures of the elements being considered. Discuss how the *ionization energies* and *atomic sizes* of elements vary, both within a vertical group (family) of the periodic table and within a horizontal row (period).

29. In general, what do we mean by a *chemical bond?* What does the *bond energy* tell us about the strength of a chemical bond? Name the principal types of chemical bonds.

30. What do we mean by *ionic* bonding? Give an example of a substance whose particles are held together by ionic bonding. What experimental evidence do we have for the existence of ionic bonding? In general, what types of substances react to produce compounds having ionic bonding?

31. What do we mean by *covalent* bonding and *polar covalent* bonding? How are these two bonding types similar and how do they differ? What circumstance must exist for a bond to be purely covalent? How does a polar covalent bond differ from an ionic bond?

32. What is meant by *electronegativity*? How is the difference in electronegativity between two bonded atoms related to the polarity of the bond? Using Figure 12.3, give an example of a bond that would be nonpolar and of a bond that would be highly polar.

33. What does it mean to say that a molecule has a dipole moment? What is the *difference* between a polar bond and a polar molecule (one that has a dipole moment)? Give an example of a molecule that has polar bonds and that has a dipole moment. Give an example of a molecule that has polar bonds, but that does *not* have a dipole moment. What are some implications of the fact that water has a dipole moment?

34. How is the attainment of a noble gas electron configuration important to our ideas of how atoms bond to each other? When atoms of a metal react with atoms of a nonmetal, what type of electron configurations do the resulting ions attain? Explain how the atoms in a covalently bonded compound can attain noble gas electron configurations.

35. Give evidence that ionic bonds are very strong. Does an ionic substance contain discrete molecules? With what general type of structure do ionic compounds occur? Sketch a representation of a general structure for an ionic compound. Why is a cation always smaller and an anion always larger than the respective parent atom? Describe the bonding in an ionic compound containing polyatomic ions.

36. Why does a Lewis structure for a molecule show only the valence electrons? What is the most important factor for the formation of a stable compound? How do we use this requirement when writing Lewis structures?

37. In writing Lewis structures for molecules, what is meant by the *duet rule?* To which element does the duet rule apply? What do we mean by the *octet rule?* Why is attaining an octet of electrons important for an atom when it forms bonds to other atoms? What is a bonding *pair* of electrons? What is a nonbonding (or *lone*) pair of electrons?

38. For three simple molecules of your own choice, *apply* the rules for writing Lewis structures. Write your discussion as if you are explaining the method to someone who is *not* familiar with Lewis structures.

39. What does a *double* bond between two atoms represent in terms of the number of electrons shared? What does a *triple* bond represent? When writing a Lewis structure, explain how we recognize when a molecule must contain double or triple bonds. What are *resonance structures?*

40. Although many simple molecules fulfill the octet rule, some common molecules are exceptions to this rule. Give three examples of molecules whose Lewis structures are exceptions to the octet rule.

41. What do we mean by the *geometric structure* of a molecule? Draw the geometric structures of at least four simple molecules of your choosing and indicate the bond angles in the structures. Explain the main ideas of the *valence shell electron pair repulsion (VSEPR) theory.* Using several examples, explain how you would *apply* the VSEPR theory to predict their geometric structures.

42. What bond angle results when there are only two valence electron pairs around an atom? What bond angle results when there are three valence pairs? What bond angle results when there are four pairs of valence electrons around the central atom in a molecule? Give examples of molecules containing these bond angles.

43. How do we predict the geometric structure of a molecule whose Lewis structure indicates that the molecule contains a double or triple bond? Give an example of such a molecule, write its Lewis structure, and show how the geometric shape is derived.

44. Write the electron configuration for the following atoms, using the appropriate noble gas to abbreviate the configuration of the core electrons.

    a. Sr, $Z = 38$ d. K, $Z = 19$
    b. Al, $Z = 13$ e. S, $Z = 16$
    c. Cl, $Z = 17$ f. As, $Z = 33$

45. Based on the electron configuration of the simple ions that the pairs of elements given below would be expected to form, predict the formula of the simple binary compound that would be formed by each pair.

    a. Al and F   d. Mg and P
    b. Li and N   e. Al and O
    c. Ca and S   f. K and S

46. Draw the Lewis structure for each of the following molecules or ions. Indicate the number and spatial orientation of the electron pairs around the boldface atom in each formula. Predict the simple geometric structure of each molecule or ion, and indicate the approximate bond angles around the boldface atom.

    a. $H_2\mathbf{O}$ d. $\mathbf{Cl}O_4^-$
    b. $\mathbf{P}H_3$ e. $\mathbf{B}F_3$
    c. $\mathbf{C}Br_4$ f. $\mathbf{Be}F_2$

Dry air (air from which the water vapor has been removed) is 78.1% N_2 molecules, 20.9% O_2 molecules, 0.9% Ar atoms, and 0.03% CO_2 molecules, along with smaller amounts of Ne, He, CH_4, Kr, and other trace components.

As a gas, water occupies 1200 times as much space as it does as a liquid at 25 °C and atmospheric pressure.

Soon after Torricelli died, a German physicist named Otto von Guericke invented an air pump. In a famous demonstration for the King of Prussia in 1683, Guericke placed two hemispheres together, pumped the air out of the resulting sphere through a valve, and showed that teams of horses could not pull the hemispheres apart. Then, after secretly opening the air valve, Guericke easily separated the hemispheres by hand. The King of Prussia was so impressed that he awarded Guericke a lifetime pension!

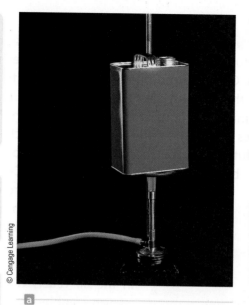

© Cengage Learning

a The pressure exerted by the gases in the atmosphere can be demonstrated by boiling water in a can and then turning off the heat and sealing the can.

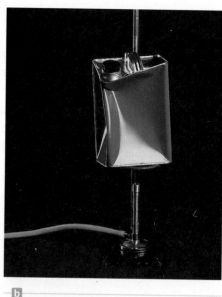

b As the can cools, the water vapor condenses, lowering the gas pressure inside the can. This causes the can to crumple.

Figure 13.1

The gases most familiar to us form the earth's atmosphere. The pressure exerted by this gaseous mixture that we call air can be dramatically demonstrated by the experiment shown in Figure 13.1. A small volume of water is placed in a metal can and the water is boiled, which fills the can with steam. The can is then sealed and allowed to cool. Why does the can collapse as it cools? It is the atmospheric pressure that crumples the can. When the can is cooled after being sealed so that no air can flow in, the water vapor (steam) inside the can condenses to a very small volume of liquid water. As a gas, the water vapor filled the can, but when it is condensed to a liquid, the liquid does not come close to filling the can. The H_2O molecules formerly present as a gas are now collected in a much smaller volume of liquid, and there are very few molecules of gas left to exert pressure outward and counteract the air pressure. As a result, the pressure exerted by the gas molecules in the atmosphere smashes the can.

A device that measures atmospheric pressure, the **barometer,** was invented in 1643 by an Italian scientist named Evangelista Torricelli (1608–1647), who had been a student of the famous astronomer Galileo. Torricelli's barometer is constructed by filling a glass tube with liquid mercury and inverting it in a dish of mercury, as shown in Figure 13.2. Notice that a large quantity of mercury stays in the tube. In fact, at sea level the height of this column of mercury averages 760 mm. Why does this mercury stay in the tube, seemingly in defiance of gravity? Figure 13.2 illustrates how the pressure exerted by the atmospheric gases on the surface of mercury in the dish keeps the mercury in the tube.

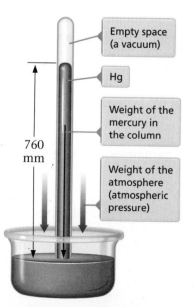

Empty space (a vacuum)

Hg

Weight of the mercury in the column

760 mm

Weight of the atmosphere (atmospheric pressure)

Figure 13.2

When a glass tube is filled with mercury and inverted in a dish of mercury at sea level, the mercury flows out of the tube until a column approximately 760 mm high remains (the height varies with atmospheric conditions). Note that the pressure of the atmosphere balances the weight of the column of mercury in the tube.

Atmospheric pressure results from the mass of the air being pulled toward the center of the earth by gravity—in other words, it results from the weight of the air. Changing weather conditions cause the atmospheric pressure to vary, so the height of the column of Hg supported by the atmosphere at sea level varies; it is not always 760 mm. The meteorologist who says a "low" is approaching means that the atmospheric pressure is going to decrease. This condition often occurs in conjunction with a storm.

Atmospheric pressure also varies with altitude. For example, when Torricelli's experiment is done in Breckenridge, Colorado (elevation 9600 feet), the atmosphere supports a column of mercury only about 520 mm high because the air is "thinner." That is, there is less air pushing down on the earth's surface at Breckenridge than at sea level.

▶ Units of Pressure

Because instruments used for measuring pressure (see Figure 13.3) often contain mercury, the most commonly used units for pressure are based on the height of the mercury column (in millimeters) that the gas pressure can support. The unit **mm Hg** (millimeters of mercury) is often called the **torr** in honor of Torricelli. The terms *torr* and *mm Hg* are used interchangeably by chemists. A related unit for pressure is the **standard atmosphere** (abbreviated atm).

> Mercury is used to measure pressure because of its high density. By way of comparison, the column of water required to measure a given pressure would be 13.6 times as high as a mercury column used for the same purpose.

1 standard atmosphere = 1.000 atm = 760.0 mm Hg = 760.0 torr

The SI unit for pressure is the **pascal** (abbreviated Pa).

1 standard atmosphere = 101,325 Pa

Thus 1 atmosphere is about 100,000 or 10^5 pascals. Because the pascal is so small we will use it sparingly in this book. A unit of pressure that is employed

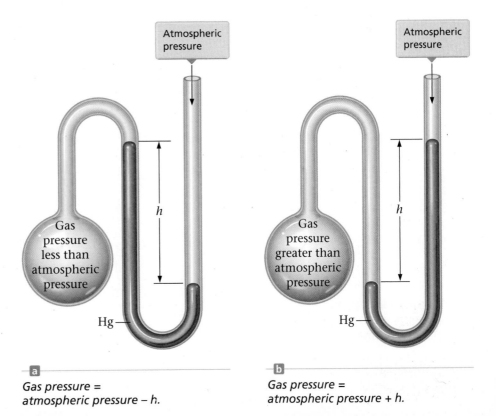

Figure 13.3

A device (called a manometer) for measuring the pressure of a gas in a container. The pressure of the gas is equal to *h* (the difference in mercury levels) in units of torr (equivalent to mm Hg).

Atmospheric pressure

Atmospheric pressure

Gas pressure less than atmospheric pressure

Gas pressure greater than atmospheric pressure

h

h

Hg

Hg

a

*Gas pressure =
atmospheric pressure – h.*

b

*Gas pressure =
atmospheric pressure + h.*

1.000 atm
760.0 mm Hg
760.0 torr
14.69 psi
101,325 Pa

in the engineering sciences and that we use for measuring tire pressure is pounds per square inch, abbreviated psi.

$$1.000 \text{ atm} = 14.69 \text{ psi}$$

Sometimes we need to convert from one unit of pressure to another. We do this by using conversion factors. The process is illustrated in Example 13.1.

EXAMPLE 13.1 | Pressure Unit Conversions

The pressure of the air in a tire is measured to be 28 psi. Represent this pressure in atmospheres, torr, and pascals.

SOLUTION

Where Are We Going?

We want to convert from units of pounds per square inch to units of atmospheres, torr, and pascals.

What Do We Know?

- 28 psi

What Information Do We Need?

- We need the equivalence statements for the units.

How Do We Get There?

To convert from pounds per square inch to atmospheres, we need the equivalence statement

$$1.000 \text{ atm} = 14.69 \text{ psi}$$

which leads to the conversion factor

$$\frac{1.000 \text{ atm}}{14.69 \text{ psi}}$$

$$28 \text{ psi} \times \frac{1.000 \text{ atm}}{14.69 \text{ psi}} = 1.9 \text{ atm}$$

To convert from atmospheres to torr, we use the equivalence statement

$$1.000 \text{ atm} = 760.0 \text{ torr}$$

which leads to the conversion factor

$$\frac{760.0 \text{ torr}}{1.000 \text{ atm}}$$

$$1.9 \text{ atm} \times \frac{760.0 \text{ torr}}{1.000 \text{ atm}} = 1.4 \times 10^3 \text{ torr}$$

To change from torr to pascals, we need the equivalence statement

$$1.000 \text{ atm} = 101,325 \text{ Pa}$$

which leads to the conversion factor

$$\frac{101,325 \text{ Pa}}{1.000 \text{ atm}}$$

$$1.9 \text{ atm} \times \frac{101,325 \text{ Pa}}{1.000 \text{ atm}} = 1.9 \times 10^5 \text{ Pa}$$

REALITY CHECK The units on the answers are the units required.

Ken O'Donoghue

Checking the air pressure in a tire.

MATH SKILL BUILDER
$1.9 \times 760.0 = 1444$
$1444 \ \blacktriangleright \ 1400 = 1.4 \times 10^3$
Round off

MATH SKILL BUILDER
$1.9 \times 101,325 = 192,517.5$
$192,517.5 \ \blacktriangleright \ 190,000 = 1.9 \times 10^5$
Round off

Self-Check **EXERCISE 13.1** On a summer day in Breckenridge, Colorado, the atmospheric pressure is 525 mm Hg. What is this air pressure in atmospheres?

See Problems 13.7 through 13.12. ∎

13.2 Pressure and Volume: Boyle's Law

OBJECTIVES: To understand the law that relates the pressure and volume of a gas. • To do calculations involving this law.

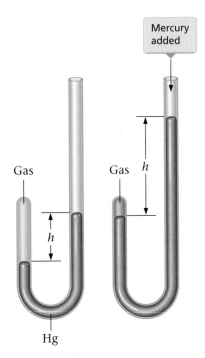

Mercury added

Gas   Gas   h

h

Hg

Figure 13.4

A J-tube similar to the one used by Boyle. The pressure on the trapped gas can be changed by adding or withdrawing mercury.

For Boyle's law to hold, the amount of gas (moles) must not be changed. The temperature must also be constant.

The fact that the constant is sometimes 1.40×10^3 instead of 1.41×10^3 is due to experimental error (uncertainties in measuring the values of P and V).

The first careful experiments on gases were performed by the Irish scientist Robert Boyle (1627–1691). Using a J-shaped tube closed at one end (Figure 13.4), which he reportedly set up in the multi-story entryway of his house, Boyle studied the relationship between the pressure of the trapped gas and its volume. Representative values from Boyle's experiments are given in Table 13.1. The units given for the volume (cubic inches) and pressure (inches of mercury) are the ones Boyle used. Keep in mind that the metric system was not in use at this time.

First let's examine Boyle's observations (Table 13.1) for general trends. Note that as the pressure increases, the volume of the trapped gas decreases. In fact, if you compare the data from experiments 1 and 4, you can see that as the pressure is doubled (from 29.1 to 58.2), the volume of the gas is halved (from 48.0 to 24.0). The same relationship can be seen in experiments 2 and 5 and in experiments 3 and 6 (approximately).

We can see the relationship between the volume of a gas and its pressure more clearly by looking at the product of the values of these two properties ($P \times V$) using Boyle's observations. This product is shown in the last column of Table 13.1. Note that for all the experiments,

$$P \times V = 1.4 \times 10^3 \text{ (in Hg)} \times \text{in.}^3$$

with only a slight variation due to experimental error. Other similar measurements on gases show the same behavior. This means that the relationship of the pressure and volume of a gas can be expressed in words as

pressure times volume equals a constant

Table 13.1 A Sample of Boyle's Observations (moles of gas and temperature both constant)

Experiment	Pressure (in Hg)	Volume (in.³)	Pressure × Volume (in Hg) × (in.³)	
			Actual	Rounded*
1	29.1	48.0	1396.8	1.40×10^3
2	35.3	40.0	1412.0	1.41×10^3
3	44.2	32.0	1414.4	1.41×10^3
4	58.2	24.0	1396.8	1.40×10^3
5	70.7	20.0	1414.0	1.41×10^3
6	87.2	16.0	1395.2	1.40×10^3
7	117.5	12.0	1410.0	1.41×10^3

*Three significant figures are allowed in the product because both of the numbers that are multiplied together have three significant figures.

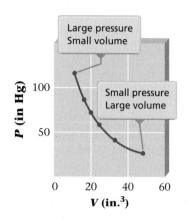

Figure 13.5

A plot of P versus V from Boyle's data in Table 13.1.

or in terms of an equation as

$$PV = k$$

which is called **Boyle's law,** where k is a constant at a specific temperature for a given amount of gas. For the data we used from Boyle's experiment, $k = 1.41 \times 10^3$ (in Hg) $\times$ in.^{3}.

It is often easier to visualize the relationships between two properties if we make a graph. Figure 13.5 uses the data given in Table 13.1 to show how pressure is related to volume. This relationship, called a plot or a graph, shows that V decreases as P increases. When this type of relationship exists, we say that volume and pressure are inversely related or *inversely proportional;* when one increases, the other decreases. Boyle's law is illustrated by the gas samples in Figure 13.6.

Boyle's law means that if we know the volume of a gas at a given pressure, we can predict the new volume if the pressure is changed, *provided that neither the temperature nor the amount of gas is changed.* For example, if we represent the original pressure and volume as P_1 and V_1 and the final values as P_2 and V_2, using Boyle's law we can write

$$P_1V_1 = k$$

and

$$P_2V_2 = k$$

We can also say

$$P_1V_1 = k = P_2V_2$$

or simply

$$P_1V_1 = P_2V_2$$

This is really another way to write Boyle's law. We can solve for the final volume (V_2) by dividing both sides of the equation by P_2.

$$\frac{P_1V_1}{P_2} = \frac{P_2V_2}{P_2}$$

Canceling the P_2 terms on the right gives

$$\frac{P_1}{P_2} \times V_1 = V_2$$

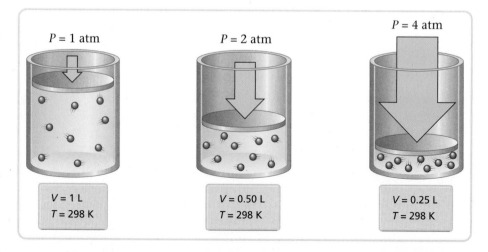

Figure 13.6

Illustration of Boyle's law. These three containers contain the same number of molecules. At 298 K, $P \times V = 1$ L atm in all three containers.

$P = 1$ atm

$V = 1$ L
$T = 298$ K

$P = 2$ atm

$V = 0.50$ L
$T = 298$ K

$P = 4$ atm

$V = 0.25$ L
$T = 298$ K

or

$$V_2 = V_1 \times \frac{P_1}{P_2}$$

This equation tells us that we can calculate the new gas volume (V_2) by multiplying the original volume (V_1) by the ratio of the original pressure to the final pressure (P_1/P_2), as illustrated in Example 13.2.

EXAMPLE 13.2   Calculating Volume Using Boyle's Law

Freon-12 (the common name for the compound CCl_2F_2) was widely used in refrigeration systems, but has now been replaced by other compounds that do not lead to the breakdown of the protective ozone in the upper atmosphere. Consider a 1.5-L sample of gaseous CCl_2F_2 at a pressure of 56 torr. If pressure is changed to 150 torr at a constant temperature,

a. Will the volume of the gas increase or decrease?

b. What will be the new volume of the gas?

SOLUTION

Where Are We Going?

We want to determine if the volume will increase or decrease when the pressure is changed, and we want to calculate the new volume.

What Do We Know?

- We know the initial and final pressures and the initial volume.
- The amount of gas and temperature are held constant.
- Boyle's law: $P_1V_1 = P_2V_2$

How Do We Get There?

a. As the first step in a gas law problem, always write down the information given, in the form of a table showing the initial and final conditions.

Initial Conditions	Final Conditions
P_1 = 56 torr	P_2 = 150 torr
V_1 = 1.5 L	V_2 = ?

Drawing a picture also is often helpful. Notice that the pressure is increased from 56 torr to 150 torr, so the volume must decrease:

P_1V_1 ➡ P_2V_2

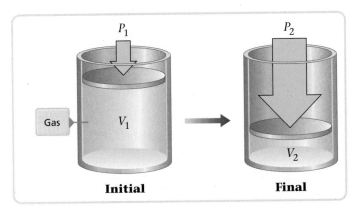

We can verify this by using Boyle's law in the form

$$V_2 = V_1 \times \frac{P_1}{P_2}$$

Note that V_2 is obtained by "correcting" V_1 using the ratio P_1/P_2. Because P_1 is less than P_2, the ratio P_1/P_2 is a fraction that is less than 1. Thus V_2 must be a fraction of (smaller than) V_1; the volume decreases.

> The fact that the volume decreases in Example 13.2 makes sense because the pressure was increased. *To help catch errors, make it a habit to check whether an answer to a problem makes physical sense.*

b. We calculate V_2 as follows:

$$V_2 = V_1 \times \frac{P_1}{P_2} = 1.5 \text{ L} \times \frac{56 \text{ torr}}{150 \text{ torr}} = 0.56 \text{ L}$$

where the P_1 corresponds to 56 torr, V_1 to 1.5 L, and P_2 to 150 torr.

REALITY CHECK   Because the pressure increases, we expect the volume to decrease. The pressure increased by almost a factor of three, and the volume decreased by about a factor of three.

Self-Check EXERCISE 13.2   A sample of neon to be used in a neon sign has a volume of 1.51 L at a pressure of 635 torr. Calculate the volume of the gas after it is pumped into the glass tubes of the sign, where it shows a pressure of 785 torr.

See Problems 13.21 and 13.22. ∎

EXAMPLE 13.3 | **Calculating Pressure Using Boyle's Law**

In an automobile engine the gaseous fuel–air mixture enters the cylinder and is compressed by a moving piston before it is ignited. In a certain engine the initial cylinder volume is 0.725 L. After the piston moves up, the volume is 0.075 L. The fuel–air mixture initially has a pressure of 1.00 atm. Calculate the pressure of the compressed fuel–air mixture, assuming that both the temperature and the amount of gas remain constant.

SOLUTION

Where Are We Going?

We want to determine the new pressure of a fuel–air mixture that has undergone a volume change.

What Do We Know?

- We know the initial and final volumes and the initial pressure.
- The amount of gas and temperature are held constant.
- Boyle's law: $P_1V_1 = P_2V_2$

How Do We Get There?

We summarize the given information in the following table:

Initial Conditions	Final Conditions
$P_1 = 1.00$ atm	$P_2 = ?$
$V_1 = 0.725$ L	$V_2 = 0.075$ L

> **MATH SKILL BUILDER**
> $$P_1V_1 = P_2V_2$$
> $$\frac{P_1V_1}{V_2} = \frac{P_2V_2}{V_2}$$
> $$P_1 \times \frac{V_1}{V_2} = P_2$$
> $$\frac{0.725}{0.075} = 9.666\ldots$$
> $$9.666 \Rightarrow 9.7$$
> Round off

Neon signs in Hong Kong.

Then we solve Boyle's law in the form $P_1V_1 = P_2V_2$ for P_2 by dividing both sides by V_2 to give the equation

$$P_2 = P_1 \times \frac{V_1}{V_2} = 1.00 \text{ atm} \times \frac{0.725 \text{ L}}{0.075 \text{ L}} = 9.7 \text{ atm}$$

REALITY CHECK   Because the volume decreases, we expect the pressure to increase. The volume decreased by about a factor of 10, and the pressure increased by about a factor of 10. ■

13.3 Volume and Temperature: Charles's Law

OBJECTIVES: To learn about absolute zero. • To learn about the law relating the volume and temperature of a sample of gas at constant moles and pressure, and to do calculations involving that law.

In the century following Boyle's findings, scientists continued to study the properties of gases. The French physicist Jacques Charles (1746–1823), who was the first person to fill a balloon with hydrogen gas and who made the first solo balloon flight, showed that the volume of a given amount of gas (at constant pressure) increases with the temperature of the gas. That is, the volume increases when the temperature increases. A plot of the volume of a given sample of gas (at constant pressure) versus its temperature (in Celsius degrees) gives a straight line. This type of relationship is called *linear,* and this behavior is shown for several gases in Figure 13.7.

The solid lines in Figure 13.7 are based on actual measurements of temperature and volume for the gases listed. As we cool the gases they eventually liquefy, so we cannot determine any experimental points below this

The air in a balloon expands when it is heated. This means that some of the air escapes from the balloon, lowering the air density inside and thus making the balloon buoyant.

Temperatures such as 0.00000002 K have been obtained in the laboratory, but 0 K has never been reached.

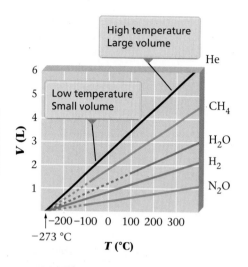

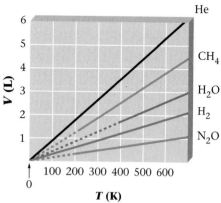

Figure 13.7

Plots of V (L) versus T (°C) for several gases. Note that each sample of gas contains a different number of moles to spread out the plots.

Figure 13.8

Plots of V versus T as in Figure 13.7, except that here the Kelvin scale is used for temperature.

temperature. However, when we extend each straight line (which is called *extrapolation* and is shown here by a dashed line), something very interesting happens. *All* of the lines extrapolate to zero volume at the same temperature: −273 °C. This suggests that −273 °C is the lowest possible temperature, because a negative volume is physically impossible. In fact, experiments have shown that matter cannot be cooled to temperatures lower than −273 °C. Therefore, this temperature is defined as **absolute zero** on the Kelvin scale.

When the volumes of the gases shown in Figure 13.7 are plotted against temperature on the Kelvin scale rather than the Celsius scale, the plots shown in Figure 13.8 result. These plots show that the volume of each gas is *directly proportional to the temperature* (in kelvins) and extrapolates to zero when the temperature is 0 K. Let's illustrate this statement with an example. Suppose we have 1 L of gas at 300 K. When we double the temperature of this gas to 600 K (without changing its pressure), the volume also doubles, to 2 L. Verify this type of behavior by looking carefully at the lines for various gases shown in Figure 13.8.

The direct proportionality between volume and temperature (in kelvins) is represented by the equation known as **Charles's law:**

$$V = bT$$

where T is in kelvins and b is the proportionality constant. Charles's law holds for a given sample of gas at constant pressure. It tells us that (for a given amount of gas at a given pressure) the volume of the gas is directly proportional to the temperature on the Kelvin scale:

$$V = bT \quad \text{or} \quad \frac{V}{T} = b = \text{constant}$$

From Figure 13.8 for Helium		
V (L)	T (K)	b
0.7	100	0.01
1.7	200	0.01
2.7	300	0.01
3.7	400	0.01
5.7	600	0.01

Notice that in the second form, this equation states that the *ratio* of V to T (in kelvins) must be constant. (This is shown for helium in the margin.) Thus, when we triple the temperature (in kelvins) of a sample of gas, the volume of the gas triples as well.

$$\frac{V}{T} = \frac{3 \times V}{3 \times T} = b = \text{constant}$$

We can also write Charles's law in terms of V_1 and T_1 (the initial conditions) and V_2 and T_2 (the final conditions).

$$\frac{V_1}{T_1} = b \quad \text{and} \quad \frac{V_2}{T_2} = b$$

> Charles's law in the form $V_1/T_1 = V_2/T_2$ applies only when both the amount of gas (moles) and the pressure are constant.

Thus

$$\frac{V_1}{T_1} = \frac{V_2}{T_2}$$

We will illustrate the use of this equation in Examples 13.4 and 13.5.

EXAMPLE 13.4 | Calculating Volume Using Charles's Law, I

A 2.0-L sample of air is collected at 298 K and then cooled to 278 K. The pressure is held constant at 1.0 atm.

   a. Does the volume increase or decrease?

   b. Calculate the volume of the air at 278 K.

SOLUTION

Where Are We Going?

We want to determine if the volume will increase or decrease when the temperature is changed, and we want to calculate the new volume.

What Do We Know?

- We know the initial and final temperatures and the initial volume.
- The amount of gas and pressure are held constant.
- Charles's law: $\dfrac{V_1}{T_1} = \dfrac{V_2}{T_2}$.

How Do We Get There?

   a. Because the gas is cooled, the volume of the gas must decrease:

$$\frac{V}{T} = \text{constant}$$

           T is decreased, so V must decrease to maintain a constant ratio.

   b. To calculate the new volume, V_2, we will use Charles's law in the form

$$\frac{V_1}{T_1} = \frac{V_2}{T_2}$$

> $\dfrac{V_1}{T_1}$ ➡ $\dfrac{V_2}{T_2}$
>
> Temperature smaller, volume smaller

We are given the following information:

Initial Conditions	Final Conditions
$T_1 = 298$ K	$T_2 = 278$ K
$V_1 = 2.0$ L	$V_2 = ?$

We want to solve the equation

$$\frac{V_1}{T_1} = \frac{V_2}{T_2}$$

for V_2. We can do this by multiplying both sides by T_2 and canceling.

$$T_2 \times \frac{V_1}{T_1} = \frac{V_2}{\cancel{T_2}} \times \cancel{T_2} = V_2$$

Thus

$$V_2 = T_2 \times \frac{V_1}{T_1} = 278 \text{ K} \times \frac{2.0 \text{ L}}{298 \text{ K}} = 1.9 \text{ L}$$

REALITY CHECK   Because the temperature decreases, we expect the volume to decrease. The temperature decreased slightly, so we would expect the volume to decrease slightly. ■

EXAMPLE 13.5   Calculating Volume Using Charles's Law, II

A sample of gas at 15 °C (at 1 atm) has a volume of 2.58 L. The temperature is then raised to 38 °C (at 1 atm).

a. Does the volume of the gas increase or decrease?

b. Calculate the new volume.

SOLUTION

Where Are We Going?

We want to determine if the volume will increase or decrease when the temperature is changed, and we want to calculate the new volume.

What Do We Know?

- We know the initial and final temperatures and the initial volume.

- The amount of gas and pressure are held constant.

- Charles's law: $\dfrac{V_1}{T_1} = \dfrac{V_2}{T_2}$.

How Do We Get There?

a. In this case we have a given sample (constant amount) of gas that is heated from 15 °C to 38 °C *while the pressure is held constant.* We know from Charles's law that the volume of a given sample of gas is directly proportional to the temperature (at constant pressure). So the increase in temperature will *increase* the volume; the new volume will be greater than 2.58 L.

b. To calculate the new volume, we use Charles's law in the form

$$\frac{V_1}{T_1} = \frac{V_2}{T_2}$$

We are given the following information:

Initial Conditions	Final Conditions
$T_1 = 15 \text{ °C}$	$T_2 = 38 \text{ °C}$
$V_1 = 2.58 \text{ L}$	$V_2 = ?$

As is often the case, the temperatures are given in Celsius degrees. However, for us to use Charles's law, the temperature *must be in kelvins.* Thus we must convert by adding 273 to each temperature.

Researchers take samples from a steaming volcanic vent at Mount Baker in Washington.

Initial Conditions

$T_1 = 15\ °C = 15 + 273$
$\qquad = 288\ K$
$V_1 = 2.58\ L$

Final Conditions

$T_2 = 38\ °C = 38 + 273$
$\qquad = 311\ K$
$V_2 = ?$

Solving for V_2 gives

$$V_2 = V_1 \times \frac{T_2}{T_1} = 2.58\ L \left(\frac{311\ \cancel{K}}{288\ \cancel{K}} \right) = 2.79\ L$$

REALITY CHECK   Because the temperature increases, we expect the volume to increase.

Self-Check EXERCISE 13.3   A child blows a bubble that contains air at 28 °C and has a volume of 23 cm³ at 1 atm. As the bubble rises, it encounters a pocket of cold air (temperature 18 °C). If there is no change in pressure, will the bubble get larger or smaller as the air inside cools to 18 °C? Calculate the new volume of the bubble.

See Problems 13.29 and 13.30. ■

Notice from Example 13.5 that we adjust the volume of a gas for a temperature change by multiplying the original volume by the ratio of the Kelvin temperatures—final (T_2) over initial (T_1). Remember to check whether your answer makes sense. When the temperature increases (at constant pressure), the volume must increase, and vice versa.

EXAMPLE 13.6   Calculating Temperature Using Charles's Law

In former times, gas volume was used as a way to measure temperature using devices called gas thermometers. Consider a gas that has a volume of 0.675 L at 35 °C and 1 atm pressure. What is the temperature (in units of °C) of a room where this gas has a volume of 0.535 L at 1 atm pressure?

SOLUTION

Where Are We Going?

We want to determine the new temperature of a gas given that the volume has decreased at constant pressure.

What Do We Know?

- We know the initial and final volumes and the initial temperature.
- The amount of gas and pressure are held constant.
- Charles's law: $\dfrac{V_1}{T_1} = \dfrac{V_2}{T_2}$.

How Do We Get There?

The information given in the problem is

Initial Conditions	**Final Conditions**
$T_1 = 35\,°C = 35 + 273 = 308\ K$	$T_2 = ?$
$V_1 = 0.675\ L$	$V_2 = 0.535\ L$
$P_1 = 1\ atm$	$P_2 = 1\ atm$

The pressure remains constant, so we can use Charles's law in the form

$$\frac{V_1}{T_1} = \frac{V_2}{T_2}$$

and solve for T_2. First we multiply both sides by T_2.

$$T_2 \times \frac{V_1}{T_1} = \frac{V_2}{\cancel{T_2}} \times \cancel{T_2} = V_2$$

Next we multiply both sides by T_1.

$$\cancel{T_1} \times T_2 \times \frac{V_1}{\cancel{T_1}} = T_1 \times V_2$$

This gives

$$T_2 \times V_1 = T_1 \times V_2$$

Now we divide both sides by V_1 (multiply by $1/V_1$),

$$\frac{1}{\cancel{V_1}} \times T_2 \times \cancel{V_1} = \frac{1}{V_1} \times T_1 \times V_2$$

and obtain

$$T_2 = T_1 \times \frac{V_2}{V_1}$$

We have now isolated T_2 on one side of the equation, and we can do the calculation.

$$T_2 = T_1 \times \frac{V_2}{V_1} = (308\ K) \times \frac{0.535\ \cancel{L}}{0.675\ \cancel{L}} = 244\ K$$

To convert from units of K to units of °C, we subtract 273 from the Kelvin temperature.

$$T_{°C} = T_K - 273 = 244 - 273 = -29\ °C$$

The room is very cold; the new temperature is $-29\ °C$.

REALITY CHECK Because the volume is smaller, we expect the temperature to be lower. ■

13.4 Volume and Moles: Avogadro's Law

OBJECTIVE: To understand the law relating the volume and the number of moles of a sample of gas at constant temperature and pressure, and to do calculations involving this law.

What is the relationship between the volume of a gas and the number of molecules present in the gas sample? Experiments show that when the number of moles of gas is doubled (at constant temperature and pressure), the volume doubles. In other words, the volume of a gas is directly proportional to the number of moles if temperature and pressure remain constant. Figure 13.9 illustrates this relationship, which can also be represented by the equation

$$V = an \qquad \text{or} \qquad \frac{V}{n} = a$$

where V is the volume of the gas, n is the number of moles, and a is the proportionality constant. Note that this equation means that the ratio of V to n is constant as long as the temperature and pressure remain constant. Thus, when the number of moles of gas is increased by a factor of 5, the volume also increases by a factor of 5,

$$\frac{V}{n} = \frac{\cancel{5} \times V}{\cancel{5} \times n} = a = \text{constant}$$

and so on. In words, this equation means that *for a gas at constant temperature and pressure, the volume is directly proportional to the number of moles of gas.* This relationship is called **Avogadro's law** after the Italian scientist Amadeo Avogadro, who first postulated it in 1811.

For cases where the number of moles of gas is changed from an initial amount to another amount (at constant T and P), we can represent Avogadro's law as

$$\underset{\substack{\text{Initial} \\ \text{amount}}}{\frac{V_1}{n_1}} = a = \underset{\substack{\text{Final} \\ \text{amount}}}{\frac{V_2}{n_2}}$$

or

$$\frac{V_1}{n_1} = \frac{V_2}{n_2}$$

We will illustrate the use of this equation in Example 13.7.

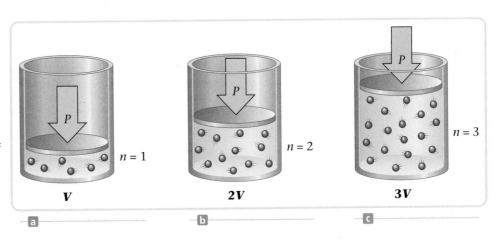

Figure 13.9

The relationship between volume V and number of moles n. As the number of moles is increased from 1 to 2 (ⓐ) to (ⓑ), the volume doubles. When the number of moles is tripled (ⓒ), the volume is also tripled. The temperature and pressure remain the same in these cases.

EXAMPLE 13.7 | Using Avogadro's Law in Calculations

Suppose we have a 12.2-L sample containing 0.50 mol oxygen gas, O_2, at a pressure of 1 atm and a temperature of 25 °C. If all of this O_2 is converted to ozone, O_3, at the same temperature and pressure, what will be the volume of the ozone formed?

SOLUTION

Where Are We Going?

We want to determine the volume of ozone (O_3) formed from 0.50 mol O_2 given the volume of oxygen.

What Do We Know?

- We know the initial number of moles of oxygen and the volume of oxygen.
- The temperature and pressure are held constant.
- Avogadro's law: $\dfrac{V_1}{T_1} = \dfrac{V_2}{T_2}$.

What Information Do We Need?

- We need the balanced equation for the reaction to determine the number of moles of ozone formed.

How Do We Get There?

To do this problem we need to compare the moles of gas originally present to the moles of gas present after the reaction. We know that 0.50 mol O_2 is present initially. To find out how many moles of O_3 will be present after the reaction, we need to use the balanced equation for the reaction.

$$3O_2(g) \rightarrow 2O_3(g)$$

We calculate the moles of O_3 produced by using the appropriate mole ratio from the balanced equation.

$$0.50 \text{ mol } O_2 \times \frac{2 \text{ mol } O_3}{3 \text{ mol } O_2} = 0.33 \text{ mol } O_3$$

Avogadro's law states that

$$\frac{V_1}{n_1} = \frac{V_2}{n_2}$$

MATH SKILL BUILDER

$$\frac{V_1}{n_1} = \frac{V_2}{n_2}$$

$$n_2 \times \frac{V_1}{n_1} = \frac{V_2}{n_2} \times n_2$$

$$V_1 \times \frac{n_2}{n_1} = V_2$$

where V_1 is the volume of n_1 moles of O_2 gas and V_2 is the volume of n_2 moles of O_3 gas. In this case we have

Initial Conditions	Final Conditions
$n_1 = 0.50$ mol	$n_2 = 0.33$ mol
$V_1 = 12.2$ L	$V_2 = ?$

Solving Avogadro's law for V_2 gives

$$V_2 = V_1 \times \frac{n_2}{n_1} = 12.2 \text{ L} \left(\frac{0.33 \text{ mol}}{0.50 \text{ mol}}\right) = 8.1 \text{ L}$$

REALITY CHECK Note that the volume decreases, as it should, because fewer molecules are present in the gas after O_2 is converted to O_3.

Self-Check EXERCISE 13.4 Consider two samples of nitrogen gas (composed of N_2 molecules). Sample 1 contains 1.5 mol N_2 and has a volume of 36.7 L at 25 °C and 1 atm. Sample 2 has a volume of 16.5 L at 25 °C and 1 atm. Calculate the number of moles of N_2 in Sample 2.

See Problems 13.41 through 13.44. ■

13.5 The Ideal Gas Law

OBJECTIVE: To understand the ideal gas law and use it in calculations.

We have considered three laws that describe the behavior of gases as it is revealed by experimental observations.

> Constant n means a constant number of moles of gas.

$$\textit{Boyle's law:}\quad PV = k \quad \text{or} \quad V = \frac{k}{P}\ (\text{at constant } T \text{ and } n)$$

$$\textit{Charles's law:}\qquad\qquad V = bT\ (\text{at constant } P \text{ and } n)$$

$$\textit{Avogadro's law:}\qquad\qquad V = an\ (\text{at constant } T \text{ and } P)$$

These relationships, which show how the volume of a gas depends on pressure, temperature, and number of moles of gas present, can be combined as follows:

$$V = R\left(\frac{Tn}{P}\right)$$

where R is the combined proportionality constant and is called the **universal gas constant.** When the pressure is expressed in atmospheres and the volume is in liters, R always has the value 0.08206 L atm/K mol. We can rearrange the above equation by multiplying both sides by P,

> $R = 0.08206\ \dfrac{\text{L atm}}{\text{K mol}}$

$$P \times V = \cancel{P} \times R\left(\frac{Tn}{\cancel{P}}\right)$$

to obtain the **ideal gas law** written in its usual form,

$$PV = nRT$$

The ideal gas law involves all the important characteristics of a gas: its pressure (P), volume (V), number of moles (n), and temperature (T). Knowledge of any three of these properties is enough to define completely the condition of the gas, because the fourth property can be determined from the ideal gas law.

It is important to recognize that the ideal gas law is based on experimental measurements of the properties of gases. A gas that obeys this equation is said to behave *ideally.* That is, this equation defines the behavior of an **ideal gas.** Most gases obey this equation closely at pressures of approximately 1 atm or lower, when the temperature is approximately 0 °C or higher. You should assume ideal gas behavior when working problems involving gases in this text.

The ideal gas law can be used to solve a variety of problems. Example 13.8 demonstrates one type, where you are asked to find one property characterizing the condition of a gas given the other three properties.

EXAMPLE 13.8 | **Using the Ideal Gas Law in Calculations**

A sample of hydrogen gas, H_2, has a volume of 8.56 L at a temperature of 0 °C and a pressure of 1.5 atm. Calculate the number of moles of H_2 present in this gas sample. (Assume that the gas behaves ideally.)

SOLUTION

Where Are We Going?

We want to determine the number of moles of hydrogen gas (H_2) present given conditions of temperature, pressure, and volume.

What Do We Know?

- We know the temperature, pressure, and volume of hydrogen gas.
- Ideal gas law: $PV = nRT$.

What Information Do We Need?

- $R = 0.08206$ L atm/mol K.

How Do We Get There?

In this problem we are given the pressure, volume, and temperature of the gas: $P = 1.5$ atm, $V = 8.56$ L, and $T = 0$ °C. Remember that the temperature must be changed to the Kelvin scale.

$$T = 0\,°C = 0 + 273 = 273\ K$$

We can calculate the number of moles of gas present by using the ideal gas law, $PV = nRT$. We solve for n by dividing both sides by RT:

$$\frac{PV}{RT} = n\frac{\cancel{RT}}{\cancel{RT}}$$

to give

$$\frac{PV}{RT} = n$$

Thus

$$n = \frac{PV}{RT} = \frac{(1.5\ \cancel{atm})(8.56\ \cancel{L})}{\left(0.08206\ \dfrac{\cancel{L}\ \cancel{atm}}{\cancel{K}\ mol}\right)(273\ \cancel{K})} = 0.57\ mol$$

Self-Check **EXERCISE 13.5**   A weather balloon contains 1.10×10^5 mol He and has a volume of 2.70×10^6 L at 1.00 atm pressure. Calculate the temperature of the helium in the balloon in kelvins and in Celsius degrees.

See Problems 13.53 through 13.60. ∎

EXAMPLE 13.9 | **Ideal Gas Law Calculations Involving Conversion of Units**

What volume is occupied by 0.250 mol carbon dioxide gas at 25 °C and 371 torr?

SOLUTION

Where Are We Going?

We want to determine the volume of carbon dioxide gas (CO_2) given the number of moles, pressure, and temperature.

What Do We Know?

- We know the number of moles, pressure, and temperature of the carbon dioxide.
- Ideal gas law: $PV = nRT$.

What Information Do We Need?

- $R = 0.08206$ L atm/mol K.

How Do We Get There?

We can use the ideal gas law to calculate the volume, but we must first convert pressure to atmospheres and temperature to the Kelvin scale.

$$P = 371 \text{ torr} = 371 \text{ torr} \times \frac{1.000 \text{ atm}}{760.0 \text{ torr}} = 0.488 \text{ atm}$$

$$T = 25\,°C = 25 + 273 = 298 \text{ K}$$

We solve for V by dividing both sides of the ideal gas law ($PV = nRT$) by P.

MATH SKILL BUILDER

$$PV = nRT$$

$$\frac{PV}{P} = \frac{nRT}{P}$$

$$V = \frac{nRT}{P}$$

$$V = \frac{nRT}{P} = \frac{(0.250 \text{ mol})\left(0.08206\,\dfrac{\text{L atm}}{\text{K mol}}\right)(298 \text{ K})}{0.488 \text{ atm}} = 12.5 \text{ L}$$

The volume of the sample of CO_2 is 12.5 L.

Self-Check EXERCISE 13.6 Radon, a radioactive gas formed naturally in the soil, can cause lung cancer. It can pose a hazard to humans by seeping into houses, and there is concern about this problem in many areas. A 1.5-mol sample of radon gas has a volume of 21.0 L at 33 °C. What is the pressure of the gas?

See Problems 13.53 through 13.60. ■

Note that R has units of L atm/K mol. Accordingly, whenever we use the ideal gas law, we must express the volume in units of liters, the temperature in kelvins, and the pressure in atmospheres. When we are given data in other units, we must first convert to the appropriate units.

The ideal gas law can also be used to calculate the changes that will occur when the conditions of the gas are changed as illustrated in Example 13.10.

EXAMPLE 13.10 | **Using the Ideal Gas Law Under Changing Conditions**

Suppose we have a 0.240-mol sample of ammonia gas at 25 °C with a volume of 3.5 L at a pressure of 1.68 atm. The gas is compressed to a volume of 1.35 L at 25 °C. Use the ideal gas law to calculate the final pressure.

SOLUTION

Where Are We Going?

We want to use the ideal gas law equation to determine the pressure of ammonia gas given a change in volume.

What Do We Know?

- We know the initial number of moles, pressure, volume, and temperature of the ammonia.

- We know the new volume.

- Ideal gas law: $PV = nRT$.

How Do We Get There?

In this case we have a sample of ammonia gas in which the conditions are changed. We are given the following information:

Initial Conditions	**Final Conditions**
$V_1 = 3.5$ L	$V_2 = 1.35$ L
$P_1 = 1.68$ atm	$P_2 = ?$
$T_1 = 25\ °C = 25 + 273 = 298$ K	$T_2 = 25\ °C = 25 + 273 = 298$ K
$n_1 = 0.240$ mol	$n_2 = 0.240$ mol

Note that both n and T remain constant—only P and V change. Thus we could simply use Boyle's law ($P_1V_1 = P_2V_2$) to solve for P_2. However, we will use the ideal gas law to solve this problem in order to introduce the idea that one equation—the ideal gas equation—can be used to do almost any gas problem. The key idea here is that in using the ideal gas law to describe a change in conditions for a gas, we always *solve the ideal gas equation in such a way that the variables that change are on one side of the equals sign and the constant terms are on the other side.* That is, we start with the ideal gas equation in the conventional form ($PV = nRT$) and rearrange it so that all the terms that change are moved to one side and all the terms that do not change are moved to the other side. In this case the pressure and volume change, and the temperature and number of moles remain constant (as does R, by definition). So we write the ideal gas law as

$$PV = nRT$$

Change   Remain constant

Because n, R, and T remain the same in this case, we can write $P_1V_1 = nRT$ and $P_2V_2 = nRT$. Combining these gives

$$P_1V_1 = nRT = P_2V_2 \quad \text{or} \quad P_1V_1 = P_2V_2$$

and

$$P_2 = P_1 \times \frac{V_1}{V_2} = (1.68\ \text{atm})\left(\frac{3.5\ \cancel{L}}{1.35\ \cancel{L}}\right) = 4.4\ \text{atm}$$

REALITY CHECK Does this answer make sense? The volume was decreased (at constant temperature and constant number of moles), which means that the pressure should increase, as the calculation indicates.

Self-Check EXERCISE 13.7 A sample of methane gas that has a volume of 3.8 L at 5 °C is heated to 86 °C at constant pressure. Calculate its new volume.

See Problems 13.61 and 13.62. ■

Note that in solving Example 13.10, we actually obtained Boyle's law ($P_1V_1 = P_2V_2$) from the ideal gas equation. You might well ask, "Why go to all this trouble?" The idea is to learn to use the ideal gas equation to solve all types of gas law problems. This way you will never have to ask yourself, "Is this a Boyle's law problem or a Charles's law problem?"

We continue to practice using the ideal gas law in Example 13.11. Remember, the key idea is to rearrange the equation so that the quantities that change are moved to one side of the equation and those that remain constant are moved to the other.

EXAMPLE 13.11 Calculating Volume Changes Using the Ideal Gas Law

A sample of diborane gas, B_2H_6, a substance that bursts into flames when exposed to air, has a pressure of 0.454 atm at a temperature of −15 °C and a volume of 3.48 L. If conditions are changed so that the temperature is 36 °C and the pressure is 0.616 atm, what will be the new volume of the sample?

SOLUTION

Where Are We Going?

We want to use the ideal gas law equation to determine the volume of diborane gas.

What Do We Know?

- We know the initial pressure, volume, and temperature of the diborane gas.
- We know the new temperature and pressure.
- Ideal gas law: $PV = nRT$.

How Do We Get There?

We are given the following information:

Initial Conditions	**Final Conditions**
$P_1 = 0.454$ atm	$P_2 = 0.616$ atm
$V_1 = 3.48$ L	$V_2 = ?$
$T_1 = -15\ °C = 273 - 15 = 258$ K	$T_2 = 36\ °C = 273 + 36 = 309$ K

MATH SKILL BUILDER

$$PV = nRT$$
$$\frac{PV}{T} = \frac{nR\cancel{T}}{\cancel{T}}$$
$$\frac{PV}{T} = nR$$

Note that the value of n is not given. However, we know that n is constant (that is, $n_1 = n_2$) because no diborane gas is added or taken away. Thus, in this experiment, n is constant and P, V, and T change. Therefore, we rearrange the ideal gas equation ($PV = nRT$) by dividing both sides by T,

$$\underset{\text{Change}}{\frac{PV}{T}} = \underset{\text{Constant}}{nR}$$

which leads to the equation

$$\frac{P_1V_1}{T_1} = nR = \frac{P_2V_2}{T_2}$$

or

$$\frac{P_1V_1}{T_1} = \frac{P_2V_2}{T_2}$$

We can now solve for V_2 by dividing both sides by P_2 and multiplying both sides by T_2.

$$\frac{1}{P_2} \times \frac{P_1V_1}{T_1} = \frac{\cancel{P_2}V_2}{T_2} \times \frac{1}{\cancel{P_2}} = \frac{V_2}{T_2}$$

$$T_2 \times \frac{P_1V_1}{P_2T_1} = \frac{V_2}{\cancel{T_2}} \times \cancel{T_2} = V_2$$

That is,

$$\frac{T_2P_1V_1}{P_2T_1} = V_2$$

Snacks Need Chemistry, Too!

Have you ever wondered what makes popcorn pop? The popping is linked with the properties of gases. What happens when a gas is heated? Charles's law tells us that if the pressure is held constant, the volume of the gas must increase as the temperature is increased. But what happens if the gas being heated is trapped at a constant volume? We can see what happens by rearranging the ideal gas law ($PV = nRT$) as follows:

$$P = \left(\frac{nR}{V}\right)T$$

When n, R, and V are held constant, the pressure of a gas is directly proportional to the temperature. Thus, as the temperature of the trapped gas increases, its pressure also increases. This is exactly what happens inside a kernel of popcorn as it is heated. The moisture inside the kernel vaporized by the heat produces increasing pressure. The pressure finally becomes so great that the kernel breaks open, allowing the starch inside to expand to about 40 times its original size.

What's special about popcorn? Why does it pop while "regular" corn doesn't? William da Silva, a biologist at the University of Campinas in Brazil, has traced the "popability" of popcorn to its outer casing, called the pericarp. The molecules in the pericarp of popcorn, which are packed in a much more orderly way than in regular corn, transfer heat unusually quickly, producing a very fast pressure jump that pops the kernel. In addition, because the pericarp of popcorn is much thicker and stronger than that of regular corn, it can withstand more pressure, leading to a more explosive pop when the moment finally comes.

Popcorn popping.

© Cengage Learning

It is sometimes convenient to think in terms of the ratios of the initial temperature and pressure and the final temperature and pressure. That is,

$$V_2 = \frac{T_2 P_1 V_1}{T_1 P_2} = V_1 \times \frac{T_2}{T_1} \times \frac{P_1}{P_2}$$

Substituting the information given yields

$$V_2 = \frac{309 \ \cancel{K}}{258 \ \cancel{K}} \times \frac{0.454 \ \cancel{atm}}{0.616 \ \cancel{atm}} \times 3.48 \ L = 3.07 \ L$$

> *Always* convert the temperature to the Kelvin scale and the pressure to atmospheres when applying the ideal gas law.

Self-Check EXERCISE 13.8 A sample of argon gas with a volume of 11.0 L at a temperature of 13 °C and a pressure of 0.747 atm is heated to 56 °C and a pressure of 1.18 atm. Calculate the final volume.

See Problems 13.61 and 13.62. ∎

The equation obtained in Example 13.11,

$$\frac{P_1 V_1}{T_1} = \frac{P_2 V_2}{T_2}$$

is often called the **combined gas law** equation. It holds when the amount of gas (moles) is held constant. While it may be convenient to remember this equation, it is not necessary because you can always use the ideal gas equation.

13.6 Dalton's Law of Partial Pressures

OBJECTIVE: To understand the relationship between the partial and total pressures of a gas mixture, and to use this relationship in calculations.

Many important gases contain a mixture of components. One notable example is air. Scuba divers who are going deeper than 150 feet use another important mixture, helium and oxygen. Normal air is not used because the nitrogen present dissolves in the blood in large quantities as a result of the high pressures experienced by the diver under several hundred feet of water. When the diver returns too quickly to the surface, the nitrogen bubbles out of the blood just as soda fizzes when it's opened, and the diver gets "the bends"—a very painful and potentially fatal condition. Because helium gas is only sparingly soluble in blood, it does not cause this problem.

Studies of gaseous mixtures show that each component behaves independently of the others. In other words, a given amount of oxygen exerts the same pressure in a 1.0-L vessel whether it is alone or in the presence of nitrogen (as in the air) or helium.

Among the first scientists to study mixtures of gases was John Dalton. In 1803, Dalton summarized his observations in this statement: *For a mixture of gases in a container, the total pressure exerted is the sum of the partial pressures of the gases present. The **partial pressure** of a gas is the pressure that the gas would exert if it were alone in the container.* This statement, known as **Dalton's law of partial pressures,** can be expressed as follows for a mixture containing three gases:

$$P_{total} = P_1 + P_2 + P_3$$

where the subscripts refer to the individual gases (gas 1, gas 2, and gas 3). The pressures P_1, P_2, and P_3 are the partial pressures; that is, each gas is responsible for only part of the total pressure (Figure 13.10).

Assuming that each gas behaves ideally, we can calculate the partial pressure of each gas from the ideal gas law:

$$P_1 = \frac{n_1RT}{V}, \; P_2 = \frac{n_2RT}{V}, \; P_3 = \frac{n_3RT}{V}$$

MATH SKILL BUILDER

$$PV = nRT$$
$$\frac{P\cancel{V}}{\cancel{V}} = \frac{nRT}{V}$$
$$P = \frac{nRT}{V}$$

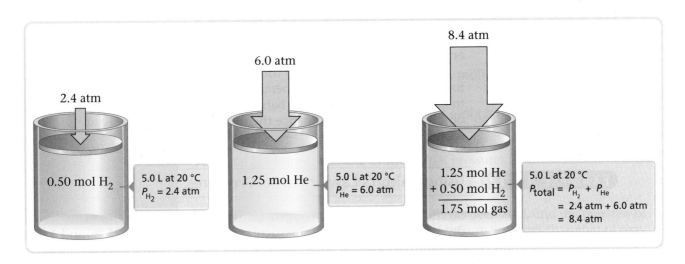

Figure 13.10

When two gases are present, the total pressure is the sum of the partial pressures of the gases.

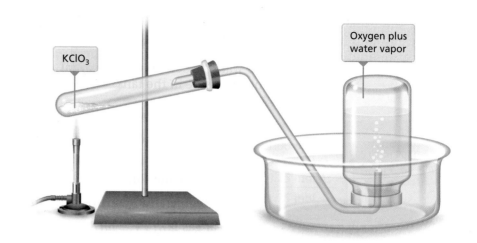

Figure 13.12

The production of oxygen by thermal decomposition of $KClO_3$.

Self-Check EXERCISE 13.9

A 2.0-L flask contains a mixture of nitrogen gas and oxygen gas at 25 °C. The total pressure of the gaseous mixture is 0.91 atm, and the mixture is known to contain 0.050 mol N_2. Calculate the partial pressure of oxygen and the moles of oxygen present.

See Problems 13.67 through 13.70. ■

Table 13.2 The Vapor Pressure of Water as a Function of Temperature	
T (°C)	P (torr)
0.0	4.579
10.0	9.209
20.0	17.535
25.0	23.756
30.0	31.824
40.0	55.324
60.0	149.4
70.0	233.7
90.0	525.8

A mixture of gases occurs whenever a gas is collected by displacement of water. For example, Figure 13.12 shows the collection of the oxygen gas that is produced by the decomposition of solid potassium chlorate. The gas is collected by bubbling it into a bottle that is initially filled with water. Thus the gas in the bottle is really a mixture of water vapor and oxygen. (Water vapor is present because molecules of water escape from the surface of the liquid and collect as a gas in the space above the liquid.) Therefore, the total pressure exerted by this mixture is the sum of the partial pressure of the gas being collected and the partial pressure of the water vapor. The partial pressure of the water vapor is called the vapor pressure of water. Because water molecules are more likely to escape from hot water than from cold water, the *vapor pressure* of water increases with temperature. This is shown by the values of vapor pressure at various temperatures in Table 13.2.

EXAMPLE 13.13 | Using Dalton's Law of Partial Pressures, II

A sample of solid potassium chlorate, $KClO_3$, was heated in a test tube (see Figure 13.12) and decomposed according to the reaction

$$2KClO_3(s) \rightarrow 2KCl(s) + 3O_2(g)$$

The oxygen produced was collected by displacement of water at 22 °C. The resulting mixture of O_2 and H_2O vapor had a total pressure of 754 torr and a volume of 0.650 L. Calculate the partial pressure of O_2 in the gas collected and the number of moles of O_2 present. The vapor pressure of water at 22 °C is 21 torr.

SOLUTION

Where Are We Going?

We want to determine the partial pressure of oxygen collected by water displacement and the number of moles of O_2 present.

What Do We Know?

- We know the temperature, total pressure, and volume of gas collected by water displacement.

13.6 Dalton's Law of Partial Pressures

OBJECTIVE: To understand the relationship between the partial and total pressures of a gas mixture, and to use this relationship in calculations.

Many important gases contain a mixture of components. One notable example is air. Scuba divers who are going deeper than 150 feet use another important mixture, helium and oxygen. Normal air is not used because the nitrogen present dissolves in the blood in large quantities as a result of the high pressures experienced by the diver under several hundred feet of water. When the diver returns too quickly to the surface, the nitrogen bubbles out of the blood just as soda fizzes when it's opened, and the diver gets "the bends"—a very painful and potentially fatal condition. Because helium gas is only sparingly soluble in blood, it does not cause this problem.

Studies of gaseous mixtures show that each component behaves independently of the others. In other words, a given amount of oxygen exerts the same pressure in a 1.0-L vessel whether it is alone or in the presence of nitrogen (as in the air) or helium.

Among the first scientists to study mixtures of gases was John Dalton. In 1803, Dalton summarized his observations in this statement: *For a mixture of gases in a container, the total pressure exerted is the sum of the partial pressures of the gases present. The* **partial pressure** *of a gas is the pressure that the gas would exert if it were alone in the container.* This statement, known as **Dalton's law of partial pressures,** can be expressed as follows for a mixture containing three gases:

$$P_{total} = P_1 + P_2 + P_3$$

where the subscripts refer to the individual gases (gas 1, gas 2, and gas 3). The pressures P_1, P_2, and P_3 are the partial pressures; that is, each gas is responsible for only part of the total pressure (Figure 13.10).

Assuming that each gas behaves ideally, we can calculate the partial pressure of each gas from the ideal gas law:

$$P_1 = \frac{n_1RT}{V}, P_2 = \frac{n_2RT}{V}, P_3 = \frac{n_3RT}{V}$$

MATH SKILL BUILDER

$$PV = nRT$$

$$\frac{P\cancel{V}}{\cancel{V}} = \frac{nRT}{V}$$

$$P = \frac{nRT}{V}$$

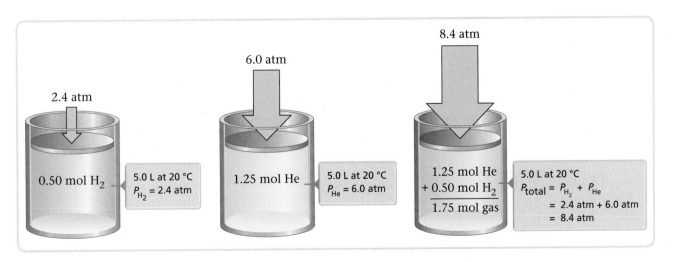

Figure 13.10

When two gases are present, the total pressure is the sum of the partial pressures of the gases.

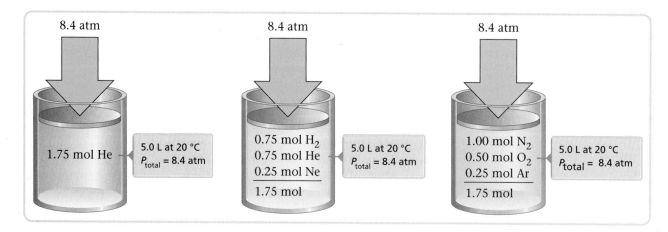

8.4 atm

1.75 mol He

5.0 L at 20 °C
P_{total} = 8.4 atm

8.4 atm

0.75 mol H_2
0.75 mol He
0.25 mol Ne
1.75 mol

5.0 L at 20 °C
P_{total} = 8.4 atm

8.4 atm

1.00 mol N_2
0.50 mol O_2
0.25 mol Ar
1.75 mol

5.0 L at 20 °C
P_{total} = 8.4 atm

Figure 13.11

The total pressure of a mixture of gases depends on the number of moles of gas particles (atoms or molecules) present, not on the identities of the particles. Note that these three samples show the same total pressure because each contains 1.75 mol gas. The detailed nature of the mixture is unimportant.

The total pressure of the mixture, P_{total}, can be represented as

$$P_{total} = P_1 + P_2 + P_3 = \frac{n_1 RT}{V} + \frac{n_2 RT}{V} + \frac{n_3 RT}{V}$$

$$= n_1\left(\frac{RT}{V}\right) + n_2\left(\frac{RT}{V}\right) + n_3\left(\frac{RT}{V}\right)$$

$$= (n_1 + n_2 + n_3)\left(\frac{RT}{V}\right)$$

$$= n_{total}\left(\frac{RT}{V}\right)$$

where n_{total} is the sum of the numbers of moles of the gases in the mixture. Thus, for a mixture of ideal gases, it is the *total number of moles of particles* that is important, not the *identity* of the individual gas particles. This idea is illustrated in Figure 13.11.

The fact that the pressure exerted by an ideal gas is affected by the *number* of gas particles and is independent of the *nature* of the gas particles tells us two important things about ideal gases:

1. The volume of the individual gas particle (atom or molecule) must not be very important.

2. The forces among the particles must not be very important.

If these factors were important, the pressure of the gas would depend on the nature of the individual particles. For example, an argon atom is much larger than a helium atom. Yet 1.75 mol argon gas in a 5.0-L container at 20 °C exerts the same pressure as 1.75 mol helium gas in a 5.0-L container at 20 °C.

The same idea applies to the forces among the particles. Although the forces among gas particles depend on the nature of the particles, this seems to have little influence on the behavior of an ideal gas. We will see that these observations strongly influence the model that we will construct to explain ideal gas behavior.

EXAMPLE 13.12 | Using Dalton's Law of Partial Pressures, I

Mixtures of helium and oxygen are used in the "air" tanks of underwater divers for deep dives. For a particular dive, 12 L of O_2 at 25 °C and 1.0 atm and 46 L of He at 25 °C and 1.0 atm were both pumped into a 5.0-L tank. Calculate the partial pressure of each gas and the total pressure in the tank at 25 °C.

SOLUTION

Where Are We Going?

We want to determine the partial pressure of helium and oxygen and the total pressure in the tank.

What Do We Know?

- We know the initial volume, pressure, and temperature of both gases.
- We know the final volume of the tank.
- The temperature remains constant.
- Ideal gas law: $PV = nRT$.
- Dalton's law of partial pressures: $P_{total} = P_1 + P_2 + \ldots$

What Information Do We Need?

- $R = 0.08206$ L atm/mol K.

How Do We Get There?

> **MATH SKILL BUILDER**
> $$PV = nRT$$
> $$\frac{PV}{RT} = \frac{nR\!\!\!/ T\!\!\!/}{R\!\!\!/ T\!\!\!/}$$
> $$\frac{PV}{RT} = n$$

Because the partial pressure of each gas depends on the moles of that gas present, we must first calculate the number of moles of each gas by using the ideal gas law in the form

$$n = \frac{PV}{RT}$$

From the above description we know that $P = 1.0$ atm, $V = 12$ L for O_2 and 46 L for He, and $T = 25 + 273 = 298$ K. Also, $R = 0.08206$ L atm/K mol (as always).

$$\text{Moles of } O_2 = n_{O_2} = \frac{(1.0\ \text{atm})(12\ \text{L})}{(0.08206\ \text{L atm/K mol})(298\ \text{K})} = 0.49\ \text{mol}$$

$$\text{Moles of He} = n_{He} = \frac{(1.0\ \text{atm})(46\ \text{L})}{(0.08206\ \text{L atm/K mol})(298\ \text{K})} = 1.9\ \text{mol}$$

The tank containing the mixture has a volume of 5.0 L, and the temperature is 25 °C (298 K). We can use these data and the ideal gas law to calculate the partial pressure of each gas.

$$P = \frac{nRT}{V}$$

$$P_{O_2} = \frac{(0.49\ \text{mol})(0.08206\ \text{L atm/K mol})(298\ \text{K})}{5.0\ \text{L}} = 2.4\ \text{atm}$$

$$P_{He} = \frac{(1.9\ \text{mol})(0.08206\ \text{L atm/K mol})(298\ \text{K})}{5.0\ \text{L}} = 9.3\ \text{atm}$$

The total pressure is the sum of the partial pressures.

$$P_{total} = P_{O_2} + P_{He} = 2.4\ \text{atm} + 9.3\ \text{atm} = 11.7\ \text{atm}$$

REALITY CHECK The volume of each gas decreased, and the pressure of each gas increased. The partial pressure of helium is greater than that of oxygen, which makes sense because the initial temperatures and pressures of helium and oxygen were the same, but the initial volume of helium was much greater than that of oxygen.

Divers use a mixture of oxygen and helium in their breathing tanks when diving to depths greater than 150 feet.

Kurt Amsler

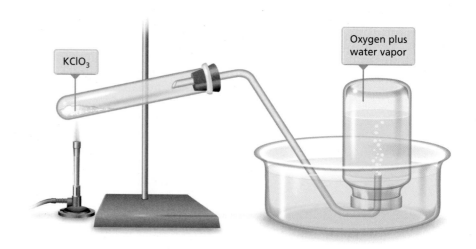

Figure 13.12

The production of oxygen by thermal decomposition of $KClO_3$.

EXERCISE 13.9   A 2.0-L flask contains a mixture of nitrogen gas and oxygen gas at 25 °C. The total pressure of the gaseous mixture is 0.91 atm, and the mixture is known to contain 0.050 mol N_2. Calculate the partial pressure of oxygen and the moles of oxygen present.

See Problems 13.67 through 13.70. ■

Table 13.2 The Vapor Pressure of Water as a Function of Temperature

T (°C)	P (torr)
0.0	4.579
10.0	9.209
20.0	17.535
25.0	23.756
30.0	31.824
40.0	55.324
60.0	149.4
70.0	233.7
90.0	525.8

A mixture of gases occurs whenever a gas is collected by displacement of water. For example, Figure 13.12 shows the collection of the oxygen gas that is produced by the decomposition of solid potassium chlorate. The gas is collected by bubbling it into a bottle that is initially filled with water. Thus the gas in the bottle is really a mixture of water vapor and oxygen. (Water vapor is present because molecules of water escape from the surface of the liquid and collect as a gas in the space above the liquid.) Therefore, the total pressure exerted by this mixture is the sum of the partial pressure of the gas being collected and the partial pressure of the water vapor. The partial pressure of the water vapor is called the vapor pressure of water. Because water molecules are more likely to escape from hot water than from cold water, the *vapor pressure* of water increases with temperature. This is shown by the values of vapor pressure at various temperatures in Table 13.2.

EXAMPLE 13.13 | Using Dalton's Law of Partial Pressures, II

A sample of solid potassium chlorate, $KClO_3$, was heated in a test tube (see Figure 13.12) and decomposed according to the reaction

$$2KClO_3(s) \rightarrow 2KCl(s) + 3O_2(g)$$

The oxygen produced was collected by displacement of water at 22 °C. The resulting mixture of O_2 and H_2O vapor had a total pressure of 754 torr and a volume of 0.650 L. Calculate the partial pressure of O_2 in the gas collected and the number of moles of O_2 present. The vapor pressure of water at 22 °C is 21 torr.

SOLUTION

Where Are We Going?

We want to determine the partial pressure of oxygen collected by water displacement and the number of moles of O_2 present.

What Do We Know?

- We know the temperature, total pressure, and volume of gas collected by water displacement.

- We know the vapor pressure of water at this temperature.
- Ideal gas law: $PV = nRT$.
- Dalton's law of partial pressures: $P_{total} = P_1 + P_2 + \ldots$

What Information Do We Need?

- $R = 0.08206$ L atm/mol K.

How Do We Get There?

We know the total pressure (754 torr) and the partial pressure of water (vapor pressure = 21 torr). We can find the partial pressure of O_2 from Dalton's law of partial pressures:

$$P_{total} = P_{O_2} + P_{H_2O} = P_{O_2} + 21 \text{ torr} = 754 \text{ torr}$$

or

$$P_{O_2} + 21 \text{ torr} = 754 \text{ torr}$$

We can solve for P_{O_2} by subtracting 21 torr from both sides of the equation.

$$P_{O_2} = 754 \text{ torr} - 21 \text{ torr} = 733 \text{ torr}$$

Next we solve the ideal gas law for the number of moles of O_2.

$$n_{O_2} = \frac{P_{O_2}V}{RT}$$

In this case, $P_{O_2} = 733$ torr. We change the pressure to atmospheres as follows:

$$\frac{733 \text{ torr}}{760 \text{ torr/atm}} = 0.964 \text{ atm}$$

MATH SKILL BUILDER

$$PV = nRT$$
$$\frac{PV}{RT} = \frac{n\cancel{R}\cancel{T}}{\cancel{R}\cancel{T}}$$
$$\frac{PV}{RT} = n$$

Then,

$$V = 0.650 \text{ L}$$
$$T = 22\,°C = 22 + 273 = 295 \text{ K}$$
$$R = 0.08206 \text{ L atm/K mol}$$

so

$$n_{O_2} = \frac{(0.964 \text{ atm})(0.650 \text{ L})}{(0.08206 \text{ L atm/K mol})(295 \text{ K})} = 2.59 \times 10^{-2} \text{ mol}$$

Self-Check EXERCISE 13.10 Consider a sample of hydrogen gas collected over water at 25 °C where the vapor pressure of water is 24 torr. The volume occupied by the gaseous mixture is 0.500 L, and the total pressure is 0.950 atm. Calculate the partial pressure of H_2 and the number of moles of H_2 present.

See Problems 13.71 through 13.74. ∎

13.7 Laws and Models: A Review

OBJECTIVE: To understand the relationship between laws and models (theories).

In this chapter we have considered several properties of gases and have seen how the relationships among these properties can be expressed by various laws written in the form of mathematical equations. The most useful of these is the ideal gas equation, which relates all the important gas properties. However, under certain conditions gases do not obey the ideal gas equation. For example, at high pressures and/or low temperatures, the properties of gases deviate significantly from the predictions of the ideal gas equation. On the other hand, as the pressure is lowered and/or the temperature is increased, almost all gases show close agreement with the ideal gas equation. This means that an ideal gas is really a hypothetical substance. At low pressures and/or high temperatures, real gases *approach* the behavior expected for an ideal gas.

At this point we want to build a model (a theory) to explain *why* a gas behaves as it does. We want to answer the question, *What are the characteristics of the individual gas particles that cause a gas to behave as it does?* However, before we do this let's briefly review the scientific method. Recall that a law is a generalization about behavior that has been observed in many experiments. Laws are very useful; they allow us to predict the behavior of similar systems. For example, a chemist who prepares a new gaseous compound can assume that that substance will obey the ideal gas equation (at least at low *P* and/or high *T*).

However, laws do not tell us *why* nature behaves the way it does. Scientists try to answer this question by constructing theories (building models). The models in chemistry are speculations about how individual atoms or molecules (microscopic particles) cause the behavior of macroscopic systems (collections of atoms and molecules in large enough numbers so that we can observe them).

A model is considered successful if it explains known behavior and predicts correctly the results of future experiments. But a model can never be proved absolutely true. In fact, by its very nature *any model is an approximation* and is destined to be modified, at least in part. Models range from the simple (to predict approximate behavior) to the extraordinarily complex (to account precisely for observed behavior). In this text, we use relatively simple models that fit most experimental results.

13.8 The Kinetic Molecular Theory of Gases

OBJECTIVE: To understand the basic postulates of the kinetic molecular theory.

go Chemistry Module 16: Gas Law and the Kinetic Molecular Theory covers concepts in this section.

A relatively simple model that attempts to explain the behavior of an ideal gas is the **kinetic molecular theory.** This model is based on speculations about the behavior of the individual particles (atoms or molecules) in a gas. The assumptions (postulates) of the kinetic molecular theory can be stated as follows:

Postulates of the Kinetic Molecular Theory of Gases

1. Gases consist of tiny particles (atoms or molecules).
2. These particles are so small, compared with the distances between them, that the volume (size) of the individual particles can be assumed to be negligible (zero).
3. The particles are in constant random motion, colliding with the walls of the container. These collisions with the walls cause the pressure exerted by the gas.
4. The particles are assumed not to attract or to repel each other.
5. The average kinetic energy of the gas particles is directly proportional to the Kelvin temperature of the gas.

The kinetic energy referred to in postulate 5 is the energy associated with the motion of a particle. Kinetic energy (*KE*) is given by the equation $KE = \frac{1}{2}mv^2$, where m is the mass of the particle and v is the velocity (speed) of the particle. The greater the mass or velocity of a particle, the greater its kinetic energy. Postulate 5 means that if a gas is heated to higher temperatures, the average speed of the particles increases; therefore, their kinetic energy increases.

Although real gases do not conform exactly to the five assumptions listed here, we will see in the next section that these postulates do indeed explain *ideal* gas behavior—behavior shown by real gases at high temperatures and/or low pressures.

13.9   The Implications of the Kinetic Molecular Theory

OBJECTIVES: To understand the term *temperature.* • To learn how the kinetic molecular theory explains the gas laws.

In this section we will discuss the *qualitative* relationships between the kinetic molecular (KM) theory and the properties of gases. That is, without going into the mathematical details, we will show how the kinetic molecular theory explains some of the observed properties of gases.

▶ The Meaning of Temperature

In Chapter 2 we introduced temperature very practically as something we measure with a thermometer. We know that as the temperature of an object increases, the object feels "hotter" to the touch. But what does temperature really mean? How does matter change when it gets "hotter"? In Chapter 10 we introduced the idea that temperature is an index of molecular motion. The kinetic molecular theory allows us to further develop this concept. As postulate 5 of the KM theory states, the temperature of a gas reflects how rapidly, on average, its individual gas particles are moving. At high temperatures the particles move very fast and hit the walls of the container frequently, whereas at low temperatures the particles' motions are more sluggish and they collide with the walls of the container much less often. Therefore, temperature really is a measure of the motions of the gas particles. In fact, the Kelvin temperature of a gas is directly proportional to the average kinetic energy of the gas particles.

▶ The Relationship Between Pressure and Temperature

To see how the meaning of temperature given above helps to explain gas behavior, picture a gas in a rigid container. As the gas is heated to a higher temperature, the particles move faster, hitting the walls more often. And, of course, the impacts become more forceful as the particles move faster. If the pressure is due to collisions with the walls, the gas pressure should increase as temperature is increased.

Is this what we observe when we measure the pressure of a gas as it is heated? Yes. A given sample of gas in a rigid container (if the volume is not changed) shows an increase in pressure as its temperature is increased.

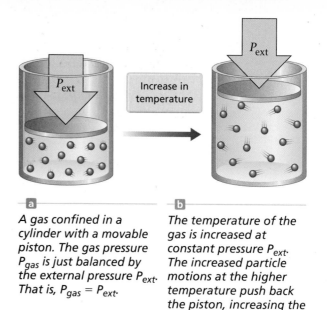

a A gas confined in a cylinder with a movable piston. The gas pressure P_{gas} is just balanced by the external pressure P_{ext}. That is, $P_{gas} = P_{ext}$.

b The temperature of the gas is increased at constant pressure P_{ext}. The increased particle motions at the higher temperature push back the piston, increasing the volume of the gas.

Figure 13.13

▶ The Relationship Between Volume and Temperature

Now picture the gas in a container with a movable piston. As shown in Figure 13.13a, the gas pressure P_{gas} is just balanced by an external pressure P_{ext}. What happens when we heat the gas to a higher temperature? As the temperature increases, the particles move faster, causing the gas pressure to increase. As soon as the gas pressure P_{gas} becomes greater than P_{ext} (the pressure holding the piston), the piston moves up until $P_{gas} = P_{ext}$. Therefore, the KM model predicts that the volume of the gas will increase as we raise its temperature at a constant pressure (Figure 13.13b). This agrees with experimental observations (as summarized by Charles's law).

EXAMPLE 13.14 | Using the Kinetic Molecular Theory to Explain Gas Law Observations

Use the KM theory to predict what will happen to the pressure of a gas when its volume is decreased (n and T constant). Does this prediction agree with the experimental observations?

SOLUTION

When we decrease the gas's volume (make the container smaller), the particles hit the walls more often because they do not have to travel so far between the walls. This would suggest an increase in pressure. This prediction on the basis of the model is in agreement with experimental observations of gas behavior (as summarized by Boyle's law). ■

In this section we have seen that the predictions of the kinetic molecular theory generally fit the behavior observed for gases. This makes it a useful and successful model.

13.10 Gas Stoichiometry

OBJECTIVES: To understand the molar volume of an ideal gas. • To learn the definition of STP. • To use these concepts and the ideal gas equation.

We have seen repeatedly in this chapter just how useful the ideal gas equation is. For example, if we know the pressure, volume, and temperature for a given sample of gas, we can calculate the number of moles present:

$n = PV/RT$. This fact makes it possible to do stoichiometric calculations for reactions involving gases. We will illustrate this process in Example 13.15.

EXAMPLE 13.15 | **Gas Stoichiometry: Calculating Volume**

Calculate the volume of oxygen gas produced at 1.00 atm and 25 °C by the complete decomposition of 10.5 g of potassium chlorate. The balanced equation for the reaction is

$$2KClO_3(s) \rightarrow 2KCl(s) + 3O_2(g)$$

SOLUTION

Where Are We Going?

We want to determine the volume of oxygen gas collected by the decomposition of $KClO_3$.

What Do We Know?

- We know the temperature and pressure of oxygen gas.
- We know the mass of $KClO_3$.
- The balanced equation: $2KClO_3(s) \rightarrow 2KCl(s) = 3O_2(g)$.
- Ideal gas law: $PV = nRT$.

What Information Do We Need?

- $R = 0.08206$ L atm/mol K.
- We need the number of moles of oxygen gas.
- Molar mass of $KClO_3$.

How Do We Get There?

This is a stoichiometry problem very much like the type we considered in Chapter 9. The only difference is that in this case, we want to calculate the volume of a gaseous product rather than the number of grams. To do so, we can use the relationship between moles and volume given by the ideal gas law.

We'll summarize the steps required to do this problem in the following schematic:

Grams of $KClO_3$ ⇨ **1** Moles of $KClO_3$ ⇨ **2** Moles of O_2 ⇨ **3** Volume of O_2

MATH SKILL BUILDER

$\frac{10.5}{122.6} = 0.085644$

$0.085644 \Rightarrow 0.0856$
 Round
  off
$0.0856 = 8.56 \times 10^{-2}$

Step 1   To find the moles of $KClO_3$ in 10.5 g, we use the molar mass of $KClO_3$ (122.6 g).

$$10.5 \text{ g } KClO_3 \times \frac{1 \text{ mol } KClO_3}{122.6 \text{ g } KClO_3} = 8.56 \times 10^{-2} \text{ mol } KClO_3$$

Step 2   To find the moles of O_2 produced, we use the mole ratio of O_2 to $KClO_3$ derived from the balanced equation.

$$8.56 \times 10^{-2} \text{ mol } KClO_3 \times \frac{3 \text{ mol } O_2}{2 \text{ mol } KClO_3} = 1.28 \times 10^{-1} \text{ mol } O_2$$

Step 3   To find the volume of oxygen produced, we use the ideal gas law $PV = nRT$, where

$$P = 1.00 \text{ atm}$$
$$V = ?$$
$$n = 1.28 \times 10^{-1} \text{ mol, the moles of } O_2 \text{ we calculated}$$
$$R = 0.08206 \text{ L atm/K mol}$$
$$T = 25 \text{ °C} = 25 + 273 = 298 \text{ K}$$

Solving the ideal gas law for V gives

$$V = \frac{nRT}{P} = \frac{(1.28 \times 10^{-1} \text{ mol})\left(0.08206 \, \frac{\text{L atm}}{\text{K mol}}\right)(298 \text{ K})}{1.00 \text{ atm}} = 3.13 \text{ L}$$

Thus 3.13 L of O_2 will be produced.

Self-Check **EXERCISE 13.11**   Calculate the volume of hydrogen produced at 1.50 atm and 19 °C by the re-action of 26.5 g of zinc with excess hydrochloric acid according to the bal-anced equation

$$Zn(s) + 2HCl(aq) \rightarrow ZnCl_2(aq) + H_2(g)$$

See Problems 13.85 through 13.92. ∎

In dealing with the stoichiometry of reactions involving gases, it is use-ful to define the volume occupied by 1 mole of a gas under certain specified conditions. For 1 mole of an ideal gas at 0 °C (273 K) and 1 atm, the volume of the gas given by the ideal gas law is

$$V = \frac{nRT}{P} = \frac{(1.00 \text{ mol})(0.08206 \text{ L atm/K mol})(273 \text{ K})}{1.00 \text{ atm}} = 22.4 \text{ L}$$

This volume of 22.4 L is called the **molar volume** of an ideal gas.

STP: 0 °C and 1 atm

The conditions 0 °C and 1 atm are called **standard temperature and pressure** (abbreviated **STP**). Properties of gases are often given under these conditions. Remember, the molar volume of an ideal gas is 22.4 L *at STP*. That is, 22.4 L contains 1 mole of an ideal gas at STP.

EXAMPLE 13.16 | Gas Stoichiometry: Calculations Involving Gases at STP

A sample of nitrogen gas has a volume of 1.75 L at STP. How many moles of N_2 are present?

SOLUTION

Where Are We Going?

We want to determine the number of moles of nitrogen gas.

What Do We Know?

- The nitrogen gas has a volume of 1.75 L at STP.

What Information Do We Need?

- STP = 1.00 atm, 0 °C.

- At STP, 1 mole of an ideal gas occupies a volume of 22.4 L.

How Do We Get There?

We could solve this problem by using the ideal gas equation, but we can take a shortcut by using the molar volume of an ideal gas at STP. Because 1 mole of an ideal gas at STP has a volume of 22.4 L, a 1.75-L sample of N_2 at STP contains considerably less than 1 mol. We can find how many moles by using the equivalence statement

$$1.000 \text{ mol} = 22.4 \text{ L (STP)}$$

which leads to the conversion factor we need:

$$1.75 \cancel{\text{L } N_2} \times \frac{1.000 \text{ mol } N_2}{22.4 \cancel{\text{L } N_2}} = 7.81 \times 10^{-2} \text{ mol } N_2$$

Self-Check **EXERCISE 13.12** Ammonia is commonly used as a fertilizer to provide a source of nitrogen for plants. A sample of $NH_3(g)$ occupies a volume of 5.00 L at 25 °C and 15.0 atm. What volume will this sample occupy at STP?

See Problems 13.95 through 13.98. ■

Standard conditions (STP) and molar volume are also useful in carrying out stoichiometric calculations on reactions involving gases, as shown in Example 13.17.

EXAMPLE 13.17 | **Gas Stoichiometry: Reactions Involving Gases at STP**

Quicklime, CaO, is produced by heating calcium carbonate, $CaCO_3$. Calculate the volume of CO_2 produced at STP from the decomposition of 152 g of $CaCO_3$ according to the reaction

$$CaCO_3(s) \rightarrow CaO(s) + CO_2(g)$$

SOLUTION

Where Are We Going?

We want to determine the volume of carbon dioxide produced from 152 g of $CaCO_3$.

What Do We Know?

- We know the temperature and pressure of carbon dioxide gas (STP).
- We know the mass of $CaCO_3$.
- The balanced equation: $CaCO_3(s) \rightarrow CaO(s) = CO_2(g)$.

What Information Do We Need?

- STP = 1.00 atm, 0 °C.
- At STP, 1 mole of an ideal gas occupies a volume of 22.4 L.
- We need the number of moles of carbon dioxide gas.
- Molar mass of $CaCO_3$.

How Do We Get There?

The strategy for solving this problem is summarized by the following schematic:

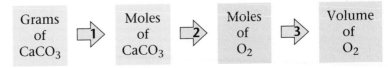

Step 1   Using the molar mass of $CaCO_3$ (100.1 g), we calculate the number of moles of $CaCO_3$.

$$152 \text{ g } CaCO_3 \times \frac{1 \text{ mol } CaCO_3}{100.1 \text{ g } CaCO_3} = 1.52 \text{ mol } CaCO_3$$

Step 2   Each mole of $CaCO_3$ produces 1 mole of CO_2, so 1.52 moles of CO_2 will be formed.

Step 3   We can convert the moles of CO_2 to volume by using the molar volume of an ideal gas, because the conditions are STP.

$$1.52 \text{ mol } CO_2 \times \frac{22.4 \text{ L } CO_2}{1 \text{ mol } CO_2} = 34.1 \text{ L } CO_2$$

Thus the decomposition of 152 g of $CaCO_3$ produces 34.1 L of CO_2 at STP. ∎

> Remember that the molar volume of an ideal gas is 22.4 L at STP.

Note that the final step in Example 13.17 involves calculating the volume of gas from the number of moles. Because the conditions were specified as STP, we were able to use the molar volume of a gas at STP. If the conditions of a problem are different from STP, we must use the ideal gas law to compute the volume, as we did in Section 13.5.

CHAPTER 13 REVIEW

Key Terms

barometer (13.1)
mm Hg (13.1)
torr (13.1)
standard atmosphere (13.1)
pascal (13.1)
Boyle's law (13.2)
absolute zero (13.3)
Charles's law (13.3)
Avogadro's law (13.4)
universal gas
  constant (13.5)

ideal gas law (13.5)
ideal gas (13.5)
combined gas law (13.5)
partial pressure (13.6)
Dalton's law of partial
  pressures (13.6)
kinetic molecular
  theory (13.8)
molar volume (13.10)
standard temperature and
  pressure (STP) (13.10)

F directs you to the *Chemistry in Focus* feature in the chapter

VP indicates visual problems

OWL interactive versions of these problems are assignable in OWL

Summary

1. Atmospheric pressure is measured with a barometer. The most commonly used units of pressure are mm Hg (torr), atmospheres, and pascals (the SI unit).

2. Boyle's law states that the volume of a given amount of gas is inversely proportional to its pressure (at constant temperature): $PV = k$ or $P = k/V$. That is, as pressure increases, volume decreases.

3. Charles's law states that, for a given amount of gas at constant pressure, the volume is directly proportional to the temperature (in kelvins): $V = bT$. At -273 °C (0 K), the volume of a gas extrapolates to zero, and this temperature is called absolute zero.

4. Avogadro's law states that for a gas at constant temperature and pressure, the volume is directly proportional to the number of moles of gas: $V = an$.

5. These three laws can be combined into the ideal gas law, $PV = nRT$, where R is called the universal gas constant. This equation makes it possible to calculate any one of the properties—volume, pressure, temperature, or moles of gas present—given the other three. A gas that obeys this equation is said to behave ideally.

6. From the ideal gas equation we can derive the combined gas law,

$$\frac{P_1 V_1}{T_1} = \frac{P_2 V_2}{T_2}$$

which holds when the amount of gas (moles) remains constant.

7. The pressure of a gas mixture is described by Dalton's law of partial pressures, which states that the total pressure of the mixture of gases in a container is the sum of the partial pressures of the gases that make up the mixture.

8. The kinetic molecular theory of gases is a model that accounts for ideal gas behavior. This model assumes that a gas consists of tiny particles with negligible volumes, that there are no interactions among particles, and that the particles are in constant motion, colliding with the container walls to produce pressure.

Active Learning Questions

These questions are designed to be considered by groups of students in class. Often these questions work well for introducing a particular topic in class.

1. As you increase the temperature of a gas in a sealed, rigid container, what happens to the density of the gas? Would the results be the same if you did the same experiment in a container with a movable piston at a constant external pressure? Explain.

VP 2. A diagram in a chemistry book shows a magnified view of a flask of air.

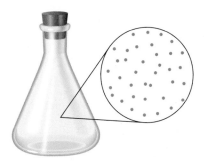

What do you suppose is between the dots (which represent air molecules)?

a. air	d. oxygen
b. dust	e. nothing
c. pollutants	

3. If you put a drinking straw in water, place your finger over the opening, and lift the straw out of the water, some water stays in the straw. Explain.

4. A chemistry student relates the following story: I noticed my tires were a bit low and went to the gas station. As I was filling the tires I thought about the kinetic molecular (KM) theory. I noticed the tires because the volume was low, and I realized that I was increasing both the pressure and volume of the tires. "Hmmm," I thought, "that goes against what I learned in chemistry, where I was told pressure and volume are inversely proportional." What is the fault of the logic of the chemistry student in this situation? Explain under what conditions pressure and volume are inversely related (draw pictures and use the KM theory).

5. Chemicals X and Y (both gases) react to form the gas XY, but it takes some time for the reaction to occur. Both X and Y are placed in a container with a piston (free to move), and you note the volume. As the reaction occurs, what happens to the volume of the container? Explain your answer.

6. Which statement best explains why a hot-air balloon rises when the air in the balloon is heated?

   a. According to Charles's law, the temperature of a gas is directly related to its volume. Thus the volume of the balloon increases, decreasing the density.
   b. Hot air rises inside the balloon, which lifts the balloon.
   c. The temperature of a gas is directly related to its pressure. The pressure therefore increases, which lifts the balloon.
   d. Some of the gas escapes from the bottom of the balloon, thus decreasing the mass of gas in the balloon. This decreases the density of the gas in the balloon, which lifts the balloon.
   e. Temperature is related to the velocity of the gas molecules. Thus the molecules are moving faster, hitting the balloon more, and lifting the balloon.

   For choices you did not pick, explain what you feel is wrong with them, and justify the choice you did pick.

7. If you release a helium balloon, it soars upward and eventually pops. Explain this behavior.

8. If you have any two gases in different containers that are the same size at the same pressure and same temperature, what is true about the moles of each gas? Why is this true?

9. Using postulates of the kinetic molecular theory, give a molecular interpretation of Boyle's law, Charles's law, and Dalton's law of partial pressures.

10. Rationalize the following observations.

    a. Aerosol cans will explode if heated.
    b. You can drink through a soda straw.
    c. A thin-walled can will collapse when the air inside is removed by a vacuum pump.
    d. Manufacturers produce different types of tennis balls for high and low altitudes.

11. Show how Boyle's law and Charles's law are special cases of the ideal gas law.

12. Look at the demonstration discussed in Figure 13.1. How would this demonstration change if water was not added to the can? Explain.

13. How does Dalton's law of partial pressures help us with our model of ideal gases? That is, which postulates of the kinetic molecular theory does it support?

14. Draw molecular-level views that show the differences among solids, liquids, and gases.

15. Explain how increasing the number of moles of gas affects the pressure (assuming constant volume and temperature).

16. Explain how increasing the number of moles of gas affects the volume (assuming constant pressure and temperature).

17. Gases are said to exert pressure. Provide a molecular-level explanation for this.

18. Why is it incorrect to say that a sample of helium at 50 °C is twice as hot as a sample of helium at 25 °C?

19. We can use different units for pressure or volume, but we must use units of Kelvin for temperature. Why must we use the Kelvin temperature scale?

20. Estimate the mass of air at normal conditions that takes up the volume of your head. Provide support for your answer.

21. You are holding two balloons of the same volume. One balloon contains 1.0 g of helium. The other balloon contains neon. Calculate the mass of neon in the balloon.

VP 22. You have helium gas in a two-bulbed container connected by a valve as shown below. Initially the valve is closed.

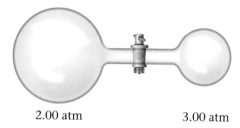

2.00 atm   3.00 atm

  a. When the valve is opened, will the total pressure in the apparatus be less than 5.00 atm, equal to 5.00 atm, or greater than 5.00 atm? Explain your answer.

  b. The left bulb has a volume of 9.00 L, and the right bulb has a volume of 3.00 L. Calculate the final pressure after the valve is opened.

VP 23. Use the graphs below to answer the following questions.

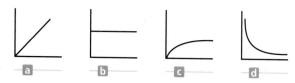

  a. Which of the above graphs best represents the relationship between the pressure and temperature (measured in kelvins) of 1 mole of an ideal gas?

  b. Which of the above graphs best represents the relationship between the pressure and volume of 1 mole of an ideal gas?

  c. Which of the above graphs best represents the relationship between the volume and temperature (measured in kelvins) of 1 mole of an ideal gas.

Questions and Problems

13.1 Pressure

QUESTIONS

1. The introduction to this chapter says that "we live immersed in a gaseous solution." What does that mean?

2. How are the three states of matter similar, and how do they differ?

3. Figure 13.1 shows an experiment that can be used effectively to demonstrate the pressure exerted by the atmosphere. Write an explanation of this experiment to a friend who has not yet taken any science courses to help him understand the concept of atmospheric pressure.

4. Describe a simple mercury barometer. How is such a barometer used to measure the pressure of the atmosphere?

5. If two gases that do not react with each other are placed in the same container, they will _____ completely with each other.

6. What are the common units used to measure pressure? Which unit is an experimental unit derived from the device used to measure atmospheric pressure?

PROBLEMS

7. Make the indicated pressure conversions.

  a. 45.2 kPa to atmospheres
  b. 755 mm Hg to atmospheres
  c. 802 torr to kilopascals
  d. 1.04 atm to millimeters of mercury

8. Make the indicated pressure conversions.

  a. 14.9 psi to atmospheres
  b. 795 torr to atmospheres
  c. 743 mm Hg to kilopascals
  d. 99,436 Pa to kilopascals

9. Make the indicated pressure conversions.

  a. 699 mm Hg to atmospheres
  b. 18.2 psi to mm Hg
  c. 862 mm Hg to torr
  d. 795 mm Hg to psi

10. Make the indicated pressure conversions.

  a. 17.3 psi to kilopascals
  b. 1.15 atm to psi
  c. 4.25 atm to mm Hg
  d. 224 psi to atmospheres

11. Make the indicated pressure conversions.

  a. 1.54×10^5 Pa to atmospheres
  b. 1.21 atm to pascals
  c. 97,345 Pa to mm Hg
  d. 1.32 kPa to pascals

12. Make the indicated pressure conversions.

  a. 6.42 atm to kilopascals
  b. 4.21 atm to torr
  c. 794 mm Hg to atmospheres
  d. 27.2 psi to atmospheres

13.2 Pressure and Volume: Boyle's Law

QUESTIONS

13. Pretend that you're talking to a friend who has not yet taken any science courses, and describe how you would explain Boyle's law to her.

14. In Figure 13.4, when additional mercury is added to the right-hand arm of the J-shaped tube, the volume of the gas trapped above the mercury in the left-hand arm of the J-tube decreases. Explain.

15. The volume of a sample of ideal gas is inversely proportional to the _____ on the gas at constant temperature.

16. A mathematical expression that summarizes Boyle's law is _____.

PROBLEMS

17. For each of the following sets of pressure/volume data, calculate the new volume of the gas sample after the pressure change is made. Assume that the temperature and the amount of gas remain the same.

    a. $V = 125$ mL at 755 mm Hg; $V = ?$ mL at 780 mm Hg
    b. $V = 223$ mL at 1.08 atm; $V = ?$ mL at 0.951 atm
    c. $V = 3.02$ L at 103 kPa; $V = ?$ L at 121 kPa

18. For each of the following sets of pressure/volume data, calculate the new volume of the gas sample after the pressure change is made. Assume that the temperature and the amount of gas remain the same.

    a. $V = 375$ mL at 1.15 atm; $V = ?$ mL at 775 mm Hg
    b. $V = 195$ mL at 1.08 atm; $V = ?$ mL at 135 kPa
    c. $V = 6.75$ L at 131 kPa; $V = ?$ L at 765 mm Hg

19. For each of the following sets of pressure/volume data, calculate the missing quantity. Assume that the temperature and the amount of gas remain constant.

    a. $V = 19.3$ L at 102.1 kPa; $V = 10.0$ L at ? kPa
    b. $V = 25.7$ mL at 755 torr; $V = ?$ at 761 mm Hg
    c. $V = 51.2$ L at 1.05 atm; $V = ?$ at 112.2 kPa

20. For each of the following sets of pressure/volume data, calculate the missing quantity after the change is made. Assume that the temperature and the amount of gas remain the same.

    a. $V = 125$ mL at 755 mm Hg; $V = 137$ mL at ? mm Hg
    b. $V = 331$ mL at 1.08 atm; $V = 299$ mL at ? atm
    c. $V = 3.02$ L at 789 mm Hg; $V = ?$ L at 135 kPa

21. What volume of gas would result if 225 mL of neon gas is compressed from 1.02 atm to 2.99 atm at constant temperature?

22. If the pressure on a 1.04-L sample of gas is doubled at constant temperature, what will be the new volume of the gas?

23. A sample of helium gas with a volume of 29.2 mL at 785 mm Hg is compressed at constant temperature until its volume is 15.1 mL. What will be the new pressure in the sample?

24. What pressure would have to be applied to a 27.2-mL sample of gas at 25 °C and 1.00 atm to compress its volume to 1.00 mL without a change in temperature?

13.3 Volume and Temperature: Charles's Law

QUESTIONS

25. Pretend that you're talking to a friend who has not yet taken any science courses, and describe how you would explain the concept of absolute zero to him.

26. Figures 13.7 and 13.8 show volume/temperature data for several samples of gases. Why do all the lines seem to extrapolate to the same point at -273 °C? Explain.

27. The volume of a sample of ideal gas is _____ proportional to its temperature (K) at constant pressure.

28. A mathematical expression that summarizes Charles's law is _____.

PROBLEMS

29. A favorite demonstration in introductory chemistry is to illustrate how the volume of a gas is affected by temperature by blowing up a balloon at room temperature and then placing the balloon into a container of dry ice or liquid nitrogen (both of which are *very* cold). Suppose a balloon containing 1.15 L of air at 25.2 °C is placed into a flask containing liquid nitrogen at -78.5 °C. What will the volume of the sample become (at constant pressure)?

30. Suppose a 375-mL sample of neon gas at 78 °C is cooled to 22 °C at constant pressure. What will be the new volume of the neon sample?

31. For each of the following sets of volume/temperature data, calculate the missing quantity after the change is made. Assume that the pressure and the amount of gas remain the same.

    a. $V = 2.03$ L at 24 °C; $V = 3.01$ L at ? °C
    b. $V = 127$ mL at 273 K; $V = ?$ mL at 373 K
    c. $V = 49.7$ mL at 34 °C; $V = ?$ at 350 K

32. For each of the following sets of volume/temperature data, calculate the missing quantity. Assume that the pressure and the mass of gas remain constant.

    a. $V = 73.5$ mL at 0 °C; $V = ?$ at 25 °C
    b. $V = 15.2$ L at 298 K; $V = 10.0$ L at ? °C
    c. $V = 1.75$ mL at 2.3 K; $V = ?$ at 0 °C

33. For each of the following sets of volume/temperature data, calculate the missing quantity after the change is made. Assume that the pressure and the amount of gas remain the same.

    a. $V = 9.14$ L at 24 °C; $V = ?$ at 48 °C
    b. $V = 24.9$ mL at -12 °C; $V = 49.9$ mL at ? °C
    c. $V = 925$ mL at 25 K; $V = ?$ at 273 K

All even-numbered Questions and Problems have answers in the back of this book and solutions in the Solutions Guide.

34. For each of the following sets of volume/temperature data, calculate the missing quantity. Assume that the pressure and the mass of gas remain constant.

    a. $V = 2.01 \times 10^2$ L at 1150 °C; $V = 5.00$ L at ? °C
    b. $V = 44.2$ mL at 298 K; $V = ?$ at 0 K
    c. $V = 44.2$ mL at 298 K; $V = ?$ at 0 °C

35. Suppose 1.25 L of argon is cooled from 291 K to 78 K. What will be the new volume of the argon sample?

36. Suppose a 125-mL sample of argon is cooled from 450 K to 250 K at constant pressure. What will be the volume of the sample at the lower temperature?

37. If a 375-mL sample of neon gas is heated from 24 °C to 72 °C at constant pressure, what will be the volume of the sample at the higher temperature?

38. A sample of gas has a volume of 127 mL in a boiling water bath at 100 °C. Calculate the volume of the sample of gas at 10 °C intervals after the heat source is turned off and the gas sample begins to cool down to the temperature of the laboratory, 20 °C.

13.4 Volume and Moles: Avogadro's Law

QUESTIONS

39. At conditions of constant temperature and pressure, the volume of a sample of ideal gas is _____ proportional to the number of moles of gas present.

40. A mathematical expression that summarizes Avogadro's law is _____.

PROBLEMS

41. If 0.00901 mol neon gas at a particular temperature and pressure occupies a volume of 242 mL, what volume would 0.00703 mol neon occupy under the same conditions?

42. If 1.04 g of chlorine gas occupies a volume of 872 mL at a particular temperature and pressure, what volume will 2.08 g of chlorine gas occupy under the same conditions?

43. If 3.25 mol argon gas occupies a volume of 100. L at a particular temperature and pressure, what volume does 14.15 mol argon occupy under the same conditions?

44. If 2.71 g of argon gas occupies a volume of 4.21 L, what volume will 1.29 mol argon occupy under the same conditions?

13.5 The Ideal Gas Law

QUESTIONS

45. What do we mean by an *ideal* gas?

46. Under what conditions do *real* gases behave most ideally?

47. Show how Boyle's gas law can be derived from the ideal gas law.

48. Show how Charles's gas law can be derived from the ideal gas law.

PROBLEMS

49. Given the following sets of values for three of the gas variables, calculate the unknown quantity.

    a. $P = 782.4$ mm Hg; $V = ?$; $n = 0.1021$ mol; $T = 26.2$ °C
    b. $P = ?$ mm Hg; $V = 27.5$ mL; $n = 0.007812$ mol; $T = 16.6$ °C
    c. $P = 1.045$ atm; $V = 45.2$ mL; $n = 0.002241$ mol; $T = ?$ °C

50. Given each of the following sets of values for an ideal gas, calculate the unknown quantity.

    a. $P = 782$ mm Hg; $V = ?$; $n = 0.210$ mol; $T = 27$ °C
    b. $P = ?$ mm Hg; $V = 644$ mL; $n = 0.0921$ mol; $T = 303$ K
    c. $P = 745$ mm Hg; $V = 11.2$ L; $n = 0.401$ mol; $T = ?$ K

51. What mass of neon gas is required to fill a 5.00-L container to a pressure of 1.02 atm at 25 °C?

52. What pressure will exist in a 10.0-L flask containing 12.2 g of argon gas at 25 °C?

53. What volume will 2.04 g of helium gas occupy at 100. °C and 785 mm Hg pressure?

54. At what temperature will 40.0 g of argon gas have a pressure of 1.00 atm when confined in a 25.0-L tank?

55. What mass of helium gas is needed to pressurize a 100.0-L tank to 255 atm at 25 °C? What mass of oxygen gas would be needed to pressurize a similar tank to the same specifications?

56. Suppose that a 1.25-g sample of neon gas is confined in a 10.1-L container at 25 °C. What will be the pressure in the container? Suppose the temperature is then raised to 50 °C. What will the new pressure be after the temperature is increased?

57. At what temperature will a 1.0-g sample of neon gas exert a pressure of 500. torr in a 5.0-L container?

58. At what temperature would 4.25 g of oxygen gas, O_2, exert a pressure of 784 mm Hg in a 2.51-L container?

59. What pressure exists in a 200-L tank containing 5.0 kg of neon gas at 300. K?

60. Which flask will have the higher pressure: a 5.00-L flask containing 4.15 g of helium at 298 K, or a 10.0-L flask containing 56.2 g of argon at 303 K?

61. Suppose a 24.3-mL sample of helium gas at 25 °C and 1.01 atm is heated to 50. °C and compressed to a volume of 15.2 mL. What will be the pressure of the sample?

62. Suppose that 1.29 g of argon gas is confined to a volume of 2.41 L at 29 °C. What would be the pressure in the container? What would the pressure become if the temperature were raised to 42 °C without a change in volume?

All even-numbered Questions and Problems have answers in the back of this book and solutions in the Solutions Guide.

63. What will the volume of the sample become if 459 mL of an ideal gas at 27 °C and 1.05 atm is cooled to 15 °C and 0.997 atm?

Ⓕ 64. The "Chemistry in Focus" segment *Snacks Need Chemistry, Too!* discusses why popcorn "pops." You can estimate the pressure inside a kernel of popcorn at the time of popping by using the ideal gas law. Basically, you determine the mass of water released when the popcorn pops by measuring the mass of the popcorn both before and after popping. Assume that the difference in mass is the mass of water vapor lost on popping. Assume that the popcorn pops at the temperature of the cooking oil (225 °C) and that the volume of the "container" is the volume of the unpopped kernel. Although we are making several assumptions, we can at least get some idea of the magnitude of the pressure inside the kernel.

Assuming a total volume of 2.0 mL for 20 kernels and a mass of 0.250 g of water lost from them on popping, calculate the pressure inside the kernels just before they "pop."

13.6 Dalton's Law of Partial Pressures

QUESTIONS

65. Explain why the measured properties of a mixture of gases depend only on the total number of moles of particles, not on the identity of the individual gas particles. How is this observation summarized as a law?

66. We often collect small samples of gases in the laboratory by bubbling the gas into a bottle or flask containing water. Explain why the gas becomes saturated with water vapor and how we must take the presence of water vapor into account when calculating the properties of the gas sample.

PROBLEMS

67. If a gaseous mixture is made of 2.41 g of He and 2.79 g of Ne in an evacuated 1.04-L container at 25 °C, what will be the partial pressure of each gas and the total pressure in the container?

68. Suppose that 1.28 g of neon gas and 2.49 g of argon gas are confined in a 9.87-L container at 27 °C. What would be the pressure in the container?

69. A tank contains a mixture of 52.5 g of oxygen gas and 65.1 g of carbon dioxide gas at 27 °C. The total pressure in the tank is 9.21 atm. Calculate the partial pressure (in atm) of each gas in the mixture.

70. What mass of neon gas would be required to fill a 3.00-L flask to a pressure of 925 mm Hg at 26 °C? What mass of argon gas would be required to fill a similar flask to the same pressure at the same temperature?

71. A sample of oxygen gas is saturated with water vapor at 27 °C. The total pressure of the mixture is 772 torr, and the vapor pressure of water is 26.7 torr at 27 °C. What is the partial pressure of the oxygen gas?

72. Suppose a gaseous mixture of 1.15 g helium and 2.91 g argon is placed in a 5.25-L container at 273 °C. What pressure would exist in the container?

73. A 500.-mL sample of O_2 gas at 24 °C was prepared by decomposing a 3% aqueous solution of hydrogen peroxide, H_2O_2, in the presence of a small amount of manganese catalyst by the reaction

$$2H_2O_2(aq) \rightarrow 2H_2O(g) + O_2(g)$$

The oxygen thus prepared was collected by displacement of water. The total pressure of gas collected was 755 mm Hg. What is the partial pressure of O_2 in the mixture? How many moles of O_2 are in the mixture? (The vapor pressure of water at 24 °C is 23 mm Hg.)

74. Small quantities of hydrogen gas can be prepared in the laboratory by the addition of aqueous hydrochloric acid to metallic zinc.

$$Zn(s) + 2HCl(aq) \rightarrow ZnCl_2(aq) + H_2(g)$$

Typically, the hydrogen gas is bubbled through water for collection and becomes saturated with water vapor. Suppose 240. mL of hydrogen gas is collected at 30. °C and has a total pressure of 1.032 atm by this process. What is the partial pressure of hydrogen gas in the sample? How many moles of hydrogen gas are present in the sample? How many grams of zinc must have reacted to produce this quantity of hydrogen? (The vapor pressure of water is 32 torr at 30 °C.)

13.7 Laws and Models: A Review

QUESTIONS

75. What is a scientific *law?* What is a *theory?* How do these concepts differ? Does a law explain a theory, or does a theory attempt to explain a law?

76. When is a scientific theory considered to be successful? Are all theories successful? Will a theory that has been successful in the past necessarily be successful in the future?

13.8 The Kinetic Molecular Theory of Gases

QUESTIONS

77. What do we assume about the volume of the actual molecules themselves in a sample of gas, compared to the bulk volume of the gas overall? Why?

78. Collisions of the molecules in a sample of gas with the walls of the container are responsible for the gas's observed _____.

79. Temperature is a measure of the average _____ of the molecules in a sample of gas.

80. The kinetic molecular theory of gases suggests that gas particles exert _____ attractive or repulsive forces on each other.

13.9 The Implications of the Kinetic Molecular Theory

QUESTIONS

81. How is the phenomenon of temperature explained on the basis of the kinetic molecular theory? What microscopic property of gas molecules is reflected in the temperature measured?

82. Explain, in terms of the kinetic molecular theory, how an increase in the temperature of a gas confined to a rigid container causes an increase in the pressure of the gas.

13.10 Gas Stoichiometry

QUESTIONS

83. What is the *molar volume* of a gas? Do all gases that behave ideally have the same molar volume?

84. What conditions are considered "standard temperature and pressure" (STP) for gases? Suggest a reason why these particular conditions might have been chosen for STP.

PROBLEMS

85. Calcium oxide can be used to "scrub" carbon dioxide from air.

$$CaO(s) + CO_2(g) \rightarrow CaCO_3(s)$$

What mass of CO_2 could be absorbed by 1.25 g of CaO? What volume would this CO_2 occupy at STP?

86. Consider the following reaction:

$$C(s) + O_2(g) \rightarrow CO_2(g)$$

What volume of oxygen gas at 25 °C and 1.02 atm would be required to react completely with 1.25 g of carbon?

87. Consider the following reaction for the combustion of octane, C_8H_{18}:

$$2C_8H_{18}(l) + 25O_2(g) \rightarrow 16CO_2(g) + 18H_2O(l)$$

What volume of oxygen gas at STP would be needed for the complete combustion of 10.0 g of octane?

88. Although we generally think of combustion reactions as involving oxygen gas, other rapid oxidation reactions are also referred to as combustions. For example, if magnesium metal is placed into chlorine gas, a rapid oxidation takes place, and magnesium chloride is produced.

$$Mg(s) + Cl_2(g) \rightarrow MgCl_2(s)$$

What volume of chlorine gas, measured at STP, is required to react completely with 1.02 g of magnesium?

89. Ammonia and gaseous hydrogen chloride combine to form ammonium chloride.

$$NH_3(g) + HCl(g) \rightarrow NH_4Cl(s)$$

If 4.21 L of $NH_3(g)$ at 27 °C and 1.02 atm is combined with 5.35 L of $HCl(g)$ at 26 °C and 0.998 atm, what mass of $NH_4Cl(s)$ will be produced? Which gas is the limiting reactant? Which gas is present in excess?

90. Calcium carbide, CaC_2, reacts with water to produce acetylene gas, C_2H_2.

$$CaC_2(s) + 2H_2O(l) \rightarrow C_2H_2(g) + Ca(OH)_2(s)$$

What volume of acetylene at 25 °C and 1.01 atm is generated by the complete reaction of 2.49 g of calcium carbide? What volume would this quantity of acetylene occupy at STP?

91. Many transition metal salts are hydrates: they contain a fixed number of water molecules bound per formula unit of the salt. For example, copper(II) sulfate most commonly exists as the pentahydrate, $CuSO_4 \cdot 5H_2O$. If 5.00 g of $CuSO_4 \cdot 5H_2O$ is heated strongly so as to drive off all of the waters of hydration as water vapor, what volume will this water vapor occupy at 350. °C and a pressure of 1.04 atm?

92. If water is added to magnesium nitride, ammonia gas is produced when the mixture is heated.

$$Mg_3N_2(s) + 3H_2O(l) \rightarrow 3MgO(s) + 2NH_3(g)$$

If 10.3 g of magnesium nitride is treated with water, what volume of ammonia gas would be collected at 24 °C and 752 mm Hg?

93. What volume does a mixture of 14.2 g of He and 21.6 g of H_2 occupy at 28 °C and 0.985 atm?

94. What volume does a mixture of 26.2 g of O_2 and 35.1 g of N_2 occupy at 35 °C and 755 mm Hg?

95. A sample of helium gas occupies a volume of 25.2 mL at 95 °C and a pressure of 892 mm Hg. Calculate the volume of the gas at STP.

96. What volume does 5.02 g of helium occupy at STP? What volume would 42.1 g of argon occupy under the same conditions?

97. A mixture contains 5.00 g *each* of O_2, N_2, CO_2, and Ne gas. Calculate the volume of this mixture at STP. Calculate the partial pressure of each gas in the mixture at STP.

98. A gaseous mixture contains 6.25 g of He and 4.97 g of Ne. What volume does the mixture occupy at STP? Calculate the partial pressure of each gas in the mixture at STP.

99. Consider the following *unbalanced* chemical equation for the combination reaction of sodium metal and chlorine gas:

$$Na(s) + Cl_2(g) \rightarrow NaCl(s)$$

What volume of chlorine gas, measured at STP, is necessary for the complete reaction of 4.81 g of sodium metal?

100. Welders commonly use an apparatus that contains a tank of acetylene (C_2H_2) gas and a tank of oxygen gas. When burned in pure oxygen, acetylene generates a large amount of heat.

$$2C_2H_2(g) + 5O_2(g) \rightarrow 2H_2O(g) + 4CO_2(g)$$

What volume of carbon dioxide gas at STP is produced if 1.00 g of acetylene is combusted completely?

101. During the making of steel, iron(II) oxide is reduced to metallic iron by treatment with carbon monoxide gas.

$$FeO(s) + CO(g) \rightarrow Fe(s) + CO_2(g)$$

Suppose 1.45 kg of Fe reacts. What volume of $CO(g)$ is required, and what volume of $CO_2(g)$ is produced, each measured at STP?

102. Consider the following reaction:

$$Zn(s) + 2HCl(aq) \rightarrow ZnCl_2(aq) + H_2(g)$$

What mass of zinc metal should be taken so as to produce 125 mL of H_2 measured at STP when reacted with excess hydrochloric acid?

Additional Problems

103. When doing any calculation involving gas samples, we must express the temperature in terms of the _____ temperature scale.

104. Two moles of ideal gas occupy a volume that is _____ the volume of 1 mole of ideal gas under the same temperature and pressure conditions.

105. Summarize the postulates of the kinetic molecular theory for gases. How does the kinetic molecular theory account for the observed properties of temperature and pressure?

106. Give a formula or equation that represents each of the following gas laws.

a. Boyle's law
b. Charles's law
c. Avogadro's law
d. the ideal gas law
e. the combined gas law

107. For a mixture of gases in the same container, the total pressure exerted by the mixture of gases is the _____ of the pressures that those gases would exert if they were alone in the container under the same conditions.

108. A helium tank contains 25.2 L of helium at 8.40 atm pressure. Determine how many 1.50-L balloons at 755 mm Hg can be inflated with the gas in the tank, assuming that the tank will also have to contain He at 755 mm Hg after the balloons are filled (that is, it is not possible to empty the tank completely). The temperature is 25 °C in all cases.

109. As weather balloons rise from the earth's surface, the pressure of the atmosphere becomes less, tending to cause the volume of the balloons to expand. However, the temperature is much lower in the upper atmosphere than at sea level. Would this temperature effect tend to make such a balloon expand or contract? Weather balloons do, in fact, expand as they rise. What does this tell you?

110. When ammonium carbonate is heated, three gases are produced by its decomposition.

$$(NH_4)_2CO_3(s) \rightarrow 2NH_3(g) + CO_2(g) + H_2O(g)$$

What total volume of gas is produced, measured at 453 °C and 1.04 atm, if 52.0 g of ammonium carbonate is heated?

111. Carbon dioxide gas, in the dry state, may be produced by heating calcium carbonate.

$$CaCO_3(s) \rightarrow CaO(s) + CO_2(g)$$

What volume of CO_2, collected dry at 55 °C and a pressure of 774 torr, is produced by complete thermal decomposition of 10.0 g of $CaCO_3$?

112. Carbon dioxide gas, saturated with water vapor, can be produced by the addition of aqueous acid to calcium carbonate.

$$CaCO_3(s) + 2H^+(aq) \rightarrow Ca^{2+}(aq) + H_2O(l) + CO_2(g)$$

How many moles of $CO_2(g)$, collected at 60. °C and 774 torr total pressure, are produced by the complete reaction of 10.0 g of $CaCO_3$ with acid? What volume does this wet CO_2 occupy? What volume would the CO_2 occupy at 774 torr if a desiccant (a chemical drying agent) were added to remove the water? (The vapor pressure of water at 60. °C is 149.4 mm Hg.)

113. Sulfur trioxide, SO_3, is produced in enormous quantities each year for use in the synthesis of sulfuric acid.

$$S(s) + O_2(g) \rightarrow SO_2(g)$$
$$2SO_2(g) + O_2(g) \rightarrow 2SO_3(g)$$

What volume of $O_2(g)$ at 350. °C and a pressure of 5.25 atm is needed to completely convert 5.00 g of sulfur to sulfur trioxide?

114. Calculate the volume of $O_2(g)$ produced at 25 °C and 630. torr when 50.0 g of $KClO_3(s)$ is heated in the presence of a small amount of MnO_2 catalyst.

115. If 10.0 g of liquid helium at 1.7 K is completely vaporized, what volume does the helium occupy at STP?

116. Perform the indicated pressure conversions.

a. 752 mm Hg into pascals
b. 458 kPa into atmospheres
c. 1.43 atm into mm Hg
d. 842 torr into mm Hg

117. Convert the following pressures into mm Hg.

a. 0.903 atm
b. 2.1240×10^6 Pa
c. 445 kPa
d. 342 torr

118. Convert the following pressures into pascals.

    a. 645 mm Hg
    b. 221 kPa
    c. 0.876 atm
    d. 32 torr

119. For each of the following sets of pressure/volume data, calculate the missing quantity. Assume that the temperature and the amount of gas remain constant.

    a. $V = 123$ L at 4.56 atm; $V = ?$ at 1002 mm Hg
    b. $V = 634$ mL at 25.2 mm Hg; $V = 166$ mL at ? atm
    c. $V = 443$ L at 511 torr; $V = ?$ at 1.05 kPa

120. For each of the following sets of pressure/volume data, calculate the missing quantity. Assume that the temperature and the amount of gas remain constant.

    a. $V = 255$ mL at 1.00 mm Hg; $V = ?$ at 2.00 torr
    b. $V = 1.3$ L at 1.0 kPa; $V = ?$ at 1.0 atm
    c. $V = 1.3$ L at 1.0 kPa; $V = ?$ at 1.0 mm Hg

121. A particular balloon is designed by its manufacturer to be inflated to a volume of no more than 2.5 L. If the balloon is filled with 2.0 L of helium at sea level, is released, and rises to an altitude at which the atmospheric pressure is only 500. mm Hg, will the balloon burst?

122. What pressure is needed to compress 1.52 L of air at 755 mm Hg to a volume of 450 mL (at constant temperature)?

123. An expandable vessel contains 729 mL of gas at 22 °C. What volume will the gas sample in the vessel have if it is placed in a boiling water bath (100. °C)?

124. For each of the following sets of volume/temperature data, calculate the missing quantity. Assume that the pressure and the amount of gas remain constant.

    a. $V = 100.$ mL at 74 °C; $V = ?$ at −74 °C
    b. $V = 500.$ mL at 100 °C; $V = 600.$ mL at ? °C
    c. $V = 10{,}000$ L at 25 °C; $V = ?$ at 0 K

125. For each of the following sets of volume/temperature data, calculate the missing quantity. Assume that the pressure and the amount of gas remain constant.

    a. $V = 22.4$ L at 0 °C; $V = 44.4$ L at ? K
    b. $V = 1.0 \times 10^{-3}$ mL at −272 °C; $V = ?$ at 25 °C
    c. $V = 32.3$ L at −40 °C; $V = 1000.$ L at ? °C

126. A 75.2-mL sample of helium at 12 °C is heated to 192 °C. What is the new volume of the helium (assuming constant pressure)?

127. If 5.12 g of oxygen gas occupies a volume of 6.21 L at a certain temperature and pressure, what volume will 25.0 g of oxygen gas occupy under the same conditions?

128. If 23.2 g of a given gas occupies a volume of 93.2 L at a particular temperature and pressure, what mass of the gas occupies a volume of 10.4 L under the same conditions?

129. Given each of the following sets of values for three of the gas variables, calculate the unknown quantity.

    a. $P = 21.2$ atm; $V = 142$ mL; $n = 0.432$ mol; $T = ?$ K
    b. $P = ?$ atm; $V = 1.23$ mL; $n = 0.000115$ mol; $T = 293$ K
    c. $P = 755$ mm Hg; $V = ?$ mL; $n = 0.473$ mol; $T = 131$ °C

130. Given each of the following sets of values for three of the gas variables, calculate the unknown quantity.

    a. $P = 1.034$ atm; $V = 21.2$ mL; $n = 0.00432$ mol; $T = ?$ K
    b. $P = ?$ atm; $V = 1.73$ mL; $n = 0.000115$ mol; $T = 182$ K
    c. $P = 1.23$ mm Hg; $V = ?$ L; $n = 0.773$ mol; $T = 152$ °C

131. What is the pressure inside a 10.0-L flask containing 14.2 g of N_2 at 26 °C?

132. Suppose three 100.-L tanks are to be filled separately with the gases CH_4, N_2, and CO_2, respectively. What mass of each gas is needed to produce a pressure of 120. atm in its tank at 27 °C?

133. At what temperature does 4.00 g of helium gas have a pressure of 1.00 atm in a 22.4-L vessel?

134. What is the pressure in a 100.-mL flask containing 55 mg of oxygen gas at 26 °C?

135. A weather balloon is filled with 1.0 L of helium at 23 °C and 1.0 atm. What volume does the balloon have when it has risen to a point in the atmosphere where the pressure is 220 torr and the temperature is −31 °C?

136. At what temperature does 100. mL of N_2 at 300. K and 1.13 atm occupy a volume of 500. mL at a pressure of 1.89 atm?

137. If 1.0 mol $N_2(g)$ is injected into a 5.0-L tank already containing 50. g of O_2 at 25 °C, what will be the total pressure in the tank?

138. A gaseous mixture contains 12.1 g of N_2 and 4.05 g of He. What is the volume of this mixture at STP?

139. A flask of hydrogen gas is collected at 1.023 atm and 35 °C by displacement of water from the flask. The vapor pressure of water at 35 °C is 42.2 mm Hg. What is the partial pressure of hydrogen gas in the flask?

140. Consider the following chemical equation:

$$N_2(g) + 3H_2(g) \rightarrow 2NH_3(g)$$

What volumes of nitrogen gas and hydrogen gas, each measured at 11 °C and 0.998 atm, are needed to produce 5.00 g of ammonia?

141. Consider the following *unbalanced* chemical equation:

$$C_6H_{12}O_6(s) + O_2(g) \rightarrow CO_2(g) + H_2O(g)$$

What volume of oxygen gas, measured at 28 °C and 0.976 atm, is needed to react with 5.00 g of $C_6H_{12}O_6$? What volume of each product is produced under the same conditions?

142. Consider the following *unbalanced* chemical equation:

$$Cu_2S(s) + O_2(g) \rightarrow Cu_2O(s) + SO_2(g)$$

What volume of oxygen gas, measured at 27.5 °C and 0.998 atm, is required to react with 25 g of copper(I) sulfide? What volume of sulfur dioxide gas is produced under the same conditions?

143. When sodium bicarbonate, $NaHCO_3(s)$, is heated, sodium carbonate is produced, with the evolution of water vapor and carbon dioxide gas.

$$2NaHCO_3(s) \rightarrow Na_2CO_3(s) + H_2O(g) + CO_2(g)$$

What total volume of gas, measured at 29 °C and 769 torr, is produced when 1.00 g of $NaHCO_3(s)$ is completely converted to $Na_2CO_3(s)$?

144. What volume does 35 moles of N_2 occupy at STP?

145. A sample of oxygen gas has a volume of 125 L at 25 °C and a pressure of 0.987 atm. Calculate the volume of this oxygen sample at STP.

146. A mixture contains 5.0 g of He, 1.0 g of Ar, and 3.5 g of Ne. Calculate the volume of this mixture at STP. Calculate the partial pressure of each gas in the mixture at STP.

147. What volume of CO_2 measured at STP is produced when 27.5 g of $CaCO_3$ is decomposed?

$$CaCO_3(s) \rightarrow CaO(s) + CO_2(g)$$

148. Concentrated hydrogen peroxide solutions are explosively decomposed by traces of transition metal ions (such as Mn or Fe):

$$2H_2O_2(aq) \rightarrow 2H_2O(l) + O_2(g)$$

What volume of pure $O_2(g)$, collected at 27 °C and 764 torr, would be generated by decomposition of 125 g of a 50.0% by mass hydrogen peroxide solution?

Table 14.1 Densities of the Three States of Water	
State	Density (g/cm³)
solid (0 °C, 1 atm)	0.9168
liquid (25 °C, 1 atm)	0.9971
gas (100 °C, 1 atm)	5.88×10^{-4}

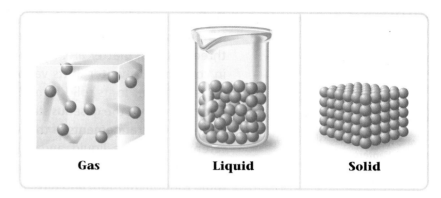

Figure 14.1

Representations of the gas, liquid, and solid states.

Ice has an unusual amount of empty space and so is less dense than liquid water, as indicated in Table 14.1.

In this chapter we will explore the important properties of liquids and solids. We will illustrate many of these properties by considering one of the earth's most important substances: water.

14.1 Water and Its Phase Changes

OBJECTIVE: To learn some of the important features of water.

In the world around us we see many solids (soil, rocks, trees, concrete, and so on), and we are immersed in the gases of the atmosphere. But the liquid we most commonly see is water; it is virtually everywhere, covering about 70% of the earth's surface. Approximately 97% of the earth's water is found in the oceans, which are actually mixtures of water and huge quantities of dissolved salts.

Water is one of the most important substances on earth. It is crucial for sustaining the reactions within our bodies that keep us alive, but it also affects our lives in many indirect ways. The oceans help moderate the earth's temperature. Water cools automobile engines and nuclear power plants. Water provides a means of transportation on the earth's surface and acts as a medium for the growth of the myriad creatures we use as food, and much more.

The water we drink often has a taste because of the substances dissolved in it. It is not pure water.

Pure water is a colorless, tasteless substance that at 1 atm pressure freezes to form a solid at 0 °C and vaporizes completely to form a gas at 100 °C. This means that (at 1 atm pressure) the liquid range of water occurs between the temperatures 0 °C and 100 °C.

What happens when we heat liquid water? First the temperature of the water rises. Just as with gas molecules, the motions of the water molecules increase as it is heated. Eventually the temperature of the water reaches 100 °C; now bubbles develop in the interior of the liquid, float to the surface, and burst—the boiling point has been reached. An interesting thing happens at the boiling point: even though heating continues, the temperature stays at 100 °C until all the water has changed to vapor. Only when all of the water has changed to the gaseous state does the temperature begin to rise

Figure 14.2

The heating/cooling curve for water heated or cooled at a constant rate. The plateau at the boiling point is longer than the plateau at the melting point, because it takes almost seven times as much energy (and thus seven times the heating time) to vaporize liquid water as to melt ice. Note that to make the diagram clear, the blue line is not drawn to scale. It actually takes more energy to melt ice and boil water than to heat water from 0 °C to 100 °C.

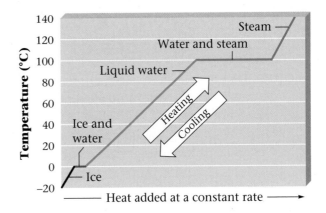

again. (We are now heating the vapor.) At 1 atm pressure, liquid water always changes to gaseous water at 100 °C, the **normal boiling point** for water.

The experiment just described is represented in Figure 14.2, which is called the **heating/cooling curve** for water. Going from left to right on this graph means energy is being added (heating). Going from right to left on the graph means that energy is being removed (cooling).

When liquid water is cooled, the temperature decreases until it reaches 0 °C, where the liquid begins to freeze (see Figure 14.2). The temperature remains at 0 °C until all the liquid water has changed to ice and then begins to drop again as cooling continues. At 1 atm pressure, water freezes (or, in the opposite process, ice melts) at 0 °C. This is called the **normal freezing point** of water. Liquid and solid water can coexist indefinitely if the temperature is held at 0 °C. However, at temperatures below 0 °C liquid water freezes, while at temperatures above 0 °C ice melts.

Interestingly, water expands when it freezes. That is, one gram of ice at 0 °C has a greater volume than one gram of liquid water at 0 °C. This has very important practical implications. For instance, water in a confined space can break its container when it freezes and expands. This accounts for the bursting of water pipes and engine blocks that are left unprotected in freezing weather.

The expansion of water when it freezes also explains why ice cubes float. Recall that density is defined as mass/volume. When one gram of liquid water freezes, its volume becomes greater (it expands). Therefore, the *density* of one gram of ice is less than the density of one gram of water, because in the case of ice we divide by a slightly larger volume. For example, at 0 °C the density of liquid water is

$$\frac{1.00 \text{ g}}{1.00 \text{ mL}} = 1.00 \text{ g/mL}$$

and the density of ice is

$$\frac{1.00 \text{ g}}{1.09 \text{ mL}} = 0.917 \text{ g/mL}$$

The lower density of ice also means that ice floats on the surface of lakes as they freeze, providing a layer of insulation that helps to prevent lakes and rivers from freezing solid in the winter. This means that aquatic life continues to have liquid water available through the winter.

14.2 Energy Requirements for the Changes of State

OBJECTIVES: To learn about interactions among water molecules. • To understand and use heat of fusion and heat of vaporization.

It is important to recognize that changes of state from solid to liquid and from liquid to gas are *physical* changes. No *chemical* bonds are broken in these processes. Ice, water, and steam all contain H_2O molecules. When water is boiled to form steam, water molecules are separated from each other (see Figure 14.3) but the individual molecules remain intact.

The bonding forces that hold the atoms of a molecule together are called **intramolecular** (within the molecule) **forces.** The forces that occur among molecules that cause them to aggregate to form a solid or a liquid are called **intermolecular** (between the molecules) **forces.** These two types of forces are illustrated in Figure 14.4.

> Remember that temperature is a measure of the random motions (average kinetic energy) of the particles in a substance.

It takes energy to melt ice and to vaporize water, because intermolecular forces between water molecules must be overcome. In ice the molecules are virtually locked in place, although they can vibrate about their positions. When energy is added, the vibrational motions increase, and the molecules eventually achieve the greater movement and disorder characteristic of liquid water. The ice has melted. As still more energy is added, the gaseous state is eventually reached, in which the individual molecules are far apart and interact relatively little. However, the gas still consists of water molecules. It would take *much* more energy to overcome the covalent bonds and decompose the water molecules into their component atoms.

The energy required to melt 1 mole of a substance is called the **molar heat of fusion.** For ice, the molar heat of fusion is 6.02 kJ/mol. The energy required to change 1 mole of liquid to its vapor is called the **molar heat of vaporization.** For water, the molar heat of vaporization is 40.6 kJ/mol at 100 °C. Notice in Figure 14.2 that the plateau that corresponds to the vaporization of water is much longer than that for the melting of ice. This occurs because it takes much more energy (almost seven times as much) to vaporize a mole of water than to melt a mole of ice. This is consistent with our models of solids, liquids, and gases (see Figure 14.1). In liquids, the particles (molecules) are relatively close together, so most of the intermolecular forces are still present. However, when the molecules go from the liquid to the gaseous state, they must be moved far apart. To separate the molecules enough to form a gas, virtually all of the intermolecular forces must be overcome, and this requires large quantities of energy.

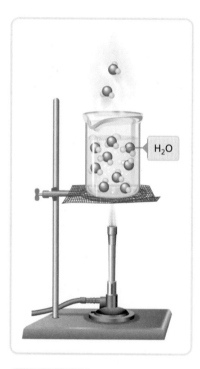

Figure 14.3

Both liquid water and gaseous water contain H_2O molecules. In liquid water the H_2O molecules are close together, whereas in the gaseous state the molecules are widely separated. The bubbles contain gaseous water.

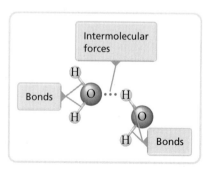

Figure 14.4

Intramolecular (bonding) forces exist between the atoms in a molecule and hold the molecule together. Intermolecular forces exist between molecules. These are the forces that cause water to condense to a liquid or form a solid at low enough temperatures. Intermolecular forces are typically much weaker than intramolecular forces.

CHEMISTRY *IN* FOCUS

Whales Need Changes of State

Sperm whales are prodigious divers. They commonly dive a mile or more into the ocean, hovering at that depth in search of schools of squid or fish. To remain motionless at a given depth, the whale must have the same density as the surrounding water. Because the density of seawater increases with depth, the sperm whale has a system that automatically increases its density as it dives. This system involves the spermaceti organ found in the whale's head. Spermaceti is a waxy substance with the formula

$$CH_3-(CH_2)_{15}-O-\underset{\underset{O}{\|}}{C}-(CH_2)_{14}-CH_3$$

which is a liquid above 30 °C. At the ocean surface the spermaceti in the whale's head is a liquid, warmed by the flow of blood through the spermaceti organ. When the whale dives, this blood flow decreases and the colder water causes the spermaceti to begin freezing. Because solid spermaceti is more dense than the liquid state, the sperm whale's density increases as it dives, matching the increase in the water's density.* When the whale wants to resurface, blood flow through the spermaceti organ increases, remelting the spermaceti and making the whale more buoyant. So the sperm whale's sophisticated density-regulating mechanism is based on a simple change of state.

*For most substances, the solid state is more dense than the liquid state. Water is an important exception.

A sperm whale.

Flip Nicklin/Minden Pictures

EXAMPLE 14.1 | Calculating Energy Changes: Solid to Liquid

Calculate the energy required to melt 8.5 g of ice at 0 °C. The molar heat of fusion for ice is 6.02 kJ/mol.

SOLUTION

Where Are We Going?

We want to determine the energy (in kJ) required to melt 8.5 g of ice at 0 °C.

What Do We Know?

- We have 8.5 g of ice (H_2O) at 0 °C.
- The molar heat of fusion of ice is 6.02 kJ/mol.

What Information Do We Need?

- We need to know the number of moles of ice in 8.5 g.

How Do We Get There?

The molar heat of fusion is the energy required to melt *1 mole* of ice. In this problem we have 8.5 g of solid water. We must find out how many moles of ice this mass represents. Because the molar mass of water is $16 + 2(1) = 18$, we know that 1 mole of water has a mass of 18 g, so we can convert 8.5 g of H_2O to moles of H_2O.

$$8.5 \text{ g } \cancel{H_2O} \times \frac{1 \text{ mol } H_2O}{18 \text{ g } \cancel{H_2O}} = 0.47 \text{ mol } H_2O$$

Because 6.02 kJ of energy is required to melt a mole of solid water, our sample will take about half this amount (we have approximately half a mole of ice). To calculate the exact amount of energy required, we will use the equivalence statement

6.02 kJ required for 1 mol H_2O

which leads to the conversion factor we need:

$$0.47 \text{ } \cancel{\text{mol } H_2O} \times \frac{6.02 \text{ kJ}}{\cancel{\text{mol } H_2O}} = 2.8 \text{ kJ}$$

This can be represented symbolically as

REALITY CHECK   Because we have just under half of 1 mole of ice, our answer should be about half the molar heat of fusion of ice. The answer of 2.8 kJ is just under half of 6.02 kJ, so this answer makes sense. ■

EXAMPLE 14.2   **Calculating Energy Changes: Liquid to Gas**

Specific heat capacity was discussed in Section 10.5.

Calculate the energy (in kJ) required to heat 25 g of liquid water from 25 °C to 100. °C and change it to steam at 100. °C. The specific heat capacity of liquid water is 4.18 J/g °C, and the molar heat of vaporization of water is 40.6 kJ/mol.

SOLUTION

Where Are We Going?

We want to determine the energy (in kJ) required to heat and vaporize a given quantity of water.

What Do We Know?

• We have 25 g of H_2O at 25 °C. The water will be heated to 100. °C and then vaporized at 100. °C

• The specific heat capacity of liquid water is 4.18 J/g °C.

• The molar vaporization of water is 40.6 kJ/mol.

• $Q = s \times m \times \Delta T$.

What Information Do We Need?

• We need to know the number of moles of water in 25 g.

How Do We Get There?

This problem can be split into two parts: (1) heating the water to its boiling point and (2) converting the liquid water to vapor at the boiling point.

Step 1: Heating to Boiling   We must first supply energy to heat the liquid water from 25 °C to 100. °C. Because 4.18 J is required to heat *one* gram of water by *one* Celsius degree, we must multiply by both the mass of water (25 g) and the temperature change (100. °C − 25 °C = 75 °C),

Energy required (Q)	=	Specific heat capacity (s)	×	Mass of water (m)	×	Temperature change (ΔT)

which we can represent by the equation

$$Q = s \times m \times \mathrm{D}T$$

Thus

$$Q = 4.18\frac{J}{g\,°C} \times 25\ g \times 75\ °C = 7.8 \times 10^3\ J$$

Energy required   Specific   Mass   Temperature
to heat 25 g of   heat   of   change
water from 25 °C   capacity   water
to 100. °C

$$= 7.8 \times 10^3\ J \times \frac{1\ kJ}{1000\ J} = 7.8\ kJ$$

Step 2: Vaporization   Now we must use the molar heat of vaporization to calculate the energy required to vaporize the 25 g of water at 100. °C. The heat of vaporization is given *per mole* rather than per gram, so we must first convert the 25 g of water to moles.

$$25\ g\ H_2O \times \frac{1\ mol\ H_2O}{18\ g\ H_2O} = 1.4\ mol\ H_2O$$

We can now calculate the energy required to vaporize the water.

$$\frac{40.6\ kJ}{mol\ H_2O} \times 1.4\ mol\ H_2O = 57\ kJ$$

Molar heat of   Moles of water
vaporization

The total energy is the sum of the two steps.

$$7.8\ kJ + 57\ kJ = 65\ kJ$$

Heat from   Change to
25 °C to   vapor
100. °C

Self-Check EXERCISE 14.1   Calculate the total energy required to melt 15 g of ice at 0 °C, heat the water to 100. °C, and vaporize it to steam at 100. °C.

HINT: Break the process into three steps and then take the sum.

See Problems 14.15 through 14.18. ■

14.3 Intermolecular Forces

OBJECTIVES:

go Chemistry **Module 17: Intermolecular Forces** covers concepts in this section.

To learn about dipole–dipole attraction, hydrogen bonding, and London dispersion forces. • To understand the effect of these forces on the properties of liquids.

We have seen that covalent bonding forces within molecules arise from the sharing of electrons, but how do intermolecular forces arise? Actually several types of intermolecular forces exist. To illustrate one type, we will consider the forces that exist among water molecules.

> The polarity of a molecule was discussed in Section 12.3.

As we saw in Chapter 12, water is a polar molecule—it has a dipole moment. When molecules with dipole moments are put together, they orient themselves to take advantage of their charge distributions. Molecules with dipole moments can attract each other by lining up so that the positive and negative ends are close to each other, as shown in Figure 14.5a. This is called a **dipole–dipole attraction.** In the liquid, the dipoles find the best compromise between attraction and repulsion, as shown in Figure 14.5b.

Dipole–dipole forces are typically only about 1% as strong as covalent or ionic bonds, and they become weaker as the distance between the dipoles increases. In the gas phase, where the molecules are usually very far apart, these forces are relatively unimportant.

> See Section 12.2 for a discussion of electronegativity.

Particularly strong dipole-dipole forces occur between molecules in which hydrogen is bound to a highly electronegative atom, such as nitrogen, oxygen, or fluorine. Two factors account for the strengths of these interactions: the great polarity of the bond and the close approach of the dipoles, which is made possible by the very small size of the hydrogen atom. Because dipole–dipole attractions of this type are so unusually strong, they are given a special name—**hydrogen bonding.** Figure 14.6 illustrates hydrogen bonding among water molecules.

Hydrogen bonding has a very important effect on various physical properties. For example, the boiling points for the covalent compounds of hydrogen with the elements in Group 6 are given in Figure 14.7. Note that the boiling point of water is much higher than would be expected from the trend shown by the other members of the series. Why? Because the especially large electronegativity value of the oxygen atom compared with that of the other group members causes the O—H bonds to be much more polar

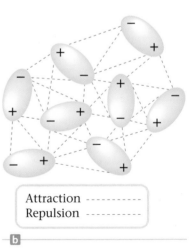

Attraction ----------
Repulsion ----------

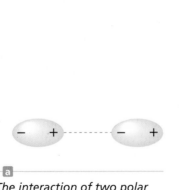

a
The interaction of two polar molecules.

b
The interaction of many dipoles in a liquid.

Figure 14.5

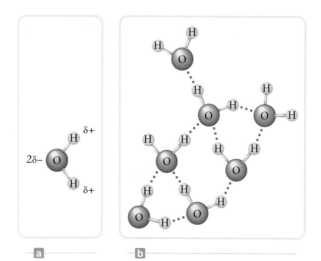

Figure 14.6

a The polar water molecule.
b Hydrogen bonding among water molecules. The small size of the hydrogen atoms allows the molecules to get very close and thus to produce strong interactions.

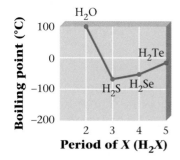

Figure 14.7

The boiling points of the covalent hydrides of elements in Group 6.

than the S—H, Se—H, or Te—H bonds. This leads to very strong hydrogen-bonding forces among the water molecules. An unusually large quantity of energy is required to overcome these interactions and separate the molecules to produce the gaseous state. That is, water molecules tend to remain together in the liquid state even at relatively high temperatures—hence the very high boiling point of water.

However, even molecules without dipole moments must exert forces on each other. We know this because all substances—even the noble gases—exist in the liquid and solid states at very low temperatures. There must be forces to hold the atoms or molecules as close together as they are in these condensed states. The forces that exist among noble gas atoms and nonpolar molecules are called **London dispersion forces.** To understand the origin of these forces, consider a pair of noble gas atoms. Although we usually assume that the electrons of an atom are uniformly distributed about the nucleus (see Figure 14.8a), this is apparently not true at every instant. Atoms

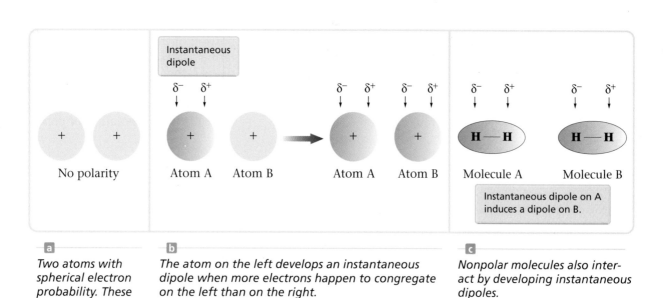

a
Two atoms with spherical electron probability. These atoms have no polarity.

b
The atom on the left develops an instantaneous dipole when more electrons happen to congregate on the left than on the right.

c
Nonpolar molecules also interact by developing instantaneous dipoles.

Figure 14.8

Table 14.2	The Freezing Points of the Group 8 Elements
Element	Freezing Point (°C)
helium*	−272.0 (25 atm)
neon	−248.6
argon	−189.4
krypton	−157.3
xenon	−111.9

*Helium will not freeze unless the pressure is increased above 1 atm.

can develop a temporary dipolar arrangement of charge as the electrons move around the nucleus (see Figure 14.8b). This *instantaneous dipole* can then *induce* a similar dipole in a neighboring atom, as shown in Figure 14.8b. The interatomic attraction thus formed is both weak and short-lived, but it can be very significant for large atoms and large molecules, as we will see.

The motions of the atoms must be greatly slowed down before the weak London dispersion forces can lock the atoms into place to produce a solid. This explains, for instance, why the noble gas elements have such low freezing points (see Table 14.2).

Nonpolar molecules such as H_2, N_2, and I_2, none of which has a permanent dipole moment, also attract each other by London dispersion forces (see Figure 14.8c). London forces become more significant as the sizes of atoms or molecules increase. Larger size means there are more electrons available to form the dipoles.

14.4 Evaporation and Vapor Pressure

OBJECTIVE: To understand the relationship among vaporization, condensation, and vapor pressure.

We all know that a liquid can evaporate from an open container. This is clear evidence that the molecules of a liquid can escape the liquid's surface and form a gas. This process, which is called **vaporization** or **evaporation,** requires energy to overcome the relatively strong intermolecular forces in the liquid.

The fact that vaporization requires energy has great practical significance; in fact, one of the most important roles that water plays in our world is to act as a coolant. Because of the strong hydrogen bonding among its molecules in the liquid state, water has an unusually large heat of vaporization (41 kJ/mol). A significant portion of the sun's energy is spent evaporating water from the oceans, lakes, and rivers rather than warming the earth. The vaporization of water is also crucial to our body's temperature-control system, which relies on the evaporation of perspiration.

Water is used to absorb heat from nuclear reactors. The water is then cooled in cooling towers before it is returned to the environment.

▶ Vapor Pressure

Vapor, not *gas,* is the term we customarily use for the gaseous state of a substance that exists naturally as a solid or liquid at 25 °C and 1 atm.

A system at equilibrium is dynamic on the molecular level, but shows no visible changes.

When we place a given amount of liquid in a container and then close it, we observe that the amount of liquid at first decreases slightly but eventually becomes constant. The decrease occurs because there is a transfer of molecules from the liquid to the vapor phase (Figure 14.9). However, as the number of vapor molecules increases, it becomes more and more likely that some of them will return to the liquid. The process by which vapor molecules form a liquid is called **condensation.** Eventually, the same number of molecules are leaving the liquid as are returning to it: the rate of condensation equals the rate of evaporation. *At this point no further change occurs in the amounts of liquid or vapor, because the two opposite processes exactly balance each other;* the system is at *equilibrium*. Note that this system is highly *dynamic* on the mo-

Figure 14.9

Behavior of a liquid in a closed container.

a *Net evaporation occurs at first, so the amount of liquid decreases slightly.*

a *As the number of vapor molecules increases, the rate of condensation increases. Finally the rate of condensation equals the rate of evaporation. The system is at equilibrium.*

lecular level—molecules are constantly escaping from and entering the liquid. However, there is no *net* change because the two opposite processes just *balance* each other. As an analogy, consider two island cities connected by a bridge. Suppose the traffic flow on the bridge is the same in both directions. There is motion—we can see the cars traveling across the bridge—but the number of cars in each city is not changing because an equal number enter and leave each one. The result is no *net* change in the number of autos in each city: an equilibrium exists.

The pressure of the vapor present at equilibrium with its liquid is called the *equilibrium vapor pressure* or, more commonly, the **vapor pressure** of the liquid. A simple barometer can be used to measure the vapor pressure of a liquid, as shown in Figure 14.10. Because mercury is so dense, any common liq-

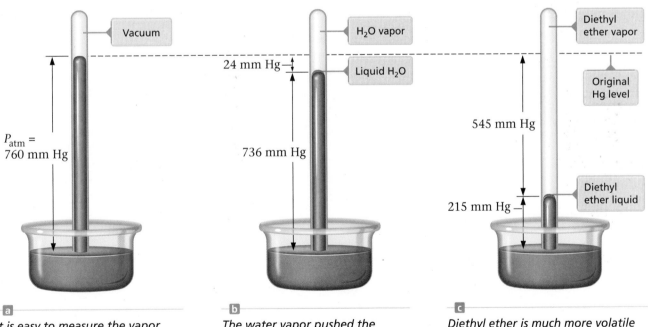

a *It is easy to measure the vapor pressure of a liquid by using a simple barometer of the type shown here.*

b *The water vapor pushed the mercury down 24 mm (760 – 736), so the vapor pressure of water is 24 mm Hg at this temperature.*

c *Diethyl ether is much more volatile than water and thus shows a higher vapor pressure. In this case, the mercury level has been pushed down 545 mm (760 – 215), so the vapor pressure of diethyl ether is 545 mm Hg at this temperature.*

Figure 14.10

uid injected at the bottom of the column of mercury floats to the top, where it produces a vapor, and the pressure of this vapor pushes some mercury out of the tube. When the system reaches equilibrium, the vapor pressure can be determined from the change in the height of the mercury column.

In effect, we are using the space above the mercury in the tube as a closed container for each liquid. However, in this case as the liquid vaporizes, the vapor formed creates a pressure that pushes some mercury out of the tube and lowers the mercury level. The mercury level stops changing when the excess liquid floating on the mercury comes to equilibrium with the vapor. The change in the mercury level (in millimeters) from its initial position (before the liquid was injected) to its final position is equal to the vapor pressure of the liquid.

The vapor pressures of liquids vary widely (see Figure 14.10). Liquids with high vapor pressures are said to be *volatile*—they evaporate rapidly.

The vapor pressure of a liquid at a given temperature is determined by the *intermolecular forces* that act among the molecules. Liquids in which the intermolecular forces are large have relatively low vapor pressures, because such molecules need high energies to escape to the vapor phase. For example, although water is a much smaller molecule than diethyl ether, C_2H_5—O—C_2H_5, the strong hydrogen-bonding forces in water cause its vapor pressure to be much lower than that of ether (see Figure 14.10).

EXAMPLE 14.3 **Using Knowledge of Intermolecular Forces to Predict Vapor Pressure**

Predict which substance in each of the following pairs will show the largest vapor pressure at a given temperature.

   a. $H_2O(l)$, $CH_3OH(l)$

   b. $CH_3OH(l)$, $CH_3CH_2CH_2CH_2OH(l)$

SOLUTION

   a. Water contains two polar O—H bonds; methanol (CH_3OH) has only one. Therefore, the hydrogen bonding among H_2O molecules is expected to be much stronger than that among CH_3OH molecules. This gives water a lower vapor pressure than methanol.

   b. Each of these molecules has one polar O—H bond. However, because $CH_3CH_2CH_2CH_2OH$ is a much larger molecule than CH_3OH, it has much greater London forces and thus is less likely to escape from its liquid. Thus $CH_3CH_2CH_2CH_2OH(l)$ has a lower vapor pressure than $CH_3OH(l)$. ∎

14.5 The Solid State: Types of Solids

OBJECTIVE: To learn about the various types of crystalline solids.

Solids play a very important role in our lives. The concrete we drive on, the trees that shade us, the windows we look through, the paper that holds this print, the diamond in an engagement ring, and the plastic lenses in eyeglasses are all important solids. Most solids, such as wood, paper, and glass, contain mixtures of various components. However, some natural solids, such as diamonds and table salt, are nearly pure substances.

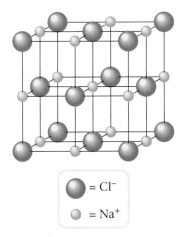

= Cl⁻

= Na⁺

Figure 14.11

The regular arrangement of sodium and chloride ions in sodium chloride, a crystalline solid.

a

Quartz, SiO₂

b

Rock salt, NaCl

c

Iron pyrite, FeS₂

Figure 14.12

Several crystalline solids.

Many substances form **crystalline solids**—those with a regular arrangement of their components. This is illustrated by the partial structure of sodium chloride shown in Figure 14.11. The highly ordered arrangement of the components in a crystalline solid produces beautiful, regularly shaped crystals such as those shown in Figure 14.12.

There are many different types of crystalline solids. For example, both sugar and salt have beautiful crystals that we can easily see. However, although both dissolve readily in water, the properties of the resulting solutions are quite different. The salt solution readily conducts an electric current; the sugar solution does not. This behavior arises from the different natures of the components in these two solids. Common salt, NaCl, is an ionic solid that contains Na⁺ and Cl⁻ ions. When solid sodium chloride dissolves in water, sodium ions and chloride ions are distributed throughout the resulting solution. These ions are free to move through the solution to conduct an electric current. Table sugar (sucrose), on the other hand, is composed of neutral molecules that are dispersed throughout the water when the solid dissolves. No ions are present, and the resulting solution does not conduct electricity. These examples illustrate two important types of crystalline solids: **ionic solids,** represented by sodium chloride; and **molecular solids,** represented by sucrose.

A third type of crystalline solid is represented by elements such as graphite and diamond (both pure carbon), boron, silicon, and all metals. These substances, which contain atoms of only one element covalently bonded to each other, are called **atomic solids.**

We have seen that crystalline solids can be grouped conveniently into three classes as shown in Figure 14.13. Notice that the names of the three classes come from the components of the solid. An ionic solid contains ions,

Figure 14.13

The classes of crystalline solids.

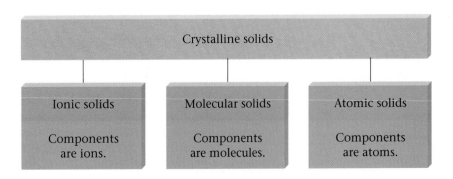

Crystalline solids

Ionic solids

Components are ions.

Molecular solids

Components are molecules.

Atomic solids

Components are atoms.

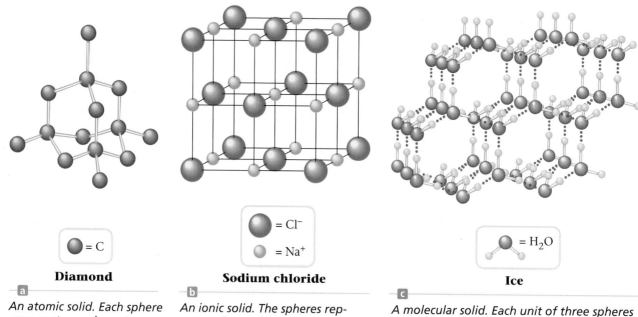

Diamond

a

An atomic solid. Each sphere represents a carbon atom in diamond.

Sodium chloride

b

An ionic solid. The spheres represent alternating Na^+ and Cl^- ions in solid sodium chloride.

Ice

c

A molecular solid. Each unit of three spheres represents an H_2O molecule in ice. The dashed lines show the hydrogen bonding among the polar water molecules.

Figure 14.14

Examples of three types of crystalline solids. Only part of the structure is shown in each case. The structures continue in three dimensions with the same patterns.

a molecular solid contains molecules, and an atomic solid contains atoms. Examples of the three types of solids are shown in Figure 14.14.

The properties of a solid are determined primarily by the nature of the forces that hold the solid together. For example, although argon, copper, and diamond are all atomic solids (their components are atoms), they have strikingly different properties. Argon has a very low melting point (-189 °C), whereas diamond and copper melt at high temperatures (about 3500 °C and 1083 °C, respectively). Copper is an excellent conductor of electricity (it is widely used for electrical wires), whereas both argon and diamond are insulators. The shape of copper can easily be changed; it is both malleable (will form thin sheets) and ductile (can be pulled into a wire). Diamond, on the other hand, is the hardest natural substance known. The marked differences in properties among these three atomic solids are due to differences in bonding. We will explore the bonding in solids in the next section.

> The internal forces in a solid determine many of the properties of the solid.

14.6 Bonding in Solids

OBJECTIVES: To understand the interparticle forces in crystalline solids. • To learn about how the bonding in metals determines metallic properties.

> Ionic solids were also discussed in Section 12.5.

We have seen that crystalline solids can be divided into three classes, depending on the fundamental particle or unit of the solid. Ionic solids consist of oppositely charged ions packed together, molecular solids contain molecules, and atomic solids have atoms as their fundamental particles. Examples of the various types of solids are given in Table 14.3.

Table 14.3	Examples of the Various Types of Solids	
Type of Solid	Examples	Fundamental Unit(s)
ionic	sodium chloride, NaCl(s)	Na^+, Cl^- ions
ionic	ammonium nitrate, $NH_4NO_3(s)$	NH_4^+, NO_3^- ions
molecular	dry ice, $CO_2(s)$	CO_2 molecules
molecular	ice, $H_2O(s)$	H_2O molecules
atomic	diamond, C(s)	C atoms
atomic	iron, Fe(s)	Fe atoms
atomic	argon, Ar(s)	Ar atoms

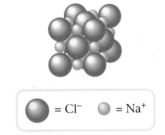

= Cl⁻   = Na⁺

Figure 14.15
The packing of Cl⁻ and Na⁺ ions in solid sodium chloride.

▶ Ionic Solids

Ionic solids are stable substances with high melting points that are held together by the strong forces that exist between oppositely charged ions. The structures of ionic solids can be visualized best by thinking of the ions as spheres packed together as efficiently as possible. For example, in NaCl the larger Cl^- ions are packed together much like one would pack balls in a box. The smaller Na^+ ions occupy the small spaces ("holes") left among the spherical Cl^- ions, as represented in Figure 14.15.

▶ Molecular Solids

In a molecular solid the fundamental particle is a molecule. Examples of molecular solids include ice (contains H_2O molecules), dry ice (contains CO_2 molecules), sulfur (contains S_8 molecules), and white phosphorus (contains P_4 molecules). The latter two substances are shown in Figure 14.16.

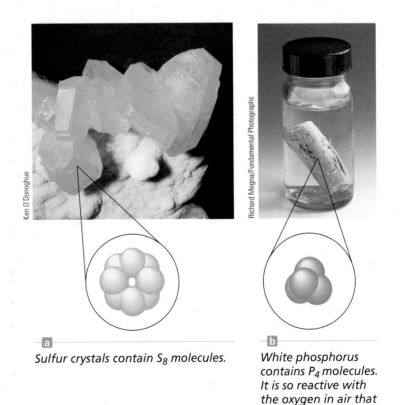

Ken O'Donoghue

Richard Megna/Fundamental Photographs

a

Sulfur crystals contain S₈ molecules.

b

White phosphorus contains P₄ molecules. It is so reactive with the oxygen in air that it must be stored under water.

Figure 14.16

Molecular solids tend to melt at relatively low temperatures because the intermolecular forces that exist among the molecules are relatively weak. If the molecule has a dipole moment, dipole–dipole forces hold the solid together. In solids with nonpolar molecules, London dispersion forces hold the solid together.

Part of the structure of solid phosphorus is represented in Figure 14.17. Note that the distances between P atoms in a given molecule are much shorter than the distances between the P_4 molecules. This is because the covalent bonds *between atoms* in the molecule are so much stronger than the London dispersion forces *between molecules*.

▶ Atomic Solids

The properties of atomic solids vary greatly because of the different ways in which the fundamental particles, the atoms, can interact with each other. For example, the solids of the Group 8 elements have very low melting points (see Table 14.2), because these atoms, having filled valence orbitals, cannot form covalent bonds with each other. So the forces in these solids are the relatively weak London dispersion forces.

On the other hand, diamond, a form of solid carbon, is one of the hardest substances known and has an extremely high melting point (about 3500 °C). The incredible hardness of diamond arises from the very strong covalent carbon–carbon bonds in the crystal, which lead to a giant

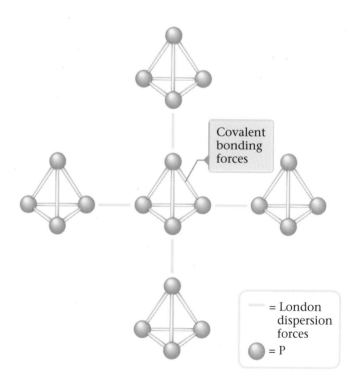

Covalent bonding forces

= London dispersion forces

= P

Figure 14.17

A representation of part of the structure of solid phosphorus, a molecular solid that contains P_4 molecules.

molecule. In fact, the entire crystal can be viewed as one huge molecule. A small part of the diamond structure is represented in Figure 14.14a. In diamond each carbon atom is bound covalently to four other carbon atoms to produce a very stable solid. Several other elements also form solids whereby the atoms join together covalently to form giant molecules. Silicon and boron are examples.

At this point you might be asking yourself, "Why aren't solids such as a crystal of diamond, which is a 'giant molecule,' classified as molecular solids?" The answer is that, by convention, a solid is classified as a molecular solid only if (like ice, dry ice, sulfur, and phosphorus) it contains small molecules. Substances like diamond that contain giant molecules are called network solids.

▶ **Bonding in Metals**

Metals represent another type of atomic solid. Metals have familiar physical properties: they can be pulled into wires, can be hammered into sheets, and are efficient conductors of heat and electricity. However, although the shapes of most pure metals can be changed relatively easily, metals are also durable and have high melting points. These facts indicate that it is difficult to separate metal atoms but relatively easy to slide them past each other. In other words, the bonding in most metals is *strong* but *nondirectional*.

The simplest picture that explains these observations is the **electron sea model,** which pictures a regular array of metal atoms in a "sea" of valence electrons that are shared among the atoms in a nondirectional way and that are quite mobile in the metal crystal. The mobile electrons can conduct heat and electricity, and the atoms can be moved rather easily, as, for example, when the metal is hammered into a sheet or pulled into a wire.

Because of the nature of the metallic crystal, other elements can be introduced relatively easily to produce substances called alloys. An **alloy** is best defined as *a substance that contains a mixture of elements and has metallic properties.* There are two common types of alloys.

In a **substitutional alloy** some of the host metal atoms are *replaced* by other metal atoms of similar sizes. For example, in brass approximately one-third of the atoms in the host copper metal have been replaced by zinc atoms, as shown in Figure 14.18a. Sterling silver (93% silver and 7% copper) and pewter (85% tin, 7% copper, 6% bismuth, and 2% antimony) are other examples of substitutional alloys.

An **interstitial alloy** is formed when some of the interstices (holes) among the closely packed metal atoms are occupied by atoms much smaller than the host atoms, as shown in Figure 14.18b. Steel, the

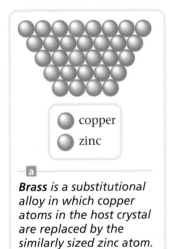

copper
zinc

a

Brass is a substitutional alloy in which copper atoms in the host crystal are replaced by the similarly sized zinc atom.

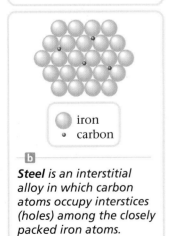

iron
carbon

b

Steel is an interstitial alloy in which carbon atoms occupy interstices (holes) among the closely packed iron atoms.

Figure 14.18

Two types of alloys.

A steel sculpture in Chicago.

Metal with a Memory

A distraught mother walks into the optical shop carrying her mangled pair of $400 eyeglasses. Her child had gotten into her purse, found her glasses, and twisted them into a pretzel. She hands them to the optometrist with little hope that they can be salvaged. The optometrist says not to worry and drops the glasses into a dish of warm water where the glasses magically spring back to their original shape. The optometrist hands the restored glasses to the woman and says there is no charge for repairing them.

How can the frames "remember" their original shape when placed in warm water? The answer is a nickel–titanium alloy called Nitinol that was developed in the late 1950s and early 1960s at the Naval Ordnance Laboratory in White Oak, Maryland, by William J. Buehler. (The name Nitinol comes from *Ni*ckel *Ti*tanium *N*aval *O*rdnance *L*aboratory.)

Nitinol has the amazing ability to remember a shape originally impressed in it. For example,

note the accompanying photos. What causes Nitinol to behave this way? Although the details are too complicated to describe here, this phenomenon results from two different forms of solid Nitinol. When Nitinol is heated to a sufficiently high temperature, the Ni and Ti atoms arrange themselves in a way that leads to the most compact and regular pattern of the atoms—a form called austenite (A). When the alloy is cooled, its atoms rearrange slightly to a form called martensite (M). The shape desired (for example, the word *ICE*) is set into the alloy at a high temperature (A form), then the metal is cooled, causing it to assume the M form. In this process no visible change is noted. Then, if the image is deformed, it will magically return if the alloy is heated (hot water works fine) to a temperature that changes it back to the A form.

Nitinol has many medical applications, including hooks used by orthopedic surgeons to attach ligaments and tendons to bone and "baskets" to catch blood clots. In the latter case a length of Nitinol wire is shaped into a tiny basket and this shape is set at a high temperature. The

best-known interstitial alloy, contains carbon atoms in the "holes" of an iron crystal. The presence of interstitial atoms changes the properties of the host metal. Pure iron is relatively soft, ductile, and malleable because of the absence of strong directional bonding. The spherical metal atoms can be moved rather easily with respect to each other. However, when carbon, which forms strong directional bonds, is introduced into an iron crystal, the presence of the directional carbon–iron bonds makes the resulting alloy harder, stronger, and less ductile than pure iron. The amount of carbon directly affects the properties of steel. *Mild steels* (containing less than 0.2% carbon) are still ductile and malleable and are used for nails, cables, and chains. *Medium steels* (containing 0.2–0.6% carbon) are harder than mild steels and are used in rails and structural steel beams. *High-carbon steels* (containing 0.6–1.5% carbon) are tough and hard and are used for springs, tools, and cutlery.

Many types of steel contain other elements in addition to iron and carbon. Such steels are often called *alloy steels* and can be viewed as being mixed interstitial (carbon) and substitutional (other metals) alloys. An example is stainless steel, which has chromium and nickel atoms substituted for some of the iron atoms. The addition of these metals greatly increases the steel's resistance to corrosion.

wires forming the basket are then straightened so they can be inserted as a small bundle through a catheter. When the wires warm up in the blood, the basket shape springs back and acts as a filter to stop blood clots from moving to the heart.

One of the most promising consumer uses of Nitinol is for eyeglass frames. Nitinol is also now being used for braces to straighten crooked teeth.

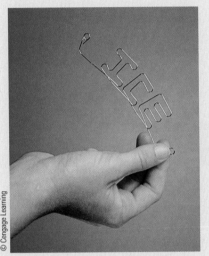

The word ICE is formed from Nitinol wire.

The wire is stretched to obliterate the word ICE.

The wire pops back to ICE when immersed in warm water.

EXAMPLE 14.4 | Identifying Types of Crystalline Solids

Name the type of crystalline solid formed by each of the following substances:

    a. ammonia

    b. iron

    c. cesium fluoride

    d. argon

    e. sulfur

SOLUTION

    a. Solid ammonia contains NH_3 molecules, so it is a molecular solid.

    b. Solid iron contains iron atoms as the fundamental particles. It is an atomic solid.

    c. Solid cesium fluoride contains the Cs^+ and F^- ions. It is an ionic solid.

d. Solid argon contains argon atoms, which cannot form covalent bonds to each other. It is an atomic solid.

e. Sulfur contains S_8 molecules, so it is a molecular solid.

Self-Check **EXERCISE 14.2**   Name the type of crystalline solid formed by each of the following substances:

a. sulfur trioxide

b. barium oxide

c. gold

See Problems 14.41 and 14.42. ■

CHAPTER 14 REVIEW

Key Terms

normal boiling
   point (14.1)
heating/cooling
   curve (14.1)
normal freezing
   point (14.1)
intramolecular
   forces (14.2)
intermolecular
   forces (14.2)
molar heat of
   fusion (14.2)
molar heat of
   vaporization (14.2)
dipole–dipole
   attraction (14.3)

hydrogen bonding (14.3)
London dispersion
   forces (14.3)
vaporization
   (evaporation) (14.4)
condensation (14.4)
vapor pressure (14.4)
crystalline solid (14.5)
ionic solid (14.5)
molecular solid (14.5)
atomic solid (14.5)
electron sea model (14.6)
alloy (14.6)
substitutional
   alloy (14.6)
interstitial alloy (14.6)

F   directs you to the *Chemistry in Focus* feature in the chapter

VP   indicates visual problems

OWL   interactive versions of these problems are assignable in OWL

Summary

1. Liquids and solids exhibit some similarities and are very different from the gaseous state.

2. The temperature at which a liquid changes its state to a gas (at 1 atm pressure) is called the normal boiling point of that liquid. Similarly, the temperature at which a liquid freezes (at 1 atm pressure) is the normal freezing point. Changes of state are physical changes, not chemical changes.

3. To convert a substance from the solid to the liquid and then to the gaseous state requires the addition of energy. Forces among the molecules in a solid or a liquid must be overcome by the input of energy. The energy required to melt 1 mole of a substance is called the molar heat of fusion, and the energy required to change 1 mole of liquid to the gaseous state is called the molar heat of vaporization.

4. There are several types of intermolecular forces. Dipole–dipole interactions occur when molecules with dipole moments attract each other. A particularly strong dipole–dipole interaction called hydrogen bonding occurs in molecules that contain hydrogen bonded to a very electronegative element such as N, O, or F. London dispersion forces occur when instantaneous dipoles in atoms or nonpolar molecules lead to relatively weak attractions.

5. The change of a liquid to its vapor is called vaporization or evaporation. The process whereby vapor molecules form a liquid is called condensation. In a closed container, the pressure of the vapor over its liquid reaches a constant value called the vapor pressure of the liquid.

6. Many solids are crystalline (contain highly regular arrangements of their components). The three types

of crystalline solids are ionic, molecular, and atomic solids. In ionic solids, the ions are packed together in a way that maximizes the attractions of oppositely charged ions and minimizes the repulsions among identically charged ions. Molecular solids are held together by dipole–dipole attractions if the molecules are polar and by London dispersion forces if the molecules are nonpolar. Atomic solids are held together by covalent bonding forces or London dispersion forces, depending on the atoms present.

Active Learning Questions

These questions are designed to be considered by groups of students in class. Often these questions work well for introducing a particular topic in class.

1. You seal a container half-filled with water. Which best describes what occurs in the container?

   a. Water evaporates until the air becomes saturated with water vapor; at this point, no more water evaporates.
   b. Water evaporates until the air becomes overly saturated (supersaturated) with water, and most of this water recondenses; this cycle continues until a certain amount of water vapor is present, and then the cycle ceases.
   c. The water does not evaporate because the container is sealed.
   d. Water evaporates, and then water evaporates and recondenses simultaneously and continuously.
   e. The water evaporates until it is eventually all in vapor form.

   Justify your choice and for choices you did not pick, explain what is wrong with them.

2. Explain the following: You add 100 mL of water to a 500-mL round-bottomed flask and heat the water until it is boiling. You remove the heat and stopper the flask, and the boiling stops. You then run cool water over the neck of the flask, and the boiling begins again. It seems as though you are boiling water by cooling it.

3. Is it possible for the dispersion forces in a particular substance to be stronger than hydrogen-bonding forces in another substance? Explain your answer.

4. Does the nature of intermolecular forces change when a substance goes from a solid to a liquid, or from a liquid to a gas? What causes a substance to undergo a phase change?

5. How does vapor pressure change with changing temperature? Explain.

6. What occurs when the vapor pressure of a liquid is equal to atmospheric pressure? Explain.

7. What is the vapor pressure of water at 100 °C? How do you know?

8. How do the following physical properties depend on the strength of intermolecular forces? Explain.

   a. melting point
   b. boiling point
   c. vapor pressure

9. Look at Figure 14.2. Why doesn't temperature increase continuously over time? That is, why does the temperature stay constant for periods of time?

10. Which are stronger, intermolecular or intramolecular forces for a given molecule? What observation(s) have you made that supports this position? Explain.

11. Why does water evaporate at all?

12. Sketch a microscopic picture of water and distinguish between *intramolecular bonds* and *intermolecular forces*. Which correspond to the bonds we draw in Lewis structures?

13. Which has the stronger intermolecular forces: N_2 or H_2O? Explain.

14. Which gas would behave more ideally at the same conditions of pressure and temperature: CO or N_2? Why?

15. You have seen that the water molecule has a bent shape and therefore is a polar molecule. This accounts for many of water's interesting properties. What if the water molecule were linear? How would this affect the properties of water? How would life be different?

16. True or false? Methane (CH_4) is more likely to form stronger hydrogen bonding than is water because each methane molecule has twice as many hydrogen atoms. Provide a concise explanation of hydrogen bonding to go with your answer.

17. Why should it make sense that N_2 exists as a gas? Given your answer, how is it possible to make liquid nitrogen? Explain why lowering the temperature works.

18. White phosphorus and sulfur both are called molecular solids even though each is made of only phosphorus and sulfur, respectively. How can they be considered molecular solids? If this is true, why isn't diamond (which is made up only of carbon) a molecular solid?

19. Why is it incorrect to use the term "molecule of NaCl" but correct to use the term "molecule of H_2O"? Is the term "molecule of diamond" correct? Explain.

20. Which would you predict should be larger for a given substance: ΔH_{vap} or ΔH_{fus}? Explain why.

VP 21. In the diagram below, which lines represent the hydrogen bonds?

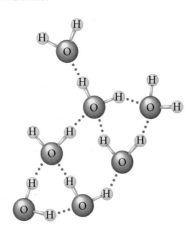

a. The dotted lines between the hydrogen atoms of one water molecule and the oxygen atoms of a different water molecule.
b. The solid lines between a hydrogen atom and oxygen atom in the same water molecule.
c. Both the solid lines and dotted lines represent the hydrogen bonds.
d. There are no hydrogen bonds represented in the diagram.

VP 22. Use the heating/cooling curve below to answer the following questions.

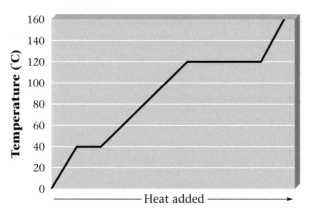

a. What is the freezing point of the liquid?
b. What is the boiling point of the liquid?
c. Which is greater: the head of fusion or the heat of vaporization? Explain.

VP 23. Assume the two-dimensional structure of an ionic compound, M_xA_y, is

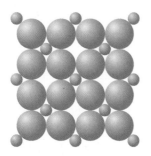

What is the empirical formula of this ionic compound?

Questions and Problems

14.1 Water and Its Phase Changes

QUESTIONS

1. Gases have (higher/lower) densities than liquids or solids.

2. Liquids and solids are (more/less) compressible than are gases.

3. What evidence do we have that the solid form of water is less dense than the liquid form of water at its freezing/melting point?

4. The enthalpy (ΔH) of *vaporization* of water is about seven times larger than water's enthalpy of *fusion* (41 kJ/mol versus 6 kJ/mol). What does this tell us about the relative similarities among the solid, liquid, and gaseous states of water?

5. Consider a sample of ice being heated from -5 °C to $+5$ °C. Describe on both a macroscopic and a microscopic basis what happens to the ice as the temperature reaches 0 °C.

6. Sketch a heating/cooling curve for water, starting out at -20 °C and going up to 120 °C, applying heat to the sample at a constant rate. Mark on your sketch the portions of the curve that represent the melting of the solid and the boiling of the liquid.

14.2 Energy Requirements for the Changes of State

QUESTIONS

7. Are changes in state *physical* or *chemical* changes for molecular solids? Why?

8. Describe in detail the microscopic processes that take place when a solid melts and when a liquid boils. What kind of forces must be overcome? Are any chemical bonds broken during these processes?

9. Explain the difference between *intra*molecular and *inter*molecular forces.

10. The forces that connect two hydrogen atoms to an oxygen atom in a water molecule are (intermolecular/intramolecular), but the forces that hold water molecules close together in an ice cube are (intermolecular/intramolecular).

11. Discuss the similarities and differences between the arrangements of molecules and the forces between molecules in liquid water versus steam, and in liquid water versus ice.

12. What does the *molar heat of fusion* of a substance represent?

PROBLEMS

13. The following data have been collected for substance X. Construct a heating curve for substance X. (The drawing does not need to be absolutely to scale, but it should clearly show relative differences.)

normal melting point	$-15\,°C$
molar heat of fusion	2.5 kJ/mol
normal boiling point	134 °C
molar heat of vaporization	55.3 kJ/mol

14. The molar heat of fusion of aluminum metal is 10.79 kJ/mol, whereas its heat of vaporization is 293.4 kJ/mol.

  a. Why is the heat of fusion of aluminum so much smaller than the heat of vaporization?
  b. What quantity of heat would be required to vaporize 1.00 g of aluminum at its normal boiling point?
  c. What quantity of heat would be evolved if 5.00 g of liquid aluminum freezes at its normal freezing point?
  d. What quantity of heat would be required to melt 0.105 mole of aluminum at its normal melting point?

15. The molar heat of fusion of benzene is 9.92 kJ/mol. Its molar heat of vaporization is 30.7 kJ/mol. Calculate the heat required to melt 8.25 g of benzene at its normal melting point. Calculate the heat required to vaporize 8.25 g of benzene at its normal boiling point. Why is the heat of vaporization more than three times the heat of fusion?

16. The molar heats of fusion and vaporization for silver are 11.3 kJ/mol and 250. kJ/mol, respectively. Silver's normal melting point is 962 °C, and its normal boiling point is 2212 °C. What quantity of heat is required to melt 12.5 g of silver at 962 °C? What quantity of heat is liberated when 4.59 g of silver vapor condenses at 2212 °C?

17. Given that the specific heat capacities of ice and steam are 2.06 J/g °C and 2.03 J/g °C, respectively, and considering the information about water given in Exercise 16, calculate the total quantity of heat evolved when 10.0 g of steam at 200. °C is condensed, cooled, and frozen to ice at −50. °C.

18. It requires 113 J to melt 1.00 g of sodium metal at its normal melting point of 98 °C. Calculate the *molar heat of fusion* of sodium.

14.3 Intermolecular Forces

QUESTIONS

19. Consider the iodine monochloride molecule, ICl. Because chlorine is more electronegative than iodine, this molecule is a dipole. How would you expect iodine monochloride molecules in the gaseous state to orient themselves with respect to each other as the sample is cooled and the molecules begin to aggregate? Sketch the orientation you would expect.

20. Dipole–dipole forces become _____ as the distance between the dipoles increases.

21. The text implies that hydrogen bonding is a special case of very strong dipole–dipole interactions possible among only certain atoms. What atoms in addition to hydrogen are necessary for hydrogen bonding? How does the small size of the hydrogen atom contribute to the unusual strength of the dipole–dipole forces involved in hydrogen bonding?

22. The normal boiling point of water is unusually high, compared to the boiling points of H_2S, H_2Se, and H_2Te. Explain this observation in terms of the *hydrogen bonding* that exists in water, but that does not exist in the other compounds.

23. Why are the dipole–dipole interactions between polar molecules *not* important in the vapor phase?

24. What are London dispersion forces, and how do they arise?

PROBLEMS

25. What type of intermolecular forces is active in the liquid state of each of the following substances?

  a. Ne
  b. CO
  c. CH_3OH
  d. Cl_2

26. Discuss the types of intermolecular forces acting in the liquid state of each of the following substances.

  a. Xe
  b. NH_3
  c. F_2
  d. ICl

27. The boiling points of the noble gas elements are listed below. Comment on the trend in the boiling points. Why do the boiling points vary in this manner?

He	$-272\,°C$	Kr	$-152.3\,°C$
Ne	$-245.9\,°C$	Xe	$-107.1\,°C$
Ar	$-185.7\,°C$	Rn	$-61.8\,°C$

28. The heats of fusion of three substances are listed below. Explain the trend this list reflects.

HI	2.87 kJ/mol
HBr	2.41 kJ/mol
HCl	1.99 kJ/mol

29. When dry ammonia gas (NH_3) is bubbled into a 125-mL sample of water, the volume of the sample (initially, at least) *decreases* slightly. Suggest a reason for this.

All even-numbered Questions and Problems have answers in the back of this book and solutions in the *Solutions Guide*.

30. When 50 mL of liquid water at 25 °C is added to 50 mL of ethanol (ethyl alcohol), also at 25 °C, the combined volume of the mixture is considerably *less* than 100 mL. Give a possible explanation.

14.4 Evaporation and Vapor Pressure

QUESTIONS

31. What is *evaporation*? What is *condensation*? Which of these processes is endothermic and which is exothermic?

32. If you've ever opened a bottle of rubbing alcohol or other solvent on a warm day, you may have heard a little "whoosh" as the vapor that had built up above the liquid escapes. Describe on a microscopic basis how a vapor pressure builds up in a closed container above a liquid. What processes in the container give rise to this phenomenon?

33. What do we mean by a *dynamic equilibrium?* Describe how the development of a vapor pressure above a liquid represents such an equilibrium.

34. Consider Figure 14.10. Imagine you are talking to a friend who has not taken any science courses, and explain how the figure demonstrates the concept of vapor pressure and enables it to be measured.

PROBLEMS

35. Which substance in each pair would be expected to have a lower boiling point? Explain your reasoning.
    a. CH_3OH or $CH_3CH_2CH_2OH$
    b. CH_3CH_3 or CH_3CH_2OH
    c. H_2O or CH_4

36. Which substance in each pair would be expected to show the largest vapor pressure at a given temperature? Explain your reasoning.
    a. $H_2O(l)$ or $HF(l)$
    b. $CH_3OCH_3(l)$ or $CH_3CH_2OH(l)$
    c. $CH_3OH(l)$ or $CH_3SH(l)$

37. Although water and ammonia differ in molar mass by only one unit, the boiling point of water is over 100 °C higher than that of ammonia. What forces in liquid water that do *not* exist in liquid ammonia could account for this observation?

38. Two molecules that contain the same number of each kind of atom but that have different molecular structures are said to be *isomers* of each other. For example, both ethyl alcohol and dimethyl ether (shown below) have the formula C_2H_6O and are isomers. Based on considerations of intermolecular forces, which substance would you expect to be more volatile? Which would you expect to have the higher boiling point? Explain.

dimethyl ether	ethyl alcohol
CH_3-O-CH_3	CH_3-CH_2-OH

14.5 The Solid State: Types of Solids

QUESTIONS

39. What are crystalline solids? What kind of microscopic structure do such solids have? How is this microscopic structure reflected in the macroscopic appearance of such solids?

40. On the basis of the smaller units that make up the crystals, cite three types of crystalline solids. For each type of crystalline solid, give an example of a substance that forms that type of solid.

14.6 Bonding in Solids

QUESTIONS

41. How do *ionic* solids differ in structure from *molecular* solids? What are the fundamental particles in each? Give two examples of each type of solid and indicate the individual particles that make up the solids in each of your examples.

42. A common prank on college campuses is to switch the salt and sugar on dining hall tables, which is usually easy because the substances look so much alike. Yet, despite the similarity in their appearance, these two substances differ greatly in their properties, since one is a molecular solid and the other is an ionic solid. How do the properties differ and why?

43. Ionic solids are generally considerably harder than most molecular solids. Explain.

44. Although crystals of table salt (sodium chloride) and table sugar (sucrose) look very similar to the naked eye, the melting point of sucrose (186 °C) is several hundred degrees less than the melting point of sodium chloride (801 °C). Explain.

45. The forces holding together a molecular solid are much (stronger/weaker) than the forces between particles in an ionic solid.

46. Explain the overall trend in melting points given below in terms of the forces among particles in the solids indicated.

Hydrogen, H_2	-259 °C
Ethyl alcohol, C_2H_5OH	-114 °C
Water, H_2O	0 °C
Sucrose, $C_{12}H_{22}O_{11}$	186 °C
Calcium chloride, $CaCl_2$	772 °C

47. What is a *network* solid? Give an example of a network solid and describe the bonding in such a solid. How does a network solid differ from a molecular solid?

48. Ionic solids do not conduct electricity in the solid state, but are strong conductors in the liquid state and when dissolved in water. Explain.

All even-numbered Questions and Problems have answers in the back of this book and solutions in the Solutions Guide.

49. What is an *alloy?* Explain the differences in structure between substitutional and interstitial alloys. Give an example of each type.

Ⓕ 50. The "Chemistry in Focus" segment *Metal with a Memory* discusses Nitinol, an alloy that "remembers" a shape originally impressed in it. Which elements compose Nitinol, and why is it classified as an alloy?

Additional Problems

MATCHING

For Exercises 51–60 choose one of the following terms to match the definition or description given.

  a. alloy
  b. specific heat
  c. crystalline solid
  d. dipole–dipole attraction
  e. equilibrium vapor pressure
  f. intermolecular
  g. intramolecular
  h. ionic solids
  i. London dispersion forces
  j. molar heat of fusion
  k. molar heat of vaporization
  l. molecular solids
  m. normal boiling point
  n. semiconductor

51. boiling point at pressure of 1 atm

52. energy required to melt 1 mole of a substance

53. forces between atoms in a molecule

54. forces between molecules in a solid

55. instantaneous dipole forces for nonpolar molecules

56. lining up of opposite charges on adjacent polar molecules

57. maximum pressure of vapor that builds up in a closed container

58. mixture of elements having metallic properties overall

59. repeating arrangement of component species in a solid

60. solids that melt at relatively low temperatures

61. Given the densities and conditions of ice, liquid water, and steam listed in Table 14.1, calculate the volume of 1.0 g of water under each of these circumstances.

62. In carbon compounds a given group of atoms can often be arranged in more than one way. This means that more than one structure may be possible for the same atoms. For example, both the molecules diethyl ether and 1-butanol have the same number of each type of atom, but they have different structures and are said to be *isomers* of one another.

  diethyl ether $CH_3-CH_2-O-CH_2-CH_3$
  1-butanol $CH_3-CH_2-CH_2-CH_2-OH$

Which substance would you expect to have the larger vapor pressure? Why?

63. Which of the substances in each of the following sets would be expected to have the highest boiling point? Explain why.

  a. Ga, KBr, O_2
  b. Hg, $NaCl$, He
  c. H_2, O_2, H_2O

64. Which of the substances in each of the following sets would be expected to have the lowest melting point? Explain why.

  a. H_2, N_2, O_2
  b. Xe, $NaCl$, C (diamond)
  c. Cl_2, Br_2, I_2

65. When a person has a severe fever, one therapy to reduce the fever is an "alcohol rub." Explain how the evaporation of alcohol from the person's skin removes heat energy from the body.

66. What is steel?

67. Some properties of potassium metal are summarized in the following table:

Normal melting point	63.5 °C
Normal boiling point	765.7 °C
Molar heat of fusion	2.334 kJ/mol
Molar heat of vaporization	79.87 kJ/mol
Specific heat of the solid	0.75 J/g °C

  a. Calculate the quantity of heat required to heat 5.00 g of potassium from 25.3 °C to 45.2 °C.
  b. Calculate the quantity of heat required to melt 1.35 moles of potassium at its normal melting point.
  c. Calculate the quantity of heat required to vaporize 2.25 g of potassium at its normal boiling point.

68. What are some important uses of water, both in nature and in industry? What is the liquid range for water?

69. Describe, on both a microscopic and a macroscopic basis, what happens to a sample of water as it is cooled from room temperature to 50 °C below its normal freezing point.

70. Cake mixes and other packaged foods that require cooking often contain special directions for use at high elevations. Typically these directions indicate that the food should be cooked longer above 5000 ft. Explain why it takes longer to cook something at higher elevations.

71. Why is there no change in *intra*molecular forces when a solid is melted? Are intramolecular forces stronger or weaker than intermolecular forces?

72. What do we call the energies required, respectively, to melt and to vaporize 1 mole of a substance? Which of these energies is always larger for a given substance? Why?

All even-numbered Questions and Problems have answers in the back of this book and solutions in the *Solutions Guide*.

73. The molar heat of vaporization of carbon disulfide, CS_2, is 28.4 kJ/mol at its normal boiling point of 46 °C. How much energy (heat) is required to vaporize 1.0 g of CS_2 at 46 °C? How much heat is evolved when 50. g of CS_2 is condensed from the vapor to the liquid form at 46 °C?

74. Which is stronger, a dipole–dipole attraction between two molecules or a covalent bond between two atoms within the same molecule? Explain.

75. For a liquid to boil, the intermolecular forces in the liquid must be overcome. Based on the types of intermolecular forces present, arrange the expected boiling points of the liquid states of the following substances in order from lowest to highest: NaCl(l), He(l), CO(l), H_2O(l).

76. What are *London dispersion forces* and how do they arise in a nonpolar molecule? Are London forces typically stronger or weaker than dipole–dipole attractions between polar molecules? Are London forces stronger or weaker than covalent bonds? Explain.

77. Discuss the types of intermolecular forces acting in the liquid state of each of the following substances.

   a. N_2
   b. NH_3
   c. He
   d. CO_2 (linear, nonpolar)

78. Explain how the evaporation of water acts as a coolant for the earth.

79. What do we mean when we say a liquid is *volatile?* Do volatile liquids have large or small vapor pressures? What types of intermolecular forces occur in highly volatile liquids?

80. Although methane, CH_4, and ammonia, NH_3, differ in molar mass by only one unit, the boiling point of ammonia is over 100 °C higher than that of methane (a nonpolar molecule). Explain.

81. Which type of solid is likely to have the highest melting point—an ionic solid, a molecular solid, or an atomic solid? Explain.

82. What types of intermolecular forces exist in a crystal of ice? How do these forces differ from the types of intermolecular forces that exist in a crystal of solid oxygen?

83. Discuss the *electron sea model* for metals. How does this model account for the fact that metals are very good conductors of electricity?

84. Water is unusual in that its solid form (ice) is less dense than its liquid form. Discuss some implications of this fact.

85. Describe in detail the microscopic processes that take place when a liquid boils. What kind of forces must be overcome? Are any chemical bonds broken during these processes?

86. Water at 100 °C (its normal boiling point) could certainly give you a bad burn if it were spilled on the skin, but steam at 100 °C could give you a much *worse* burn. Explain.

87. What is a *dipole–dipole attraction?* Give three examples of liquid substances in which you would expect dipole–dipole attractions to be large.

88. What is meant by *hydrogen bonding?* Give three examples of substances that would be expected to exhibit hydrogen bonding in the liquid state.

89. Although the noble gas elements are monatomic and could not give rise to dipole–dipole forces or hydrogen bonding, these elements still can be liquefied and solidified. Explain.

90. Describe, on a microscopic basis, the processes of *evaporation* and *condensation*. Which process requires an input of energy? Why?

15

Solutions

● Seawater is an aqueous solution. *(Georgette Douwma/Getty Images)*

Most of the important chemistry that keeps plants, animals, and humans functioning occurs in aqueous solutions. Even the water that comes out of a tap is not pure water but a solution of various materials in water. For example, tap water may contain dissolved chlorine to disinfect it, dissolved minerals that make it "hard," and traces of many other substances that result from natural and human-initiated pollution. We encounter many other chemical solutions in our daily lives: air, shampoo, orange soda, coffee, gasoline, cough syrup, and many others.

A **solution** is a homogeneous mixture, a mixture in which the components are uniformly intermingled. This means that a sample from one part is the same as a sample from any other part. For example, the first sip of coffee is the same as the last sip.

The atmosphere that surrounds us is a gaseous solution containing $O_2(g)$, $N_2(g)$, and other gases randomly dispersed. Solutions can also be solids. For example, brass is a homogeneous mixture—a solution—of copper and zinc.

These examples illustrate that a solution can be a gas, a liquid, or a solid (see Table 15.1). The substance present in the largest amount is called the **solvent,** and the other substance or substances are called **solutes.** For example, when we dissolve a teaspoon of sugar in a glass of water, the sugar is the solute and the water is the solvent.

Aqueous solutions are solutions with water as the solvent. Because they are so important, in this chapter we will concentrate on the properties of aqueous solutions.

Brass, a solid solution of copper and zinc, is used to make musical instruments and many other objects.

iStockphoto.com

15.1 Solubility

OBJECTIVES: To understand the process of dissolving. • To learn why certain components dissolve in water.

What happens when you put a teaspoon of sugar in your iced tea and stir it, or when you add salt to water for cooking vegetables? Why do the sugar and salt "disappear" into the water? What does it mean when something dissolves—that is, when a solution forms?

Table 15.1	Various Types of Solutions		
Example	State of Solution	Original State of Solute	State of Solvent
air, natural gas	gas	gas	gas
vodka in water, antifreeze in water	liquid	liquid	liquid
brass	solid	solid	solid
carbonated water (soda)	liquid	gas	liquid
seawater, sugar solution	liquid	solid	liquid

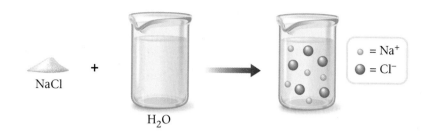

NaCl

H_2O

= Na⁺
= Cl⁻

Figure 15.1

When solid sodium chloride dissolves, the ions are dispersed randomly throughout the solution.

We saw in Chapter 7 that when sodium chloride dissolves in water, the resulting solution conducts an electric current. This convinces us that the solution contains *ions* that can move (this is how the electric current is conducted). The dissolving of solid sodium chloride in water is represented in Figure 15.1. Notice that in the solid state the ions are packed closely together. However, when the solid dissolves, the ions are separated and dispersed throughout the solution. The strong ionic forces that hold the sodium chloride crystal together are overcome by the strong attractions between the ions and the polar water molecules. This process is represented in Figure 15.2. Notice that each polar water molecule orients itself in a way to maximize its attraction with a Cl⁻ or Na⁺ ion. The negative end of a water molecule is attracted to a Na⁺ ion, while the positive end is attracted to a Cl⁻ ion. The strong forces holding the positive and negative ions in the solid are replaced by strong water–ion interactions, and the solid dissolves (the ions disperse).

Cations are positive ions.
Anions are negative ions.

It is important to remember that when an ionic substance (such as a salt) dissolves in water, it breaks up into *individual* cations and anions, which are dispersed in the water. For instance, when ammonium nitrate, NH_4NO_3, dissolves in water, the resulting solution contains NH_4^+ and NO_3^- ions, which move around independently. This process can be represented as

$$NH_4NO_3(s) \xrightarrow{H_2O(l)} NH_4^+(aq) + NO_3^-(aq)$$

where (*aq*) indicates that the ions are surrounded by water molecules.

Figure 15.2

Polar water molecules interact with the positive and negative ions of a salt. These interactions replace the strong ionic forces holding the ions together in the undissolved solid, thus assisting in the dissolving process.

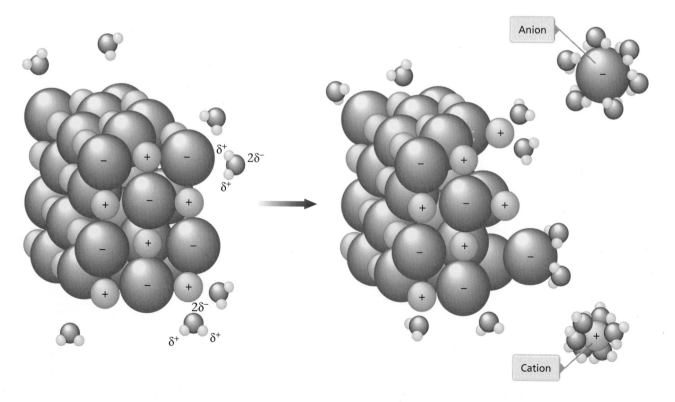

Anion

Cation

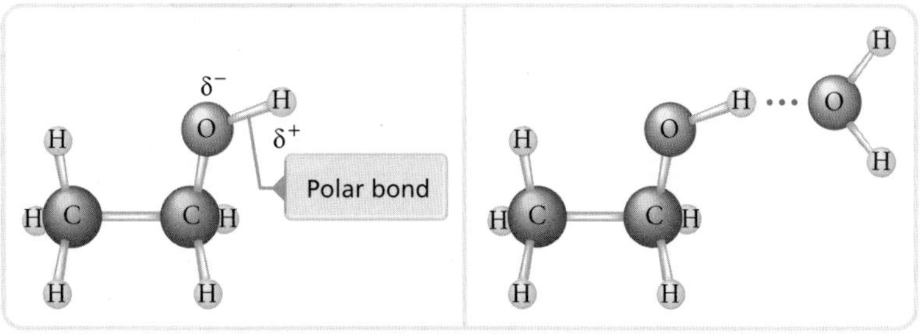

Figure 15.3

a The ethanol molecule contains a polar O—H bond similar to those in the water molecule.

b The polar water molecule interacts strongly with the polar O—H bond in ethanol.

A satellite photo of an oil spill in Tokyo Bay.

Water also dissolves many nonionic substances. Sugar is one example of a nonionic solute that is very soluble in water. Another example is ethanol, C_2H_5OH. Wine, beer, and mixed drinks are aqueous solutions of ethanol (and other substances). Why is ethanol so soluble in water? The answer lies in the structure of the ethanol molecule (Figure 15.3a). The molecule contains a polar O—H bond like those in water, which makes it very compatible with water. Just as hydrogen bonds form among water molecules in pure water (see Figure 14.6), ethanol molecules can form hydrogen bonds with water molecules in a solution of the two. This is shown in Figure 15.3b.

The sugar molecule (common table sugar has the chemical name sucrose) is shown in Figure 15.4. Notice that this molecule has many polar O—H groups, each of which can hydrogen-bond to a water molecule. Because of the attractions between sucrose and water molecules, solid sucrose is quite soluble in water.

Many substances do not dissolve in water. For example, when petroleum leaks from a damaged tanker, it does not disperse uniformly in the water (does not dissolve) but rather floats on the surface because its density is less than that of water. Petroleum is a mixture of molecules like the one shown in Figure 15.5. Since carbon and hydrogen have very similar electronegativities, the bonding electrons are shared almost equally and the

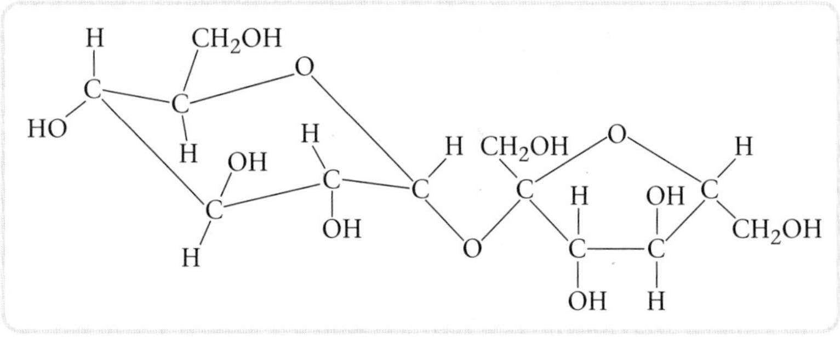

Figure 15.4

The structure of common table sugar (called sucrose). The large number of polar O—H groups in the molecule causes sucrose to be very soluble in water.

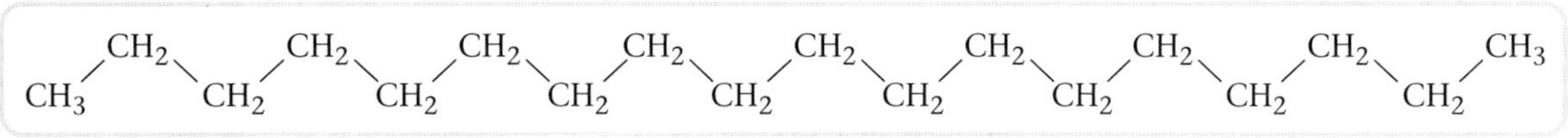

Figure 15.5

A molecule typical of those found in petroleum. The bonds are not polar.

What Do We Know?

- We have 1.00 g ethanol (C_2H_5OH) in 100.0 g water (H_2O).

- Mass percent $= \dfrac{\text{mass of solute}}{\text{mass of solution}} \times 100\%$.

How Do We Get There?

In this case we have 1.00 g of solute (ethanol) and 100.0 g of solvent (water). We now apply the definition of mass percent.

$$\text{Mass percent } C_2H_5OH = \left(\frac{\text{grams of } C_2H_5OH}{\text{grams of solution}}\right) \times 100\%$$

$$= \left(\frac{1.00 \text{ g } C_2H_5OH}{100.0 \text{ g } H_2O + 1.00 \text{ g } C_2H_5OH}\right) \times 100\%$$

$$= \frac{1.00 \text{ g}}{101.0 \text{ g}} \times 100\%$$

$$= 0.990\% \ C_2H_5OH$$

REALITY CHECK The percent mass is just under 1%, which makes sense because we have 1.00 g of ethanol in a bit more than 100.0 g of solution.

Self-Check **EXERCISE 15.1** A 135-g sample of seawater is evaporated to dryness, leaving 4.73 g of solid residue (the salts formerly dissolved in the seawater). Calculate the mass percent of solute present in the original seawater.

See Problems 15.15 and 15.16. ■

EXAMPLE 15.2 | **Solution Composition: Determining Mass of Solute**

Although milk is not a true solution (it is really a suspension of tiny globules of fat, protein, and other substrates in water), it does contain a dissolved sugar called lactose. Cow's milk typically contains 4.5% by mass of lactose, $C_{12}H_{22}O_{11}$. Calculate the mass of lactose present in 175 g of milk.

SOLUTION

Where Are We Going?

We want to determine the mass of lactose present in 175 g of milk.

What Do We Know?

- We have 175 g of milk.

- Milk contains 4.5% by mass of lactose, $C_{12}H_{22}O_{11}$.

- Mass percent $= \dfrac{\text{mass of solute}}{\text{mass of solution}} \times 100\%$.

How Do We Get There?

Using the definition of mass percent, we have

$$\text{Mass percent} = \frac{\text{grams of solute}}{\text{grams of solution}} \times 100\%$$

We now substitute the quantities we know:

$$\text{Mass percent} = \underbrace{\frac{\overbrace{\text{grams of solute}}^{\text{Mass of lactose}}}{\underset{\text{Mass of milk}}{175 \text{ g}}} \times 100\%}_{} = \overset{\text{Mass percent}}{4.5\%}$$

We now solve for grams of solute by multiplying both sides by 175 g,

$$\cancel{175 \text{ g}} \times \frac{\text{grams of solute}}{\cancel{175 \text{ g}}} \times 100\% = 4.5\% \times 175 \text{ g}$$

and then dividing both sides by 100%,

$$\text{Grams of solute} \times \frac{\cancel{100\%}}{\cancel{100\%}} = \frac{4.5\%}{100\%} \times 175 \text{ g}$$

to give

$$\text{Grams of solute} = 0.045 \times 175 \text{ g} = 7.9 \text{ g lactose}$$

Self-Check EXERCISE 15.2   What mass of water must be added to 425 g of formaldehyde to prepare a 40.0% (by mass) solution of formaldehyde? This solution, called formalin, is used to preserve biological specimens.

HINT: Substitute the known quantities into the definition for mass percent, and then solve for the unknown quantity (mass of solvent).

See Problems 15.17 and 15.18. ∎

15.4 Solution Composition: Molarity

OBJECTIVES: To understand molarity. • To learn to use molarity to calculate the number of moles of solute present.

When a solution is described in terms of mass percent, the amount of solution is given in terms of its mass. However, it is often more convenient to measure the volume of a solution than to measure its mass. Because of this, chemists often describe a solution in terms of concentration. We define the *concentration* of a solution as the amount of solute in a *given volume* of solution. The most commonly used expression of concentration is **molarity (M).** Molarity describes the amount of solute in moles and the volume of the solution in liters. Molarity is *the number of moles of solute per volume of solution in liters.* That is

$$M = \text{molarity} = \frac{\text{moles of solute}}{\text{liters of solution}} = \frac{\text{mol}}{\text{L}}$$

A solution that is 1.0 molar (written as 1.0 M) contains 1.0 mole of solute per liter of solution.

EXAMPLE 15.3   Solution Composition: Calculating Molarity, I

Calculate the molarity of a solution prepared by dissolving 11.5 g of solid NaOH in enough water to make 1.50 L of solution.

SOLUTION

Where Are We Going?

We want to determine the concentration (M) of a solution of NaOH.

What Do We Know?

- 11.5 g of NaOH is dissolved in 1.50 L of solution.
- $M = \dfrac{\text{moles of solute}}{\text{liters of solution}}$.

What Information Do We Need?

- We need to know the number of moles of NaOH in 11.5 g NaOH.

How Do We Get There?

We have the mass (in grams) of solute, so we need to convert the mass of solute to moles (using the molar mass of NaOH). Then we can divide the number of moles by the volume in liters.

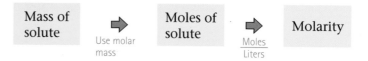

We compute the number of moles of solute, using the molar mass of NaOH (40.0 g).

$$11.5 \ \text{g NaOH} \times \frac{1 \ \text{mol NaOH}}{40.0 \ \text{g NaOH}} = 0.288 \ \text{mol NaOH}$$

Then we divide by the volume of the solution in liters.

$$\text{Molarity} = \frac{\text{moles of solute}}{\text{liters of solution}} = \frac{0.288 \ \text{mol NaOH}}{1.50 \ \text{L solution}} = 0.192 \ M \ \text{NaOH} \ \blacksquare$$

EXAMPLE 15.4   Solution Composition: Calculating Molarity, II

Calculate the molarity of a solution prepared by dissolving 1.56 g of gaseous HCl into enough water to make 26.8 mL of solution.

SOLUTION

Where Are We Going?

We want to determine the concentration (M) of a solution of HCl.

What Do We Know?

- 1.56 g of HCl is dissolved in 26.8 mL of solution.
- $M = \dfrac{\text{moles of solute}}{\text{liters of solution}}$.

What Information Do We Need?

- We need to know the number of moles of HCl in 1.56 g.
- We need to know the volume of the solution in liters.

How Do We Get There?

We must change 1.56 g of HCl to moles of HCl, and then we must change 26.8 mL to liters (because molarity is defined in terms of liters). First we calculate the number of moles of HCl (molar mass = 36.5 g).

$$1.56 \text{ g HCl} \times \frac{1 \text{ mol HCl}}{36.5 \text{ g HCl}} = 0.0427 \text{ mol HCl}$$

$$= 4.27 \times 10^{-2} \text{ mol HCl}$$

Next we change the volume of the solution from milliliters to liters, using the equivalence statement 1 L = 1000 mL, which gives the appropriate conversion factor.

$$26.8 \text{ mL} \times \frac{1 \text{ L}}{1000 \text{ mL}} = 0.0268 \text{ L}$$

$$= 2.68 \times 10^{-2} \text{ L}$$

Finally, we divide the moles of solute by the liters of solution.

$$\text{Molarity} = \frac{4.27 \times 10^{-2} \text{ mol HCl}}{2.68 \times 10^{-2} \text{ L solution}} = 1.59 \text{ M HCl}$$

Self-Check EXERCISE 15.3 Calculate the molarity of a solution prepared by dissolving 1.00 g of ethanol, C_2H_5OH, in enough water to give a final volume of 101 mL.

See Problems 15.37 through 15.42. ∎

It is important to realize that the description of a solution's composition may not accurately reflect the true chemical nature of the solute as it is present in the dissolved state. Solute concentration is always written in terms of the form of the solute *before* it dissolves. For example, describing a solution as 1.0 M NaCl means that the solution was prepared by dissolving 1.0 mole of solid NaCl in enough water to make 1.0 L of solution; it does not mean that the solution contains 1.0 mole of NaCl units. Actually the solution contains 1.0 mole of Na^+ ions and 1.0 mole of Cl^- ions. That is, it contains 1.0 M Na^+ and 1.0 M Cl^-.

EXAMPLE 15.5 | **Solution Composition: Calculating Ion Concentration from Molarity**

Remember, ionic compounds separate into the component ions when they dissolve in water.

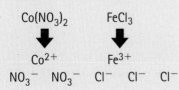

Give the concentrations of all the ions in each of the following solutions:

a. 0.50 M $Co(NO_3)_2$

b. 1 M $FeCl_3$

SOLUTION

a. When solid $Co(NO_3)_2$ dissolves, it produces ions as follows:

$$Co(NO_3)_2(s) \xrightarrow{H_2O(l)} Co^{2+}(aq) + 2NO_3^-(aq)$$

which we can represent as

$$1 \text{ mol Co(NO}_3)_2(s) \xrightarrow{\text{H}_2\text{O}(l)} 1 \text{ mol Co}^{2+}(aq) + 2 \text{ mol NO}_3^-(aq)$$

Therefore, a solution that is 0.50 M Co(NO$_3$)$_2$ contains 0.50 M Co^{2+} and (2 × 0.50) M NO$_3^-$, or 1.0 M NO$_3^-$.

b. When solid FeCl$_3$ dissolves, it produces ions as follows:

$$\text{FeCl}_3(s) \xrightarrow{\text{H}_2\text{O}(l)} \text{Fe}^{3+}(aq) + 3\text{Cl}^-(aq)$$

or

$$1 \text{ mol FeCl}_3(s) \xrightarrow{\text{H}_2\text{O}(l)} 1 \text{ mol Fe}^{3+}(aq) + 3 \text{ mol Cl}^-(aq)$$

A solution that is 1 M FeCl$_3$ contains 1 M Fe^{3+} ions and 3 M Cl$^-$ ions.

Self-Check **EXERCISE 15.4** Give the concentrations of the ions in each of the following solutions:

a. 0.10 M Na$_2$CO$_3$

b. 0.010 M Al$_2$(SO$_4$)$_3$

See Problems 15.49 and 15.50. ∎

MATH SKILL BUILDER

$$M = \frac{\text{moles of solute}}{\text{liters of solution}}$$

Liters × M ➡ Moles of solute

Often we need to determine the number of moles of solute present in a given volume of a solution of known molarity. To do this, we use the definition of molarity. When we multiply the molarity of a solution by the volume (in liters), we get the moles of solute present in that sample:

$$\text{Liters of solution} \times \text{molarity} = \text{liters of solution} \times \frac{\text{moles of solute}}{\text{liters of solution}}$$
$$= \text{moles of solute}$$

EXAMPLE 15.6

> ## Solution Composition: Calculating Number of Moles from Molarity

How many moles of Ag$^+$ ions are present in 25 mL of a 0.75 M AgNO$_3$ solution?

SOLUTION

Where Are We Going?

We want to determine the number of moles of Ag$^+$ in a solution.

What Do We Know?

• We have 25 mL of 0.75 M AgNO$_3$.

• $M = \dfrac{\text{moles of solute}}{\text{liters of solution}}$.

How Do We Get There?

A 0.75 M AgNO$_3$ solution contains 0.75 M Ag$^+$ ions and 0.75 M NO$_3^-$ ions. Next we must express the volume in liters. That is, we must convert from mL to L.

A solution of cobalt(II) nitrate.

Tom Pantages

$$25 \ \cancel{mL} \times \frac{1 \text{ L}}{1000 \ \cancel{mL}} = 0.025 \text{ L} = 2.5 \times 10^{-2} \text{ L}$$

Now we multiply the volume times the molarity.

$$2.5 \times 10^{-2} \ \cancel{\text{L solution}} \times \frac{0.75 \text{ mol Ag}^+}{\cancel{\text{L solution}}} = 1.9 \times 10^{-2} \text{ mol Ag}^+$$

Self-Check EXERCISE 15.5   Calculate the number of moles of Cl^- ions in 1.75 L of 1.0×10^{-3} *M* $AlCl_3$.

See Problems 15.49 and 15.50. ∎

A **standard solution** is a solution whose *concentration is accurately known*. When the appropriate solute is available in pure form, a standard solution can be prepared by weighing out a sample of solute, transferring it completely to a *volumetric flask* (a flask of accurately known volume), and adding enough solvent to bring the volume up to the mark on the neck of the flask. This procedure is illustrated in Figure 15.7.

EXAMPLE 15.7 | Solution Composition: Calculating Mass from Molarity

To analyze the alcohol content of a certain wine, a chemist needs 1.00 L of an aqueous 0.200 *M* $K_2Cr_2O_7$ (potassium dichromate) solution. How much solid $K_2Cr_2O_7$ (molar mass = 294.2 g) must be weighed out to make this solution?

SOLUTION

Where Are We Going?

We want to determine the mass of $K_2Cr_2O_7$ needed to make a given solution.

What Do We Know?

- We want 1.00 L of 0.200 *M* $K_2Cr_2O_7$.

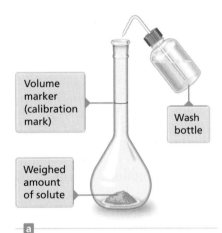

Volume marker (calibration mark)

Wash bottle

Weighed amount of solute

a

Put a weighed amount of a substance (the solute) into the volumetric flask, and add a small quantity of water.

b

Dissolve the solid in the water by gently swirling the flask (with the stopper in place).

c

Add more water (with gentle swirling) until the level of the solution just reaches the mark etched on the neck of the flask. Then mix the solution thoroughly by inverting the flask several times.

Figure 15.7

Steps involved in the preparation of a standard aqueous solution.

• The molar mass of $K_2Cr_2O_7$ is 294.2 g/mol.

• $M = \dfrac{\text{moles of solute}}{\text{liters of solution}}$.

How Do We Get There?

We need to calculate the number of grams of solute ($K_2Cr_2O_7$) present (and thus the mass needed to make the solution). First we determine the number of moles of $K_2Cr_2O_7$ present by multiplying the volume (in liters) by the molarity.

Liters $\times$ M ➡ Moles of solute

$$1.00 \text{ L solution} \times \frac{0.200 \text{ mol } K_2Cr_2O_7}{\text{L solution}} = 0.200 \text{ mol } K_2Cr_2O_7$$

Then we convert the moles of $K_2Cr_2O_7$ to grams, using the molar mass of $K_2Cr_2O_7$ (294.2 g).

$$0.200 \text{ mol } K_2Cr_2O_7 \times \frac{294.2 \text{ g } K_2Cr_2O_7}{\text{mol } K_2Cr_2O_7} = 58.8 \text{ g } K_2Cr_2O_7$$

Therefore, to make 1.00 L of 0.200 M $K_2Cr_2O_7$, the chemist must weigh out 58.8 g of $K_2Cr_2O_7$ and dissolve it in enough water to make 1.00 L of solution. This is most easily done by using a 1.00-L volumetric flask (see Figure 15.7).

Self-Check EXERCISE 15.6 Formalin is an aqueous solution of formaldehyde, HCHO, used as a preservative for biologic specimens. How many grams of formaldehyde must be used to prepare 2.5 L of 12.3 M formalin?

See Problems 15.51 and 15.52. ■

15.5 Dilution

OBJECTIVE: To learn to calculate the concentration of a solution made by diluting a stock solution.

To save time and space in the laboratory, solutions that are routinely used are often purchased or prepared in concentrated form (called *stock solutions*). Water (or another solvent) is then added to achieve the molarity desired for a particular solution. The process of adding more solvent to a solution is called **dilution.** For example, the common laboratory acids are purchased as concentrated solutions and diluted with water as they are needed. A typical dilution calculation involves determining how much water must be added to an amount of stock solution to achieve a solution of the desired concentration. The key to doing these calculations is to remember that *only water is added in the dilution.* The amount of solute in the final, more dilute solution is the *same* as the amount of solute in the original, concentrated stock solution. That is,

> The molarities of stock solutions of the common concentrated acids are:
>
> | Sulfuric (H_2SO_4) | 18 M |
> | Nitric (HNO_3) | 16 M |
> | Hydrochloric (HCl) | 12 M |

Moles of solute after dilution = moles of solute before dilution

> Dilution with water doesn't alter the number of moles of solute present.

The number of moles of solute stays the same but more water is added, increasing the volume, so the molarity decreases.

$$M = \frac{\text{moles of solute}}{\text{volume (L)}}$$

Remains constant

Decreases   Increases
(water added)

For example, suppose we want to prepare 500. mL of 1.00 M acetic acid, $HC_2H_3O_2$, from a 17.5 M stock solution of acetic acid. What volume of the stock solution is required?

The first step is to determine the number of moles of acetic acid needed in the final solution. We do this by multiplying the volume of the solution by its molarity.

$$\begin{array}{c}\text{Volume of dilute} \\ \text{solution (liters)}\end{array} \times \begin{array}{c}\text{molarity of} \\ \text{dilute solution}\end{array} = \begin{array}{c}\text{moles of solute} \\ \text{present}\end{array}$$

The number of moles of solute present in the more dilute solution equals the number of moles of solute that must be present in the more concentrated (stock) solution, because this is the only source of acetic acid.

Because molarity is defined in terms of liters, we must first change 500. mL to liters and then multiply the volume (in liters) by the molarity.

$$\underbrace{500. \text{ mL solution}}_{\substack{V_{\text{dilute solution}} \\ \text{(in mL)}}} \times \underbrace{\frac{1 \text{ L solution}}{1000 \text{ mL solution}}}_{\text{Convert mL to L}} = 0.500 \text{ L solution}$$

$$0.500 \text{ L solution} \times \underbrace{\frac{1.00 \text{ mol } HC_2H_3O_2}{\text{L solution}}}_{M_{\text{dilute solution}}} = 0.500 \text{ mol } HC_2H_3O_2$$

MATH SKILL BUILDER
Liters $\times$ M ➡ Moles of solute

Now we need to find the volume of 17.5 M acetic acid that contains 0.500 mole of $HC_2H_3O_2$. We will call this unknown volume V. Because volume $\times$ molarity = moles, we have

$$V \text{ (in liters)} \times \frac{17.5 \text{ mol } HC_2H_3O_2}{\text{L solution}} = 0.500 \text{ mol } HC_2H_3O_2$$

Solving for V $\left(\text{by dividing both sides by } \dfrac{17.5 \text{ mol}}{\text{L solution}}\right)$ gives

$$V = \frac{0.500 \text{ mol } HC_2H_3O_2}{\dfrac{17.5 \text{ mol } HC_2H_3O_2}{\text{L solution}}} = 0.0286 \text{ L, or } 28.6 \text{ mL, of solution}$$

Therefore, to make 500. mL of a 1.00 M acetic acid solution, we take 28.6 mL of 17.5 M acetic acid and dilute it to a total volume of 500. mL. This process is illustrated in Figure 15.8. Because the moles of solute remain the same before and after dilution, we can write

$$\begin{array}{ccccccc} \multicolumn{3}{c}{\text{Initial Conditions}} & & & \multicolumn{3}{c}{\text{Final Conditions}} \\ M_1 & \times & V_1 & = \text{moles of solute} = & M_2 & \times & V_2 \\ \text{Molarity} & & \text{Volume} & & \text{Molarity} & & \text{Volume} \\ \text{before} & & \text{before} & & \text{after} & & \text{after} \\ \text{dilution} & & \text{dilution} & & \text{dilution} & & \text{dilution} \end{array}$$

We can check our calculations on acetic acid by showing that $M_1 \times V_1 = M_2 \times V_2$. In the above example, $M_1 = 17.5$ M, $V_1 = 0.0286$ L, $V_2 = 0.500$ L, and $M_2 = 1.00$ M, so

$$M_1 \times V_1 = 17.5 \frac{\text{mol}}{\text{L}} \times 0.0286 \text{ L} = 0.500 \text{ mol}$$

$$M_2 \times V_2 = 1.00 \frac{\text{mol}}{\text{L}} \times 0.500 \text{ L} = 0.500 \text{ mol}$$

and therefore

$$M_1 \times V_1 = M_2 \times V_2$$

This shows that the volume (V_2) we calculated is correct.

500 mL

a 28.6 mL of 17.5 M acetic acid solution is transferred to a volumetric flask that already contains some water.

b Water is added to the flask (with swirling) to bring the volume to the calibration mark, and the solution is mixed by inverting the flask several times.

c The resulting solution is 1.00 M acetic acid.

Figure 15.8

EXAMPLE 15.8 | **Calculating Concentrations of Diluted Solutions**

What volume of 16 *M* sulfuric acid must be used to prepare 1.5 L of a 0.10 *M* H_2SO_4 solution?

SOLUTION

Where Are We Going?

We want to determine the volume of sulfuric acid needed to prepare a given volume of a more dilute solution.

What Do We Know?

Initial Conditions (concentrated)	Final Conditions (dilute)
$M_1 = 16 \dfrac{\text{mol}}{\text{L}}$	$M_2 = 0.10 \dfrac{\text{mol}}{\text{L}}$
$V_1 = ?$	$V_2 = 1.5 \text{ L}$

$$\text{Moles of solute} = M_1 \times V_1 = M_2 \times V_2$$

How Do We Get There?

We can solve the equation

$$M_1 \times V_1 = M_2 \times V_2$$

Approximate dilutions can be carried out using a calibrated beaker. Here, concentrated sulfuric acid is being added to water to make a dilute solution.

Tom Pantages

for V_1 by dividing both sides by M_1,

$$\frac{\not{M_1} \times V_1}{\not{M_1}} = \frac{M_2 \times V_2}{M_1}$$

to give

$$V_1 = \frac{M_2 \times V_2}{M_1}$$

Now we substitute the known values of M_2, V_2, and M_1.

$$V_1 = \frac{\left(0.10 \frac{\text{mol}}{\text{L}}\right)(1.5 \text{ L})}{16 \frac{\text{mol}}{\text{L}}} = 9.4 \times 10^{-3} \text{ L}$$

$$9.4 \times 10^{-3} \not{\text{L}} \times \frac{1000 \text{ mL}}{1 \not{\text{L}}} = 9.4 \text{ mL}$$

> It is always best to add concentrated acid to water, not water to the acid. That way, if any splashing occurs accidentally, it is dilute acid that splashes.

Therefore, $V_1 = 9.4 \times 10^{-3}$ L, or 9.4 mL. To make 1.5 L of 0.10 M H_2SO_4 using 16 M H_2SO_4, we must take 9.4 mL of the concentrated acid and dilute it with water to a final volume of 1.5 L. The correct way to do this is to add the 9.4 mL of acid to about 1 L of water and then dilute to 1.5 L by adding more water.

Self-Check EXERCISE 15.7   What volume of 12 M HCl must be taken to prepare 0.75 L of 0.25 M HCl?

See Problems 15.57 and 15.58. ∎

15.6 Stoichiometry of Solution Reactions

OBJECTIVE: To understand the strategy for solving stoichiometric problems for solution reactions.

Because so many important reactions occur in solution, it is important to be able to do stoichiometric calculations for solution reactions. The principles needed to perform these calculations are very similar to those developed in Chapter 9. It is helpful to think in terms of the following steps:

Steps for Solving Stoichiometric Problems Involving Solutions

> See Section 7.3 for a discussion of net ionic equations.

Step 1 Write the balanced equation for the reaction. For reactions involving ions, it is best to write the net ionic equation.

Step 2 Calculate the moles of reactants.

Step 3 Determine which reactant is limiting.

Step 4 Calculate the moles of other reactants or products, as required.

Step 5 Convert to grams or other units, if required.

EXAMPLE 15.9 | Solution Stoichiometry: Calculating Mass of Reactants and Products

Calculate the mass of solid NaCl that must be added to 1.50 L of a 0.100 M $AgNO_3$ solution to precipitate all of the Ag^+ ions in the form of AgCl. Calculate the mass of AgCl formed.

SOLUTION

Where Are We Going?

We want to determine the mass of NaCl.

What Do We Know?

- We have 1.50 L of a 0.100 M $AgNO_3$ solution.

What Information Do We Need?

- We need the balanced equation between $AgNO_3$ and NaCl.
- We need the molar mass of NaCl.

How Do We Get There?

Step 1 *Write the balanced equation for the reaction.*
When added to the $AgNO_3$ solution (which contains Ag^+ and NO_3^- ions), the solid NaCl dissolves to yield Na^+ and Cl^- ions. Solid AgCl forms according to the following balanced net ionic reaction:

> This reaction was discussed in Section 7.2.

$$Ag^+(aq) + Cl^-(aq) \rightarrow AgCl(s)$$

Step 2 *Calculate the moles of reactants.*
In this case we must add enough Cl^- ions to just react with all the Ag^+ ions present, so we must calculate the moles of Ag^+ ions present in 1.50 L of a 0.100 M $AgNO_3$ solution. (Remember that a 0.100 M $AgNO_3$ solution contains 0.100 M Ag^+ ions and 0.100 M NO_3^- ions.)

MATH SKILL BUILDER
Liters $\times M$ ➡ Moles of solute

$$1.50 \; \cancel{L} \times \frac{0.100 \; \text{mol Ag}^+}{\cancel{L}} = 0.150 \; \text{mol Ag}^+$$

Moles of Ag⁺ present
in 1.50 L of 0.100 M AgNO₃

Step 3 *Determine which reactant is limiting.*
In this situation we want to add just enough Cl^- to react with the Ag^+ present. That is, we want to precipitate *all* the Ag^+ in the solution. Thus the Ag^+ present determines the amount of Cl^- needed.

Step 4 *Calculate the moles of Cl^- required.*
We have 0.150 mole of Ag^+ ions and, because one Ag^+ ion reacts with one Cl^- ion, we need 0.150 mole of Cl^-,

Richard Megna/Fundamental Photographs

$$0.150 \; \cancel{\text{mol Ag}^+} \times \frac{1 \; \text{mol Cl}^-}{1 \; \cancel{\text{mol Ag}^+}} = 0.150 \; \text{mol Cl}^-$$

When aqueous sodium chloride is added to a solution of silver nitrate, a white silver chloride precipitate forms.

so 0.150 mole of AgCl will be formed.

$$0.150 \; \text{mol Ag}^+ + 0.150 \; \text{mol Cl}^- \rightarrow 0.150 \; \text{mol AgCl}$$

Step 5 *Convert to grams of NaCl required.*
To produce 0.150 mol Cl⁻, we need 0.150 mol NaCl. We calculate the mass of NaCl required as follows:

$$0.150 \; \text{mol NaCl} \times \frac{58.4 \; \text{g NaCl}}{\text{mol NaCl}} = 8.76 \; \text{g NaCl}$$

| Moles | times molar mass | Mass |

The mass of AgCl formed is

$$0.150 \; \text{mol AgCl} \times \frac{143.3 \; \text{g AgCl}}{\text{mol AgCl}} = 21.5 \; \text{g AgCl} \; ■$$

EXAMPLE 15.10

Solution Stoichiometry: Determining Limiting Reactants and Calculating Mass of Products

See Section 7.2 for a discussion of this reaction.

When $Ba(NO_3)_2$ and K_2CrO_4 react in aqueous solution, the yellow solid $BaCrO_4$ is formed. Calculate the mass of $BaCrO_4$ that forms when 3.50×10^{-3} mole of solid $Ba(NO_3)_2$ is dissolved in 265 mL of 0.0100 M K_2CrO_4 solution.

SOLUTION

Where Are We Going?

We want to determine the mass of $BaCrO_4$ that forms in a reaction of known amounts of solutions.

What Do We Know?

- We react 3.50×10^{-3} mol $BaNO_3$ with 265 mL of 0.0100 M K_2CrO_4.

What Information Do We Need?

- We will need the balanced equation between $BaNO_3$ and K_2CrO_4.
- We will need the molar mass of $BaCrO_4$.

How Do We Get There?

Step 1 The original K_2CrO_4 solution contains the ions K^+ and CrO_4^{2-}. When the $Ba(NO_3)_2$ is dissolved in this solution, Ba^{2+} and NO_3^- ions are added. The Ba^{2+} and CrO_4^{2-} ions react to form solid $BaCrO_4$. The balanced net ionic equation is

$$Ba^{2+}(aq) + CrO_4^{2-}(aq) \rightarrow BaCrO_4(s)$$

Step 2 Next we determine the moles of reactants. We are told that 3.50×10^{-3} mole of $Ba(NO_3)_2$ is added to the K_2CrO_4 solution. Each formula unit of $Ba(NO_3)_2$ contains one Ba^{2+} ion, so 3.50×10^{-3} mole of $Ba(NO_3)_2$ gives 3.50×10^{-3} mole of Ba^{2+} ions in solution.

| 3.50×10^{-3} mol $Ba(NO_3)_2$ | dissolves to give | 3.50×10^{-3} mol Ba^{2+} |

Because $V \times M$ = moles of solute, we can compute the moles of K_2CrO_4 in the solution from the volume and molarity of the original solution. First we must convert the volume of the solution (265 mL) to liters.

$$265 \; \text{mL} \times \frac{1 \; \text{L}}{1000 \; \text{mL}} = 0.265 \; \text{L}$$

Barium chromate precipitating.

Next we determine the number of moles of K_2CrO_4, using the molarity of the K_2CrO_4 solution (0.0100 M).

$$0.265 \; \cancel{L} \times \frac{0.0100 \; \text{mol } K_2CrO_4}{\cancel{L}} = 2.65 \times 10^{-3} \; \text{mol } K_2CrO_4$$

We know that

2.65×10^{-3} mol K_2CrO_4	dissolves to give	2.65×10^{-3} mol CrO_4^{2-}

so the solution contains 2.65×10^{-3} mole of CrO_4^{2-} ions.

Step 3   The balanced equation tells us that one Ba^{2+} ion reacts with one CrO_4^{2-} ion. Because the number of moles of CrO_4^{2-} ions (2.65×10^{-3}) is smaller than the number of moles of Ba^{2+} ions (3.50×10^{-3}), the CrO_4^{2-} will run out first.

$$Ba^{2+}(aq) \quad + \quad CrO_4^{2-}(aq) \quad \rightarrow \quad BaCrO_4(s)$$

3.50×10^{-3} mol	2.65×10^{-3} mol

Smaller (runs out first)

Therefore, the CrO_4^{2-} is limiting.

Moles of CrO_4^{2-}	limits	Moles of $BaCrO_4$

Step 4   The 2.65×10^{-3} mole of CrO_4^{2-} ions will react with 2.65×10^{-3} mole of Ba^{2+} ions to form 2.65×10^{-3} mole of $BaCrO_4$.

2.65×10^{-3} mol Ba^{2+}	+	2.65×10^{-3} mol CrO_4^{2-}		2.65×10^{-3} mol $BaCrO_4(s)$

Step 5   The mass of $BaCrO_4$ formed is obtained from its molar mass (253.3 g) as follows:

$$2.65 \times 10^{-3} \; \cancel{\text{mol } BaCrO_4} \times \frac{253.3 \; \text{g } BaCrO_4}{\cancel{\text{mol } BaCrO_4}} = 0.671 \; \text{g } BaCrO_4$$

Self-Check EXERCISE 15.8   When aqueous solutions of Na_2SO_4 and $Pb(NO_3)_2$ are mixed, $PbSO_4$ precipitates. Calculate the mass of $PbSO_4$ formed when 1.25 L of 0.0500 M $Pb(NO_3)_2$ and 2.00 L of 0.0250 M Na_2SO_4 are mixed.

HINT: Calculate the moles of Pb^{2+} and SO_4^{2-} in the mixed solution, decide which ion is limiting, and calculate the moles of $PbSO_4$ formed.

See Problems 15.65 through 15.68. ■

15.7 Neutralization Reactions

OBJECTIVE: To learn how to do calculations involved in acid–base reactions.

So far we have considered the stoichiometry of reactions in solution that result in the formation of a precipitate. Another common type of solution reaction occurs between an acid and a base. We introduced these reactions in Section 7.4. Recall from that discussion that an acid is a substance that furnishes H^+ ions. A strong acid, such as hydrochloric acid, HCl, dissociates (ionizes) completely in water.

$$HCl(aq) \rightarrow H^+(aq) + Cl^-(aq)$$

Strong bases are water-soluble metal hydroxides, which are completely dissociated in water. An example is NaOH, which dissolves in water to give Na^+ and OH^- ions.

$$NaOH(s) \xrightarrow{H_2O(l)} Na^+(aq) + OH^-(aq)$$

When a strong acid and a strong base react, the net ionic reaction is

$$H^+(aq) + OH^-(aq) \rightarrow H_2O(l)$$

An acid–base reaction is often called a **neutralization reaction.** When just enough strong base is added to react exactly with the strong acid in a solution, we say the acid has been *neutralized.* One product of this reaction is always water. The steps in dealing with the stoichiometry of any neutralization reaction are the same as those we followed in the previous section.

EXAMPLE 15.11 | Solution Stoichiometry: Calculating Volume in Neutralization Reactions

What volume of a 0.100 *M* HCl solution is needed to neutralize 25.0 mL of a 0.350 *M* NaOH solution?

SOLUTION

Where Are We Going?

We want to determine the volume of a given solution of HCl required to react with a known amount of NaOH.

What Do We Know?

- We have 25.0 mL of 0.350 *M* NaOH.
- The concentration of the HCl solution is 0.100 *M*.

What Information Do We Need?

- We need the balanced equation between HCl and NaOH.

How Do We Get There?

Step 1 *Write the balanced equation for the reaction.*
Hydrochloric acid is a strong acid, so all the HCl molecules dissociate to produce H^+ and Cl^- ions. Also, when the strong base NaOH dissolves, the solution contains Na^+ and OH^- ions. When these two solutions are mixed, the H^+ ions from the hydrochloric acid react with the OH^- ions from the sodium

hydroxide solution to form water. The balanced net ionic equation for the reaction is

$$H^+(aq) + OH^-(aq) \rightarrow H_2O(l)$$

Step 2 *Calculate the moles of reactants.*
In this problem we are given a volume (25.0 mL) of 0.350 M NaOH, and we want to add just enough 0.100 M HCl to provide just enough H^+ ions to re-act with all the OH^-. Therefore, we must calculate the number of moles of OH^- ions in the 25.0-mL sample of 0.350 M NaOH. To do this, we first change the volume to liters and multiply by the molarity.

$$25.0 \text{ mL NaOH} \times \frac{1 \text{ L}}{1000 \text{ mL}} \times \frac{0.350 \text{ mol OH}^-}{\text{L NaOH}} = 8.75 \times 10^{-3} \text{ mol OH}^-$$

Moles of OH^- present
in 25.0 mL of
0.350 M NaOH

Step 3 *Determine which reactant is limiting.*
This problem requires the addition of just enough H^+ ions to react exactly with the OH^- ions present, so the number of moles of OH^- ions present de-termines the number of moles of H^+ that must be added. The OH^- ions are limiting.

Step 4 *Calculate the moles of H^+ required.*
The balanced equation tells us that the H^+ and OH^- ions react in a 1:1 ratio, so 8.75×10^{-3} mole of H^+ ions is required to neutralize (exactly react with) the 8.75×10^{-3} mole of OH^- ions present.

Step 5 Calculate the volume of 0.100 M *HCl required.*
Next we must find the volume (V) of 0.100 M HCl required to furnish this amount of H^+ ions. Because the volume (in liters) times the molarity gives the number of moles, we have

$$V \times \frac{0.100 \text{ mol H}^+}{\text{L}} = 8.75 \times 10^{-3} \text{ mol H}^+$$

Unknown
volume
(in liters) Moles of
H^+ needed

Now we must solve for V by dividing both sides of the equation by 0.100.

$$V \times \frac{0.100 \text{ mol H}^+}{0.100 \text{ L}} = \frac{8.75 \times 10^{-3} \text{ mol H}^+}{0.100}$$

$$V = 8.75 \times 10^{-2} \text{ L}$$

Changing liters to milliliters, we have

$$V = 8.75 \times 10^{-2} \text{ L} \times \frac{1000 \text{ mL}}{\text{L}} = 87.5 \text{ mL}$$

Therefore, 87.5 mL of 0.100 M HCl is required to neutralize 25.0 mL of 0.350 M NaOH.

Self-Check **EXERCISE 15.9**   Calculate the volume of 0.10 M HNO_3 needed to neutralize 125 mL of 0.050 M KOH.

See Problems 15.69 through 15.74. ∎

15.8 Solution Composition: Normality

OBJECTIVES: To learn about normality and equivalent weight. • To learn to use these concepts in stoichiometric calculations.

Normality is another unit of concentration that is sometimes used, especially when dealing with acids and bases. The use of normality focuses mainly on the H^+ and OH^- available in an acid–base reaction. Before we discuss normality, however, we need to define some terms. One **equivalent of an acid** is the *amount of that acid that can furnish 1 mole of H^+ ions*. Similarly, one **equivalent of a base** is defined as the *amount of that base that can furnish 1 mole of OH^- ions*. The **equivalent weight** of an acid or a base is the mass in grams of 1 equivalent (equiv) of that acid or base.

The common strong acids are HCl, HNO_3, and H_2SO_4. For HCl and HNO_3 each molecule of acid furnishes one H^+ ion, so 1 mole of HCl can furnish 1 mole of H^+ ions. This means that

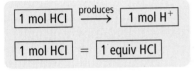

$$\text{Furnishes 1 mol } H^+$$
$$\downarrow$$
$$1 \text{ mol HCl} = 1 \text{ equiv HCl}$$
$$\text{Molar mass (HCl)} = \text{equivalent weight (HCl)}$$

Likewise, for HNO_3,

$$1 \text{ mol } HNO_3 = 1 \text{ equiv } HNO_3$$
$$\text{Molar mass (}HNO_3\text{)} = \text{equivalent weight (}HNO_3\text{)}$$

However, H_2SO_4 can furnish *two* H^+ ions per molecule, so 1 mole of H_2SO_4 can furnish *two* moles of H^+. This means that

$$1 \text{ mol } H_2SO_4 \xrightarrow{\text{furnishes}} 2 \text{ mol } H^+$$

$$\tfrac{1}{2} \text{ mol } H_2SO_4 \xrightarrow{\text{furnishes}} 1 \text{ mol } H^+$$

$$\tfrac{1}{2} \text{ mol } H_2SO_4 = 1 \text{ equiv } H_2SO_4 \Rightarrow 1 \text{ mol } H^+$$

Because each mole of H_2SO_4 can furnish 2 moles of H^+, we need only to take $\tfrac{1}{2}$ mole of H_2SO_4 to get 1 equiv of H_2SO_4. Therefore,

$$\tfrac{1}{2} \text{ mol } H_2SO_4 = 1 \text{ equiv } H_2SO_4$$

and

$$\text{Equivalent weight (}H_2SO_4\text{)} = \tfrac{1}{2} \text{ molar mass (}H_2SO_4\text{)}$$
$$= \tfrac{1}{2} (98 \text{ g}) = 49 \text{ g}$$

The equivalent weight of H_2SO_4 is 49 g.

The common strong bases are NaOH and KOH. For NaOH and KOH, each formula unit furnishes one OH^- ion, so we can say

$$1 \text{ mol NaOH} = 1 \text{ equiv NaOH}$$
$$\text{Molar mass (NaOH)} = \text{equivalent weight (NaOH)}$$
$$1 \text{ mol KOH} = 1 \text{ equiv KOH}$$
$$\text{Molar mass (KOH)} = \text{equivalent weight (KOH)}$$

These ideas are summarized in Table 15.2.

Table 15.2 The Molar Masses and Equivalent Weights of the Common Strong Acids and Bases

	Molar Mass (g)	Equivalent Weight (g)
Acid		
HCl	36.5	36.5
HNO_3	63.0	63.0
H_2SO_4	98.0	$49.0 = \dfrac{98.0}{2}$
Base		
NaOH	40.0	40.0
KOH	56.1	56.1

EXAMPLE 15.12   Solution Stoichiometry: Calculating Equivalent Weight

Phosphoric acid, H_3PO_4, can furnish three H^+ ions per molecule. Calculate the equivalent weight of H_3PO_4.

SOLUTION

Where Are We Going?

We want to determine the equivalent weight of phosphoric acid.

What Do We Know?

- The formula for phosphoric acid is H_3PO_4.
- The equivalent weight of an acid is the amount of acid that can furnish 1 mole of H^+ ions.

What Information Do We Need?

- We need to know the molar mass of H_3PO_4.

How Do We Get There?

The key point here involves how many protons (H^+ ions) each molecule of H_3PO_4 can furnish.

$$H_3PO_4 \quad \xrightarrow{\text{furnishes}} \quad ?\ H^+$$

Because each H_3PO_4 can furnish three H^+ ions, 1 mole of H_3PO_4 can furnish 3 moles of H^+ ions:

$$\begin{array}{c}1\ \text{mol} \\ H_3PO_4\end{array} \quad \xrightarrow{\text{furnishes}} \quad \begin{array}{c}3\ \text{mol} \\ H^+\end{array}$$

So 1 equiv of H_3PO_4 (the amount that can furnish 1 mole of H^+) is one-third of a mole.

$$\begin{array}{c}\tfrac{1}{3}\ \text{mol} \\ H_3PO_4\end{array} \quad \xrightarrow{\text{furnishes}} \quad \begin{array}{c}1\ \text{mol} \\ H^+\end{array}$$

This means the equivalent weight of H_3PO_4 is one-third its molar mass.

$$\text{Equivalent weight} = \frac{\text{Molar mass}}{3}$$

$$\text{Equivalent weight } (H_3PO_4) = \frac{\text{molar mass } (H_3PO_4)}{3}$$

$$= \frac{98.0 \text{ g}}{3} = 32.7 \text{ g} \blacksquare$$

Normality (*N*) is defined as the number of equivalents of solute per liter of solution.

$$\text{Normality} = N = \frac{\text{number of equivalents}}{1 \text{ liter of solution}} = \frac{\text{equivalents}}{\text{liter}} = \frac{\text{equiv}}{L}$$

This means that a 1 *N* solution contains 1 equivalent of solute per liter of solution. Notice that when we multiply the volume of a solution in liters by the normality, we get the number of equivalents.

MATH SKILL BUILDER
Liters × Normality ➡ Equiv

$$N \times V = \frac{\text{equiv}}{\cancel{L}} \times \cancel{L} = \text{equiv}$$

EXAMPLE 15.13 | **Solution Stoichiometry: Calculating Normality**

A solution of sulfuric acid contains 86 g of H_2SO_4 per liter of solution. Calculate the normality of this solution.

SOLUTION

Where Are We Going?

We want to determine the normality of a given solution of H_2SO_4.

What Do We Know?

Whenever you need to calculate the concentration of a solution, first write the appropriate definition. Then decide how to calculate the quantities shown in the definition.

- We have 86 g of H_2SO_4 per liter of solution.
- $N = \dfrac{\text{equivalents}}{L}$.

What Information Do We Need?

- We need to know the molar mass of H_2SO_4.

How Do We Get There?

To find the number of equivalents present, we must calculate the number of equivalents represented by 86 g of H_2SO_4. To do this calculation, we focus on the definition of the equivalent: it is the amount of acid that furnishes 1 mole of H^+. Because H_2SO_4 can furnish two H^+ ions per molecule, 1 equiv of H_2SO_4 is $\frac{1}{2}$ mole of H_2SO_4, so

$$\text{Equivalent weight } (H_2SO_4) = \frac{\text{molar mass } (H_2SO_4)}{2}$$

$$= \frac{98.0 \text{ g}}{2} = 49.0 \text{ g}$$

We have 86 g of H_2SO_4.

$$86 \text{ g } H_2SO_4 \times \frac{1 \text{ equiv } H_2SO_4}{49.0 \text{ g } H_2SO_4} = 1.8 \text{ equiv } H_2SO_4$$

$$N = \frac{\text{equiv}}{\text{L}} = \frac{1.8 \text{ equiv } H_2SO_4}{1.0 \text{ L}} = 1.8 \text{ N } H_2SO_4$$

REALITY CHECK   We know that 86 g is more than 1 equiv of H_2SO_4 (49 g), so this answer makes sense.

Self-Check **EXERCISE 15.10** Calculate the normality of a solution containing 23.6 g of KOH in 755 mL of solution.

See Problems 15.79 and 15.80. ■

The main advantage of using equivalents is that 1 equiv of acid contains the same number of available H^+ ions as the number of OH^- ions present in 1 equiv of base. That is,

0.75 equiv (base) will react exactly with 0.75 equiv (acid).

0.23 equiv (base) will react exactly with 0.23 equiv (acid).

And so on.

In each of these cases, the *number of* H^+ ions furnished by the sample of acid is the same as the *number of* OH^- ions furnished by the sample of base. The point is that *n equivalents of any acid will exactly neutralize n equivalents of any base.*

$$\boxed{\begin{array}{c} n \text{ equiv} \\ \text{acid} \end{array}} \quad \leftarrow \text{ reacts exactly with } \rightarrow \quad \boxed{\begin{array}{c} n \text{ equiv} \\ \text{base} \end{array}}$$

Because we know that equal equivalents of acid and base are required for neutralization, we can say that

$$\text{equiv (acid)} = \text{equiv (base)}$$

That is,

$$N_{acid} \times V_{acid} = \text{equiv (acid)} = \text{equiv (base)} = N_{base} \times V_{base}$$

Therefore, for any neutralization reaction, the following relationship holds:

$$N_{acid} \times V_{acid} = N_{base} \times V_{base}$$

EXAMPLE 15.14 | Solution Stoichiometry: Using Normality in Calculations

What volume of a 0.075 N KOH solution is required to react exactly with 0.135 L of 0.45 N H_3PO_4?

SOLUTION

Where Are We Going?

We want to determine the volume of a given solution of KOH required to react with a known solution of H_3PO_4.

What Do We Know?

- We have 0.135 L of 0.45 N H_3PO_4.
- The concentration of the KOH solution is 0.075 N.
- We know equivalents$_{acid}$ = equivalents$_{base}$.
- $N_{acid} \times V_{acid} = N_{base} \times V_{base}$

How Do We Get There?

We know that for neutralization, equiv (acid) = equiv (base), or

$$N_{acid} \times V_{acid} = N_{base} \times V_{base}$$

We want to calculate the volume of base, V_{base}, so we solve for V_{base} by dividing both sides by N_{base}.

$$\frac{N_{acid} \times V_{acid}}{N_{base}} = \frac{\cancel{N_{base}} \times V_{base}}{\cancel{N_{base}}} = V_{base}$$

Now we can substitute the given values N_{acid} = 0.45 N, V_{acid} = 0.135 L, and N_{base} = 0.075 N into the equation.

$$V_{base} = \frac{N_{acid} \times V_{acid}}{N_{base}} = \frac{\left(0.45 \, \dfrac{\text{equiv}}{\text{L}}\right)(0.135 \text{ L})}{0.075 \, \dfrac{\text{equiv}}{\text{L}}} = 0.81 \text{ L}$$

This gives V_{base} = 0.81 L, so 0.81 L of 0.075 N KOH is required to react exactly with 0.135 L of 0.45 N H_3PO_4.

Self-Check EXERCISE 15.11 What volume of 0.50 N H_2SO_4 is required to react exactly with 0.250 L of 0.80 N KOH?

See Problems 15.85 and 15.86. ■

CHAPTER 15 REVIEW

Key Terms

solution (p. 475)
solvent (p. 475)
solute (p. 475)
aqueous solution (p. 475)
saturated (15.2)
unsaturated (15.2)
concentrated (15.2)
dilute (15.2)
mass percent (15.3)
molarity (M) (15.4)

standard solution (15.4)
dilution (15.5)
neutralization
  reaction (15.7)
equivalent of an
  acid (15.8)
equivalent of a
  base (15.8)
equivalent weight (15.8)
normality (N) (15.8)

ⓕ directs you to the *Chemistry in Focus* feature in the chapter
VP indicates visual problems
ⓌWL interactive versions of these problems are assignable in OWL

Summary

1. A solution is a homogeneous mixture. The solubility of a solute in a given solvent depends on the interactions between the solvent and solute particles. Water dissolves many ionic compounds and compounds with polar molecules, because strong forces occur between the solute and the polar water molecules.

Nonpolar solvents tend to dissolve nonpolar solutes. "Like dissolves like."

2. Solution composition can be described in many ways. Two of the most important are in terms of mass percent of solute:

$$\text{Mass percent} = \frac{\text{mass of solute}}{\text{mass of solution}} \times 100\%$$

and molarity:

$$\text{Molarity} = \frac{\text{moles of solute}}{\text{liters of solution}}$$

3. A standard solution is one whose concentration is accurately known. Solutions are often made from a stock solution by dilution. When a solution is diluted, only solvent is added, which means that

Moles of solute after dilution = moles of solute before dilution

4. Normality is defined as the number of equivalents per liter of solution. One equivalent of acid is the amount of acid that furnishes 1 mole of H^+ ions. One equivalent of base is the amount of base that furnishes 1 mole of OH^- ions.

Active Learning Questions

These questions are designed to be considered by groups of students in class. Often these questions work well for introducing a particular topic in class.

1. You have a solution of table salt in water. What happens to the salt concentration (increases, decreases, or stays the same) as the solution boils? Draw pictures to explain your answer.

2. Consider a sugar solution (solution A) with concentration x. You pour one-third of this solution into a beaker, and add an equivalent volume of water (solution B).

   a. What is the ratio of sugar in solutions A and B?
   b. Compare the volumes of solutions A and B.
   c. What is the ratio of the concentrations of sugar in solutions A and B?

3. You need to make 150.0 mL of a 0.10 M NaCl solution. You have solid NaCl, and your lab partner has a 2.5 M NaCl solution. Explain how you each independently make the solution you need.

4. You have two solutions containing solute A. To determine which solution has the highest concentration of A in molarity, which of the following must you know? (There may be more than one answer.)

   a. the mass in grams of A in each solution
   b. the molar mass of A
   c. the volume of water added to each solution
   d. the total volume of the solution

   Explain your answer.

5. Which of the following do you need to know to calculate the molarity of a salt solution? (There may be more than one answer.)

   a. the mass of salt added
   b. the molar mass of the salt
   c. the volume of water added
   d. the total volume of the solution

   Explain your answer.

6. Consider separate aqueous solutions of HCl and H_2SO_4 with the same concentrations in terms of molarity. You wish to neutralize an aqueous solution of NaOH. For which acid solution would you need to add more volume (in mL) to neutralize the base?

   a. The HCl solution.
   b. The H_2SO_4 solution.
   c. You need to know the acid concentrations to answer this question.
   d. You need to know the volume and concentration of the NaOH solution to answer this question.
   e. c and d

   Explain your answer.

7. Draw molecular-level pictures to differentiate between concentrated and dilute solutions.

8. Can one solution have a greater concentration than another in terms of weight percent, but a lower concentration in terms of molarity? Explain.

9. Explain why the formula $M_1V_1 = M_2V_2$ works when solving dilution problems.

10. You have equal masses of different solutes dissolved in equal volumes of solution. Which of the solutes listed below would make the solution with the highest concentration measured in molarity? Defend your answer.

$$\text{NaCl, MgSO}_4\text{, LiF, KNO}_3$$

11. Which of the following solutions contains the greatest number of particles? Support your answer.

   a. 400.0 mL of 0.10 M sodium chloride
   b. 300.0 mL of 0.10 M calcium chloride
   c. 200.0 mL of 0.10 M iron(III) chloride
   d. 200.0 mL of 0.10 M potassium bromide
   e. 800.0 mL of 0.10 M sucrose (table sugar)

12. As with all quantitative problems in chemistry, make sure not to get "lost in the math." In particular, work on visualizing solutions at a molecular level. For example, consider the following.

   You have two separate beakers with aqueous solutions, one with 4 "units" of potassium sulfate and one with 3 "units" of barium nitrate.

   a. Draw molecular-level diagrams of both solutions.
   b. Draw a molecular-level diagram of the mixture of the two solutions before a reaction has taken place.
   c. Draw a molecular-level diagram of the product and solution formed after the reaction has taken place.

VP 13. The figures below are molecular-level representations of four aqueous solutions of the same solute. Arrange the solutions from most to least concentrated.

| **Solution A** | **Solution B** |
| Volume = 1.0 L | Volume = 4.0 L |

| **Solution C** | **Solution D** |
| Volume = 2.0 L | Volume = 2.0 L |

VP 14. The drawings below represent aqueous solutions. Solution A is 2.00 L of a 2.00 *M* aqueous solution of copper(II) nitrate. Solution B is 2.00 L of a 3.00 *M* aqueous solution of potassium hydroxide.

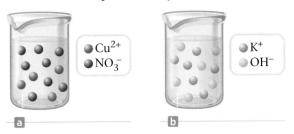

- Cu^{2+}
- NO_3^-
- K^+
- OH^-

a. Draw a picture of the solution made by mixing solutions A and B together after the precipitation reaction takes place. Make sure this picture shows the correct relative volume compared to solutions A and B and the correct relative number of ions, along with the correct relative amount of solid formed.
b. Determine the concentrations (in *M*) of all ions left in solution (from part a) and the mass of solid formed.

Questions and Problems

15.1 Solubility

QUESTIONS

1. A solution is a *homogeneous mixture*. Can you give an example of a gaseous homogeneous mixture? A liquid homogeneous mixture? A solid homogeneous mixture?

2. How do the properties of a *non*homogeneous (heterogeneous) mixture differ from those of a solution? Give two examples of *non*homogeneous mixtures.

3. Suppose you dissolved a teaspoon of sugar in a glass of water. Which substance is the *solvent?* Which substance is the *solute?*

4. A metallic alloy, such as brass, is an example of a _____ solution.

5. In Chapter 14, you learned that the bonding forces in ionic solids such as NaCl are very strong, yet many ionic solids dissolve readily in water. Explain.

6. An oil spill spreads out on the *surface* of water, rather than *dissolving* in the water. Explain why.

F 7. The "Chemistry in Focus" segment *Water, Water Everywhere, But . . .* discusses the desalinization of ocean water. Explain why many salts are soluble in water. Include molecular-level diagrams in your answer.

F 8. The "Chemistry in Focus" segment *Green Chemistry* discusses the use of gaseous carbon dioxide in place of CFCs and of liquid carbon dioxide in place of the dry-cleaning chemical PERC. Would you expect carbon dioxide to be very soluble in water? Explain your answer.

15.2 Solution Composition: An Introduction

QUESTIONS

9. What does it mean to say that a solution is *saturated* with a solute?

10. If additional solute is added to a(n) _____ solution, it will dissolve.

11. A solution is a homogeneous mixture and, unlike a compound, has _____ composition.

12. The label "concentrated H_2SO_4" on a bottle means that there is a relatively _____ amount of H_2SO_4 present in the solution.

15.3 Solution Composition: Mass Percent

QUESTIONS

13. How do we define the *mass percent* composition of a solution? Give an example of a solution, and explain the relative amounts of solute and solvent present in the solution in terms of the mass percent composition.

14. A solution that is 9% by mass glucose contains 9 g of glucose in every _____ g of solution.

PROBLEMS

15. Calculate the percent by mass of solute in each of the following solutions.

a. 2.14 g of potassium chloride dissolved in 12.5 g of water

b. 2.14 g of potassium chloride dissolved in 25.0 g of water

c. 2.14 g of potassium chloride dissolved in 37.5 g of water

d. 2.14 g of potassium chloride dissolved in 50.0 g of water

16. Calculate the percent by mass of solute in each of the following solutions.

a. 6.11 mg of calcium chloride dissolved in 5.25 g of water

b. 6.11 mg of calcium chloride dissolved in 52.5 g of water

c. 6.11 g of calcium chloride dissolved in 52.5 g of water

d. 6.11 kg of calcium chloride dissolved in 52.5 kg of water

17. Calculate the mass, in grams, of solute present in each of the following solutions.

a. 375 g of 1.51% ammonium chloride solution
b. 125 g of 2.91% sodium chloride solution
c. 1.31 kg of 4.92% potassium nitrate solution
d. 478 mg of 12.5% ammonium nitrate solution

18. Calculate how many grams of solute and solvent are needed to prepare the following solutions.

a. 525 g of 3.91% iron(III) chloride solution
b. 225 g of 11.9% sucrose solution
c. 1.45 kg of 12.5% sodium chloride solution
d. 635 g of 15.1% potassium nitrate solution

19. A sample of an iron alloy contains 92.1 g Fe, 2.59 g C, and 1.59 g Cr. Calculate the percent by mass of each component present in the alloy sample.

20. Consider the iron alloy described in Question 19. Suppose it is desired to prepare 1.00 kg of this alloy. What mass of each component would be necessary?

21. An aqueous solution is to be prepared that will be 7.51% by mass ammonium nitrate. What mass of NH_4NO_3 and what mass of water will be needed to prepare 1.25 kg of the solution?

22. If 67.1 g of $CaCl_2$ is added to 275 g of water, calculate the mass percent of $CaCl_2$ in the solution.

23. A solution is to be prepared that will be 4.50% by mass calcium chloride. To prepare 175 g of the solution, what mass of calcium chloride will be needed?

24. How many grams of KBr are contained in 125 g of a 6.25% (by mass) KBr solution?

25. What mass of each solute is present in 285 g of a solution that contains 5.00% by mass NaCl and 7.50% by mass Na_2CO_3?

26. Hydrogen peroxide solutions sold in drugstores as an antiseptic typically contain 3.0% of the active ingredient, H_2O_2. Hydrogen peroxide decomposes into water and oxygen gas when applied to a wound according to the balanced chemical equation

$$2H_2O_2(aq) \rightarrow 2H_2O(l) + O_2(g)$$

What approximate mass of hydrogen peroxide solution would be needed to produce 1.00 g of oxygen gas?

27. Sulfuric acid has a great affinity for water, and for this reason, the most concentrated form of sulfuric acid available is actually a 98.3% solution. The density of concentrated sulfuric acid is 1.84 g/mL. What mass of sulfuric acid is present in 1.00 L of the concentrated solution?

28. A solvent sold for use in the laboratory contains 0.95% of a stabilizing agent that prevents the solvent from reacting with the air. What mass of the stabilizing agent is present in 1.00 kg of the solvent?

15.4 Solution Composition: Molarity

QUESTIONS

29. A solution you used in last week's lab experiment was labeled "3 *M* HCl." Describe in words the composition of this solution.

30. A solution labeled "0.110 *M* $CaCl_2$" would contain _____ mol Ca^{2+} and _____ mol Cl^- in each liter of the solution.

31. What is a *standard* solution? Describe the steps involved in preparing a standard solution.

32. To prepare 500. mL of 1.02 *M* sugar solution, which of the following would you need?

a. 500. mL of water and 1.02 mole of sugar
b. 1.02 mole of sugar and enough water to make the total volume 500. mL
c. 500. g of water and 1.02 mole of sugar
d. 0.51 mole of sugar and enough water to make the total volume 500. mL

PROBLEMS

33. For each of the following solutions, the number of moles of solute is given, followed by the total volume of the solution prepared. Calculate the molarity of each solution.

a. 0.521 mol NaCl; 125 mL
b. 0.521 mol NaCl; 250. mL
c. 0.521 mol NaCl; 500. mL
d. 0.521 mol NaCl; 1.00 L

34. For each of the following solutions, the number of moles of solute is given, followed by the total volume of the solution prepared. Calculate the molarity of each solution.

a. 0.754 mol KNO_3; 225 mL
b. 0.0105 mol $CaCl_2$; 10.2 mL
c. 3.15 mol NaCl; 5.00 L
d. 0.499 mol NaBr; 100. mL

All even-numbered Questions and Problems have answers in the back of this book and solutions in the Solutions Guide.

35. For each of the following solutions, the mass of solute is given, followed by the total volume of the solution prepared. Calculate the molarity of each solution.

   a. 3.51 g NaCl; 25 mL
   b. 3.51 g NaCl; 50. mL
   c. 3.51 g NaCl; 75 mL
   d. 3.51 g NaCl; 1.00 L

36. For each of the following solutions, the mass of solute is given, followed by the total volume of the solution prepared. Calculate the molarity of each solution.

   a. 5.59 g $CaCl_2$; 125 mL
   b. 2.34 g $CaCl_2$; 125 mL
   c. 8.73 g $CaCl_2$; 125 mL
   d. 11.5 g $CaCl_2$; 125 mL

37. A laboratory assistant needs to prepare 225 mL of 0.150 M $CaCl_2$ solution. How many grams of calcium chloride will she need?

38. What mass of potassium bromide is contained in 135 mL of 0.251 M KBr solution?

39. Standard solutions of calcium ion used to test for water hardness are prepared by dissolving pure calcium carbonate, $CaCO_3$, in dilute hydrochloric acid. A 1.745-g sample of $CaCO_3$ is placed in a 250.0-mL volumetric flask and dissolved in HCl. Then the solution is diluted to the calibration mark of the volumetric flask. Calculate the resulting molarity of calcium ion.

40. An alcoholic iodine solution ("tincture" of iodine) is prepared by dissolving 5.15 g of iodine crystals in enough alcohol to make a volume of 225 mL. Calculate the molarity of iodine in the solution.

41. If 42.5 g of NaOH is dissolved in water and diluted to a final volume of 225 mL, calculate the molarity of the solution.

42. It is desired to prepare a standard solution of potassium nitrate. If 1.21 g of KNO_3 is placed in a 25.0-mL volumetric flask, and the solute is then dissolved and diluted to the calibration mark on the flask, what will be the molarity of the solution?

43. How many *moles* of the indicated solute does each of the following solutions contain?

   a. 4.25 mL of 0.105 M $CaCl_2$ solution
   b. 11.3 mL of 0.405 M NaOH solution
   c. 1.25 L of 12.1 M HCl solution
   d. 27.5 mL of 1.98 M NaCl solution

44. How many *moles* of the indicated solute does each of the following solutions contain?

   a. 12.5 mL of 0.104 M HCl
   b. 27.3 mL of 0.223 M NaOH
   c. 36.8 mL of 0.501 M HNO_3
   d. 47.5 mL of 0.749 M KOH

45. What *mass* of the indicated solute does each of the following solutions contain?

   a. 2.50 L of 13.1 M HCl solution
   b. 15.6 mL of 0.155 M NaOH solution
   c. 135 mL of 2.01 M HNO_3 solution
   d. 4.21 L of 0.515 M $CaCl_2$ solution

46. What *mass* of the indicated solute does each of the following solutions contain?

   a. 17.8 mL of 0.119 M $CaCl_2$
   b. 27.6 mL of 0.288 M KCl
   c. 35.4 mL of 0.399 M $FeCl_3$
   d. 46.1 mL of 0.559 M KNO_3

47. What mass of NaOH pellets is required to prepare 3.5 L of 0.50 M NaOH solution?

48. What mass of solute is present in 225 mL of 0.355 M KBr solution?

49. Calculate the number of moles of the indicated ion present in each of the following solutions.

   a. Na^+ ion in 1.00 L of 0.251 M Na_2SO_4 solution
   b. Cl^- ion in 5.50 L of 0.10 M $FeCl_3$ solution
   c. NO_3^- ion in 100. mL of 0.55 M $Ba(NO_3)_2$ solution
   d. NH_4^+ ion in 250. mL of 0.350 M $(NH_4)_2SO_4$ solution

50. Calculate the number of moles of *each* ion present in each of the following solutions.

   a. 10.2 mL of 0.451 M $AlCl_3$ solution
   b. 5.51 L of 0.103 M Na_3PO_4 solution
   c. 1.75 mL of 1.25 M $CuCl_2$ solution
   d. 25.2 mL of 0.00157 M $Ca(OH)_2$ solution

51. An experiment calls for 125 mL of 0.105 M NaCl solution. What mass of NaCl is required? What mass of NaCl would be required for 1.00 L of the same solution?

52. Strong acid solutions may have their concentration determined by reaction with measured quantities of standard sodium carbonate solution. What mass of Na_2CO_3 is needed to prepare 250. mL of 0.0500 M Na_2CO_3 solution?

15.5 Dilution

QUESTIONS

53. When a concentrated stock solution is diluted to prepare a less concentrated reagent, the number of _____ is the same both before and after the dilution.

54. When the volume of a given solution is doubled (by adding water), the new concentration of solute is _____ the original concentration.

PROBLEMS

55. Calculate the new molarity if each of the following dilutions is made. Assume the volumes are additive.

   a. 55.0 mL of water is added to 25.0 mL of 0.119 M NaCl solution
   b. 125 mL of water is added to 45.3 mL of 0.701 M NaOH solution
   c. 550. mL of water is added to 125 mL of 3.01 M KOH solution
   d. 335 mL of water is added to 75.3 mL of 2.07 M $CaCl_2$ solution

56. Calculate the new molarity if each of the following dilutions is made. Assume the volumes are additive.

    a. 25.0 mL of water is added to 10.0 mL of 0.251 M $CaCl_2$ solution
    b. 97.5 mL of water is added to 125 mL of 3.00 M HCl solution
    c. 25.0 mL of 0.851 M NH_3 solution is transferred by pipet to a 500.-mL volumetric flask and water is added to the 500.-mL mark
    d. 25.0 mL of 1.25 M NaCl solution is diluted with an equal volume of water

57. Many laboratories keep bottles of 3.0 M solutions of the common acids on hand. Given the following molarities of the concentrated acids, determine how many milliliters of each concentrated acid would be required to prepare 225 mL of a 3.0 M solution of the acid.

Acid	Molarity of Concentrated Reagent
HCl	12.1 M
HNO_3	15.9 M
H_2SO_4	18.0 M
$HC_2H_3O_2$	17.5 M
H_3PO_4	14.9 M

58. For convenience, one form of sodium hydroxide that is sold commercially is the saturated solution. This solution is 19.4 M, which is approximately 50% by mass sodium hydroxide. What volume of this solution would be needed to prepare 3.50 L of 3.00 M NaOH solution?

59. How would you prepare 275 mL of 0.350 M NaCl solution using an available 2.00 M solution?

60. Suppose 325 mL of 0.150 M NaOH is needed for your experiment. How would you prepare this if all that is available is a 1.01 M NaOH solution?

61. How much *water* must be added to 500. mL of 0.200 M HCl to produce a 0.150 M solution? (Assume that the volumes are additive.)

62. An experiment calls for 100. mL of 1.25 M HCl. All that is available in the lab is a bottle of concentrated HCl, whose label indicates that it is 12.1 M. How much of the concentrated HCl would be needed to prepare the desired solution?

15.6 Stoichiometry of Solution Reactions

PROBLEMS

63. The amount of nickel(II) present in an aqueous solution can be determined by precipitating the nickel with the organic chemical reagent dimethylglyoxime $[CH_3C(NOH)C(NOH)CH_3$, commonly abbreviated as "DMG"].

    $$Ni^{2+}(aq) + 2DMG(aq) \rightarrow Ni(DMG)_2(s)$$

    How many milliliters of 0.0703 M DMG solution is required to precipitate all the nickel(II) present in 10.0 mL of 0.103 M nickel(II) sulfate solution?

64. Generally only the carbonates of the Group 1 elements and the ammonium ion are soluble in water; most other carbonates are *insoluble*. How many milliliters of 0.125 M sodium carbonate solution would be needed to precipitate the calcium ion from 37.2 mL of 0.105 M $CaCl_2$ solution?

    $$Na_2CO_3(aq) + CaCl_2(aq) \rightarrow CaCO_3(s) + 2NaCl(s)$$

65. Many metal ions are precipitated from solution by the sulfide ion. As an example, consider treating a solution of copper(II) sulfate with sodium sulfide solution:

    $$CuSO_4(aq) + Na_2S(aq) \rightarrow CuS(s) + Na_2SO_4(aq)$$

    What volume of 0.105 M Na_2S solution would be required to precipitate all of the copper(II) ion from 27.5 mL of 0.121 M $CuSO_4$ solution?

66. Calcium oxalate, CaC_2O_4, is very insoluble in water. What mass of sodium oxalate, $Na_2C_2O_4$, is required to precipitate the calcium ion from 37.5 mL of 0.104 M $CaCl_2$ solution?

67. When aqueous solutions of lead(II) ion are treated with potassium chromate solution, a bright yellow precipitate of lead(II) chromate, $PbCrO_4$, forms. How many grams of lead chromate form when a 1.00-g sample of $Pb(NO_3)_2$ is added to 25.0 mL of 1.00 M K_2CrO_4 solution?

68. Aluminum ion may be precipitated from aqueous solution by addition of hydroxide ion, forming $Al(OH)_3$. A large excess of hydroxide ion must not be added, however, because the precipitate of $Al(OH)_3$ will redissolve as a soluble compound containing aluminum ions and hydroxide ions begins to form. How many grams of solid NaOH should be added to 10.0 mL of 0.250 M $AlCl_3$ to just precipitate all the aluminum?

15.7 Neutralization Reactions

PROBLEMS

69. What volume of 0.502 M NaOH solution would be required to neutralize 27.2 mL of 0.491 M HNO_3 solution?

70. What volume of 0.995 M HCl solution could be neutralized by 125 mL of 3.01 M NaOH solution?

71. A sample of sodium hydrogen carbonate solid weighing 0.1015 g requires 47.21 mL of a hydrochloric acid solution to react completely.

    $$HCl(aq) + NaHCO_3(s) \rightarrow NaCl(aq) + H_2O(l) + CO_2(g)$$

    Calculate the molarity of the hydrochloric acid solution.

72. The total acidity in water samples can be determined by neutralization with standard sodium hydroxide solution. What is the total concentration of hydrogen ion, H^+, present in a water sample if 100. mL of the sample requires 7.2 mL of $2.5 \times 10^{-3} M$ NaOH to be neutralized?

73. What volume of 1.00 M NaOH is required to neutralize each of the following solutions?

    a. 25.0 mL of 0.154 M acetic acid, $HC_2H_3O_2$
    b. 35.0 mL of 0.102 M hydrofluoric acid, HF
    c. 10.0 mL of 0.143 M phosphoric acid, H_3PO_4
    d. 35.0 mL of 0.220 M sulfuric acid, H_2SO_4

74. What volume of 0.101 M HNO_3 is required to neutralize each of the following solutions?

    a. 12.7 mL of 0.501 M NaOH
    b. 24.9 mL of 0.00491 M $Ba(OH)_2$
    c. 49.1 mL of 0.103 M NH_3
    d. 1.21 L of 0.102 M KOH

15.8 Solution Composition: Normality

QUESTIONS

75. One equivalent of an acid is the amount of the acid required to provide _____.

76. A solution that contains 1 equivalent of acid or base per liter is said to be a _____ solution.

77. Explain why the equivalent weight of H_2SO_4 is half the molar mass of this substance. How many hydrogen ions does each H_2SO_4 molecule produce when reacting with an excess of OH^- ions?

78. How many equivalents of hydroxide ion are needed to react with 1.53 equivalents of hydrogen ion? How did you know this when no balanced chemical equation was provided for the reaction?

PROBLEMS

79. For each of the following solutions, calculate the normality.

    a. 25.2 mL of 0.105 M HCl diluted with water to a total volume of 75.3 mL
    b. 0.253 M H_3PO_4
    c. 0.00103 M $Ca(OH)_2$

80. For each of the following solutions, the mass of solute taken is indicated, along with the total volume of solution prepared. Calculate the normality of each solution.

    a. 0.113 g NaOH; 10.2 mL
    b. 12.5 mg $Ca(OH)_2$; 100. mL
    c. 12.4 g H_2SO_4; 155 mL

81. Calculate the normality of each of the following solutions.

    a. 0.250 M HCl
    b. 0.105 M H_2SO_4
    c. 5.3×10^{-2} M H_3PO_4

82. Calculate the normality of each of the following solutions.

    a. 0.134 M NaOH
    b. 0.00521 M $Ca(OH)_2$
    c. 4.42 M H_3PO_4

83. A solution of phosphoric acid, H_3PO_4, is found to contain 35.2 g of H_3PO_4 per liter of solution. Calculate the molarity and normality of the solution.

84. A solution of the sparingly soluble base $Ca(OH)_2$ is prepared in a volumetric flask by dissolving 5.21 mg of $Ca(OH)_2$ to a total volume of 1000. mL. Calculate the molarity and normality of the solution.

85. How many milliliters of 0.50 N NaOH are required to neutralize exactly 15.0 mL of 0.35 N H_2SO_4?

86. What volume of 0.104 N H_2SO_4 is required to neutralize 15.2 mL of 0.152 N NaOH? What volume of 0.104 M H_2SO_4 is required to neutralize 15.2 mL of 0.152 M NaOH?

    $$H_2SO_4(aq) + 2NaOH(aq) \rightarrow Na_2SO_4(aq) + 2H_2O(l)$$

87. What volume of 0.151 N NaOH is required to neutralize 24.2 mL of 0.125 N H_2SO_4? What volume of 0.151 N NaOH is required to neutralize 24.1 mL of 0.125 M H_2SO_4?

88. Suppose that 27.34 mL of standard 0.1021 M NaOH is required to neutralize 25.00 mL of an unknown H_2SO_4 solution. Calculate the molarity and the normality of the unknown solution.

Additional Problems

89. A mixture is prepared by mixing 50.0 g of ethanol, 50.0 g of water, and 5.0 g of sugar. What is the mass percent of each component in the mixture? How many grams of the mixture should one take in order to have 1.5 g of sugar? How many grams of the mixture should one take to have 10.0 g of ethanol?

90. Explain the difference in meaning between the following two solutions: "50. g of NaCl dissolved in 1.0 L of water" and "50. g of NaCl dissolved in enough water to make 1.0 L of solution." For which solution can the molarity be calculated directly (using the molar mass of NaCl)?

91. Suppose 50.0 mL of 0.250 M $CoCl_2$ solution is added to 25.0 mL of 0.350 M $NiCl_2$ solution. Calculate the concentration, in moles per liter, of each of the ions present after mixing. Assume that the volumes are additive.

92. If 500. g of water is added to 75 g of 25% NaCl solution, what is the percent by mass of NaCl in the diluted solution?

93. Calculate the mass of AgCl formed, and the concentration of silver ion remaining in solution, when 10.0 g of solid $AgNO_3$ is added to 50. mL of 1.0×10^{-2} M NaCl solution. Assume there is no volume change upon addition of the solid.

94. Baking soda (sodium hydrogen carbonate, $NaHCO_3$) is often used to neutralize spills of acids on the benchtop in the laboratory. What mass of $NaHCO_3$ would be needed to neutralize a spill consisting of 25.2 mL of 6.01 M hydrochloric acid solution?

All even-numbered Questions and Problems have answers in the back of this book and solutions in the Solutions Guide.

95. Many metal ions form insoluble sulfide compounds when a solution of the metal ion is treated with hydrogen sulfide gas. For example, nickel(II) precipitates nearly quantitatively as NiS when H_2S gas is bubbled through a nickel ion solution. How many milliliters of gaseous H_2S at STP are needed to precipitate all the nickel ion present in 10. mL of 0.050 M $NiCl_2$ solution?

96. Strictly speaking, the solvent is the component of a solution that is present in the largest amount on a *mole* basis. For solutions involving water, water is almost always the solvent because there tend to be many more water molecules present than molecules of any conceivable solute. To see why this is so, calculate the number of moles of water present in 1.0 L of water. Recall that the density of water is very nearly 1.0 g/mL under most conditions.

97. Aqueous ammonia is typically sold by chemical supply houses as the saturated solution, which has a concentration of 14.5 mol/L. What volume of NH_3 at STP is required to prepare 100. mL of concentrated ammonia solution?

98. What volume of hydrogen chloride gas at STP is required to prepare 500. mL of 0.100 M HCl solution?

99. What do we mean when we say that "like dissolves like"? Do two molecules have to be identical to be able to form a solution in one another?

100. The concentration of a solution of HCl is 33.1% by mass, and its density was measured to be 1.147 g/mL. How many milliliters of the HCl solution are required to obtain 10.0 g of HCl?

101. An experiment calls for 1.00 g of silver nitrate, but all that is available in the laboratory is a 0.50% solution of $AgNO_3$. Assuming the density of the silver nitrate solution to be very nearly that of water because it is so dilute, determine how many milliliters of the solution should be used.

102. If 14.2 g of $CaCl_2$ is added to a 50.0-mL volumetric flask, and after dissolving the salt, water is added to the calibration mark of the flask, calculate the molarity of the solution.

103. A solution is 0.1% by mass calcium chloride. Therefore, 100. g of the solution contains _____ g of calcium chloride.

104. Calculate the mass percent of KNO_3 in each of the following solutions.

a. 5.0 g of KNO_3 in 75 g of water
b. 2.5 mg of KNO_3 in 1.0 g of water
c. 11 g of KNO_3 in 89 g of water
d. 11 g of KNO_3 in 49 g of water

105. A 15.0% (by mass) NaCl solution is available. Determine what mass of the solution should be taken to obtain the following quantities of NaCl.

a. 10.0 g   c. 100.0 g
b. 25.0 g   d. 1.00 lb

106. A certain grade of steel is made by dissolving 5.0 g of carbon and 1.5 g of nickel per 100. g of molten iron. What is the mass percent of each component in the finished steel?

107. A sugar solution is prepared in such a way that it contains 10.% dextrose by mass. What quantity of this solution do we need to obtain 25 g of dextrose?

108. How many grams of Na_2CO_3 are contained in 500. g of a 5.5% by mass Na_2CO_3 solution?

109. What mass of KNO_3 is required to prepare 125 g of 1.5% KNO_3 solution?

110. A solution contains 7.5% by mass NaCl and 2.5% by mass KBr. What mass of *each* solute is contained in 125 g of the solution?

111. How many moles of each ion are present in 11.7 mL of 0.102 M Na_3PO_4 solution?

112. For each of the following solutions, the number of moles of solute is given, followed by the total volume of solution prepared. Calculate the molarity.

a. 0.10 mole of $CaCl_2$; 25 mL
b. 2.5 moles of KBr; 2.5 L
c. 0.55 mole of $NaNO_3$; 755 mL
d. 4.5 moles of Na_2SO_4; 1.25 L

113. For each of the following solutions, the mass of the solute is given, followed by the total volume of solution prepared. Calculate the molarity.

a. 5.0 g of $BaCl_2$; 2.5 L
b. 3.5 g of KBr; 75 mL
c. 21.5 g of Na_2CO_3; 175 mL
d. 55 g of $CaCl_2$; 1.2 L

114. If 125 g of sucrose, $C_{12}H_{22}O_{11}$, is dissolved in enough water to make 450. mL of solution, calculate the molarity.

115. Concentrated hydrochloric acid is made by pumping hydrogen chloride gas into distilled water. If concentrated HCl contains 439 g of HCl per liter, what is the molarity?

116. If 1.5 g of NaCl is dissolved in enough water to make 1.0 L of solution, what is the molarity of NaCl in the solution?

117. How many *moles* of the indicated solute does each of the following solutions contain?

a. 1.5 L of 3.0 M H_2SO_4 solution
b. 35 mL of 5.4 M NaCl solution
c. 5.2 L of 18 M H_2SO_4 solution
d. 0.050 L of 1.1×10^{-3} M NaF solution

118. How many *moles* and how many *grams* of the indicated solute does each of the following solutions contain?

a. 4.25 L of 0.105 M KCl solution
b. 15.1 mL of 0.225 M $NaNO_3$ solution
c. 25 mL of 3.0 M HCl
d. 100. mL of 0.505 M H_2SO_4

119. If 10. g of $AgNO_3$ is available, what volume of 0.25 M $AgNO_3$ solution can be prepared?

120. Calculate the number of moles of *each* ion present in each of the following solutions.

    a. 1.25 L of 0.250 M Na_3PO_4 solution
    b. 3.5 mL of 6.0 M H_2SO_4 solution
    c. 25 mL of 0.15 M $AlCl_3$ solution
    d. 1.50 L of 1.25 M $BaCl_2$ solution

121. Calcium carbonate, $CaCO_3$, can be obtained in a very pure state. Standard solutions of calcium ion are usually prepared by dissolving calcium carbonate in acid. What mass of $CaCO_3$ should be taken to prepare 500. mL of 0.0200 M calcium ion solution?

122. Calculate the new molarity when 150. mL of water is added to each of the following solutions.

    a. 125 mL of 0.200 M HBr
    b. 155 mL of 0.250 M $Ca(C_2H_3O_2)_2$
    c. 0.500 L of 0.250 M H_3PO_4
    d. 15 mL of 18.0 M H_2SO_4

123. How many milliliters of 18.0 M H_2SO_4 are required to prepare 35.0 mL of 0.250 M solution?

124. When 50. mL of 5.4 M NaCl is diluted to a final volume of 300. mL, what is the concentration of NaCl in the diluted solution?

125. When 10. L of water is added to 3.0 L of 6.0 M H_2SO_4, what is the molarity of the resulting solution? Assume the volumes are additive.

126. How many milliliters of 0.10 M Na_2S solution are required to precipitate all the nickel, as NiS, from 25.0 mL of 0.20 M $NiCl_2$ solution?

$$NiCl_2(aq) + Na_2S(aq) \rightarrow NiS(s) + 2NaCl(aq)$$

127. How many grams of $Ba(NO_3)_2$ are required to precipitate all the sulfate ion present in 15.3 mL of 0.139 M H_2SO_4 solution?

$$Ba(NO_3)_2(aq) + H_2SO_4(aq) \rightarrow BaSO_4(s) + 2HNO_3(aq)$$

128. What volume of 0.150 M HNO_3 solution is needed to exactly neutralize 35.0 mL of 0.150 M NaOH solution?

129. What volume of 0.250 M HCl is required to neutralize each of the following solutions?

    a. 25.0 mL of 0.103 M sodium hydroxide, NaOH
    b. 50.0 mL of 0.00501 M calcium hydroxide, $Ca(OH)_2$
    c. 20.0 mL of 0.226 M ammonia, NH_3
    d. 15.0 mL of 0.0991 M potassium hydroxide, KOH

130. For each of the following solutions, the mass of solute taken is indicated, as well as the total volume of solution prepared. Calculate the normality of each solution.

    a. 15.0 g of HCl; 500. mL
    b. 49.0 g of H_2SO_4; 250. mL
    c. 10.0 g of H_3PO_4; 100. mL

131. Calculate the normality of each of the following solutions.

    a. 0.50 M acetic acid, $HC_2H_3O_2$
    b. 0.00250 M sulfuric acid, H_2SO_4
    c. 0.10 M potassium hydroxide, KOH

132. A sodium dihydrogen phosphate solution was prepared by dissolving 5.0 g of NaH_2PO_4 in enough water to make 500. mL of solution. What are the molarity and normality of the resulting solution?

133. How many milliliters of 0.105 M NaOH are required to neutralize exactly 14.2 mL of 0.141 M H_3PO_4?

134. If 27.5 mL of 3.5×10^{-2} N $Ca(OH)_2$ solution is needed to neutralize 10.0 mL of nitric acid solution of unknown concentration, what is the normality of the nitric acid?

QUESTIONS

1. What are some of the general properties of gases that distinguish them from liquids and solids?

2. How does the pressure of the atmosphere arise? Sketch a representation of the device commonly used to measure the pressure of the atmosphere. Your textbook described a simple experiment to demonstrate the pressure of the atmosphere. Explain this experiment.

3. What is the SI unit of pressure? What units of pressure are commonly used in the United States? Why are these common units more convenient to use than the SI unit? Describe a *manometer* and explain how such a device can be used to measure the pressure of gas samples.

4. Your textbook gives several definitions and formulas for Boyle's law for gases. Write, in your *own* words, what this law really tells us about gases. Now write two mathematical expressions that describe Boyle's law. Do these two expressions tell us different things, or are they different representations of the same phenomena? Sketch the general shape of a graph of pressure versus volume for an ideal gas.

5. When using Boyle's law in solving problems in the textbook, you may have noticed that questions were often qualified by stating that "the temperature and amount of gas remain the same." Why was this qualification necessary?

6. What does Charles's law tell us about how the volume of a gas sample varies as the temperature of the sample is changed? How does this volume–temperature relationship *differ* from the volume–pressure relationship of Boyle's law? Give two mathematical expressions that describe Charles's law. For Charles's law to hold true, why must the pressure and amount of gas remain the same? Sketch the general shape of a graph of volume versus temperature (at constant pressure) for an ideal gas.

7. Explain how the concept of absolute zero came about through Charles's studies of gases. *Hint:* What would happen to the volume of a gas sample at absolute zero (if the gas did not liquefy first)? What temperature scale is defined with its lowest point as the absolute zero of temperature? What is absolute zero in Celsius degrees?

8. What does Avogadro's law tell us about the relationship between the volume of a sample of gas and the number of molecules the gas contains? Why must the temperature and pressure be held constant for valid comparisons using Avogadro's law? Does Avogadro's law describe a direct or an inverse relationship between the volume and the number of moles of gas?

9. What do we mean specifically by an *ideal* gas? Explain why the *ideal gas law* ($PV = nRT$) is actually a combination of Boyle's, Charles's, and Avogadro's gas laws. What is the numerical value and what are the specific units of the universal gas constant, *R?* Why is close attention to *units* especially important when doing ideal gas law calculations?

10. Dalton's law of partial pressures concerns the properties of mixtures of gases. What is meant by the *partial pressure* of an individual gas in a mixture? How does the *total pressure* of a gaseous mixture depend on the partial pressures of the individual gases in the mixture? How does Dalton's law help us realize that in an ideal gas sample, the volume of the individual molecules is insignificant compared with the bulk volume of the sample?

11. What happens to a gas sample when it is collected by displacement of, or by bubbling through, water? How is this taken into account when calculating the pressure of the gas?

12. Without consulting your textbook, list and explain the main postulates of the kinetic molecular theory for gases. How do these postulates help us account for the following bulk properties of a gas: the pressure of the gas and why the pressure of the gas increases with increased temperature; the fact that a gas fills its entire container; and the fact that the volume of a given sample of gas increases as its temperature is increased.

13. What does "STP" stand for? What conditions correspond to STP? What is the volume occupied by one mole of an ideal gas at STP?

14. In general, how do we envision the structures of solids and liquids? Explain how the densities and compressibilities of solids and liquids contrast with those properties of gaseous substances. How do we know that the structures of the solid and liquid states of a substance are more comparable to each other than to the properties of the substance in the gaseous state?

15. Describe some of the physical properties of water. Why is water one of the most important substances on earth?

16. Define the *normal* boiling point of water. Why does a sample of boiling water remain at the same temperature until all the water has been boiled? Define the normal freezing point of water. Sketch a representation of a heating/cooling curve for water, marking clearly the normal freezing and boiling points.

17. Are changes in state physical or chemical changes? Explain. What type of forces must be overcome to melt or vaporize a substance (are these forces *intra*molecular or *inter*molecular)? Define the *molar heat of fusion* and *molar heat of vaporization*. Why is the molar heat of vaporization of water so much larger than its molar heat of fusion? Why does the boiling point of a liquid vary with altitude?

18. What is a *dipole–dipole attraction?* How do the strengths of dipole–dipole forces compare with the strengths of typical covalent bonds? What is *hydrogen bonding?* What conditions are necessary for hydrogen bonding to exist in a substance or mixture? What experimental evidence do we have for hydrogen bonding?

19. Define *London dispersion forces*. Draw a picture showing how London forces arise. Are London forces relatively strong or relatively weak? Explain. Although London forces exist among all molecules, for what type of molecule are they the *only* major intermolecular force?

20. Why does the process of *vaporization* require an input of energy? Why is it so important that water has a large heat of vaporization? What is *condensation?* Explain how the processes of vaporization and condensation represent an *equilibrium* in a closed container. Define the *equilibrium vapor pressure* of a liquid. Describe how this pressure arises in a closed container. Describe an experiment that demonstrates vapor pressure and enables us to measure the magnitude of that pressure. How is the magnitude of a liquid's vapor pressure related to the intermolecular forces in the liquid?

21. Define a *crystalline solid*. Describe in detail some important types of crystalline solids and name a substance that is an example of each type of solid. Explain how the particles are held together in each type of solid (the interparticle forces that exist). How do the interparticle forces in a solid influence the bulk physical properties of the solid?

22. Define the bonding that exists in metals and how this model explains some of the unique physical properties of metals. What are metal *alloys?* Identify the two main types of alloys, and describe how their structures differ. Give several examples of each type of alloy.

23. Define a *solution*. Describe how an ionic solute such as NaCl dissolves in water to form a solution. How are the strong bonding forces in a crystal of ionic solute overcome? Why do the ions in a solution not attract each other so strongly as to reconstitute the ionic solute? How does a molecular solid such as sugar dissolve in water? What forces between water molecules and the molecules of a molecular solid may help the solute dissolve? Why do some substances *not* dissolve in water at all?

24. Define a *saturated* solution. Does saturated mean the same thing as saying the solution is *concentrated?* Explain. Why does a solute dissolve only to a particular extent in water? How does formation of a saturated solution represent an equilibrium?

25. The concentration of a solution may be expressed in various ways. Suppose 5.00 g of NaCl were dissolved in 15.0 g of water, which resulted in 16.1 mL of solution after mixing. Explain how you would calculate the *mass percent* of NaCl and the *molarity* of NaCl.

26. When a solution is diluted by adding additional solvent, the *concentration* of solute changes but the *amount* of solute present does not change. Explain. Suppose 250. mL of water is added to 125 mL of 0.551 *M* NaCl solution. Explain *how* you would calculate the concentration of the solution after dilution.

27. What is one *equivalent* of an acid? What does an equivalent of a base represent? How is the equivalent weight of an acid or a base related to the substance's molar mass? Give an example of an acid and a base that have equivalent weights *equal* to their molar masses. Give an example of an acid and a base that have equivalent weights that are *not equal* to their molar masses. What is a *normal* solution of an acid or a base? How is the *normality* of an acid or a base solution related to its *molarity?* Give an example of a solution whose normality is equal to its molarity, and an example of a solution whose normality is *not* the same as its molarity.

PROBLEMS

28. a. If the pressure on a 125-mL sample of gas is increased from 755 mm Hg to 899 mm Hg at constant temperature, what will the volume of the sample become?

   b. If a sample of gas is compressed from an initial volume of 455 mL at 755 mm Hg to a final volume of 327 mL at constant temperature, what will be the new pressure in the gas sample?

29. a. If the temperature of a 255-mL sample of gas is increased from 35 °C to 55 °C at constant pressure, what will be the new volume of the gas sample?

   b. If a 325-mL sample of gas at 25 °C is immersed in liquid nitrogen at –196 °C, what will be the new volume of the gas sample?

30. Calculate the indicated quantity for each gas sample.

   a. The volume occupied by 1.15 g of helium gas at 25 °C and 1.01 atm pressure.

   b. The partial pressure of each gas if 2.27 g of H_2 and 1.03 g of He are confined to a 5.00-L container at 0 °C.

   c. The pressure existing in a 9.97-L tank containing 42.5 g of argon gas at 27 °C.

31. Chlorine gas, Cl_2, can be generated in small quantities by addition of concentrated hydrochloric acid to manganese(IV) oxide.

   $$MnO_2(s) + 4HCl(aq) \rightarrow MnCl_2(aq) + 2H_2O(l) + Cl_2(g)$$

   The chlorine gas is bubbled through water to dissolve any traces of HCl remaining and then is dried by bubbling through concentrated sulfuric acid.

   After drying, what volume of Cl_2 gas at STP would be expected if 4.05 g of MnO_2 is treated with excess concentrated HCl?

32. When calcium carbonate is heated strongly, it evolves carbon dioxide gas.

   $$CaCO_3(s) \rightarrow CaO(s) + CO_2(g)$$

If 1.25 g of $CaCO_3$ is heated, what mass of CO_2 would be produced? What volume would this quantity of CO_2 occupy at STP?

33. If an electric current is passed through molten sodium chloride, elemental chlorine gas is generated (see Chapter 18) as the sodium chloride is decomposed.

$$2NaCl(l) \rightarrow 2Na(s) + Cl_2(g)$$

What volume of chlorine gas measured at 767 mm Hg at 25 °C would be generated by complete decomposition of 1.25 g of NaCl?

34. Calculate the indicated quantity for each solution.
   a. The percent by mass of solute when 2.05 g of NaCl is dissolved in 19.2 g of water.
   b. The mass of solute contained in 26.2 g of 10.5% $CaCl_2$ solution.
   c. The mass of NaCl required to prepare 225 g of 5.05% NaCl solution.

35. Calculate the indicated quantity for each solution.
   a. The mass of solute present in 235 mL of 0.251 M NaOH solution.
   b. The molarity of the solution when 0.293 mole of KNO_3 is dissolved in water to a final volume of 125 mL.
   c. The number of moles of HCl present in 5.05 L of 6.01 M solution.

36. Calculate the molarities of the solutions resulting when the indicated dilutions are made. Assume that the volumes are additive.
   a. 25 mL of water is added to 12.5 mL of 1.515 M NaOH solution.
   b. 75.0 mL of 0.252 M HCl is diluted to a volume of 225 mL.
   c. 52.1 mL fo 0.751 M HNO_3 is added to 250. mL of water.

37. Calculate the volume (in milliliters) of each of the following acid solutions that would be required to neutralize 36.2 mL of 0.259 M NaOH solution.
   a. 0.271 M HCl
   b. 0.119 M H_2SO_4
   c. 0.171 M H_3PO_4

38. If 125 mL of concentrated sulfuric acid solution (density 1.84 g/mL, 98.3% H_2SO_4 by mass) is diluted to a final volume of 3.01 L, calculate the following information.
   a. the mass of pure H_2SO_4 in the 125-mL sample.
   b. the molarity of the *concentrated* acid solution
   c. the molarity of the *dilute* acid solution
   d. the normality of the dilute acid solution
   e. the quantity of the dilute acid solution needed to neutralize 45.3 mL of 0.532 M NaOH solution

$$NaOH(s) \xrightarrow{\text{H}_2\text{O}} Na^+(aq) + OH^-(aq)$$

This solution is called a strong base.

Although the **Arrhenius concept of acids and bases** was a major step forward in understanding acid–base chemistry, this concept is limited because it allows for only one kind of base—the hydroxide ion. A more general definition of acids and bases was suggested by the Danish chemist Johannes Brønsted and the English chemist Thomas Lowry. In the **Brønsted–Lowry model,** *an acid is a proton (H$^+$) donor, and a base is a proton acceptor.* According to the Brønsted–Lowry model, the general reaction that occurs when an acid is dissolved in water can best be represented as an acid (HA) donating a proton to a water molecule to form a new acid (the **conjugate acid**) and a new base (the **conjugate base**).

> Recall that (aq) means the substance is hydrated—it has water molecules clustered around it.

$$\underset{\text{Acid}}{HA(aq)} + \underset{\text{Base}}{H_2O(l)} \rightarrow \underset{\substack{\text{Conjugate} \\ \text{acid}}}{H_3O^+(aq)} + \underset{\substack{\text{Conjugate} \\ \text{base}}}{A^-(aq)}$$

This model emphasizes the significant role of the polar water molecule in pulling the proton from the acid. Note that the conjugate base is everything that remains of the acid molecule after a proton is lost. The conjugate acid is formed when the proton is transferred to the base. A **conjugate acid–base pair** consists of two substances related to each other by the donating and accepting of a *single proton.* In the above equation there are two conjugate acid–base pairs: HA (acid) and A$^-$ (base), and H$_2$O (base) and H$_3$O$^+$ (acid). For example, when hydrogen chloride is dissolved in water it behaves as an acid.

Acid–conjugate base pair

$$HCl(aq) + H_2O(l) \rightarrow H_3O^+(aq) + Cl^-(aq)$$

Base–conjugate acid pair

In this case HCl is the acid that loses an H$^+$ ion to form Cl$^-$, its conjugate base. On the other hand, H$_2$O (behaving as a base) gains an H$^+$ ion to form H$_3$O$^+$ (the conjugate acid).

How can water act as a base? Remember that the oxygen of the water molecule has two unshared electron pairs, either of which can form a covalent bond with an H$^+$ ion. When gaseous HCl dissolves in water, the following reaction occurs:

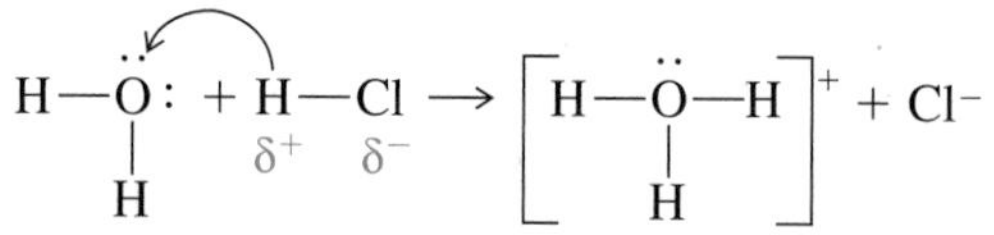

$$H-\overset{..}{\underset{|}{O}}: + \underset{\delta^+}{H}-\underset{\delta^-}{Cl} \rightarrow \left[H-\overset{..}{\underset{|}{O}}-H \right]^+ + Cl^-$$
$$\qquad H \qquad \qquad \qquad \qquad H$$

Note that an H$^+$ ion is transferred from the HCl molecule to the water molecule to form H$_3$O$^+$, which is called the **hydronium ion.**

EXAMPLE 16.1 | Identifying Conjugate Acid–Base Pairs

Which of the following represent conjugate acid–base pairs?

a. HF, F$^-$

b. NH$_4^+$, NH$_3$

c. HCl, H$_2$O

CHEMISTRY IN FOCUS

Gum That Foams

Mad Dawg chewing gum is a practical joker's dream come true. It is noticeably sour when someone first starts to chew it, but the big surprise comes about ten chews later when brightly colored foam oozes from the person's mouth. Although the effect is dramatic, the cause is simple acid–base chemistry.

The foam consists of sugar and saliva churned into a bubbling mess by carbon dioxide released from the gum. The carbon dioxide is formed when sodium bicarbonate ($NaHCO_3$) present in the gum is mixed with citric acid and malic acid (also present in the gum) in the moist environment of the mouth. As $NaHCO_3$ dissolves in the water of the saliva, it separates into its ions:

$$NaHCO_3(s) \xrightarrow{H_2O} Na^+(aq) + HCO_3^-(aq)$$

The bicarbonate ion, when exposed to H^+ ions from acids, decomposes to carbon dioxide and water:*

$$H^+(aq) + HCO_3^-(aq) \rightarrow H_2O(l) + CO_2(g)$$

The acids present in the gum also cause it to be sour, stimulating extra salivation and thus extra foam.

Although the chemistry behind Mad Dawg is well understood, the development of the gum into a safe, but fun, product was not so easy. In fact, early versions of the gum exploded because the acids and the sodium bicarbonate mixed prematurely. As solids, citric and malic acids and sodium bicarbonate do not react with each other. However, the presence of water frees the ions to move and react. In the manufacture of the gum, colorings and flavorings are applied as aqueous solutions. The water caused the gum to explode in early attempts to manufacture it. The makers of Mad Dawg obviously solved the problem. Buy some Mad Dawg and cut it open to see how they did it.

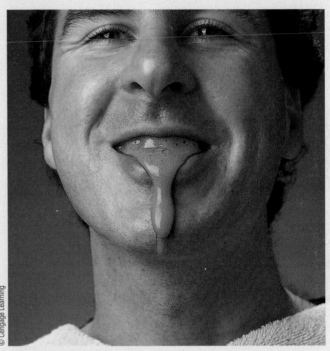

Chewing Mad Dawg gum.

© Cengage Learning

*This reaction is often used to power "bottle rockets" by adding vinegar (dilute acetic acid) to baking soda (sodium bicarbonate).

SOLUTION

a. and b. HF, F^- and NH_4^+, NH_3 are conjugate acid–base pairs because the two species differ by one H^+.

$$HF \rightarrow H^+ + F^-$$
$$NH_4^+ \rightarrow H^+ + NH_3$$

c. HCl and H_2O are not a conjugate acid–base pair because they are not related by the removal or addition of one H^+. The conjugate base of HCl is Cl^-. The conjugate acid of H_2O is H_3O^+. ∎

EXAMPLE 16.2 | **Writing Conjugate Bases**

Write the conjugate base for each of the following:

a. $HClO_4$ b. H_3PO_4 c. $CH_3NH_3{}^+$

SOLUTION

To get the conjugate base for an acid, we must remove an H^+ ion.

a. $\underset{\text{Acid}}{HClO_4} \rightarrow H^+ + \underset{\text{Conjugate base}}{ClO_4^-}$

b. $\underset{\text{Acid}}{H_3PO_4} \rightarrow H^+ + \underset{\text{Conjugate base}}{H_2PO_4^-}$

c. $\underset{\text{Acid}}{CH_3NH_3^+} \rightarrow H^+ + \underset{\text{Conjugate base}}{CH_3NH_2}$

Self-Check **EXERCISE 16.1**   Which of the following represent conjugate acid–base pairs?

a. H_2O, H_3O^+

b. OH^-, HNO_3

c. H_2SO_4, $SO_4{}^{2-}$

d. $HC_2H_3O_2$, $C_2H_3O_2{}^-$

See Problems 16.7 through 16.14. ■

16.2   Acid Strength

OBJECTIVES: To understand what acid strength means. • To understand the relationship between acid strength and the strength of the conjugate base.

We have seen that when an acid dissolves in water, a proton is transferred from the acid to water:

$$HA(aq) + H_2O(l) \rightarrow H_3O^+(aq) + A^-(aq)$$

In this reaction a new acid, H_3O^+ (called the conjugate acid), and a new base, A^- (the conjugate base), are formed. The conjugate acid and base can react with one another,

$$H_3O^+(aq) + A^-(aq) \rightarrow HA(aq) + H_2O(l)$$

to re-form the parent acid and a water molecule. Therefore, this reaction can occur "in both directions." The forward reaction is

$$HA(aq) + H_2O(l) \rightarrow H_3O^+(aq) + A^-(aq)$$

and the reverse reaction is

$$H_3O^+(aq) + A^-(aq) \rightarrow HA(aq) + H_2O(l)$$

Note that the products in the forward reaction are the reactants in the reverse reaction. We usually represent the situation in which the reaction can occur in both directions by double arrows:

$$HA(aq) + H_2O(l) \rightleftharpoons H_3O^+(aq) + A^-(aq)$$

This situation represents a competition for the H^+ ion between H_2O (in the forward reaction) and A^- (in the reverse reaction). If H_2O "wins" this competition—that is, if H_2O has a very high attraction for H^+ compared to A^-—then the solution will contain mostly H_3O^+ and A^-. We describe this situation by saying that the H_2O molecule is a much stronger base (more attraction for H^+) than A^-. In this case the forward reaction predominates:

$$HA(aq) + H_2O(l) \Longrightarrow H_3O^+(aq) + A^-(aq)$$

We say that the acid HA is **completely ionized** or **completely dissociated.** This situation represents a **strong acid.**

The opposite situation can also occur. Sometimes A^- "wins" the competition for the H^+ ion. In this case A^- is a much stronger base than H_2O and the reverse reaction predominates:

$$HA(aq) + H_2O(l) \Longleftarrow H_3O^+(aq) + A^-(aq)$$

Here, A^- has a much larger attraction for H^+ than does H_2O, and most of the HA molecules remain intact. This situation represents a **weak acid.**

We can determine what is actually going on in a solution by measuring its ability to conduct an electric current. Recall from Chapter 7 that a solution can conduct a current in proportion to the number of ions that are present (see Figure 7.2). When 1 mole of solid sodium chloride is dissolved in 1 L of water, the resulting solution is an excellent conductor of an electric current because the Na^+ and Cl^- ions separate completely. We call NaCl a strong electrolyte. Similarly, when 1 mole of hydrogen chloride is dissolved in 1 L of water, the resulting solution is an excellent conductor. Therefore, hydrogen chloride is also a strong electrolyte, which means that each HCl molecule must produce H^+ and Cl^- ions. This tells us that the forward reaction predominates:

$$HCl(aq) + H_2O(l) \Longrightarrow H_3O^+(aq) + Cl^-(aq)$$

(Accordingly, the arrow pointing right is longer than the arrow pointing left.) In solution there are virtually no HCl molecules, only H^+ and Cl^- ions. This shows that Cl^- is a very poor base compared to the H_2O molecule; it has virtually no ability to attract H^+ ions in water. This aqueous solution of hydrogen chloride (called *hydrochloric acid*) is a strong acid.

In general, the strength of an acid is defined by the position of its ionization (dissociation) reaction:

$$HA(aq) + H_2O(l) \Longrightarrow H_3O^+(aq) + A^-(aq)$$

A strong acid is one for which *the forward reaction predominates.* This means that almost all the original HA is dissociated (ionized) (see Figure 16.1a). There is an important connection between the strength of an acid and that of its conjugate base. *A strong acid contains a relatively weak conjugate base*—one that has a low attraction for protons. A strong acid can be described as an acid whose conjugate base is a much weaker base than water (Figure 16.2). In this case the water molecules win the competition for the H^+ ions.

In contrast to hydrochloric acid, when acetic acid, $HC_2H_3O_2$, is dissolved in water, the resulting solution conducts an electric current only weakly. That is, acetic acid is a weak electrolyte, which means that only a few ions are present. In other words, for the reaction

$$HC_2H_3O_2(aq) + H_2O(l) \Longrightarrow H_3O^+(aq) + C_2H_3O_2^-(aq)$$

A hydrochloric acid solution readily conducts electric current, as shown by the brightness of the bulb.

A strong acid is completely dissociated in water. No HA molecules remain. Only H_3O^+ and A^- are present.

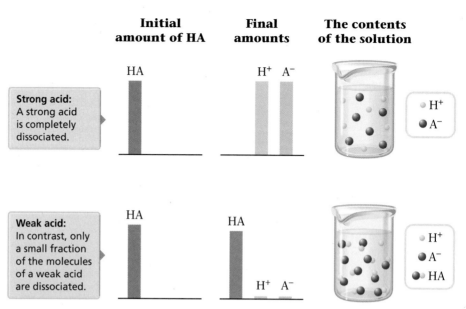

Figure 16.1

Graphical representation of the behavior of acids of different strengths in aqueous solution.

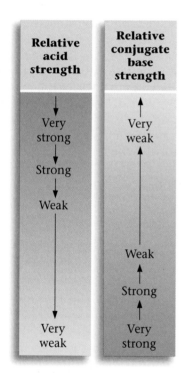

Figure 16.2

The relationship of acid strength and conjugate base strength for the dissociation reaction

HA(*aq*) + H$_2$O(*l*) $\rightleftharpoons$
Acid

        H$_3$O$^+$(*aq*) + A$^-$(*aq*)
                Conjugate base

the reverse reaction predominates (thus the arrow pointing left is longer). In fact, measurements show that only about one in one hundred (1%) of the HC$_2$H$_3$O$_2$ molecules is dissociated (ionized) in a 0.1 *M* solution of acetic acid. Thus acetic acid is a weak acid. When acetic acid molecules are placed in water, almost all of the molecules remain undissociated. This tells us that the acetate ion, C$_2$H$_3$O$_2$$^-$, is an effective base—it very successfully attracts H$^+$ ions in water. This means that acetic acid remains largely in the form of HC$_2$H$_3$O$_2$ molecules in solution. A weak acid is one for which the *reverse reaction predominates*.

$$HA(aq) + H_2O(l) \; \Leftarrow \; H_3O^+(aq) + A^-(aq)$$

Most of the acid originally placed in the solution is still present as HA at equilibrium. That is, a weak acid dissociates (ionizes) only to a very small extent in aqueous solution (see Figure 16.1b). In contrast to a strong acid, a weak acid has a conjugate base that is a much stronger base than water. In this case a water molecule is not very successful in pulling an H$^+$ ion away from the conjugate base. *A weak acid contains a relatively strong conjugate base* (Figure 16.2).

The various ways of describing the strength of an acid are summarized in Table 16.1.

Table 16.1 Ways to Describe Acid Strength

Property	Strong Acid	Weak Acid
the acid ionization (dissociation) reaction	forward reaction predominates	reverse reaction predominates
strength of the conjugate base compared with that of water	A$^-$ is a much weaker base than H$_2$O	A$^-$ is a much stronger base than H$_2$O

Carbonation—A Cool Trick

The sensations of taste and smell greatly affect our daily experience. For example, memories are often triggered by an odor that matches one that occurred when an event was originally stored in our memory banks. Likewise, the sense of taste has a powerful effect on our lives. For example, many people crave the intense sensation produced by the compounds found in chili peppers.

One sensation that is quite refreshing for most people is the effect of a chilled, carbonated beverage in the mouth. The sharp, tingling sensation experienced is not directly due to the bubbling of the dissolved carbon dioxide in the beverage. Rather, it arises because protons are produced as the CO_2 interacts with the water in the tissues of the mouth:

$$CO_2 + H_2O \rightleftharpoons H^+ + HCO_3^-$$

This reaction is speeded up by a biologic catalyst—an enzyme—called carbonic anhydrase. The acidification of the fluids in the nerve endings in the mouth leads to the sharp sensation produced by carbonated drinks.

Carbon dioxide also stimulates nerve sites that detect "coolness" in the mouth. In fact, researchers have identified a mutual enhancement between cooling and the presence of CO_2. Studies show that at a given concentration of CO_2, a colder drink feels more "pungent" than a warmer one. When tests were conducted on drinks in which the carbon dioxide concentration was varied, the results showed that a drink felt colder as the CO_2 concentration was increased, even though the drinks were all actually at the same temperature.

Thus a beverage can seem colder if it has a higher concentration of carbon dioxide. At the same time, cooling a carbonated beverage can intensify the tingling sensation caused by the acidity induced by the CO_2. This is truly a happy synergy.

An acetic acid solution conducts only a small amount of current as shown by the dimly lit bulb.

© Cengage Learning

The common strong acids are sulfuric acid, $H_2SO_4(aq)$; hydrochloric acid, $HCl(aq)$; nitric acid, $HNO_3(aq)$; and perchloric acid, $HClO_4(aq)$. Sulfuric acid is actually a **diprotic acid,** an acid that can furnish two protons. The acid H_2SO_4 is a strong acid that is virtually 100% dissociated in water:

$$H_2SO_4(aq) \rightarrow H^+(aq) + HSO_4^-(aq)$$

The HSO_4^- ion is also an acid but it is a weak acid:

$$HSO_4^-(aq) \rightleftharpoons H^+(aq) + SO_4^{2-}(aq)$$

Most of the HSO_4^- ions remain undissociated.

Most acids are **oxyacids,** in which the acidic hydrogen is attached to an oxygen atom (several oxyacids are shown at the bottom of the following page). The strong acids we have mentioned, except hydrochloric acid, are typical examples. **Organic acids,** those with a carbon-atom backbone, commonly contain the **carboxyl group:**

$$-C\begin{smallmatrix} O \\ \\ O-H \end{smallmatrix}$$

Acids of this type are usually weak. An example is acetic acid, CH_3COOH, which is often written as $HC_2H_3O_2$.

Plants Fight Back

Plants sometimes do not seem to get much respect. We often think of them as rather dull life forms. We are used to animals communicating with each other, but we think of plants as mute. However, this perception is now changing. It is now becoming clear that plants communicate with other plants and also with insects. Ilya Roskin and his colleagues at Rutgers University, for example, have found that tobacco plants under attack by disease signal distress using the chemical salicylic acid, a precursor of aspirin. When a tobacco plant is infected with tobacco mosaic virus (TMV), which forms dark blisters on leaves and causes them to pucker and yellow, the sick plant produces large amounts of salicylic acid to alert its immune system to fight the virus. In addition, some of the salicylic acid is converted to methyl salicylate, a volatile compound that evaporates from the sick plant. Neighboring plants absorb this chemical and turn it back to salicylic acid, thus triggering their immune systems to protect them against the impending attack by TMV. Thus, as a tobacco plant gears up to fight an attack by TMV, it also warns its neighbors to be ready for this virus.

In another example of plant communication, a tobacco leaf under attack by a caterpillar emits a chemical signal that attracts a parasitic wasp that stings and kills the insect. Even more impressive is the ability of the plant to customize the emitted signal so that the wasp attracted will be the one that specializes in killing the particular caterpillar involved in the attack. The plant does this by changing the proportions of two chemicals emitted when a caterpillar chews on a leaf. Studies have shown that other plants, such as corn and cotton, also emit wasp-attracting chemicals when they face attack by caterpillars.

This research shows that plants can "speak up" to protect themselves. Scientists hope to learn to help them do this even more effectively.

Agricultural Research Service/USDA

A wasp lays its eggs on a gypsy moth caterpillar on the leaf of a corn plant.

Salicylic acid

Methyl salicylate

Phosphoric acid

Acetic acid

Nitrous acid

Hypochlorous acid

There are some important acids in which the acidic proton is attached to an atom other than oxygen. The most significant of these are the hydrohalic acids HX, where X represents a halogen atom. Examples are HCl(aq), a strong acid, and HF(aq), a weak acid.

16.3 Water as an Acid and a Base

OBJECTIVE: To learn about the ionization of water.

A substance is said to be *amphoteric* if it can behave either as an acid or as a base. Water is the most common **amphoteric substance.** We can see this clearly in the **ionization of water,** which involves the transfer of a proton from one water molecule to another to produce a hydroxide ion and a hydronium ion.

$$H_2O(l) + H_2O(l) \rightleftharpoons H_3O^+(aq) + OH^-(aq)$$

In this reaction one water molecule acts as an acid by furnishing a proton, and the other acts as a base by accepting the proton. The forward reaction for this process does not occur to a very great extent. That is, in pure water only a tiny amount of H_3O^+ and OH^- exist. At 25 °C the actual concentrations are

$$[H_3O^+] = [OH^-] = 1.0 \times 10^{-7} \, M$$

Notice that in pure water the concentrations of $[H_3O^+]$ and $[OH^-]$ are equal because they are produced in equal numbers in the ionization reaction.

One of the most interesting and important things about water is that the mathematical *product* of the H_3O^+ and OH^- concentrations is always constant. We can find this constant by multiplying the concentrations of H_3O^+ and OH^- at 25 °C:

$$[H_3O^+][OH^-] = (1.0 \times 10^{-7})(1.0 \times 10^{-7}) = 1.0 \times 10^{-14}$$

We call this constant K_w. Thus at 25 °C

$$[H_3O^+][OH^-] = 1.0 \times 10^{-14} = K_w$$

To simplify the notation we often write H_3O^+ as just H^+. Thus we would write the K_w expression as follows:

$$[H^+][OH^-] = 1.0 \times 10^{-14} = K_w$$

$\boldsymbol{K_w}$ is called the **ion-product constant** for water. The units are customarily omitted when the value of the constant is given and used.

It is important to recognize the meaning of K_w. In any aqueous solution at 25 °C, *no matter what it contains,* the product of $[H^+]$ and $[OH^-]$ must always equal 1.0×10^{-14}. This means that if the $[H^+]$ goes up, the $[OH^-]$ must go down so that the product of the two is still 1.0×10^{-14}. For example, if HCl gas is dissolved in water, increasing the $[H^+]$, the $[OH^-]$ must decrease.

> At 25 °C, $K_w = [H^+][OH^-]$
> $= 1.0 \times 10^{-14}$

There are three possible situations we might encounter in an aqueous solution. If we add an acid (an H^+ donor) to water, we get an *acidic solution.* In this case, because we have added a source of H^+, the $[H^+]$ will be greater than the $[OH^-]$. On the other hand, if we add a base (a source of OH^-) to water, the $[OH^-]$ will be greater than the $[H^+]$. This is a *basic solution.* Finally, we might have a situation in which $[H^+] = [OH^-]$. This is called a *neutral solution.* Pure water is automatically neutral but we can also obtain a neutral solution by adding equal amounts of H^+ and OH^-. It is very important that you understand the definitions of neutral, acidic, and basic solutions. In summary:

Remember that H^+ represents H_3O^+.

1. In a **neutral solution,** $[H^+] = [OH^-]$
2. In an **acidic solution,** $[H^+] > [OH^-]$
3. In a **basic solution,** $[OH^-] > [H^+]$

In each case, however, $K_w = [H^+][OH^-] = 1.0 \times 10^{-14}$.

EXAMPLE 16.3 | Calculating Ion Concentrations in Water

Calculate $[H^+]$ or $[OH^-]$ as required for each of the following solutions at 25 °C, and state whether the solution is neutral, acidic, or basic.

  a. $1.0 \times 10^{-5}\ M\ OH^-$ b. $1.0 \times 10^{-7}\ M\ OH^-$ c. $10.0\ M\ H^+$

SOLUTION

  a. **Where Are We Going?**

   We want to determine $[H^+]$ in a solution of given $[OH^-]$ at 25 °C.

   What Do We Know?

   • At 25 °C, $K_w = [H^+][OH^-] = 1.0 \times 10^{-14}$
   • $[OH^-] = 1.0 \times 10^{-5}\ M$

   How Do We Get There?

MATH SKILL BUILDER
$K_w = [H^+][OH^-]$
$\dfrac{K_w}{[OH^-]} = [H^+]$

   We know that $K_w = [H^+][OH^-] = 1.0 \times 10^{-14}$. We need to calculate the $[H^+]$. However, the $[OH^-]$ is given—it is $1.0 \times 10^{-5}\ M$—so we will solve for $[H^+]$ by dividing both sides by $[OH^-]$.

$$[H^+] = \frac{1.0 \times 10^{-14}}{[OH^-]} = \frac{1.0 \times 10^{-14}}{1.0 \times 10^{-5}} = 1.0 \times 10^{-9}\ M$$

   Because $[OH^-] = 1.0 \times 10^{-5}\ M$ is greater than $[H^+] = 1.0 \times 10^{-9}\ M$, the solution is basic. (Remember: The more negative the exponent, the smaller the number.)

  b. **Where Are We Going?**

   We want to determine $[H^+]$ in a solution of given $[OH^-]$ at 25 °C.

   What Do We Know?

   • At 25 °C, $K_w = [H^+][OH^-] = 1.0 \times 10^{-14}$
   • $[OH^-] = 1.0 \times 10^{-7}\ M$

   How Do We Get There?

   Again the $[OH^-]$ is given, so we solve the K_w expression for $[H^+]$.

$$[H^+] = \frac{1.0 \times 10^{-14}}{[OH^-]} = \frac{1.0 \times 10^{-14}}{1.0 \times 10^{-7}} = 1.0 \times 10^{-7}\ M$$

   Here $[H^+] = [OH^-] = 1.0 \times 10^{-7}\ M$, so the solution is neutral.

  c. **Where Are We Going?**

   We want to determine $[OH^-]$ in a solution of given $[H^+]$ at 25 °C.

What Do We Know?

- At 25 °C, $K_w = [H^+][OH^-] = 1.0 \times 10^{-14}$
- $[H^+] = 10.0\ M$

How Do We Get There?

In this case the $[H^+]$ is given, so we solve for $[OH^-]$.

$$[OH^-] = \frac{1.0 \times 10^{-14}}{[H^+]} = \frac{1.0 \times 10^{-14}}{10.0} = 1.0 \times 10^{-15}\ M$$

Now we compare $[H^+] = 10.0\ M$ with $[OH^-] = 1.0 \times 10^{-15}\ M$. Because $[H^+]$ is greater than $[OH^-]$, the solution is acidic.

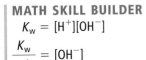

MATH SKILL BUILDER

$K_w = [H^+][OH^-]$

$\dfrac{K_w}{[H^+]} = [OH^-]$

Self-Check EXERCISE 16.2   Calculate $[H^+]$ in a solution in which $[OH^-] = 2.0 \times 10^{-2}\ M$. Is this solution acidic, neutral, or basic?

See Problems 16.31 through 16.34. ∎

EXAMPLE 16.4 | **Using the Ion-Product Constant in Calculations**

Is it possible for an aqueous solution at 25 °C to have $[H^+] = 0.010\ M$ and $[OH^-] = 0.010\ M$?

SOLUTION

The concentration 0.010 M can also be expressed as $1.0 \times 10^{-2}\ M$. Thus, if $[H^+] = [OH^-] = 1.0 \times 10^{-2}\ M$, the product

$$[H^+][OH^-] = (1.0 \times 10^{-2})(1.0 \times 10^{-2}) = 1.0 \times 10^{-4}$$

This is not possible. The product of $[H^+]$ and $[OH^-]$ must always be 1.0×10^{-14} in water at 25 °C, so a solution could not have $[H^+] = [OH^-] = 0.010\ M$. If H^+ and OH^- are added to water in these amounts, they will react with each other to form H_2O,

$$H^+ + OH^- \rightarrow H_2O$$

until the product $[H^+][OH^-] = 1.0 \times 10^{-14}$.

This is a general result. When H^+ and OH^- are added to water in amounts such that the product of their concentrations is greater than 1.0×10^{-14}, they will react to form water until enough H^+ and OH^- are consumed so that $[H^+][OH^-] = 1.0 \times 10^{-14}$. ∎

16.4 The pH Scale

OBJECTIVE: To understand pH and pOH. • To learn to find pOH and pH for various solutions. • To learn to use a calculator in these calculations.

To express small numbers conveniently, chemists often use the "p scale," which is based on common logarithms (base 10 logs). In this system, if N represents some number, then

$$pN = -\log N = (-1) \times \log N$$

CHEMISTRY *IN* FOCUS

Airplane Rash

Because airplanes remain in service for many years, it is important to spot corrosion that might weaken the structure at an early stage. In the past, looking for minute signs of corrosion has been very tedious and labor-intensive, especially for large planes. This situation has changed, however, thanks to the paint system developed by Gerald S. Frankel and Jian Zhang of Ohio State University. The paint they created turns pink in areas that are beginning to corrode, making these areas easy to spot.

The secret to the paint's magic is phenolphthalein, the common acid–base indicator that turns pink in a basic solution. The corrosion of the aluminum skin of the airplane involves a reaction that forms OH^- ions, producing a basic area at the site of the corrosion that turns the phenolphthalein pink. Because this system is highly sensitive, corrosion can be corrected before it damages the plane.

Next time you fly, if the plane has pink spots you might want to wait for a later flight!

go Chemistry **Module 9a: pH (Pt. 1)** covers concepts in this section.

That is, the p means to take the log of the number that follows and multiply the result by -1. For example, to express the number 1.0×10^{-7} on the p scale, we need to take the negative log of 1.0×10^{-7}.

$$p(1.0 \times 10^{-7}) = -\log(1.0 \times 10^{-7}) = 7.00$$

The pH scale provides a compact way to represent solution acidity.

Because the $[H^+]$ in an aqueous solution is typically quite small, using the p scale in the form of the **pH scale** provides a convenient way to represent solution acidity. The pH is defined as

$$pH = -\log[H^+]$$

go Chemistry **Module 9b: pH (Pt. 2)** covers concepts in this section.

To obtain the pH value of a solution, we must compute the negative log of the $[H^+]$.

In the case where $[H^+] = 1.0 \times 10^{-5}\ M$, the solution has a pH value of 5.00.

To represent pH to the appropriate number of significant figures, you need to know the following rule for logarithms: *the number of decimal places for a log must be equal to the number of significant figures in the original number.* Thus

2 significant figures

$$[H^+] = 1.0 \times 10^{-5}\ M$$

and

$$pH = 5.00$$

2 decimal places

EXAMPLE 16.5 | Calculating pH

Calculate the pH value for each of the following solutions at 25 °C.

a. A solution in which $[H^+] = 1.0 \times 10^{-9}$ M

b. A solution in which $[OH^-] = 1.0 \times 10^{-6}$ M

SOLUTION

a. For this solution $[H^+] = 1.0 \times 10^{-9}$.

$$-\log 1.0 \times 10^{-9} = 9.00$$
$$pH = 9.00$$

b. In this case we are given the $[OH^-]$. Thus we must first calculate $[H^+]$ from the K_w expression. We solve

$$K_w = [H^+][OH^-] = 1.0 \times 10^{-14}$$

for $[H^+]$ by dividing both sides by $[OH^-]$.

$$[H^+] = \frac{1.0 \times 10^{-14}}{[OH^-]} = \frac{1.0 \times 10^{-14}}{1.0 \times 10^{-6}} = 1.0 \times 10^{-8}$$

Now that we know the $[H^+]$, we can calculate the pH because pH = $-\log[H^+] = -\log[1.0 \times 10^{-8}] = 8.00$.

Self-Check EXERCISE 16.3   Calculate the pH value for each of the following solutions at 25 °C.

a. A solution in which $[H^+] = 1.0 \times 10^{-3}$ M

b. A solution in which $[OH^-] = 5.0 \times 10^{-5}$ M

See Problems 16.41 through 16.44. ■

Table 16.2 The Relationship of the H+ Concentration of a Solution to Its pH

$[H^+]$	pH
1.0×10^{-1}	1.00
1.0×10^{-2}	2.00
1.0×10^{-3}	3.00
1.0×10^{-4}	4.00
1.0×10^{-5}	5.00
1.0×10^{-6}	6.00
1.0×10^{-7}	7.00

The pH decreases as $[H^+]$ increases, and vice versa.

Because the pH scale is a log scale based on 10, *the pH changes by 1 for every power-of-10 change in the $[H^+]$*. For example, a solution of pH 3 has an H^+ concentration of 10^{-3} M, which is 10 times that of a solution of pH 4 ($[H^+] = 10^{-4}$ M) and 100 times that of a solution of pH 5. This is illustrated in Table 16.2. Also note from Table 16.2 that *the pH decreases as the $[H^+]$ increases*. That is, a lower pH means a more acidic solution. The pH scale and the pH values for several common substances are shown in Figure 16.3.

We often measure the pH of a solution by using a pH meter, an electronic device with a probe that can be inserted into a solution of unknown pH. A pH meter is shown in Figure 16.4. Colored indicator paper is also commonly used to measure the pH of a solution when less accuracy is needed. A drop of the solution to be tested is placed on this special paper, which promptly turns to a color characteristic of a given pH (see Figure 16.5).

Log scales similar to the pH scale are used for representing other quantities. For example,

The symbol p means $-\log$.

$$pOH = -\log[OH^-]$$

Therefore, in a solution in which

$$[OH^-] = 1.0 \times 10^{-12} \text{ M}$$

the pOH is

$$-\log[OH^-] = -\log(1.0 \times 10^{-12}) = 12.00$$

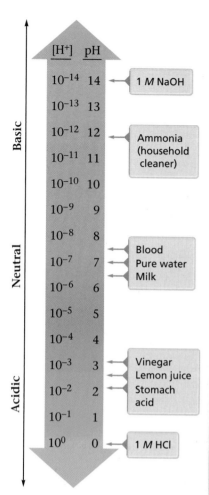

Figure 16.3

The pH scale and pH values of some common substances.

Figure 16.4

A pH meter. The electrodes on the right are placed in the solution with unknown pH. The difference between the [H$^+$] in the solution sealed into one of the electrodes and the [H$^+$] in the solution being analyzed is translated into an electrical potential and registered on the meter as a pH reading.

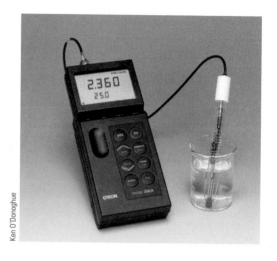

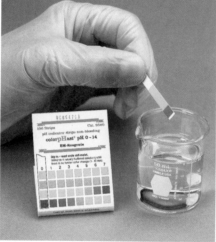

Figure 16.5

Indicator paper being used to measure the pH of a solution. The pH is determined by comparing the color that the solution turns the paper to the color chart.

EXAMPLE 16.6 | Calculating pH and pOH

Calculate the pH and pOH for each of the following solutions at 25 °C.

   a. 1.0×10^{-3} M OH$^-$

   b. 1.0 M H$^+$

SOLUTION

a. We are given the [OH$^-$], so we can calculate the pOH value by taking $-\log[\text{OH}^-]$.

$$\text{pOH} = -\log[\text{OH}^-] = -\log(1.0 \times 10^{-3}) = 3.00$$

To calculate the pH, we must first solve the K_w expression for [H$^+$].

$$[\text{H}^+] = \frac{K_w}{[\text{OH}^-]} = \frac{1.0 \times 10^{-14}}{1.0 \times 10^{-3}} = 1.0 \times 10^{-11} \, M$$

Now we compute the pH.

$$pH = -\log[H^+] = -\log(1.0 \times 10^{-11}) = 11.00$$

b. In this case we are given the $[H^+]$ and we can compute the pH.

$$pH = -\log[H^+] = -\log(1.0) = 0$$

We next solve the K_w expression for $[OH^-]$.

$$[OH^-] = \frac{K_w}{[H^+]} = \frac{1.0 \times 10^{-14}}{1.0} = 1.0 \times 10^{-14}\,M$$

Now we compute the pOH.

$$pOH = -\log[OH^-] = -\log(1.0 \times 10^{-14}) = 14.00 \ \blacksquare$$

We can obtain a convenient relationship between pH and pOH by starting with the K_w expression $[H^+][OH^-] = 1.0 \times 10^{-14}$ and taking the negative log of both sides.

$$-\log([H^+][OH^-]) = -\log(1.0 \times 10^{-14})$$

Because the log of a product equals the sum of the logs of the terms—that is, $\log(A \times B) = \log A + \log B$—we have

$$\underbrace{-\log[H^+]}_{pH}\ \underbrace{-\log[OH^-]}_{pOH} = -\log(1.0 \times 10^{-14}) = 14.00$$

which gives the equation

$$pH + pOH = 14.00$$

This means that once we know either the pH or the pOH for a solution, we can calculate the other. For example, if a solution has a pH of 6.00, the pOH is calculated as follows:

$$pH + pOH = 14.00$$
$$pOH = 14.00 - pH$$
$$pOH = 14.00 - 6.00 = 8.00$$

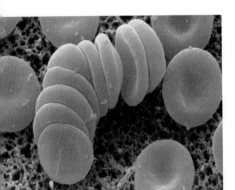

Red blood cells can exist only over a narrow range of pH.

EXAMPLE 16.7   Calculating pOH from pH

The pH of blood is about 7.4. What is the pOH of blood?

SOLUTION

$$pH + pOH = 14.00$$
$$pOH = 14.00 - pH$$
$$= 14.00 - 7.4$$
$$= 6.6$$

The pOH of blood is 6.6.

Self-Check **EXERCISE 16.4**   A sample of rain in an area with severe air pollution has a pH of 3.5. What is the pOH of this rainwater?

See Problems 16.45 and 16.46. ■

It is also possible to find the $[H^+]$ or $[OH^-]$ from the pH or pOH. To find the $[H^+]$ from the pH, we must go back to the definition of pH:

$$pH = -\log[H^+]$$

or

$$-pH = \log[H^+]$$

To arrive at $[H^+]$ on the right-hand side of this equation we must "undo" the log operation. This is called taking the *antilog* or the *inverse* log.

Inverse log $(-pH)$ = inverse log $(\log[H^+])$
Inverse log $(-pH)$ = $[H^+]$

There are different methods for carrying out the inverse log operation on various calculators. One common method is the two-key (inv) (log) sequence. (Consult the user's manual for your calculator to find out how to do the antilog or inverse log operation.) The steps in going from pH to $[H^+]$ are as follows:

MATH SKILL BUILDER
This operation may involve a 10^x key on some calculators.

Steps for Calculating [H⁺] from pH

Step 1 Take the inverse log (antilog) of $-pH$ to give $[H^+]$ by using the (inv) (log) keys in that order. (Your calculator may require different keys for this operation.)

Step 2 Press the minus $[-]$ key.

Step 3 Enter the pH.

For practice, we will convert pH = 7.0 to $[H^+]$.

$$pH = 7.0$$
$$-pH = -7.0$$

David Woodfall/Stone/Getty Images

Measuring the pH of the water in a river.

The inverse log of -7.0 gives 1×10^{-7}.

$$[H^+] = 1 \times 10^{-7}\ M$$

This process is illustrated further in Example 16.8.

EXAMPLE 16.8 | Calculating [H$^+$] from pH

The pH of a human blood sample was measured to be 7.41. What is the [H$^+$] in this blood?

SOLUTION

$$pH = 7.41$$
$$-pH = -7.41$$
$$[H^+] = \text{inverse log of } -7.41 = 3.9 \times 10^{-8}$$
$$[H^+] = 3.9 \times 10^{-8}\ M$$

Notice that because the pH has two decimal places, we need two significant figures for [H$^+$].

Self-Check EXERCISE 16.5   The pH of rainwater in a polluted area was found to be 3.50. What is the [H$^+$] for this rainwater?

See Problems 16.49 and 16.50. ■

A similar procedure is used to change from pOH to [OH$^-$], as shown in Example 16.9.

EXAMPLE 16.9 | Calculating [OH$^-$] from pOH

The pOH of the water in a fish tank is found to be 6.59. What is the [OH$^-$] for this water?

SOLUTION

We use the same steps as for converting pH to [H$^+$], except that we use the pOH to calculate the [OH$^-$].

$$pOH = 6.59$$
$$-pOH = -6.59$$

$$[OH^-] = \text{inverse log of } -6.59 = 2.6 \times 10^{-7}$$

$$[OH^-] = 2.6 \times 10^{-7}\ M$$

Note that two significant figures are required.

Self-Check EXERCISE 16.6   The pOH of a liquid drain cleaner was found to be 10.50. What is the [OH$^-$] for this cleaner?

See Problems 16.51 and 16.52. ■

CHEMISTRY IN FOCUS

Garden-Variety Acid–Base Indicators

What can flowers tell us about acids and bases? Actually, some flowers can tell us whether the soil they are growing in is acidic or basic. For example, in acidic soil, bigleaf hydrangea blossoms will be blue; in basic (alkaline) soil, the flowers will be red. What is the secret? The pigment in the flower is an acid–base indicator.

Generally, acid–base indicators are dyes that are weak acids. Because indicators are usually complex molecules, we often symbolize them as HIn. The reaction of the indicator with water can be written as

$$HIn(aq) + H_2O(l) \rightleftharpoons H_3O^+(aq) + In^-(aq)$$

To work as an acid–base indicator, the conjugate acid–base forms of these dyes must have different colors. The acidity level of the solution will determine whether the indicator is present mainly in its acidic form (HIn) or its basic form (In$^-$).

When placed in an acidic solution, most of the basic form of the indicator is converted to the acidic form by the reaction

$$In^-(aq) + H^+(aq) \rightarrow HIn(aq)$$

When placed in a basic solution, most of the acidic form of the indicator is converted to the basic form by the reaction

$$HIn(aq) + OH^-(aq) \rightarrow In^-(aq) + H_2O(l)$$

It turns out that many fruits, vegetables, and flowers can act as acid–base indicators. Red, blue, and purple plants often contain a class of chemicals called anthocyanins, which change color based on the acidity level of the surroundings. Perhaps the most famous of these plants is red cabbage. Red cabbage contains a mixture of anthocyanins and other pigments that allow it to be used as a "universal indicator." Red cabbage juice appears deep red at a pH of 1–2, purple at a pH of 4, blue at a pH of 8, and green at a pH of 11.

16.5 Calculating the pH of Strong Acid Solutions

OBJECTIVE: To learn to calculate the pH of solutions of strong acids.

In this section we will learn to calculate the pH for a solution containing a strong acid of known concentration. For example, if we know a solution contains 1.0 M HCl, how can we find the pH of the solution? To answer this question we must know that when HCl dissolves in water, each molecule dissociates (ionizes) into H$^+$ and Cl$^-$ ions. That is, we must know that HCl is a strong acid. Thus, although the label on the bottle says 1.0 M HCl, the solution contains virtually no HCl molecules. A 1.0 M HCl solution contains H$^+$ and Cl$^-$ ions rather than HCl molecules. Typically, container labels indicate the substance(s) used to make up the solution but do not necessarily describe the solution components after dissolution. In this case,

$$1.0\ M\ HCl \rightarrow 1.0\ M\ H^+ \text{ and } 1.0\ M\ Cl^-$$

Therefore, the [H$^+$] in the solution is 1.0 M. The pH is then

$$pH = -\log[H^+] = -\log(1.0) = 0$$

Other natural indicators include the skins of beets (which change from red to purple in very basic solutions), blueberries (which change from blue to red in acidic solutions), and a wide variety of flower petals, including delphiniums, geraniums, morning glories, and, of course, hydrangeas.

EXAMPLE 16.10 | Calculating the pH of Strong Acid Solutions

Calculate the pH of 0.10 M HNO$_3$.

SOLUTION

HNO$_3$ is a strong acid, so the ions in solution are H$^+$ and NO$_3^-$. In this case,

$$0.10 \ M \ \text{HNO}_3 \rightarrow 0.10 \ M \ \text{H}^+ \ \text{and} \ 0.10 \ M \ \text{NO}_3^-$$

Thus

$$[\text{H}^+] = 0.10 \ M \quad \text{and} \quad \text{pH} = -\log(0.10) = 1.00$$

Self-Check **EXERCISE 16.7** Calculate the pH of a solution of $5.0 \times 10^{-3} \ M$ HCl.

See Problems 16.57 and 16.58. ∎

Buffered Solutions

OBJECTIVE: To understand the general characteristics of buffered solutions.

> Water: pH = 7
> 0.01 M HCl: pH = 2

A **buffered solution** is one that resists a change in its pH even when a strong acid or base is added to it. For example, when 0.01 mole of HCl is added to 1 L of pure water, the pH changes from its initial value of 7 to 2, a change of 5 pH units. However, when 0.01 mole of HCl is added to a solution containing both 0.1 M acetic acid ($HC_2H_3O_2$) and 0.1 M sodium acetate ($NaC_2H_3O_2$), the pH changes from an initial value of 4.74 to 4.66, a change of only 0.08 pH unit. The latter solution is buffered—it undergoes only a very slight change in pH when a strong acid or base is added to it.

Buffered solutions are vitally important to living organisms whose cells can survive only in a very narrow pH range. Many goldfish have died because their owners did not realize the importance of buffering the aquarium water at an appropriate pH. For humans to survive, the pH of the blood must be maintained between 7.35 and 7.45. This narrow range is maintained by several different buffering systems.

A solution is **buffered** by the *presence of a weak acid and its conjugate base*. An example of a buffered solution is an aqueous solution that contains acetic acid and sodium acetate. The sodium acetate is a salt that furnishes acetate ions (the conjugate base of acetic acid) when it dissolves. To see how this system acts as a buffer, we must recognize that the species present in this solution are

$$HC_2H_3O_2, \quad Na^+, \quad C_2H_3O_2^-$$

When $NaC_2H_3O_2$ is dissolved, it produces the separated ions

For goldfish to survive, the pH of the water must be carefully controlled.

What happens in this solution when a strong acid such as HCl is added? In pure water, the H^+ ions from the HCl would accumulate, thus lowering the pH.

$$HCl \xrightarrow{100\%} H^+ + Cl^-$$

However, this buffered solution contains $C_2H_3O_2^-$ ions, which are basic. That is, $C_2H_3O_2^-$ has a strong affinity for H^+, as evidenced by the fact that $HC_2H_3O_2$ is a weak acid. This means that the $C_2H_3O_2^-$ and H^+ ions do not exist together in large numbers. Because the $C_2H_3O_2^-$ ion has a high affinity for H^+, these two combine to form $HC_2H_3O_2$ molecules. Thus the H^+ from the added HCl does not accumulate in solution but reacts with the $C_2H_3O_2^-$ as follows:

$$H^+(aq) + C_2H_3O_2^-(aq) \rightarrow HC_2H_3O_2(aq)$$

Next consider what happens when a strong base such as sodium hydroxide is added to the buffered solution. If this base were added to pure water, the OH^- ions from the solid would accumulate and greatly change (raise) the pH.

$$NaOH \xrightarrow{100\%} Na^+ + OH^-$$

However, in the buffered solution the OH^- ion, which has a *very strong* affinity for H^+, reacts with $HC_2H_3O_2$ molecules as follows:

$$HC_2H_3O_2(aq) + OH^-(aq) \rightarrow H_2O(l) + C_2H_3O_2^-(aq)$$

> **Table 16.3** The Characteristics of a Buffer
> 1. The solution contains a weak acid HA and its conjugate base A⁻.
> 2. The buffer resists changes in pH by reacting with any added H^+ or OH^- so that these ions do not accumulate.
> 3. Any added H^+ reacts with the base A⁻.
> $$H^+(aq) + A^-(aq) \rightarrow HA(aq)$$
> 4. Any added OH^- reacts with the weak acid HA.
> $$OH^-(aq) + HA(aq) \rightarrow H_2O(l) + A^-(aq)$$

This happens because, although $C_2H_3O_2^-$ has a strong affinity for H^+, OH^- has a much stronger affinity for H^+ and thus can remove H^+ ions from acetic acid molecules.

Note that the buffering materials dissolved in the solution prevent added H^+ or OH^- from building up in the solution. Any added H^+ is trapped by $C_2H_3O_2^-$ to form $HC_2H_3O_2$. Any added OH^- reacts with $HC_2H_3O_2$ to form H_2O and $C_2H_3O_2^-$.

The general properties of a buffered solution are summarized in Table 16.3.

CHAPTER 16 REVIEW

Key Terms

acid (16.1)
base (16.1)
Arrhenius concept of acids and bases (16.1)
Brønsted–Lowry model (16.1)
conjugate acid (16.1)
conjugate base (16.1)
conjugate acid–base pair (16.1)
hydronium ion (16.1)
completely ionized (dissociated) (16.2)
strong acid (16.2)
weak acid (16.2)

diprotic acid (16.2)
oxyacid (16.2)
organic acid (16.2)
carboxyl group (16.2)
amphoteric substance (16.3)
ionization of water (16.3)
ion-product constant, K_w (16.3)
neutral solution (16.3)
acidic solution (16.3)
basic solution (16.3)
pH scale (16.4)
buffered solution (16.6)
buffered (16.6)

F directs you to the *Chemistry in Focus* feature in the chapter

VP indicates visual problems

OWL interactive versions of these problems are assignable in OWL

more general: an acid is a proton donor, and a base is a proton acceptor. Water acts as a Brønsted–Lowry base when it accepts a proton from an acid to form a hydronium ion:

$$HA(aq) + H_2O(l) \rightleftharpoons H_3O^+(aq) + A^-(aq)$$

Acid   Base   Conjugate   Conjugate
acid   base

A conjugate base is everything that remains of the acid molecule after the proton is lost. A conjugate acid is formed when a proton is transferred to the base. Two substances related in this way are called a conjugate acid–base pair.

2. A strong acid or base is one that is completely ionized (dissociated). A weak acid is one that is ionized (dissociated) only to a slight extent. Strong acids have weak conjugate bases. Weak acids have relatively strong conjugate bases.

3. Water is an amphoteric substance—it can behave either as an acid or as a base. The ionization of water reveals this property; one water molecule transfers a

Summary

1. Acids or bases in water are commonly described by two different models. Arrhenius postulated that acids produce H^+ ions in aqueous solutions and that bases produce OH^- ions. The Brønsted–Lowry model is

proton to another water molecule to produce a hydronium ion and a hydroxide ion.

$$H_2O(l) + H_2O(l) \rightleftharpoons H_3O^+(aq) + OH^-(aq)$$

The expression

$$K_w = [H_3O^+][OH^-] = [H^+][OH^-]$$

is called the ion-product constant. It has been shown experimentally that at 25 °C,

$$[H^+] = [OH^-] = 1.0 \times 10^{-7}\ M$$

so $K_w = 1.0 \times 10^{-14}$.

4. In an acidic solution, $[H^+]$ is greater than $[OH^-]$. In a basic solution, $[OH^-]$ is greater than $[H^+]$. In a neutral solution, $[H^+] = [OH^-]$.

5. To describe $[H^+]$ in aqueous solutions, we use the pH scale.

$$pH = -\log[H^+]$$

Note that the pH decreases as $[H^+]$ (acidity) increases.

6. The pH of strong acid solutions can be calculated directly from the concentration of the acid, because 100% dissociation occurs in aqueous solution.

7. A buffered solution is one that resists a change in its pH even when a strong acid or base is added to it. A buffered solution contains a weak acid and its conjugate base.

Active Learning Questions

These questions are designed to be considered by groups of students in class. Often these questions work well for introducing a particular topic in class.

1. You are asked for the H^+ concentration in a solution of $NaOH(aq)$. Because sodium hydroxide is a strong base, can we say there is no H^+, since having H^+ would imply that the solution is acidic?

2. Explain why Cl^- does not affect the pH of an aqueous solution.

3. Write the general reaction for an acid acting in water. What is the base in this case? The conjugate acid? The conjugate base?

4. Differentiate among the terms *concentrated, dilute, weak,* and *strong* in describing acids. Use molecular-level pictures to support your answer.

5. What is meant by "pH"? True or false: A strong acid always has a lower pH than a weak acid does. Explain.

6. Consider two separate solutions: one containing a weak acid, HA, and one containing HCl. Assume that you start with 10 molecules of each.

   a. Draw a molecular-level picture of what each solution looks like.

   b. Arrange the following from strongest to weakest base: Cl^-, H_2O, A^-. Explain.

7. Why is the pH of water at 25 °C equal to 7.00?

8. Can the pH of a solution be negative? Explain.

9. Stanley's grade-point average (GPA) is 3.28. What is Stanley's p(GPA)?

10. A friend asks the following: "Consider a buffered solution made up of the weak acid HA and its salt NaA. If a strong base like NaOH is added, the HA reacts with the OH^- to make A^-. Thus, the amount of acid (HA) is decreased, and the amount of base (A^-) is increased. Analogously, adding HCl to the buffered solution forms more of the acid (HA) by reacting with the base (A^-). How can we claim that a buffered solution resists changes in the pH of the solution?" How would you explain buffering to your friend?

11. Mixing together aqueous solutions of acetic acid and sodium hydroxide can make a buffered solution. Explain.

12. Could a buffered solution be made by mixing aqueous solutions of HCl and NaOH? Explain.

13. Consider the equation: $HA(aq) + H_2O \rightleftharpoons H_3O^+(aq) + A^-(aq)$.

   a. If water is a better base than A^-, which way will equilibrium lie?

   b. If water is a better base than A^-, does this mean that HA is a strong or a weak acid?

   c. If water is a better base than A^-, is the value for K_a greater or less than 1?

14. Choose the answer that best completes the following statement and defend your answer. When 100.0 mL of water is added to 100.0 mL of 1.00 M HCl,

   a. the pH decreases because the solution is diluted.

   b. the pH does not change because water is neutral.

   c. the pH is doubled because the volume is now doubled.

   d. the pH increases because the concentration of H^+ decreases.

   e. the solution is completely neutralized.

15. You mix a solution of a strong acid with a pH of 4 and an equal volume of a strong acid solution with a pH of 6. Is the final pH less than 4, between 4 and 5, 5, between 5 and 6, or greater than 6? Explain.

VP 16. The following figures are molecular-level representations of acid solutions. Label each as a strong acid or a weak acid.

17. Answer the following questions concerning buffered solutions.

   a. Explain what a buffered solution does.

   b. Describe the substances that make up a buffered solution.

   c. Explain how a buffered solution works.

Questions and Problems

16.1 Acids and Bases

QUESTIONS

1. What are some physical properties that historically led chemists to classify various substances as acids and bases?

2. Write an equation showing how HCl(g) behaves as an Arrhenius acid when dissolved in water. Write an equation showing how NaOH(s) behaves as an Arrhenius base when dissolved in water.

3. According to the Brønsted-Lowry model, an acid is a "proton donor" and a base is a "proton acceptor." Explain.

4. How do the components of a conjugate acid–base pair differ from one another? Give an example of a conjugate acid–base pair to illustrate your answer.

5. Given the general equation illustrating the reaction of the acid HA in water,

$$HA(aq) + H_2O(l) \rightarrow H_3O^+(aq) + A^-(aq)$$

explain why water is considered a *base* in the Brønsted-Lowry model.

F 6. The "Chemistry in Focus" segment *Gum That Foams* discusses Mad Dawg chewing gum. One of the ingredients in the gum is baking soda, sodium bicarbonate, $NaHCO_3$. Does baking soda behave as an acid or as a base in the gum?

PROBLEMS

7. Which of the following do *not* represent a conjugate acid–base pair? For those pairs that are not conjugate acid–base pairs, write the correct conjugate acid–base pair for each species in the pair.

 a. HI, I$^-$
 b. HClO, HClO$_2$
 c. H$_3$PO$_4$, PO$_4^{3-}$
 d. H$_2$CO$_3$, CO$_3^{2-}$

8. Which of the following do *not* represent a conjugate acid–base pair? For those pairs that are not conjugate acid–base pairs, write the correct conjugate acid–base pair for each species in the pair.

 a. HClO$_4$, ClO$_4^-$
 b. NH$_4^+$, NH$_3$
 c. NH$_3$, NH$_2^-$
 d. H$_2$O, O^{2-}

9. In each of the following chemical equations, identify the conjugate acid–base pairs.

 a. HF(aq) + H$_2$O(l) $\rightleftharpoons$ F$^-$(aq) + H$_3$O$^+$(aq)
 b. CN$^-$(aq) + H$_2$O(l) $\rightleftharpoons$ HCN(aq) + OH$^-$(aq)
 c. HCO$_3^-$(aq) + H$_2$O(l) $\rightleftharpoons$ H$_2$CO$_3$(aq) + OH$^-$(aq)

10. In each of the following chemical reactions, identify the conjugate acid–base pairs.

 a. NH$_3$(aq) + H$_2$O(l) $\rightleftharpoons$ NH$_4^+$(aq) + OH$^-$(aq)
 b. NH$_4^+$(aq) + H$_2$O(l) $\rightleftharpoons$ NH$_3$(aq) + H$_3$O$^+$(aq)
 c. NH$_2^-$(aq) + H$_2$O(l) $\rightarrow$ NH$_3$(aq) + OH$^-$(aq)

11. Write the conjugate *acid* for each of the following bases:

 a. PO$_4^{3-}$ c. NO$_3^-$
 b. IO$_3^-$ d. NH$_2^-$

12. Write the conjugate *acid* for each of the following bases.

 a. ClO$^-$ c. ClO$_3^-$
 b. Cl$^-$ d. ClO$_4^-$

13. Write the conjugate *base* for each of the following acids:

 a. H$_2$S   c. NH$_3$
 b. HS$^-$ d. H$_2$SO$_3$

14. Write the conjugate *base* for each of the following acids.

 a. HBrO   c. HSO$_3^-$
 b. HNO$_2$ d. CH$_3$NH$_3^+$

15. Write a chemical equation showing how each of the following species can behave as indicated when dissolved in water.

 a. HSO$_3^-$ as an acid
 b. CO$_3^{2-}$ as a base
 c. H$_2$PO$_4^-$ as an acid
 d. C$_2$H$_3$O$_2^-$ as a base

16. Write a chemical equation showing how each of the following species can behave as indicated when dissolved in water.

 a. O^{2-} as a base
 b. NH$_3$ as a base
 c. HSO$_4^-$ as an acid
 d. HNO$_2$ as an acid

16.2 Acid Strength

QUESTIONS

17. What does it mean to say that an acid is *strong* in aqueous solution? What does this reveal about the ability of the acid's anion to attract protons?

18. What does it mean to say that an acid is *weak* in aqueous solution? What does this reveal about the ability of the acid's anion to attract protons?

19. How is the strength of an acid related to the fact that a competition for protons exists in aqueous solution between water molecules and the anion of the acid?

20. A strong acid has a weak conjugate base, whereas a weak acid has a relatively strong conjugate base. Explain.

All even-numbered Questions and Problems have answers in the back of this book and solutions in the Solutions Guide.

21. Write the formula for the *hydronium* ion. Write an equation for the formation of the hydronium ion when an acid is dissolved in water.

22. Name four strong acids. For each of these, write the equation showing the acid dissociating in water.

23. Organic acids contain the carboxyl group

Using acetic acid, CH_3—COOH, and propionic acid, CH_3CH_2—COOH, write equations showing how the carboxyl group enables these substances to behave as weak acids when dissolved in water.

24. What is an *oxyacid?* Write the formulas of three acids that are oxyacids. Write the formulas of three acids that are *not* oxyacids.

25. Which of the following acids have relatively *strong* conjugate bases?

   a. HCN
   b. H_2S
   c. $HBrO_4$
   d. HNO_3

F 26. The "Chemistry in Focus" segment *Plants Fight Back* discusses how tobacco plants under attack by disease produce salicylic acid. Examine the structure of salicylic acid and predict whether it behaves as a monoprotic or a diprotic acid.

16.3 Water as an Acid and a Base

QUESTIONS

27. Water is the most common *amphoteric* substance, which means that, depending on the circumstances, water can behave either as an acid or as a base. Using HF as an example of an acid and NH_3 as an example of a base, write equations for these substances reacting with water, in which water behaves as a base and as an acid, respectively.

28. Anions containing hydrogen (for example, HCO_3^- and $H_2PO_4^{2-}$) show amphoteric behavior when reacting with other acids or bases. Write equations illustrating the amphoterism of these anions.

29. What is meant by the *ion-product constant* for water, K_w? What does this constant signify? Write an equation for the chemical reaction from which the constant is derived.

30. What happens to the hydroxide ion concentration in aqueous solutions when we increase the hydrogen ion concentration by adding an acid? What happens to the hydrogen ion concentration in aqueous solutions when we increase the hydroxide ion concentration by adding a base? Explain.

PROBLEMS

31. Calculate the $[H^+]$ in each of the following solutions, and indicate whether the solution is acidic or basic.

   a. $[OH^-] = 2.32 \times 10^{-4}\ M$
   b. $[OH^-] = 8.99 \times 10^{-10}\ M$
   c. $[OH^-] = 4.34 \times 10^{-6}\ M$
   d. $[OH^-] = 6.22 \times 10^{-12}\ M$

32. Calculate the $[H^+]$ in each of the following solutions, and indicate whether the solution is acidic or basic.

   a. $[OH^-] = 3.44 \times 10^{-1}\ M$
   b. $[OH^-] = 9.79 \times 10^{-11}\ M$
   c. $[OH^-] = 4.89 \times 10^{-6}\ M$
   d. $[OH^-] = 3.78 \times 10^{-7}\ M$

33. Calculate the $[OH^-]$ in each of the following solutions, and indicate whether the solution is acidic or basic.

   a. $[H^+] = 4.01 \times 10^{-4}\ M$
   b. $[H^+] = 7.22 \times 10^{-6}\ M$
   c. $[H^+] = 8.05 \times 10^{-7}\ M$
   d. $[H^+] = 5.43 \times 10^{-9}\ M$

34. Calculate the $[OH^-]$ in each of the following solutions, and indicate whether the solution is acidic or basic.

   a. $[H^+] = 1.02 \times 10^{-7}\ M$
   b. $[H^+] = 9.77 \times 10^{-8}\ M$
   c. $[H^+] = 3.41 \times 10^{-3}\ M$
   d. $[H^+] = 4.79 \times 10^{-11}\ M$

35. For each pair of concentrations, tell which represents the more acidic solution.

   a. $[H^+] = 1.2 \times 10^{-3}\ M$ or $[H^+] = 4.5 \times 10^{-4}\ M$
   b. $[H^+] = 2.6 \times 10^{-6}\ M$ or $[H^+] = 4.3 \times 10^{-8}\ M$
   c. $[H^+] = 0.000010\ M$ or $[H^+] = 0.0000010\ M$

36. For each pair of concentrations, tell which represents the more *basic* solution.

   a. $[H^+] = 3.99 \times 10^{-6}\ M$ or $[OH^-] = 6.03 \times 10^{-4}\ M$
   b. $[H^+] = 1.79 \times 10^{-5}\ M$ or $[OH^-] = 4.21 \times 10^{-6}\ M$
   c. $[H^+] = 7.81 \times 10^{-3}\ M$ or $[OH^-] = 8.04 \times 10^{-4}\ M$

16.4 The pH Scale

QUESTIONS

37. Why do scientists tend to express the acidity of a solution in terms of its pH, rather than in terms of the molarity of hydrogen ion present? How is pH defined mathematically?

38. Using Figure 16.3, list the approximate pH value of five "everyday" solutions. How do the familiar properties (such as the sour taste for acids) of these solutions correspond to their indicated pH?

39. For a hydrogen ion concentration of $2.33 \times 10^{-6}\ M$, how many *decimal places* should we give when expressing the pH of the solution?

All even-numbered Questions and Problems have answers in the back of this book and solutions in the Solutions Guide.

40. The "Chemistry in Focus" segment *Garden-Variety Acid–Base Indicators* discusses acid–base indicators found in nature. What colors are exhibited by red cabbage juice under acid conditions? Under basic conditions?

PROBLEMS

41. Calculate the pH corresponding to each of the hydrogen ion concentrations given below, and indicate whether each solution is acidic or basic.

a. $[H^+] = 4.02 \times 10^{-3} M$
b. $[H^+] = 8.99 \times 10^{-7} M$
c. $[H^+] = 2.39 \times 10^{-6} M$
d. $[H^+] = 1.89 \times 10^{-10} M$

42. Calculate the pH corresponding to each of the hydrogen ion concentrations given below, and indicate whether each solution is acidic or basic.

a. $[H^+] = 9.35 \times 10^{-2} M$
b. $[H^+] = 3.75 \times 10^{-4} M$
c. $[H^+] = 8.36 \times 10^{-6} M$
d. $[H^+] = 5.42 \times 10^{-8} M$

43. Calculate the pH corresponding to each of the hydroxide ion concentrations given below, and indicate whether each solution is acidic or basic.

a. $[OH^-] = 4.73 \times 10^{-4} M$
b. $[OH^-] = 5.99 \times 10^{-1} M$
c. $[OH^-] = 2.87 \times 10^{-8} M$
d. $[OH^-] = 6.39 \times 10^{-3} M$

44. Calculate the pH corresponding to each of the hydroxide ion concentrations given below, and indicate whether each solution is acidic or basic.

a. $[OH^-] = 8.63 \times 10^{-3} M$
b. $[OH^-] = 7.44 \times 10^{-6} M$
c. $[OH^-] = 9.35 \times 10^{-9} M$
d. $[OH^-] = 1.21 \times 10^{-11} M$

45. Calculate the pH corresponding to each of the pOH values listed, and indicate whether each solution is acidic, basic, or neutral.

a. pOH = 4.32   c. pOH = 1.81
b. pOH = 8.90   d. pOH = 13.1

46. Calculate the pOH value corresponding to each of the pH values listed, and tell whether each solution is acidic or basic.

a. pH = 9.78   c. pH = 2.79
b. pH = 4.01   d. pH = 11.21

47. For each hydrogen ion concentration listed, calculate the pH of the solution as well as the concentration of hydroxide ion in the solution. Indicate whether each solution is acidic or basic.

a. $[H^+] = 4.76 \times 10^{-8} M$
b. $[H^+] = 8.92 \times 10^{-3} M$
c. $[H^+] = 7.00 \times 10^{-5} M$
d. $[H^+] = 1.25 \times 10^{-12} M$

48. For each hydrogen ion concentration listed, calculate the pH of the solution as well as the concentration of hydroxide ion in the solution. Indicate whether each solution is acidic or basic.

a. $[H^+] = 1.91 \times 10^{-2} M$
b. $[H^+] = 4.83 \times 10^{-7} M$
c. $[H^+] = 8.92 \times 10^{-11} M$
d. $[H^+] = 6.14 \times 10^{-5} M$

49. Calculate the hydrogen ion concentration, in moles per liter, for solutions with each of the following pH values.

a. pH = 9.01   c. pH = 1.02
b. pH = 6.89   d. pH = 7.00

50. Calculate the hydrogen ion concentration, in moles per liter, for solutions with each of the following pH values.

a. pH = 11.21   c. pH = 7.44
b. pH = 4.39   d. pH = 1.38

51. Calculate the hydrogen ion concentration, in moles per liter, for solutions with each of the following pOH values.

a. pOH = 4.95
b. pOH = 7.00
c. pOH = 12.94
d. pOH = 1.02

52. Calculate the hydrogen ion concentration, in moles per liter, for solutions with each of the following pH or pOH values.

a. pOH = 4.99
b. pH = 7.74
c. pOH = 10.74
d. pH = 2.25

53. Calculate the pH of each of the following solutions from the information given.

a. $[H^+] = 4.78 \times 10^{-2} M$
b. pOH = 4.56
c. $[OH^-] = 9.74 \times 10^{-3} M$
d. $[H^+] = 1.24 \times 10^{-8} M$

54. Calculate the pH of each of the following solutions from the information given.

a. $[H^+] = 4.39 \times 10^{-6} M$
b. pOH = 10.36
c. $[OH^-] = 9.37 \times 10^{-9} M$
d. $[H^+] = 3.31 \times 10^{-1} M$

16.5 Calculating the pH of Strong Acid Solutions

QUESTIONS

55. When 1 mole of gaseous hydrogen chloride is dissolved in enough water to make 1 L of solution, approximately how many HCl molecules remain in the solution? Explain.

All even-numbered Questions and Problems have answers in the back of this book and solutions in the *Solutions Guide*.

56. A bottle of acid solution is labeled "3 M HNO$_3$." What are the substances that are actually present in the solution? Are any HNO$_3$ molecules present? Why or why not?

PROBLEMS

57. Calculate the hydrogen ion concentration and the pH of each of the following solutions of strong acids.

a. 1.04×10^{-4} M HCl
b. 0.00301 M HNO$_3$
c. 5.41×10^{-4} M HClO$_4$
d. 6.42×10^{-2} M HNO$_3$

58. Calculate the pH of each of the following solutions of strong acids.

a. 1.21×10^{-3} M HNO$_3$
b. 0.000199 M HClO$_4$
c. 5.01×10^{-5} M HCl
d. 0.00104 M HBr

16.6 Buffered Solutions

QUESTIONS

59. What characteristic properties do buffered solutions possess?

60. What two components make up a buffered solution? Give an example of a combination that would serve as a buffered solution.

61. Which component of a buffered solution is capable of combining with an added strong acid? Using your example from Exercise 60, show how this component would react with added HCl.

62. Which component of a buffered solution consumes added strong base? Using your example from Exercise 60, show how this component would react with added NaOH.

PROBLEMS

63. Which of the following combinations would act as buffered solutions?

a. HCl and NaCl
b. CH$_3$COOH and KCH$_3$COO
c. H$_2$S and NaHS
d. H$_2$S and Na$_2$S

64. A buffered solution is prepared containing acetic acid, HC$_2$H$_3$O$_2$, and sodium acetate, Na$^+$C$_2$H$_3$O$_2^-$, both at 0.5 M. Write a chemical equation showing how this buffered solution would resist a decrease in its pH if a few drops of aqueous strong acid HCl solution were added to it. Write a chemical equation showing how this buffered solution would resist an increase in its pH if a few drops of aqueous strong base NaOH solution were added to it.

Additional Problems

65. The concepts of acid–base equilibria were developed in this chapter for aqueous solutions (in aqueous solutions, water is the solvent and is intimately involved in the equilibria). However, the Brønsted–Lowry acid–base theory can be extended easily to other solvents. One such solvent that has been investigated in depth is liquid ammonia, NH$_3$.

a. Write a chemical equation indicating how HCl behaves as an acid in liquid ammonia.
b. Write a chemical equation indicating how OH$^-$ behaves as a base in liquid ammonia.

66. *Strong bases* are bases that completely ionize in water to produce hydroxide ion, OH$^-$. The strong bases include the hydroxides of the Group 1 elements. For example, if 1.0 mole of NaOH is dissolved per liter, the concentration of OH$^-$ ion is 1.0 M. Calculate the [OH$^-$], pOH, and pH for each of the following strong base solutions.

a. 0.10 M NaOH
b. 2.0×10^{-4} M KOH
c. 6.2×10^{-3} M CsOH
d. 0.0001 M NaOH

67. Which of the following conditions indicate an *acidic* solution?

a. pH = 3.04
b. [H$^+$] > 1.0×10^{-7} M
c. pOH = 4.51
d. [OH$^-$] = 3.21×10^{-12} M

68. Which of the following conditions indicate a *basic* solution?

a. pOH = 11.21
b. pH = 9.42
c. [OH$^-$] > [H$^+$]
d. [OH$^-$] > 1.0×10^{-7} M

69. Buffered solutions are mixtures of a weak acid and its conjugate base. Explain why a mixture of a *strong* acid and its conjugate base (such as HCl and Cl$^-$) is not buffered.

70. Which of the following acids are classified as *strong* acids?

a. HNO$_3$
b. CH$_3$COOH (HC$_2$H$_3$O$_2$)
c. HCl
d. HF
e. HClO$_4$

71. Is it possible for a solution to have [H$^+$] = 0.002 M and [OH$^-$] = 5.2×10^{-6} M at 25 °C? Explain.

72. Despite HCl's being a strong acid, the pH of 1.00×10^{-7} M HCl is *not* exactly 7.00. Can you suggest a reason why?

73. According to Arrhenius, bases are species that produce _____ ion in aqueous solution.

74. According to the Brønsted–Lowry model, a base is a species that _____ protons.

75. A conjugate acid–base pair consists of two substances related by the donating and accepting of a(n) _____.

All even-numbered Questions and Problems have answers in the back of this book and solutions in the Solutions Guide.

76. Acetate ion, $C_2H_3O_2^-$, has a stronger affinity for protons than does water. Therefore, when dissolved in water, acetate ion behaves as a(n) _____.

77. An acid such as HCl that strongly conducts an electric current when dissolved in water is said to be a(n) _____ acid.

78. Draw the structure of the carboxyl group, —COOH. Show how a molecule containing the carboxyl group behaves as an acid when dissolved in water.

79. Because of _____, even pure water contains measurable quantities of H^+ and OH^-.

80. The ion-product constant for water, K_w, has the value _____ at 25 °C.

81. The number of _____ in the logarithm of a number is equal to the number of significant figures in the number.

82. A solution with pH = 4 has a (higher/lower) hydrogen ion concentration than a solution with pOH = 4.

83. A 0.20 M HCl solution contains _____ M hydrogen ion and _____ M chloride ion concentrations.

84. A buffered solution is one that resists a change in _____ when either a strong acid or a strong base is added to it.

85. A(n) _____ solution contains a conjugate acid–base pair and through this is able to resist changes in its pH.

86. When sodium hydroxide, NaOH, is added dropwise to a buffered solution, the _____ component of the buffer consumes the added hydroxide ion.

87. When hydrochloric acid, HCl, is added dropwise to a buffered solution, the _____ component of the buffer consumes the added hydrogen ion.

88. Which of the following represent conjugate acid–base pairs? For those pairs that are not conjugates, write the correct conjugate acid or base for each species in the pair.

   a. H_2O, OH^-
   b. H_2SO_4, SO_4^{2-}
   c. H_3PO_4, $H_2PO_4^-$
   d. $HC_2H_3O_2$, $C_2H_3O_2^-$

89. In each of the following chemical equations, identify the conjugate acid–base pairs.

   a. $CH_3NH_2 + H_2O \rightleftharpoons CH_3NH_3^+ + OH^-$
   b. $CH_3COOH + NH_3 \rightleftharpoons CH_3COO^- + NH_4^+$
   c. $HF + NH_3 \rightleftharpoons F^- + NH_4^+$

90. Write the conjugate *acid* for each of the following.

   a. NH_3 c. H_2O
   b. NH_2^- d. OH^-

91. Write the conjugate *base* for each of the following.

   a. H_3PO_4
   b. HCO_3^-
   c. HF
   d. H_2SO_4

92. Write chemical equations showing the ionization (dissociation) in water for each of the following acids.

   a. CH_3CH_2COOH (Only the last H is acidic.)
   b. NH_4^+
   c. H_2SO_4
   d. H_3PO_4

93. Which of the following bases have relatively *strong* conjugate acids?

   a. F^-
   b. Cl^-
   c. HSO_4^-
   d. NO_3^-

94. Calculate $[H^+]$ in each of the following solutions, and indicate whether the solution is acidic, basic, or neutral.

   a. $[OH^-] = 4.22 \times 10^{-3}\ M$
   b. $[OH^-] = 1.01 \times 10^{-13}\ M$
   c. $[OH^-] = 3.05 \times 10^{-7}\ M$
   d. $[OH^-] = 6.02 \times 10^{-6}\ M$

95. Calculate $[OH^-]$ in each of the following solutions, and indicate whether the solution is acidic, basic, or neutral.

   a. $[H^+] = 4.21 \times 10^{-7}\ M$
   b. $[H^+] = 0.00035\ M$
   c. $[H^+] = 0.00000010\ M$
   d. $[H^+] = 9.9 \times 10^{-6}\ M$

96. For each pair of concentrations, tell which represents the more basic solution.

   a. $[H^+] = 0.000013\ M$ or $[OH^-] = 0.0000032\ M$
   b. $[H^+] = 1.03 \times 10^{-6}\ M$ or $[OH^-] = 1.54 \times 10^{-8}\ M$
   c. $[OH^-] = 4.02 \times 10^{-7}\ M$ or $[OH^-] = 0.0000001\ M$

97. Calculate the pH of each of the solutions indicated below. Tell whether the solution is acidic, basic, or neutral.

   a. $[H^+] = 1.49 \times 10^{-3}\ M$
   b. $[OH^-] = 6.54 \times 10^{-4}\ M$
   c. $[H^+] = 9.81 \times 10^{-9}\ M$
   d. $[OH^-] = 7.45 \times 10^{-10}\ M$

98. Calculate the pH corresponding to each of the hydroxide ion concentrations given below. Tell whether each solution is acidic, basic, or neutral.

   a. $[OH^-] = 1.4 \times 10^{-6}\ M$
   b. $[OH^-] = 9.35 \times 10^{-9}\ M$
   c. $[OH^-] = 2.21 \times 10^{-1}\ M$
   d. $[OH^-] = 7.98 \times 10^{-12}\ M$

99. Calculate the pOH corresponding to each of the pH values listed, and indicate whether each solution is acidic, basic, or neutral.

   a. pH = 1.02
   b. pH = 13.4
   c. pH = 9.03
   d. pH = 7.20

100. For each hydrogen or hydroxide ion concentration listed, calculate the concentration of the complementary ion and the pH and pOH of the solution.

a. $[H^+] = 5.72 \times 10^{-4}\ M$
b. $[OH^-] = 8.91 \times 10^{-5}\ M$
c. $[H^+] = 2.87 \times 10^{-12}\ M$
d. $[OH^-] = 7.22 \times 10^{-8}\ M$

101. Calculate the hydrogen ion concentration, in moles per liter, for solutions with each of the following pH values.

a. pH = 8.34   c. pH = 2.65
b. pH = 5.90   d. pH = 12.6

102. Calculate the hydrogen ion concentration, in moles per liter, for solutions with each of the following pH or pOH values.

a. pH = 5.41
b. pOH = 12.04
c. pH = 11.91
d. pOH = 3.89

103. Calculate the hydrogen ion concentration, in moles per liter, for solutions with each of the following pH or pOH values.

a. pOH = 0.90
b. pH = 0.90
c. pOH = 10.3
d. pH = 5.33

104. Calculate the hydrogen ion concentration and the pH of each of the following solutions of strong acids.

a. $1.4 \times 10^{-3}\ M\ HClO_4$
b. $3.0 \times 10^{-5}\ M\ HCl$
c. $5.0 \times 10^{-2}\ M\ HNO_3$
d. $0.0010\ M\ HCl$

105. Write the formulas for *three* combinations of weak acid and salt that would act as buffered solutions. For each of your combinations, write chemical equations showing how the components of the buffered solution would consume added acid and base.

Using Your Calculator

In this section we will review how to use your calculator to perform common mathematical operations. This discussion assumes that your calculator uses the algebraic operating system, the system used by most brands.

One very important principle to keep in mind as you use your calculator is that it is not a substitute for your brain. Keep thinking as you do the calculations. Keep asking yourself, "Does the answer make sense?"

Addition, Subtraction, Multiplication, and Division

Performing these operations on a pair of numbers always involves the following steps:

1. Enter the first number, using the numbered keys and the decimal (.) key if needed.
2. Enter the operation to be performed.
3. Enter the second number.
4. Press the "equals" key to display the answer.

For example, the operation

$$15.1 + 0.32$$

is carried out as follows:

Press	Display
15.1	15.1
+	15.1
.32	0.32
=	15.42

The answer given by the display is 15.42. If this is the final result of a calculation, you should round it off to the correct number of significant figures (15.4), as discussed in Section 2.5. If this number is to be used in further calculations, use it exactly as it appears on the display. Round off only the final answer in the calculation.

Do the following operations for practice. The detailed procedures are given below.

a. $1.5 + 32.86$ c. 0.33×153

b. $23.5 - 0.41$ d. $\dfrac{9.3}{0.56}$ or $9.3 \div 0.56$

Procedures

a. Press	Display	b. Press	Display
1.5	1.5	23.5	23.5
+	1.5	−	23.5
32.86	32.86	.41	0.41
=	34.36	=	23.09
Rounded:	34.4	Rounded:	23.1

c. Press	Display	d. Press	Display
.33	0.33	9.3	9.3
×	0.33	÷	9.3
153	153	.56	0.56
=	50.49	=	16.607143
Rounded:	50.	Rounded:	17

Squares, Square Roots, Reciprocals, and Logs

Now we will consider four additional operations that we often need to solve chemistry problems.

The *squaring* of a number is done with a key labeled X^2. The *square root* key is usually labeled $\sqrt{X}$. To take the *reciprocal* of a number, you need the 1/X key. The *logarithm* of a number is determined by using a key labeled log or logX.

To perform these operations, take the following steps:

1. Enter the number.
2. Press the appropriate function key.
3. The answer is displayed automatically.

For example, let's calculate the square root of 235.

Press	Display
235	235
$\sqrt{X}$	15.32971
Rounded:	15.3

We can obtain the log of 23 as follows:

Press	Display
23	23
log	1.3617278
Rounded:	1.36

Often a key on a calculator serves two functions. In this case, the first function is listed on the key and the second is shown on the calculator just above the key. For example, on some calculators the top row of keys appears as follows:

1/X X^2

[2nd] [R/S] [$\sqrt{X}$] [off] [on/C]

To make the calculator square a number, we must use 2nd and then $\sqrt{X}$; pressing 2nd tells the calculator we want the function that is listed *above* the key. Thus we can obtain the square of 11.56 on this calculator as follows:

Press	Display
11.56	11.56
2nd then $\sqrt{X}$	133.6336
Rounded:	133.6

We obtain the reciprocal of 384 (1/384) on this calculator as follows:

Press	Display
384	384
2nd then R/S	0.0026042
Rounded:	0.00260

Your calculator may be different. See the user's manual if you are having trouble with these operations.

Chain Calculations

In solving problems you often have to perform a series of calculations—a calculation chain. This is generally quite easy if you key in the chain as you read the numbers and operations in order. For example, to perform the calculation

$$\frac{14.68 + 1.58 - 0.87}{0.0850}$$

you should use the appropriate keys as you read it to yourself:

14.68 plus 1.58 equals; minus .87 equals;
divided by 0.0850 equals

The details follow.

Press	Display
14.68	14.68
+	14.68
1.58	1.58
=	16.26
−	16.26
.87	0.87
=	15.39
÷	15.39
.0850	0.0850
=	181.05882
Rounded:	181

Note that you must press $\boxed{=}$ after every operation to keep the calculation "up to date."

For more practice, consider the calculation

$$(0.360)(298) + \frac{(14.8)(16.0)}{1.50}$$

Here you are adding two numbers, but each must be obtained by the indicated calculations. One procedure is to calculate each number first and then add them. The first term is

$$(0.360)(298) = 107.28$$

The second term,

$$\frac{(14.8)(16.0)}{1.50}$$

can be computed easily by reading it to yourself. It "reads"

14.8 times 16.0 equals; divided by 1.50 equals

and is summarized as follows:

Press	Display
14.8	14.8
×	14.8
16.0	16.0
=	236.8
÷	236.8
1.50	1.50
=	157.86667

Now we can keep this last number on the calculator and add it to 107.28 from the first calculation.

Press	Display
+	157.86667
107.28	107.28
=	265.14667
Rounded:	265

To summarize,

$$(0.360)(298) + \frac{(14.8)(16.0)}{1.50}$$

becomes

$$107.28 + 157.86667$$

and the sum is 265.14667 or, rounded to the correct number of significant figures, 265. There are other ways to do this calculation, but this is the safest way (assuming you are careful).

A common type of chain calculation involves a number of terms multiplied together in the numerator and the denominator, as in

$$\frac{(323)(.0821)(1.46)}{(4.05)(76)}$$

There are many possible sequences by which this calculation can be carried out, but the following seems the most natural.

323 times .0821 equals; times 1.46 equals;
divided by 4.05 equals; divided by 76 equals

This sequence is summarized as follows:

Press	Display
323	323
×	323
.0821	0.0821
=	26.5183
×	26.5183
1.46	1.46
=	38.716718
÷	38.716718
4.05	4.05
=	9.5596835
÷	9.5596835
76	76
=	0.1257853

The answer is 0.1257853, which, when rounded to the correct number of significant figures, is 0.13. Note that when two or more numbers are multiplied in the denominator, you must divide by *each* one.

Here are some additional chain calculations (with solutions) to give you more practice.

a. $15 - (0.750)(243)$

b. $\dfrac{(13.1)(43.5)}{(1.8)(63)}$

c. $\dfrac{(85.8)(0.142)}{(16.46)(18.0)} + \dfrac{(131)(0.0156)}{10.17}$

d. $(18.1)(0.051) - \dfrac{(325)(1.87)}{(14.0)(3.81)} + \dfrac{1.56 - 0.43}{1.33}$

Solutions

a. $15 - 182 = -167$

b. 5.0

c. $0.0411 + 0.201 = 0.242$

d. $0.92 - 11.4 + 0.850 = -9.6$

In performing chain calculations, take the following steps in the order listed.

1. Perform any additions and subtractions that appear inside parentheses.

2. Complete the multiplications and divisions of individual terms.

3. Add and subtract individual terms as required.

Basic Algebra

In solving chemistry problems you will use, over and over again, relatively few mathematical procedures. In this section we review the few algebraic manipulations that you will need.

Solving an Equation

In the course of solving a chemistry problem, we often construct an algebraic equation that includes the unknown quantity (the thing we want to calculate). An example is

$$(1.5)V = (0.23)(0.08206)(298)$$

We need to "solve this equation for V." That is, we need to isolate V on one side of the equals sign with all the numbers on the other side. How can we do this? The key idea in solving an algebraic equation is that *doing the same thing on both sides of the equals sign* does not change the equality. That is, it is always "legal" to do the same thing to both sides of the equation. Here we want to solve for V, so we must get the number 1.5 on the other side of the equals sign. We can do this by dividing *both sides* by 1.5.

$$\frac{(1.5)V}{1.5} = \frac{(0.23)(0.08206)(298)}{1.5}$$

Now the 1.5 in the denominator on the left cancels the 1.5 in the numerator:

$$\frac{(\cancel{1.5})V}{\cancel{1.5}} = \frac{(0.23)(0.08206)(298)}{1.5}$$

to give

$$V = \frac{(0.23)(0.08206)(298)}{1.5}$$

Using the procedures in "Using Your Calculator" for chain calculations, we can now obtain the value for V with a calculator.

$$V = 3.7$$

Sometimes it is necessary to solve an equation that consists of symbols. For example, consider the equation

$$\frac{P_1 V_1}{T_1} = \frac{P_2 V_2}{T_2}$$

Let's assume we want to solve for T_2. That is, we want to isolate T_2 on one side of the equation. There are several possible ways to proceed, keeping in mind that we always do the same thing on both sides of the equals sign. First we multiply both sides by T_2.

$$T_2 \times \frac{P_1 V_1}{T_1} = \frac{P_2 V_2}{\cancel{T_2}} \times \cancel{T_2}$$

This cancels T_2 on the right. Next we multiply both sides by T_1.

$$T_2 \times \frac{P_1 V_1}{\cancel{T_1}} \times \cancel{T_1} = P_2 V_2 T_1$$

This cancels T_1 on the left. Now we divide both sides by $P_1 V_1$.

$$T_2 \times \frac{\cancel{P_1 V_1}}{\cancel{P_1 V_1}} = \frac{P_2 V_2 T_1}{P_1 V_1}$$

This yields the desired equation,

$$T_2 = \frac{P_2 V_2 T_1}{P_1 V_1}$$

For practice, solve each of the following equations for the variable indicated.

a. $PV = k$; solve for P

b. $1.5x + 6 = 3$; solve for x

c. $PV = nRT$; solve for n

d. $\dfrac{P_1 V_1}{T_1} = \dfrac{P_2 V_2}{T_2}$; solve for V_2

e. $\dfrac{°F - 32}{°C} = \dfrac{9}{5}$; solve for $°C$

f. $\dfrac{°F - 32}{°C} = \dfrac{9}{5}$; solve for $°F$

Solutions

a. $\dfrac{P\cancel{V}}{\cancel{V}} = \dfrac{k}{V}$

$P = \dfrac{k}{V}$

b. $1.5x + 6 - 6 = 3 - 6$

$1.5x = -3$

$\dfrac{\cancel{1.5}x}{\cancel{1.5}} = \dfrac{-3}{1.5}$

$x = -\dfrac{3}{1.5} = -2$

c. $\dfrac{PV}{RT} = \dfrac{n\cancel{R}\cancel{T}}{\cancel{R}\cancel{T}}$

$\dfrac{PV}{RT} = n$

d. $\dfrac{P_1 V_1}{T_1} \times T_2 = \dfrac{P_2 V_2}{\cancel{T_2}} \times \cancel{T_2}$

$\dfrac{P_1 V_1 T_2}{T_1 P_2} = \dfrac{\cancel{P_2} V_2}{\cancel{P_2}}$

$\dfrac{P_1 V_1 T_2}{T_1 P_2} = V_2$

e. $\dfrac{°F - 32}{°\cancel{C}} \times °\cancel{C} = \dfrac{9}{5}\,°C$

$\dfrac{5}{9}\,(°F - 32) = \dfrac{\cancel{5}}{\cancel{9}} \times \dfrac{\cancel{9}}{\cancel{5}}\,°C$

$\dfrac{5}{9}\,(°F - 32) = °C$

f. $\dfrac{°F - 32}{°\cancel{C}} \times °\cancel{C} = \dfrac{9}{5}\,°C$

$°F - \cancel{32} + \cancel{32} = \dfrac{9}{5}\,°C + 32$

$°F = \dfrac{9}{5}\,°C + 32$

Scientific (Exponential) Notation

The numbers we must work with in scientific measurements are often very large or very small; thus it is convenient to express them using powers of 10. For example, the number 1,300,000 can be expressed as 1.3×10^6, which means multiply 1.3 by 10 six times, or

$$1.3 \times 10^6 = 1.3 \times \underbrace{10 \times 10 \times 10 \times 10 \times 10 \times 10}_{10^6 \;=\; 1 \text{ million}}$$

A number written in scientific notation always has the form:

A number (between 1 and 10) times
the appropriate power of 10

To represent a large number such as 20,500 in scientific notation, we must move the decimal point in such a way as to achieve a number between 1 and 10 and then multiply the result by a power of 10 to compensate for moving the decimal point. In this case, we must move the decimal point four places to the left.

$$2\ 0\ 5\ 0\ 0$$
$$4\ \ 3\ \ 2\ \ 1$$

to give a number between 1 and 10:

$$2.05$$

where we retain only the significant figures (the number 20,500 has three significant figures). To compensate for moving the decimal point four places to the left, we must multiply by 10^4. Thus

$$20{,}500 = 2.05 \times 10^4$$

As another example, the number 1985 can be expressed as 1.985×10^3. To end up with the number 1.985, which is between 1 and 10, we had to move the decimal point three places to the left. To compensate for that, we must multiply by 10^3. Some other examples are given in the accompanying list.

Number	Exponential Notation
5.6	5.6×10^0 or 5.6×1
39	3.9×10^1
943	9.43×10^2
1126	1.126×10^3

So far, we have considered numbers greater than 1. How do we represent a number such as 0.0034 in exponential notation? First, to achieve a number between 1 and 10, we start with 0.0034 and move the decimal point three places to the right.

$$0.0\ 0\ 3\ 4$$
$$1\ 2\ 3$$

This yields 3.4. Then, to compensate for moving the decimal point to the right, we must multiply by a power of 10 with a negative exponent—in this case, 10^{-3}. Thus

$$0.0034 = 3.4 \times 10^{-3}$$

In a similar way, the number 0.00000014 can be written as 1.4×10^{-7}, because going from 0.00000014 to 1.4 requires that we move the decimal point seven places to the right.

Mathematical Operations with Exponentials

We next consider how various mathematical operations are performed using exponential numbers. First we cover the various rules for these operations; then we consider how to perform them on your calculator.

Multiplication and Division

When two numbers expressed in exponential notation are multiplied, the initial numbers are multiplied and the exponents of 10 are *added*.

$$(M \times 10^m)(N \times 10^n) = (MN) \times 10^{m+n}$$

For example (to two significant figures, as required),

$$(3.2 \times 10^4)(2.8 \times 10^3) = 9.0 \times 10^7$$

When the numbers are multiplied, if a result greater than 10 is obtained for the initial number, the decimal point is moved one place to the left and the exponent of 10 is increased by 1.

$$(5.8 \times 10^2)(4.3 \times 10^8) = 24.9 \times 10^{10}$$
$$= 2.49 \times 10^{11}$$
$$= 2.5 \times 10^{11} \text{ (two significant figures)}$$

Division of two numbers expressed in exponential notation involves normal division of the initial numbers and *subtraction* of the exponent of the divisor from that of the dividend. For example,

$$\frac{4.8 \times 10^8}{\underbrace{2.1 \times 10^3}_{\text{Divisor}}} = \frac{4.8}{2.1} \times 10^{(8-3)} = 2.3 \times 10^5$$

If the initial number resulting from the division is less than 1, the decimal point is moved one place to the right and the exponent of 10 is decreased by 1. For example,

$$\frac{6.4 \times 10^3}{8.3 \times 10^5} = \frac{6.4}{8.3} \times 10^{(3-5)} = 0.77 \times 10^{-2}$$
$$= 7.7 \times 10^{-3}$$

Addition and Subtraction

In order for us to add or subtract numbers expressed in exponential notation, *the exponents of the numbers must be the same*. For example, to add 1.31×10^5 and 4.2×10^4, we must rewrite one number so that the exponents of both are the same. The number 1.31×10^5 can be written 13.1×10^4: decreasing the exponent by 1 compensates for moving the decimal point one place to the right. Now we can add the numbers.

$$\begin{array}{r} 13.1 \times 10^4 \\ + \ 4.2 \times 10^4 \\ \hline 17.3 \times 10^4 \end{array}$$

In correct exponential notation, the result is expressed as 1.73×10^5.

To perform addition or subtraction with numbers expressed in exponential notation, we add or subtract only the initial numbers. The exponent of the result is the same as the exponents of the numbers being added or subtracted. To subtract 1.8×10^2 from 8.99×10^3, we first convert 1.8×10^2 to 0.18×10^3 so that both numbers have the same exponent. Then we subtract.

$$\begin{array}{r} 8.99 \times 10^3 \\ -0.18 \times 10^3 \\ \hline 8.81 \times 10^3 \end{array}$$

Powers and Roots

When a number expressed in exponential notation is taken to some power, the initial number is taken to the appropriate power and the exponent of 10 is *multiplied* by that power.

$$(N \times 10^n)^m = N^m \times 10^{m \times n}$$

For example,

$$(7.5 \times 10^2)^2 = (7.5)^2 \times 10^{2 \times 2}$$
$$= 56. \times 10^4$$
$$= 5.6 \times 10^5$$

When a root is taken of a number expressed in exponential notation, the root of the initial number is taken and the exponent of 10 is divided by the number representing the root. For example, we take the square root of a number as follows:

$$\sqrt{N \times 10^n} = (N \times 10^n)^{1/2} = \sqrt{N} \times 10^{n/2}$$

For example,

$$(2.9 \times 10^6)^{1/2} = \sqrt{2.9} \times 10^{6/2}$$
$$= 1.7 \times 10^3$$

Using a Calculator to Perform Mathematical Operations on Exponentials

In dealing with exponential numbers, you must first learn to enter them into your calculator. First the number is keyed in and then the exponent. There is a special key that must be pressed just before the exponent is entered. This key is often labeled (EE) or (exp). For example, the number 1.56×10^6 is entered as follows:

Press	Display
1.56	1.56
EE or exp	1.56 00
6	1.56 06

To enter a number with a negative exponent, use the change-of-sign key (+/−) after entering the exponent number. For example, the number 7.54×10^{-3} is entered as follows:

Press	Display
7.54	7.54
EE or exp	7.54 00
3	7.54 03
+/−	7.54 −03

Once a number with an exponent is entered into your calculator, the mathematical operations are performed exactly the same as with a "regular" number. For example, the numbers 1.0×10^3 and 1.0×10^2 are multiplied as follows:

Press	Display	
1.0	1.0	
EE or exp	1.0	00
3	1.0	03
×	1	03
1.0	1.0	
EE or exp	1.0	00
2	1.0	02
=	1	05

The answer is correctly represented as 1.0×10^5.

The numbers 1.50×10^5 and 1.1×10^4 are added as follows:

Press	Display	
1.5	1.50	
EE or exp	1.50	00
5	1.50	05
+	1.5	05
1.1	1.1	
EE or exp	1.1	00
4	1.1	04
=	1.61	05

The answer is correctly represented as 1.61×10^5. Note that when exponential numbers are added, the calculator automatically takes into account any difference in exponents.

To take the power, root, or reciprocal of an exponential number, enter the number first, then press the appropriate key or keys. For example, the square root of 5.6×10^3 is obtained as follows:

Press	Display	
5.6	5.6	
EE or exp	5.6	00
3	5.6	03
$\sqrt{\text{X}}$	7.4833148	01

The answer is correctly represented as 7.5×10^1.

Practice by performing the following operations that involve exponential numbers. The answers follow the exercises.

a. $7.9 \times 10^2 \times 4.3 \times 10^4$

b. $\dfrac{5.4 \times 10^3}{4.6 \times 10^5}$

c. $1.7 \times 10^2 + 1.63 \times 10^3$

d. $4.3 \times 10^{-3} + 1 \times 10^{-4}$

e. $(8.6 \times 10^{-6})^2$

f. $\dfrac{1}{8.3 \times 10^2}$

g. $\log(1.0 \times 10^{-7})$

h. $-\log(1.3 \times 10^{-5})$

i. $\sqrt{6.7 \times 10^9}$

Solutions

a. 3.4×10^7

b. 1.2×10^{-2}

c. 1.80×10^3

d. 4.4×10^{-3}

e. 7.4×10^{-11}

f. 1.2×10^{-3}

g. -7.00

h. 4.89

i. 8.2×10^4

Graphing Functions

In interpreting the results of a scientific experiment, it is often useful to make a graph. If possible, the function to be graphed should be in a form that gives a straight line. The equation for a straight line (a *linear equation*) can be represented in the general form

$$y = mx + b$$

where y is the *dependent variable*, x is the *independent variable*, m is the *slope*, and b is the *intercept* with the y axis.

To illustrate the characteristics of a linear equation, the function $y = 3x + 4$ is plotted in Figure A.1. For this equation $m = 3$ and $b = 4$. Note that the y intercept occurs when $x = 0$. In this case the y intercept is 4, as can be seen from the equation ($b = 4$).

The slope of a straight line is defined as the ratio of the rate of change in y to that in x:

$$m = \text{slope} = \frac{\Delta y}{\Delta x}$$

For the equation $y = 3x + 4$, y changes three times as fast as x (because x has a coefficient of 3). Thus the slope in

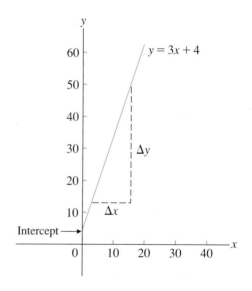

Figure A.1

Graph of the linear equation $y = 3x + 4$.

this case is 3. This can be verified from the graph. For the triangle shown in Figure A.1,

$$\Delta y = 15 - 16 = 36 \qquad \text{and} \qquad \Delta x = 15 - 3 = 12$$

Thus

$$\text{Slope} = \frac{\Delta y}{\Delta x} = \frac{36}{12} = 3$$

This example illustrates a general method for obtaining the slope of a line from the graph of that line. Simply draw a triangle with one side parallel to the y axis and the other side parallel to the x axis, as shown in Figure A.1. Then determine the lengths of the sides to get Δy and Δx, respectively, and compute the ratio $\Delta y/\Delta x$.

SI Units and Conversion Factors

These conversion factors are given with more significant figures than those typically used in the body of the text.

Length	SI Unit: Meter (m)
1 meter	= 1.0936 yards
1 centimeter	= 0.39370 inch
1 inch	= 2.54 centimeters (exactly)
1 kilometer	= 0.62137 mile
1 mile	= 5280. feet
	= 1.6093 kilometers

Mass	SI Unit: Kilogram (kg)
1 kilogram	= 1000 grams
	= 2.2046 pounds
1 pound	= 453.59 grams
	= 0.45359 kilogram
	= 16 ounces
1 atomic mass unit	= 1.66057×10^{-27} kilograms

Volume	SI Unit: Cubic Meter (m³)
1 liter	= 10^{-3} m^3
	= 1 dm^3
	= 1.0567 quarts
1 gallon	= 4 quarts
	= 8 pints
	= 3.7854 liters
1 quart	= 32 fluid ounces
	= 0.94635 liter

Pressure	SI Unit: Pascal (Pa)
1 atmosphere	= 101.325 kilopascals
	= 760. torr (mm Hg)
	= 14.70 pounds per square inch

Energy	SI Unit: Joule (J)
1 joule	= 0.23901 calorie
1 calorie	= 4.184 joules

Chapter 2

Self-Check Exercise 2.1

$357 = 3.57 \times 10^2$

$0.0055 = 5.5 \times 10^{-3}$

Self-Check Exercise 2.2

a. Three significant figures. The leading zeros (to the left of the 1) do not count, but the trailing zeros do.

b. Five significant figures. The one captive zero and the two trailing zeros all count.

c. This is an exact number obtained by counting the cars. It has an unlimited number of significant figures.

Self-Check Exercise 2.3

a. $12.6 \times 0.53 = 6.678 = 6.7$
   Limiting

b. $12.6 \times 0.53 = 6.7;$ 6.7 Limiting
   Limiting $\underline{-4.59}$
   $2.11 = 2.1$

c. 25.36 $\dfrac{21.21}{2.317} = 9.15408 = 9.154$
   $\underline{-4.15}$
   21.21

Self-Check Exercise 2.4

$$0.750 \; \cancel{L} \times \frac{1.06 \text{ qt}}{1 \; \cancel{L}} = 0.795 \text{ qt}$$

Self-Check Exercise 2.5

$$225 \; \frac{\cancel{\text{mi}}}{\text{h}} \times \frac{1760 \; \cancel{\text{yd}}}{1 \; \cancel{\text{mi}}} \times \frac{1 \; \cancel{\text{m}}}{1.094 \; \cancel{\text{yd}}} \times \frac{1 \text{ km}}{1000 \; \cancel{\text{m}}} = 362 \; \frac{\text{km}}{\text{h}}$$

Self-Check Exercise 2.6

The best way to solve this problem is to convert 172 K to Celsius degrees. To do this we will use the formula $T_{\circ C} = T_K - 273$.
   In this case

$$T_{\circ C} = T_K - 273 = 172 - 273 = -101$$

So 172 K $= -101$ °C, which is a lower temperature than -75 °C. Thus 172 K is colder than -75 °C.

Self-Check Exercise 2.7

The problem is 41 °C $=$? °F.
   Using the formula

$$T_{\circ F} = 1.80\,(T_{\circ C}) + 32$$

we have

$$T_{\circ F} = ? \; \text{°F} = 1.80(41) + 32 = 74 + 32 = 106$$

That is, 41 °C $=$ 106 °F.

Self-Check Exercise 2.8

This problem can be stated as 239 °F $=$? °C.
   Using the formula

$$T_{\circ C} = \frac{T_{\circ F} - 32}{1.80}$$

we have in this case

$$T_{\circ C} = ? \; \text{°C} = \frac{239 - 32}{1.80} = \frac{207}{1.80} = 115$$

That is, 239 °F $=$ 115 °C.

Self-Check Exercise 2.9

We obtain the density of the cleaner by dividing its mass by its volume.

$$\text{Density} = \frac{\text{mass}}{\text{volume}} = \frac{28.1 \text{ g}}{35.8 \text{ mL}} = 0.785 \text{ g/mL}$$

This density identifies the liquid as isopropyl alcohol.

Chapter 3

Self-Check Exercise 3.1

Items (a) and (c) are physical properties. When the solid gallium melts, it forms liquid gallium. There is no change in composition. Items (b) and (d) reflect the ability to change composition and are thus chemical properties. Statement (b) means that platinum does not react with oxygen to form some new substance. Statement (d) means that copper does react in the air to form a new substance, which is green.

Self-Check Exercise 3.2

a. Milk turns sour because new substances are formed. This is a chemical change.

b. Melting the wax is a physical change (a change of state). When the wax burns, new substances are formed. This is a chemical change.

Self-Check Exercise 3.3

a. Maple syrup is a homogeneous mixture of sugar and other substances dispersed uniformly in water.

b. Helium and oxygen form a homogeneous mixture.

c. Oil and vinegar salad dressing is a heterogeneous mixture. (Note the two distinct layers the next time you look at a bottle of dressing.)

d. Common salt is a pure substance (sodium chloride), so it always has the same composition. (Note that other substances such as iodine are often added to commercial preparations of table salt, which is mostly sodium chloride. Thus commercial table salt is a homogeneous mixture.)

Chapter 4

Self-Check Exercise 4.1

a. P_4O_{10} b. UF_6 c. $AlCl_3$

Self-Check Exercise 4.2

In the symbol $^{90}_{38}Sr$, the number 38 is the atomic number, which represents the number of protons in the nucleus of a strontium atom. Because the atom is neutral overall, it must also have 38 electrons. The number 90 (the mass number) represents the number of protons plus the number of neutrons. Thus the number of neutrons is $A - Z = 90 - 38 = 52$.

Self-Check Exercise 4.3

The atom $^{201}_{80}Hg$ has 80 protons, 80 electrons, and $201 - 80 = 121$ neutrons.

Self-Check Exercise 4.4

The atomic number for phosphorus is 15 and the mass number is $15 + 17 = 32$. Thus the symbol for the atom is $^{32}_{15}P$.

Self-Check Exercise 4.5

Element	Symbol	Atomic Number	Metal or Nonmetal	Family Name
a. argon	Ar	18	nonmetal	noble gas
b. chlorine	Cl	17	nonmetal	halogen
c. barium	Ba	56	metal	alkaline earth metal
d. cesium	Cs	55	metal	alkali metal

Self-Check Exercise 4.6

a. KI $(1+) + (1-) = 0$

b. Mg_3N_2 $3(2+) + 2(3-) = (6+) + (6-) = 0$

c. Al_2O_3 $2(3+) + 3(2-) = 0$

Chapter 5

Self-Check Exercise 5.1

a. rubidium oxide

b. strontium iodide

c. potassium sulfide

Self-Check Exercise 5.2

a. The compound $PbBr_2$ must contain Pb^{2+}—named lead(II)—to balance the charges of the two Br^- ions. Thus the name is lead(II) bromide. The compound $PbBr_4$ must contain Pb^{4+}—named lead(IV)—to balance the charges of the four Br^- ions. The name is therefore lead(IV) bromide.

b. The compound FeS contains the S^{2-} ion (sulfide) and thus the iron cation present must be Fe^{2+}, iron(II). The name is iron(II) sulfide. The compound Fe_2S_3 contains three S^{2-} ions and two iron cations of unknown charge. We can determine the iron charge from the following:

$$2(?+) + 3(2-) = 0$$

$\qquad\qquad\uparrow\qquad\quad\uparrow$

$\qquad\qquad$ Iron $\qquad S^{2-}$

$\qquad\qquad$ charge $\quad$ charge

In this case, ? must represent 3 because

$$2(3+) + 3(2-) = 0$$

Thus Fe_2S_3 contains Fe^{3+} and S^{2-}, and its name is iron(III) sulfide.

c. The compound $AlBr_3$ contains Al^{3+} and Br^-. Because aluminum forms only one ion (Al^{3+}), no Roman numeral is required. The name is aluminum bromide.

d. The compound Na_2S contains Na^+ and S^{2-} ions. The name is sodium sulfide. (Because sodium forms only Na^+, no Roman numeral is needed.)

e. The compound $CoCl_3$ contains three Cl^- ions. Thus the cobalt cation must be Co^{3+}, which is named cobalt(III) because cobalt is a transition metal and can form more than one type of cation. Thus the name of $CoCl_3$ is cobalt(III) chloride.

Self-Check Exercise 5.3

Compound	Individual Names	Prefixes	Name
a. CCl_4	carbon chloride	none *tetra-*	carbon tetrachloride
b. NO_2	nitrogen oxide	none *di-*	nitrogen dioxide
c. IF_5	iodine fluoride	none *penta-*	iodine pentafluoride

Self-Check Exercise 5.4

a. silicon dioxide

b. dioxygen difluoride

c. xenon hexafluoride

Self-Check Exercise 5.5

a. chlorine trifluoride

b. vanadium(V) fluoride

c. copper(I) chloride

d. manganese(IV) oxide

e. magnesium oxide

f. water

Self-Check Exercise 5.6

a. calcium hydroxide

b. sodium phosphate

c. potassium permanganate

d. ammonium dichromate

e. cobalt(II) perchlorate (Perchlorate has a 1− charge, so the cation must be Co^{2+} to balance the two ClO_4^- ions.)

f. potassium chlorate

g. copper(II) nitrite (This compound contains two NO_2^- (nitrite) ions and thus must contain a Cu^{2+} cation.)

Self-Check Exercise 5.7

Compound	Name
a. $NaHCO_3$	sodium hydrogen carbonate

Contains Na^+ and HCO_3^-; often called sodium bicarbonate (common name).

b. $BaSO_4$	barium sulfate

Contains Ba^{2+} and SO_4^{2-}.

c. $CsClO_4$	cesium perchlorate

Contains Cs^+ and ClO_4^-.

d. BrF_5	bromine pentafluoride

Both nonmetals (Type III binary).

e. NaBr	sodium bromide

Contains Na^+ and Br^- (Type I binary).

f. KOCl	potassium hypochlorite

Contains K^+ and OCl^-.

g. $Zn_3(PO_4)_2$	zinc(II) phosphate

Contains Zn^{2+} and PO_4^{3-}; Zn is a transition metal and officially requires a Roman numeral. However, because Zn forms only the Zn^{2+} cation, the II is usually left out. Thus the name of the compound is usually given as zinc phosphate.

Self-Check Exercise 5.8

Name	Chemical Formula
a. ammonium sulfate	$(NH_4)_2SO_4$

Two ammonium ions (NH_4^+) are required for each sulfate ion (SO_4^{2-}) to achieve charge balance.

b. vanadium(V) fluoride	VF_5

The compound contains V^{5+} ions and requires five F^- ions for charge balance.

c. disulfur dichloride	S_2Cl_2

The prefix *di-* indicates two of each atom.

d. rubidium peroxide	Rb_2O_2

Because rubidium is in Group 1, it forms only 1+ ions. Thus two Rb^+ ions are needed to balance the 2− charge on the peroxide ion (O_2^{2-}).

e. aluminum oxide	Al_2O_3

Aluminum forms only 3+ ions. Two Al^{3+} ions are required to balance the charge on three O^{2-} ions.

Chapter 6

Self-Check Exercise 6.1

a. $Mg(s) + H_2O(l) \rightarrow Mg(OH)_2(s) + H_2(g)$

Note that magnesium (which is in Group 2) always forms the Mg^{2+} cation and thus requires two OH^- anions for a zero net charge.

b. Ammonium dichromate contains the polyatomic ions NH_4^+ and $Cr_2O_7^{2-}$ (you should have these memorized). Because NH_4^+ has a 1+ charge, two NH_4^+ cations are required for each $Cr_2O_7^{2-}$, with it 2− charge, to give the formula $(NH_4)_2Cr_2O_7$. Chromium(III) oxide contains Cr^{3+} ions—signified by chromium(III)—and O^{2-} (the oxide ion). To achieve a net charge of zero, the solid must contain two Cr^{3+} ions for every three O^{2-} ions, so the formula is Cr_2O_3. Nitrogen gas contains diatomic molecules and is written $N_2(g)$, and gaseous water is written $H_2O(g)$. Thus the unbalanced equation for the decomposition of ammonium dichromate is

$$(NH_4)_2Cr_2O_7(s) \rightarrow Cr_2O_3(s) + N_2(g) + H_2O(g)$$

c. Gaseous ammonia, $NH_3(g)$, and gaseous oxygen, $O_2(g)$, react to form nitrogen monoxide gas, $NO(g)$, plus gaseous water, $H_2O(g)$. The unbalanced equation is

$$NH_3(g) + O_2(g) \rightarrow NO(g) + H_2O(g)$$

Self-Check Exercise 6.2

Step 1 The reactants are propane, $C_3H_8(g)$, and oxygen, $O_2(g)$; the products are carbon dioxide, $CO_2(g)$, and water, $H_2O(g)$. All are in the gaseous state.

Step 2 The unbalanced equation for the reaction is

$$C_3H_8(g) + O_2(g) \rightarrow CO_2(g) + H_2O(g)$$

Step 3 We start with C_3H_8 because it is the most complicated molecule. C_3H_8 contains three carbon atoms per molecule, so a coefficient of 3 is needed for CO_2.

$$C_3H_8(g) + O_2(g) \rightarrow 3CO_2(g) + H_2O(g)$$

Also, each C_3H_8 molecule contains eight hydrogen atoms, so a coefficient of 4 is required for H_2O.

$$C_3H_8(g) + O_2(g) \rightarrow 3CO_2(g) + 4H_2O(g)$$

The final element to be balanced is oxygen. Note that the left side of the equation now has two oxygen atoms, and the right side has ten. We can balance the oxygen by using a coefficient of 5 for O_2.

$$C_3H_8(g) + 5O_2(g) \rightarrow 3CO_2(g) + 4H_2O(g)$$

Step 4 Check:

3 C, 8 H, 10 O → 3 C, 8 H, 10 O

Reactant   Product
atoms   atoms

We cannot divide all coefficients by a given integer to give smaller integer coefficients.

Self-Check Exercise 6.3

a. $NH_4NO_2(s) \rightarrow N_2(g) + H_2O(g)$ (unbalanced)
$NH_4NO_2(s) \rightarrow N_2(g) + 2H_2O(g)$ (balanced)
b. $NO(g) \rightarrow N_2O(g) + NO_2(g)$ (unbalanced)
$3NO(g) \rightarrow N_2O(g) + NO_2(g)$ (balanced)
c. $HNO_3(l) \rightarrow NO_2(g) + H_2O(l) + O_2(g)$ (unbalanced)
$4HNO_3(l) \rightarrow 4NO_2(g) + 2H_2O(l) + O_2(g)$ (balanced)

Chapter 7

Self-Check Exercise 7.1

a. The ions present are

$$Ba^{2+}(aq) + 2NO_3^-(aq) + Na^+(aq) + Cl^-(aq) \rightarrow$$

Ions in   Ions in
$Ba(NO_3)_2(aq)$ $NaCl(aq)$

Exchanging the anions gives the possible solid products $BaCl_2$ and $NaNO_3$. Using Table 7.1, we see that both substances are very soluble (rules 1, 2, and 3). Thus no solid forms.

b. The ions present in the mixed solution before any reaction occurs are

$$2Na^+(aq) + S^{2-}(aq) + Cu^{2+}(aq) + 2NO_3^-(aq) \rightarrow$$

Ions in   Ions in
$Na_2S(aq)$ $Cu(NO_3)_2(aq)$

Exchanging the anions gives the possible solid products CuS and $NaNO_3$. According to rules 1 and 2 in Table 7.1, $NaNO_3$ is soluble, and by rule 6, CuS should be insoluble. Thus CuS will precipitate. The balanced equation is

$$Na_2S(aq) + Cu(NO_3)_2(aq) \rightarrow CuS(s) + 2NaNO_3(aq)$$

c. The ions present are

$$NH_4^+(aq) + Cl^-(aq) + Pb^{2+}(aq) + 2NO_3^-(aq) \rightarrow$$

Ions in   Ions in
$NH_4Cl(aq)$ $Pb(NO_3)_2(aq)$

Exchanging the anions gives the possible solid products NH_4NO_3 and $PbCl_2$. NH_4NO_3 is soluble (rules 1 and 2) and $PbCl_2$ is insoluble (rule 3). Thus $PbCl_2$ will precipitate. The balanced equation is

$$2NH_4Cl(aq) + Pb(NO_3)_2(aq) \rightarrow PbCl_2(s) + 2NH_4NO_3(aq)$$

Self-Check Exercise 7.2

a. *Molecular equation:*
$Na_2S(aq) + Cu(NO_3)_2(aq) \rightarrow CuS(s) + 2NaNO_3(aq)$
Complete ionic equation:
$2Na^+(aq) + S^{2-}(aq) + Cu^{2+}(aq) + 2NO_3^-(aq) \rightarrow$
$\qquad\qquad\qquad\qquad CuS(s) + 2Na^+(aq) + 2NO_3^-(aq)$

Net ionic equation:
$S^{2-}(aq) + Cu^{2+}(aq) \rightarrow CuS(s)$

b. *Molecular equation:*
$2NH_4Cl(aq) + Pb(NO_3)_2(aq) \rightarrow PbCl_2(s) + 2NH_4NO_3(aq)$
Complete ionic equation:
$2NH_4^+(aq) + 2Cl^-(aq) + Pb^{2+}(aq) + 2NO_3^-(aq) \rightarrow$
$\qquad\qquad\qquad PbCl_2(s) + 2NH_4^+(aq) + 2NO_3^-(aq)$

Net ionic equation:
$2Cl^-(aq) + Pb^{2+}(aq) \rightarrow PbCl_2(s)$

Self-Check Exercise 7.3

a. The compound NaBr contains the ions Na^+ and Br^-. Thus each sodium atom loses one electron ($Na \rightarrow Na^+ + e^-$), and each bromine atom gains one electron ($Br + e^- \rightarrow Br^-$).

$$Na + Na + Br - Br \rightarrow (Na^+Br^-) + (Na^+Br^-)$$

$e^- \quad e^-$

b. The compound CaO contains the Ca^{2+} and O^{2-} ions. Thus each calcium atom loses two electrons ($Ca \rightarrow Ca^{2+} + 2e^-$), and each oxygen atom gains two electrons ($O + 2e^- \rightarrow O^{2-}$).

$$Ca + Ca + O - O \rightarrow (Ca^{2+}O^{2-}) + (Ca^{2+}O^{2-})$$

$2e^- \quad 2e^-$

Self-Check Exercise 7.4

a. oxidation–reduction reaction; combustion reaction
b. synthesis reaction; oxidation–reduction reaction; combustion reaction
c. synthesis reaction; oxidation–reduction reaction
d. decomposition reaction; oxidation–reduction reaction
e. precipitation reaction (and double displacement)
f. synthesis reaction; oxidation–reduction reaction
g. acid–base reaction (and double displacement)
h. combustion reaction; oxidation–reduction reaction

Chapter 8

Self-Check Exercise 8.1

The average mass of nitrogen is 14.01 amu. The appropriate equivalence statement is 1 N atom = 14.01 amu, which yields the conversion factor we need:

$$23 \text{ N atoms} \times \frac{14.01 \text{ amu}}{\text{N atom}} = 322.2 \text{ amu}$$

(exact)

Self-Check Exercise 8.2

The average mass of oxygen is 16.00 amu, which gives the equivalence statement 1 O atom = 16.00 amu. The number of oxygen atoms present is

$$288 \text{ amu} \times \frac{1 \text{ O atom}}{16.00 \text{ amu}} = 18.0 \text{ O atoms}$$

Self-Check Exercise 8.3

Note that the sample of 5.00×10^{20} atoms of chromium is less than 1 mole (6.022×10^{23} atoms) of chromium. What fraction of a mole it represents can be determined as follows:

$$5.00 \times 10^{20} \text{ atoms Cr} \times \frac{1 \text{ mol Cr}}{6.022 \times 10^{23} \text{ atoms Cr}} =$$
$$8.30 \times 10^{-4} \text{ mol Cr}$$

Because the mass of 1 mole of chromium atoms is 52.00 g, the mass of 5.00×10^{20} atoms can be determined as follows:

$$8.30 \times 10^{-4} \text{ mol Cr} \times \frac{52.00 \text{ g Cr}}{1 \text{ mol Cr}} = 4.32 \times 10^{-2} \text{ g Cr}$$

Self-Check Exercise 8.4

Each molecule of C_2H_3Cl contains two carbon atoms, three hydrogen atoms, and one chlorine atom, so 1 mole of C_2H_3Cl molecules contains 2 moles of C atoms, 3 moles of H atoms, and 1 mole of Cl atoms.

Mass of 2 mol C atoms: $2 \times 12.01 = 24.02$ g
Mass of 3 mol H atoms: $3 \times 1.008 = 3.024$ g
Mass of 1 mol Cl atoms: $1 \times 35.45 = \underline{35.45 \text{ g}}$
62.494 g

The molar mass of C_2H_3Cl is 62.49 g (rounding to the correct number of significant figures).

Self-Check Exercise 8.5

The formula for sodium sulfate is Na_2SO_4. One mole of Na_2SO_4 contains 2 moles of sodium ions and 1 mole of sulfate ions.

1 mole of $Na_2SO_4 \rightarrow$ 1 mole of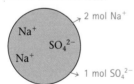
2 mol Na^+
1 mol SO_4^{2-}

Mass of 2 mol Na^+ = 2×22.99 = 45.98 g
Mass of 1 mol SO_4^{2-} = $32.07 + 4(16.00)$ = $\underline{96.07 \text{ g}}$
Mass of 1 mol Na_2SO_4 = 142.05 g

The molar mass for sodium sulfate is 142.05 g.

A sample of sodium sulfate with a mass of 300.0 g represents more than 1 mol. (Compare 300.0 g to the molar mass of Na_2SO_4.) We calculate the number of moles of Na_2SO_4 present in 300.0 g as follows:

$$300.0 \text{ g } Na_2SO_4 \times \frac{1 \text{ mol } Na_2SO_4}{142.05 \text{ g } Na_2SO_4} = 2.112 \text{ mol } Na_2SO_4$$

Self-Check Exercise 8.6

First we must compute the mass of 1 mole of C_2F_4 molecules (the molar mass). Because 1 mole of C_2F_4 contains 2 moles of C atoms and 4 moles of F atoms, we have

$$2 \text{ mol C} \times \frac{12.01 \text{ g}}{\text{mol}} = 24.02 \text{ g C}$$

$$4 \text{ mol F} \times \frac{19.00 \text{ g}}{\text{mol}} = 76.00 \text{ g F}$$

Mass of 1 mole of C_2F_4: 100.02 g = molar mass

Using the equivalence statement 100.02 g C_2F_4 = 1 mole C_2F_4, we calculate the moles of C_2F_4 units in 135 g of Teflon.

$$135 \text{ g } C_2F_4 \text{ units} \times \frac{1 \text{ mol } C_2F_4}{100.02 \text{ g } C_2F_4} = 1.35 \text{ mol } C_2F_4 \text{ units}$$

Next, using the equivalence statement 1 mol = 6.022×10^{23} units, we calculate the number of C_2F_4 units in 135 mol of Teflon.

$$135 \text{ mol } C_2F_4 \times \frac{6.022 \times 10^{23} \text{ units}}{1 \text{ mol}} = 8.13 \times 10^{23} \text{ } C_2F_4 \text{ units}$$

Self-Check Exercise 8.7

The molar mass of penicillin F is computed as follows:

$$C: 14 \text{ mol} \times 12.01 \frac{g}{\text{mol}} = 168.1 \text{ g}$$

$$H: 20 \text{ mol} \times 1.008 \frac{g}{\text{mol}} = 20.16 \text{ g}$$

$$N: 2 \text{ mol} \times 14.01 \frac{g}{\text{mol}} = 28.02 \text{ g}$$

$$S: 1 \text{ mol} \times 32.07 \frac{g}{\text{mol}} = 32.07 \text{ g}$$

$$O: 4 \text{ mol} \times 16.00 \frac{g}{\text{mol}} = 64.00 \text{ g}$$

Mass of 1 mole of $C_{14}H_{20}N_2SO_4$ = 312.39 g = 312.4 g

$$\text{Mass percent of C} = \frac{168.1 \text{ g C}}{312.4 \text{ g } C_{14}H_{20}N_2SO_4} \times 100\%$$
$$= 53.81\%$$

$$\text{Mass percent of H} = \frac{20.16 \text{ g H}}{312.4 \text{ g } C_{14}H_{20}N_2SO_4} \times 100\%$$
$$= 6.453\%$$

$$\text{Mass percent of N} = \frac{28.02 \text{ g N}}{312.4 \text{ g } C_{14}H_{20}N_2SO_4} \times 100\%$$
$$= 8.969\%$$

$$\text{Mass percent of S} = \frac{32.07 \text{ g S}}{312.4 \text{ g } C_{14}H_{20}N_2SO_4} \times 100\%$$
$$= 10.27\%$$

$$\text{Mass percent of O} = \frac{64.00 \text{ g O}}{312.4 \text{ g } C_{14}H_{20}N_2SO_4} \times 100\%$$
$$= 20.49\%$$

Check: The percentages add up to 99.99%.

Self-Check Exercise 8.8

Step 1 0.6884 g lead and 0.2356 g chlorine

Step 2 $0.6884 \text{ g Pb} \times \dfrac{1 \text{ mol Pb}}{207.2 \text{ g Pb}} = 0.003322 \text{ mol Pb}$

$0.2356 \text{ g Cl} \times \dfrac{1 \text{ mol Cl}}{35.45 \text{ g Cl}} = 0.006646 \text{ mol Cl}$

Step 3 $\dfrac{0.003322 \text{ mol Pb}}{0.003322} = 1.000 \text{ mol Pb}$

$\dfrac{0.006646 \text{ mol Cl}}{0.003322} = 2.001 \text{ mol Cl}$

These numbers are very close to integers, so step 4 is unnecessary. The empirical formula is $PbCl_2$.

Self-Check Exercise 8.9

Step 1 0.8007 g C, 0.9333 g N, 0.2016 g H, and 2.133 g O

Step 2 $0.8007 \text{ g C} \times \dfrac{1 \text{ mol C}}{12.01 \text{ g C}} = 0.06667 \text{ mol C}$

$0.9333 \text{ g N} \times \dfrac{1 \text{ mol N}}{14.01 \text{ g N}} = 0.06662 \text{ mol N}$

$0.2016 \text{ g H} \times \dfrac{1 \text{ mol H}}{1.008 \text{ g H}} = 0.2000 \text{ mol H}$

$2.133 \text{ g O} \times \dfrac{1 \text{ mol O}}{16.00 \text{ g O}} = 0.1333 \text{ mol O}$

Step 3 $\dfrac{0.06667 \text{ mol C}}{0.06667} = 1.001 \text{ mol C}$

$\dfrac{0.06662 \text{ mol N}}{0.06667} = 1.000 \text{ mol N}$

$\dfrac{0.2000 \text{ mol H}}{0.06662} = 3.002 \text{ mol H}$

$\dfrac{0.1333 \text{ mol O}}{0.06662} = 2.001 \text{ mol O}$

The empirical formula is CNH_3O_2.

Self-Check Exercise 8.10

Step 1 In 100.00 g of Nylon-6 the masses of elements present are 63.68 g C, 12.38 g N, 9.80 g H, and 14.14 g O.

Step 2 $63.68 \text{ g C} \times \dfrac{1 \text{ mol C}}{12.01 \text{ g C}} = 5.302 \text{ mol C}$

$12.38 \text{ g N} \times \dfrac{1 \text{ mol N}}{14.01 \text{ g N}} = 0.8837 \text{ mol N}$

$9.80 \text{ g H} \times \dfrac{1 \text{ mol H}}{1.008 \text{ g H}} = 9.72 \text{ mol H}$

$14.14 \text{ g O} \times \dfrac{1 \text{ mol O}}{16.00 \text{ g O}} = 0.8838 \text{ mol O}$

Step 3 $\dfrac{5.302 \text{ mol C}}{0.8836} = 6.000 \text{ mol C}$

$\dfrac{0.8837 \text{ mol N}}{0.8837} = 1.000 \text{ mol N}$

$\dfrac{9.72 \text{ mol H}}{0.8837} = 11.0 \text{ mol H}$

$\dfrac{0.8838 \text{ mol O}}{0.8837} = 1.000 \text{ mol O}$

The empirical formula for Nylon-6 is $C_6NH_{11}O$.

Self-Check Exercise 8.11

Step 1 First we convert the mass percents to mass in grams. In 100.0 g of the compound, there are 71.65 g of chlorine, 24.27 g of carbon, and 4.07 g of hydrogen.

Step 2 We use these masses to compute the moles of atoms present.

$71.65 \text{ g Cl} \times \dfrac{1 \text{ mol Cl}}{35.45 \text{ g Cl}} = 2.021 \text{ mol Cl}$

$24.27 \text{ g C} \times \dfrac{1 \text{ mol C}}{12.01 \text{ g C}} = 2.021 \text{ mol C}$

$4.07 \text{ g H} \times \dfrac{1 \text{ mol H}}{1.008 \text{ g H}} = 4.04 \text{ mol H}$

Step 3 Dividing each mole value by 2.021 (the smallest number of moles present), we obtain the empirical formula $ClCH_2$.

To determine the molecular formula, we must compare the empirical formula mass to the molar mass. The empirical formula mass is 49.48.

Cl:	35.45
C:	12.01
2 H: 2 × (1.008)	
$ClCH_2$:	49.48 = empirical formula mass

The molar mass is known to be 98.96. We know that

Molar mass = n × (empirical formula mass)

So we can obtain the value of n as follows:

$$\dfrac{\text{Molar mass}}{\text{Empirical formula mass}} = \dfrac{98.96}{49.48} = 2$$

Molecular formula = $(ClCH_2)_2 = Cl_2C_2H_4$

This substance is composed of molecules with the formula $Cl_2C_2H_4$.

Chapter 9

Self-Check Exercise 9.1

The problem can be stated as follows:

$$4.30 \text{ mol } C_3H_8 \xrightarrow[\text{yields}]{} ? \text{ mol } CO_2$$

From the balanced equation

$$C_3H_8(g) + 5O_2(g) \rightarrow 3CO_2(g) + 4H_2O(g)$$

we derive the equivalence statement

$$1 \text{ mol } C_3H_8 = 3 \text{ mol } CO_2$$

The appropriate conversion factor (moles of C_3H_8 must cancel) is 3 mol CO_2/1 mol C_3H_8, and the calculation is

$$4.30 \text{ mol } C_3H_8 \times \dfrac{3 \text{ mol } CO_2}{1 \text{ mol } C_3H_8} = 12.9 \text{ mol } CO_2$$

Thus we can say

$$4.30 \text{ mol } C_3H_8 \text{ yields } 12.9 \text{ mol } CO_2$$

Self-Check Exercise 9.2

The problem can be sketched as follows:

$$C_3H_8(g) + 5O_2(g) \rightarrow 3CO_2(g) + 4H_2O(g)$$

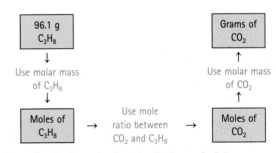

We have already done the first step in Example 9.4.

To find out how many moles of CO_2 can be produced from 2.18 moles of C_3H_8, we see from the balanced equation that 3 moles of CO_2 is produced for each mole of C_3H_8 reacted. The mole ratio we need is 3 mol CO_2/1 mol C_3H_8. The conversion is therefore

$$2.18 \ \text{mol } C_3H_8 \times \frac{3 \ \text{mol } CO_2}{1 \ \text{mol } C_3H_8} = 6.54 \ \text{mol } CO_2$$

Next, using the molar mass of CO_2, which is $12.01 + 32.00 = 44.01$ g, we calculate the mass of CO_2 produced.

$$6.54 \ \text{mol } CO_2 \times \frac{44.01 \ \text{g } CO_2}{1 \ \text{mol } CO_2} = 288 \ \text{g } CO_2$$

The sequence of steps we took to find the mass of carbon dioxide produced from 96.1 g of propane is summarized in the following diagram.

96.1 g C_3H_8	→	$\dfrac{1 \ \text{mol } C_3H_8}{44.09 \ \text{g } C_3H_8}$	→	2.18 mol C_3H_8
2.18 mol C_3H_8	→	$\dfrac{3 \ \text{mol } CO_2}{1 \ \text{mol } C_3H_8}$	→	6.54 mol CO_2
6.54 mol CO_2	→	$\dfrac{44.01 \ \text{g } CO_2}{1 \ \text{mol } CO_2}$	→	288 g CO_2
Mass				Moles

Self-Check Exercise 9.3

We sketch the problem as follows:

$$C_3H_8(g) + 5O_2(g) \rightarrow 3CO_2(g) + 4H_2O(g)$$

96.1 g C_3H_8				Grams of H_2O
↓				↑
$\dfrac{1 \ \text{mol } C_3H_8}{44.09 \ \text{g}}$				$\dfrac{18.02 \ \text{g}}{\text{mol } H_2O}$
↓				↑
Moles of C_3H_8	→	$\dfrac{4 \ \text{mol } H_2O}{1 \ \text{mol } C_3H_8}$	→	Moles of H_2O

Then we do the calculations.

96.1 g C_3H_8	→	$\dfrac{1 \ \text{mol } C_3H_8}{44.09 \ \text{g}}$	→	2.18 mol C_3H_8
2.18 mol C_3H_8	→	$\dfrac{4 \ \text{mol } H_2O}{1 \ \text{mol } C_3H_8}$	→	8.72 mol H_2O
8.72 mol H_2O	→	$\dfrac{18.02 \ \text{g}}{\text{mol } H_2O}$	→	157 g H_2O

Therefore, 157 g of H_2O is produced from 96.1 g C_3H_8.

Self-Check Exercise 9.4

a. We first write the balanced equation.

$$SiO_2(s) + 4HF(aq) \rightarrow SiF_4(g) + 2H_2O(l)$$

The map of the steps required is

$$SiO_2(s) + 4HF(aq) \rightarrow SiF_4(g) + 2H_2O(l)$$

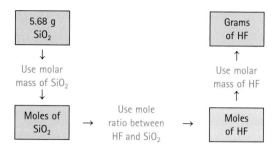

We convert 5.68 g of SiO_2 to moles as follows:

$$5.68 \ \text{g } SiO_2 \times \frac{1 \ \text{mol } SiO_2}{60.09 \ \text{g } SiO_2} = 9.45 \times 10^{-2} \ \text{mol } SiO_2$$

Using the balanced equation, we obtain the appropriate mole ratio and convert to moles of HF.

$$9.45 \times 10^{-2} \ \text{mol } SiO_2 \times \frac{4 \ \text{mol } HF}{1 \ \text{mol } SiO_2} = 3.78 \times 10^{-1} \ \text{mol } HF$$

Finally, we calculate the mass of HF by using its molar mass.

$$3.78 \times 10^{-1} \ \text{mol } HF \times \frac{20.01 \ \text{g } HF}{\text{mol } HF} = 7.56 \ \text{g } HF$$

b. The map for this problem is

$$SiO_2(s) + 4HF(aq) \rightarrow SiF_4(g) + 2H_2O(l)$$

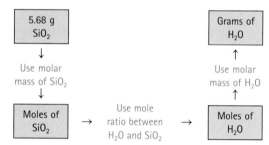

We have already accomplished the first conversion in part a. Using the balanced equation, we obtain moles of H_2O as follows:

$$9.45 \times 10^{-2} \ \text{mol } SiO_2 \times \frac{2 \ \text{mol } H_2O}{1 \ \text{mol } SiO_2} = 1.89 \times 10^{-1} \ \text{mol } H_2O$$

The mass of water formed is

$$1.89 \times 10^{-1} \ \text{mol } H_2O \times \frac{18.02 \ \text{g } H_2O}{\text{mol } H_2O} = 3.41 \ \text{g } H_2O$$

Self-Check Exercise 9.5

In this problem, we know the mass of the product to be formed by the reaction

$$CO(g) + 2H_2(g) \rightarrow CH_3OH(l)$$

and we want to find the masses of reactants needed. The procedure is the same one we have been following. We must first convert the mass of CH_3OH to moles, then use the balanced equation to obtain moles of H_2 and CO needed, and then convert these moles to masses. Using the molar mass of CH_3OH (32.04 g/mol), we convert to moles of CH_3OH.

First we convert kilograms to grams.

$$6.0 \ \text{kg } CH_3OH \times \frac{1000 \ \text{g}}{\text{kg}} = 6.0 \times 10^3 \ \text{g } CH_3OH$$

Next we convert 6.0×10^3 g CH_3OH to moles of CH_3OH, using the conversion factor 1 mol CH_3OH/32.04 g CH_3OH.

$$6.0 \times 10^3 \ \text{g } CH_3OH \times \frac{1 \ \text{mol } CH_3OH}{32.04 \ \text{g } CH_3OH} = 1.9 \times 10^2 \ \text{mol } CH_3OH$$

Then we have two questions to answer:

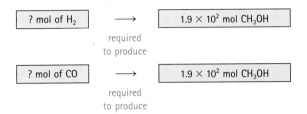

To answer these questions, we use the balanced equation

$$CO(g) + 2H_2(g) \rightarrow CH_3OH(l)$$

to obtain mole ratios between the reactants and the products. In the balanced equation the coefficients for both CO and CH_3OH are 1, so we can write the equivalence statement

$$1 \text{ mol CO} = 1 \text{ mol } CH_3OH$$

Using the mole ratio 1 mol CO/1 mol CH_3OH, we can now convert from moles of CH_3OH to moles of CO.

$$1.9 \times 10^2 \text{ mol } CH_3OH \times \frac{1 \text{ mol CO}}{1 \text{ mol } CH_3OH} = 1.9 \times 10^2 \text{ mol CO}$$

To calculate the moles of H_2 required, we construct the equivalence statement between CH_3OH and H_2, using the coefficients in the balanced equation.

$$2 \text{ mol } H_2 = 1 \text{ mol } CH_3OH$$

Using the mole ratio 2 mol H_2/1 mol CH_3OH, we can convert moles of CH_3OH to moles of H_2.

$$1.9 \times 10^2 \text{ mol } CH_3OH \times \frac{2 \text{ mol } H_2}{1 \text{ mol } CH_3OH} = 3.8 \times 10^2 \text{ mol } H_2$$

We now have the moles of reactants required to produce 6.0 kg of CH_3OH. Since we need the masses of reactants, we must use the molar masses to convert from moles to mass.

$$1.9 \times 10^2 \text{ mol CO} \times \frac{28.01 \text{ g CO}}{1 \text{ mol CO}} = 5.3 \times 10^3 \text{ g CO}$$

$$3.8 \times 10^2 \text{ mol } H_2 \times \frac{2.016 \text{ g } H_2}{1 \text{ mol } H_2} = 7.7 \times 10^2 \text{ } H_2$$

Therefore, we need 5.3×10^3 g CO to react with 7.7×10^2 g H_2 to form 6.0×10^3 g (6.0 kg) of CH_3OH. This whole process is mapped in the following diagram.

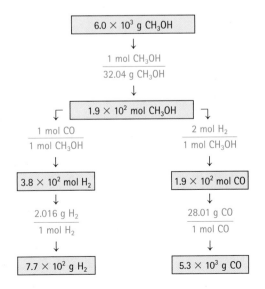

Self-Check Exercise 9.6

Step 1 The balanced equation for the reaction is

$$6Li(s) + N_2(g) \rightarrow 2Li_3N(s)$$

Step 2 To determine the limiting reactant, we must convert the masses of lithium (atomic mass = 6.941 g) and nitrogen (molar mass = 28.02 g) to moles.

$$56.0 \text{ g Li} \times \frac{1 \text{ mol Li}}{6.941 \text{ g Li}} = 8.07 \text{ mol Li}$$

$$56.0 \text{ g } N_2 \times \frac{1 \text{ mol } N_2}{28.02 \text{ g } N_2} = 2.00 \text{ mol } N_2$$

Step 3 Using the mole ratio from the balanced equation, we can calculate the moles of lithium required to react with 2.00 moles of nitrogen.

$$2.00 \text{ mol } N_2 \times \frac{6 \text{ mol Li}}{1 \text{ mol } N_2} = 12.0 \text{ mol Li}$$

Therefore, 12.0 moles of Li is required to react with 2.00 moles of N_2. However, we have only 8.07 mol of Li, so lithium is limiting. It will be consumed before the nitrogen runs out.

Step 4 Because lithium is the limiting reactant, we must use the 8.07 moles of Li to determine how many moles of Li_3N can be formed.

$$8.07 \text{ mol Li} \times \frac{2 \text{ mol } Li_3N}{6 \text{ mol Li}} = 2.69 \text{ mol } Li_3N$$

Step 5 We can now use the molar mass of Li_3N (34.83 g) to calculate the mass of Li_3N formed.

$$2.69 \text{ mol } Li_3N \times \frac{34.83 \text{ g } Li_3N}{1 \text{ mol } Li_3N} = 93.7 \text{ g } Li_3N$$

Self-Check Exercise 9.7

a. **Step 1** The balanced equation is

$$TiCl_4(g) + O_2(g) \rightarrow TiO_2(s) + 2Cl_2(g)$$

Step 2 The numbers of moles of reactants are

$$6.71 \times 10^3 \text{ g } TiCl_4 \times \frac{1 \text{ mol } TiCl_4}{189.68 \text{ g } TiCl_4} = 3.54 \times 10^1 \text{ mol } TiCl_4$$

$$2.45 \times 10^3 \text{ g } O_2 \times \frac{1 \text{ mol } O_2}{32.00 \text{ g } O_2} = 7.66 \times 10^1 \text{ mol } O_2$$

Step 3 In the balanced equation both $TiCl_4$ and O_2 have coefficients of 1, so

$$1 \text{ mol } TiCl_4 = 1 \text{ mol } O_2$$

and

$$3.54 \times 10^1 \text{ mol } TiCl_4 \times \frac{1 \text{ mol } O_2}{1 \text{ mol } TiCl_4}$$
$$= 3.54 \times 10^1 \text{ mol } O_2 \text{ required}$$

We have 7.66×10^1 moles of O_2, so the O_2 is in excess and the $TiCl_4$ is limiting. This makes sense. $TiCl_4$ and O_2 react in a 1:1 mole ratio, so the $TiCl_4$ is limiting because fewer moles of $TiCl_4$ are present than moles of O_2.

Step 4 We will now use the moles of $TiCl_4$ (the limiting reactant) to determine the moles of TiO_2 that would form if the reaction produced 100% of the expected yield (the theoretical yield).

$$3.54 \times 10^1 \text{ mol } TiCl_4 \times \frac{1 \text{ mol } TiO_2}{1 \text{ mol } TiCl_4} = 3.54 \times 10^1 \text{ mol } TiO_2$$

The mass of TiO_2 expected for 100% yield is

$$3.54 \times 10^1 \text{ mol } TiO_2 \times \frac{79.88 \text{ g } TiO_2}{1 \text{ mol } TiO_2} = 2.83 \times 10^3 \text{ g } TiO_2$$

This amount represents the theoretical yield.

b. Because the reaction is said to give only a 75.0% yield of TiO_2, we use the definition of percent yield,

$$\frac{\text{Actual yield}}{\text{Theoretical yield}} \times 100\% = \% \text{ yield}$$

to write the equation

$$\frac{\text{Actual yield}}{2.83 \times 10^3 \text{ g } TiO_2} \times 100\% = 75.0\% \text{ yield}$$

We now want to solve for the actual yield. First we divide both sides by 100%.

$$\frac{\text{Actual yield}}{2.83 \times 10^3 \text{ g } TiO_2} \times \frac{100\%}{100\%} = \frac{75.0}{100} = 0.750$$

Then we multiply both sides by 2.83×10^3 g TiO_2.

$$2.83 \times 10^3 \text{ g } TiO_2 \times \frac{\text{Actual yield}}{2.83 \times 10^3 \text{ g } TiO_2}$$
$$= 0.750 \times 2.83 \times 10^3 \text{ g } TiO_2$$
$$\text{Actual yield} = 0.750 \times 2.83 \times 10^3 \text{ g } TiO_2$$
$$= 2.12 \times 10^3 \text{ g } TiO_2$$

Thus 2.12×10^3 g of $TiO_2(s)$ is actually obtained in this reaction.

Chapter 10

Self-Check Exercise 10.1

The conversion factor needed is $\dfrac{1 \text{ cal}}{4.184 \text{ J}}$, and the conversion is

$$28.4 \text{ J} \times \frac{1 \text{ cal}}{4.184 \text{ J}} = 6.79 \text{ cal}$$

Self-Check Exercise 10.2

We know that it takes 4.184 J of energy to change the temperature of each gram of water by 1 °C, so we must multiply 4.184 by the mass of water (454 g) and the temperature change (98.6 °C − 5.4 °C = 93.2 °C).

$$4.184 \frac{\text{J}}{\text{g} \cdot °C} \times 454 \text{ g} \times 93.2 \text{ °C} = 1.77 \times 10^5 \text{ J}$$

Self-Check Exercise 10.3

From Table 10.1, the specific heat capacity for solid gold is 0.13 J/g °C. Because it takes 0.13 J to change the temperature of *one* gram of gold by *one* Celsius degree, we must multiply 0.13 by the sample size (5.63 g) and the change in temperature (32 °C − 21 °C = 11 °C).

$$0.13 \frac{\text{J}}{\text{g} \cdot °C} \times 5.63 \text{ g} \times 11 \text{ °C} = 8.1 \text{ J}$$

We can change this energy to units of calories as follows:

$$8.1 \text{ J} \times \frac{1 \text{ cal}}{4.184 \text{ J}} = 1.9 \text{ cal}$$

Self-Check Exercise 10.4

Table 10.1 lists the specific heat capacities of several metals. We want to calculate the specific heat capacity (s) for this metal and then use Table 10.1 to identify the metal. Using the equation

$$Q = s \times m \times \Delta T$$

we can solve for s by dividing both sides by m (the mass of the sample) and by ΔT:

$$\frac{Q}{m \times \Delta T} = s$$

In this case,

Q = energy (heat) required = 10.1 J
m = 2.8 g
ΔT = temperature change = 36 °C − 21 °C = 15 °C

so

$$s = \frac{Q}{m \times \Delta T} = \frac{10.1 \text{ J}}{(2.8 \text{ g})(15 \text{ °C})} = 0.24 \text{ J/g °C}$$

Table 10.1 shows that silver has a specific heat capacity of 0.24 J/g °C. The metal is silver.

Self-Check Exercise 10.5

We are told that 1652 kJ of energy is *released* when 4 moles of Fe reacts. We first need to determine what number of moles 1.00 g Fe represents.

$$1.00 \text{ g Fe} \times \frac{1 \text{ mol}}{55.85 \text{ g}} = 1.79 \times 10^{-2} \text{ mol Fe}$$

$$1.79 \times 10^{-2} \text{ mol Fe} \times \frac{1652 \text{ kJ}}{4 \text{ mol Fe}} = 7.39 \text{ kJ}$$

Thus 7.39 kJ of energy (as heat) is released when 1.00 g of iron reacts.

Self-Check Exercise 10.6

Noting the reactants and products in the desired reaction

$$S(s) + O_2(g) \rightarrow SO_2(g)$$

We need to reverse the second equation and multiply it by $\frac{1}{2}$. This reverses the sign and cuts the amount of energy by a factor of 2.

$$\frac{1}{2}[2SO_3(g) \rightarrow 2SO_2(g) + O_2(g)] \qquad \Delta H = \frac{198.2 \text{ kJ}}{2}$$

or

$$SO_3(g) \rightarrow SO_2(g) + \tfrac{1}{2}O_2(g) \qquad \Delta H = 99.1 \text{ kJ}$$

Now we add this reaction to the first reaction.

$$
\begin{array}{ll}
S(s) + \tfrac{3}{2}O_2(g) \rightarrow SO_3(g) & \Delta H = -395.2 \text{ kJ} \\
\underline{SO_3(g) \rightarrow SO_2(g) + \tfrac{1}{2}O_2(g)} & \underline{\Delta H = 99.1 \text{ kJ}} \\
S(s) + O_2(g) \rightarrow SO_2(g) & \Delta H = -296.1 \text{ kJ}
\end{array}
$$

Chapter 11

Self-Check Exercise 11.1

a. Circular pathways for electrons in the Bohr model.
b. Three-dimensional probability maps that represent the likelihood that the electron will occupy a given point in space.
c. The surface that contains 90% of the total electron probability.
d. A set of orbitals of a given type of orbital within a principal energy level. For example, there are three sublevels in principal energy level 3 (s, p, d).

Self-Check Exercise 11.2

Element	Electron Configuration	Orbital Diagram				
		$1s$	$2s$	$2p$	$3s$	$3p$
Al	$1s^22s^22p^63s^23p^1$ [Ne]$3s^23p^1$	↑↓	↑↓	↑↓ ↑↓ ↑↓	↑↓	↑ □ □
Si	[Ne]$3s^23p^2$	↑↓	↑↓	↑↓ ↑↓ ↑↓	↑↓	↑ ↑ □
P	[Ne]$3s^23p^3$	↑↓	↑↓	↑↓ ↑↓ ↑↓	↑↓	↑ ↑ ↑
S	[Ne]$3s^23p^4$	↑↓	↑↓	↑↓ ↑↓ ↑↓	↑↓	↑↓ ↑ ↑
Cl	[Ne]$3s^23p^5$	↑↓	↑↓	↑↓ ↑↓ ↑↓	↑↓	↑↓ ↑↓ ↑
Ar	[Ne]$3s^23p^6$	↑↓	↑↓	↑↓ ↑↓ ↑↓	↑↓	↑↓ ↑↓ ↑↓

Self-Check Exercise 11.3

F: $1s^22s^22p^5$ or [He]$2s^22p^5$

Si: $1s^22s^22p^63s^23p^2$ or [Ne]$3s^23p^2$

Cs: $1s^22s^22p^63s^23p^64s^23d^{10}4p^65s^24d^{10}5p^66s^1$ or [Xe]$6s^1$

Pb: $1s^22s^22p^63s^23p^64s^23d^{10}4p^65s^24d^{10}5p^66s^24f^{14}5d^{10}6p^2$ or [Xe]$6s^24f^{14}5d^{10}6p^2$

I: $1s^22s^22p^63s^23p^64s^23d^{10}4p^65s^24d^{10}5p^5$ or [Kr]$5s^24d^{10}5p^5$

Silicon (Si): In Group 4 and Period 3, it is the second of the "$3p$ elements." The configuration is $1s^22s^22p^63s^23p^2$, or [Ne]$3s^23p^2$.

Cesium (Cs): In Group 1 and Period 6, it is the first of the "$6s$ elements." The configuration is $1s^22s^22p^63s^23p^64s^23d^{10}4p^65s^24d^{10}5p^66s^1$, or [Xe]$6s^1$.

Lead (Pb): In Group 4 and Period 6, it is the second of the "$6p$ elements." The configuration is [Xe]$6s^24f^{14}5d^{10}6p^2$.

Iodine (I): In Group 7 and Period 5, it is the fifth of the "$5p$ elements." The configuration is [Kr]$5s^24d^{10}5p^5$.

Chapter 12

Self-Check Exercise 12.1

Using the electronegativity values given in Figure 12.3, we choose the bond in which the atoms exhibit the largest difference in electronegativity. (Electronegativity values are shown in parentheses.)

a. H—C   >   H—P
   (2.1)(2.5)   (2.1)(2.1)

b. O—I   >   O—F
   (3.5)(2.5)   (3.5)(4.0)

c. S—O   >   N—O
   (2.5)(3.5)   (3.0)(3.5)

d. N—H   >   Si—H
   (3.0)(2.1)   (1.8)(2.1)

Self-Check Exercise 12.2

H has one electron, and Cl has seven valence electrons. This gives a total of eight valence electrons. We first draw in the bonding pair:

H—Cl, which could be drawn as H:Cl

We have six electrons yet to place. The H already has two electrons, so we place three lone pairs around the chlorine to satisfy the octet rule.

H—C̈l: or H:C̈l:

Self-Check Exercise 12.3

Step 1 O_3: 3(6) = 18 valence electrons

Step 2 O—O—O

Step 3 Ö=Ö—Ö: and :Ö—Ö=Ö

This molecule shows resonance (it has two valid Lewis structures).

Self-Check Exercise 12.4

See table on top of page A10.

Self-Check Exercise 12.5

a. NH_4^+

The Lewis structure is   [H—N—H with H above and H below]$^+$

(See Self-Check Exercise 12.4.) There are four pairs of electrons around the nitrogen. This requires a tetrahedral arrangement of electron pairs. The NH_4^+ ion has a tetrahedral molecular structure (row 3 in Table 12.4), because all electron pairs are shared.

b. SO_4^{2-}

The Lewis structure is   [:Ö—S—Ö: with O above and below]$^{2-}$

(See Self-Check Exercise 12.4.) The four electron pairs around the sulfur require a tetrahedral arrangement. The SO_4^{2-} has a tetrahedral molecular structure (row 3 in Table 12.4).

c. NF_3

The Lewis structure is   :F̈—N—F̈: with F below

(See Self-Check Exercise 12.4.) The four pairs of electrons on the nitrogen require a tetrahedral arrangement. In this case, only three of the pairs are shared with the fluorine atoms, leaving one lone pair. Thus the molecular structure is a trigonal pyramid (row 4 in Table 12.4).

d. H_2S

The Lewis structure is   H—S̈—H

(See Self-Check Exercise 12.4.) The four pairs of electrons around the sulfur require a tetrahedral arrangement. In this case, two pairs are shared with hydrogen atoms, leaving two lone pairs. Thus the molecular structure is bent or V-shaped (row 5 in Table 12.4).

e. ClO_3^-

The Lewis structure is   [:Ö—Cl—Ö: with O below]$^-$

(See Self-Check Exercise 12.4.) The four pairs of electrons require a tetrahedral arrangement. In this case, three pairs are shared with oxygen atoms, leaving one lone pair. Thus the molecular structure is a trigonal pyramid (row 4 in Table 12.4).

Molecule or Ion	Total Valence Electrons	Draw Single Bonds	Calculate Number of Electrons Remaining	Use Remaining Electrons to Achieve Noble Gas Configurations	Check Atoms	Check Electrons
a. NF_3	$5 + 3(7) = 26$	F—N(F)(F)	$26 - 6 = 20$	:F—N—F: / :F:	N / F	8 / 8
b. O_2	$2(6) = 12$	O—O	$12 - 2 = 10$	:O=O:	O	8
c. CO	$4 + 6 = 10$	C—O	$10 - 2 = 8$	:C≡O:	C / O	8 / 8
d. PH_3	$5 + 3(1) = 8$	H—P(H)—H	$8 - 6 = 2$	H—P̈—H / H	P / H	8 / 2
e. H_2S	$2(1) + 6 = 8$	H—S—H	$8 - 4 = 4$	H—S̈—H	S / H	8 / 2
f. SO_4^{2-}	$6 + 4(6) + 2 = 32$	O—S(O)(O)—O	$32 - 8 = 24$	$\left[\begin{array}{c}:Ö: \\ :Ö—S—Ö: \\ :Ö:\end{array}\right]^{2-}$	S / O	8 / 8
g. NH_4^+	$5 + 4(1) - 1 = 8$	H—N(H)(H)—H	$8 - 8 = 0$	$\left[\begin{array}{c}H \\ H—N—H \\ H\end{array}\right]^+$	N / H	8 / 2
h. ClO_3^-	$7 + 3(6) + 1 = 26$	Cl(O)(O)O	$26 - 6 = 20$	$\left[:Ö—Cl—Ö: / :Ö:\right]^-$	Cl / O	8 / 8
i. SO_2	$6 + 2(6) = 18$	O—S—O	$18 - 4 = 14$	Ö=S—Ö: and :Ö—S=Ö	S / O	8 / 8

Answer to Self-Check Exercise 12.4.

f. BeF_2

The Lewis structure is : F̈—Be—F̈ :

The two electron pairs on beryllium require a linear arrangement. Because both pairs are shared by fluorine atoms, the molecular structure is also linear (row 1 in Table 12.4).

Chapter 13

Self-Check Exercise 13.1

We know that 1.000 atm = 760.0 mm Hg. So

$$525 \text{ mm Hg} \times \frac{1.000 \text{ atm}}{760.0 \text{ mm Hg}} = 0.691 \text{ atm}$$

Self-Check Exercise 13.2

Initial Conditions	Final Conditions
$P_1 = 635$ torr	$P_2 = 785$ torr
$V_1 = 1.51$ L	$V_2 = ?$

Solving Boyle's law ($P_1V_1 = P_2V_2$) for V_2 gives

$$V_2 = V_1 \times \frac{P_1}{P_2}$$

$$= 1.51 \text{ L} \times \frac{635 \text{ torr}}{785 \text{ torr}} = 1.22 \text{ L}$$

Note that the volume decreased, as the increase in pressure led us to expect.

Self-Check Exercise 13.3

Because the temperature of the gas inside the bubble decreases (at constant pressure), the bubble gets smaller. The conditions are

Initial Conditions
$T_1 = 28 °C = 28 + 273 = 301$ K
$V_1 = 23 \text{ cm}^3$

Final Conditions
$T_2 = 18 °C = 18 + 273 = 291$ K
$V_2 = ?$

Solving Charles's law,

$$\frac{V_1}{T_1} = \frac{V_2}{T_2}$$

for V_2 gives

$$V_2 = V_1 \times \frac{T_2}{T_1} = 23 \text{ cm}^3 \times \frac{291 \text{ K}}{301 \text{ K}} = 22 \text{ cm}^3$$

Self-Check Exercise 13.4

Because the temperature and pressure of the two samples are the same, we can use Avogadro's law in the form

$$\frac{V_1}{n_1} = \frac{V_2}{n_2}$$

The following information is given:

Sample 1	Sample 2
$V_1 = 36.7$ L	$V_2 = 16.5$ L
$n_1 = 1.5$ mol	$n_2 = ?$

We can now solve Avogadro's law for the value of n_2 (the moles of N_2 in sample 2):

$$n_2 = n_1 \times \frac{V_2}{V_1} = 1.5 \text{ mol} \times \frac{16.5 \text{ L}}{36.7 \text{ L}} = 0.67 \text{ mol}$$

Here n_2 is smaller than n_1, which makes sense in view of the fact that V_2 is smaller than V_1.
Note: We isolate n_2 from Avogadro's law as given above by multiplying both sides of the equation by n_2 and then by n_1/V_1,

$$\left(n_2 \times \frac{n_1}{V_1}\right)\frac{V_1}{n_1} = \left(n_2 \times \frac{n_1}{V_1}\right)\frac{V_2}{n_2}$$

to give $n_2 = n_1 \times V_2/V_1$.

Self-Check Exercise 13.5

We are given the following information:

$$P = 1.00 \text{ atm}$$
$$V = 2.70 \times 10^6 \text{ L}$$
$$n = 1.10 \times 10^5 \text{ mol}$$

We solve for T by dividing both sides of the ideal gas law by nR:

$$\frac{PV}{nR} = \frac{nRT}{nR}$$

to give

$$T = \frac{PV}{nR} = \frac{(1.00 \text{ atm})(2.70 \times 10^6 \text{ L})}{(1.10 \times 10^5 \text{ mol})\left(0.08206 \dfrac{\text{L atm}}{\text{K mol}}\right)}$$
$$= 299 \text{ K}$$

The temperature of the helium is 299 K, or $299 - 273 = 26 \text{ °C}$.

Self-Check Exercise 13.6

We are given the following information about the radon sample:

$$n = 1.5 \text{ mol}$$
$$V = 21.0 \text{ L}$$
$$T = 33 \text{ °C} = 33 + 273 = 306 \text{ K}$$
$$P = ?$$

We solve the ideal gas law ($PV = nRT$) for P by dividing both sides of the equation by V:

$$P = \frac{nRT}{V} = \frac{(1.5 \text{ mol})\left(0.08206 \dfrac{\text{L atm}}{\text{K mol}}\right)(306 \text{ K})}{21.0 \text{ L}}$$
$$= 1.8 \text{ atm}$$

Self-Check Exercise 13.7

To solve this problem, we take the ideal gas law and separate those quantities that change from those that remain constant (on opposite sides of the equation). In this case, volume and temperature change, and number of moles and pressure (and, of course, R) remain constant. So $PV = nRT$ becomes $V/T = nR/P$, which leads to

$$\frac{V_1}{T_1} = \frac{nR}{P} \quad \text{and} \quad \frac{V_2}{T_2} = \frac{nR}{P}$$

Combining these gives

$$\frac{V_1}{T_1} = \frac{nR}{P} = \frac{V_2}{T_2} \quad \text{or} \quad \frac{V_1}{T_1} = \frac{V_2}{T_2}$$

We are given

Initial Conditions
$T_1 = 5 \text{ °C} = 5 + 273 = 278 \text{ K}$
$V_1 = 3.8 \text{ L}$
Final Conditions
$T_2 = 86 \text{ °C} = 86 + 273 = 359 \text{ K}$
$V_2 = ?$

Thus

$$V_2 = \frac{T_2 V_1}{T_1} = \frac{(359 \text{ K})(3.8 \text{ L})}{278 \text{ K}} = 4.9 \text{ L}$$

Check: Is the answer sensible? In this case, the temperature was increased (at constant pressure), so the volume should increase. The answer makes sense.

Note that this problem could be described as a "Charles's law problem." The real advantage of using the ideal gas law is that you need to remember only *one* equation to do virtually any problem involving gases.

Self-Check Exercise 13.8

We are given the following information:

Initial Conditions
$P_1 = 0.747 \text{ atm}$
$T_1 = 13 \text{ °C} = 13 + 273 = 286 \text{ K}$
$V_1 = 11.0 \text{ L}$
Final Conditions
$P_2 = 1.18 \text{ atm}$
$T_2 = 56 \text{ °C} = 56 + 273 = 329 \text{ K}$
$V_2 = ?$

In this case, the number of moles remains constant. Thus we can say

$$\frac{P_1 V_1}{T_1} = nR \quad \text{and} \quad \frac{P_2 V_2}{T_2} = nR$$

or

$$\frac{P_1 V_1}{T_1} = \frac{P_2 V_2}{T_2}$$

Solving for V_2 gives

$$V_2 = V_1 \times \frac{T_2}{T_1} \times \frac{P_1}{P_2} = (11.0 \text{ L})\left(\frac{329 \text{ K}}{286 \text{ K}}\right)\left(\frac{0.747 \text{ atm}}{1.18 \text{ atm}}\right)$$
$$= 8.01 \text{ L}$$

Self-Check Exercise 13.9

As usual when dealing with gases, we can use the ideal gas equation $PV = nRT$. First consider the information given:

$$P = 0.91 \text{ atm} = P_{\text{total}}$$
$$V = 2.0 \text{ L}$$
$$T = 25 \text{ °C} = 25 + 273 = 298 \text{ K}$$

Given this information, we can calculate the number of moles of gas in the mixture: $n_{total} = n_{N_2} + n_{O_2}$. Solving for n in the ideal gas equation gives

$$n_{total} = \frac{P_{total}V}{RT} = \frac{(0.91 \text{ atm})(2.0 \text{ L})}{\left(0.08206 \dfrac{\text{L atm}}{\text{K mol}}\right)(298 \text{ K})} = 0.074 \text{ mol}$$

We also know that 0.050 mole of N_2 is present. Because

$$n_{total} = n_{N_2} + n_{O_2} = 0.074 \text{ mol}$$
$$\uparrow$$
$$(0.050 \text{ mol})$$

we can calculate the moles of O_2 present.

$$0.050 \text{ mol} + n_{O_2} = 0.074 \text{ mol}$$
$$n_{O_2} = 0.074 \text{ mol} - 0.050 \text{ mol} = 0.024 \text{ mol}$$

Now that we know the moles of oxygen present, we can calculate the partial pressure of oxygen from the ideal gas equation.

$$P_{O_2} = \frac{n_{O_2}RT}{V} = \frac{(0.024 \text{ mol})\left(0.08206 \dfrac{\text{L atm}}{\text{K mol}}\right)(298 \text{ K})}{2.0 \text{ L}}$$
$$= 0.29 \text{ atm}$$

Although it is not requested, note that the partial pressure of the N_2 must be 0.62 atm, because

$$0.62 \text{ atm} + 0.29 \text{ atm} = 0.91 \text{ atm}$$
$$\underbrace{\qquad}_{P_{N_2}} \quad \underbrace{\qquad}_{P_{O_2}} \quad \underbrace{\qquad}_{P_{total}}$$

Self-Check Exercise 13.10

The volume is 0.500 L, the temperature is 25 °C (or 25 + 273 = 298 K), and the total pressure is given as 0.950 atm. Of this total pressure, 24 torr is due to the water vapor. We can calculate the partial pressure of the H_2 because we know that

$$P_{total} = P_{H_2} + P_{H_2O} = 0.950 \text{ atm}$$
$$\uparrow$$
$$24 \text{ torr}$$

Before we carry out the calculation, however, we must convert the pressures to the same units. Converting P_{H_2O} to atmospheres gives

$$24 \text{ torr} \times \frac{1.000 \text{ atm}}{760.0 \text{ torr}} = 0.032 \text{ atm}$$

Thus

$$P_{total} = P_{H_2} + P_{H_2O} = 0.950 \text{ atm} = P_{H_2} + 0.032 \text{ atm}$$

and

$$P_{H_2} = 0.950 \text{ atm} - 0.032 \text{ atm} = 0.918 \text{ atm}$$

Now that we know the partial pressure of the hydrogen gas, we can use the ideal gas equation to calculate the moles of H_2.

$$n_{H_2} = \frac{P_{H_2}V}{RT} = \frac{(0.918 \text{ atm})(0.500 \text{ L})}{\left(0.08206 \dfrac{\text{L atm}}{\text{K mol}}\right)(298 \text{ K})}$$
$$= 0.0188 \text{ mol} = 1.88 \times 10^{-2} \text{ mol}$$

The sample of gas contains 1.88×10^{-2} mole of H_2, which exerts a partial pressure of 0.918 atm.

Self-Check Exercise 13.11

We will solve this problem by taking the following steps:

Grams of zinc	⟹	Moles of zinc	⟹	Moles of H_2	⟹	Volume of H_2

Step 1   Using the atomic mass of zinc (65.38), we calculate the moles of zinc in 26.5 g.

$$26.5 \text{ g Zn} \times \frac{1 \text{ mol Zn}}{65.38 \text{ g Zn}} = 0.405 \text{ mol Zn}$$

Step 2   Using the balanced equation, we next calculate the moles of H_2 produced.

$$0.405 \text{ mol Zn} \times \frac{1 \text{ mol H}_2}{1 \text{ mol Zn}} = 0.405 \text{ mol H}_2$$

Step 3   Now that we know the moles of H_2, we can compute the volume of H_2 by using the ideal gas law, where

$$P = 1.50 \text{ atm}$$
$$V = ?$$
$$n = 0.405 \text{ mol}$$
$$R = 0.08206 \text{ L atm/K mol}$$
$$T = 19 \text{ °C} = 19 + 273 = 292 \text{ K}$$

$$V = \frac{nRT}{P} = \frac{(0.405 \text{ mol})\left(0.08206 \dfrac{\text{L atm}}{\text{K mol}}\right)(292 \text{ K})}{1.50 \text{ atm}}$$
$$= 6.47 \text{ L of H}_2$$

Self-Check Exercise 13.12

Although there are several possible ways to do this problem, the most convenient method involves using the molar volume at STP. First we use the ideal gas equation to calculate the moles of NH_3 present:

$$n = \frac{PV}{RT}$$

where $P = 15.0$ atm, $V = 5.00$ L, and $T = 25$ °C + 273 = 298 K.

$$n = \frac{(15.0 \text{ atm})(5.00 \text{ L})}{\left(0.08206 \dfrac{\text{L atm}}{\text{K mol}}\right)(298 \text{ K})} = 3.07 \text{ mol}$$

We know that at STP each mole of gas occupies 22.4 L. Therefore, 3.07 mol has the volume

$$3.07 \text{ mol} \times \frac{22.4 \text{ L}}{1 \text{ mol}} = 68.8 \text{ L}$$

The volume of the ammonia at STP is 68.8 L.

Chapter 14

Self-Check Exercise 14.1

Energy to melt the ice:

$$15 \text{ g H}_2O \times \frac{1 \text{ mol H}_2O}{18 \text{ g H}_2O} = 0.83 \text{ mol H}_2O$$

$$0.83 \text{ mol H}_2O \times 6.02 \frac{\text{kJ}}{\text{mol H}_2O} = 5.0 \text{ kJ}$$

Energy to heat the water from 0 °C to 100 °C:

$$4.18 \frac{\text{J}}{\text{g °C}} \times 15 \text{ g} \times 100 \text{ °C} = 6300 \text{ J}$$

$$6300 \text{ J} \times \frac{1 \text{ kJ}}{1000 \text{ J}} = 6.3 \text{ kJ}$$

Energy to vaporize the water at 100 °C:

$$0.83 \text{ mol H}_2O \times 40.6 \frac{\text{kJ}}{\text{mol H}_2O} = 34 \text{ kJ}$$

Total energy required:

$$5.0 \text{ kJ} + 6.3 \text{ kJ} + 34 \text{ kJ} = 45 \text{ kJ}$$

Self-Check Exercise 14.2

a. Contains SO_3 molecules—a molecular solid.
b. Contains Ba^{2+} and O^{2-} ions—an ionic solid.
c. Contains Au atoms—an atomic solid.

Chapter 15

Self-Check Exercise 15.1

$$\text{Mass percent} = \frac{\text{mass of solute}}{\text{mass of solution}} \times 100\%$$

For this sample, the mass of solution is 135 g and the mass of the solute is 4.73 g, so

$$\text{Mass percent} = \frac{4.73 \text{ g solute}}{135 \text{ g solution}} \times 100\%$$
$$= 3.50\%$$

Self-Check Exercise 15.2

Using the definition of mass percent, we have

$$\frac{\text{Mass of solute}}{\text{Mass of solution}} =$$

$$\frac{\text{grams of solute}}{\text{grams of solute} + \text{grams of solvent}} \times 100\% = 40.0\%$$

There are 425 grams of solute (formaldehyde). Substituting, we have

$$\frac{425 \text{ g}}{425 \text{ g} + \text{grams of solvent}} \times 100\% = 40.0\%$$

We must now solve for grams of solvent (water). This will take some patience, but we can do it if we proceed step by step. First we divide both sides by 100%.

$$\frac{425 \text{ g}}{425 \text{ g} + \text{grams of solvent}} \times \frac{100\%}{100\%} = \frac{40.0\%}{100\%} = 0.400$$

Now we have

$$\frac{425 \text{ g}}{425 \text{ g} + \text{grams of solvent}} = 0.400$$

Next we multiply both sides by (425 g + grams of solvent).

$$(425 \text{ g} + \text{grams of solvent}) \times \frac{425 \text{ g}}{425 \text{ g} + \text{grams of solvent}}$$
$$= 0.400 \times (425 \text{ g} + \text{grams of solvent})$$

This gives

$$425 \text{ g} = 0.400 \times (425 \text{ g} + \text{grams of solvent})$$

Carrying out the multiplication gives

$$425 \text{ g} = 170. \text{ g} + 0.400 \text{ (grams of solvent)}$$

Now we subtract 170. g from both sides,

$$425 \text{ g} - 170. \text{ g} = 170. \text{ g} - 170. \text{ g} + 0.400 \text{ (grams of solvent)}$$
$$255 \text{ g} = 0.400 \text{ (grams of solvent)}$$

and divide both sides by 0.400.

$$\frac{255 \text{ g}}{0.400} = \frac{0.400}{0.400} \text{ (grams of solvent)}$$

We finally have the answer:

$$\frac{255 \text{ g}}{0.400} = 638 \text{ g} = \text{grams of solvent}$$
$$= \text{mass of water needed}$$

Self-Check Exercise 15.3

The moles of ethanol can be obtained from its molar mass (46.1).

$$1.00 \text{ g } C_2H_5OH \times \frac{1 \text{ mol } C_2H_5OH}{46.1 \text{ g } C_2H_5OH} = 2.17 \times 10^{-2} \text{ mol } C_2H_5OH$$

$$\text{Volume in liters} = 101 \text{ mL} \times \frac{1 \text{ L}}{1000 \text{ mL}} = 0.101 \text{ L}$$

$$\text{Molarity of } C_2H_5OH = \frac{\text{moles of } C_2H_5OH}{\text{liters of solution}}$$
$$= \frac{2.17 \times 10^{-2} \text{ mol}}{0.101 \text{ L}}$$
$$= 0.215 \text{ M}$$

Self-Check Exercise 15.4

When Na_2CO_3 and $Al_2(SO_4)_3$ dissolve in water, they produce ions as follows:

$$Na_2CO_3(s) \xrightarrow{H_2O(l)} 2Na^+(aq) + CO_3^{2-}(aq)$$

$$Al_2(SO_4)_3(s) \xrightarrow{H_2O(l)} 2Al^{3+}(aq) + 3SO_4^{2-}(aq)$$

Therefore, in a 0.10 M Na_2CO_3 solution, the concentration of Na^+ ions is $2 \times 0.10 \text{ M} = 0.20 \text{ M}$ and the concentration of CO_3^{2-} ions is 0.10 M. In a 0.010 M $Al_2(SO_4)_3$ solution, the concentration of Al^{3+} ions is $2 \times 0.010 \text{ M} = 0.020 \text{ M}$ and the concentration of SO_4^{2-} ions is $3 \times 0.010 \text{ M} = 0.030 \text{ M}$.

Self-Check Exercise 15.5

When solid $AlCl_3$ dissolves, it produces ions as follows:

$$AlCl_3(s) \xrightarrow{H_2O(l)} Al^{3+}(aq) + 3Cl^-(aq)$$

so a 1.0×10^{-3} M $AlCl_3$ solution contains 1.0×10^{-3} M Al^{3+} ions and 3.0×10^{-3} M Cl^- ions.

To calculate the moles of Cl^- ions in 1.75 L of the 1.0×10^{-3} M $AlCl_3$ solution, we must multiply the volume by the molarity.

1.75 L solution $\times 3.0 \times 10^{-3}$ M Cl^-

$$= 1.75 \text{ L solution} \times \frac{3.0 \times 10^{-3} \text{ mol } Cl^-}{\text{L solution}}$$

$$= 5.25 \times 10^{-3} \text{ mol } Cl^- = 5.3 \times 10^{-3} \text{ mol } Cl^-$$

Self-Check Exercise 15.6

We must first determine the number of moles of formaldehyde in 2.5 L of 12.3 M formalin. Remember that volume of solution (in liters) times molarity gives moles of solute. In this case, the volume of solution is 2.5 L and the molarity is 12.3 moles of HCHO per liter of solution.

$$2.5 \text{ L solution} \times \frac{12.3 \text{ mol HCHO}}{\text{L solution}} = 31 \text{ mol HCHO}$$

Next, using the molar mass of HCHO (30.0 g), we convert 31 moles of HCHO to grams.

$$31 \text{ mol HCHO} \times \frac{30.0 \text{ g HCHO}}{1 \text{ mol HCHO}} = 9.3 \times 10^2 \text{ g HCHO}$$

Therefore, 2.5 L of 12.3 M formalin contains 9.3×10^2 g of formaldehyde. We must weigh out 930 g of formaldehyde and dissolve it in enough water to make 2.5 L of solution.

Self-Check Exercise 15.7

We are given the following information:

$$M_1 = 12 \frac{\text{mol}}{\text{L}} \qquad\qquad M_2 = 0.25 \frac{\text{mol}}{\text{L}}$$

$V_1 = ?$ (what we need to find) $V_2 = 0.75 \text{ L}$

Using the fact that the moles of solute do not change upon dilution, we know that

$$M_1 \times V_1 = M_2 \times V_2$$

Solving for V_1 by dividing both sides by M_1 gives

$$V_1 = \frac{M_2 \times V_2}{M_1} = \frac{0.25 \frac{\text{mol}}{\text{L}} \times 0.75 \text{ L}}{12 \frac{\text{mol}}{\text{L}}}$$

and

$$V_1 = 0.016 \text{ L} = 16 \text{ mL}$$

Self-Check Exercise 15.8

Step 1 When the aqueous solutions of Na_2SO_4 (containing Na^+ and SO_4^{2-} ions) and $Pb(NO_3)_2$ (containing Pb^{2+} and NO_3^- ions) are mixed, solid $PbSO_4$ is formed.

$$Pb^{2+}(aq) + SO_4^{2-}(aq) \rightarrow PbSO_4(s)$$

Step 2   We must first determine whether Pb^{2+} or SO_4^{2-} is the limiting reactant by calculating the moles of Pb^{2+} and SO_4^{2-} ions present. Because 0.0500 M $Pb(NO_3)_2$ contains 0.0500 M Pb^{2+} ions, we can calculate the moles of Pb^{2+} ions in 1.25 L of this solution as follows:

$$1.25 \; \cancel{L} \times \frac{0.0500 \text{ mol } Pb^{2+}}{\cancel{L}} = 0.0625 \text{ mol } Pb^{2+}$$

The 0.0250 M Na_2SO_4 solution contains 0.0250 M SO_4^{2-} ions, and the number of moles of SO_4^{2-} ions in 2.00 L of this solution is

$$2.00 \; \cancel{L} \times \frac{0.0250 \text{ mol } SO_4^{2-}}{\cancel{L}} = 0.0500 \text{ mol } SO_4^{2-}$$

Step 3 Pb^{2+} and SO_4^{2-} react in a 1:1 ratio, so the amount of SO_4^{2-} ions is limiting because SO_4^{2-} is present in the smaller number of moles.

Step 4   The Pb^{2+} ions are present in excess, and only 0.0500 mole of solid $PbSO_4$ will be formed.

Step 5   We calculate the mass of $PbSO_4$ by using the molar mass of $PbSO_4$ (303.3 g).

$$0.0500 \; \cancel{\text{mol PbSO}_4} \times \frac{303.3 \text{ g } PbSO_4}{1 \; \cancel{\text{mol PbSO}_4}} = 15.2 \text{ g } PbSO_4$$

Self-Check Exercise 15.9

Step 1   Because nitric acid is a strong acid, the nitric acid solution contains H^+ and NO_3^- ions. The KOH solution contains K^+ and OH^- ions. When these solutions are mixed, the H^+ and OH^- react to form water.

$$H^+(aq) + OH^-(aq) \rightarrow H_2O(l)$$

Step 2   The number of moles of OH^- present in 125 mL of 0.050 M KOH is

$$125 \; \cancel{\text{mL}} \times \frac{1 \; \cancel{L}}{1000 \; \cancel{\text{mL}}} \times \frac{0.050 \text{ mol } OH^-}{\cancel{L}} = 6.3 \times 10^{-3} \text{ mol } OH^-$$

Step 3 H^+ and OH^- react in a 1:1 ratio, so we need 6.3×10^{-3} mole of H^+ from the 0.100 M HNO_3.

Step 4 6.3×10^{-3} mole of OH^- requires 6.3×10^{-3} mole of H^+ to form 6.3×10^{-3} mole of H_2O. Therefore,

$$V \times \frac{0.100 \text{ mol } H^+}{L} = 6.3 \times 10^{-3} \text{ mol } H^+$$

where V represents the volume in liters of 0.100 M HNO_3 required. Solving for V, we have

$$V = \frac{6.3 \times 10^{-3} \; \cancel{\text{mol } H^+}}{\dfrac{0.100 \; \cancel{\text{mol } H^+}}{L}} = 6.3 \times 10^{-2} \text{ L}$$

$$= 6.3 \times 10^{-2} \; \cancel{L} \times \frac{1000 \text{ mL}}{\cancel{L}} = 63 \text{ mL}$$

Self-Check Exercise 15.10

From the definition of normality, $N = \text{equiv/L}$, we need to calculate (1) the equivalents of KOH and (2) the volume of the solution in liters. To find the number of equivalents, we use the equivalent weight of KOH, which is 56.1 g (see Table 15.2).

$$23.6 \text{ g } \cancel{\text{KOH}} \times \frac{1 \text{ equiv KOH}}{56.1 \text{ g } \cancel{\text{KOH}}} = 0.421 \text{ equiv KOH}$$

Next we convert the volume to liters.

$$755 \; \cancel{\text{mL}} \times \frac{1 \text{ L}}{1000 \; \cancel{\text{mL}}} = 0.755 \text{ L}$$

Finally, we substitute these values into the equation that defines normality.

$$\text{Normality} = \frac{\text{equiv}}{L} = \frac{0.421 \text{ equiv}}{0.755 \text{ L}} = 0.558 \text{ N}$$

Self-Check Exercise 15.11

To solve this problem, we use the relationship

$$N_{acid} \times V_{acid} = N_{base} \times V_{base}$$

where

$$N_{acid} = 0.50 \; \frac{\text{equiv}}{L}$$
$$V_{acid} = ?$$
$$N_{base} = 0.80 \; \frac{\text{equiv}}{L}$$
$$V_{base} = 0.250 \text{ L}$$

We solve the equation

$$N_{acid} \times V_{acid} = N_{base} \times V_{base}$$

for V_{acid} by dividing both sides by N_{acid}.

$$\frac{N_{acid} \times V_{acid}}{N_{acid}} = \frac{N_{base} \times V_{base}}{N_{acid}}$$

$$V_{acid} = \frac{N_{base} \times V_{base}}{N_{acid}} = \frac{(0.80 \; \cancel{\frac{\text{equiv}}{L}}) \times (0.250 \text{ L})}{0.50 \; \cancel{\frac{\text{equiv}}{L}}}$$

$$V_{acid} = 0.40 \text{ L}$$

Therefore, 0.40 L of 0.50 N H_2SO_4 is required to neutralize 0.250 L of 0.80 N KOH.

Chapter 16

Self-Check Exercise 16.1

The conjugate acid–base pairs are

$$\begin{array}{cc} H_2O, & H_3O^+ \\ \text{Base} & \text{Conjugate acid} \end{array}$$

and

$$\begin{array}{cc} HC_2H_3O_2, & C_2H_3O_2^- \\ \text{Acid} & \text{Conjugate base} \end{array}$$

The members of both pairs differ by one H^+.

Self-Check Exercise 16.2

Because $[H^+][OH^-] = 1.0 \times 10^{-14}$, we can solve for $[H^+]$.

$$[H^-] = \frac{1.0 \times 10^{-14}}{[OH^-]} = \frac{1.0 \times 10^{-14}}{2.0 \times 10^{-2}} = 5.0 \times 10^{-13} \text{ M}$$

This solution is basic: $[OH^-] = 2.0 \times 10^{-2}$ M is greater than $[H^+] = 5.0 \times 10^{-13}$ M.

Self-Check Exercise 16.3

a.   Because $[H^+] = 1.0 \times 10^{-3}$ M, we get pH = 3.00 because pH = $-\log[H^+] = -\log[1.0 \times 10^{-3}] = 3.00$.

b.   Because $[OH^-] = 5.0 \times 10^{-5}$ M, we can find $[H^+]$ from the K_w expression.

$$[H^+] = \frac{K_w}{[OH^-]} = \frac{1.0 \times 10^{-14}}{5.0 \times 10^{-5}} = 2.0 \times 10^{-10} \text{ M}$$

$$pH = -\log[H^+] = -\log[2.0 \times 10^{-10}] = 9.70$$

Self-Check Exercise 16.4

$$pOH + pH = 14.00$$
$$pOH = 14.00 - pH = 14.00 - 3.5$$
$$pOH = 10.5$$

Self-Check Exercise 16.5

Step 1   pH = 3.50

Step 2 $-$pH = -3.50

Step 3 $\boxed{\text{inv}}\boxed{\text{log}}$ $-3.50 = 3.2 \times 10^{-4}$

$[H^+] = 3.2 \times 10^{-4}\ M$

Self-Check Exercise 16.6

Step 1 pOH $= 10.50$

Step 2 $-$pOH $= -10.50$

Step 3 $\boxed{\text{inv}}\boxed{\text{log}}$ $-10.50 = 3.2 \times 10^{-11}$

$[OH^-] = 3.2 \times 10^{-11}\ M$

Self-Check Exercise 16.7

Because HCl is a strong acid, it is completely dissociated:

$5.0 \times 10^{-3}\ M\ \text{HCl} \rightarrow 5.0 \times 10^{-3}\ M\ H^+$ and $5.0 \times 10^{-3}\ M\ Cl^-$

so $[H^+] = 5.0 \times 10^{-3}\ M$.

$\text{pH} = -\log(5.0 \times 10^{-3}) = 2.30$

Chapter 1

2. The answer depends on the student's experiences.
4. Answers will depend on the student's responses.
6. Answers will depend on the student's choices.
8. Recognize the problem and state it clearly; propose possible solutions or explanations; decide which solution/explanation is best through experiments.
10. Answers will depend on student responses. A quantitative observation must include a number, such as "There are three windows in this room." A qualitative observation could include something like "The chair is blue."
12. The answer depends on the student's responses/examples.
14. Chemistry is not just a set of facts that have to be memorized. To be successful in chemistry, you have to be able to apply what you have learned to new situations, new phenomena, new experiments. Rather than just learning a list of facts or studying someone else's solution to a problem, your instructor hopes you will learn *how* to solve problems *yourself*, so that you will be able to apply what you have learned in future circumstances.
16. In real-life situations, the problems and applications likely to be encountered are not simple textbook examples. You must be able to observe an event, hypothesize a cause, and then test this hypothesis. You must be able to carry what has been learned in class forward to new, different situations.

Chapter 2

2. "Scientific notation" means we have to put the decimal point after the first significant figure, and then express the order of magnitude of the number as a power of 10. So we want to put the decimal point after the first 2:

$$2421 \rightarrow 2.421 \times 10^{\text{to some power}}$$

To be able to move the decimal point three places to the left in going from 2421 to 2.421 means you will need a power of 10^3 after the number, where the exponent 3 shows that you moved the decimal point three places to the left:

$$2421 \rightarrow 2.421 \times 10^{\text{to some power}} = 2.421 \times 10^3$$

4. (a) 10^4; (b) 10^{-3}; (c) 10^2; (d) 10^{-30}
6. (a) negative; (b) zero; (c) positive; (d) negative
8. (a) 2789; (b) 0.002789; (c) 93,000,000; (d) 42.89; (e) 99,990; (f) 0.00009999
10. (a) three places to the left; (b) one place to the left; (c) five places to the right; (d) one place to the left; (e) two places to the right; (f) two places to the left
12. (a) 6244; (b) 0.09117; (c) 82.99; (d) 0.0001771; (e) 545.1; (f) 0.00002934
14. (a) 3.1×10^3; (b) 1×10^6; (c) 1 or 1×10^0; (d) 1.8×10^{-5}; (e) 1×10^7; (f) 1.00×10^6; (g) 1.00×10^{-7}; (h) 1×10^1
16. Answer depends on the student's examples.
18. about ¼ pound   20. about an inch   22. 2-liter bottle
24. the woman   26. (a) centimeter; (b) meter; (c) kilometer
28. d
30. Typically we read the scale on measuring devices to 0.1 unit of the smallest scale division on the device. We estimate this final significant figure, which makes the final significant figure in the measurement uncertain.

32. The scale of the ruler is marked to the nearest tenth of a centimeter. Writing 2.850 would imply that the scale was marked to the nearest hundredth of a centimeter (and that the zero in the thousandths place had been estimated).
34. (a) three: the relationship is exact; (b) two; (c) five; (d) probably two
36. It is better to round off only the final answer and to carry through extra digits in intermediate calculations. If there are enough steps to the calculation, rounding off in each step may lead to a cumulative error in the final answer.
38. (a) 4.18×10^{-6}; (b) 3.87×10^4; (c) 9.11×10^{-30}; (d) 5.46×10^6
40. (a) 8.8×10^{-4}; (b) 9.375×10^4; (c) 8.97×10^{-1}; (d) 1.00×10^3
42. The total mass would be determined by the number of decimal places available on the readout of the scale/balance. For example, if a balance whose readout is to the nearest 0.01 g were used, the total mass would be reported to the second decimal place. For example, 42.05 g + 29.15 g + 31.09 g would be reported as 102.29 to the second decimal place. Even though there are only four significant figures in each of the measurements, there are five significant figures in the answer because we look at the decimal place when adding (or subtracting) numbers.
44. Most calculators would say 0.66666666. If the 2 and 3 were experimentally determined numbers, this quotient would imply far too many significant figures.
46. none
48. (a) 2.3; (b) 9.1×10^2; (c) 1.323×10^3; (d) 6.63×10^{-13}
50. (a) one; (b) four; (c) two; (d) three
52. (a) 2.045; (b) 3.8×10^3; (c) 5.19×10^{-5}; (d) 3.8418×10^{-7}
54. an infinite number, a definition
56. $\dfrac{2.54\ \text{cm}}{1\ \text{in.}}$; $\dfrac{1\ \text{in.}}{2.54\ \text{cm}}$ 58. $\dfrac{1\ \text{lb}}{\$0.79}$
60. (a) 50.5 in.; (b) 3.11 ft; (c) 452 mm; (d) 76.12 cm; (e) 1.32 qt; (f) 8.42 pt; (g) 13.7 lb; (h) 28.0 oz
62. (a) 1.03598 atm; (b) 3.13 qt; (c) 0.510 kg; (d) 1.007 cal; (e) 8617 ft; (f) 9.04 qt; (g) 262 g; (h) 1.76 qt
64. 4117 km   66. 1×10^{-8} cm; 4×10^{-9} in.; 0.1 nm
68. freezing/melting   70. 273
72. Fahrenheit (F)
74. (a) 195 K; (b) 502 °C; (c) 216 °C; (d) 297 K
76. (a) 173 °F; (b) 104 °F; (c) −459 °F; (d) 90. °F
78. (a) 2 °C; (b) 28 °C; (c) −5.8 °F (−6 °F); (d) −40 °C (−40 is where both temperature scales have the same value)
80. g/cm³ (g/mL)   82. 100 in.³
84. Density is a characteristic property of a pure substance.
86. copper
88. (a) 22 g/cm³; (b) 0.034 g/cm³; (c) 0.962 g/cm³; (d) 2.1×10^{-5} g/cm³
90. 2.94×10^3 g; 159 mL   92. float   94. 11.7 mL
96. (a) 966 g; (b) 394 g; (c) 567 g; (d) 135 g
98. (a) 301,100,000,000,000,000,000,000; (b) 5,091,000,000; (c) 720; (d) 123,400; (e) 0.000432002; (f) 0.03001; (g) 0.00000029901; (h) 0.42
100. (a) cm; (b) m; (c) km; (d) cm; (e) mm

102. (a) 5.07×10^4 kryll;   (b) 0.12 blim;   (c) 3.70×10^{-5} blim^2

104. 20. in.   **106.** \$1.33   **108.** °X = 1.26 °C + 14

110. 3.50 g/L (3.50×10^{-3} g/cm^3)   **112.** 959 g

114. (a) negative;   (b) negative;   (c) positive;   (d) zero;
(e) negative

116. (a) 2, positive;   (b) 11, negative;   (c) 3, positive;
(d) 5, negative;   (e) 5, positive;   (f) 0, zero;
(g) 1, negative;   (h) 7, negative

118. (a) 1, positive;   (b) 3, negative;   (c) 0, zero;
(d) 3, positive;   (e) 9, negative

120. (a) 0.0000298;   (b) 4,358,000,000;   (c) 0.0000019928;
(d) 602,000,000,000,000,000,000,000;   (e) 0.101;
(f) 0.00787;   (g) 98,700,000;   (h) 378.99;   (i) 0.1093;
(j) 2.9004;   (k) 0.00039;   (l) 0.00000001904

122. (a) 1×10^{-2};   (b) 1×10^2;   (c) 5.5×10^{-2};   (d) 3.1×10^9;
(e) 1×10^3;   (f) 1×10^8;   (g) 2.9×10^2;   (h) 3.453×10^4

124. kelvin, K   **126.** centimeter   **128.** 0.105 m

130. 1 kg   **132.** 10

134. 2.8 (the hundredths place is estimated)

136. (a) 0.000426;   (b) 4.02×10^{-5};   (c) 5.99×10^6;
(d) 400.;   (e) 0.00600

138. (a) 2149.6;   (b) 5.37×10^3;   (c) 3.83×10^{-2};
(d) -8.64×10^5

140. (a) 7.6166×10^6;   (b) 7.24×10^3;   (c) 1.92×10^{-5};
(d) 2.4482×10^{-3}

142. $\dfrac{1 \text{ yr}}{12 \text{ mo}}$; $\dfrac{12 \text{ mo}}{1 \text{ yr}}$

144. (a) 25.7 kg;   (b) 3.38 gal;   (c) 0.132 qt;
(d) 1.09×10^4 mL;   (e) 2.03×10^3 g;   (f) 0.58 qt

146. for exactly 6 gross, 864 pencils

148. (a) 352 K;   (b) -18 °C;   (c) -43 °C;   (d) 257 °F

150. 78.2 g   **152.** 0.59 g/cm^3

154. (a) 23 °F;   (b) 32 °F;   (c) -321 °F;   (d) -459 °F;
(e) 187 °F;   (f) -459 °F

156. (a) $100 \text{ km} \times \dfrac{1 \text{ mile}}{1.6093 \text{ km}} = 62$ miles, or about 60 miles,

taking significant figures into account.

(b) $22{,}300 \text{ kg} \times \dfrac{2.2046 \text{ lbs}}{1 \text{ kg}} = 49{,}200$ lbs. of fuel was

needed; 22,300 lbs. were added, so 26,900 additional
pounds were needed.

158. $\dfrac{10^{-8} \text{ g}}{\text{L}} \times \dfrac{3.7854 \text{ L}}{1 \text{ gallon}} \times \dfrac{1 \text{ lb.}}{453.59 \text{ g}} \approx 10^{-11}$ lb/gal

Chapter 3

2. forces among the particles in the matter

4. liquids   **6.** gaseous   **8.** stronger

10. Because gases are mostly empty space, they can be *compressed* easily to smaller volumes. In solids and liquids, most of the sample's bulk volume is filled with the molecules, leaving little empty space.

12. chemical   **14.** malleable; ductile   **16.** c

18. (a) physical;   (b) chemical;   (c) chemical;   (d) chemical;
(e) physical;   (f) physical;   (g) chemical;   (h) physical;
(i) physical;   (j) physical;   (k) chemical

20. Compounds consist of two or more elements combined together chemically in a fixed composition, no matter what their source may be. For example, water on earth consists of molecules containing one oxygen atom and two hydrogen atoms. Water on Mars (or any other planet) has the same composition.

22. compounds

24. In general, the properties of a compound are very different from the properties of its constituent elements. For example, the properties of water are altogether different from the properties of the elements (hydrogen gas and oxygen gas) that make it up.

26. no; heating causes a reaction to form iron(II) sulfide, a pure substance

28. Heterogeneous mixtures: salad dressing, jelly beans, the change in my pocket; solutions: window cleaner, shampoo, rubbing alcohol

30. (a) primarily a pure compound, but fillers and anti–caking agents may have been added;   (b) mixture;   (c) mixture;   (d) pure substance

32. Concrete is a mixture. It consists of sand, gravel, water, and cement (which consists of limestone, clay, shale, and gypsum). The composition of concrete can vary.

34. Consider a mixture of salt (sodium chloride) and sand. Salt is soluble in water; sand is not. The mixture is added to water and stirred to dissolve the salt, and is then filtered. The salt solution passes through the filter; the sand remains on the filter. The water can then be evaporated from the salt.

36. Each component of the mixture retains its own identity during the separation.

38. compound   **40.** physical   **42.** far apart

44. chemical   **46.** physical   **48.** electrolysis

50. (a) heterogeneous;   (b) heterogeneous;   (c) homogeneous (if no lumps!);   (d) heterogeneous (although it may appear homogeneous);   (e) heterogeneous

52. Answers depend on student responses.

54. physical; chemical

56. O_2 and P_4 are both still elements, even though the ordinary forms of these elements consist of molecules containing more than one atom (but all atoms in each respective molecule are the same). P_2O_5 is a compound, because it is made up of two or more different elements (not all the atoms in the P_2O_5 molecule are the same).

58. Assuming there is enough water present in the mixture to have dissolved all the salt, filter the mixture to separate out the sand from the mixture. Then distill the filtrate (consisting of salt and water), which will boil off the water, leaving the salt.

60. The most obvious difference is the physical states: water is a liquid under room conditions, hydrogen and oxygen are both gases. Hydrogen is flammable. Oxygen supports combustion. Water does neither.

Chapter 4

2. Robert Boyle

4. 116 elements are presently known; 88 occur naturally; the remainder are manmade. Table 4.1 lists the most common elements on the earth.

6. (a) Trace elements are elements that are present in tiny amounts. Trace elements in the body, while present in small amounts, are essential.
(b) Answers will vary. For example, chromium assists in the metabolism of sugars and cobalt is present in vitamin B$_{12}$.

8. Answer depends on student choices/examples.

10. (a) 9;   (b) 6;   (c) 8;   (d) 12;   (e) 11;   (f) 13;   (g) 3;
(h) 5;   (i) 4;   (j) 2

12. zirconium; Cs; selenium; Au; cerium

14. B: barium, Ba; berkelium, Bk; beryllium, Be; bismuth, Bi; bohrium, Bh; boron, B; bromine, Br
N: neodymium, Nd; neon, Ne; neptunium, Np; nickel, Ni; niobium, Nb; nitrogen, N; nobelium, No
P: palladium, Pd; phosphorus, P; platinum, Pt; plutonium, Pu; polonium, Po; potassium, K; praseodymium, Pr; promethium, Pm; protactinium, Pa
S: samarium, Sm; scandium, Sc; seaborgium, Sg; selenium, Se; silicon, Si; silver, Ag; sodium, Na; strontium, Sr; sulfur, S

16. (a) Elements are made of tiny particles called atoms.   (b) All atoms of a given element are identical;   (c) The atoms of a given element are different from those of any other element; (d) A given compound always has the same numbers and types of atoms;   (e) Atoms are neither created nor destroyed in chemical processes. A chemical reaction simply changes the way the atoms are grouped together.

18. According to Dalton, all atoms of the same element are *identical;* in particular, every atom of a given element has the same *mass* as every other atom of that element. If a given compound always contains the *same relative numbers* of atoms of each kind, and those atoms always have the same *masses,* then the compound made from those elements always contains the same relative masses of its elements.

20. (a) CO_2;   (b) CO;   (c) $CaCO_3$;   (d) H_2SO_4;   (e) $BaCl_2$; (f) Al_2S_3

22. (a) False; Rutherford's bombardment experiments with metal foil suggested that the α particles were being deflected by coming near a *dense, positively charged* atomic nucleus; (b) False; the proton and the electron have opposite charges, but the mass of the electron is *much smaller* than the mass of the proton;   (c) True

24. The protons and neutrons are found in the nucleus. The protons are positively charged; the neutrons have no charge. The protons and neutrons each weigh approximately the same.

26. neutron; electron   28. The electrons; outside the nucleus

30. The atomic number represents the number of protons in the nucleus of the atom and makes the atom a particular element. The mass number represents the total number of protons and neutrons in the nucleus of an atom and distinguishes one isotope of an element from another.

32. Neutrons are uncharged and contribute only to the mass.

34. Atoms of the same element (atoms with the same number of protons in the nucleus) may have different numbers of neutrons, and so will have different masses.

36.

Z	Symbol	Name
14	Si	silicon
54	Xe	xenon
79	Au	gold
56	Ba	barium
53	I	iodine
50	Sn	tin
48	Cd	cadmium

38. (a) $^{54}_{26}Fe$;   (b) $^{56}_{26}Fe$;   (c) $^{57}_{26}Fe$;   (d) $^{14}_{7}N$;   (e) $^{15}_{7}N$;   (f) $^{15}_{7}N$

40. Researchers have found that the concentrations of hydrogen-2 (deuterium) and oxygen-18 in drinking water vary significantly from region to region in the United States. By collecting hair samples around the country, they have also found that 86% of the variations in the hair samples' hydrogen and oxygen isotopes result from the isotopic composition of the local water.

42.

Name	Symbol	Atomic Number	Mass Number	Number of Neutrons
oxygen	$^{17}_{8}O$	8	17	9
oxygen	$^{17}_{8}O$	8	17	9
neon	$^{20}_{10}Ne$	10	20	10
iron	$^{56}_{26}Fe$	26	56	30
plutonium	$^{244}_{94}Pu$	94	244	150
mercury	$^{202}_{80}Hg$	80	202	122
cobalt	$^{59}_{27}Co$	27	59	32
nickel	$^{56}_{28}Ni$	28	56	28
fluorine	$^{19}_{9}F$	9	19	10
chromium	$^{50}_{24}Cr$	24	50	26

44. vertical; groups

46. Metallic elements are found toward the *left* and *bottom* of the periodic table; there are far more metallic elements than nonmetals.

48. nonmetallic gaseous elements: oxygen, nitrogen, fluorine, chlorine, hydrogen, and the noble gases; There are no metallic gaseous elements at room conditions

50. A metalloid is an element that has some properties common to both metallic and nonmetallic elements. The metalloids are found in the "stair-step" region marked on most periodic tables.

52. (a) fluorine, chlorine, bromine, iodine, astatine;   (b) lithium, sodium, potassium, rubidium, cesium, francium;   (c) beryllium, magnesium, calcium, strontium, barium, radium; (d) helium, neon, argon, krypton, xenon, radon

54. Arsenic is a metalloid. Other elements in the same group (5A) include nitrogen (N), phosphorus (P), antinomy (Sb), and bismuth (Bi).

56. Most elements are too reactive to be found in the uncombined form in nature and are found only in compounds.

58. These elements are found uncombined in nature and do not readily react with other elements. Although these elements were once thought to form no compounds, this now has been shown to be untrue.

60. diatomic gases: H_2, N_2, O_2, F_2, Cl_2; monatomic gases: He, Ne, Kr, Xe, Rn, Ar

62. chlorine   64. diamond   66. electrons   68. 3+

70. -ide   72. nonmetallic

74. (a) 36;   (b) 36;   (c) 21;   (d) 36;   (e) 80;   (f) 27

76. (a) two electrons gained;   (b) three electrons gained; (c) three electrons lost;   (d) two electrons lost; (e) one electron lost;   (f) two electrons lost

78. (a) P^{3-};   (b) Ra^{2+};   (c) At^-;   (d) no ion;   (e) Cs^+;   (f) Se^{2-}

80. Sodium chloride is an *ionic* compound, consisting of Na^+ and Cl^- ions. When NaCl is dissolved in water, these ions are *set free* and can move independently to conduct the electric current. Sugar crystals, although they may *appear* similar visually, contain *no* ions. When sugar is dissolved in water, it dissolves as uncharged *molecules*. No electrically charged species are present in a sugar solution to carry the electric current.

82. The total number of positive charges must equal the total number of negative charges so that the crystals of an ionic compound have *no net charge*. A macroscopic sample of compound ordinarily has no net charge.

84. (a) CsI, BaI_2, AlI_3;   (b) Cs_2O, BaO, Al_2O_3;   (c) Cs_3P, Ba_3P_2, AlP;   (d) Cs_2Se, BaSe, Al_2Se_3;   (e) CsH, BaH_2, AlH_3

86. (a) 7, halogens;   (b) 8, noble gases;   (c) 2, alkaline earth elements;   (d) 2, alkaline earth elements;   (e) 4;   (f) 6; (g) 8, noble gases;   (h) 1, alkali metals

88.

	Element	Symbol	Atomic Number
Group 3	boron	B	5
	aluminum	Al	13
	gallium	Ga	31
	indium	In	49
Group 5	nitrogen	N	7
	phosphorus	P	15
	arsenic	As	33
	antimony	Sb	51
Group 6	oxygen	O	8
	sulfur	S	16
	selenium	Se	34
	tellurium	Te	52
Group 8	helium	He	2
	neon	Ne	10
	argon	Ar	18
	krypton	Kr	36

90. Most of an atom's mass is concentrated in the nucleus: the *protons* and *neutrons* that constitute the nucleus have similar masses and are each nearly 2000 times more massive than electrons. The chemical properties of an atom depend on the number and location of the *electrons* it possesses. Electrons are found in the outer regions of the atom and are involved in interactions between atoms.

92. $C_6H_{12}O_6$

94. (a) 29 electrons, 34 neutrons, 29 electrons;
(b) 35 protons, 45 neutrons, 35 electrons;
(c) 12 protons, 12 neutrons, 12 electrons

96. The chief use of gold in ancient times was as *ornamentation*, whether in statuary or in jewelry. Gold possesses an especially beautiful luster; since it is relatively soft and malleable, it can be worked finely by artisans. Among the metals, gold is inert to attack by most substances in the environment.

98. (a) I; (b) Si; (c) W; (d) Fe; (e) Cu; (f) Co

100. (a) Br; (b) Bi; (c) Hg; (d) V; (e) F; (f) Ca

102. (a) osmium; (b) zirconium; (c) rubidium;
(d) radon; (e) uranium; (f) manganese;
(g) nickel; (h) bromine

104. (a) CO_2; (b) $AlCl_3$; (c) $HClO_4$; (d) SCl_6

106. (a) $^{13}_{6}C$; (b) $^{13}_{6}C$; (c) $^{13}_{6}C$; (d) $^{44}_{19}K$; (e) $^{41}_{20}Ca$; (f) $^{35}_{19}K$

108.

Symbol	Number of Protons	Number of Neutrons	Mass Number
$^{41}_{20}Ca$	20	21	41
$^{55}_{25}Mn$	25	30	55
$^{109}_{47}Ag$	47	62	109
$^{45}_{21}Sc$	21	24	45

Chapter 5

2. A binary chemical compound contains only two elements; the major types are ionic (compounds of a metal and a nonmetal) and nonionic or molecular (compounds between two nonmetals). Answers depend on student responses.

4. cation (positive ion)

6. Some substances do not contain molecules; the formula we write reflects only the relative number of each type of atom present.

8. Roman numeral

10. (a) lithium chloride; (b) barium fluoride;
(c) calcium oxide; (d) aluminum iodide;
(e) magnesium sulfide; (f) rubidium oxide

12. (a) correct; (b) incorrect, copper(I) oxide;
(c) incorrect; potassium oxide; (d) correct;
(e) incorrect, rubidium sulfide

14. (a) copper(II) chloride; (b) chromium(III) oxide;
(c) mercury(II) chloride; (d) mercury(I) oxide;
(e) gold(III) bromide; (f) manganese(IV) oxide

16. (a) cobaltic chloride; (b) ferrous bromide;
(c) plumbic oxide; (d) stannic chloride;
(e) mercuric iodide; (f) ferrous sulfide

18. (a) chlorine pentafluoride; (b) xenon dichloride;
(c) selenium dioxide; (d) dinitrogen trioxide;
(e) diiodine hexachloride; (f) carbon disulfide

20. (a) lead(IV) sulfide, plumbic sulfide;
(b) lead(II) sulfide, plumbous sulfide;
(c) silicon dioxide;
(d) tin(IV) fluoride, stannic fluoride;
(e) dichlorine heptoxide;
(f) cobalt(III) sulfide, cobaltic sulfide

22. (a) barium fluoride; (b) radium oxide;
(c) dinitrogen oxide; (d) rubidium oxide;
(e) diarsenic pent(a)oxide; (f) calcium nitride

24. An oxyanion is a polyatomic ion containing a given element and one or more oxygen atoms. The oxyanions of chlorine and bromine are given below:

Oxyanion	Name	Oxyanion	Name
ClO^-	hypochlorite	BrO^-	hypobromite
ClO_2^-	chlorite	BrO_2^-	bromite
ClO_3^-	chlorate	BrO_3^-	bromate
ClO_4^-	perchlorate	BrO_4^-	perbromate

26. *hypo-* (fewest); *per-* (most)

28. IO^-, hypoiodite; IO_2^-, iodite; IO_3^-, iodate; IO_4^-, periodate

30. (a) NO_3^-; (b) NO_2^-; (c) NH_4^+; (d) CN^-

32. CN^-, cyanide; CO_3^{2-}, carbonate; HCO_3^-, hydrogen carbonate; $C_2H_3O_2^-$, acetate

34. (a) ammonium ion; (b) dihydrogen phosphate ion;
(c) sulfate ion; (d) hydrogen sulfite ion (bisulfite ion);
(e) perchlorate ion; (f) iodate ion

36. (a) sodium permanganate; (b) aluminum phosphate;
(c) chromium(II) carbonate, chromous carbonate;
(d) calcium hypochlorite; (e) barium carbonate;
(f) calcium chromate

38. oxygen

40. (a) hypochlorous acid; (b) sulfurous acid; (c) bromic acid;
(d) hypoiodous acid; (e) perbromic acid; (f) hydrosulfuric acid; (g) hydroselenic acid; (h) phosphorous acid

42. (a) MgF_2; (b) FeI_2; (c) HgS; (d) Ba_3N_2; (e) $PbCl_2$;
(f) SnF_4; (g) Ag_2O; (h) K_2Se

44. (a) N_2O; (b) NO_2; (c) N_2O_4; (d) SF_6; (e) PBr_3; (f) CI_4;
(g) OCl_2

46. (a) $NH_4C_2H_3O_2$; (b) $Fe(OH)_2$; (c) $Co_2(CO_3)_3$; (d) $BaCr_2O_7$;
(e) $PbSO_4$; (f) KH_2PO_4; (g) Li_2O_2; (h) $Zn(ClO_3)_2$

48. (a) HCN; (b) HNO_3; (c) H_2SO_4; (d) H_3PO_4;
(e) $HClO$ or $HOCl$; (f) HBr; (g) $HBrO_2$; (h) HF

50. (a) $Ca(HSO_4)_2$; (b) $Zn_3(PO_4)_2$; (c) $Fe(ClO_4)_3$; (d) $Co(OH)_3$;
(e) K_2CrO_4; (f) $Al(H_2PO_4)_3$; (g) $LiHCO_3$; (h) $Mn(C_2H_3O_2)_2$;
(i) $MgHPO_4$; (j) $CsClO_2$; (k) BaO_2; (l) $NiCO_3$

52. A moist paste of NaCl would contain Na^+ and Cl^- ions in solution and would serve as a *conductor* of electrical impulses.

54. $H \rightarrow H^+$ (hydrogen ion) $+ e^-$; $H + e^- \rightarrow H^-$ (hydride ion)

56. ClO_4^-, $HClO_4$; IO_3^-, HIO_3; ClO^-, $HClO$; BrO_2^-, $HBrO_2$; ClO_2^-, $HClO_2$

58. (a) gold(III) bromide (auric bromide); (b) cobalt(III) cyanide (cobaltic cyanide); (c) magnesium hydrogen phosphate;
(d) diboron hexahydride (common name diborane);
(e) ammonia; (f) silver(I) sulfate (usually called silver sulfate); (g) beryllium hydroxide

60. (a) ammonium carbonate; (b) ammonium hydrogen carbonate, ammonium bicarbonate; (c) calcium phosphate;
(d) sulfurous acid; (e) manganese(IV) oxide; (f) iodic acid;
(g) potassium hydride

62. (a) $M(C_2H_3O_2)_4$; (b) $M(MnO_4)_4$; (c) MO_2; (d) $M(HPO_4)_2$;
(e) $M(OH)_4$; (f) $M(NO_2)_4$

64. M^+ compounds: MD, M_2E, M_3F; M^{2+} compounds: MD_2, ME, M_3F_2; M^{3+} compounds: MD_3, M_2E_3, MF

66.

$Ca(NO_3)_2$	$CaSO_4$	$Ca(HSO_4)_2$	$Ca(H_2PO_4)_2$	CaO	$CaCl_2$
$Sr(NO_3)_2$	$SrSO_4$	$Sr(HSO_4)_2$	$Sr(H_2PO_4)_2$	SrO	$SrCl_2$
NH_4NO_3	$(NH_4)_2SO_4$	NH_4HSO_4	$NH_4H_2PO_4$	$(NH_4)_2O$	NH_4Cl
$Al(NO_3)_3$	$Al_2(SO_4)_3$	$Al(HSO_4)_3$	$Al(H_2PO_4)_3$	Al_2O_3	$AlCl_3$
$Fe(NO_3)_3$	$Fe_2(SO_4)_3$	$Fe(HSO_4)_3$	$Fe(H_2PO_4)_3$	Fe_2O_3	$FeCl_3$
$Ni(NO_3)_2$	$NiSO_4$	$Ni(HSO_4)_2$	$Ni(H_2PO_4)_2$	NiO	$NiCl_2$
$AgNO_3$	Ag_2SO_4	$AgHSO_4$	AgH_2PO_4	Ag_2O	$AgCl$
$Au(NO_3)_3$	$Au_2(SO_4)_3$	$Au(HSO_4)_3$	$Au(H_2PO_4)_3$	Au_2O_3	$AuCl_3$
KNO_3	K_2SO_4	$KHSO_4$	KH_2PO_4	K_2O	KCl
$Hg(NO_3)_2$	$HgSO_4$	$Hg(HSO_4)_2$	$Hg(H_2PO_4)_2$	HgO	$HgCl_2$
$Ba(NO_3)_2$	$BaSO_4$	$Ba(HSO_4)_2$	$Ba(H_2PO_4)_2$	BaO	$BaCl_2$

68. helium   70. F_2, Cl_2 (gas); Br_2 (liquid); I_2, At_2 (solid)
72. 1−   74. 1−
76. (a) Al(13e) → Al^{3+}(10e) + 3e⁻;   (b) S(16e) + 2e⁻ → S^{2-}(18e);
    (c) Cu(29e) → Cu^+(28e) + e⁻;   (d) F(9e) + e⁻ → F^-(10e);
    (e) Zn(30e) → Zn^{2+}(28e) + 2e⁻;   (f) P(15e) + 3e⁻ → P^{3-}(18e)
78. (a) Na_2S;   (b) KCl;   (c) BaO;   (d) MgSe;   (e) $CuBr_2$;
    (f) AlI_3;   (g) Al_2O_3;   (h) Ca_3N_2
80. (a) silver(I) oxide or just silver oxide;   (b) correct;
    (c) iron(III) oxide;   (d) plumbic oxide;   (e) correct
82. (a) stannous chloride;   (b) ferrous oxide;   (c) stannic oxide;
    (d) plumbous sulfide;   (e) cobaltic sulfide;   (f) chromous chloride
84. (a) iron(III) acetate;   (b) bromine monofluoride;
    (c) potassium peroxide;   (d) silicon tetrabromide;
    (e) copper(II) permanganate;   (f) calcium chromate
86. (a) CO_3^{2-};   (b) HCO_3^-;   (c) $C_2H_3O_2^-$;   (d) CN^-
88. (a) carbonate;   (b) chlorate;   (c) sulfate;   (d) phosphate;
    (e) perchlorate;   (f) permanganate
90. Answer depends on student choices.
92. (a) NaH_2PO_4;   (b) $LiClO_4$;   (c) $Cu(HCO_3)_2$;   (d) $KC_2H_3O_2$;
    (e) BaO_2;   (f) Cs_2SO_3

Chapter 6

2. Most of these products contain a peroxide, which decomposes and releases oxygen gas.
4. Bubbling takes place as the hydrogen peroxide chemically decomposes into water and oxygen gas.
6. The appearance of the black color actually signals the breakdown of starches and sugars in the bread to elemental carbon. You may also see steam coming from the bread (water produced by the breakdown of the carbohydrates).
8. atoms
10. Balancing an equation ensures that no atoms are created or destroyed during the reaction. The total mass after the reaction must be the same as the total mass before the reaction.
12. Solid, (s); liquid, (l); gas, (g)
14. $H_2O_2(aq) → H_2(g) + O_2(g)$
16. $N_2H_4(l) → N_2(g) + H_2(g)$
18. $C_3H_8(g) + O_2(g) → CO_2(g) + H_2O(g)$;
    $C_3H_8(g) + O_2(g) → CO(g) + H_2O(g)$
20. $CaCO_3(s) + HCl(aq) → CaCl_2(aq) + H_2O(l) + CO_2(g)$
22. $SiO_2(s) + C(s) → Si(s) + CO(g)$
24. $Fe(s) + H_2O(l) → FeO(s) + H_2(g)$
26. $SO_2(g) + H_2O(l) → H_2SO_3(aq)$; $SO_3(g) + H_2O(l) → H_2SO_4(aq)$
28. $NO(g) + O_3(g) → NO_2(g) + O_2(g)$
30. $P_4(s) + O_2(g) → P_2O_5(s)$ 32. $Xe(g) + F_2(g) → XeF_4(s)$
34. $NH_3(g) + O_2(g) → HNO_3(aq) + H_2O(l)$
36. To balance a chemical equation we must have the same number of each type of atom on both sides of the equation. In addition, we must balance the equation we are given, that is, we are not to change the nature of the substances.

    For example, the equation $2H_2O_2(aq) → 2H_2O(l) + O_2(g)$ can be represented as

    The equation $H_2O_2(aq) → H_2(g) + O_2(g)$ can be represented as

38. (a) $Zn(s) + CuO(s) → ZnO(s) + Cu(l)$;   (b) $P_4(s) + 6F_2(g) → 4PF_3(g)$;   (c) $Xe(g) + 2F_2(g) → XeF_4(s)$;   (d) $2NH_4Cl(g) + Mg(OH)_2(s) → 2NH_3(g) + 2H_2O(g) + MgCl_2(s)$;   (e) $2SiO(s) + 4Cl_2(g) → 2SiCl_4(l) + O_2(g)$;   (f) $Cs_2O(s) + H_2O(l) → 2CsOH(aq)$;   (g) $N_2O_3(g) + H_2O(l) → 2HNO_2(aq)$;   (h) $Fe_2O_3(s) + 3H_2SO_4(l) → Fe_2(SO_4)_3(s) + 3H_2O(g)$

40. (a) $Na_2SO_4(aq) + CaCl_2(aq) → CaSO_4(s) + 2NaCl(aq)$;
    (b) $3Fe(s) + 4H_2O(g) → Fe_3O_4(s) + 4H_2(g)$;
    (c) $Ca(OH)_2(aq) + 2HCl(aq) → CaCl_2(aq) + 2H_2O(l)$;
    (d) $Br_2(g) + 2H_2O(l) + SO_2(g) → 2HBr(aq) + H_2SO_4(aq)$;
    (e) $3NaOH(s) + H_3PO_4(aq) → Na_3PO_4(aq) + 3H_2O(l)$;
    (f) $2NaNO_3(s) → 2NaNO_2(s) + O_2(g)$;   (g) $2Na_2O_2(s) + 2H_2O(l) → 4NaOH(aq) + O_2(g)$;   (h) $4Si(s) + S_8(s) → 2Si_2S_4(s)$
42. (a) $4NaCl(s) + 2SO_2(g) + 2H_2O(g) + O_2(g) → 2Na_2SO_4(s) + 4HCl(g)$;
    (b) $3Br_2(l) + I_2(s) → 2IBr_3(s)$;
    (c) $Ca(s) + 2H_2O(g) → Ca(OH)_2(aq) + H_2(g)$;
    (d) $2BF_3(g) + 3H_2O(g) → B_2O_3(s) + 6HF(g)$;
    (e) $SO_2(g) + 2Cl_2(g) → SOCl_2(l) + Cl_2O(g)$;
    (f) $Li_2O(s) + H_2O(l) → 2LiOH(aq)$;
    (g) $Mg(s) + CuO(s) → MgO(s) + Cu(l)$;
    (h) $Fe_3O_4(s) + 4H_2(g) → 3Fe(l) + 4H_2O(g)$
44. (a) $Ba(NO_3)_2(aq) + Na_2CrO_4(aq) → BaCrO_4(s) + 2NaNO_3(aq)$;
    (b) $PbCl_2(aq) + K_2SO_4(aq) → PbSO_4(s) + 2KCl(aq)$;   (c) $C_2H_5OH(l) + 3O_2(g) → 2CO_2(g) + 3H_2O(l)$;   (d) $CaC_2(s) + 2H_2O(l) → Ca(OH)_2(s) + C_2H_2(g)$;   (e) $Sr(s) + 2HNO_3(aq) → Sr(NO_3)_2(aq) + H_2(g)$;   (f) $BaO_2(s) + H_2SO_4(aq) → BaSO_4(s) + H_2O_2(aq)$;   (g) $2AsI_3(s) → 2As(s) + 3I_2(s)$;   (h) $2CuSO_4(aq) + 4KI(s) → 2CuI(s) + I_2(s) + 2K_2SO_4(aq)$
46. $Na(s) + O_2(g) → Na_2O_2(s)$; $Na_2O_2(s) + H_2O(l) → NaOH(aq) + O_2(g)$
48. $C_{12}H_{22}O_{11}(aq) + H_2O(l) → 4C_2H_5OH(aq) + 4CO_2(g)$
50. $2Al_2O_3(s) + 3C(s) → 4Al(s) + 3CO_2(g)$
52. $2Li(s) + S(s) → Li_2S(s)$; $2Na(s) + S(s) → Na_2S(s)$; $2K(s) + S(s) → K_2S(s)$; $2Rb(s) + S(s) → Rb_2S(s)$; $2Cs(s) + S(s) → Cs_2S(s)$; $2Fr(s) + S(s) → Fr_2S(s)$
54. $BaO_2(s) + H_2O(l) → BaO(s) + H_2O_2(aq)$
56. $2KClO_3(s) → 2KCl(s) + 3O_2(g)$
58. $NH_3(g) + HCl(g) → NH_4Cl(s)$
60. The senses we call "odor" and "taste" are really chemical reactions of the receptors in our body with molecules in the food we are eating. The fact that the receptors no longer detect the "fishy" odor or taste suggests that adding the lemon juice or vinegar has changed the nature of the amines in the fish.
62. $Fe(s) + S(s) → FeS(s)$
64. $K_2CrO_4(aq) + BaCl_2(aq) → BaCrO_4(s) + 2KCl(aq)$
66. $2NaCl(aq) + 2H_2O(l) → Cl_2(g) + H_2(g) + 2NaOH(aq, s)$
    $2NaBr(aq) + 2H_2O(l) → Br_2(l) + H_2(g) + 2NaOH(aq, s)$
    $2NaI(aq) + 2H_2O(l) → I_2(s) + H_2(g) + 2NaOH(aq, s)$
68. $CaC_2(s) + 2H_2O(l) → Ca(OH)_2(s) + C_2H_2(g)$
70. $CuO(s) + H_2SO_4(aq) → CuSO_4(aq) + H_2O(l)$
72. $Na_2SO_3(aq) + S(s) → Na_2S_2O_3(aq)$
74. (a) $Cl_2(g) + 2KI(aq) → 2KCl(aq) + I_2(s)$;   (b) $CaC_2(s) + 2H_2O(l) → Ca(OH)_2(s) + C_2H_2(g)$;   (c) $2NaCl(s) + H_2SO_4(l) → Na_2SO_4(s) + 2HCl(g)$;   (d) $CaF_2(s) + H_2SO_4(l) → CaSO_4(s) + 2HF(g)$;   (e) $K_2CO_3(s) → K_2O(s) + CO_2(g)$;   (f) $3BaO(s) + 2Al(s) → Al_2O_3(s) + 3Ba(s)$;   (g) $2Al(s) + 3F_2(g) → 2AlF_3(s)$;   (h) $CS_2(g) + 3Cl_2(g) → CCl_4(l) + S_2Cl_2(g)$
76. (a) $Pb(NO_3)_2(aq) + K_2CrO_4(aq) → PbCrO_4(s) + 2KNO_3(aq)$;
    (b) $BaCl_2(aq) + Na_2SO_4(aq) → BaSO_4(s) + 2NaCl(aq)$;
    (c) $2CH_3OH(l) + 3O_2(g) → 2CO_2(g) + 4H_2O(g)$;
    (d) $Na_2CO_3(aq) + S(s) + SO_2(g) → CO_2(g) + Na_2S_2O_3(aq)$;
    (e) $Cu(s) + 2H_2SO_4(aq) → CuSO_4(aq) + SO_2(g) + 2H_2O(l)$;
    (f) $MnO_2(s) + 4HCl(aq) → MnCl_2(aq) + Cl_2(g) + 2H_2O(l)$;
    (g) $As_2O_3(s) + 6KI(aq) + 6HCl(aq) → 2AsI_3(s) + 6KCl(aq) + 3H_2O(l)$;   (h) $2Na_2S_2O_3(aq) + I_2(aq) → Na_2S_4O_6(aq) + 2NaI(aq)$

Chapter 7

2. Driving forces are types of *changes* in a system that pull a reaction in the *direction of product formation;* driving forces include formation of a *solid,* formation of *water,* formation of a *gas,* and transfer of electrons.

4. A reactant in aqueous solution is indicated with (*aq*); formation of a solid is indicated with (*s*).

6. There are twice as many chloride ions as magnesium ions.

8. The simplest evidence is that solutions of ionic substances conduct electricity.

10. Answer depends on student choices.

12. (a) soluble; Rule 3;   (b) soluble; Rule 2;   (c) soluble; Rule 2;   (d) insoluble; Rule 5;   (e) soluble; Rule 2;   (f) soluble; Rule 1;   (g) soluble; Rule 4;   (h) insoluble; Rule 6

14. (a) Rule 6;   (b) Rule 6;   (c) Rule 6;   (d) Rule 3;   (e) Rule 4

16. (a) $MnCO_3$, Rule 6;   (b) $CaSO_4$, Rule 4;   (c) Hg_2Cl_2, Rule 3;   (d) no precipitate, most sodium and nitrate salts are soluble;   (e) $Ni(OH)_2$, Rule 5;   (f) $BaSO_4$, Rule 4

18. (a) $Na_2CO_3(aq) + CuSO_4(aq) \rightarrow Na_2SO_4(aq) + \underline{CuCO_3(s)}$
    (b) $HCl(aq) + AgC_2H_3O_2(aq) \rightarrow HC_2H_3O_2(aq) + \underline{AgCl(s)}$
    (c) no precipitate
    (d) $3(NH_4)_2S(aq) + 2FeCl_3(aq) \rightarrow 6NH_4Cl(aq) + Fe_2S_3(s)$
    (e) $H_2SO_4(aq) + Pb(NO_3)_2(aq) \rightarrow 2HNO_3(aq) + \underline{PbSO_4(s)}$
    (f) $2K_3PO_4(aq) + 3CaCl_2(aq) \rightarrow 6KCl(aq) + \underline{Ca_3(PO_4)_2(s)}$

20. (a) $CaCl_2(aq) + 2AgNO_3(aq) \rightarrow Ca(NO_3)_2(aq) + 2AgCl(s)$;
    (b) $2AgNO_3(aq) + K_2CrO_4(aq) \rightarrow Ag_2CrO_4(s) + 2KNO_3(aq)$;
    (c) $BaCl_2(aq) + K_2SO_4(aq) \rightarrow BaSO_4(s) + 2KCl(aq)$

22. (a) $Na_2CO_3(aq) + K_2SO_4(aq) \rightarrow$ no precipitate; all combinations are soluble   (b) $CuCl_2(aq) + (NH_4)_2CO_3(aq) \rightarrow 2NH_4Cl(aq) + \underline{CuCO_3(s)}$ (c) $K_3PO_4(aq) + AlCl_3(aq) \rightarrow 3KCl(aq) + \underline{AlPO_4(s)}$

24. Spectator ions are ions that *remain in solution* during a precipitation/double-displacement reaction. For example, in the reaction $BaCl_2(aq) + K_2SO_4(aq) \rightarrow BaSO_4(s) + 2KCl(aq)$, the K^+ and Cl^- ions are spectator ions.

26. (a) $Ca^{2+}(aq) + SO_4^{2-}(aq) \rightarrow CaSO_4(s)$;   (b) $Ni^{2+}(aq) + 2OH^-(aq) \rightarrow Ni(OH)_2(s)$;   (c) $2Fe^{3+}(aq) + 3S^{2-}(aq) \rightarrow Fe_2S_3(s)$

28. $Ag^+(aq) + Cl^-(aq) \rightarrow AgCl(s)$; $Pb^{2+}(aq) + 2Cl^-(aq) \rightarrow PbCl_2(s)$; $Hg_2^{2+}(aq) + 2Cl^-(aq) \rightarrow Hg_2Cl_2(s)$

30. $Co^{2+}(aq) + S^{2-}(aq) \rightarrow CoS(s)$; $2Co^{3+}(aq) + 3S^{2-}(aq) \rightarrow Co_2S_3(s)$; $Fe^{2+}(aq) + S^{2-}(aq) \rightarrow FeS(s)$; $2Fe^{3+}(aq) + 3S^{2-}(aq) \rightarrow Fe_2S_3(s)$

32. The strong bases are those hydroxide compounds that dissociate fully when dissolved in water. The strong bases that are highly soluble in water (NaOH, KOH) are also strong electrolytes.

34. acids: HCl (hydrochloric), HNO_3 (nitric), H_2SO_4 (sulfuric); bases: hydroxides of Group 1A elements: NaOH, KOH, RbOH, CsOH

36. A salt is the ionic product remaining in solution when an acid neutralizes a base. For example, in the reaction $HCl(aq) + NaOH(aq) \rightarrow NaCl(aq) + H_2O(l)$, sodium chloride is the salt produced by the neutralization reaction.

38. $RbOH(s) \rightarrow Rb^+(aq) + OH^-(aq)$; $CsOH(s) \rightarrow Cs^+(aq) + OH^-(aq)$

40. (a) $H_2SO_4(aq) + 2KOH(aq) \rightarrow K_2SO_4(aq) + 2H_2O(l)$
    (b) $HNO_3(aq) + NaOH(aq) \rightarrow NaNO_3(aq) + H_2O(l)$
    (c) $2HCl(aq) + Ca(OH)_2(aq) \rightarrow CaCl_2(aq) + 2H_2O(l)$
    (d) $2HClO_4(aq) + Ba(OH)_2(aq) \rightarrow Ba(ClO_4)_2(aq) + 2H_2O(l)$

42. Answer depends on student choice of example: $Na(s) + Cl_2(g) \rightarrow 2NaCl(s)$ is an example.

44. The metal loses electrons, the nonmetal gains electrons.

46. Each magnesium atom would lose two electrons. Each oxygen atom would gain two electrons (so the O_2 molecule would gain four electrons). Two magnesium atoms would be required to react with each O_2 molecule. Magnesium ions are charged 2+, oxide ions are charged 2−.

48. Each potassium atom loses one electron. The sulfur atom gains two electrons. So two potassium atoms are required to react with one sulfur atom.

$2 \times (K \rightarrow K^+ + e^-)$
$S + 2e^- \rightarrow S^{2-}$

50. (a) $P_4(s) + 5O_2(g) \rightarrow P_4O_{10}(s)$;   (b) $MgO(s) + C(s) \rightarrow Mg(s) + CO(g)$;   (c) $Sr(s) + 2H_2O(l) \rightarrow Sr(OH)_2(aq) + H_2(g)$;   (d) $Co(s) + 2HCl(aq) \rightarrow CoCl_2(aq) + H_2(g)$

52. The reaction includes aluminum metal as a reactant and products that contain aluminum ions. For this reaction, electrons must be transferred. That is, to make an aluminum cation, electrons must be removed from the metal. An oxidation reduction is one that involves transfers of electrons.

54. (a) oxidation–reduction;   (b) oxidation–reduction;   (c) acid–base;   (d) acid–base, precipitation;   (e) precipitation;   (f) precipitation;   (g) oxidation–reduction;   (h) oxidation–reduction;   (i) acid–base

56. oxidation–reduction

58. A decomposition reaction is one in which a given compound is broken down into simpler compounds or constituent elements. The reactions $CaCO_3(s) \rightarrow CaO(s) + CO_2(g)$ and $2HgO(s) \rightarrow 2Hg(l) + O_2(g)$ represent decomposition reactions. Such reactions often may be classified in other ways. For example, the reaction of $HgO(s)$ is also an oxidation--reduction reaction.

60. (a) $C_3H_8(g) + 5O_2(g) \rightarrow 3CO_2(g) + 4H_2O(g)$;
    (b) $C_2H_4(g) + 3O_2(g) \rightarrow 2CO_2(g) + 2H_2O(g)$;
    (c) $2C_8H_{18}(l) + 25O_2(g) \rightarrow 16CO_2(g) + 18H_2O(g)$

62. Answer depends on student selection.

64. (a) $8Fe(s) + S_8(s) \rightarrow 8FeS(s)$;   (b) $4Co(s) + 3O_2(g) \rightarrow 2Co_2O_3(s)$;   (c) $Cl_2O_7(g) + H_2O(l) \rightarrow 2HClO_4(aq)$

66. (a) $2Al(s) + 3Br_2(l) \rightarrow 2AlBr_3(s)$
    (b) $Zn(s) + 2HClO_4(aq) \rightarrow Zn(ClO_4)_2(aq) + H_2(g)$
    (c) $3Na(s) + P(s) \rightarrow Na_3P(s)$
    (d) $CH_4(g) + 4Cl_2(g) \rightarrow CCl_4(l) + 4HCl(g)$
    (e) $Cu(s) + 2AgNO_3(aq) \rightarrow Cu(NO_3)_2(aq) + 2Ag(s)$

68. (a) silver ion: $Ag^+(aq) + Cl^-(aq) \rightarrow AgCl(s)$; lead(II) ion: $Pb^{2+}(aq) + 2Cl^-(aq) \rightarrow PbCl_2(s)$; mercury(I) ion: $Hg_2^{2+}(aq) + 2Cl^-(aq) \rightarrow Hg_2Cl_2(s)$;   (b) sulfate ion: $Ca^{2+}(aq) + SO_4^{2-}(aq) \rightarrow CaSO_4(s)$; carbonate ion: $Ca^{2+}(aq) + CO_3^{2-}(aq) \rightarrow CaCO_3(s)$; phosphate ion: $3Ca^{2+}(aq) + 2PO_4^{3-}(aq) \rightarrow Ca_3(PO_4)_2(s)$;   (c) hydroxide ion: $Fe^{3+}(aq) + 3OH^-(aq) \rightarrow Fe(OH)_3(s)$; sulfide ion: $2Fe^{3+}(aq) + 3S^{2-}(aq) \rightarrow Fe_2S_3(s)$; phosphate ion: $Fe^{3+}(aq) + PO_4^{3-}(aq) \rightarrow FePO_4(s)$;   (d) barium ion: $Ba^{2+}(aq) + SO_4^{2-}(aq) \rightarrow BaSO_4(s)$; calcium ion: $Ca^{2+}(aq) + SO_4^{2-}(aq) \rightarrow CaSO_4(s)$; lead(II) ion: $Pb^{2+}(aq) + SO_4^{2-}(aq) \rightarrow PbSO_4(s)$;   (e) chloride ion: $Hg_2^{2+}(aq) + 2Cl^-(aq) \rightarrow Hg_2Cl_2(s)$; sulfide ion: $Hg_2^{2+}(aq) + S^{2-}(aq) \rightarrow Hg_2S(s)$; carbonate ion: $Hg_2^{2+}(aq) + CO_3^{2-}(aq) \rightarrow Hg_2CO_3(s)$;   (f) chloride ion: $Ag^+(aq) + Cl^-(aq) \rightarrow AgCl(s)$; hydroxide ion: $Ag^+(aq) + OH^-(aq) \rightarrow AgOH(s)$; carbonate ion: $2Ag^+(aq) + CO_3^{2-}(aq) \rightarrow Ag_2CO_3(s)$

70. (a) $HNO_3(aq) + KOH(aq) \rightarrow H_2O(l) + \underline{KNO_3(aq)}$;
    (b) $H_2SO_4(aq) + Ba(OH)_2(aq) \rightarrow \underline{BaSO_4(s)} + 2H_2O(l)$;
    (c) $HClO_4(aq) + NaOH(aq) \rightarrow H_2O(l) + \underline{NaClO_4(aq)}$;
    (d) $2HCl(aq) + Ca(OH)_2(aq) \rightarrow \underline{CaCl_2(aq)} + H_2O(l)$

72. (a) soluble (Rule 2: most potassium salts are soluble);   (b) soluble (Rule 2: most ammonium salts are soluble);   (c) insoluble (Rule 6: most carbonate salts are only slightly soluble);   (d) insoluble (Rule 6: most phosphate salts are only slightly soluble);   (e) soluble (Rule 2: most sodium salts are soluble);   (f) insoluble (Rule 6: most carbonate salts are only slightly soluble);   (g) soluble (Rule 3: most chloride salts are soluble)

74. (a) $AgNO_3(aq) + HCl(aq) \rightarrow \underline{AgCl(s)} + HNO_3(aq)$;
    (b) $CuSO_4(aq) + (NH_4)_2CO_3(aq) \rightarrow \underline{CuCO_3(s)} + (NH_4)_2SO_4(aq)$;
    (c) $FeSO_4(aq) + K_2CO_3(aq) \rightarrow \underline{FeCO_3(s)} + K_2SO_4(aq)$;
    (d) no reaction;   (e) $Pb(NO_3)_2(aq) + Li_2CO_3(aq) \rightarrow \underline{PbCO_3(s)} + 2LiNO_3(aq)$;   (f) $SnCl_4(aq) + 4NaOH(aq) \rightarrow \underline{Sn(OH)_4(s)} + 4NaCl(aq)$

76. $Fe^{2+}(aq) + S^{2-}(aq) \to FeS(s)$; $2Cr^{3+}(aq) + 3S^{2-}(aq) \to Cr_2S_3(s)$; $Ni^{2+}(aq) + S^{2-}(aq) \to NiS(s)$

78. These anions tend to form insoluble precipitates with many metal ions. The following are illustrative for cobalt(II) chloride, tin(II) chloride, and copper(II) nitrate reacting with sodium salts of the given anions.
(a) $CoCl_2(aq) + Na_2S(aq) \to CoS(s) + 2NaCl(aq)$; $SnCl_2(aq) + Na_2S(aq) \to SnS(s) + 2NaCl(aq)$; $Cu(NO_3)_2(aq) + Na_2S(aq) \to CuS(s) + 2NaNO_3(aq)$; (b) $CoCl_2(aq) + Na_2CO_3(aq) \to CoCO_3(s) + 2NaCl(aq)$; $SnCl_2(aq) + Na_2CO_3(aq) \to SnCO_3(s) + 2NaCl(aq)$; $Cu(NO_3)_2(aq) + Na_2CO_3(aq) \to CuCO_3(s) + 2NaNO_3(aq)$; (c) $CoCl_2(aq) + 2NaOH(aq) \to Co(OH)_2(s) + 2NaCl(aq)$; $SnCl_2(aq) + 2NaOH(aq) \to Sn(OH)_2(s) + 2NaCl(aq)$; $Cu(NO_3)_2(aq) + 2NaOH(aq) \to Cu(OH)_2(s) + 2NaNO_3(aq)$; (d) $3CoCl_2(aq) + 2Na_3PO_4(aq) \to Co_3(PO_4)_2(s) + 6NaCl(aq)$; $3SnCl_2(aq) + 2Na_3PO_4(aq) \to Sn_3(PO_4)_2(s) + 6NaCl(aq)$; $3Cu(NO_3)_2(aq) + 2Na_3PO_4(aq) \to Cu_3(PO_4)_2(s) + 6NaNO_3(aq)$

80. (a) $2Na(s) + O_2(g) \to Na_2O_2(s)$; (b) $Fe(s) + H_2SO_4(aq) \to FeSO_4(aq) + H_2(g)$; (c) $2Al_2O_3(s) \to 4Al(s) + 3O_2(g)$; (d) $2Fe(s) + 3Br_2(l) \to 2FeBr_3(s)$; (e) $Zn(s) + 2HNO_3(aq) \to Zn(NO_3)_2(aq) + H_2(g)$

82. (a) $2C_4H_{10}(l) + 13O_2(g) \to 8CO_2(g) + 10H_2O(g)$; (b) $C_4H_{10}O(l) + 6O_2(g) \to 4CO_2(g) + 5H_2O(g)$; (c) $2C_4H_{10}O_2(l) + 11O_2(g) \to 8CO_2(g) + 10H_2O(g)$

84. (a) $2NaHCO_3(s) \to Na_2CO_3(s) + H_2O(g) + CO_2(g)$; (b) $2NaClO_3(s) \to 2NaCl(s) + 3O_2(g)$; (c) $2HgO(s) \to 2Hg(l) + O_2(g)$; (d) $C_{12}H_{22}O_{11}(s) \to 12C(s) + 11H_2O(g)$; (e) $2H_2O_2(l) \to 2H_2O(l) + O_2(g)$

86. $Fe(s) + H_2SO_4(aq) \to FeSO_4(aq) + H_2(g)$; $Zn(s) + H_2SO_4(aq) \to ZnSO_4(aq) + H_2(g)$; $Mg(s) + H_2SO_4(aq) \to MgSO_4(aq) + H_2(g)$; $Co(s) + H_2SO_4(aq) \to CoSO_4(aq) + H_2(g)$; $Ni(s) + H_2SO_4(aq) \to NiSO_4(aq) + H_2(g)$

88. (a) one; (b) one; (c) two; (d) two; (e) three

90. The reaction $C(s) + O_2(g) \to CO_2(g)$ is such an example.

92. (a) $2C_3H_8O(l) + 9O_2(g) \to 6CO_2(g) + 8H_2O(g)$; oxidation–reduction, combustion; (b) $HCl(aq) + AgC_2H_3O_2(aq) \to AgCl(s) + HC_2H_3O_2(aq)$, precipitation, double-displacement; (c) $3HCl(aq) + Al(OH)_3(s) \to AlCl_3(aq) + 3H_2O(l)$, acid–base, double-displacement; (d) $2H_2O_2(aq) \to 2H_2O(l) + O_2(g)$, oxidation–reduction, decomposition; (e) $N_2H_4(l) + O_2(g) \to N_2(g) + 2H_2O(g)$, oxidation–reduction, combustion

94. $2Na(s) + Cl_2(g) \to 2NaCl(s)$; $2Al(s) + 3Cl_2(g) \to 2AlCl_3(s)$; $Zn(s) + Cl_2(g) \to ZnCl_2(s)$; $Ca(s) + Cl_2(g) \to CaCl_2(s)$; $2Fe(s) + 3Cl_2(g) \to 2FeCl_3(s)$

Chapter 8

2. The empirical formula is the lowest whole-number ratio of atoms in the compound. The graphic of PVDF shows four of each type of atom (carbon, hydrogen, and fluorine). So, the empirical formula is CHF.

4. The average atomic mass takes into account the various isotopes of an element and the relative abundances in which those isotopes are found.

6. (a) one; (b) five; (c) ten; (d) 50; (e) ten

8. A sample containing 35 tin atoms would weigh 4155 amu; 2967.5 amu of tin would represent 25 tin atoms.

10. 26.98   12. 3.011×10^{23} atoms Ne; 2.002 g He   14. 177 g

16. 1.99×10^{-23} g   18. 0.50 mol Ne atoms

20. (a) 3.500 moles of F atoms; (b) 2.000 mmol Hg; (c) 3.000 mol Si; (d) 0.2500 mol Pt; (e) 100.0 mol Mg; (f) 0.5000 mol Mo

22. (a) 0.221 g; (b) 0.0676 g; (c) 3.64×10^3 g; (d) 1.84×10^{-5} g; (e) 86.4 g; (f) 7.47×10^{-3} g

24. (a) 1.16×10^{-20} g; (b) 6.98×10^3 amu; (c) 2.24 mol; (d) 6.98×10^3 g; (e) 1.35×10^{24} atoms; (f) 7.53×10^{25} atoms

26. The molar mass is calculated by summing the individual atomic masses of the atoms in the formula.

28. (a) potassium hydrogen carbonate; 100.12 g; (b) mercury(I) chloride, mercurous chloride; 472.1 g; (c) hydrogen peroxide; 34.02 g; (d) beryllium chloride; 79.91 g; (e) aluminum sulfate; 342.2 g; (f) potassium chlorate; 122.55 g

30. (a) $LiClO_4$; 106.39 g; (b) $NaHSO_4$; 120.07 g; (c) $MgCO_3$; 84.32 g; (d) $AlBr_3$; 266.7 g; (e) Cr_2S_3; 200.2 g

32. (a) 0.463 mol; (b) 11.3 mol; (c) 7.18×10^{-3} mol; (d) 2.36×10^{-7} mol; (e) 0.362 mol; (f) 0.0129 mol

34. (a) 2.64×10^{-5} mol; (b) 38.1 mol; (c) 7.76×10^{-6} mol; (d) 3.49×10^{-2} mol; (e) 2.09×10^{-3} mol; (f) 2.69×10^{-2} mol

36. (a) 41.2 g; (b) 0.194 g; (c) 3.63×10^4 g; (d) 0.773 g; (e) 6.68×10^5 g; (f) 0.270 g

38. (a) 77.6 g; (b) 177 g; (c) 6.09×10^{-3} g; (d) 0.220 g; (e) 1.26×10^3 g; (f) 3.78×10^{-2} g

40. (a) 3.84×10^{24} molecules; (b) 1.37×10^{23} molecules; (c) 8.76×10^{16} molecules; (d) 1.58×10^{18} molecules; (e) 4.03×10^{22} molecules

42. (a) 0.0141 mol S; (b) 0.0159 mol S; (c) 0.0258 mol S; (d) 0.0127 mol S

44. less

46. (a) 80.34% Zn; 19.66% O; (b) 58.91% Na; 41.09% S; (c) 41.68% Mg; 54.86% O; 3.456% H; (d) 5.926% H; 94.06% O; (e) 95.20% Ca; 4.789% H; (f) 83.01% K; 16.99% O

48. (a) 81.10% Ba; (b) 89.56% Ba; (c) 26.94% Co; (d) 19.73% Co; (e) 62.61% Sn; (f) 45.57% Sn; (g) 87.32% Li; (h) 89.93% Al

50. (a) 78.16% I; (b) 63.65% N; (c) 46.68% N; (d) 73.89% Hg; (e) 84.98% Hg; (f) 21.96% S; (g) 77.55% Xe; (h) 63.19% Mn

52. (a) 47.06% S^{2-}; (b) 63.89% Cl^-; (c) 10.44% O^{2-}; (d) 62.08% SO_4^{2-}

54. The empirical formula indicates the smallest whole-number ratio of the number and type of atoms present in a molecule. For example, NO_2 and N_2O_4 both have two oxygen atoms for every nitrogen atom and therefore have the same empirical formula.

56. a, c   58. NCl_3 60. BH_3 62. $SnCl_4$ 64. Co_2S_3

66. AlF_3 68. Li_2O 70. Li_3N

72. Co_2O_3 74. PCl_3, PCl_5

76. molar mass   78. C_6H_6 80. $C_4H_{10}O_2$

82. Both are 30.45% N, 69.55% O

84. 5.00 g Al, 0.185 mol, 1.12×10^{23} atoms; 0.140 g Fe, 0.00250 mole, 1.51×10^{21} atoms; 2.7×10^2 g Cu, 4.3 mol, 2.6×10^{24} atoms; 0.00250 g Mg, 1.03×10^{-4} mol, 6.19×10^{19} atoms; 0.062 g Na, 2.7×10^{-3} mol, 1.6×10^{21} atoms; 3.95×10^{-18} g U, 1.66×10^{-20} mol, 1.00×10^4 atoms

86. 24.8% X, 17.4% Y, 57.8% Z. If the molecular formula were actually $X_4Y_2Z_6$, the percent composition would be the same: the *relative* mass of each element present would not change. The molecular formula is always a whole-number multiple of the empirical formula.

88. Cu_2O, CuO

90. (a) 2.82×10^{23} H atoms, 1.41×10^{23} O atoms; (b) 9.32×10^{22} C atoms, 1.86×10^{23} O atoms; (c) 1.02×10^{19} C atoms and H atoms; (d) 1.63×10^{25} C atoms, 2.99×10^{25} H atoms, 1.50×10^{25} O atoms

92. (a) 4.141 g C, 52.96% C, 2.076×10^{23} C atoms; (b) 0.0305 g C, 42.88% C, 1.53×10^{21} C atoms; (c) 14.4 g C, 76.6% C, 7.23×10^{23} C atoms

94. 2.12 g Fe   **96.** 7.86 g Hg   **98.** 2.554×10^{-22} g

100. (a) 0.9331 g N;   (b) 1.388 g N;   (c) 0.8537 g N;
(d) 1.522 g N

102. MgN_2O_6 [$Mg(NO_3)_2$]

104. The average mass takes into account not only the exact masses of the isotopes of an element, but also the relative abundance of the isotopes in nature.

106. 8.61×10^{11} sodium atoms; 6.92×10^{24} amu

108. (a) 2.0×10^2 g K;   (b) 0.0612 g Hg;   (c) 1.27×10^{-3} g Mn;
(d) 325 g P;   (e) 2.7×10^6 g Fe;   (f) 868 g Li;
(g) 0.2290 g F

110. (a) 151.9 g;   (b) 454.4 g;   (c) 150.7 g;   (d) 129.8 g;
(e) 187.6 g

112. (a) 0.311 mol;   (b) 0.270 mol;   (c) 0.0501 mol;
(d) 2.8 mol;   (e) 6.2 mol

114. (a) 4.2 g;   (b) 3.05×10^5 g;   (c) 0.533 g;   (d) 1.99×10^3 g;
(e) 4.18×10^3 g

116. (a) 1.15×10^{22} molecules;   (b) 2.08×10^{24} molecules;
(c) 4.95×10^{22} molecules;   (d) 2.18×10^{22} molecules;
(e) 6.32×10^{20} formula units (substance is ionic)

118. (a) 38.76% Ca, 19.97% P, 41.27% O;   (b) 53.91% Cd,
15.38% S, 30.70% O;   (c) 27.93% Fe, 24.06% S, 48.01% O;
(d) 43.66% Mn, 56.34% Cl;   (e) 29.16% N, 8.392% H,
12.50% C, 49.95% O;   (f) 27.37% Na, 1.200% H, 14.30% C,
57.14% O;   (g) 27.29% C, 72.71% O;   (h) 63.51% Ag,
8.246% N, 28.25% O

120. (a) 36.76% Fe;   (b) 93.10% Ag;   (c) 55.28% Sr;
(d) 55.80% C;   (e) 37.48% C;   (f) 52.92% Al;
(g) 36.70% K;   (h) 52.45% K

122. $C_3H_7NO_2$ **124.** HgO   **126.** $BaCl_2$

Chapter 9

2. The coefficients of the balanced chemical equation indicate the *relative numbers of molecules* (or moles) of each reactant that combine, as well as the number of molecules (or moles) of each product formed.

4. Balanced chemical equations tell us in what molar ratios substances combine to form products, not in what mass proportions they combine.

6. (a) $(NH_4)_2CO_3(s) \rightarrow 2NH_3(g) + CO_2(g) + H_2O(g)$.
One formula unit of solid ammonium carbonate decomposes to produce two molecules of ammonia gas, one molecule of carbon dioxide gas, and one molecule of water vapor. One mole of solid ammonium carbonate decomposes into two moles of gaseous ammonia, one mole of carbon dioxide gas, and one mole of water vapor.
(b) $6Mg(s) + P_4(s) \rightarrow 2Mg_3P_2(s)$.
Six atoms of magnesium metal react with one molecule of solid phosphorus (P_4) to make two formula units of solid magnesium phosphide. Six moles of magnesium metal react with one mole of solid phosphorus (P_4) to produce two moles of solid magnesium phosphide.
(c) $4Si(s) + S_8(s) \rightarrow 2Si_2S_4(l)$.
Four atoms of solid silicon react with one molecule of solid sulfur (S_8) to form two molecules of liquid disilicon tetrasulfide. Four moles of solid silicon react with one mole of solid sulfur (S_8) to form two moles of liquid disilicon tetrasulfide.
(d) $C_2H_5OH(l) + 3O_2(g) \rightarrow 2CO_2(g) + 3H_2O(g)$.
One molecule of liquid ethanol burns with three molecules of oxygen gas to produce two molecules of carbon dioxide gas and three molecules of water vapor. One mole of liquid ethanol burns with three moles of oxygen gas to produce two moles of gaseous carbon dioxide and three moles of water vapor.

8. Balanced chemical equations tell us in what molar ratios substances combine to form products, not in what mass propor-

tions they combine. How could 2 g of reactant produce a total of 3 g of products?

10. $\dfrac{3 \text{ mol } H_2SO_4}{1 \text{ mol } Fe_2O_3}; \dfrac{1 \text{ mol } Fe_2(SO_4)_3}{1 \text{ mol } Fe_2O_3}; \dfrac{3 \text{ mol } H_2O}{1 \text{ mol } Fe_2O_3}$

12. (a) 0.125 mol Bi_2O_3;   (b) 0.250 mol Sn; 0.500 mol H_2O;
(c) 0.250 mol SiO_2; 1.00 mol HCl;   (d) 0.500 mol HNO_3

14. (a) 165 g CO_2; 81.1 g H_2O;   (b) 27.0 g H_2O; 33.0 g CO_2;
(c) 175 g $BaHPO_4$; 27.0 g H_2O;   (d) 69.1 g C_2H_5OH; 66.0 g CO_2

16. (a) 0.469 mol O_2;   (b) 0.938 mol Se;   (c) 0.625 mol
CH_3CHO;   (d) 1.25 mol Fe

18. Stoichiometry is the process of using a chemical equation to calculate the relative masses of reactants and products involved in a reaction.

20. (a) 1.81×10^{-3} mol;   (b) 0.692 mol;   (c) 1.40×10^4 mol;
(d) 9.37×10^{-6} mol;   (e) 13.9 mol

22. (a) 98.3 g;   (b) 0.361 g;   (c) 3.55×10^8 g;   (d) 0.0140 g;
(e) 0.0103 g

24. (a) 0.0310 mol;   (b) 0.00555 mol;   (c) 0.00475 mol;
(d) 0.139 mol

26. (a) 1.38 g B, 14.0 g HCl;   (b) 13.5 g Cu_2O, 6.04 g SO_2;
(c) 35.9 g Cu, 6.04 g SO_2;   (d) 29.0 g $CaSiO_3$, 11.0 g CO_2

28. 1.52 g C_2H_2 **30.** 0.959 g Na_2CO_3

32. 2.68 g ethyl alcohol   **34.** 0.443 g NH_3

36. 8.62 kg Hg   **38.** 0.501 g C

40. Gas mileage is about 19 miles per gallon.
Balanced equation:
$2C_8H_{18} + 25O_2 \rightarrow 16CO_2 + 18H_2O$

$1 \text{ gallon of gasoline} \times \dfrac{3.7854 \text{ L}}{1 \text{ gallon}} \times \dfrac{1000 \text{ mL}}{1 \text{ L}} \times$

$\dfrac{0.75 \text{ g } C_8H_{18}}{1 \text{ mL}} \times \dfrac{1 \text{ mol } C_8H_{18}}{114.224 \text{ g } C_8H_{18}} \times \dfrac{16 \text{ mol } CO_2}{2 \text{ mol } C_8H_{18}} \times$

$\dfrac{44.01 \text{ g } CO_2}{1 \text{ mol } CO_2} \times \dfrac{1 \text{ lb } CO_2}{453.59 \text{ g } CO_2} \times \dfrac{1 \text{ mile}}{1 \text{ lb } CO_2} = 19.29 \text{ miles traveled}$

42. To determine the limiting reactant, first calculate the number of moles of each reactant present. Then determine how these numbers of moles correspond to the stoichiometric ratio indicated by the balanced chemical equation for the reaction. For each reactant, use the stoichiometric ratios from the balanced chemical equation to calculate how much of the *other* reactants would be required to react completely.

44. A reactant is present in excess if there is more of that reactant present than is required to react with the limiting reactant. The limiting reactant, by definition, cannot be present in excess. No.

46. (a) H_2SO_4 is limiting, 4.90 g SO_2, 0.918 g H_2O;   (b) H_2SO_4 is limiting, 6.30 g $Mn(SO_4)_2$, 0.918 g H_2O;   (c) O_2 is limiting, 6.67 g SO_2, 1.88 g H_2O;   (d) $AgNO_3$ is limiting, 3.18 g Ag, 2.09 g $Al(NO_3)_3$

48. (a) O_2 is limiting, 0.458 g CO_2;   (b) CO_2 is limiting, 0.409 g H_2O;   (c) MnO_2 is limiting, 0.207 g H_2O;   (d) I_2 is limiting, 1.28 g ICl

50. (a) CO is limiting reactant; 11.4 mg CH_3OH;   (b) I_2 is limiting reactant; 10.7 mg AlI_3;   (c) HBr is limiting reactant; 12.4 mg $CaBr_2$; 2.23 mg H_2O;   (d) H_3PO_4 is limiting reactant; 15.0 mg $CrPO_4$; 0.309 mg H_2

52. CuO   **54.** 1.79 g Fe$_2O_3$

56. Sodium sulfate is the limiting reactant; calcium chloride is present in excess.

58. 0.67 kg SiC

60. If the reaction occurs in a solvent, the product may have a substantial solubility in the solvent; the reaction may come to equilibrium before the full yield of product is achieved (see Chapter 17); loss of product may occur through operator error.

62. 1.86 g in theory; 81.3% yield

64. $2LiOH(s) + CO_2(g) \rightarrow Li_2CO_3(s) + H_2O(g)$. 142 g of CO_2 can be ultimately absorbed; 102 g is 71.8% of the canister's capacity.
66. theoretical, 2.72 g $BaSO_4$; percent, 74.3%
68. 28.6 g $NaHCO_3$
70. $C_6H_{12}O_6 + 6O_2 \rightarrow 6CO_2 + 6H_2O$; 1.47 g CO_2
72. at least 325 mg
74. (a) $UO_2(s) + 4HF(aq) \rightarrow UF_4(aq) + 2H_2O(l)$. One formula unit of uranium(IV) oxide combines with four molecules of hydrofluoric acid, producing one uranium(IV) fluoride molecule and two water molecules. One mole of uranium(IV) oxide combines with four moles of hydrofluoric acid to produce one mole of uranium(IV) fluoride and two moles of water; (b) $2NaC_2H_3O_2(aq) + H_2SO_4(aq) \rightarrow Na_2SO_4(aq) + 2HC_2H_3O_2(aq)$. Two molecules (formula units) of sodium acetate react exactly with one molecule of sulfuric acid, producing one molecule (formula unit) of sodium acetate and two molecules of acetic acid. Two moles of sodium acetate combine with one mole of sulfuric acid, producing one mole of sodium sulfate and two moles of acetic acid; (c) $Mg(s) + 2HCl(aq) \rightarrow MgCl_2(aq) + H_2(g)$. One magnesium atom reacts with two hydrochloric acid molecules (formula units) to produce one molecule (formula unit) of magnesium chloride and one molecule of hydrogen gas. One mole of magnesium combines with two moles of hydrochloric acid, producing one mole of magnesium chloride and one mole of gaseous hydrogen; (d) $B_2O_3(s) + 3H_2O(l) \rightarrow 2B(OH)_3(s)$. One molecule (formula unit) of diboron trioxide reacts exactly with three molecules of water, producing two molecules of boron trihydroxide (boric acid). One mole of diboron trioxide combines with three moles of water to produce two moles of boron trihydroxide (boric acid).
76. for O_2, 5 mol O_2/1 mol C_3H_8; for CO_2, 3 mol CO_2/1 mol C_3H_8; for H_2O, 4 mol H_2O/1 mol C_3H_8
78. (a) 0.0588 mol NH_4Cl; (b) 0.0178 mol $CaCO_3$; (c) 0.0217 mol Na_2O; (d) 0.0323 mol PCl_3
80. (a) 3.2×10^2 g HNO_3; (b) 0.0612 g Hg; (c) 4.49×10^{-3} g K_2CrO_4; (d) 1.40×10^3 g $AlCl_3$; (e) 7.2×10^6 g SF_6; (f) 2.13×10^3 g NH_3; (g) 0.9397 g Na_2O_2
82. 1.9×10^2 kg SO_3 84. 0.667 g O_2 86. 0.0771 g H_2
88. (a) Br_2 is limiting reactant, 6.4 g NaBr; (b) $CuSO_4$ is limiting reactant, 5.1 g $ZnSO_4$, 2.0 g Cu; (c) NH_4Cl is limiting reactant, 1.6 g NH_3, 1.7 g H_2O, 5.5 g NaCl; (d) Fe_2O_3 is limiting reactant, 3.5 g Fe, 4.1 g CO_2
90. 0.624 mol N_2, 17.5 g N_2; 1.25 mol H_2O, 22.5 g H_2O
92. 5.0 g

Chapter 10

2. Potential energy is energy due to position or composition. A stone at the top of a hill possesses potential energy because the stone may eventually roll down the hill. A gallon of gasoline possesses potential energy because heat will be released when the gasoline is burned.
4. The total energy of the universe is constant. Energy cannot be created or destroyed, but can only be converted from one form to another.
6. Ball A initially possesses potential energy by virtue of its position at the top of the hill. As ball A rolls down the hill, its potential energy is converted to kinetic energy and frictional (heat) energy. When ball A reaches the bottom of the hill and hits ball B, it transfers its kinetic energy to ball B. Ball A then has only the potential energy corresponding to its new position.
8. The hot tea is at a higher temperature, which means the particles in the hot tea have higher average kinetic energies. When the tea spills on the skin, energy flows from the hot tea to the skin, until the tea and skin are at the same temperature. This sudden inflow of energy causes the burn.
10. Temperature is the concept by which we express the thermal energy contained in a sample. We cannot measure the motions of the particles/kinetic energy in a sample of matter directly. We know, however, that if two objects are at different temperatures, the one with the higher temperature has molecules that have higher average kinetic energies than the molecules of the object at the lower temperature.
12. When the chemical system evolves energy, the energy evolved from the reacting chemicals is transferred to the surroundings.
14. exactly equal to   16. internal   18. losing
20. gaining
22. (a) $\dfrac{1\ J}{4.184\ cal}$; (b) $\dfrac{4.184\ cal}{1\ J}$; (c) $\dfrac{1\ kcal}{1000\ cal}$; (d) $\dfrac{1000\ J}{1\ kJ}$
24. 6540 J = 6.54 kJ
26. (a) 8.254 kcal; (b) 0.0415 kcal; (c) 8.231 kcal; (d) 752.9 kcal
28. (a) 243 kJ to three significant figures; (b) 0.004184 kJ; (c) 0.000251 kJ; (d) 0.4503 kJ
30. (a) 9.174×10^4 cal; (b) 425.7 cal; (c) 1.032 kcal; (d) 383.8 kJ
32. 5.8×10^2 J (two significant figures)   34. 29 °C
36. exothermic
38. 14.6 kJ (~15 kJ to one significant figure)
40. A calorimeter is an insulated device in which reactions are performed and temperature changes measured, enabling the calculation of heat flows. See Figure 10.6.
42. (a) −9.23 kJ; (b) −148 kJ; (c) +296 kJ/mol
44. (a) −29.5 kJ; (b) $\Delta H = -1360$ kJ; (c) 453 kJ/mol H_2O
46. −220 kJ   48. −233 kJ
50. Once everything in the universe is at the same temperature, no further thermodynamic work can be done. Even though the total energy of the universe will be the same, the energy will have been dispersed evenly, making it effectively useless.
52. Concentrated sources of energy, such as petroleum, are being used so as to disperse the energy they contain, making that energy unavailable for further human use.
54. Petroleum consists mainly of hydrocarbons, which are molecules containing chains of carbon atoms with hydrogen atoms attached to the chains. The fractions are based on the number of carbon atoms in the chains: for example, gasoline is a mixture of hydrocarbons with 5–10 carbon atoms in the chains, whereas asphalt is a mixture of hydrocarbons with 25 or more carbon atoms in the chains. Different fractions have different physical properties and uses, but all can be combusted to produce energy. See Table 10.3.
56. Tetraethyl lead was used as an additive for gasoline to promote smoother running of engines. It is no longer widely used because of concerns about the lead being released into the environment as the leaded gasoline burns.
58. The greenhouse effect is a warming effect due to the presence of gases in the atmosphere that absorb infrared radiation that has reached the earth from the sun; the gases do not allow the energy to pass back into space. A limited greenhouse effect is desirable because it moderates the temperature changes in the atmosphere that would otherwise be more drastic between daytime when the sun is shining and nighttime. Having too high a concentration of greenhouse gases, however, will elevate the temperature of the earth too much, affecting climate, crops, the polar ice caps, the temperatures of the oceans, and so on. Carbon dioxide produced by combustion reactions is our greatest concern as a greenhouse gas.
60. If a proposed reaction involves either or both of those phenomena, the reaction will tend to be favorable.

62. Formation of a solid precipitate represents a concentration of matter.

64. The molecules in liquid water are moving around freely and are therefore more "disordered" than when the molecules are held rigidly in a solid lattice in ice. The entropy increases during melting.

66. (a) 110.5 kcal; (b) 4.369 kcal; (c) 0.2424 kcal; (d) 45.53 kcal

68. 7.65 kcal **70.** 2.0×10^2 J (two significant figures)

72. 3.8×10^5 J **74.** 62.5 °C = 63 °C **76.** 9.0 J

78.

Substance	Specific Heat Capacity	Temperature Change
water (l)	4.184 J/g °C	23.9 °C
water (s)	2.03 J/g °C	49.3 °C
water (g)	2.0 J/g °C	50. °C
aluminum	0.89 J/g °C	1.1×10^2 °C
iron	0.45 J/g °C	2.2×10^2 °C
mercury	0.14 J/g °C	7.1×10^2 °C
carbon	0.71 J/g °C	1.4×10^2 °C
silver	0.24 J/g °C	4.2×10^2 °C
gold	0.13 J/g °C	7.7×10^2 °C

80. (a) exothermic; (b) exothermic; (c) endothermic; (d) endothermic

82. $\frac{1}{2}C + F \rightarrow A + B + D$ $\Delta H = 47.0$ kJ

84. Approximately 9 hr

Chapter 11

2. Rutherford's experiments determined that the atom had a nucleus containing positively charged particles called protons. He established that the nucleus was very small compared to the overall size of the atom. He was not able to determine where the electrons were in the atom or what they were doing.

4. The different forms of electromagnetic radiation all exhibit the same wavelike behavior and are propagated through space at the same speed (the "speed of light"). The types of electromagnetic radiation differ in their frequency (and wavelength) and in the resulting amount of energy carried per photon.

6. The frequency of electromagnetic radiation represents how many waves pass a given location per second. The speed of electromagnetic radiation represents how fast the waves propagate through space. The frequency and the speed are not the same.

8. The greenhouse gases do not absorb light in the visible wavelengths. Therefore, this light passes through the atmosphere and warms the earth, keeping the earth much warmer than it would be without these gases. As we are increasing our use of fossil fuels, the level of CO_2 in the atmosphere is increasing gradually but significantly. An increase in the level of CO_2 will warm the earth further, eventually changing the weather patterns on the earth's surface and melting the polar ice caps.

10. exactly equal to **12.** It is emitted as a photon.

14. absorbs

16. When excited hydrogen atoms emit their excess energy, the photons of radiation emitted always have exactly the same wavelength and energy. This means that the hydrogen atom possesses only certain allowed energy states, and that the photons emitted correspond to the electron changing from one of these allowed energy states to another allowed energy state. The energy of the photon emitted corresponds to the energy difference between the allowed states. If the hydrogen atom did *not* possess discrete energy levels, then the photons emitted would have random wavelengths and energies.

18. They are identical.

20. Energy is emitted at wavelengths corresponding to specific transitions for the electron among the energy levels of hydrogen.

22. The electron moves to an orbit farther from the nucleus of the atom.

24. Bohr's theory explained the experimentally observed line spectrum of hydrogen exactly. The theory was discarded because the calculated properties did not correspond closely to experimental measurements for atoms other than hydrogen.

26. An orbit refers to a definite, exact circular pathway around the nucleus, in which Bohr postulated that an electron would be found. An orbital represents a region of space in which there is a high probability of finding the electron.

28. The firefly analogy is intended to demonstrate the concept of a probability map for electron density. In the wave mechanical model of the atom, we cannot say specifically where the electron is in the atom; we can say only where there is a high probability of finding the electron. The analogy is to imagine a time-exposure photograph of a firefly in a closed room. Most of the time, the firefly will be found near the center of the room.

30. The drawing is a contour map, indicating a 90% probability that the electron is within the region of space bounded by that region. The electron may be anywhere within this region.

32. two-lobed ("dumbbell"-shaped); lower in energy and closer to the nucleus; similar shape

34. 1

36.

Value of n	Possible Subshells
1	1s
2	2s, 2p
3	3s, 3p, 3d
4	4s, 4p, 4d, 4f

38. Electrons have an intrinsic spin (they spin on their own axes). Geometrically, there are only two senses possible for spin (clockwise or counterclockwise). This means only two electrons can occupy an orbital, with the opposite sense or direction of spin. This idea is called the Pauli exclusion principle.

40. increases

42. paired (opposite spin)

44. (a) not possible; (b) possible; (c) possible; (d) not possible

46. For a hydrogen atom in its ground state, the electron is in the 1s orbital. The 1s orbital has the lowest energy of all hydrogen orbitals.

48. similar type of orbitals being filled in the same way; chemical properties of the members of the group are similar

50. (a) silicon; (b) beryllium; (c) neon; (d) argon

52. (a) selenium; (b) scandium; (c) sulfur; (d) iodine

54. (a) [↑↓] [↑↓] [↑↓][↑↓][↑↓] [↑↓]
        1s   2s   2p   3s

(b) [↑↓] [↑↓] [↑↓][↑↓][↑↓] [↑↓] [↑↑][↑][↑]
    1s   2s   2p   3s   3p

(c) [↑↓] [↑]
    1s   2s

(d) [↑↓] [↑↓] [↑↓][↑↓][↑↓] [↑↓] [↑↓][↑↓][↑↓] [↑↓]
    1s   2s   2p   3s   3p   4s
    [↑↓][↑↓][↑↓][↑↓][↑↓] [↑][↑][↑]
          3d   4p

56. Specific answers depend on student choice of elements. Any Group 1 element would have one valence electron. Any Group 3 element would have three valence electrons. Any Group 5 element would have five valence electrons. Any Group 7 element would have seven valence electrons.

58. The properties of Rb and Sr suggest that they are members of Groups 1 and 2, respectively, and so must be filling the 5s orbital. The 5s orbital is lower in energy than (and fills before) the 4d orbitals.

60. (a) aluminum; (b) potassium; (c) bromine; (d) tin

62. (a) $[Ne]3s^23p^3$; (b) $[Ne]3s^23p^5$; (c) $[Ne]3s^2$; (d) $[Ar]4s^23d^{10}$

64. (a) 1; (b) 2; (c) 0; (d) 10

66. (a) 5f; (b) 5f; (c) 4f; (d) 6p   **68.** $[Rn]7s^25f^{14}6d^5$

70. The metallic elements lose electrons and form positive ions (cations); the nonmetallic elements gain electrons and form negative ions (anions).

72. All exist as diatomic molecules (F_2, Cl_2, Br_2, I_2); are nonmetals; have relatively high electronegativities; and form 1− ions in reacting with metallic elements.

74. Elements at the left of a period (horizontal row) lose electrons most readily; at the left of a period (given principal energy level) the nuclear charge is the smallest and the electrons are least tightly held.

76. The elements of a given period (horizontal row) have valence electrons in the same subshells, but nuclear charge increases across a period going from left to right. Atoms at the left side have smaller nuclear charges and bind their valence electrons less tightly.

78. When substances absorb energy, the electrons become excited (move to higher energy levels). Upon returning to the ground state, energy is released, some of which is in the visible spectrum. Because we see colors, this tells us only certain wavelengths of light are released, which means that only certain transitions are allowed. This is what is meant by quantized energy levels. If all wavelengths of light were emitted, we would see white light.

80. (a) Li; (b) Ca; (c) Cl; (d) S

82. (a) Na; (b) S; (c) N; (d) F

84. speed of light   **86.** photons   **88.** quantized

90. orbital   **92.** transition metal   **94.** spins

96. (a) $1s^22s^22p^63s^23p^64s^1$; $[Ar]4s^1$;

$\uparrow\downarrow$	$\uparrow\downarrow$	$\uparrow\downarrow$ $\uparrow\downarrow$ $\uparrow\downarrow$	$\uparrow\downarrow$	$\uparrow\downarrow$ $\uparrow\downarrow$ $\uparrow\downarrow$	$\uparrow$
1s	2s	2p	3s	3p	4s

(b) $1s^22s^22p^63s^23p^64s^23d^2$; $[Ar]4s^23d^2$;

$\uparrow\downarrow$	$\uparrow\downarrow$	$\uparrow\downarrow$ $\uparrow\downarrow$ $\uparrow\downarrow$	$\uparrow\downarrow$	$\uparrow\downarrow$ $\uparrow\downarrow$ $\uparrow\downarrow$	$\uparrow\downarrow$
1s	2s	2p	3s	3p	4s

$\uparrow$	$\uparrow$		
3d			

(c) $1s^22s^22p^63s^23p^2$; $[Ne]3s^23p^2$;

$\uparrow\downarrow$	$\uparrow\downarrow$	$\uparrow\downarrow$ $\uparrow\downarrow$ $\uparrow\downarrow$	$\uparrow\downarrow$	$\uparrow$ $\uparrow$
1s	2s	2p	3s	3p

(d) $1s^22s^22p^63s^23p^64s^23d^6$; $[Ar]4s^23d^6$;

$\uparrow\downarrow$	$\uparrow\downarrow$	$\uparrow\downarrow$ $\uparrow\downarrow$ $\uparrow\downarrow$	$\uparrow\downarrow$	$\uparrow\downarrow$ $\uparrow\downarrow$ $\uparrow\downarrow$	$\uparrow\downarrow$
1s	2s	2p	3s	3p	4s

$\uparrow\downarrow$	$\uparrow$	$\uparrow$	$\uparrow$	$\uparrow$
3d				

(e) $1s^22s^22p^63s^23p^64s^23d^{10}$; $[Ar]4s^23d^{10}$;

$\uparrow\downarrow$	$\uparrow\downarrow$	$\uparrow\downarrow$ $\uparrow\downarrow$ $\uparrow\downarrow$	$\uparrow\downarrow$	$\uparrow\downarrow$ $\uparrow\downarrow$ $\uparrow\downarrow$	$\uparrow\downarrow$
1s	2s	2p	3s	3p	4s

$\uparrow\downarrow$ $\uparrow\downarrow$ $\uparrow\downarrow$ $\uparrow\downarrow$ $\uparrow\downarrow$
3d

98. (a) ns^2; (b) ns^2np^5; (c) ns^2np^4; (d) ns^1; (e) ns^2np^4

100. (a) 2.7×10^{-12} m; (b) 4.4×10^{-34} m; (c) 2×10^{-35} m; the wavelengths for the ball and the person are infinitesimally small, whereas the wavelength for the electron is nearly the same order of magnitude as the diameter of a typical atom.

102. Light is emitted from the hydrogen atom only at certain fixed wavelengths. If the energy levels of hydrogen were continuous, a hydrogen atom would emit energy at all possible wavelengths.

104. The third principal energy level of hydrogen is divided into three sublevels (3s, 3p, and 3d); there is a single 3s orbital, a set of three 3p orbitals, and a set of five 3d orbitals. See Figures 11.25 – 11.28 for the shapes of these orbitals.

106. Answer depends on student choice of examples.

108. (a) $1s^22s^22p^63s^23p^64s^23d^{10}4p^5$
(b) $1s^22s^22p^63s^23p^64s^23d^{10}4p^65s^24d^{10}5p^6$
(c) $1s^22s^22p^63s^23p^64s^23d^{10}4p^65s^24d^{10}5p^66s^2$
(d) $1s^22s^22p^63s^23p^64s^23d^{10}4p^4$

110. (a) five (2s, 2p); (b) seven (3s, 3p); (c) one (3s);
(d) three (3s, 3p)

112. (a) $[Kr]5s^24d^2$; (b) $[Kr]5s^24d^{10}5p^5$; (c) $[Ar]4s^23d^{10}4p^2$;
(d) $[Xe]6s^1$

114. (a) Se; (b) Se; (c) Rb; (d) V

116. metals, low; nonmetals, high

118. (a) Ca; (b) P; (c) K

Chapter 12

2. The *bond energy* represents the energy required to break a chemical bond.

4. A covalent bond represents the *sharing* of electrons by nuclei.

6. In H_2 and HF, the bonding is covalent in nature, with an electron pair being shared between the atoms. In H_2, the two atoms are identical and so the sharing is equal; in HF, the two atoms are different and so the bonding is polar covalent. Both of these are in marked contrast to the situation in NaF: NaF is an ionic compound, and an electron is completely transferred from sodium to fluorine, thereby producing the separate ions.

8. A bond is polar if the centers of positive and negative charge do not coincide at the same point. The bond has a negative end and a positive end. Any molecule in which the atoms in the bonds are not identical will have polar bonds (although the molecule as a whole may not be polar). Two simple examples are HCl and HF.

10. The difference in electronegativity between the atoms in the bond

12. (a) I is most electronegative, Rb is least electronegative;
(b) Mg is most electronegative, Ca and Sr have similar electronegativities; (c) Br is most electronegative, K is least electronegative

14. (a) ionic; (b) polar covalent; (c) covalent

16. c and d

18. (a) O—Br; (b) N—F; (c) P—O; (d) H—O

20. (a) Ca–Cl; (b) Ba–Cl; (c) Fe–I; (d) Be–F

22. The presence of strong bond dipoles and a large overall dipole moment makes water a very polar substance. Properties of water that are dependent on its dipole moment involve its freezing point, melting point, vapor pressure, and ability to dissolve many substances.

24. (a) H; (b) Cl; (c) I

26. (a) $^{\delta+}S \rightarrow O^{\delta-}$; (b) $^{\delta+}S \rightarrow N^{\delta-}$; (c) $^{\delta+}S \rightarrow F^{\delta-}$; (d) $^{\delta+}S \rightarrow Cl^{\delta-}$

28. (a) $^{\delta+}H \rightarrow C^{\delta-}$; (b) $^{\delta+}N \rightarrow O^{\delta-}$;
(c) $^{\delta+}S \rightarrow N^{\delta-}$; (d) $^{\delta+}C \rightarrow N^{\delta-}$;

30. preceding

32. Atoms in covalent molecules gain a configuration like that of a noble gas by sharing one or more pairs of electrons between atoms: such shared pairs of electrons "belong" to each of the bonding atoms at the same time. In ionic bonding, one atom completely donates one or more electrons to another atom, and then the resulting ions behave independently of one another (they are not "attached" to one another, although they are mutually attracted).

34. (a) Br^- [Kr]; (b) Cs^+ [Xe]; (c) P^{3-} [Ar]; (d) S^{2-} [Ar]

36. (a) F^-, O^{2-}, N^{3-}; (b) Cl^-, S^{2-}, P^{3-};
(c) F^-, O^{2-}, N^{3-}; (d) Br^-, Se^{2-}, As^{3-}

38. (a) $AlBr_3$; (b) Al_2O_3; (c) AlP; (d) AlH_3

40. Answers depend on student choice of examples.

42. An ionic solid such as NaCl consists of an array of alternating positively and negatively charged ions: that is, each positive ion has as its nearest neighbors a group of negative ions, and each negative ion has a group of positive ions surrounding it. In most ionic solids, the ions are packed as tightly as possible.

44. In forming an anion, an atom gains additional electrons in its outermost (valence) shell. Having additional electrons in the valence shell increases the repulsive forces between electrons, and the outermost shell becomes larger to accommodate this.

46. (a) F^- is larger than Li^+. The F^- ion has a filled $n = 2$ shell. A lithium atom has *lost* the electron from its $n = 2$ shell, leaving the $n = 1$ shell as its outermost. (b) Cl^- is larger than Na^+, since its valence electrons are in the $n = 3$ shell (Na^+ has lost its $3s$ electron). (c) Ca is larger than Ca^{2+}. Positive ions are always smaller than the atoms from which they are formed. (d) I^- is larger. Both Cs^+ and I^- have the same electron configuration (isoelectronic with Xe) and have their valence electrons in the same shell. However, Cs^+ has two more positive charges in its nucleus than does I^-; this charge causes the $n = 5$ shell of Cs^+ to be smaller than that of I^- (the electrons are pulled in closer to the nucleus by the positive charge).

48. (a) I; (b) F^-; (c) F^-

50. When atoms form covalent bonds, they try to attain a valence-electron configuration similar to that of the following noble gas element. When the elements in the first few horizontal rows of the periodic table form covalent bonds, they attempt to achieve the configurations of the noble gases helium (two valence electrons, duet rule) and neon and argon (eight valence electrons, octet rule).

52. These elements attain a total of eight valence electrons, giving the valence-electron configurations of the noble gases Ne and Ar.

54. Two atoms in a molecule are connected by a triple bond if the atoms share three pairs of electrons (six electrons) to complete their outermost shells. A simple molecule containing a triple bond is acetylene, C_2H_2 (H:C:::C:H).

56. (a) Mg:; (b) :Br·; (c) :S·; (d) :Si

58. (a) 24; (b) 16; (c) 20; (d) 17

60. (a) H—H (b) H—Cl:

(c) (d)

62. (a) (b)

(c) (d) H—N—N—H

64. :O≡C—Ö: ⟷ Ö=C=Ö ⟷ :Ö—C≡O:

66. (a) ClO_3^-

(b) O_2^{2-}

(c) $C_2H_3O_2^-$

68. (a)

(b) (c)

70. The geometric structure of NH_3 is that of a trigonal pyramid. The nitrogen atom of NH_3 is surrounded by four electron pairs (three are bonding, one is a lone pair). The H—N—H bond angle is somewhat less than 109.5° (because of the presence of the lone pair).

72. SiF_4 has a tetrahedral geometric structure; eight pairs of electrons on Si; ~109.5°

74. The general molecular structure of a molecule is determined by how many electron pairs surround the central atom in the molecule, and by which of those pairs are used for bonding to the other atoms of the molecule.

76. Geometry shows that only two points in space are needed to indicate a straight line. A diatomic molecule represents two points in space.

78. In NF_3, the nitrogen atom has *four* pairs of valence electrons; in BF_3, only *three* pairs of valence electrons surround the boron atom. The nonbonding pair on nitrogen in NF_3 pushes the three F atoms out of the plane of the N atom.

80. (a) four pairs of electrons in a (distorted) tetrahedral arrangement; (b) four pairs of electrons in a (slightly distorted) tetrahedral arrangement; (c) four pairs of electrons in a tetrahedral arrangement

82. (a) trigonal pyramidal; (b) trigonal pyramidal; (c) nonlinear (bent, V-shaped)

84. (a) basically tetrahedral arrangement of the oxygens around the phosphorus; (b) tetrahedral; (c) trigonal pyramid

86. (a) approximately tetrahedral (a little less than 109.5°); (b) approximately tetrahedral (a little less than 109.5°); (c) tetrahedral (109.5°); (d) trigonal planar (120°) because of the double bond

88. 120° around the carbon atoms in the rings; 120° also for the C—N—N and N—N—C bond angles. The double bonds influence the bond angles greatly, with each atom having only three "effective pairs" of electrons around the atom.

90. double

92. (a) S—F; (b) P—O; (c) C—H

94. The bond energy is the energy required to break the bond.

96. (a) Be; (b) N; (c) F

98. a, c

100. (a) O; (b) Br; (c) I

102. (a) Al: $1s^2 2s^2 2p^6 3s^2 3p^1$; Al^{3+}: $1s^2 2s^2 2p^6$; Ne has the same configuration as Al^{3+}; (b) Br: $1s^2 2s^2 2p^6 3s^2 3p^6 4s^2 3d^{10} 4p^5$; Br$^-$: $1s^2 2s^2 2p^6 3s^2 3p^6 4s^2\ 3d^{10} 4p^6$; Kr has the same configuration as Br$^-$; (c) Ca: $1s^2 2s^2 2p^6 3s^2 3p^6 4s^2$; Ca^{2+}: $1s^2 2s^2 2p^6 3s^2 3p^6$; Ar has the same configuration as Ca^{2+}; (d) Li: $1s^2 2s^1$; Li$^+$: $1s^2$; He has the same configuration as Li$^+$; (e) F: $1s^2 2s^2 2p^5$; F$^-$: $1s^2 2s^2 2p^6$; Ne has the same configuration as F$^-$.

104. (a) Na$_2$Se; (b) RbF; (c) K$_2$Te; (d) BaSe; (e) KAt; (f) FrCl

106. (a) Na$^+$; (b) Al^{3+}; (c) F$^-$; (d) Na$^+$

108. (a) 24; (b) 32; (c) 32; (d) 32

110. (a) N$_2$H$_4$ $\quad$ H—N̈—N̈—H
$\qquad\qquad$ | $\ \,$ |
$\qquad\qquad$ H $\ $ H

(b)
$\qquad\qquad$ H $\ $ H
$\qquad\qquad$ | $\ \,$ |
C$_2$H$_6$ $\ $ H—C—C—H
$\qquad\qquad$ | $\ \,$ |
$\qquad\qquad$ H $\ $ H

(c) NCl$_3$ $\quad$:C̈l—N̈—C̈l:
$\qquad\qquad\qquad$ |
$\qquad\qquad\qquad$:C̈l:

(d)
$\qquad\qquad\qquad$:C̈l:
$\qquad\qquad\qquad$ |
SiCl$_4$ $\ $:C̈l—Si—C̈l:
$\qquad\qquad\qquad$ |
$\qquad\qquad\qquad$:C̈l:

112. (a) NO$_3^-$ $\quad \left[\ddot{O}=N—\ddot{O}: \right]^- \ \leftrightarrow \ \left[:\ddot{O}—N=\ddot{O} \right]^- \ \leftrightarrow$
$\qquad\qquad\qquad$ | $\qquad\qquad\qquad$ |
$\qquad\qquad\qquad$:Ö: $\qquad\qquad\qquad$:Ö:

$\qquad\qquad \left[:\ddot{O}—N=\ddot{O}: \right]^-$
$\qquad\qquad\qquad$ ‖
$\qquad\qquad\qquad$:O:

(b) CO$_3^{2-}$ $\quad \left[\ddot{O}=C—\ddot{O}: \right]^{2-} \leftrightarrow \left[:\ddot{O}—C=\ddot{O} \right]^{2-} \leftrightarrow$
$\qquad\qquad\qquad$ | $\qquad\qquad\qquad$ |
$\qquad\qquad\qquad$:Ö: $\qquad\qquad\qquad$:Ö:

$\qquad\qquad \left[:\ddot{O}—C=\ddot{O}: \right]^{2-}$
$\qquad\qquad\qquad$ ‖
$\qquad\qquad\qquad$:O:

(c) NH$_4^+$ $\quad \left[\begin{array}{c} H \\ | \\ H—N—H \\ | \\ H \end{array} \right]^+$

114. (a) four pairs arranged tetrahedrally; (b) four pairs arranged tetrahedrally; (c) three pairs arranged trigonally (planar)

116. (a) trigonal pyramid; (b) nonlinear (V-shaped); (c) tetrahedral

118. (a) nonlinear (V-shaped); (b) trigonal planar; (c) basically trigonal planar around C, distorted somewhat by H; (d) linear

120. Ionic compounds tend to be hard, crystalline substances with relatively high melting and boiling points. Covalently bonded substances tend to be gases, liquids, or relatively soft solids, with much lower melting and boiling points.

Chapter 13

2. Solids are rigid and incompressible and have definite shapes and volumes. Liquids are less rigid than solids; although they have definite volumes, liquids take the shape of their con-

tainers. Gases have no fixed volume or shape; they take the volume and shape of their container and are affected more by changes in their pressure and temperature than are solids or liquids.

4. A mercury barometer consists of a tube filled with mercury that is then inverted over a reservoir of mercury, the surface of which is open to the atmosphere. The pressure of the atmosphere is reflected in the height to which the column of mercury in the tube is supported.

6. Pressure units include mm Hg, torr, pascals, and psi. The unit "mm Hg" is derived from the barometer, because in a traditional mercury barometer, we measure the height of the mercury column (in millimeters) above the reservoir of mercury.

8. (a) 1.01 atm; (b) 1.05 atm; (c) 99.1 kPa; (d) 99.436 kPa

10. (a) 119 kPa; (b) 16.9 psi; (c) 3.23×10^3 mm Hg; (d) 15.2 atm

12. (a) 651 kPa; (b) 3.20×10^3 torr; (c) 1.04 atm; (d) 1.85 atm

14. Additional mercury increases the pressure on the gas sample, causing the volume of the gas upon which the pressure is exerted to decrease (Boyle's law).

16. $PV = k$; $P_1 V_1 = P_2 V_2$

18. (a) 423 mL; (b) 158 mL; (c) 8.67 L

20. (a) 689 mm Hg; (b) 1.20 atm; (c) 2.35 L

22. 0.520 L

24. 27.2 atm

26. Charles's law indicates that an ideal gas decreases by 1/273 of its volume for every Celsius degree its temperature is lowered. This means an ideal gas would approach a volume of zero at $-273\ °C$.

28. $V = bT$; $V_1/T_1 = V_2/T_2$

30. 315 mL

32. (a) 80.2 mL; (b) $-77\ °C$ (196 K); (c) 208 mL (2.1×10^2 mL)

34. (a) 35.4 K = $-238\ °C$; (b) 0 mL (absolute zero; a real gas would condense to a solid or liquid); (c) 40.5 mL

36. 69.4 mL (69 mL to two significant figures)

38. 90 °C, 124 mL; 80 °C, 121 mL; 70 °C, 117 mL; 60 °C, 113 mL; 50 °C, 110. mL; 40 °C, 107 mL; 30 °C, 103 mL; 20 °C, 99.8 mL

40. $V = an$; $V_1/n_1 = V_2/n_2$

42. 1744 mL (1.74×10^3 mL)

44. 80.1 L

46. Real gases behave most ideally at relatively high temperatures and relatively low pressures. We usually assume that a real gas's behavior approaches ideal behavior if the temperature is over 0 °C (273 K) and the pressure is 1 atm or lower.

48. For an ideal gas, $PV = nRT$ is true under any conditions. Consider a particular sample of gas (n remains constant) at a particular fixed pressure (P remains constant). Suppose that at temperature T_1 the volume of the gas sample is V_1. For this set of conditions, the ideal gas equation would be given by $PV_1 = nRT_1$. If the temperature of the gas sample changes to a new temperature, T_2, then the volume of the gas sample changes to a new volume, V_2. For this new set of conditions, the ideal gas equation would be given by $PV_2 = nRT_2$. If we make a *ratio* of these two expressions for the ideal gas equation for this gas sample, and cancel out terms that are constant for this situation (P, n, and R), we get

$$\frac{PV_1}{PV_2} = \frac{nRT_1}{nRT_2}, \text{ or } \frac{V_1}{V_2} = \frac{T_1}{T_2},$$

which can be rearranged to the familiar form of Charles's law,

$$\frac{V_1}{T_1} = \frac{V_2}{T_2}.$$

50. (a) 5.02 L;   (b) 3.56 atm = 2.70×10^3 mm Hg;   (c) 334 K

52. 0.747 atm

54. 304 K, 31 °C

56. 0.150 atm; 0.163 atm

58. 238 K/−35 °C

60. The helium (5.07 atm) is at a higher pressure than the argon (3.50 atm).

62. 0.332 atm; 0.346 atm

64. ~283 atm (2.8×10^2 atm)

66. As a gas is bubbled through water, the bubbles of gas become saturated with water vapor, thus forming a gaseous mixture. The total pressure for a sample of gas that has been collected by bubbling through water is made up of two components: the pressure of the sample gas and the pressure of water vapor. The partial pressure of the gas equals the total pressure of the sample minus the vapor pressure of water.

68. 0.314 atm

70. 3.00 g Ne; 5.94 g Ar

72. 3.07 atm

74. $P_{hydrogen}$ = 0.990 atm; 9.55×10^{-3} mol H_2; 0.625 g Zn

76. A theory is successful if it explains known experimental observations. Theories that have been successful in the past may not be successful in the future (for example, as technology evolves, more sophisticated experiments may be possible in the future).

78. pressure

80. no

82. If the temperature of a sample of gas is increased, the average kinetic energy of the particles of gas increases. This means that the speeds of the particles increase. If the particles have a higher speed, they hit the walls of the container more frequently and with greater force, thereby increasing the pressure.

84. STP = 0 °C, 1 atm pressure. These conditions were chosen because they are easy to attain and reproduce *experimentally*. The barometric pressure within a laboratory will usually be near 1 atm, and 0 °C can be attained with a simple ice bath.

86. 2.50 L O_2

88. 0.941 L

90. 0.941 L; 0.870 L

92. 5.03 L (dry volume)

94. 52.7 L

96. 28.1 L He; 23.6 L Ar

98. 40.5 L; P_{He} = 0.864 atm; P_{Ne} = 0.136 atm

100. 1.72 L

102. 0.365 g

104. twice

106. (a) $PV = k$; $P_1V_1 = P_2V_2$;   (b) $V = bT$; $V_1/T_1 = V_2/T_2$;   (c) $V = an$; $V_1/n_1 = V_2/n_2$;   (d) $PV = nRT$;   (e) $P_1V_1/T_1 = P_2V_2/T_2$

108. 125 balloons

110. 124 L

112. 0.0999 mol CO_2; 3.32 L wet; 2.68 L dry

114. 18.1 L O_2

116. (a) 1.00×10^5 Pa;   (b) 4.52 atm;   (c) 1087 (1.09×10^3) mm Hg;   (d) 842 mm Hg

118. (a) 8.60×10^4 Pa;   (b) 2.21×10^5 Pa;   (c) 8.88×10^4 Pa;   (d) 4.3×10^3 Pa

120. (a) 128 mL;   (b) 1.3×10^{-2} L;   (c) 9.8 L

122. 2.55×10^3 mm Hg

124. (a) 57.3 mL;   (b) 448 K = 175 °C;   (c) zero (absolute zero; a real gas would condense to a solid or liquid)

126. 123 mL

128. 2.59 g

130. (a) 61.8 K;   (b) 0.993 atm;   (c) 1.66×10^4 L

132. 487 mol gas needed; 7.79 kg CH_4; 13.6 kg N_2; 21.4 kg CO_2

134. 0.42 atm

136. 2.51×10^3 K

138. 32.4 L

140. 3.43 L N_2; 10.3 L H_2

142. 5.8 L O_2; 3.9 L SO_2

144. 7.8×10^2 L

146. 32 L; P_{He} = 0.86 atm; P_{Ar} = 0.017 atm; P_{Ne} = 0.12 atm

148. 22.4 L O_2

Chapter 14

2. less

4. Because it requires so much more energy to vaporize water than to melt ice, this suggests that the gaseous state is significantly different from the liquid state, but that the liquid and solid states are relatively similar.

6. See Figure 14.2.

8. When a solid is heated, the molecules begin to vibrate/move more quickly. When enough energy has been added to overcome the intermolecular forces that hold the molecules in a crystal lattice, the solid melts. As the liquid is heated, the molecules begin to move more quickly and more randomly. When enough energy has been added, molecules having sufficient kinetic energy will begin to escape from the surface of the liquid. Once the pressure of vapor coming from the liquid is equal to the pressure above the liquid, the liquid boils. Only intermolecular forces need to be overcome in this process: no chemical bonds are broken.

10. intramolecular; intermolecular

12. The quantity of energy that must be applied to melt 1 mole of the substance.

14. (a) In going from a liquid to a gas, a considerably larger amount of the heat being applied has to be converted to the kinetic energy of the atoms escaping from the liquid;   (b) 10.9 kJ;   (c) −2.00 kJ (heat is evolved);   (d) 1.13 kJ

16. 2.44 kJ; −10.6 kJ (heat is evolved)

18. 2.60 kJ/mol

20. weaker

22. The hydrogen bonding that can exist when H is bonded to O (or N or F) is an additional intermolecular force, which means additional energy must be added to separate the molecules during boiling.

24. London dispersion forces are instantaneous dipole forces that arise when the electron cloud of an atom is momentarily distorted by a nearby dipole, temporarily separating the centers of positive and negative charge in the atom.

26. (a) London dispersion forces;   (b) hydrogen bonding (H bonded to N); London dispersion forces;   (c) London dispersion forces;   (d) dipole–dipole forces (polar molecules); London dispersion forces

28. An increase in the heat of fusion is observed for an increase in the size of the halogen atom (the electron cloud of a larger atom is more easily polarized by a neighboring dipole, thus giving larger London dispersion forces).

30. For a homogeneous mixture to form, the forces between molecules of the two substances being mixed must be at least *comparable in magnitude* to the intermolecular forces within each separate substance. In the case of a water–ethanol mixture, the forces that exist when water and ethanol are mixed are stronger than water–water or ethanol–ethanol forces in the separate substances. Ethanol and water molecules can approach one another more closely in the mixture than either substance's molecules could approach a like molecule in the separate substances. Strong hydrogen bonding occurs in both ethanol and water.

32. When a liquid is placed into a closed container, a dynamic equilibrium is set up, in which vaporization of the liquid and condensation of the vapor are occurring at the same rate. Once the equilibrium has been achieved, there is a net concentration of molecules in the vapor state, which gives rise to the observed vapor pressure.

34. A liquid is injected at the bottom of the column of mercury and rises to the surface of the mercury, where the liquid evaporates into the vacuum above the mercury column. As the liquid evaporates, the pressure of the vapor increases in the space above the mercury and presses down on the mercury. The level of mercury therefore drops, and the amount by which the mercury level drops (in mm Hg) is equivalent to the vapor pressure of the liquid.

36. (a) HF: Although both substances are capable of hydrogen bonding, water has two O—H bonds that can be involved in hydrogen bonding versus only one F—H bond in HF; (b) CH_3OCH_3: Because no H is attached to the O atom, no hydrogen bonding can exist. Thus, the molecule should be relatively more volatile than CH_3CH_2OH even though it contains the same number of atoms of each element; (c) CH_3SH: Hydrogen bonding is not as important for a S—H bond (because S has a lower electronegativity than O). Since there is relatively little hydrogen bonding, CH_3SH is more volatile than CH_3OH.

38. Both substances have the same molar mass. Ethyl alcohol contains a hydrogen atom directly bonded to an oxygen atom, however. Therefore, hydrogen bonding can exist in ethyl alcohol, whereas only weak dipole–dipole forces exist in dimethyl ether. Dimethyl ether is more volatile; ethyl alcohol has a higher boiling point.

40. *Ionic* solids have positive and negative ions as their fundamental particles; a simple example is sodium chloride, in which Na^+ and Cl^- ions are held together by strong electrostatic forces. *Molecular* solids have molecules as their fundamental particles, with the molecules being held together in the crystal by dipole–dipole forces, hydrogen-bonding forces, or London dispersion forces (depending on the identity of the substance); simple examples of molecular solids include ice (H_2O) and ordinary table sugar (sucrose). *Atomic* solids have simple atoms as their fundamental particles, with the atoms being held together in the crystal by either covalent bonding (as in graphite or diamond) or metallic bonding (as in copper or other metals).

42. sugar: molecular solid, relatively "soft," melts at a relatively low temperature, dissolves as molecules, does not conduct electricity when dissolved or melted; salt: ionic solid, relatively "hard," melts at a high temperature, dissolves as positively and negatively charged ions, conducts electricity when dissolved or melted.

44. Sodium chloride is an ionic substance in which a crystal lattice of alternating positive and negative ions holds the substance together with very strong forces that are difficult to overcome. Sucrose is a molecular substance in which the molecules are held together in the solid by dipole–dipole (and H-bonding) forces, which are weaker than the ionic forces.

46. In liquid hydrogen, the only intermolecular forces are weak London dispersion forces. In ethyl alcohol and water, hydrogen bonding is possible, but the hydrogen bonding forces are weaker in ethyl alcohol because of the influence of the remainder of the molecule. In sucrose, hydrogen bonding also is possible but now at several places in the molecule, leading to stronger forces. In calcium chloride, there exists an ionic crystal lattice with even stronger forces between the particles.

48. Although ions exist in both the solid and liquid states, in the solid state the ions are rigidly held in place in the crystal lattice and cannot move so as to conduct an electric current.

50. Nitinol is an alloy of nickel and titanium. When nickel and titanium are heated to a sufficiently high temperature during the production of Nitinol, the atoms arrange themselves in a compact and regular pattern of the atoms.

52. j

54. f

56. d

58. a

60. l

62. Diethyl ether has the larger vapor pressure. No hydrogen bonding is possible because the O atom does not have a hydrogen atom attached. Hydrogen bonding can occur *only* when a hydrogen atom is *directly* attached to a strongly electronegative atom (such as N, O, or F). Hydrogen bonding *is* possible in 1-butanol (1-butano contains an —OH group).

64. (a) H_2. London dispersion forces are the only intermolecular forces present in these nonpolar molecules; typically these forces become larger with increasing atomic size (as the atoms become bigger, the edge of the electron cloud lies farther from the nucleus and becomes more easily distorted); (b) Xe. Only the relatively weak London forces exist in a crystal of Xe atoms, whereas in NaCl strong ionic forces exist, and in diamond strong covalent bonding exists between carbon atoms; (c) Cl_2. Only London forces exist among such nonpolar molecules.

66. *Steel* is a general term applied to alloys consisting primarily of iron, but with small amounts of other substances added. Whereas pure iron itself is relatively soft, malleable, and ductile, steels are typically much stronger and harder and much less subject to damage.

68. Water is the solvent in which cellular processes take place in living creatures. Water in the oceans moderates the earth's temperature. Water is used in industry as a cooling agent, and it serves as a means of transportation. The liquid range is 0 °C to 100 °C at 1 atm pressure.

70. At higher altitudes, the boiling points of liquids are lower because there is a lower atmospheric pressure above the liquid. The temperature at which food cooks is determined by the temperature to which the water in the food can be heated before it escapes as steam. Thus, food cooks at a lower temperature at high elevations where the boiling point of water is lowered.

72. Heat of fusion (melt); heat of vaporization (boil). The heat of vaporization is always larger, because virtually all of the intermolecular forces must be overcome to form a gas. In a liquid, considerable intermolecular forces remain. Going from a solid to a liquid requires less energy than going from a liquid to a gas.

74. Dipole–dipole interactions are typically 1% as strong as a covalent bond. Dipole–dipole interactions represent electrostatic attractions between portions of molecules that carry only a *partial* positive or negative charge, and such forces require the molecules that are interacting to come *near* each other.

76. London dispersion forces are relatively weak forces that arise among noble gas atoms and in nonpolar molecules. London forces arise from *instantaneous dipoles* that develop when one atom (or molecule) momentarily distorts the electron cloud of another atom (or molecule). London forces are typically weaker than either permanent dipole–dipole forces or covalent bonds.

78. For each mole of liquid water that evaporates, several kilojoules of heat must be absorbed by the water from its surroundings to overcome attractive forces among the molecules.

80. In NH_3, strong hydrogen bonding can exist. Because CH_4 molecules are nonpolar, only the relatively weak London dispersion forces exist.

82. Strong *hydrogen-bonding* forces are present in an ice crystal, while only the much weaker *London forces* exist in the crystal of a nonpolar substance like oxygen.

84. Ice floats on liquid water; water expands when it is frozen.

86. Although they are at the same *temperature*, steam at 100 °C contains a larger amount of *energy* than hot water, equal to the heat of vaporization of water.

88. Hydrogen bonding is a special case of dipole–dipole interactions that occur among molecules containing hydrogen atoms bonded to highly electronegative atoms such as fluorine, oxygen, or nitrogen. The bonds are very polar, and the small size of the hydrogen atom (compared to other atoms) allows the dipoles to approach each other very closely. Examples: H_2O, NH_3, HF.

90. Evaporation and condensation are opposite processes. Evaporation is an endothermic process; condensation is an exothermic process. Evaporation requires an input of energy to provide the increased kinetic energy possessed by the molecules when they are in the gaseous state. It occurs when the molecules in a liquid are moving fast enough and randomly enough that molecules are able to escape from the surface of the liquid and enter the vapor phase.

Chapter 15

2. A *non*homogeneous mixture may differ in composition in various places in the mixture, whereas a solution (a homogeneous mixture) has the same composition throughout. Examples of nonhomogeneous mixtures include spaghetti sauce, a jar of jelly beans, and a mixture of salt and sugar.

4. solid

6. "Like dissolves like." The hydrocarbons in oil have intermolecular forces that are very different from those in water, so the oil spreads out rather than dissolving in the water.

8. Carbon dioxide is somewhat soluble in water, especially if pressurized (otherwise, the soda you may be drinking while studying chemistry would be "flat"). Carbon dioxide's solubility in water is approximately 1.5 g/L at 25 °C under a pressure of approximately 1 atm. The carbon dioxide molecule overall is nonpolar, because the two individual C—O bond dipoles cancel each other due to the linearity of the molecule. However, these bond dipoles are able to interact with water, making CO_2 more soluble in water than nonpolar molecules such as O_2 or N_2, which do not possess individual bond dipoles.

10. unsaturated

12. large

14. 100.

16. (a) 0.116%; (b) 0.0116%; (c) 10.4%; (d) 10.4%

18. (a) 20.5 g $FeCl_3$; 504.5 g (505 g) water; (b) 26.8 g sucrose; 198.2 g (198 g) water; (c) 181.3 g (181 g) NaCl; 1268.7 (1.27×10^3) g water; (d) 95.9 g KNO_3; 539.1 (539) g water

20. 957 g Fe; 26.9 g C; 16.5 g Cr

22. 19.6% $CaCl_2$

24. 7.81 g KBr

26. approximately 71 g

28. 9.5 g

30. 0.110 mol; 0.220 mol

32. b

34. (a) 3.35 M; (b) 1.03 M; (c) 0.630 M; (d) 4.99 M

36. (a) 0.403 M; (b) 0.169 M; (c) 0.629 M; (d) 0.829 M

38. 4.03 g KBr

40. 0.0902 M

42. 0.479 M

44. (a) 0.00130 mol; (b) 0.00609 mol; (c) 0.0184 mol; (d) 0.0356 mol

46. (a) 0.235 g; (b) 0.593 g; (c) 2.29 g; (d) 2.61 g

48. 9.51 g

50. (a) 4.60×10^{-3} mol Al^{3+}, 1.38×10^{-2} mol Cl^-; (b) 1.70 mol Na^+, 0.568 mol PO_4^{3-}; (c) 2.19×10^{-3} mol Cu^{2+}, 4.38×10^{-3} mol Cl^-; (d) 3.96×10^{-5} mol Ca^{2+}, 7.91×10^{-5} mol OH^-

52. 1.33 g

54. half

56. (a) 0.0717 M; (b) 1.69 M; (c) 0.0426 M; (d) 0.625 M

58. 0.541 L (541 mL)

60. Dilute 48.3 mL of the 1.01 M solution to a final volume of 325 mL.

62. 10.3 mL

64. 31.2 mL

66. 0.523 g

68. 0.300 g

70. 378 mL

72. 1.8×10^{-4} M

74. (a) 63.0 mL; (b) 2.42 mL; (c) 50.1 mL; (d) 1.22 L

76. 1 N

78. 1.53 equivalents OH^- ion. By definition, one equivalent of OH^- ion exactly neutralizes one equivalent of H^+ ion.

80. (a) 0.277 N; (b) 3.37×10^{-3} N; (c) 1.63 N

82. (a) 0.134 N; (b) 0.0104 N; (c) 13.3 N

84. 7.03×10^{-5} M, 1.41×10^{-4} N

86. 22.2 mL, 11.1 mL

88. 0.05583 M, 0.1117 N

90. Molarity is defined as the number of moles of solute contained in 1 liter of *total* solution volume (solute plus solvent after mixing). In the first example, the total volume after mixing is *not* known and the molarity cannot be calculated. In the second example, the final volume after mixing is known and the molarity can be calculated simply.

92. 3.3%

94. 12.7 g $NaHCO_3$

96. 56 mol

98. 1.12 L HCl at STP

100. 26.3 mL

102. 2.56 M

104. (a) 6.3% KNO_3; (b) 0.25% KNO_3; (c) 11% KNO_3; (d) 18% KNO_3

106. 4.7% C, 1.4% Ni, 93.9% Fe

108. 28 g Na_2CO_3

110. 9.4 g NaCl, 3.1 g KBr

112. (a) 4.0 M; (b) 1.0 M; (c) 0.73 M; (d) 3.6 M

114. 0.812 M

116. 0.026 M

118. (a) 0.446 mol, 33.3 g; (b) 0.00340 mol, 0.289 g; (c) 0.075 mol, 2.7 g; (d) 0.0505 mol, 4.95 g

120. (a) 0.938 mol Na^+, 0.313 mol PO_4^{3-}; (b) 0.042 mol H^+, 0.021 mol SO_4^{2-}; (c) 0.0038 mol Al^{3+}, 0.011 mol Cl^-; (d) 1.88 mol Ba^{2+}, 3.75 mol Cl^-

122. (a) 0.0909 M; (b) 0.127 M; (c) 0.192 M; (d) 1.6 M

124. 0.90 M

126. 50. mL

128. 35.0 mL

130. (a) 0.822 N HCl; (b) 4.00 N H_2SO_4; (c) 3.06 N H_3PO_4

132. 0.083 M NaH_2PO_4, 0.17 N NaH_2PO_4

134. 9.6×10^{-2} N HNO_3

Chapter 16

2. $HCl(g) \xrightarrow{H_2O} H^+(aq) + Cl^-(aq)$; $NaOH(s) \xrightarrow{H_2O} Na^+(aq) + OH^-(aq)$

4. A conjugate acid–base pair differs by one hydrogen ion, H^+. For example, $HC_2H_3O_2$ (acetic acid) differs from its conjugate base, $C_2H_3O_2^-$ (acetate ion), by a single H^+ ion.

$$HC_2H_3O_2(aq) \rightleftharpoons C_2H_3O_2^-(aq) + H^+(aq)$$

6. In addition to sodium bicarbonate, the gum also contains citric acid and malic acid. When the gum is exposed to moisture in the mouth, the bicarbonate ion behaves as a base and reacts with hydrogen ion from the acids: $H^+ (aq) + HCO_3^- (aq) \rightarrow H_2O (l) + CO_2 (g)$.

8. (a) conjugate pair; (b) conjugate pair; (c) conjugate pair; (d) not a conjugate pair; H_2O, OH^-; OH^-, O^{2-}

10. (a) $NH_3(aq)$(base) + $H_2O(l)$(acid) $\rightleftharpoons NH_4^+(aq)$(acid) + $OH^-(aq)$(base);
    (b) $NH_4^+(aq)$(acid) + $H_2O(l)$(base) $\rightleftharpoons NH_3(aq)$(base) + $H_3O^+(aq)$(acid);
    (c) $NH_2^-(aq)$(base) + $H_2O(l)$(acid) $\rightarrow NH_3(aq)$(acid) + $OH^-(aq)$(base)

12. (a) $HClO$; (b) HCl; (c) $HClO_3$; (d) $HClO_4$

14. (a) BrO^-; (b) HSO_3^-; (c) SO_3^{2-}; (d) CH_3NH_2

16. (a) $O^{2-}(aq) + H_2O(l) \rightleftharpoons OH^-(aq) + OH^-(aq)$;
    (b) $NH_3(aq) + H_2O(l) \rightleftharpoons NH_4^+(aq) + OH^-(aq)$;
    (c) $HSO_4^-(aq) + H_2O(l) \rightleftharpoons SO_4^{2-}(aq) + H_3O^+(aq)$;
    (d) $HNO_2(aq) + H_2O(l) \rightleftharpoons NO_2^-(aq) + H_3O^+(aq)$

18. If an acid is weak in aqueous solution, it does not easily transfer protons to water (and does not fully ionize). If an acid does not lose protons easily, then the acid's anion must strongly attract protons.

20. A strong acid loses its protons easily and fully ionizes in water; the acid's conjugate base is poor at attracting and holding protons and is a relatively weak base. A weak acid resists loss of its protons and does not ionize to a great extent in water; the acid's conjugate base attracts and holds protons tightly and is a relatively strong base.

22. H_2SO_4 (sulfuric): $H_2SO_4 + H_2O \rightarrow HSO_4^- + H_3O^+$;
    HCl (hydrochloric): $HCl + H_2O \rightarrow Cl^- + H_3O^+$;
    HNO_3 (nitric): $HNO_3 + H_2O \rightarrow NO_3^- + H_3O^+$;
    $HClO_4$ (perchloric): $HClO_4 + H_2O \rightarrow ClO_4^- + H_3O^+$

24. An oxyacid is an acid containing a particular element that is bonded to one or more oxygen atoms. HNO_3, H_2SO_4, and $HClO_4$ are oxyacids. HCl, HF, and HBr are not oxyacids.

26. Salicylic acid is a monoprotic acid: only the hydrogen of the carboxyl group ionizes.

28. HCO_3^- can behave as an acid if it reacts with a substance that more strongly gains protons than does HCO_3^- itself. For example, HCO_3^- would behave as an acid when reacting with hydroxide ion (a much stronger base): $HCO_3^-(aq) + OH^-(aq) \rightarrow CO_3^{2-}(aq) + H_2O(l)$. On the other hand, HCO_3^- would behave as a base when reacted with a substance that more readily loses protons than does HCO_3^- itself. For example, HCO_3^- would behave as a base when reacting with hydrochloric acid (a much stronger acid): $HCO_3^-(aq) + HCl(aq) \rightarrow H_2CO_3(aq) + Cl^-(aq)$. $H_2PO_4^- + OH^- \rightarrow HPO_4^{2-} + H_2O$ and $H_2PO_4^- + H_3O^+ \rightarrow H_3PO_4 + H_2O$.

30. The concentrations of H^+ and OH^- ions in water and in dilute aqueous solutions are *not* independent of one another. Rather, they are related by the ion product equilibrium constant, K_w. $K_w = [H^+(aq)][OH^-(aq)] = 1.00 \times 10^{-14}$ at 25 °C. If the concentration of one ion is *increased* by addition of a reagent producing H^+ or OH^-, then the concentration of the complementary ion will *decrease* so that the constant's value will hold true. If an acid is added to a solution, the concen-

tration of hydroxide ion in the solution will decrease. Similarly, if a base is added to a solution, then the concentration of hydrogen ion will decrease.

32. (a) $[H^+] = 2.9 \times 10^{-14}$ M; basic;
    (b) $[H^+] = 1.0 \times 10^{-4}$ M; acidic;
    (c) $[H^+] = 2.0 \times 10^{-9}$ M; basic;
    (d) $[H^+] = 2.6 \times 10^{-8}$ M; basic

34. (a) $[OH^-] = 9.8 \times 10^{-8}$ M; acidic;
    (b) $[OH^-] = 1.02 \times 10^{-7}$ M (1.0×10^{-7} M); basic;
    (c) $[OH^-] = 2.9 \times 10^{-12}$ M; acidic;
    (d) $[OH^-] = 2.1 \times 10^{-4}$ M; basic

36. (a) $[OH^-] = 6.03 \times 10^{-4}$ M; (b) $[OH^-] = 4.21 \times 10^{-6}$ M;
    (c) $[OH^-] = 8.04 \times 10^{-4}$ M

38. Answers will depend on student choices.

40. pH 1–2, deep red; pH 4, purple; pH 8, blue; pH 11, green

42. (a) pH = 1.029; acidic; (b) 3.426; acidic;
    (c) 5.078; acidic; (d) 7.266; basic

44. (a) pH = 11.94; basic; (b) pH = 8.87; basic;
    (c) pH = 5.97; acidic; (d) pH = 3.08; acidic

46. (a) 4.22, basic; (b) 9.99, acidic; (c) 11.21, acidic;
    (d) 2.79, basic

48. (a) pH = 1.719, $[OH^-] = 5.2 \times 10^{-13}$ M;
    (b) pH = 6.316, $[OH^-] = 2.1 \times 10^{-8}$ M;
    (c) pH = 10.050, $[OH^-] = 1.1 \times 10^{-4}$ M;
    (d) pH = 4.212, $[OH^-] = 1.6 \times 10^{-10}$ M

50. (a) 6.2×10^{-12} M; (b) 4.1×10^{-5} M; (c) 3.6×10^{-8} M;
    (d) 4.2×10^{-2} M

52. (a) 9.8×10^{-10} M; (b) 1.8×10^{-8} M; (c) 5.5×10^{-4} M;
    (d) 5.6×10^{-3} M

54. (a) 5.358; (b) 3.64; (c) 5.97; (d) 0.480

56. The solution contains water molecules, H_3O^+ ions (protons), and NO_3^- ions. Because HNO_3 is a strong acid that is completely ionized in water, no HNO_3 molecules are present.

58. (a) pH = 2.917; (b) pH = 3.701; (c) pH = 4.300;
    (d) pH = 2.983

60. A buffered solution consists of a mixture of a weak acid and its conjugate base; one example of a buffered solution is a mixture of acetic acid ($HC_2H_3O_2$) and sodium acetate ($NaC_2H_3O_2$).

62. The weak acid component of a buffered solution is capable of reacting with added strong base. For example, using the buffered solution given as an example in Exercise 60, acetic acid would consume added sodium hydroxide as follows: $HC_2H_3O_2(aq) + NaOH(aq) \rightarrow NaC_2H_3O_2(aq) + H_2O(l)$. Acetic acid *neutralizes* the added NaOH and prevents it from affecting the overall pH of the solution.

64. $CH_3COO^- + HCl \rightarrow CH_3COOH + Cl^-$; $CH_3COOH + NaOH \rightarrow H_2O + NaCH_3COO$

66. (a) $[OH^-(aq)] = 0.10$ M, pOH = 1.00, pH = 13.00;
    (b) $[OH^-(aq)] = 2.0 \times 10^{-4}$ M, pOH = 3.70, pH = 10.30;
    (c) $[OH^-(aq)] = 6.2 \times 10^{-3}$ M, pOH = 2.21, pH = 11.79;
    (d) $[OH^-(aq)] = 0.0001$ M, pOH = 4.0, pH = 10.0

68. b, c, d   70. a, c, e

72. Having a concentration as small as 10^{-7} M for HCl means that the contribution to the total hydrogen ion concentration from the dissociation of water must also be considered in determining the pH of the solution.

74. accepts

76. base

78. $-C\overset{\displaystyle O}{\underset{\displaystyle OH}{\big\|}}$; $CH_3COOH + H_2O \rightleftharpoons C_2H_3O_2^- + H_3O^+$

80. 1.0×10^{-14}

82. higher

84. pH

86. weak acid

88. (a) H_2O and OH^- are a conjugate acid–base pair (H_2O is the acid, having one more proton than the base, OH^-); (b) H_2SO_4 and SO_4^{2-} are *not* a conjugate acid–base pair (they differ by *two* protons). The conjugate base of H_2SO_4 is HSO_4^-; the conjugate acid of SO_4^{2-} is also HSO_4^-; (c) H_3PO_4 and $H_2PO_4^-$ are a conjugate acid–base pair (H_3PO_4 is the acid, having one more proton than the base, $H_2PO_4^-$); (d) $HC_2H_3O_2$ and $C_2H_3O_2^-$ are a conjugate acid–base pair ($HC_2H_3O_2$ is the acid, having one more proton than the base, $C_2H_3O_2^-$)

90. (a) NH_4^+; (b) NH_3; (c) H_3O^+; (d) H_2O

92. (a) $CH_3CH_2COOH + H_2O \rightleftharpoons CH_3CH_2COO^- + H_3O^+$;
(b) $NH_4^+ + H_2O \rightleftharpoons NH_3 + H_3O^+$;
(c) $H_2SO_4 + H_2O \rightarrow HSO_4^- + H_3O^+$;
(d) $H_3PO_4 + H_2O \rightleftharpoons H_2PO_4^- + H_3O^+$

94. (a) $[H^+(aq)] = 2.4 \times 10^{-12}$ M, solution is basic;
(b) $[H^+(aq)] = 9.9 \times 10^{-2}$ M, solution is acidic;
(c) $[H^+(aq)] = 3.3 \times 10^{-8}$ M, solution is basic;
(d) $[H^+(aq)] = 1.7 \times 10^{-9}$ M, solution is basic

96. (a) $[OH^-(aq)] = 0.0000032$ M;
(b) $[OH^-(aq)] = 1.54 \times 10^{-8}$ M;
(c) $[OH^-(aq)] = 4.02 \times 10^{-7}$ M

98. (a) pH = 8.15; solution is basic; (b) pH = 5.97; solution is acidic; (c) pH = 13.34; solution is basic; (d) pH = 2.90; solution is acidic

100. (a) $[OH^-(aq)] = 1.8 \times 10^{-11}$ M, pH = 3.24, pOH = 10.76;
(b) $[H^+(aq)] = 1.1 \times 10^{-10}$ M, pH = 9.95, pOH = 4.05;
(c) $[OH^-(aq)] = 3.5 \times 10^{-3}$ M, pH = 11.54, pH = 2.46;
(d) $[H^+(aq)] = 1.4 \times 10^{-7}$ M, pH = 6.86, pOH = 7.14

102. (a) $[H^+] = 3.9 \times 10^{-6}$ M; (b) $[H^+] = 1.1 \times 10^{-2}$ M;
(c) $[H^+] = 1.2 \times 10^{-12}$ M; (d) $[H^+] = 7.8 \times 10^{-11}$ M

104. (a) $[H^+(aq)] = 1.4 \times 10^{-3}$ M, pH = 2.85;
(b) $[H^+(aq)] = 3.0 \times 10^{-5}$ M, pH = 4.52;
(c) $[H^+(aq)] = 5.0 \times 10^{-2}$ M, pH = 1.30;
(d) $[H^+(aq)] = 0.0010$ M, pH = 3.00

Chapters 1–3

2. After having covered three chapters in this book, you should have adopted an "active" approach to your study of chemistry. You can't just sit and take notes in class, or just review the solved examples in the textbook. You must learn to *interpret* problems and reduce them to simple mathematical relationships.

4. Some courses, particularly those in your major field, have obvious and immediate utility. Other courses—chemistry included—provide general *background* knowledge that will prove useful in understanding your own major, or other subjects related to your major.

6. Whenever a scientific measurement is made, we always employ the instrument or measuring device to the limits of its precision. This usually means that we *estimate* the last significant figure of the measurement. An example of the uncertainty in the last significant figure is given for measuring the length of a pin in the text in Figure 2.5. Scientists appreciate the limits of experimental techniques and instruments and always *assume* that the last digit in a number representing a measurement has been estimated. Because instruments or measuring devices always have a limit to their precision, uncertainty cannot be completely excluded from measurements.

8. Dimensional analysis is a method of problem solving that pays particular attention to the units of measurements and uses these units as if they were algebraic symbols that multiply, divide, and cancel. Consider the following example: One dozen eggs costs $1.25. Suppose we want to know how much one egg costs, and also how much three dozen eggs will cost. To solve these problems, we need two equivalence statements:

   1 dozen eggs = 12 eggs

   1 dozen eggs = $1.25

   The calculations are

   $$\frac{\$1.25}{12 \text{ eggs}} = \$0.104 = \$0.10$$

   as the cost of one egg and

   $$\frac{\$1.25}{1 \text{ dozen}} \times 3 \text{ dozen} = \$3.75$$

   as the cost of three dozen eggs. See Section 2.6 of the text for how we construct conversion factors from equivalence statements.

10. Scientists say that matter is anything that "has mass and occupies space." Matter is the "stuff" of which everything is made. It can be classified and subdivided in many ways, depending on what we are trying to demonstrate. All the types of matter we have studied are made of atoms. They differ in whether these atoms are all of one element, or are of more than one element, and also in whether these atoms are in physical mixtures or chemical combinations.
    Matter can also be classified according to its physical state (solid, liquid, or gas). In addition, it can be classified as a pure substance (one type of molecule) or a mixture (more than one type of molecule).

12. An element is a fundamental substance that cannot be broken down into simpler substances by chemical methods. An element consists of atoms of only one type. Compounds, on the other hand, *can* be broken down into simpler substances. For example, both sulfur and oxygen are *elements*. When sulfur and oxygen are placed together and heated, the *compound* sulfur dioxide (SO_2) forms. Each molecule of sulfur dioxide contains one sulfur atom and two oxygen atoms. On a mass basis, SO_2 always consists of 50% each, by mass, sulfur and oxygen—that is, sulfur dioxide has a constant composition. Sulfur dioxide from any source would have the same composition (or it wouldn't be sulfur dioxide!).

14. (a) 8.917×10^{-4}; (b) 0.0002795; (c) 4913;
    (d) 8.51×10^7; (e) 1.219×10^2; (f) 3.396×10^{-9}

16. (a) two; (b) two; (c) three; (d) three; (e) one;
    (f) two; (g) two; (h) three

18. (a) 0.785 g/mL; (b) 2.03 L; (c) 1.06 kg;
    (d) 9.33 cm³; (e) 2.0×10^2 g

Chapters 4–5

2. Although you don't have to memorize all the elements, you should at least be able to give the symbol or name for the most common elements (listed in Table 4.3).

4. The main postulates of Dalton's theory are: (1) elements are made up of tiny particles called atoms; (2) all atoms of a given element are identical; (3) although all atoms of a given element are identical, these atoms are different from the atoms of all other elements; (4) atoms of one element can combine with atoms of another element to form a compound that will always have the same relative numbers and types of atoms for its composition; and (5) atoms are merely rearranged into new groupings during an ordinary chemical reaction, and no atom is ever destroyed and no new atom is ever created during such a reaction.

6. The expression "nuclear atom" indicates that the atom has a dense center of positive charge (nucleus) around which the electrons move through primarily empty space. Rutherford's experiment involved shooting a beam of α particles at a thin sheet of metal foil. According to the "plum pudding" model of the atom, these positively charged α particles should have passed through the foil. Rutherford detected that a small number of α particles bounced backward to the source of α particles or were deflected from the foil at large angles. Rutherford realized that his observations could be explained if the atoms of the metal foil had a small, dense, positively charged nucleus, with a significant amount of empty space between nuclei. The empty space between nuclei would allow most of the α particles to pass through the foil. If an α particle were to hit a nucleus head-on, it would be deflected backward. If a positively charged α particle passed *near* a positively charged nucleus, then the α particle would be deflected by the repulsive forces. Rutherford's experiment disproved the "plum pudding" model, which envisioned the atom as a uniform sphere of positive charge, with enough negatively charged electrons scattered throughout to balance out the positive charge.

8. Isotopes represent atoms of the same element that have different atomic masses. Isotopes result from the different numbers of neutrons in the nuclei of atoms of a given element. They have the same atomic number (number of protons in the nucleus) but have different mass numbers (total number of protons and neutrons in the nucleus). The different isotopes of an atom are indicated by the form $^A_Z X$, in which Z

represents the atomic number and A the mass number of element X. For example, $^{13}_{6}C$ represents a nuclide of carbon with atomic number 6 (6 protons in the nucleus) and mass number 13 (6 protons plus 7 neutrons in the nucleus). The various isotopes of an element have identical *chemical* properties. The *physical* properties of the isotopes of an element may differ slightly because of the small difference in mass.

10. Most elements are too reactive to be found in nature in other than the combined form. Gold, silver, platinum, and some of the gaseous elements (such as O_2, N_2, He, and Ar) are found in the elemental form.

12. Ionic compounds typically are hard, crystalline solids with high melting and boiling points. The ability of aqueous solutions of ionic substances to conduct electricity means that ionic substances consist of positively and negatively charged particles (ions). A sample of an ionic substance has no net electrical charge because the total number of positive charges is *balanced* by an equal number of negative charges. An ionic compound could not consist of only cations or only anions because a net charge of zero cannot be obtained when all ions have the same charge. Also, ions of like charge will repel each other.

14. When naming ionic compounds, the positive ion (cation) is named first. For simple binary Type I ionic compounds, the ending *-ide* is added to the root name of the negative ion (anion). For example, the name for K_2S would be "potassium sul*fide*"—potassium is the cation, sulfide is the anion. Type II compounds, which involve elements that form more than one stable ion, are named by either of two systems: the Roman numeral system (which is preferred by most chemists) and the *-ous/-ic* system. For example, iron can react with oxygen to form either of two stable oxides, FeO or Fe_2O_3. Under the Roman numeral system, FeO would be named iron(II) oxide to show that it contains Fe^{2+} ions; Fe_2O_3 would be named iron(III) oxide to indicate that it contains Fe^{3+} ions. Under the *-ous/-ic* system, FeO is named fer*rous* oxide and Fe_2O_3 is called fer*ric* oxide. Type II compounds usually involve transition metals and nonmetals.

16. A polyatomic ion is an ion containing more than one atom. Some common polyatomic ions are listed in Table 5.4. Parentheses are used in writing formulas containing polyatomic ions to indicate how many polyatomic ions are present. For example, the correct formula for calcium phosphate is $Ca_3(PO_4)_2$, which indicates that three calcium ions are combined for every two phosphate ions. If we did *not* write the parentheses around the formula for the phosphate ion (that is, if we wrote Ca_3PO_{42}), people might think that 42 oxygen atoms were present!

18. Acids are substances that produce protons (H^+ ions) when dissolved in water. For acids that do *not* contain oxygen, the prefix *hydro-* and the suffix *-ic* are used with the root name of the element present in the acid (for example: HCl, *hydro*chloric acid; H_2S, *hydro*sulfuric acid; HF, *hydro*fluoric acid). For acids whose anions contain oxygen, a series of prefixes and suffixes is used with the name of the central atom in the anion: these prefixes and suffixes indicate the relative (not actual) number of oxygen atoms present in the anion. Most elements that form oxyanions form *two* such anions—for example, sulfur forms sulf*ite* ion (SO_3^{2-}) and sulf*ate* ion (SO_4^{2-}). For an element that forms two oxyanions, the acid containing the anions will have the ending *-ous* if the *-ite* anion is involved and the ending *-ic* if the *-ate* anion is present. For example, H_2SO_3 is sulfur*ous* acid and H_2SO_4 is sulfur*ic* acid. The Group 7 elements each form *four* oxyanions/oxyacids. The prefix *hypo-* is used for the oxyacid that contains fewer oxygen atoms than the *-ite* anion, and the prefix *per-* is used for the oxyacid that contains more oxygen atoms than the *-ate* anion. For example,

Acid	Name	Anion	Name
HBrO	*hypo*brom*ous* acid	BrO^-	hypobromite
$HBrO_2$	brom*ous* acid	BrO_2^-	bromite
$HBrO_3$	brom*ic* acid	BrO_3^-	bromate
$HBrO_4$	*per*brom*ic* acid	BrO_4^-	perbromate

20. Elements in the same family have the same electron configuration and tend to undergo similar chemical reactions with other groups. For example, Li, Na, K, Rb, and Cs all react with elemental chlorine gas, Cl_2, to form an ionic compound of general formula M^+Cl^-.

22. (a) 8, 8, 9; (b) 92, 92, 143; (c) 17, 17, 20; (d) 1, 1, 2; (e) 2, 2, 2; (f) 50, 50, 69; (g) 54, 54, 70; h) 30, 30, 34

24. (a) 12 protons, 10 electrons; (b) 26 protons, 24 electrons; (c) 26 protons, 23 electrons; (d) 9 protons, 10 electrons; (e) 28 protons, 26 electrons; (f) 30 protons; 28 electrons; (g) 27 protons, 24 electrons; (h) 7 protons, 10 electrons; (i) 16 protons, 18 electrons; (j) 37 protons, 36 electrons; (k) 34 protons, 36 electrons; (l) 19 protons, 18 electrons

26. (a) CuI; (b) $CoCl_2$; (c) Ag_2S; (d) Hg_2Br_2; (e) HgO; (f) Cr_2S_3; (g) PbO_2; (h) K_3N; (i) SnF_2; (j) Fe_2O_3

28. (a) NH_4^+, ammonium ion; (b) SO_3^{2-}, sulfite ion; (c) NO_3^-, nitrate ion; (d) SO_4^{2-}, sulfate ion; (e) NO_2^-, nitrite ion; (f) CN^-, cyanide ion; (g) OH^-, hydroxide ion; (h) ClO_4^-, perchlorate ion; (i) ClO^-, hypochlorite ion; (j) PO_4^{3-}, phosphate ion

30. (a) xenon dioxide; (b) iodine pentachloride; (c) phosphorus trichloride; (d) carbon monoxide; (e) oxygen difluoride; (f) diphosphorus pentoxide; (g) arsenic triiodide; (h) sulfur trioxide

Chapters 6–7

2. A chemical equation indicates the substances necessary for a given chemical reaction, and the substances produced by that chemical reaction. The substances to the left of the arrow are called the *reactants;* those to the right of the arrow are called the *products.* A *balanced* equation indicates the relative numbers of molecules in the reaction.

4. Never change the *subscripts* of a *formula:* changing the subscripts changes the *identity* of a substance and makes the equation invalid. When balancing a chemical equation, we adjust only the *coefficients* in front of a formula: changing a coefficient changes the *number* of molecules being used in the reaction, *without* changing the *identity* of the substance.

6. A precipitation reaction is one in which a solid is produced when two aqueous solutions are combined. The driving force in such a reaction is the formation of the solid, thus removing ions from the solution. Examples depend on student input.

8. Nearly all compounds containing the nitrate, sodium, potassium, and ammonium ions are soluble in water. Most salts containing the chloride and sulfate ions are soluble in water, with specific exceptions (see Table 7.1). Most compounds containing the hydroxide, sulfide, carbonate, and phosphate ions are *not* soluble in water (unless the compound also contains Na^+, K^+, or NH_4^+). For example, suppose we combine barium chloride and sulfuric acid solutions:

$BaCl_2(aq) + H_2SO_4(aq) \rightarrow BaSO_4(s) + 2HCl(aq)$
$Ba^{2+}(aq) + SO_4^{2-}(aq) \rightarrow BaSO_4(s)$ [net ionic reaction]

Because barium sulfate is not soluble in water, a precipitate of $BaSO_4(s)$ forms.

10. Acids (such as the acetic acid found in vinegar) were first noted primarily because of their sour taste, whereas bases were first characterized by their bitter taste and slippery feel on the skin.

Acids and bases neutralize each other, forming water: $H^+(aq)$ + $OH^-(aq) \rightarrow H_2O(l)$. Strong acids and bases ionize *fully* when dissolved in water, which means they are also strong electrolytes.

Strong acids: HCl, HNO_3, and H_2SO_4

Strong bases: Group 1 hydroxides (for example, $NaOH$ and KOH)

12. Oxidation–reduction reactions; oxidation; reduction; No: if one species is going to lose electrons, there must be another species present capable of gaining them; Examples depend on student input.

14. In a synthesis reaction, elements or simple compounds react to produce more complex substances. For example,

$$N_2(g) + 3H_2(g) \rightarrow 2NH_3(g)$$
$$NaOH(aq) + CO_2(g) \rightarrow NaHCO_3(s)$$

Decomposition reactions represent the breakdown of complex substances into simpler substances. For example, $2H_2O_2(aq) \rightarrow 2H_2O(l) + O_2(g)$. Synthesis and decomposition reactions are often oxidation–reduction reactions, although not always. For example, the synthesis reaction between $NaOH$ and CO_2 does *not* represent oxidation–reduction.

16. (a) $C(s) + O_2(g) \rightarrow CO_2(g)$; (b) $2C(s) + O_2(g) \rightarrow 2CO(g)$;
(c) $2Li(l) + 2C(s) \rightarrow Li_2C_2(s)$; (d) $FeO(s) + C(s) \rightarrow Fe(l) + CO(g)$; (e) $C(s) + 2F_2(g) \rightarrow CF_4(g)$

18. (a) $Ba(NO_3)_2(aq) + K_2CrO_4(aq) \rightarrow BaCrO_4(s) + 2KNO_3(aq)$;
(b) $NaOH(aq) + HC_2H_3O_2(aq) \rightarrow H_2O(l) + NaC_2H_3O_2(aq)$ (then evaporate the water from the solution);
(c) $AgNO_3(aq) + NaCl(aq) \rightarrow AgCl(s) + NaNO_3(aq)$;
(d) $Pb(NO_3)_2(aq) + H_2SO_4(aq) \rightarrow PbSO_4(s) + 2HNO_3(aq)$;
(e) $2NaOH(aq) + H_2SO_4(aq) \rightarrow Na_2SO_4(aq) + 2H_2O(l)$ (then evaporate the water from the solution); (f) $Ba(NO_3)_2(aq) + 2Na_2CO_3(aq) \rightarrow BaCO_3(s) + 2NaNO_3(aq)$

20. (a) $FeO(s) + 2HNO_3(aq) \rightarrow Fe(NO_3)_2(aq) + H_2O(l)$; acid–base; double-displacement; (b) $2Mg(s) + 2CO_2(g) + O_2(g) \rightarrow 2MgCO_3(s)$; synthesis; oxidation–reduction;
(c) $2NaOH(s) + CuSO_4(aq) \rightarrow Cu(OH)_5(s) + Na_2SO_4(aq)$; precipitation; double-displacement; (d) $HI(aq) + KOH(aq) \rightarrow KI(aq) + H_2O(l)$; acid–base; double-displacement;
(e) $C_3H_8(g) + 5O_2(g) \rightarrow 3CO_2(g) + 4H_2O(g)$; combustion; oxidation–reduction; (f) $Co(NH_3)_6Cl_2(s) \rightarrow CoCl_2(s) + 6NH_3(g)$; decomposition; (g) $2HCl(aq) + Pb(C_2H_3O_2)_2(aq) \rightarrow 2HC_2H_3O_2(aq) + PbCl_2(aq)$; precipitation; double-displacement; (h) $C_{12}H_{22}O_{11}(s) \rightarrow 12C(s) + 11H_2O(g)$; decomposition; oxidation–reduction; (i) $2Al(s) + 6HNO_3(aq) \rightarrow 2Al(NO_3)_3(aq) + 3H_2(g)$; oxidation–reduction; single-displacement; (j) $4B(s) + 3O_2(g) \rightarrow 2B_2O_3(s)$; synthesis; oxidation–reduction

22. Answer will depend on student examples.

24. (a) no reaction (all combinations are soluble)
(b) $Ca^{2+}(aq) + SO_4^{2-}(aq) \rightarrow CaSO_4(s)$
(c) $Pb^{2+}(aq) + S^{2-}(aq) \rightarrow PbS(s)$
(d) $2Fe^{3+}(aq) + 3CO_3^{2-}(aq) \rightarrow Fe_2(CO_3)_3(s)$
(e) $Hg_2^{2+}(aq) + 2Cl^-(aq) \rightarrow Hg_2Cl_2(s)$
(f) $Ag^+(aq) + Cl^-(aq) \rightarrow AgCl(s)$
(g) $3Ca^{2+}(aq) + 2PO_4^{3-}(aq) \rightarrow Ca_3(PO_4)_2(s)$
(h) no reaction (all combinations are soluble)

Chapters 8–9

2. On a microscopic basis, one mole of a substance represents Avogadro's number (6.022×10^{23}) of individual units (atoms or molecules) of the substance. On a macroscopic basis, one mole of a substance represents the amount of substance present when the molar mass of the substance in grams is taken. Chemists have chosen these definitions so that a simple relationship will exist between measurable amounts of substances (grams) and the actual number of atoms or molecules present, and so that the number of particles present in samples of *different* substances can easily be compared.

4. The molar mass of a compound is the mass in grams of one mole of the compound and is calculated by summing the average atomic masses of all the atoms present in a molecule of the compound. For example, for H_3PO_4: molar mass H_3PO_4 = $3(1.008\ g) + 1(30.97\ g) + 4(16.00\ g) = 97.99\ g$.

6. The *empirical* formula of a compound represents the *relative* number of atoms of each type present in a molecule of the compound, whereas the *molecular* formula represents the *actual* number of atoms of each type present in a real molecule. For example, both acetylene (molecular formula C_2H_2) and benzene (molecular formula C_6H_6) have the same relative number of carbon and hydrogen atoms, and thus have the same empirical formula (CH). The molar mass of the compound must be determined before calculating the actual molecular formula. Since real molecules cannot contain fractional *parts* of atoms, the molecular formula is always a *whole-number multiple* of the empirical formula.

8. Answer depends on student examples chosen for Exercise 7.

10. for O_2: $\dfrac{5\ mol\ O_2}{1\ mol\ C_3H_8}$; $0.55\ mol\ C_3H_8 \times \dfrac{5\ mol\ O_2}{1\ mol\ C_3H_8} =$ 2.8 (2.75) mol O_2

for CO_2: $\dfrac{3\ mol\ CO_2}{1\ mol\ C_3H_8}$; $0.55\ mol\ C_3H_8 \times \dfrac{3\ mol\ CO_2}{1\ mol\ C_3H_8} =$ 1.7 (1.65) mol CO_2

for H_2O: $\dfrac{4\ mol\ H_2O}{1\ mol\ C_3H_8}$; $0.55\ mol\ C_3H_8 \times \dfrac{4\ mol\ H_2O}{1\ mol\ C_3H_8} =$ 2.2 mol H_2O

12. When arbitrary amounts of reactants are used, one reactant will be present, stoichiometrically, in the least amount: this substance is called the *limiting reactant*. It *limits* the amount of product that can form in the experiment, because once this substance has reacted completely, the reaction must *stop*. The other reactants in the experiment are present *in excess,* which means that a portion of these reactants will be present *unchanged* after the reaction ends.

14. The *theoretical yield* for an experiment is the mass of product calculated assuming the limiting reactant for the experiment is completely consumed. The *actual yield* for an experiment is the mass of product actually collected by the experimenter. Any experiment is restricted by the skills of the experimenter and by the inherent limitations of the experimental method: for these reasons, the actual yield is often less than the theoretical yield. Although one would expect that the actual yield should never exceed the theoretical yield, in real experiments, sometimes this happens. However, an actual yield greater than a theoretical yield usually means that something is *wrong* in either the experiment (for example, impurities may be present) or the calculations.

16. (a) 92.26% C; (b) 32.37% Na; (c) 15.77% C;
(d) 20.24% Al; (e) 88.82% Cu; (f) 79.89% Cu;
(g) 71.06% Co; (h) 40.00% C

18. (a) 53.0 g $SiCl_4$, 3.75 g C; (b) 20.0 g LiOH;
(c) 12.8 g NaOH, 2.56 g O_2; (d) 9.84 g Sn, 2.99 g H_2O

20. 11.7 g CO; 18.3 g CO_2

Chapters 10–12

2. Temperature is a measure of the random motions of the components of a substance; in other words, temperature is a measure of the average kinetic energy of the particles in a sample. The molecules in warm water must be moving faster than the molecules in cold water (the molecules have the same

mass, so if the temperature is higher, the average velocity of the particles must be higher in the warm water). Heat is the energy that flows because of a difference in temperature.

4. Thermodynamics is the study of energy and energy changes. The first law of thermodynamics is the law of conservation of energy: the energy of the universe is constant. Energy cannot be created or destroyed, only transferred from one place to another or from one form to another. The internal energy of a system, E, represents the total of the kinetic and potential energies of all particles in a system. A flow of heat may be produced when there is a change in internal energy in the system, but it is not correct to say that the system "contains" the heat: part of the internal energy is *converted* to heat energy during the process (under other conditions, the change in internal energy might be expressed as work rather than a heat flow).

6. The enthalpy change represents the heat energy that flows (at constant pressure) on a molar basis when a reaction occurs. The enthalpy change is a state function (which we make great use of in Hess's law calculations). Enthalpy changes are typically measured in insulated reaction vessels called calorimeters (a simple calorimeter is shown in Figure 10.6).

8. Consider petroleum. A gallon of gasoline contains concentrated, stored energy. We can use that energy to make a car move, but when we do, the energy stored in the gasoline is dispersed throughout the environment. Although the energy is still there (it is conserved), it is no longer in a concentrated, useful form. Thus, although the energy content of the universe remains constant, the energy that is now stored in concentrated forms in oil, coal, wood, and other sources is gradually being dispersed to the universe, where it can do no work.

10. A driving force is an effect that tends to make a process occur. Two important driving forces are dispersion of energy during a process or dispersion of matter during a process (energy spread and matter spread). For example, a log burns in a fireplace because the energy contained in the log is dispersed to the universe when it burns. If we put a teaspoon of sugar into a glass of water, the dissolving of the sugar is a favorable process because the matter of the sugar is dispersed when it dissolves. Entropy is a measure of the randomness or disorder in a system. The entropy of the universe is constantly increasing because of matter spread and energy spread. A spontaneous process is one that occurs without outside intervention: the spontaneity of a reaction depends on the energy spread and matter spread if the reaction takes place. A reaction that disperses energy and also disperses matter will always be spontaneous. Reactions that require an input of energy may still be spontaneous if the matter spread is large enough.

12. (a) 464 kJ; (b) 69.3 kJ; (c) 1.40 mol (22.5 g)

14. An atom in its *ground state* is in its lowest possible energy state. When an atom possesses more energy than in its ground state, the atom is in an *excited state*. An atom is promoted from its ground state to an excited state by absorbing energy; when the atom returns from an excited state to its ground state it emits the excess energy as electromagnetic radiation. Atoms do not gain or emit radiation randomly, but rather do so only in discrete bundles of radiation called *photons*. The photons of radiation emitted by atoms are characterized by the wavelength (color) of the radiation: longer-wavelength photons carry less energy than shorter-wavelength photons. The energy of a photon emitted by an atom corresponds *exactly* to the difference in energy between two allowed energy states in an atom.

16. Bohr pictured the electron moving in certain circular orbits around the nucleus, with each orbit being associated with a specific energy (resulting from the attraction between the nucleus and the electron and from the kinetic energy of the electron). Bohr assumed that when an atom absorbs energy, the electron moves from its ground state ($n = 1$) to an orbit farther away from the nucleus ($n = 2, 3, 4, \ldots$). Bohr postulated that when an excited atom returns to its ground state, the atom emits the excess energy as radiation. Because the Bohr orbits are located at fixed distances from the nucleus and from each other, when an electron moves from one fixed orbit to another, the energy change is of a definite amount, which corresponds to the emission of a photon with a particular characteristic wavelength and energy. When the simple Bohr model for the atom was applied to the emission spectra of other elements, however, the theory could not predict or explain the observed emission spectra of these elements.

18. The lowest-energy hydrogen atomic orbital is called the 1s orbital. The 1s orbital is spherical in shape (the electron density around the nucleus is uniform in all directions). The orbital does *not* have a sharp edge (it appears fuzzy) because the probability of finding the electron gradually decreases as distance from the nucleus increases. The orbital does *not* represent just a spherical surface on which the electron moves (this would be similar to Bohr's original theory)—instead, the 1s orbital represents a probability map of electron density around the nucleus for the first principal energy level.

20. The third principal energy level of hydrogen is divided into three sublevels: the 3s, 3p, and 3d sublevels. The 3s subshell consists of the single 3s orbital, which is spherical in shape. The 3p subshell consists of a set of three equal-energy 3p orbitals: each of these 3p orbitals has the same shape ("dumbbell"), but each of the 3p orbitals is oriented in a different direction in space. The 3d subshell consists of a set of five 3d orbitals with shapes as indicated in Figure 11.28, which are oriented in different directions around the nucleus. The fourth principal energy level of hydrogen is divided into four sublevels: the 4s, 4p, 4d, and 4f orbitals. The 4s subshell consists of the single 4s orbital. The 4p subshell consists of a set of three 4p orbitals. The 4d subshell consists of a set of five 4d orbitals. The shapes of the 4s, 4p, and 4d orbitals are the *same* as the shapes of the orbitals of the third principal energy level—the orbitals of the fourth principal energy level are *larger* and *farther from the nucleus* than the orbitals of the third level, however. The fourth principal energy level also contains a 4f subshell consisting of seven 4f orbitals (the shapes of the 4f orbitals are beyond the scope of this text).

22. Atoms have a series of *principal energy levels* indexed by the letter n. The $n = 1$ level is closest to the nucleus, and the energies of the levels increase as the value of n (and distance from the nucleus) increases. Each principal energy level is divided into *sublevels* (sets of orbitals) of different characteristic shapes designated by the letters s, p, d, and f. Each s subshell consists of a single s orbital; each p subshell consists of a set of three p orbitals; each d subshell consists of a set of five d orbitals; and so on. An orbital can be empty or it can contain one or two electrons, but never more than two electrons (if an orbital contains two electrons, then the electrons must have opposite spins). The shape of an orbital represents a probability map for finding electrons—it does not represent a trajectory or pathway for electron movements.

24. The valence electrons are the electrons in an atom's outermost shell. The valence electrons are those most likely to be involved in chemical reactions because they are at the outside edge of the atom.

26. The general periodic table you drew for Question 25 should resemble that found in Figure 11.31. From the column and row location of an element, you should be able to determine its valence configuration. For example, the element in the third horizontal row of the second vertical column has $3s^2$ as its valence configuration. The element in the seventh vertical column of the second horizontal row has valence configuration $2s^2 2p^5$.

28. The ionization energy of an atom represents the energy required to remove an electron from the atom in the gas phase. Moving from top to bottom in a vertical group on the periodic table, the ionization energies decrease. The ionization energies increase when going from left to right within a horizontal row within the periodic table. The relative sizes of atoms also vary systematically with the location of an element on the periodic table. Within a given vertical group, the atoms become progressively larger when going from the top of the group to the bottom. Moving from left to right within a horizontal row on the periodic table, the atoms become progressively smaller.

30. To form an ionic compound, a metallic element reacts with a nonmetallic element, with the metallic element losing electrons to form a positive ion and the nonmetallic element gaining electrons to form a negative ion. The aggregate form of such a compound consists of a crystal lattice of alternating positively and negatively charged ions: a given positive ion is attracted by surrounding negatively charged ions, and a given negative ion is attracted by surrounding positively charged ions. Similar electrostatic attractions exist in three dimensions throughout the crystal of the ionic solid, leading to a very stable system (with very high melting and boiling points, for example). As evidence for the existence of ionic bonding, ionic solids do not conduct electricity (the ions are rigidly held), but melts or solutions of such substances do conduct electric current. For example, when sodium metal and chlorine gas react, a typical ionic substance (sodium chloride) results: $2Na(s) + Cl_2(g) \rightarrow 2Na^+Cl^-(s)$.

32. Electronegativity represents the relative ability of an atom in a molecule to attract shared electrons to itself. The larger the difference in electronegativity between two atoms joined in a bond, the more polar is the bond. Examples depend on student choice of elements.

34. It has been observed over many, many experiments that when an active metal like sodium or magnesium reacts with a nonmetal, the sodium atoms always form Na^+ ions and the magnesium atoms always form Mg^{2+} ions. It has also been observed that when nonmetallic elements like nitrogen, oxygen, or fluorine form simple ions, the ions are always N^{3-}, O^{2-}, and F^-, respectively. Observing that these elements always form the same ions and those ions all contain eight electrons in the outermost shell, scientists speculated that a species that has an octet of electrons (like the noble gas neon) must be very fundamentally stable. The *repeated* observation that so many elements, when reacting, tend to attain an electron configuration that is isoelectronic with a noble gas led chemists to speculate that *all* elements try to attain such a configuration for their outermost shells. Covalently and polar covalently bonded molecules also strive to attain pseudo–noble gas electron configurations. For a covalently bonded molecule like F_2, each F atom provides one electron of the pair of electrons that constitutes the covalent bond. Each F atom feels also the influence of the other F atom's electron in the shared pair, and each F atom effectively fills its outermost shell.

36. Bonding between atoms to form a molecule involves only the outermost electrons of the atoms, so only these *valence* electrons are shown in the Lewis structures of molecules. The most important requisite for the formation of a stable compound is that each atom of a molecule attain a noble gas electron configuration. In Lewis structures, arrange the bonding and nonbonding valence electrons to try to complete the octet (or duet) for as many atoms as possible.

38. You could choose practically any molecules for your discussion. Let's illustrate the method for ammonia, NH_3. First, count the total number of valence electrons available in the molecule (without regard to their source). For NH_3, since ni-

trogen is in Group 5, one nitrogen atom would contribute five valence electrons. Since hydrogen atoms have only one electron each, the three hydrogen atoms provide an additional three valence electrons, for a total of eight valence electrons overall. Next, write down the symbols for the atoms in the molecule, and use one pair of electrons (represented by a line) to form a bond between each pair of bound atoms.

$$\begin{array}{c} H-N-H \\ | \\ H \end{array}$$

These three bonds use six of the eight valence electrons. Because each hydrogen already has its duet and the nitrogen atom has only six electrons around it so far, the final two valence electrons must represent a lone pair on the nitrogen.

$$\begin{array}{c} H-\ddot{N}-H \\ | \\ H \end{array}$$

40. Boron and beryllium compounds sometimes do not fit the octet rule. For example, in BF_3, the boron atom has only six valence electrons in its outermost shell, whereas in BeF_2, the beryllium atom has only four electrons in its outermost shell. Other exceptions to the octet rule include any molecule with an odd number of valence electrons (such as NO or NO_2).

42.

Number of Valence Pairs	Bond Angle	Examples
2	180°	BeF_2, BeH_2
3	120°	BCl_3
4	109.5°	CH_4, CCl_4, GeF_4

44. (a) $[Kr]5s^2$; (b) $[Ne]3s^23p^1$; (c) $[Ne]3s^23p^5$; (d) $[Ar]4s^1$; (e) $[Ne]3s^23p^4$; (f) $[Ar]4s^23d^{10}4p^3$

46.

$H-\ddot{O}-H$ 4 electron pairs tetrahedrally oriented on O; nonlinear (bent, V-shaped) geometry; H—O—H bond angle slightly less than 109.5° because of lone pairs

$\begin{array}{c} H-\ddot{P}-H \\ | \\ H \end{array}$ 4 electron pairs tetrahedrally oriented on P; trigonal pyramidal geometry; H—P—H bond angles slightly less than 109.5° because of lone pair

$\begin{array}{c} :\ddot{B}r: \\ | \\ :\ddot{B}r-C-\ddot{B}r: \\ | \\ :\ddot{B}r: \end{array}$ 4 electron pairs tetrahedrally oriented on C; overall tetrahedral geometry; Br—C—Br bond angles 109.5°

$\left[\begin{array}{c} :\ddot{O}: \\ | \\ :\ddot{O}-Cl-\ddot{O}: \\ | \\ :\ddot{O}: \end{array}\right]^-$ 4 electron pairs tetrahedrally oriented on Cl; overall tetrahedral geometry; O—Cl—O bond angles 109.5°

$\begin{array}{c} :\ddot{F} \\ \diagdown \\ B-\ddot{F}: \\ \diagup \\ :\ddot{F} \end{array}$ 3 electron pairs trigonally oriented on B (exception to octet rule); overall trigonal geometry; F—B—F bond angles 120°

$:\ddot{F}-Be-\ddot{F}:$ 2 electron pairs linearly oriented on Be (exception to octet rule); overall linear geometry; F—Be—F bond angle 180°

Chapters 13–15

2. The pressure of the atmosphere represents the mass of the gases in the atmosphere pressing down on the surface of the earth. The device most commonly used to measure the pressure of the atmosphere is the mercury barometer, shown in Figure 13.2. A simple experiment to demonstrate the pressure of the atmosphere is shown in Figure 13.1.

4. Boyle's law says that the volume of a gas sample will decrease if you squeeze it harder (at constant temperature, for a fixed amount of gas). Two mathematical statements of Boyle's law are

$$P \times V = \text{constant}$$
$$P_1 \times V_1 = P_2 \times V_2$$

These two mathematical formulas say the same thing: if the pressure on a sample of gas is increased, the volume of the sample will decrease. A graph of Boyle's law data is given as Figure 13.5: this type of graph ($xy = k$) is known to mathematicians as a *hyperbola*.

6. Charles's law says that if you heat a sample of gas, the volume of the sample will increase (assuming the pressure and amount of gas remain the same). When the temperature is given in kelvins, Charles's law expresses a *direct* proportionality (if you *increase* T, then V *increases*), whereas Boyle's law expresses an *inverse* proportionality (if you *increase* P, then V *decreases*). Two mathematical statements of Charles's law are $V = bT$ and $(V_1/T_1) = (V_2/T_2)$. With this second formulation, we can determine volume–temperature information for a given gas sample under two sets of conditions. Charles's law holds true only if the amount of gas remains the same (the volume of a gas sample would increase if more gas were present) and also if the pressure remains the same (a change in pressure also changes the volume of a gas sample). A graph of volume versus temperature (at constant pressure) for an ideal gas is a straight line with an intercept at –273 °C (see Figure 13.7).

8. Avogadro's law says that the volume of a sample of gas is directly proportional to the number of moles (or molecules) of gas present (at constant temperature and pressure). Avogadro's law holds true only for gas samples compared under the same conditions of temperature and pressure. Avogadro's law expresses a direct proportionality: the more gas in a sample, the larger the sample's volume.

10. The "partial" pressure of an individual gas in a mixture of gases represents the pressure the gas would exert in the same container at the same temperature if it were the *only* gas present. The *total* pressure in a mixture of gases is the sum of the individual partial pressures of the gases present in the mixture. The fact that the partial pressures of the gases in a mixture are additive suggests that the total pressure in a container is a function of the *number* of molecules present, and not of the identity of the molecules or of any other property (such as the molecules' inherent atomic size).

12. The main postulates of the kinetic molecular theory for gases are: (a) gases consist of tiny particles (atoms or molecules), and the size of these particles themselves is negligible compared with the bulk volume of a gas sample;   (b) the particles in a gas are in constant random motion, colliding with each other and with the walls of the container;   (c) the particles in a gas sample do not assert any attractive or repulsive forces on one another; and   (d) the average kinetic energy of the gas particles is directly related to the absolute temperature of the gas sample. The pressure exerted by a gas results from the molecules colliding with (and pushing on) the walls of the container; the pressure increases with temperature because, at a higher temperature, the molecules move faster and hit the walls of the container with greater force. A gas fills the volume available to it because the molecules in a gas are in constant *random* motion: the randomness of the molecules' motion means that they eventually will move out into the available volume until the distribution of molecules is uniform; at constant pressure, the volume of a gas sample increases as the

temperature is increased because with each collision having greater force, the container must expand so that the molecules are farther apart if the pressure is to remain constant.

14. The molecules are much closer together in solids and liquids than in gaseous substances and interact with each other to a much greater extent. Solids and liquids have much greater densities than do gases, and are much less compressible, because so little room exists between the molecules in the solid and liquid states (the volume of a solid or liquid is not affected very much by temperature or pressure). We know that the solid and liquid states of a substance are similar to each other in structure, since it typically takes only a few kilojoules of energy to melt 1 mole of a solid, whereas it may take 10 times more energy to convert a liquid to the vapor state.

16. The *normal* boiling point of water—that is, water's boiling point at a pressure of exactly 760 mm Hg—is 100 °C. Water remains at 100 °C while boiling, because the additional energy added to the sample is used to overcome attractive forces among the water molecules as they go from the condensed, liquid state to the gaseous state. The normal (760 mm Hg) freezing point of water is exactly 0 °C. A cooling curve for water is given in Figure 14.2.

18. Dipole–dipole forces arise when molecules with permanent dipole moments try to orient themselves so that the positive end of one polar molecule can attract the negative end of another polar molecule. Dipole–dipole forces are not nearly as strong as ionic or covalent bonding forces (only about 1% as strong as covalent bonding forces) since electrostatic attraction is related to the *magnitude* of the charges of the attracting species and drops off rapidly with distance. Hydrogen bonding is an especially strong dipole–dipole attractive force that can exist when hydrogen atoms are directly bonded to the most electronegative atoms (N, O, and F). Because the hydrogen atom is so small, dipoles involving N—H, O—H, and F—H bonds can approach each other much more closely than can other dipoles; because the magnitude of dipole–dipole forces is related to distance, unusually strong attractive forces can exist. The much higher boiling point of water than that of the other covalent hydrogen compounds of the Group 6 elements is evidence for the special strength of hydrogen bonding.

20. The vaporization of a liquid requires an input of energy to overcome the intermolecular forces that exist between the molecules in the liquid state. The large heat of vaporization of water is essential to life since much of the excess energy striking the earth from the sun is dissipated in vaporizing water. Condensation refers to the process by which molecules in the vapor state form a liquid. In a closed container containing a liquid with some empty space above the liquid, an equilibrium occurs between vaporization and condensation. When the liquid is first placed in the container, the liquid phase begins to evaporate into the empty space. As the number of molecules in the vapor phase increases, however, some of these molecules begin to reenter the liquid phase. Eventually, each time a molecule of liquid somewhere in the container enters the vapor phase, another molecule of vapor reenters the liquid phase. No further net change occurs in the amount of liquid phase. The pressure of the vapor in such an equilibrium situation is characteristic for the liquid at each temperature. A simple experiment to determine the vapor pressure of a liquid is shown in Figure 14.10. Typically, liquids with strong intermolecular forces have smaller vapor pressures (they have more difficulty in evaporating) than do liquids with very weak intermolecular forces.

22. The *electron sea model* explains many properties of metallic elements. This model pictures a regular array of metal atoms set in a "sea" of mobile valence electrons. The electrons can

move easily throughout the metal to conduct heat or electricity, and the lattice of atoms and cations can be deformed with little effort, allowing the metal to be hammered into a sheet or stretched into wire. An alloy is a material that contains a mixture of elements that overall has metallic properties. *Substitutional* alloys consist of a host metal in which some of the atoms in the metal's crystalline structure are replaced by atoms of other metallic elements. For example, sterling silver is an alloy in which some silver atoms have been replaced by copper atoms. An *interstitial alloy* is formed when other, smaller atoms enter the interstices (holes) between atoms in the host metal's crystal structure. Steel is an interstitial alloy in which carbon atoms enter the interstices of a crystal of iron atoms.

24. A saturated solution contains as much solute as can dissolve at a particular temperature. Saying that a solution is *saturated* does not *necessarily* mean that the solute is present at a high concentration—for example, magnesium hydroxide dissolves only to a very small extent before the solution is saturated. A saturated solution is in equilibrium with undissolved solute: as molecules of solute dissolve from the solid in one place in the solution, dissolved molecules rejoin the solid phase in another part of the solution. Once the rates of dissolving and solid formation become equal, no further net change occurs in the concentration of the solution and the solution is saturated.

26. Adding more solvent to a solution to dilute the solution does *not* change the number of moles of solute present, but changes only the *volume* in which the solute is dispersed. If molarity is used to describe the solution's concentration, then the number of *liters* is changed when solvent is added and the number of *moles per liter* (the molarity) changes, but the actual number of *moles* of solute does *not* change. For example, 125 mL of 0.551 *M* NaCl contains 0.0689 mole of NaCl. The solution will *still* contain 0.0689 mole of NaCl after 250 mL of water is added to it. The volume and the concentration will change, but the number of moles of solute in the solution will *not* change. The 0.0689 mole of NaCl, divided by the total volume of the diluted solution in liters, gives the new molarity (0.184 *M*).

28. (a) 105 mL; (b) 1.05×10^3 mm Hg

30. (a) 6.96 L; (b) $P_{\text{hydrogen}} = 5.05$ atm; $P_{\text{helium}} = 1.15$ atm; (c) 2.63 atm

32. 0.550 g CO_2; 0.280 L CO_2 at STP

34. (a) 9.65% NaCl; (b) 2.75 g $CaCl_2$; (c) 11.4 g NaCl

36. (a) 0.505 *M*; (b) 0.0840 *M*; (c) 0.130 *M*

38. (a) 226 g; (b) 18.4 *M*; (c) 0.764 *M*; (d) 1.53 *N*; (e) 15.8 mL

Page numbers followed by *n* refer to margin notes. Page numbers followed by *f* refer to figures. Page numbers followed by *t* refer to tables.

Table 5.1 — Common Simple Cations and Anions

Cation	Name	Anion	Name*
H^+	hydrogen	H^-	hydride
Li^+	lithium	F^-	fluoride
Na^+	sodium	Cl^-	chloride
K^+	potassium	Br^-	bromide
Cs^+	cesium	I^-	iodide
Be^{2+}	beryllium	O^{2-}	oxide
Mg^{2+}	magnesium	S^{2-}	sulfide
Ca^{2+}	calcium		
Ba^{2+}	barium		
Al^{3+}	aluminum		
Ag^+	silver		
Zn^{2+}	zinc		

*The root is given in color.

Table 5.2 — Common Type II Cations

Ion	Systematic Name	Older Name
Fe^{3+}	iron(III)	ferric
Fe^{2+}	iron(II)	ferrous
Cu^{2+}	copper(II)	cupric
Cu^+	copper(I)	cuprous
Co^{3+}	cobalt(III)	cobaltic
Co^{2+}	cobalt(II)	cobaltous
Sn^{4+}	tin(IV)	stannic
Sn^{2+}	tin(II)	stannous
Pb^{4+}	lead(IV)	plumbic
Pb^{2+}	lead(II)	plumbous
Hg^{2+}	mercury(II)	mercuric
Hg_2^{2+}*	mercury(I)	mercurous

*Mercury(I) ions always occur bound together in pairs to form Hg_2^{2+}.

Table 5.4 — Names of Common Polyatomic Ions

Ion	Name	Ion	Name
NH_4^+	ammonium	CO_3^{2-}	carbonate
NO_2^-	nitrite	HCO_3^-	hydrogen carbonate (bicarbonate is a widely used common name)
NO_3^-	nitrate		
SO_3^{2-}	sulfite		
SO_4^{2-}	sulfate	ClO^-	hypochlorite
HSO_4^-	hydrogen sulfate (bisulfate is a widely used common name)	ClO_2^-	chlorite
		ClO_3^-	chlorate
		ClO_4^-	perchlorate
OH^-	hydroxide	$C_2H_3O_2^-$	acetate
CN^-	cyanide	MnO_4^-	permanganate
PO_4^{3-}	phosphate	$Cr_2O_7^{2-}$	dichromate
HPO_4^{2-}	hydrogen phosphate	CrO_4^{2-}	chromate
$H_2PO_4^-$	dihydrogen phosphate	O_2^{2-}	peroxide

Student Solutions Manual

Introductory Chemistry: A Foundation, Introductory Chemistry, Basic Chemistry

SEVENTH EDITION

Steven S. Zumdahl
University of Illinois Urbana-Champaign

Donald J. DeCoste
University of Illinois Urbana-Champaign

Written by

James F. Hall
University of Massachusetts Lowell

BROOKS/COLE
CENGAGE Learning

Australia • Brazil • Japan • Korea • Mexico • Singapore • Spain • United Kingdom • United States

Contents

Preface

This guide contains the even-numbered solutions for the end-of-chapter problems in the seventh editions of *Introductory Chemistry*, *Introductory Chemistry: A Foundation*, and *Basic Chemistry* by Steven S. Zumdahl and Donald J. DeCoste. Several hundred new problems and questions have been prepared for the new editions of the text, which we hope will be of even greater help to students in gaining an understanding of the fundamental principles of chemistry.

We have tried to give the most detailed solutions possible to all the problems, even though some problems give repeat drill practice on the same subject. Our chief attempt at brevity is to give molar masses for compounds without showing the calculation (after the subject of molar mass itself has been discussed). We have also made a conscious effort in this guide to solve each problem in the manner discussed in the textbook. The instructor, of course, may wish to discuss alternative methods of solution with his or her students.

One topic that causes many students concern is the matter of significant figures and the determination of the number of digits to which a solution to a problem should be reported. To avoid truncation errors in the solutions contained in this guide, the solutions typically report intermediate answers to one more digit than appropriate for the final answer. The final answer to each problem is then given to the correct number of significant figures based on the data provided in the problem.

I wish you the best of luck and success in your study of chemistry!

James F. Hall

University of Massachusetts Lowell

CHAPTER 1

Chemistry: An Introduction

2. The answer will depend on student examples.

4. Answer depends on student responses/examples.

6. This answer depends on your own experience, but consider the following examples: oven cleaner (the label says it contains sodium hydroxide; it converts the burned-on grease in the oven to a soapy material that washes away); drain cleaner (the label says it contains sodium hydroxide; it dissolves the clog of hair in the drain); stomach antacid (the label says it contains calcium carbonate; it makes me belch and makes my stomach feel better); hydrogen peroxide (the label says it is a 3% solution of hydrogen peroxide; when applied to a wound, it bubbles); depilatory cream (the label says it contains sodium hydroxide; it removes unwanted hair from skin).

8. The scientist must recognize the problem and state it clearly, propose possible solutions or explanations, and then decide through experimentation which solution or explanation is best.

10. Answer depends on student response. A quantitative observation must include a number. For example "There are two windows in this room" represents a quantitative observation, but "The walls of this room are yellow" is a qualitative observation.

12. Answer depends on student responses/examples.

14. Chemistry is not just a set of facts that have to be memorized. To be successful in chemistry, you have to be able to apply what you have learned to new situations, new phenomena, and new experiments. Rather than just learning a list of facts or studying someone else's solution to a problem, your instructor hopes you will learn *how* to solve problems *yourself,* so that you will be able to apply what you have learned in future circumstances.

16. In real life situations, the problems and applications likely to be encountered are not simple textbook examples. One must be able to observe an event, hypothesize a cause, and then test this hypothesis. One must be able to carry what has been learned in class forward to new, different situations.

CHAPTER 2

Measurements and Calculations

2. "Scientific notation" means we have to put the decimal point after the first significant figure, and then express the order of magnitude of the number as a power of ten. So we want to put the decimal point after the first 2:

    $$2{,}421 \rightarrow 2.421 \times 10^{\text{to some power}}$$

    To be able to move the decimal point three places to the left in going from 2,421 to 2.421, means I will need a power of 10^3 after the number, where the exponent 3 shows that I moved the decimal point 3 places to the left.

    $$2{,}421 \rightarrow 2.421 \times 10^{\text{to some power}} = 2.421 \times 10^3$$

4. a. 10^4

    b. 10^{-3}

    c. 10^2

    d. 10^{-30}

6. a. negative

    b. zero

    c. positive

    d. negative

8. a. The decimal point must be moved three spaces to the right: 2789

    b. The decimal point must be moved three spaces to the left: 0.002789

    c. The decimal point must be moved seven spaces to the right: 93,000,000.

    d. The decimal point must be moved one space to the right: 42.89.

    e. The decimal point must be moved 4 spaces to the right: 99,990.

    f. The decimal point must be moved 5 spaces to the left: 0.00009999.

10. a. three spaces to the left

    b. one space to the left

    c. five spaces to the right

    d. one space to the left

    e. two spaces to the right

    f. two spaces to the left

12.
a. The decimal point must be moved 3 places to the right: 6244

b. The decimal point must be moved 2 spaces to the left: 0.09117

c. The decimal point must be moved 1 space to the right: 82.99

d. The decimal point must be moved 4 spaces to the left: 0.0001771

e. The decimal point must be moved 2 spaces to the right: 545.1

f. The decimal point must be moved 5 spaces to the left: 0.00002934

14.
a. $1/0.00032 = 3.1 \times 10^3$

b. $10^3/10^{-3} = 1 \times 10^6$

c. $10^3/10^3 = 1 \ (1 \times 10^0)$; any number divided by itself is unity.

d. $1/55,000 = 1.8 \times 10^{-5}$

e. $(10^5)(10^4)(10^{-4})/10^{-2} = 1 \times 10^7$

f. $43.2/(4.32 \times 10^{-5}) = \dfrac{4.32 \times 10^1}{4.32 \times 10^{-5}} = 1.00 \times 10^6$

g. $(4.32 \times 10^{-5})/432 = \dfrac{4.32 \times 10^{-5}}{4.32 \times 10^2} = 1.00 \times 10^{-7}$

h. $1/(10^5)(10^{-6}) = 1/(10^{-1}) = 1 \times 10^1$

16. The metric system uses prefixes to indicate multiples of the basic SI units. For example, a *centi*meter is $\frac{1}{100}$ of a meter; a *kilo*meter is 1000 meters.

18. Since a pound is 453.6 grams, the 125-g can will be slightly more than ¼ pound.

20. Since 1 inch = 2.54 cm, the nail is approximately an inch long.

22. Since a liter is slightly more than a quart, the 2–liter bottle is larger.

24. 1.62 m is approximately 5 ft, 4 in. The woman is slightly taller.

26.
a. centimeter

b. meter

c. kilometer

28. d (the other units would give very large numbers for the distance).

30. When we use a measuring device with an analog scale, we estimate the reading to 0.1 of the smallest scale divisions on the measuring scale. Since this last reading is decided by the user, not by the divisions on the measuring scale, the final digit of the measurement is uncertain no matter how careful we may be in making the determination.

32. The scale of the ruler shown is only marked to the nearest *tenth* of a centimeter; writing 2.850 would imply that the scale was marked to the nearest *hundredth* of a centimeter (and that the zero in the thousandths place had been estimated).

34.   a.   three (the relationship is exact)

       b.   two (a counting number)

       c.   five (

       d.   only two since there is no decimal point indicated

36.   It is better to round off only the final answer, and to carry through extra digits in intermediate calculations. If there are enough steps to the calculation, rounding off in each step may lead to a cumulative error in the final answer.

38.   a. 4.18×10^{-6}

       b. 3.87×10^{4}

       c. 9.11×10^{-30}

       d. 5.46×10^{6}

40.   a. 8.8×10^{-4}

       b. 9.375×10^{4}

       c. 8.97×10^{-1}

       d. 1.00×10^{3}

42.   The total mass would be determined by the number of decimal places available on the readout of the scale/balance. For example, if a balance whose readout is to the nearest 0.01 g were used, the total mass would be reported to the second decimal place. For example 32.05 g + 29.15 g + 31.09 g would be reported as 92.29 g to the second decimal place. For the calculation 44.05 g + 33.91 g + 48.38 g, the sum would be reported as 126.34 g (a total of five significant figures, but given to the second decimal place).

44.   Most calculators would display 0.66666666. If the 2 and 3 were *experimentally determined* numbers, this quotient would imply far too many significant figures.

46.   none (10,434 is only known to the nearest whole number)

48.   a.   2.3 (the answer can only be given to two significant figures because 3.1 is only known to two significant figures)

       b. 9.1×10^{2}: (the answer can only be given to the first decimal place because 4.1 is only given to the first decimal place; both numbers have the same power of ten)

       c. 1.323×10^{3}: (the numbers must be first expressed as the same power of ten; $1.091 \times 10^{3} + 0.221 \times 10^{3} + 0.0114 \times 10^{3} = 1.323 \times 10^{3}$)

       d. 6.63×10^{-13} (the answer can only be given to three significant figures because 4.22×10^{6} is only given to three significant figures)

50.   a.   one (the factor of 2 has only one significant figure)

       b.   four (the sum within the parentheses will contain four significant figures)

       c.   two (based on the factor 4.7×10^{-6} only having two significant figures)

       d.   three (based on the factor 63.9 having only three significant figures)

52.   a. $(2.0944 + 0.0003233 + 12.22)/7.001 = (14.31)/7.001 = 2.045$

       b. $(1.42 \times 10^2 + 1.021 \times 10^3)/(3.1 \times 10^{-1}) =$

             $(142 + 1021)/(3.1 \times 10^{-1}) = (1163)/(3.1 \times 10^{-1}) = 3752 = 3.8 \times 10^3$

       c. $(9.762 \times 10^{-3})/(1.43 \times 10^2 + 4.51 \times 10^1) =$

             $(9.762 \times 10^{-3})/(143 + 45.1) = (9.762 \times 10^{-3})/(188.1) = 5.19 \times 10^{-5}$

       d. $(6.1982 \times 10^{-4})^2 = (6.1982 \times 10^{-4})(6.1982 \times 10^{-4}) = 3.8418 \times 10^{-7}$

54.   an infinite number (a definition)

56. $\dfrac{2.54 \text{ cm}}{1 \text{ in}}$ and $\dfrac{1 \text{ in}}{2.54 \text{ cm}}$

58. $\dfrac{1 \text{ lb}}{\$0.79}$

60.   a. $4.21 \text{ ft} \times \dfrac{12 \text{ in}}{1 \text{ ft}} = 50.5 \text{ in}$

       b. $37.3 \text{ in} \times \dfrac{1 \text{ ft}}{12 \text{ in}} = 3.11 \text{ ft}$

       c. $45.2 \text{ cm} \times \dfrac{10 \text{ mm}}{1 \text{ cm}} = 452 \text{ mm}$

       d. $761.2 \text{ mm} \times \dfrac{1 \text{ cm}}{10 \text{ mm}} = 76.12 \text{ cm}$

       e. $1.25 \text{ L} \times \dfrac{1.0567 \text{ qt}}{1 \text{ L}} = 1.32 \text{ qt}$

       f. $4.21 \text{ qt} \times \dfrac{2 \text{ pt}}{1 \text{ qt}} = 8.42 \text{ pt}$

       g. $6.21 \text{ kg} \times \dfrac{2.2046 \text{ lb}}{1 \text{ kg}} = 13.7 \text{ lb}$

       h. $1.75 \text{ lb} \times \dfrac{16 \text{ oz}}{1 \text{ lb}} = 28.0 \text{ oz}$

62.   a. $104.971 \text{ kPa} \times \dfrac{1 \text{ atm}}{101.325 \text{ kPa}} = 1.03598 \text{ atm}$

       b. $6.25 \text{ pt} \times \dfrac{1 \text{ qt}}{2 \text{ pt}} = 3.13 \text{ qt}$

       c. $18.0 \text{ oz} \times \dfrac{1 \text{ lb}}{16 \text{ oz}} \times \dfrac{1 \text{ kg}}{2.2046 \text{ lb}} = 0.510 \text{ kg}$

d. $4.213 \text{ J} \times \dfrac{1 \text{ cal}}{4.184 \text{ J}} = 1.007 \text{ cal}$

e. $1.632 \text{ mi} \times \dfrac{5280 \text{ ft}}{1 \text{ mi}} = 8617 \text{ ft}$

f. $4.52 \text{ qt} \times \dfrac{2 \text{ pt}}{1 \text{ qt}} = 9.04 \text{ qt}$

g. $9.25 \text{ oz} \times \dfrac{453.59 \text{ g}}{16 \text{ oz}} = 262 \text{ g}$

h. $56.2 \text{ fl oz} \times \dfrac{1 \text{ qt}}{32 \text{ fl oz}} = 1.76 \text{ qt}$

64. $2558 \text{ mi} \times \dfrac{1.6093 \text{ km}}{1 \text{ mi}} = 4117 \text{ km}$

66. $1 \times 10^{-10} \text{ m} \times \dfrac{100 \text{ cm}}{1 \text{ m}} = 1 \times 10^{-8} \text{ cm}$

$1 \times 10^{-8} \text{ cm} \times \dfrac{1 \text{ in}}{2.54 \text{ cm}} = 4 \times 10^{-9} \text{ in.}$

$1 \times 10^{-8} \text{ cm} \times \dfrac{1 \text{ m}}{100 \text{ cm}} \times \dfrac{10^{9} \text{ nm}}{1 \text{ m}} = 0.1 \text{ nm}$

68.   freezing

70.   273

72.   Fahrenheit (F)

74. $T_{K} = T_{C} + 273$ $T_{C} = T_{K} - 273$

a. $-78.1 + 273 = 194.9 \text{ K } (195 \text{ K})$

b. $775 \text{ K} - 273 = 502\text{°C}$

c. $489 \text{ K} - 273 = 216\text{°C}$

d. $24.3\text{°C} + 273 = 297.3 \text{ K } (297 \text{ K})$

76. $T_{F} = 1.80(T_{C}) + 32$

a. $1.80(78.1) + 32 = 173\text{°F}$

b. $1.80(40.) + 32 = 104\text{°F}$

c. $1.80(-273) + 32 = -459\text{°F}$

d. $1.80(32) + 32 = 90.\text{°F}$

78. $T_F = 1.80(T_C) + 32$ $\qquad$ $T_C = (T_F - 32)/1.80$ $\qquad$ $T_K = T_C + 273$

    a. $\quad 275 - 273 = 2°C$

    b. $\quad (82 - 32)/1.80 = 28°C$

    c. $\quad 1.80(-21) + 32 = -5.8°F$ ($-6°F$)

    d. $\quad (-40 - 32)/1.80 = -40\ °C$ (Celsius and Fahrenheit temperatures are the same at -40).

80. g/cm^3 (g/mL)

82. $100\ in.^3$

84. Density is a *characteristic* property, which is always the same for a pure substance.

86. copper

88. $density = \dfrac{mass}{volume}$

    a. $\quad d = \dfrac{122.4\ g}{5.5\ cm^3} = 22\ g/cm^3$

    b. $\quad v = 0.57\ m^3 \times \left(\dfrac{100\ cm}{1\ m}\right)^3 = 5.7 \times 10^5\ cm^3$

    $\quad d = \dfrac{1.9302 \times 10^4\ g}{5.7 \times 10^5\ cm} = 0.034\ g/cm^3$

    c. $\quad m = 0.0175\ kg \times \dfrac{1000\ g}{1\ kg} = 17.5\ g$

    $\quad d = \dfrac{17.5\ g}{18.2\ mL} = 0.962\ g/mL = 0.962\ g/cm^3$

    d. $\quad v = 0.12\ m^3 \times \left(\dfrac{100\ cm}{1\ m}\right)^3 = 1.2 \times 10^5\ cm^3$

    $\quad d = \dfrac{2.49\ g}{1.2 \times 10^5\ cm^3} = 2.1 \times 10^{-5}\ g/cm^3$

90. $3.75\ L = 3750\ mL$

    $3750\ mL \times \dfrac{0.785\ g}{1\ ml} = 2944\ g = 2.94 \times 10^3\ g$

    $125\ g \times \dfrac{1\ mL}{0.785\ g} = 159\ mL$

92. $m = 3.5 \text{ lb} \times \dfrac{453.59 \text{ g}}{1 \text{ lb}} = 1.59 \times 10^3 \text{ g}$

$v = 1.2 \times 10^4 \text{ in.}^3 \times \left(\dfrac{2.54 \text{ cm}}{1 \text{ in}} \right)^3 = 1.97 \times 10^5 \text{ cm}^3$

$d = \dfrac{1.59 \times 10^3 \text{ g}}{1.97 \times 10^5 \text{ cm}^3} = 8.1 \times 10^{-3} \text{ g/cm}^3$

The material will float.

94. $5.25 \text{ g} \times \dfrac{1 \text{ cm}^3}{10.5 g} = 0.500 \text{ cm}^3 = 0.500 \text{ mL}$

$11.2 \text{ mL} + 0.500 \text{ mL} = 11.7 \text{ mL}$

96. a. $50.0 \text{ cm}^3 \times \dfrac{19.32 \text{ g}}{1 \text{ cm}^3} = 966 \text{ g}$

b. $50.0 \text{ cm}^3 \times \dfrac{7.87 \text{ g}}{1 \text{ cm}^3} = 394 \text{ g}$

c. $50.0 \text{ cm}^3 \times \dfrac{11.34 \text{ g}}{1 \text{ cm}^3} = 567 \text{ g}$

d. $50.0 \text{ cm}^3 \times \dfrac{2.70 \text{ g}}{1 \text{ cm}^3} = 135 \text{ g}$

98. a. $3.011 \times 10^{23} = 301,100,000,000,000,000,000,000$

b. $5.091 \times 10^9 = 5,091,000,000$

c. $7.2 \times 10^2 = 720$

d. $1.234 \times 10^5 = 123,400$

e. $4.32002 \times 10^{-4} = 0.000432002$

f. $3.001 \times 10^{-2} = 0.03001$

g. $2.9901 \times 10^{-7} = 0.00000029901$

h. $4.2 \times 10^{-1} = 0.42$

100. a. centimeters

b. meters

c. kilometers

d. centimeters

e. millimeters

102. a. $36.2 \text{ blim} \times \dfrac{1400 \text{ kryll}}{1 \text{ blim}} = 5.07 \times 10^4 \text{ kryll}$

      b. $170 \text{ kryll} \times \dfrac{1 \text{ blim}}{1400 \text{ kryll}} = 0.12 \text{ blim}$

      c. $72.5 \text{ kryll}^2 \times \left(\dfrac{1 \text{ blim}}{1400 \text{ kryll}} \right)^2 = 3.70 \times 10^{-5} \text{ blim}^2$

104. $52 \text{ cm} \times \dfrac{1 \text{ in}}{2.54 \text{ cm}} = 20. \text{ in.}$

106. $1 \text{ lb} \times \dfrac{1 \text{ kg}}{2.2 \text{ lb}} \times \dfrac{\$1.20}{1 \text{ euro}} \times \dfrac{2.45 \, euro}{1 \text{ kg}} = \; = \$1.33 \text{ per pound}$

108. $°X = 1.26°C + 14$

110. $d = \dfrac{36.8 \text{ g}}{10.5 \text{ L}} = 3.50 \text{ g/L} \quad (3.50 \times 10^{-3} \text{ g/cm}^3)$

112. For ethanol, $100. \text{ mL} \times \dfrac{0.785 \text{ g}}{1 \text{ mL}} = 78.5 \text{ g}$

      For benzene, $1000 \text{ mL} \times \dfrac{0.880 \text{ g}}{1 \text{ mL}} = 880. \text{ g}$

      total mass, $78.5 + 880. = 959 \text{ g}$

114. a.   negative

      b.   negative

      c.   positive

      d.   zero

      e.   negative

116. a.   2; positive

      b.   11; negative

      c.   3; positive

      d.   5; negative

      e.   5; positive

      f.   0; zero

      g.   1; negative

      h.   7; negative

118.   a.   1; positive

       b.   3; negative

       c.   0; zero

       d.   3; positive

       e.   9; negative

120.   a.   The decimal point must be moved five places to the left; $2.98 \times 10^{-5} = 0.0000298$.

       b.   The decimal point must be moved nine places to the right; $4.358 \times 10^{9} = 4{,}358{,}000{,}000$.

       c.   The decimal point must be moved six places to the left; $1.9928 \times 10^{-6} = 0.0000019928$.

       d.   The decimal point must be moved 23 places to the right; $6.02 \times 10^{23} = 602{,}000{,}000{,}000{,}000{,}000{,}000{,}000$.

       e.   The decimal point must be moved one place to the left; $1.01 \times 10^{-1} = 0.101$.

       f.   The decimal point must be moved three places to the left; $7.87 \times 10^{-3} = 0.00787$.

       g.   The decimal point must be moved seven places to the right; $9.87 \times 10^{7} = 98{,}700{,}000$.

       h.   The decimal point must be moved two places to the right; $3.7899 \times 10^{2} = 378.99$.

       i.   The decimal point must be moved one place to the left; $1.093 \times 10^{-1} = 0.1093$.

       j.   The decimal point must be moved zero places; $2.9004 \times 10^{0} = 2.9004$.

       k.   The decimal point must be moved four places to the left; $3.9 \times 10^{-4} = 0.00039$.

       l.   The decimal point must be moved eight places to the left; $1.904 \times 10^{-8} = 0.00000001904$.

122.   a. $1/10^{2} = 1 \times 10^{-2}$

       b. $1/10^{-2} = 1 \times 10^{2}$

       c. $55/10^{3} = \dfrac{5.5 \times 10^{1}}{1 \times 10^{3}} = 5.5 \times 10^{-2}$

       d. $(3.1 \times 10^{6})/10^{-3} = \dfrac{3.1 \times 10^{6}}{1 \times 10^{-3}} = 3.1 \times 10^{9}$

       e. $(10^{6})^{1/2} = 1 \times 10^{3}$

       f. $(10^{6})(10^{4})/(10^{2}) = \dfrac{(1 \times 10^{6})(1 \times 10^{4})}{(1 \times 10^{2})} = 1 \times 10^{8}$

       g. $1/0.0034 = \dfrac{1}{3.4 \times 10^{-3}} = 2.9 \times 10^{2}$

       h. $3.453/10^{-4} = \dfrac{3.453}{1 \times 10^{-4}} = 3.453 \times 10^{4}$

124.   Kelvin, K

126.   centimeter

128.   0.105 m

130.   1 kg (100 g = 0.1 kg)

132.   10 cm (1 cm = 10 mm)

134.   2.8 (the hundredths place is estimated)

136.   a.   0.000426

b. 4.02×10^{-5}

c. 5.99×10^{6}

d.   400.

e.   0.00600

138.   a.   2149.6 (the answer can only be given to the first decimal place, because 149.2 is only known to the first decimal place)

b. 5.37×10^{3} (the answer can only be given to two decimal places because 4.34 is only known to two decimal places; moreover, since the power of ten is the same for each number, the calculation can be performed directly)

c.   Before performing the calculation, the numbers have to be converted so that they contain the same power of ten.

$4.03 \times 10^{-2} - 2.044 \times 10^{-3} = 4.03 \times 10^{-2} - 0.2044 \times 10^{-2} = 3.83 \times 10^{-2}$ (the answer can only be given the second decimal place because 4.03×10^{-2} is only known to the second decimal place)

d.   Before performing the calculation, the numbers have to be converted so that they contain the same power of ten.

$2.094 \times 10^{5} - 1.073 \times 10^{6} = 2.094 \times 10^{5} - 10.73 \times 10^{5} = -8.64 \times 10^{5}$

140.   a. $(2.9932 \times 10^{4})(2.4443 \times 10^{2} + 1.0032 \times 10^{1}) =$

$(2.9932 \times 10^{4})(24.443 \times 10^{1} + 1.0032 \times 10^{1}) =$

$(2.9932 \times 10^{4})(25.446 \times 10^{1}) = 7.6166 \times 10^{6}$

b. $(2.34 \times 10^{2} + 2.443 \times 10^{-1})/(0.0323) =$

$(2.34 \times 10^{2} + 0.002443 \times 10^{2})/(0.0323) =$

$(2.34 \times 10^{2})/(0.0323) = 7.24 \times 10^{3}$

c. $(4.38 \times 10^{-3})^{2} = 1.92 \times 10^{-5}$

d. $(5.9938 \times 10^{-6})^{1/2} = 2.4482 \times 10^{-3}$

142. $\dfrac{1 \text{ year}}{12 \text{ months}}; \dfrac{12 \text{ months}}{1 \text{ year}}$

144. a. $908 \text{ oz} \times \dfrac{1 \text{ lb}}{16 \text{ oz}} \times \dfrac{1 \text{ kg}}{2.2046 \text{ lb}} = 25.7 \text{ kg}$

    b. $12.8 \text{ L} \times \dfrac{1 \text{ qt}}{0.94633 \text{ L}} \times \dfrac{1 \text{ gal}}{4 \text{ qt}} = 3.38 \text{ gal}$

    c. $125 \text{ mL} \times \dfrac{1 \text{ L}}{1000 \text{ mL}} \times \dfrac{1 \text{ qt}}{0.94633 \text{ L}} = 0.132 \text{ qt}$

    d. $2.89 \text{ gal} \times \dfrac{4 \text{ qt}}{1 \text{ gal}} \times \dfrac{1 \text{ L}}{1.0567 \text{ qt}} \times \dfrac{1000 \text{ mL}}{1 \text{ L}} = 1.09 \times 10^4 \text{ mL}$

    e. $4.48 \text{ lb} \times \dfrac{453.59 \text{ g}}{1 \text{ lb}} = 2.03 \times 10^3 \text{ g}$

    f. $550 \text{ mL} \times \dfrac{1 \text{ L}}{1000 \text{ mL}} \times \dfrac{1.0567 \text{ qt}}{1 \text{ L}} = 0.58 \text{ qt}$

146. Assuming exactly 6 gross, 864 pencils

148. a. Celsius temperature = (175 – 32)/1.80 = 79.4°C

       Kelvin temperature = 79.4 + 273 = 352 K

    b. 255 – 273 = –18 °C

    c. (–45 – 32)/1.80 = –43°C

    d. 1.80(125) + 32 = 257°F

150. $85.5 \text{ mL} \times \dfrac{0.915 \text{ g}}{1 \text{ mL}} = 78.2 \text{ g}$

152. $m = 155 \text{ lb} \times \dfrac{453.59 \text{ g}}{1 \text{ lb}} = 7.031 \times 10^4 \text{ g}$

    $v = 4.2 \text{ ft}^3 \times \left(\dfrac{12 \text{ in}}{1 \text{ ft}}\right)^3 \times \left(\dfrac{2.54 \text{ cm}}{1 \text{ in}}\right)^3 = 1.189 \times 10^5 \text{ cm}^3$

    $d = \dfrac{7.031 \times 10^4 \text{ g}}{1.189 \times 10^5 \text{ cm}^3} = 0.59 \text{ g/cm}^3$

154. $T_F = 1.80(T_C) + 32$

    a. 23 °F

    b. 32 °F

    c. –321 °F

    d. –459 °F

    e. 187 °F

    f. –459 °F

156.   a.   The Mars Climate Orbiter dipped 100 km lower in the Mars atmosphere than was planned. Using the conversion factor between miles and kilometers found inside the cover of this text

$$100 \text{ km} \times \frac{1 \text{ mi}}{1.6093 \text{ km}} = 62 \text{ mi}$$

   b.   The aircraft required 22,300 kg of fuel, but only 22,300 lb of fuel was loaded. Using the conversion factor between pounds and kilograms found inside the cover of this text, the amount of fuel required in pounds was

$$22,300 \text{ kg} \times \frac{2.2046 \text{ lb}}{1 \text{ kg}} = 49,163 \text{ lb}$$

Therefore, $(49,163 - 22,300) = 26,863 = 2.69 \times 10^4$ lb additional fuel was needed.

158. $\dfrac{10^{-8} \text{ g}}{\text{L}} \times \dfrac{1 \text{ lb}}{453.59 \text{ g}} \times \dfrac{1 \text{ L}}{1.0567 \text{ qt}} \times \dfrac{4 \text{ qt}}{1 \text{ gal}} = 8 \times 10^{-11} \text{ lb/gal}$

CHAPTER 3

Matter

2. intermolecular forces

4. liquids

6. gaseous

8. The *stronger* the inter-particle forces, the more rigid is the sample overall.

10. Gases are easily compressed into smaller volumes, whereas solids and liquids are not. Because a gaseous sample consists mostly of empty space, it is this empty space that is compressed when pressure is applied to a gas.

12. This is a chemical property: the red liquid bromine disappears and is replaced by a white solid.

14. Magnesium is malleable and ductile.

16. c

18. a. physical; the iron is only being heated.

    b. chemical; the sugars in the marshmallow are being reduced to carbon.

    c. chemical; most strips contain a peroxide which decomposes.

    d. chemical; the bleach oxidizes dyes in the fabric.

    e. physical; evaporation is only a change of state.

    f physical; the salt is only modifying the physical properties of the solution, not undergoing a chemical reaction.

    g. chemical; the drain cleaner breaks bonds in the hair.

    h. physical; students will most likely reply that this is a physical change since the perfume is evaporating; the sensation of smell, however, depends on chemical processes.

    i. physical; the sublimation is only a change of state.

    j. physical; the wood is only being physically divided into smaller pieces.

    k. chemical; the cellulose in the wood is reacting with oxygen gas

20. Compounds consist of two or more elements combined together chemically in a fixed composition, no matter what their source may be. For example, water on earth consists of molecules containing one oxygen atom and two hydrogen atoms. Water on Mars (or any other planet) has the same composition.

22. compounds

24. Typically, the properties of a compound and the elements that constitute it are very different. Consider the properties of liquid *water* and the hydrogen and oxygen gases from which the water was prepared. Consider the properties of *sodium chloride* (table salt) and the sodium metal and chlorine gas from which it might have been prepared.

26.   Given that the product of the process is no longer attracted by the magnet, this strongly suggests that the iron has been converted to an iron/sulfur compound—a pure substance.

28.   solutions: window cleaner, shampoo, rubbing alcohol

       mixtures: salad dressing, jelly beans, the change in my pocket

30.   a.   primarily a pure compound   c.   mixture

       b.   mixture   d.   pure substance

32.   Concrete is a mixture: the various components of the particular concrete are still distinguishable within the concrete if examined closely.

34.   Consider a mixture of salt (sodium chloride) and sand. Salt is soluble in water, sand is not. The mixture is added to water and stirred to dissolve the salt and is then filtered. The salt solution passes through the filter; the sand remains on the filter. The water can then be evaporated from the salt.

36.   The chemical identities of the components of the mixture are not changed by filtration or distillation: the various components are separated by physical, not chemical, means.

38.   Since X is a pure substance, the fact that two different solids form when electrical current is passed indicates that X must be a compound.

40.   Because vaporized water is still the *same substance* as solid water, no chemical reaction has occurred. Sublimation is a physical change.

42.   far apart

44.   chemical

46.   physical

48.   electrolysis

50.   a.   heterogeneous

       b.   heterogeneous

       c.   heterogeneous (unless you work hard to get all the lumps out!)

       d.   although strictly heterogeneous, it may appear homogeneous

       e.   heterogeneous

52.   Answer depends on student response

54.   physical, chemical

56. O_2 and P_4 are both still elements, even though the ordinary forms of these elements consist of molecules containing more than one atom (but all atoms in each respective molecule are the same). P_2O_5 is a compound, because it is made up of two or more different elements (not all the atoms in the P_2O_5 molecule are the same).

58.   Assuming there is enough water present in the mixture to have dissolved all the salt, filter the mixture to separate out the sand from the mixture. Then distill the filtrate (consisting of salt and water), which will boil off the water, leaving the salt.

60.   The most obvious difference is the physical states: water is a liquid under room conditions, hydrogen and oxygen are both gases. Hydrogen is flammable. Oxygen supports combustion. Water does neither.

CUMULATIVE REVIEW

Chapters 1–3

2. By now, after having covered three chapters in this book, it is hoped that you have adopted an "active" approach to your study of chemistry. You may have discovered (perhaps through a disappointing grade on a quiz (though we hope not), that you really have to get involved with chemistry. You can't just sit and take notes, or just look over the solved examples in the textbook. You have to learn to solve problems. You have to learn how to interpret problems, and how to reduce them to the simple mathematical relationships you have studied. Whereas in some courses you might get by on just giving back on exams the facts or ideas presented in class, in chemistry you have to be able to extend and synthesize what has been discussed and to apply the material to new situations. Don't get discouraged if this is difficult at first: it's difficult for everyone at first.

4. It is difficult sometimes for students (especially beginning students) to understand why certain subjects are required for a given college major. The faculty of your major department, however, have collectively many years of experience in the subject in which you have chosen to specialize. They really do know what courses will be helpful to you in the future. They may have had trouble with the same courses that now give you trouble, but they realize that all the work will be worth it in the end. Some courses you take, particularly in your major field itself, have obvious and immediate utility. Other courses, often times chemistry included, are provided to give you a general background knowledge, which may prove useful in understanding your own major or other subjects related to your major. In perhaps a burst of bravado, chemistry has been called "the central science" by one team of textbook authors. This moniker is very true however: in order to understand biology, physics, nutrition, farming, home economics, or whatever (it helps to have a general background in chemistry).

6. Whenever a scientific measurement is made, we always employ the instrument or measuring device we are using to the limits of its precision. On a practical basis, this usually means that we *estimate* our reading of the last significant figure of the measurement. An example of the uncertainty in the last significant figure is given for measuring the length of a pin in the text in Figure 2.5. Scientists appreciate the limits of experimental techniques and instruments, and always assume that the last digit in a number representing a measurement has been estimated. Because the last significant figure in every measurement is assumed to be estimated, it is never possible to exclude uncertainty from measurements. The best we can do is to try to improve our techniques and instruments so that we get more significant figures for our measurements.

8. Dimensional analysis is a method of problem solving that pays particular attention to the units of measurements and uses these units as if they were algebraic symbols that multiply, divide, and cancel. Consider the following example. A dozen eggs costs $1.25. Suppose we want to know how much one egg costs, and also how much three dozens of eggs will cost. To solve these problems, we need to make use of two equivalence statements:

   1 dozen eggs = 12 eggs

   1 dozen eggs = $1.25

   The first of these equivalence statements is obvious: everyone knows that 12 eggs is "equivalent" to one dozen. The second statement also expresses an equivalence: if you give the grocer $1.25,

16

he or she will give you a dozen eggs. From these equivalence statements, we can construct the conversion factors we need to answer the two questions. For the first question (what does one egg cost) we can set up the calculation as follows

$$\frac{\$1.25}{12 \text{ eggs}} = \$0.104 = \$0.10$$

as the cost of one egg. Similarly, for the second question (the cost of 3 dozens eggs), we can set up the conversion as follows

$$3 \text{ dozens} \times \frac{\$1.25}{1 \text{ dozen}} = \$3.75$$

as the cost of three dozens eggs. See Section 2.6 of the text for how we construct conversion factors from equivalence statements.

10. Defining what scientists mean by "matter" often seems circular to students. Scientists say that matter is something that "has mass and occupies space", without ever really explaining what it means to "have mass" or to "occupy space"! The concept of matter is so basic and fundamental, that it becomes difficult to give a good textbook definition other than to say that matter is the "stuff" of which everything is made. Matter can be classified and subdivided in many ways, depending on what we are trying to demonstrate.

On the most fundamental basis, all matter is composed of tiny particles (such as protons, electrons, neutrons, and the other subatomic particles). On one higher level, these tiny particles are combined in a systematic manner into units called atoms. Atoms, in turn, may be combined to constitute molecules. And finally, large groups of molecules may be placed together to form a bulk sample of substance that we can see.

Matter can also be classified as to the physical state a particular substance happens to take. Some substances are solids, some are liquids, and some are gases. Matter can also be classified as to whether it is a pure substance (one type of molecule) or a mixture (more than one type of molecule), and furthermore whether a mixture is homogeneous or heterogeneous.

12. Chemists tend to give a functional definition of what they mean by an "element": an element is a fundamental substance that cannot be broken down into any simpler substances by chemical methods. Compounds, on the other hand, can be broken down into simpler substances (the elements of which the compound is composed). For example, sulfur and oxygen are both elements (sulfur occurs as S_8 molecules and oxygen as O_2 molecules). When sulfur and oxygen are placed together and heated, the compound sulfur dioxide (SO_2) forms. When we analyze the sulfur dioxide produced, we notice that each and every molecule consists of one sulfur atom and two oxygen atoms, and on a mass basis, consists of 50% each of sulfur and oxygen. We describe this by saying that sulfur dioxide has a constant composition. The fact that a given compound has constant composition is usually expressed in terms of the mass percentages of the elements present in the compound. The reason the mass percentages are constant is because of a constant number of atoms of each type present in the compound's molecules. If a scientist anywhere in the universe analyzed sulfur dioxide, he or she would find the same composition: if a scientist finds something that does not have the same composition, then the substance cannot be sulfur dioxide.

14.   a.   The decimal point must be moved four places to the right: 8.917×10^{-4}

        b.   The decimal point must be moved four places to the left: 0.0002795

        c.   The decimal point must be moved three places to the right: 4913

    d.   The decimal point must be moved seven places to the left: 8.51×10^7

    e.   The arithmetic must be performed and then the exponents combined: 1.219×10^2

    f.   The arithmetic must be performed and then the exponents combined: 3.396×10^{-9}

16.   a.   two (based on the factor of 2.1 in the denominator)

    b.   two (based on the factor of 5.2 in the numerator)

    c.   three (one before the decimal point, and two after the decimal point)

    d.   three (based on the sum of 5.338 and 2.11)

    e.   one (based on 9 only having one significant figure)

    f.   two (based on the sum of 4.2005 and 2.7)

    g.   two (based on the factor of 0.15)

    h.   three (two before the decimal point, and one after the decimal point)

18.   density = mass/volume   mass = volume × density   volume = mass/density

    a. $\text{density} = \dfrac{78.5\ \text{g}}{100.\ \text{mL}} = 0.785\ \text{g/mL}$

    b. $\text{volume} = \text{mass/density} = \dfrac{1.590\ \text{kg} \times \dfrac{1000\ \text{g}}{1\ \text{kg}}}{0.785\ \text{g/mL}} = 2025\ \text{mL} = 2.03\ \text{L}$

    c. $\text{mass} = \text{volume} \times \text{density} = 1.35\ \text{L} \times \dfrac{1000\ \text{mL}}{1\ \text{L}} \times \dfrac{0.785\ \text{g}}{1\ \text{mL}} = 1060\ \text{g} = 1.06\ \text{kg}$

    d. $\text{volume} = \text{mass/density} = \dfrac{25.2\ \text{g}}{2.70\ \text{g/cm}^3} = 9.33\ \text{cm}^3$

    e. $\text{volume} = 12.0\ \text{cm} \times 2.5\ \text{cm} \times 2.5\ \text{cm} = 75\ \text{cm}^3$

            $\text{mass} = \text{volume} \times \text{density} = 75\ \text{cm}^3 \times 2.70\ \text{g/cm}^3 = 202.5\ \text{g} = 2.0 \times 10^2\ \text{g}$

CHAPTER 4

Chemical Foundations: Elements, Atoms, and Ions

2.   Robert Boyle

4.   There are over 116 elements presently known; of these 88 occur naturally and the remaining are manmade. Table 4.1 lists the most common elements on the Earth.

6.   a.   Trace elements are those elements which are present in only tiny amounts in the body, but are critical for many bodily processes and functions.   /

        b.   Answer depends on your choice of elements

8.   Sometimes the symbol for an element is based on its common name in another language. This is true for many of the more common metals since their existence was known to the ancients: some examples are iron, sodium, potassium, silver, and tin (the symbols come from their name in Latin); tungsten (the symbol comes from its name in German).

10.   a.   9

        b.   6

        c.   8

        d.   12

        e.   11

        f.   13

        g.   3

        h.   5

        i.   4

        j.   2

12.   Zr   zirconium

        Cs   cesium

        Se   selenium

        Au   gold

        Ce   cerium

14.   B: barium, Ba; berkelium, Bk; beryllium, Be; bismuth, Bi; bohrium, Bh; boron, B; bromine, Br

        N: neodymium, Nd; neon, Ne; neptunium, Np; nickel, Ni; niobium, Nb; nitrogen, N; nobelium, No

P: palladium, Pd; phosphorus, P; platinum, Pt; plutonium, Pu; polonium, Po; potassium, K; praseodymium, Pr; promethium, Pm; protactinium, Pa

S: samarium, Sm; scandium, Sc; seaborgium, Sg; selenium, Se; silicon, Si; silver, Ag; sodium, Na; strontium, Sr; sulfur, S

16. a. Elements are made of tiny particles called atoms.

b. All the atoms of a given element are identical

c. The atoms of a given element are different from those of any other element.

d. A given compound always has the same numbers and types of atoms.

e. Atoms are neither created nor destroyed in chemical processes. A chemical reaction simply changes the way the atoms are grouped together.

18. According to Dalton, all atoms of the same element are *identical*; in particular, every atom of a given element has the same *mass* as every other atom of that element. If a given compound always contains the *same relative numbers* of atoms of each kind, and those atoms always have the *same masses*, then it follows that the compound made from those elements would always contain the same relative masses of its elements.

20. a. CO_2 d. H_2SO_4

b. CO e. $BaCl_2$

c. $CaCO_3$ f. Al_2S_3

22. a. False; Rutherford's bombardment experiments with metal foil suggested that the alpha particles were being deflected by coming near a *dense, positively charged* atomic nucleus.

b. False; The proton and the electron have opposite charges, but the mass of the electron is *much smaller* than the mass of the proton.

c. True

24. The protons and neutrons are found in the nucleus. The protons are positively charged; the neutrons have no electrical charge. Protons and neutrons each have approximately the same mass.

26. neutron; electron

28. Because they are located in the exterior regions of the atom, it is the electrons of an atom that most interact with other atoms and are therefore most responsible for the atom's chemical behavior.

30. The atomic number represents the number of protons in the nucleus of the atom, and makes the atom a particular element. The mass number represents the total number of protons and neutrons in the nucleus of an atom, and distinguishes one isotope of an element from another.

32. Neutrons are uncharged and contribute only to the mass.

34. Atoms of the same element (i.e., atoms with the same number of protons in the nucleus) may have different numbers of neutrons, and so will have different masses.

36.

Z	Symbol	Name
14	Si	silicon
54	Xe	xenon
79	Au	gold
56	Ba	barium
53	I	iodine
50	Sn	tin
48	Cd	cadmium

38. a. $^{54}_{26}\text{Fe}$

b. $^{56}_{26}\text{Fe}$

c. $^{57}_{26}\text{Fe}$

d. $^{14}_{7}\text{N}$

e. $^{15}_{7}\text{N}$

f. $^{15}_{7}\text{N}$

40. The relative amounts of ^{2}H and ^{18}O in a person's hair, compared to other isotopes of these elements, vary significantly from region to region in the United States and is related to the isotopic abundances in the drinking water in a region.

42.

Name	Symbol	Atomic Number	Mass Number	Number of neutrons
oxygen	$^{17}_{8}\text{O}$	8	17	9
oxygen	$^{17}_{8}\text{O}$	8	17	9
Neon	$^{20}_{10}\text{Ne}$	10	20	10
iron	$^{56}_{26}\text{Fe}$	26	56	30
plutonium	$^{244}_{94}\text{Pu}$	94	244	150
mercury	$^{202}_{80}\text{Hg}$	80	202	122
cobalt	$^{59}_{27}\text{Co}$	27	59	32
nickel	$^{56}_{28}\text{Ni}$	28	56	28
fluorine	$^{19}_{9}\text{F}$	9	19	10
chromium	$^{50}_{24}\text{Cr}$	24	50	26

44. Elements with similar chemical properties are aligned *vertically* in families known as *groups*.

46. Metallic elements are found towards the *left* and *bottom* of the periodic table; there are far more metallic elements than there are nonmetals.

48. The gaseous nonmetallic elements are hydrogen, nitrogen, oxygen, fluorine, chlorine, plus all the group 8 elements (noble gases). There are no gaseous metallic elements under room conditions.

50.   The metalloids are the elements found on either side of the "stairstep" region that is marked on most periodic tables. The metalloid elements show some properties of both metals and nonmetals.

52.   a.   fluorine, chlorine, bromine, iodine, astatine

       b.   lithium, sodium, potassium, rubidium, cesium, francium

       c.   beryllium, magnesium, calcium, strontium, barium, radium

       d.   helium, neon, argon, krypton, xenon, radon

54.   Arsenic, atomic number 33, is located on the dividing line between the metallic elements and the non-metallic elements, and is therefore classified as a metalloid. Arsenic is in Group 5 of the periodic table, whose other principal members are N, P, Sb, and Bi.

56.   Most of the elements are too reactive to be found in the uncombined form in nature and are found only in compounds.

58.   These elements are found *uncombined* in nature and do not readily react with other elements. For many years it was thought that these elements formed no compounds at all, although this has now been shown to be untrue.

60.   diatomic gases: H_2, N_2, O_2, Cl_2, and F_2

       monatomic gases: He, Ne, Kr, Xe, Rn, and Ar

62.   chlorine

64.   diamond

66.   electrons

68.   3+

70.   *-ide*

72.   nonmetallic

74.   a.   36   d.   36

       b.   36   e.   80

       c.   21   f.   27

76.   a.   two electrons gained

       b.   three electrons gained

       c.   three electrons lost

       d.   two electrons lost

       e.   one electron lost

       f.   two electrons lost.

78.   a. P^{3-}

    b. Ra^{2+}

    c. At^-

    d.   no ion

    e. Cs^+

    f. Se^{2-}

80.   Sodium chloride is an *ionic* compound, consisting of Na^+ and Cl^- *ions*. When NaCl is dissolved in water, these ions are *set free*, and can move independently to conduct the electrical current. Sugar crystals, although they may visually *appear* similar contain *no* ions. When sugar is dissolved in water, it dissolves as uncharged *molecules*. There are no electrically charged species present in a sugar solution to carry the electrical current.

82.   The total number of positive charges must equal the total number of negative charges so that there will be *no net charge* on the crystals of an ionic compound. A macroscopic sample of compound must ordinarily not have any net charge.

84.   a. CsI, BaI_2, AlI_3

    b. Cs_2O, BaO, Al_2O_3

    c. Cs_3P, Ba_3P_2, AlP

    d. Cs_2Se, $BaSe$, Al_2Se_3

    e. CsH, BaH_2, AlH_3

86.   a.   7; halogens

    b.   8; noble gases

    c.   2; alkaline earth elements

    d.   2; alkaline earth elements

    e.   4

    f.   6; (the members of group 6 are sometimes called the chalcogens)

    g.   8; noble gases

    h.   1; alkali metals

88.

	Element	*Symbol*	*Atomic Number*
Group 3	boron	B	5
	aluminum	Al	13
	gallium	Ga	31
	indium	In	49
Group 5	nitrogen	N	7
	phosphorus	P	15
	arsenic	As	33
	antimony	Sb	51

Group 6	oxygen	O	8
	sulfur	S	16
	selenium	Se	34
	tellurium	Te	52
Group 8	helium	He	2
	neon	Ne	10
	argon	Ar	18
	krypton	Kr	36

90.   Most of the mass of an atom is concentrated in the nucleus: the *protons* and *neutrons* that
constitute the nucleus have similar masses, and these particles are nearly two thousand times
heavier than electrons. The chemical properties of an atom depend on the number and location of
the *electrons* it possesses. Electrons are found in the outer regions of the atom and are the
particles most likely to be involved in interactions between atoms.

92. $C_6H_{12}O_6$

94.   a.   29 protons; 34 neutrons; 29 electrons

        b.   35 protons; 45 neutrons; 35 electrons

        c.   12 protons; 12 neutrons; 12 electrons

96.   The chief use of gold in ancient times was as *ornamentation*, whether in statuary or in jewelry.
Gold possesses an especially beautiful luster, and because it is relatively soft and malleable, it
could be worked finely by artisans. Among the metals, gold is particularly inert to attack by most
substances in the environment.

98.   a.   I

        b.   Si

        c.   W

        d.   Fe

        e.   Cu

        f.   Co

100.   a.   Br

        b.   Bi

        c.   Hg

        d.   V

        e.   F

        f.   Ca

102.   a.   osmium

        b.   zirconium

        c.   rubidium

        d.   radon

    e.   uranium

    f.   manganese

    g.   nickel

    h.   bromine

104.   a. CO_2

         b. $AlCl_3$

         c. $HClO_4$

         d. SCl_6

106.   a. $^{13}_{6}C$

         b. $^{13}_{6}C$

         c. $^{13}_{6}C$

         d. $^{44}_{19}K$

         e. $^{41}_{20}Ca$

         f. $^{35}_{19}K$

108.

Symbol	Protons	Neutrons	Mass Number
$^{41}_{20}Ca$	20	21	41
$^{55}_{25}Mn$	25	30	55
$^{109}_{47}Ag$	47	62	109
$^{45}_{21}Sc$	21	24	45

CHAPTER 5

Nomenclature

2.   A binary compound contains only two elements: the major types of binary compounds are *ionic* (compounds that contain a metal and a nonmetal) and *nonionic* (compounds containing two nonmetals).

4.   cation

6.   Some substances do not contain molecules. For example, the substance sodium chloride consists of an extended lattice array of sodium ions, Na^+, and chloride ions, Cl^-. Each sodium ion is surrounded by several chloride ions, and each chloride ion is surrounded by several sodium ions. We write the formula as NaCl to indicate the relative number of each ion in the substance, not to indicate that there are "molecules" of sodium chloride.

8.   Roman numeral

10.   a.   lithium chloride

b.   barium fluoride

c.   calcium oxide

d.   aluminum iodide

e.   magnesium sulfide

f.   rubidium oxide

12.   a.   correct

b.   incorrect; copper(I) oxide

c.   incorrect; potassium oxide

d.   correct

e.   incorrect; rubidium sulfide

14.   a.   As the chloride ion has a 1– charge, the copper ion must have a 2+ charge: the name is copper(II) chloride.

b.   As the oxide ion has a 2– charge, the chromium ion must have a 3+ charge: the name is chromium(III) oxide.

c.   As the chloride ion has a 1– charge, the mercury ion must have a 2+ charge: the name is mercury(II) chloride.

d.   As the oxide ion has a 2– charge, each mercury ion must have a 1+ charge: the name is mercury(I) oxide.

e.   As the bromide ion has a 1– charge, the gold ion must have a 3+ charge: the name is gold(III) bromide.

f.   As the oxide ion has a 2– charge, the manganese ion must have a 4+ charge: the name is manganese(IV) oxide.

16. a.   As each chloride ion has a 1– charge, the cobalt ion must have a 3+ charge: the name is cobalt*ic* chloride.

b.   As each bromide ion has a 1– charge, the iron ion must have a 2+ charge: the name is ferr*ous* bromide.

c.   As each oxide ion has a 2– charge, the lead ion must have a 4+ charge: the name is plumb*ic* oxide.

d.   As each chloride ion has a 1– charge, the tin ion must have a 4+ charge: the name is stann*ic* chloride.

e.   As the iodide ion has a 1– charge, the mercury ion must have a 2+ charge: the name is mercur*ic* iodide.

f.   As the sulfide ion has a 2– charge, the iron ion must have a 2+ charge: the name is ferr*ous* sulfide.

18. Remember that for this type of compound of nonmetals, numerical prefixes are used to indicate how many of each type of atom are present. However, if only one atom of the first element mentioned in the compound is present in a molecule, the prefix *mono–* is not needed.

a.   chlorine pentafluoride

b.   xenon dichloride

c.   selenium dioxide

d.   dinitrogen trioxide

e.   diiodine hexachloride

f.   carbon disulfide

20. a.   lead(IV) sulfide, plumbic sulfide – ionic

b.   lead(II) sulfide, plumbous sulfide – ionic

c.   silicon dioxide – nonionic

d.   tin(IV) fluoride, stannic fluoride – ionic

e.   dichlorine heptoxide – nonionic

f.   cobalt(III) sulfide, cobaltic sulfide – ionic

22. a.   barium fluoride – ionic

b.   radium oxide – ionic

c.   dinitrogen oxide – nonionic

d.   rubidium oxide – ionic

e.   diarsenic pentoxide – nonionic

f.   calcium nitride – ionic

24.   An oxyanion is a polyatomic ion containing a given element and one or more oxygen atoms. The oxyanions of chlorine and bromine are given below:

Oxyanion	Name	Oxyanion	Name
ClO^-	hypochlorite	BrO^-	hypobromite
ClO_2^-	chlorite	BrO_2^-	bromite
ClO_3^-	chlorate	BrO_3^-	bromate
ClO_4^-	perchlorate	BrO_4^-	perbromate

26.   For a series of oxyanions, the prefix *hypo–* is used for the anion with the fewest oxygen atoms, and the prefix *per–* is used for the anion with the most oxygen atoms.

28. IO^- hypoiodite

       IO_2^- iodite

       IO_3^- iodate

       IO_4^- periodate

30.   a. NO_3^-

       b. NO_2^-

       c. NH_4^+

       d. CN^-

32. CN^- cyanide

       CO_3^{2-} carbonate

       HCO_3^- hydrogen carbonate

       $C_2H_3O_2^-$ acetate

34.   a.   ammonium

       b.   dihydrogen phosphate

       c.   sulfate

       d.   hydrogen sulfite (also called *bi*sulfite)

       e.   perchlorate

       f.   iodate

36.   a.   sodium permanganate

       b.   aluminum phosphate

       c.   chromium(II) carbonate, chromous carbonate

       d.   calcium hypochlorite

       e.   barium carbonate

       f.   calcium chromate

38.   oxygen (commonly referred to as *oxy*acids)

40.   a.   hypochlorous acid

       b.   sulfurous acid

       c.   bromic acid

       d.   hypoiodous acid

       e.   perbromic acid

       f.   hydrosulfuric acid

       g.   hydroselenic acid

       h.   phosphorous acid

42.   a. MgF_2

       b. FeI_3

       c. HgS

       d. Ba_3N_2

       e. $PbCl_2$

       f. SnF_4

       g. Ag_2O

       h. K_2Se

44.   a. N_2O

       b. NO_2

       c. N_2O_4

       d. SF_6

       e. PBr_3

       f. CI_4

       g. OCl_2

46.   a. $NH_4C_2H_3O_2$

       b. $Fe(OH)_2$

       c. $Co_2(CO_3)_3$

       d. $BaCr_2O_7$

       e. $PbSO_4$

       f. KH_2PO_4

       g. Li_2O_2

       h. $Zn(ClO_3)_2$

48.   a. HCN

       b. HNO_3

c. H_2SO_4

d. H_3PO_4

e. HClO or HOCl

f. HBr

g. $HBrO_2$

h. HF

50. a. $Ca(HSO_4)_2$

b. $Zn_3(PO_4)_2$

c. $Fe(ClO_4)_3$

d. $Co(OH)_3$

e. K_2CrO_4

f. $Al(H_2PO_4)_3$

g. $LiHCO_3$

h. $Mn(C_2H_3O_2)_2$

i. $MgHPO_4$

j. $CsClO_2$

k. BaO_2

l. $NiCO_3$

52. A moist paste of NaCl would contain Na^+ and Cl^- ions in solution, and would serve as a *conductor* of electrical impulses.

54. $H \rightarrow H^+$ (hydrogen ion: a cation) $+ e^-$

$H + e^- \rightarrow H^-$ (hydr*ide* ion: an anion)

56. missing oxyanions: IO_3^-; ClO_2^-

missing oxyacids: $HClO_4$; HClO; $HBrO_2$

58. a. gold(III) bromide, auric bromide

b. cobalt(III) cyanide, cobaltic cyanide

c. magnesium hydrogen phosphate

d. diboron hexahydride (diborane is its common name)

e. ammonia

f. silver(I) sulfate (usually called silver sulfate)

g. beryllium hydroxide

60. a. ammonium carbonate

b. ammonium hydrogen carbonate, ammonium bicarbonate

    c.   calcium phosphate

    d.   sulfurous acid

    e.   manganese(IV) oxide

    f.   iodic acid

    g.   potassium hydride

62.   a. $M(C_2H_3O_2)_4$

       b. $M(MnO_4)_4$

       c. MO_2

       d. $M(HPO_4)_2$

       e. $M(OH)_4$

       f. $M(NO_2)_4$

64. M^+ compounds: MD, M_2E, M_3F

       M^{2+} compounds: MD_2, ME, M_3F_2

       M^{3+} compounds: MD_3, M_2E_3, MF

66.

$Ca(NO_3)_2$	$CaSO_4$	$Ca(HSO_4)_2$	$Ca(H_2PO_4)_2$	CaO	$CaCl_2$
$Sr(NO_3)_2$	$SrSO_4$	$Sr(HSO_4)_2$	$Sr(H_2PO_4)_2$	SrO	$SrCl_2$
NH_4NO_3	$(NH_4)_2SO_4$	NH_4HSO_4	$NH_4H_2PO_4$	$(NH_4)_2O$	NH_4Cl
$Al(NO_3)_3$	$Al_2(SO_4)_3$	$Al(HSO_4)_3$	$Al(H_2PO_4)_3$	Al_2O_3	$AlCl_3$
$Fe(NO_3)_3$	$Fe_2(SO_4)_3$	$Fe(HSO_4)_3$	$Fe(H_2PO_4)_3$	Fe_2O_3	$FeCl_3$
$Ni(NO_3)_2$	$NiSO_4$	$Ni(HSO_4)_2$	$Ni(H_2PO_4)_2$	NiO	$NiCl_2$
$AgNO_3$	Ag_2SO_4	$AgHSO_4$	AgH_2PO_4	Ag_2O	$AgCl$
$Au(NO_3)_3$	$Au_2(SO_4)_3$	$Au(HSO_4)_3$	$Au(H_2PO_4)_3$	Au_2O_3	$AuCl_3$
KNO_3	K_2SO_4	$KHSO_4$	KH_2PO_4	K_2O	KCl
$Hg(NO_3)_2$	$HgSO_4$	$Hg(HSO_4)_2$	$Hg(H_2PO_4)_2$	HgO	$HgCl_2$
$Ba(NO_3)_2$	$BaSO_4$	$Ba(HSO_4)_2$	$Ba(H_2PO_4)_2$	BaO	$BaCl_2$

68.   helium

70.   iodine (solid), bromine (liquid), fluorine and chlorine (gases)

72.   1–

74.   1–

76.   a. $Al(13e^-) \rightarrow Al^{3+}(10e^-) + 3e^-$

       b. $S(16e^-) + 2e^- \rightarrow S^{2-}(18e^-)$

       c. $Cu(29e^-) \rightarrow Cu^+(28e^-) + e^-$

       d. $F(9e^-) + e^- \rightarrow F^-(10e^-)$

       e. $Zn(30e^-) \rightarrow Zn^{2+}(28e^-) + 2e^-$

       f. $P(15e^-) + 3e^- \rightarrow P^{3-}(18e^-)$

78.	a.	Two 1+ ions are needed to balance a 2– ion, so the formula must have two Na^+ ions for each S^{2-} ion: Na_2S.

	b.	One 1+ ion exactly balances a 1– ion, so the formula should have an equal number of K^+ and Cl^- ions: KCl.

	c.	One 2+ ion exactly balances a 2– ion, so the formula must have an equal number of Ba^{2+} and O^{2-} ions: BaO.

	d.	One 2+ ion exactly balances a 2– ion, so the formula must have an equal number of Mg^{2+} and Se^{2-} ions: MgSe.

	e.	One 2+ ion requires two 1– ions to balance charge, so the formula must have twice as many Br^- ions as Cu^{2+} ions: $CuBr_2$.

	f.	One 3+ ion requires three 1– ions to balance charge, so the formula must have three times as many I^- ions as Al^{3+} ions: AlI_3.

	g.	Two 3+ ions give a total of 6+, whereas three 2– ions will give a total of 6–. The formula then should contain two Al^{3+} ions and three O^{2-} ions: Al_2O_3.

	h.	Three 2+ ions are required to balance two 3– ions, so the formula must contain three Ca^{2+} ions for every two N^{3-} ions: Ca_3N_2.

80.	a.	silver(I) oxide or just silver oxide

	b.	correct

	c.	iron(III) oxide

	d.	plumbic oxide

	e.	correct

82.	a.	stannous chloride

	b.	ferrous oxide

	c.	stannic oxide

	d.	plumbous sulfide

	e.	cobaltic sulfide

	f.	chromous chloride

84.	a.	iron(III) acetate, ferric acetate

	b.	bromine monofluoride

	c.	potassium peroxide

	d.	silicon tetrabromide

	e.	copper(II) permanganate, cupric permanganate

	f.	calcium chromate

86.	a.	CO_3^{2-}

	b.	HCO_3^-

    c. $C_2H_3O_2^-$

    d. CN^-

88.   a.   carbonate

    b.   chlorate

    c.   sulfate

    d.   phosphate

    e.   perchlorate

    f.   permanganate

90.   Answer depends on student choices.

92.   a. NaH_2PO_4

    b. $LiClO_4$

    c. $Cu(HCO_3)_2$

    d. $KC_2H_3O_2$

    e. BaO_2

    f. Cs_2SO_3

CUMULATIVE REVIEW

Chapters 4 and 5

2.   How many elements could you name? Although you certainly don't have to memorize all the elements, you should at least be able to give the symbol or name for the most common elements (listed in Table 4.3).

4.   Dalton's atomic theory as presented in this text consists of five main postulates. Although Dalton's theory was exceptional scientific thinking for its time, some of the postulates have been modified as our scientific instruments and calculation methods have become increasingly more sophisticated. The main postulates of Dalton's theory are as follows: (1) Elements are made up of tiny particles called atoms; (2) all atoms of a given element are identical; (3) although all atoms of a given element are identical, these atoms are different from the atoms of all other elements; (4) atoms of one element can combine with atoms of another element to form a compound, and such a compound will always have the same relative numbers and types of atoms for its composition; and (5) atoms are merely rearranged into new groupings during an ordinary chemical reaction, and no atom is ever destroyed and no new atom is ever created during such a reaction.

6.   The expression *nuclear* atom indicates that we view the atom as having a dense center of positive charge (called the nucleus) around which the electrons move through primarily empty space. Rutherford's experiment involved shooting a beam of particles at a thin sheet of metal foil. According to the then current "plum pudding" model of the atom, most of these positively-charged particles should have passed right through the foil. However, Rutherford detected that a significant number of particles effectively bounced off something and were deflected backwards to the source of particles, and that other particles were deflected from the foil at large angles. Rutherford realized that his observations could be explained if the atoms of the metal foil had a small, dense, positively-charged nucleus, with a significant amount of empty space between nuclei. The empty space between nuclei would allow most of the particles to pass through the atom. However, if a particle hit a nucleus head-on, it would be deflected backwards at the source. If a positively-charged particle passed near a positively-charged nucleus (but did not hit the nucleus head-on), then the particle would be deflected by the repulsive forces between the positive charges. Rutherford's experiment conclusively disproved the "plum pudding" model for the atom, which envisioned the atom as a uniform sphere of positive charge, with enough negatively-charged electrons scattered through the atom to balance out the positive charge.

8.   Isotopes represent atoms of the same element which have different atomic masses. Isotopes are a result of the fact that atoms of a given element may have different numbers of neutrons in their nuclei. Isotopes have the same atomic number (number of protons in the nucleus) but have different mass numbers (total number of protons and neutrons in the nucleus). The different isotopes of an atom are indicated by symbolism of the form $_Z^A X$ in which Z represents the atomic number, and A the mass number, of element X. For example, $_6^{13}C$ represents a nuclide of carbon with atomic number 6 (6 protons in the nucleus) and mass number 13 (reflecting 6 protons plus 7 neutrons in the nucleus). The various isotopes of an element have identical chemical properties because the chemical properties of an atom are a function of the electrons in the atom (*not* the

34

nucleus). The physical properties of the isotopes of an element (and compounds containing those isotopes) may differ because of the difference in mass of the isotopes.

10.   Most elements are too reactive to be found in nature in other than the combined form. Aside from the noble metals gold, silver, and platinum, the only other elements commonly found in nature in the uncombined state are some of the gaseous elements (such as O2, N2, He, Ar, etc.), and the solid nonmetals carbon and sulfur.

12.   Ionic compounds typically are hard, crystalline solids with high melting and boiling points. Ionic substances like sodium chloride, when dissolved in water or when melted, conduct electrical currents: chemists have taken this evidence to mean that ionic substances consist of positively– and negatively–charged particles (ions). Although an ionic substance is made up of positively– and negatively–charged particles, there is no net electrical charge on a sample of such a substance because the total number of positive charges is balanced by an equal number of negative charges. An ionic compound could not possibly exist of just cations or just anions: there must be a balance of charge or the compound would be very unstable (like charges repel each other).

14.   When naming ionic compounds, we name the positive ion (cation) first. For simple binary Type I ionic compounds, the ending –ide is added to the root name of the element that is the negative ion (anion). For example, for the Type I ionic compound formed between potassium and sulfur, K_2S, the name would be potassium sulfide: potassium is the cation, sulfur is the anion (with the suffix –ide added). Type II compounds are named by either of two systems, the "*ous–ic*" system (which is falling out of use), and the "Roman numeral" system which is preferred by most chemists. Type II compounds involve elements that form more than one stable ion. It is therefore necessary to specify *which* ion is present in a given compound. For example, iron forms two types of stable ion: Fe^{2+} and Fe^{3+}. Iron can react with oxygen to form either of two stable oxides, FeO or Fe_2O_3, depending on which cation is involved. Under the Roman numeral naming system, FeO would be named iron(II) oxide to show that it contains Fe^{2+} ions; Fe_2O_3 would be named iron(III) oxide to indicate that it contains Fe^{3+} ions. The Roman numeral used in a name corresponds to the charge of the specific ion present in the compound. Under the less-favored "ous–ic" system, for an element that forms two stable ions, the ending –*ous* is used to indicate the lower-charged ion, whereas the ending –*ic* is used to indicate the higher-charged ion. FeO and Fe_2O_3 would thus be named ferr*ous* oxide and ferr*ic* oxide, respectively. The "ous–ic" system has fallen out of favor because it does not indicate the actual charge on the ion, but only that it is the lower or higher charged of the two. This can lead to confusion: for example Fe^{2+} is called ferrous ion in this system, but Cu^{2+} is called cupric ion (since there is also a Cu^+ stable ion).

16.   A polyatomic ion is an ion containing more than one atom. Some common polyatomic ions you should be familiar with are listed in Table 5.4. Parentheses are used in writing formulas containing polyatomic ions to indicate unambiguously how many of the polyatomic ion are present in the formula, to make certain that there is no mistake as to what is meant by the formula. For example, consider the substance calcium phosphate. The correct formula for this substance is $Ca_3(PO_4)_2$, which indicates that three calcium ions are combined for every two phosphate ions (check the total number of positive and negative charges to see why this is so). If we did not write the parenthesis around the formula for the phosphate ion, that is, if we had written Ca_3PO_{42}, people reading this formula might think that there were 42 oxygen atoms present!

18.   Acids, in general, are substances that produce protons (H^+ ions) when dissolved in water. For acids that do not contain oxygen, the prefix *hydro–* and the suffix –*ic* are used with the root name of the element present in the acid (for example: HCl, hydrochloric acid; H_2S, hydrosulfuric acid;

HF, hydrofluoric acid). The nomenclature of acids whose anions contain oxygen is more complicated. A series of prefixes and suffixes is used with the name of the non-oxygen atom in the anion of the acid: these prefixes and suffixes indicate the relative (not actual) number of oxygen atoms present in the anion. Most of the elements that form oxyanions form two such anions: for example, sulfur forms sulfite ion (SO_3^{2-}) and sulfate ion (SO_4^{2-}), and nitrogen forms nitrite ion (NO_2^-) and nitrate ion (NO_3^-). For an element that forms two oxyanions, the acid containing the anions will have the ending *–ous* if the anion is the *–ite* anion and the ending *–ic* if the anion is the *–ate* anion. For example, HNO_2 is nitr*ous* acid and HNO_3 is nitr*ic* acid; H_2SO_3 is sulfur*ous* acid and H_2SO_4 is sulfur*ic* acid. The halogen elements (Group 7) each form four oxyanions, and consequently, four oxyacids. The prefix *hypo–* is used for the oxyacid that contains fewer oxygen atoms than the *–ite* anion, and the prefix *per–* is used for the oxyacid that contains more oxygen atoms than the *–ate* anion. For example,

Acid	Name	Anion	Anion name
$HBrO$	*hypo*brom*ous* acid	BrO^-	*hypo*brom*ite*
$HBrO_2$	brom*ous* acid	BrO_2^-	brom*ite*
$HBrO_3$	brom*ic* acid	BrO_3^-	brom*ate*
$HBrO_4$	*per*brom*ic* acid	BrO_4^-	*per*brom*ate*

20. How many elements in each family could you name? Elements in the same family have the same type of electronic configuration, and tend to undergo similar chemical reactions with other groups. For example, Li, Na, K, Rb, Cs all react with elemental chlorine gas, Cl_2, to form an ionic compound of general formula M^+Cl^-.

22. a. 8 electrons, 8 protons, 9 neutrons

    b. 92 electrons, 92 protons, 143 neutrons

    c. 17 electrons, 17 protons, 20 neutrons

    d. 1 electrons, 1 protons, 2 neutrons

    e. 2 electrons, 2 protons, 2 neutrons

    f. 50 electrons, 50 protons, 69 neutrons

    g. 54 electrons, 54 protons, 70 neutrons

    h. 30 electrons, 30 protons, 34 neutrons

24. a. 12 protons, 10 electrons

    b. 26 protons, 24 electrons

    c. 26 protons, 23 electrons

    d. 9 protons, 10 electrons

    e. 28 protons, 26 electrons

    f. 30 protons, 28 electrons

    g. 27 protons, 24 electrons

    h. 7 protons, 10 electrons

    i. 16 protons, 18 electrons

j.   37 protons, 36 electrons

k.   34 protons, 36 electrons

l.   19 protons, 18 electrons

26.   a.   CuI

b. $CoCl_2$

c. Ag_2S

d. Hg_2Br_2

e.   HgO

f. Cr_2S_3

g. PbO_2

h. K_3N

i. SnF_2

j. Fe_2O_3

28.   a. NH_4^+, ammonium ion

b. SO_3^{2-}, sulfite ion

c. NO_3^-, nitrate ion

d. SO_4^{2-}, sulfate ion

e. NO_2^-, nitrite ion

f. CN^-, cyanide ion

g. OH^-, hydroxide ion

h. ClO_4^-, perchlorate ion

i. ClO^-, hypochlorite ion

j. PO_4^{3-}, phosphate ion

30.   a.   xenon dioxide

b.   iodine pentachloride

c.   phosphorus trichloride

d.   carbon monoxide

e.   oxygen difluoride

f.   diphosphorus pentoxide

g.   arsenic triiodide

h.   sulfur trioxide

CHAPTER 6

Chemical Reactions: An Introduction

2.   Most of these products contain a peroxide, which decomposes releasing oxygen gas.

4.   Bubbling takes place as the hydrogen peroxide chemically decomposes into water and oxygen gas.

6.   The appearance of the black color actually signals the breakdown of starches and sugars in the bread to elemental carbon. You may also see steam coming from the bread (water produced by the breakdown of the carbohydrates).

8.   atoms

10.   Balancing an equation ensures that no atoms are created or destroyed during the reaction. The total mass after the reaction must be the same as the total mass before the reaction.

12.   For solids we use (s), for liquids we use (l), and for gases we use (g).

14. $H_2O_2(aq) \rightarrow H_2(g) + O_2(g)$

16. $N_2H_4(l) \rightarrow N_2(g) + H_2(g)$

18. $C_3H_8(g) + O_2(g) \rightarrow CO_2(g) + H_2O(g)$

      $C_3H_8(g) + O_2(g) \rightarrow CO(g) + H_2O(g)$

20. $CaCO_3(s) + HCl(aq) \rightarrow CaCl_2(aq) + H_2O(l) + CO_2(g)$

22. $SiO_2(s) + C(s) \rightarrow Si(s) + CO(g)$

24. $Fe(s) + H_2O(g) \rightarrow FeO(s) + H_2(g)$

26. $SO_2(g) + H_2O(l) \rightarrow H_2SO_3(aq)$

      $SO_3(g) + H_2O(l) \rightarrow H_2SO_4(aq)$

28. $NO(g) + O_3(g) \rightarrow NO_2(g) + O_2(g)$

30. $P_4(s) + O_2(g) \rightarrow P_2O_5(s)$

32. $Xe(g) + F_2(g) \rightarrow XeF_4(s)$

34. $NH_3(g) + O_2(g) \rightarrow HNO_3(aq) + H_2O(l)$

36.   We cannot change the identities or formulas of the reactants or products in a chemical equation when balancing the equation. The proposed equation has incorrectly changed one of the products from water to hydrogen gas.

38.   a. $Zn(s) + CuO(s) \rightarrow ZnO(s) + Cu(l)$

The equation is already balanced.

b. $P_4(s) + F_2(g) \rightarrow PF_3(g)$

balance phosphorus: $P_4(s) + F_2(g) \rightarrow \mathbf{4}PF_3(g)$

balance fluorine: $P_4(s) + \mathbf{6}F_2(g) \rightarrow 4PF_3(g)$

balanced equation: $P_4(s) + 6F_2(g) \rightarrow 4PF_3(g)$

c. $Xe(g) + F_2(g) \rightarrow XeF_4(s)$

balance fluorine: $Xe(g) + \mathbf{2}F_2(g) \rightarrow XeF_4(s)$

balanced equation: $Xe(g) + 2F_2(g) \rightarrow XeF_4(s)$

d. $NH_4Cl(g) + Mg(OH)_2(s) \rightarrow NH_3(g) + H_2O(g) + MgCl_2(s)$

balance chlorine: $\mathbf{2}NH_4Cl(g) + Mg(OH)_2(s) \rightarrow NH_3(g) + H_2O(g) + MgCl_2(s)$

balance nitrogen: $2NH_4Cl(g) + Mg(OH)_2(s) \rightarrow \mathbf{2}NH_3(g) + H_2O(g) + MgCl_2(s)$

balance oxygen: $2NH_4Cl(g) + Mg(OH)_2(s) \rightarrow 2NH_3(g) + \mathbf{2}H_2O(g) + MgCl_2(s)$

balanced equation: $2NH_4Cl(g) + Mg(OH)_2(s) \rightarrow 2NH_3(g) + 2H_2O(g) + MgCl_2(s)$

e. $SiO(s) + Cl_2(g) \rightarrow SiCl_4(l) + O_2(g)$

balance oxygen: $\mathbf{2}SiO(s) + Cl_2(g) \rightarrow SiCl_4(l) + O_2(g)$

balanced silicon: $2SiO(s) + Cl_2(g) \rightarrow \mathbf{2}SiCl_4(l) + O_2(g)$

balance chlorine: $2SiO(s) + \mathbf{4}Cl_2(g) \rightarrow 2SiCl_4(l) + O_2(g)$

balanced equation: $2SiO(s) + 4Cl_2(g) \rightarrow 2SiCl_4(l) + O_2(g)$

f. $Cs_2O(s) + H_2O(l) \rightarrow CsOH(aq)$

balance cesium: $Cs_2O(s) + H_2O(l) \rightarrow \mathbf{2}CsOH(aq)$

balanced equation: $Cs_2O(s) + H_2O(l) \rightarrow 2CsOH(aq)$

g. $N_2O_3(g) + H_2O(l) \rightarrow HNO_2(aq)$

balance hydrogen: $N_2O_3(g) + H_2O(l) \rightarrow \mathbf{2}HNO_2(aq)$

balanced equation: $N_2O_3(g) + H_2O(l) \rightarrow 2HNO_2(aq)$

h. $Fe_2O_3(s) + H_2SO_4(l) \rightarrow Fe_2(SO_4)_3(s) + H_2O(g)$

balance sulfate ions: $Fe_2O_3(s) + \mathbf{3}H_2SO_4(l) \rightarrow Fe_2(SO_4)_3(s) + H_2O(g)$

balance hydrogen: $Fe_2O_3(s) + \mathbf{3}H_2SO_4(l) \rightarrow Fe_2(SO_4)_3(s) + \mathbf{3}H_2O(g)$

balanced equation: $Fe_2O_3(s) + \mathbf{3}H_2SO_4(l) \rightarrow Fe_2(SO_4)_3(s) + \mathbf{3}H_2O(g)$

40.   a. $Na_2SO_4(aq) + CaCl_2(aq) \rightarrow CaSO_4(s) + 2NaCl(aq)$

b. $3Fe(s) + 4H_2O(g) \rightarrow Fe_3O_4(s) + 4H_2(g)$

c. $Ca(OH)_2(aq) + 2HCl(aq) \rightarrow CaCl_2(aq) + 2H_2O(l)$

d. $Br_2(g) + 2H_2O(l) + SO_2(g) \rightarrow 2HBr(aq) + H_2SO_4(aq)$

e. $3NaOH(s) + H_3PO_4(aq) \rightarrow Na_3PO_4(aq) + 3H_2O(l)$

f. $2NaNO_3(s) \rightarrow 2NaNO_2(s) + O_2(g)$

g. $2Na_2O_2(s) + 2H_2O(l) \rightarrow 4NaOH(aq) + O_2(g)$

h. $4Si(s) + S_8(s) \rightarrow 2Si_2S_4(s)$

42.   a. $4NaCl(s) + 2SO_2(g) + 2H_2O(g) + O_2(g) \rightarrow 2Na_2SO_4(s) + 4HCl(g)$

b. $3Br_2(l) + I_2(s) \rightarrow 2IBr_3(s)$

c. $Ca(s) + 2H_2O(g) \rightarrow Ca(OH)_2(aq) + H_2(g)$

d. $2BF_3(g) + 3H_2O(g) \rightarrow B_2O_3(s) + 6HF(g)$

e. $SO_2(g) + 2Cl_2(g) \rightarrow SOCl_2(l) + Cl_2O(g)$

f. $Li_2O(s) + H_2O(l) \rightarrow 2LiOH(aq)$

g. $Mg(s) + CuO(s) \rightarrow MgO(s) + Cu(l)$

h. $Fe_3O_4(s) + 4H_2(g) \rightarrow 3Fe(l) + 4H_2O(g)$

44.   a. $Ba(NO_3)_2(aq) + Na_2CrO_4(aq) \rightarrow BaCrO_4(s) + 2NaNO_3(aq)$

b. $PbCl_2(aq) + K_2SO_4(aq) \rightarrow PbSO_4(s) + 2KCl(aq)$

c. $C_2H_5OH(l) + 3O_2(g) \rightarrow 2CO_2(g) + 3H_2O(l)$

d. $CaC_2(s) + 2H_2O(l) \rightarrow Ca(OH)_2(s) + C_2H_2(g)$

e. $Sr(s) + 2HNO_3(aq) \rightarrow Sr(NO_3)_2(aq) + H_2(g)$

f. $BaO_2(s) + H_2SO_4(aq) \rightarrow BaSO_4(s) + H_2O_2(aq)$

g. $2AsI_3(s) \rightarrow 2As(s) + 3I_2(s)$

h. $2CuSO_4(aq) + 4KI(s) \rightarrow 2CuI(s) + I_2(s) + 2K_2SO_4(aq)$

46. $Na(s) + O_2(g) \rightarrow Na_2O_2(s)$

$Na_2O_2(s) + H_2O(l) \rightarrow NaOH(aq) + O_2(g)$

48. $C_{12}H_{22}O_{11}(aq) + H_2O(l) \rightarrow 4C_2H_5OH(aq) + 4CO_2(g)$

50. $2Al_2O_3(s) + 3C(s) \rightarrow 4Al(s) + 3CO_2(g)$

52. $2Li(s) + S(s) \rightarrow Li_2S(s)$

$2Na(s) + S(s) \rightarrow Na_2S(s)$

$2K(s) + S(s) \rightarrow K_2S(s)$

$2Rb(s) + S(s) \rightarrow Rb_2S(s)$

$2Cs(s) + S(s) \rightarrow Cs_2S(s)$

$2Fr(s) + S(s) \rightarrow Fr_2S(s)$

54. $BaO_2(s) + H_2O(l) \rightarrow BaO(s) + H_2O_2(aq)$

56. $2KClO_3(s) \rightarrow 2KCl(s) + 3O_2(g)$

58. $NH_3(g) + HCl(g) \rightarrow NH_4Cl(s)$

60.   The senses we call "odor" and "taste" are really chemical reactions of the receptors in our body with molecules in the food we are eating. The fact that the receptors no longer detect the "fishy" odor or taste suggest that adding the lemon juice or vinegar has changed the nature of the amines in the fish.

62. $Fe(s) + S(s) \rightarrow FeS(s)$

64. $K_2CrO_4(aq) + BaCl_2(aq) \rightarrow BaCrO_4(s) + 2KCl(aq)$

66. $2NaCl(aq) + 2H_2O(l) \rightarrow 2NaOH(aq) + H_2(g) + Cl_2(g)$

   $2NaBr(aq) + 2H_2O(l) \rightarrow 2NaOH(aq) + H_2(g) + Br_2(g)$

   $2NaI(aq) + 2H_2O(l) \rightarrow 2NaOH(aq) + H_2(g) + I_2(g)$

68. $CaC_2(s) + 2H_2O(l) \rightarrow Ca(OH)_2(s) + C_2H_2(g)$

70. $CuO(s) + H_2SO_4(aq) \rightarrow CuSO_4(aq) + H_2O(l)$

72. $Na_2SO_3(aq) + S(s) \rightarrow Na_2S_2O_3(aq)$

74.   a. $Cl_2(g) + 2KI(aq) \rightarrow 2KCl(aq) + I_2(s)$

   b. $CaC_2(s) + 2H_2O(l) \rightarrow Ca(OH)_2(s) + C_2H_2(g)$

   c. $2NaCl(s) + H_2SO_4(l) \rightarrow Na_2SO_4(s) + 2HCl(g)$

   d. $CaF_2(s) + H_2SO_4(l) \rightarrow CaSO_4(s) + 2HF(g)$

   e. $K_2CO_3(s) \rightarrow K_2O(s) + CO_2(g)$

   f. $3BaO(s) + 2Al(s) \rightarrow Al_2O_3(s) + 3Ba(s)$

   g. $2Al(s) + 3F_2(g) \rightarrow 2AlF_3(s)$

   h. $CS_2(g) + 3Cl_2(g) \rightarrow CCl_4(l) + S_2Cl_2(g)$

76.   a. $Pb(NO_3)_2(aq) + K_2CrO_4(aq) \rightarrow PbCrO_4(s) + 2KNO_3(aq)$

   b. $BaCl_2(aq) + Na_2SO_4(aq) \rightarrow BaSO_4(s) + 2NaCl(aq)$

   c. $2CH_3OH(l) + 3O_2(g) \rightarrow 2CO_2(g) + 4H_2O(g)$

   d. $Na_2CO_3(aq) + S(s) + SO_2(g) \rightarrow CO_2(g) + Na_2S_2O_3(aq)$

   e. $Cu(s) + 2H_2SO_4(aq) \rightarrow CuSO_4(aq) + SO_2(g) + 2H_2O(l)$

   f. $MnO_2(s) + 4HCl(aq) \rightarrow MnCl_2(aq) + Cl_2(g) + 2H_2O(l)$

   g. $As_2O_3(s) + 6KI(aq) + 6HCl(aq) \rightarrow 2AsI_3(s) + 6KCl(aq) + 3H_2O(l)$

   h. $2Na_2S_2O_3(aq) + I_2(aq) \rightarrow Na_2S_4O_6(aq) + 2NaI(aq)$

CHAPTER 7

Reactions in Aqueous Solution

2. Driving forces are types of *changes* in a system that push a reaction in the *direction of product formation*; driving forces discussed in Chapter 7 include: formation of a *solid*, formation of *water*, formation of a *gas*, and transfer of electrons.

4. A reactant in aqueous solution is indicated with (*aq*). Formation of a solid is indicated with (*s*)

6. Because each formula unit of $MgCl_2$ contains two chloride ions for each magnesium ion, that ratio will be preserved in the solution when $MgCl_2$ is dissolved in water.

8. Chemists know that a solution contains independent ions because such a solution will readily allow an electrical current to pass through it. The simplest experiment that demonstrates this uses the sort of light–bulb conductivity apparatus described in the text: if the light bulb glows strongly, then the solution must contain a lot of ions to be conducting the electricity well.

10. Answer depends on student choices.

12. a. soluble (Rule 3: most chloride salts are soluble.)

   b. soluble (Rule 2: most salts of NH_4^+ are soluble.)

   c. soluble (Rule 2: most salts of Na^+ are soluble.)

   d. insoluble (Rule 5: most hydroxide compounds are insoluble.)

   e. soluble (Rule 2: most salts of K^+ are soluble.)

   f. soluble (Rule 1: most nitrate salts are soluble.)

   g. soluble (Rule 4: most sulfate salts are soluble.)

   h. insoluble (Rule 6: most sulfide salts are insoluble.)

14. a. Rule 6: Most sulfide salts are insoluble.

   b. Rule 6: Most carbonate salts are insoluble.

   c. Rule 6: Most phosphate salts are insoluble.

   d. Rule 3: Exception to the rule for chloride salts.

   e. Rule 4: Exception to the rule for sulfate salts.

16. a. $MnCO_3$: Rule 6 (most carbonates are only slightly soluble).

   b. $CaSO_4$: Rule 4 (exception for sulfates).

   c. Hg_2Cl_2: Rule 3: (exception for chlorides).

   d. soluble

    e. $Ni(OH)_2$: Rule 5 (most hydroxides are only slightly soluble).

    f. $BaSO_4$: Rule 4 (exception for sulfates).

18.   The formulas of the precipitates are in boldface type.

    a.   Rule 6: Most carbonate salts are insoluble.

        $Na_2CO_3(aq) + CuSO_4(aq) \rightarrow Na_2SO_4(aq) + \mathbf{CuCO_3(s)}$

    b.   Rule 3: Exception for chloride salts.

        $HCl(aq) + AgC_2H_3O_2(aq) \rightarrow HC_2H_3O_2(aq) + \mathbf{AgCl(s)}$

    c.   No precipitate

    d.   Rule 6: Most sulfide salts are insoluble.

        $3(NH_4)_2S(aq) + 2FeCl_3(aq) \rightarrow 6NH_4Cl(aq) + \mathbf{Fe_2S_3(s)}$

    e.   Rule 4: Exception for sulfate salts

        $H_2SO_4(aq) + Pb(NO_3)_2(aq) \rightarrow 2HNO_3(aq) + \mathbf{PbSO_4(s)}$

    f.   Rule 6: Most phosphate salts are insoluble.

        $2K_3PO_4(aq) + 3CaCl_2(aq) \rightarrow 6KCl(aq) + \mathbf{Ca_3(PO_4)_2(s)}$

20.   Hint: when balancing equations involving polyatomic ions, especially in precipitation reactions, balance the polyatomic ions as a *unit*, not in terms of the atoms the polyatomic ions contain (e.g., treat nitrate ion, NO_3^- as a single entity, not as one nitrogen and three oxygen atoms). When finished balancing, however, be sure to count the individual number of atoms of each type on each side of the equation.

    a. $CaCl_2 (aq) + AgNO_3 (aq) \rightarrow Ca(NO_3)_2 (aq) + AgCl (s)$

        balance chlorine: $CaCl_2 (aq) + AgNO_3 (aq) \rightarrow Ca(NO_3)_2 (aq) + \mathbf{2}AgCl (s)$

        balance silver: $CaCl_2 (aq) + \mathbf{2}AgNO_3 (aq) \rightarrow Ca(NO_3)_2 (aq) + 2AgCl (s)$

        balanced equation: $CaCl_2 (aq) + 2AgNO_3 (aq) \rightarrow Ca(NO_3)_2 (aq) + 2AgCl (s)$

    b. $AgNO_3(aq) + K_2CrO_4(aq) \rightarrow Ag_2CrO_4(s) + KNO_3(aq)$

        balance silver: $\mathbf{2}AgNO_3(aq) + K_2CrO_4(aq) \rightarrow Ag_2CrO_4(s) + KNO_3(aq)$

        balance nitrate ion: $2AgNO_3(aq) + K_2CrO_4(aq) \rightarrow Ag_2CrO_4(s) + \mathbf{2}KNO_3(aq)$

        balanced equation: $2AgNO_3(aq) + K_2CrO_4(aq) \rightarrow Ag_2CrO_4(s) + 2KNO_3(aq)$

    c. $BaCl_2(aq) + K_2SO_4(aq) \rightarrow BaSO_4(s) + KCl(aq)$

        balance potassium: $BaCl_2(aq) + K_2SO_4(aq) \rightarrow BaSO_4(s) + \mathbf{2}KCl(aq)$

        balanced equation: $BaCl_2(aq) + K_2SO_4(aq) \rightarrow BaSO_4(s) + 2KCl(aq)$

22.   The products are determined by having the ions "switch partners." For example, for a general reaction $AB + CD \rightarrow$, the possible products are AD and CB if the ions switch partners. If either AD or CB is insoluble, then a precipitation reaction has occurred. In the following reactions, the formula of the precipitate is given in boldface type.

    a. $Na_2CO_3(aq) + K_2SO_4(aq) \rightarrow$ no precipitate; all combinations are soluble

b. $CuCl_2(aq) + (NH_4)_2CO_3(aq) \rightarrow 2NH_4Cl(aq) + \mathbf{CuCO_3(s)}$

Rule 6: Most carbonate salts are only slightly soluble.

c. $K_3PO_4(aq) + AlCl_3(aq) \rightarrow 3KCl(aq) + \mathbf{AlPO_4(s)}$

Rule 6: Most phosphate salts are only slightly soluble.

24. Spectator ions are ions which *remain in solution* during a precipitation/double displacement reaction. For example in the reaction

$$BaCl_2(aq) + K_2SO_4(aq) \rightarrow BaSO_4(s) + 2KCl(aq)$$

the K^+ and Cl^- ions are the spectator ions.

26. The net ionic equation for a reaction indicates *only those ions that go to form the precipitate* and does not show the spectator ions present in the solutes mixed. The identity of the precipitate is determined from the Solubility Rules (Table 7.1).

a. $Ca(NO_3)_2(aq) + H_2SO_4(aq) \rightarrow CaSO_4(s) + 2HNO_3(aq)$

$Ca^{2+}(aq) + SO_4^{2-}(aq) \rightarrow CaSO_4(s)$

b. $Ni(NO_3)_2(aq) + 2NaOH(aq) \rightarrow Ni(OH)_2(s) + 2NaNO_3(aq)$

$Ni^{2+}(aq) + 2OH^-(aq) \rightarrow Ni(OH)_2(s)$

c. $3(NH_4)_2S(aq) + 2FeCl_3(aq) \rightarrow Fe_2S_3(s) + 6NH_4Cl(aq)$

$2Fe^{3+}(aq) + 3S^{2-}(aq) \rightarrow Fe_2S_3(s)$

28. $Ag^+(aq) + Cl^-(aq) \rightarrow AgCl(s)$

$Pb^{2+}(aq) + 2Cl^-(aq) \rightarrow PbCl_2(s)$

$Hg_2^{2+}(aq) + 2Cl^-(aq) \rightarrow Hg_2Cl_2(s)$

30. $Co^{2+}(aq) + S^{2-}(aq) \rightarrow CoS(s)$

$2Co^{3+}(aq) + 3S^{2-}(aq) \rightarrow Co_2S_3(s)$

$Fe^{2+}(aq) + S^{2-}(aq) \rightarrow FeS(s)$

$2Fe^{3+}(aq) + 3S^{2-}(aq) \rightarrow Fe_2S_3(s)$

32. Strong bases fully produce hydroxide ions when dissolved in water. The strong bases are also strong electrolytes.

34. acids: HCl, H_2SO_4, HNO_3, $HClO_4$, HBr

bases: NaOH, KOH, RbOH, CsOH

36. A salt is the ionic product remaining in solution when an acid neutralizes a base. For example, in the reaction $HCl (aq) + NaOH(aq) \rightarrow NaCl(aq) + H_2O(l)$ sodium chloride is the salt produced by the neutralization reaction.

38. $RbOH(s) \rightarrow Rb^+(aq) + OH^-(aq)$

$CsOH(s) \rightarrow Cs^+(aq) + OH^-(aq)$

40.   In general, the salt formed in an aqueous acid–base reaction consists of the *positive ion of the base* involved in the reaction, combined with the *negative ion of the acid*. The hydrogen ion of the strong acid combines with the hydroxide ion of the strong base to produce water, which is the other product of the acid–base reactions.

    a. $H_2SO_4(aq) + 2KOH(aq) \rightarrow K_2SO_4(aq) + 2H_2O(l)$

    b. $HNO_3(aq) + NaOH(aq) \rightarrow NaNO_3(aq) + H_2O(l)$

    c. $2HCl(aq) + Ca(OH)_2(aq) \rightarrow CaCl_2(aq) + 2H_2O(l)$

    d. $2HClO_4(aq) + Ba(OH)_2(aq) \rightarrow Ba(ClO_4)_2(aq) + 2H_2O(l)$

42.   Answer depends on student choice of example: $Na(s) + Cl_2(g) \rightarrow 2NaCl(s)$ is an example.

44.   The metallic element *loses* electrons and the nonmetallic element *gains* electrons.

46.   Each magnesium atom would lose two electrons. Each oxygen atom would gain two electrons (so the O_2 molecule would gain four electrons). Two magnesium atoms would be required to react with each oxygen, O_2, molecule. Magnesium ions are charged 2+, oxide ions are charged 2–.

48.   Each potassium atom loses one electron. The sulfur atom gains two electrons. So two potassium atoms are required to react with one sulfur atom.

$$2 \times (K \rightarrow K^+ + e^-)$$
$$S + 2e^- \rightarrow S^{2-}$$

50.   a. $P_4(s) + O_2(g) \rightarrow P_4O_{10}(s)$

         balance oxygen: $P_4(s) + \mathbf{5}O_2(g) \rightarrow P_4O_{10}(s)$

         balanced equation: $P_4(s) + 5O_2(g) \rightarrow P_4O_{10}(s)$

    b. $MgO(s) + C(s) \rightarrow Mg(s) + CO(g)$

         This equation is already balanced.

    c. $Sr(s) + H_2O(l) \rightarrow Sr(OH)_2(aq) + H_2(g)$

         balance oxygen: $Sr(s) + \mathbf{2}H_2O(l) \rightarrow Sr(OH)_2(aq) + H_2(g)$

         balanced equation: $Sr(s) + 2H_2O(l) \rightarrow Sr(OH)_2(aq) + H_2(g)$

    d. $Co(s) + HCl(aq) \rightarrow CoCl_2(aq) + H_2(g)$

         balance hydrogen: $Co(s) + \mathbf{2}HCl(aq) \rightarrow CoCl_2(aq) + H_2(g)$

         balanced equation: $Co(s) + 2HCl(aq) \rightarrow CoCl_2(aq) + H_2(g)$

52.   A reaction must be an oxidation–reduction reaction if any of the oxidation numbers of the atoms in the equation change. Aluminum changes oxidation state from 0 in Al to +3 (oxidation) in Al_2O_3 and $AlCl_3$; nitrogen changes oxidation state from –3 in NH_4^+ to +2 in NO (oxidation); chlorine changes oxidation state from +7 in ClO_4^- to –1 in $AlCl_3$ (reduction)

54.   For each reaction, the type of reaction is first identified, followed by some of the reasoning that leads to this choice (there may be more than one way in which you can recognize a particular type of reaction).

    a.   oxidation–reduction (Oxygen changes from the combined state to the elemental state.)

    b.   oxidation–reduction (Zinc changes from the elemental to the combined state; hydrogen changes from the combined to the elemental state.)

    c.   acid–base (H_2SO_4 is a strong acid and NaOH is a strong base; water and a salt are formed.)

    d.   acid–base, precipitation (H_2SO_4 is a strong acid, and $Ba(OH)_2$ is a base; water and a salt are formed; an insoluble product forms.)

    e.   precipitation (From the Solubility Rules of Table 7.1, AgCl is only slightly soluble.)

    f.   precipitation (From the Solubility Rules of Table 7.1, $Cu(OH)_2$ is only slightly soluble.)

    g.   oxidation–reduction (Chlorine and fluorine change from the elemental to the combined state.)

    h.   oxidation–reduction (Oxygen changes from the elemental to the combined state.)

    i.   acid–base (HNO_3 is a strong acid and $Ca(OH)_2$ is a strong base; a salt and water are formed.)

56.   oxidation–reduction

58.   A decomposition reaction is one in which a given compound is broken down into simpler compounds or constituent elements. The reactions

$$CaCO_3(s) \rightarrow CaO(s) + CO_2(g)$$

$$2HgO(s) \rightarrow 2Hg(l) + O_2(g)$$

both represent decomposition reactions. Such reactions often (but not necessarily always) may be classified in other ways. For example, the reaction of HgO(s) is also an oxidation–reduction reaction.

60.   Compounds like those in this problem, containing only carbon and hydrogen, are called *hydrocarbons*. When a hydrocarbon is reacted with oxygen (O_2), the hydrocarbon is almost always converted to carbon dioxide and water vapor. Because water molecules contain an odd number of oxygen atoms, and O_2 contains an even number of oxygen atoms, it is often difficult to balance such equations. For this reason, it is simpler to balance the equation using fractional coefficients if necessary, and then to multiply by a factor that will give whole number coefficients for the final balanced equation.

    a. $C_3H_8(g) + O_2(g) \rightarrow CO_2(g) + H_2O(g)$

        balance carbon: $C_3H_8(g) + O_2(g) \rightarrow \mathbf{3}CO_2(g) + H_2O(g)$

        balance hydrogen: $C_3H_8(g) + O_2(g) \rightarrow 3CO_2(g) + \mathbf{4}H_2O(g)$

        balance oxygen: $C_3H_8(g) + \mathbf{5}O_2(g) \rightarrow 3CO_2(g) + 4H_2O(g)$

        balanced equation: $C_3H_8(g) + 5O_2(g) \rightarrow 3CO_2(g) + 4H_2O(g)$

b. $C_2H_4(g) + O_2(g) \rightarrow CO_2(g) + H_2O(g)$

balance carbon: $C_2H_4(g) + O_2(g) \rightarrow \mathbf{2}CO_2(g) + H_2O(g)$

balance hydrogen: $C_2H_4(g) + O_2(g) \rightarrow \mathbf{2}CO_2(g) + \mathbf{2}H_2O(g)$

balance oxygen: $C_2H_4(g) + \mathbf{3}O_2(g) \rightarrow \mathbf{2}CO_2(g) + \mathbf{2}H_2O(g)$

balanced equation: $C_2H_4(g) + 3O_2(g) \rightarrow 2CO_2(g) + 2H_2O(g)$

c. $C_4H_{10}(g) + O_2(g) \rightarrow CO_2(g) + H_2O(g)$

balance carbon: $C_4H_{10}(g) + O_2(g) \rightarrow \mathbf{4}CO_2(g) + H_2O(g)$

balance hydrogen: $C_4H_{10}(g) + O_2(g) \rightarrow 4CO_2(g) + \mathbf{5}H_2O(g)$

balance oxygen: $C_4H_{10}(g) + \frac{13}{2}O_2(g) \rightarrow 4CO_2(g) + 5H_2O(g)$

balanced equation: $2C_4H_{10}(g) + 13O_2(g) \rightarrow 8CO_2(g) + 10H_2O(g)$

62.   A reaction in which small molecules or atoms combine to make a larger molecule is called a *synthesis* reaction. An example would be the synthesis of sodium chloride from the elements

$2Na(s) + Cl_2(g) \rightarrow 2NaCl(s).$

A reaction in which a molecule is broken down into simpler molecules or atoms is called a *decomposition* reaction. An example would be the decomposition of sodium hydrogen carbonate when heated.

$2NaHCO_3(s) \rightarrow Na_2CO_3(s) + CO_2(g) + H_2O(g).$

Specific examples will depend on the students' input.

64.   a. $8Fe(s) + S_8(s) \rightarrow 8FeS(s)$

b. $4Co(s) + 3O_2(g) \rightarrow 2Co_2O_3(s)$

c. $Cl_2O_7(g) + H_2O(l) \rightarrow 2HClO_4(aq)$

66.   a. $2Al(s) + 3Br_2(l) \rightarrow 2AlBr_3(s)$

b. $Zn(s) + 2HClO_4(aq) \rightarrow Zn(ClO_4)_2(aq) + H_2(g)$

c. $3Na(s) + P(s) \rightarrow Na_3P(s)$

d. $CH_4(g) + 4Cl_2(g) \rightarrow CCl_4(l) + 4HCl(g)$

e. $Cu(s) + 2AgNO_3(aq) \rightarrow Cu(NO_3)_2(aq) + 2Ag(s)$

68.   In several cases, the given ion may be precipitated by *many* reactants. The following are only three of the possible examples.

a.   Chloride ion would precipitate when treated with solutions containing silver ion, lead(II) ion, or mercury(I) ion.

$Ag^+(aq) + Cl^-(aq) \rightarrow AgCl(s)$

$Pb^{2+}(aq) + 2Cl^-(aq) \rightarrow PbCl_2(s)$

$Hg_2^{2+}(aq) + 2Cl^-(aq) \rightarrow Hg_2Cl_2(s)$

b. Calcium ion would precipitate when treated with solutions containing sulfate ion, carbonate ion, and phosphate ion.

$$Ca^{2+}(aq) + SO_4^{2-}(aq) \rightarrow CaSO_4(s)$$

$$Ca^{2+}(aq) + CO_3^{2-}(aq) \rightarrow CaCO_3(s)$$

$$3Ca^{2+}(aq) + 2PO_4^{3-}(aq) \rightarrow Ca_3(PO_4)_2(s)$$

c. Iron(III) ion would precipitate when treated with solutions containing hydroxide, sulfide, or carbonate ions.

$$Fe^{3+}(aq) + 3OH^-(aq) \rightarrow Fe(OH)_3(s)$$

$$2Fe^{3+}(aq) + 3S^{2-}(aq) \rightarrow Fe_2S_3(s)$$

$$2Fe^{3+}(aq) + 3CO_3^{2-}(aq) \rightarrow Fe_2(CO_3)_3(s)$$

d. Sulfate ion would precipitate when treated with solutions containing barium ion, calcium ion, or lead(II) ion.

$$Ba^{2+}(aq) + SO_4^{2-}(aq) \rightarrow BaSO_4(s)$$

$$Ca^{2+}(aq) + SO_4^{2-}(aq) \rightarrow CaSO_4(s)$$

$$Pb^{2+}(aq) + SO_4^{2-}(aq) \rightarrow PbSO_4(s)$$

e. Mercury(I) ion would precipitate when treated with solutions containing chloride ion, sulfide ion, or carbonate ion.

$$Hg_2^{2+}(aq) + 2Cl^-(aq) \rightarrow Hg_2Cl_2(s)$$

$$Hg_2^{2+}(aq) + S^{2-}(aq) \rightarrow Hg_2S(s)$$

$$Hg_2^{2+}(aq) + CO_3^{2-}(aq) \rightarrow Hg_2CO_3(s)$$

f. Silver ion would precipitate when treated with solutions containing chloride ion, sulfide ion, or carbonate ion.

$$Ag^+(aq) + Cl^-(aq) \rightarrow AgCl(s)$$

$$2Ag^+(aq) + S^{2-}(aq) \rightarrow Ag_2S(s)$$

$$2Ag^+(aq) + CO_3^{2-}(aq) \rightarrow Ag_2CO_3(s)$$

70. The formulas of the salts are indicated in boldface type.

a. $HNO_3(aq) + KOH(aq) \rightarrow H_2O(l) + \textbf{KNO}_3(aq)$

b. $H_2SO_4(aq) + Ba(OH)_2(aq) \rightarrow 2H_2O(l) + \textbf{BaSO}_4(s)$

c. $HClO_4(aq) + NaOH(aq) \rightarrow H_2O(l) + \textbf{NaClO}_4(aq)$

d. $2HCl(aq) + Ca(OH)_2(aq) \rightarrow 2H_2O(l) + \textbf{CaCl}_2(aq)$

72. a.   soluble (Rule 2: Most potassium salts are soluble.)

b.   soluble (Rule 2: Most ammonium salts are soluble.)

c.   insoluble (Rule 6: Most carbonate salts are only slightly soluble.)

d.   insoluble (Rule 6: Most phosphate salts are only slightly soluble.)

e.   soluble (Rule 2: Most sodium salts are soluble.)

    f.   insoluble (Rule 6: Most carbonate salts are only slightly soluble.)

    g.   soluble (Rule 3: Most chloride salts are soluble.)

74.   The precipitates are marked in boldface type.

    a.   Rule 3: AgCl is listed as an exception

$$AgNO_3(aq) + HCl(aq) \rightarrow \textbf{AgCl}(s) + HNO_3(aq)$$

    b.   Rule 6: Most carbonate salts are only slightly soluble.

$$CuSO_4(aq) + (NH_4)_2CO_3(aq) \rightarrow \textbf{CuCO}_3(s) + (NH_4)_2SO_4(aq)$$

    c.   Rule 6: Most carbonate salts are only slightly soluble.

$$FeSO_4(aq) + K_2CO_3(aq) \rightarrow \textbf{FeCO}_3(s) + K_2SO_4(aq)$$

    d.   no reaction

    e.   Rule 6: Most carbonate salts are only slightly soluble.

$$Pb(NO_3)_2(aq) + Li_2CO_3(aq) \rightarrow \textbf{PbCO}_3(s) + 2LiNO_3(aq)$$

    f.   Rule 5: Most hydroxide compounds are only slightly soluble.

$$SnCl_4(aq) + 4NaOH(aq) \rightarrow \textbf{Sn(OH)}_4(s) + 4NaCl(aq)$$

76. $Fe^{2+}(aq) + S^{2-}(aq) \rightarrow FeS(s)$

    $2Cr^{3+}(aq) + 3S^{2-}(aq) \rightarrow Cr_2S_3(s)$

    $Ni^{2+}(aq) + S^{2-}(aq) \rightarrow NiS(s)$

78.   These anions tend to form insoluble precipitates with *many* metal ions. The following are illustrative for cobalt(II) chloride, tin(II) chloride, and copper(II) nitrate reacting with the sodium salts of the given anions.

    a. $CoCl_2(aq) + Na_2S(aq) \rightarrow CoS(s) + 2NaCl(aq)$

             $SnCl_2(aq) + Na_2S(aq) \rightarrow SnS(s) + 2NaCl(aq)$

             $Cu(NO_3)_2(aq) + Na_2S(aq) \rightarrow CuS(s) + 2NaNO_3(aq)$

    b. $CoCl_2(aq) + Na_2CO_3(aq) \rightarrow CoCO_3(s) + 2NaCl(aq)$

             $SnCl_2(aq) + Na_2CO_3(aq) \rightarrow SnCO_3(s) + 2NaCl(aq)$

             $Cu(NO_3)_2(aq) + Na_2CO_3(aq) \rightarrow CuCO_3(s) + 2NaNO_3(aq)$

    c. $CoCl_2(aq) + 2NaOH(aq) \rightarrow Co(OH)_2(s) + 2NaCl(aq)$

             $SnCl_2(aq) + 2NaOH(aq) \rightarrow Sn(OH)_2(s) + 2NaCl(aq)$

             $Cu(NO_3)_2(aq) + 2NaOH(aq) \rightarrow Cu(OH)_2(s) + 2NaNO_3(aq)$

    d. $3CoCl_2(aq) + 2Na_3PO_4(aq) \rightarrow Co_3(PO_4)_2(s) + 6NaCl(aq)$

             $3SnCl_2(aq) + 2Na_3PO_4(aq) \rightarrow Sn_3(PO_4)_2(s) + 6NaCl(aq)$

             $3Cu(NO_3)_2(aq) + 2Na_3PO_4(aq) \rightarrow Cu_3(PO_4)_2(s) + 6NaNO_3(aq)$

80. a. $Na + O_2 \rightarrow Na_2O_2$

    Balance sodium: $\mathbf{2}Na + O_2 \rightarrow Na_2O_2$

    Balanced equation: $2Na(s) + O_2(g) \rightarrow Na_2O_2(s)$

    b. $Fe(s) + H_2SO_4(aq) \rightarrow FeSO_4(aq) + H_2(g)$

    Equation is already balanced!

    c. $Al_2O_3 \rightarrow Al + O_2$

    Balance oxygen: $\mathbf{2}Al_2O_3 \rightarrow Al + \mathbf{3}O_2$

    Balance aluminum: $2Al_2O_3 \rightarrow \mathbf{4}Al + 3O_2$

    Balanced equation: $2Al_2O_3(s) \rightarrow 4Al(s) + 3O_2(g)$

    d. $Fe + Br_2 \rightarrow FeBr_3$

    Balance bromine: $Fe + \mathbf{3}Br_2 \rightarrow \mathbf{2}FeBr_3$

    Balance iron: $\mathbf{2}Fe + 3Br_2 \rightarrow 2FeBr_3$

    Balanced equation: $2Fe(s) + 3Br_2(l) \rightarrow 2FeBr_3(s)$

    e. $Zn + HNO_3 \rightarrow Zn(NO_3)_2 + H_2$

    Balance nitrate ions: $Zn + \mathbf{2}HNO_3 \rightarrow Zn(NO_3)_2 + H_2$

    Balanced equation: $Zn(s) + 2HNO_3(aq) \rightarrow Zn(NO_3)_2(aq) + H_2(g)$

82. a. $2C_4H_{10}(l) + 13O_2(g) \rightarrow 8CO_2(g) + 10H_2O(g)$

    b. $C_4H_{10}O(l) + 6O_2(g) \rightarrow 4CO_2(g) + 5H_2O(g)$

    c. $2C_4H_{10}O_2(l) + 11O_2(g) \rightarrow 8CO_2(g) + 10H_2O(g)$

84. a. $2NaHCO_3(s) \rightarrow Na_2CO_3(s) + H_2O(g) + CO_2(g)$

    b. $2NaClO_3(s) \rightarrow 2NaCl(s) + 3O_2(g)$

    c. $2HgO(s) \rightarrow 2Hg(l) + O_2(g)$

    d. $C_{12}H_{22}O_{11}(s) \rightarrow 12C(s) + 11H_2O(g)$

    e. $2H_2O_2(l) \rightarrow 2H_2O(l) + O_2(g)$

86. $Al(s) + H_2SO_4(aq) \rightarrow Al_2(SO_4)_3(aq) + H_2(g)$

    $Zn(s) + H_2SO_4(aq) \rightarrow ZnSO_4(aq) + H_2(g)$

    $Mg(s) + H_2SO_4(aq) \rightarrow MgSO_4(aq) + H_2(g)$

    $Co(s) + H_2SO_4(aq) \rightarrow CoSO_4(aq) + H_2(g)$

    $Ni(s) + H_2SO_4(aq) \rightarrow NiSO_4(aq) + H_2(g)$

88. a. one

    b. one

    c. two

    d.   two

    e.   three

90.   A very simple example that fits the bill is: $C(s) + O_2(g) \rightarrow CO_2(g)$

92.   a. $2C_3H_8O(l) + 9O_2(g) \rightarrow 6CO_2(g) + 8H_2O(g)$

              oxidation–reduction, combustion

       b. $HCl(aq) + AgC_2H_3O_2(aq) \rightarrow AgCl(s) + HC_2H_3O_2(aq)$

              precipitation, double–displacement

       c. $3HCl(aq) + Al(OH)_3(s) \rightarrow AlCl_3(aq) + 3H_2O(l)$

              acid–base, double–displacement

       d. $2H_2O_2(aq) \rightarrow 2H_2O(l) + O_2(g)$

              oxidation–reduction, decomposition

       e. $N_2H_4(l) + O_2(g) \rightarrow N_2(g) + 2H_2O(g)$

              oxidation–reduction, combustion

94. $2Na(s) + Cl_2(g) \rightarrow 2NaCl(s)$

       $2Al(s) + 3Cl_2(g) \rightarrow 2AlCl_3(s)$

       $Zn(s) + Cl_2(g) \rightarrow ZnCl_2(s)$

       $Ca(s) + Cl_2(g) \rightarrow CaCl_2(s)$

       $2Fe(s) + 3Cl_2(g) \rightarrow 2FeCl_3(s); Fe(s) + Cl_2(g) \rightarrow FeCl_2(s)$

CUMULATIVE REVIEW

Chapters 6 and 7

2.   A chemical equation indicates the substances necessary for a chemical reaction to take place, as well as what is produced by that chemical reaction. The substances to the left of the arrow in a chemical equation are called the reactants; those to the right of the arrow are referred to as the products. In addition, if a chemical equation has been balanced, then the equation indicates the relative proportions in which the reactant molecules combine to form the product molecules.

4.   It is *never* permissible to change the subscripts of a formula when balancing a chemical equation: changing the subscripts changes the *identity* of a substance from one chemical to another. For example, consider the unbalanced chemical equation

$$H_2(g) + O_2(g) \rightarrow H_2O(l).$$

If you changed the *formula* of the product from $H_2O(l)$ to $H_2O_2(l)$, the equation would appear to be "balanced". However, H_2O is water, whereas H_2O_2 is hydrogen peroxide–a completely different chemical substance (which is not prepared by reaction of the elements hydrogen and oxygen).

When we balance a chemical equation, it is permitted only to adjust the *coefficients* of a formula, so changing a coefficient merely changes the number of molecules of a substance being used in the reaction, without changing the identity of the substance. For the example above, we can balance the equation by putting coefficients of 2 in front of the formulas of H_2 and H_2O: these coefficients do not change the nature of what is reacting and what product is formed.

$$2H_2(g) + O_2(g) \rightarrow 2H_2O(l)$$

6.   A precipitation reaction is one in which a *solid* forms when the reactants are combined: the solid is called a precipitate. The driving force in such a reaction is the formation of the solid, thus *removing ions* from the solution. There are many examples of such precipitation reactions: consult the solubility rules in Table 7.1 if you need help. One example would be to combine barium nitrate and sodium carbonate solutions: a precipitate of barium carbonate would form.

The molecular equation for this reaction is:

$$Ba(NO_3)_2(aq) + Na_2CO_3(aq) \rightarrow BaCO_3(s) + 2NaNO_3(aq)$$

The net ionic equation for this reaction is:

$$Ba^{2+}(aq) + CO_3^{2-}(aq) \rightarrow BaCO_3(s)$$

8.   In summary, nearly all compounds containing the nitrate, sodium, potassium, and ammonium ions are soluble in water. Most salts containing the chloride and sulfate ions are soluble in water, with specific exceptions (see Table 7.1 for these exceptions). Most compounds containing the hydroxide, sulfide, carbonate, and phosphate ions are not soluble in water, unless the compound also contains one of the cations mentioned above (Na^+, K^+, NH_4^+).

The solubility rules are phrased as if you had a sample of a given solute and wanted to see if you could dissolve it in water. These rules can also be applied, however, to predict the identity of the solid produced in a precipitation reaction: a given combination of ions will not be soluble in water whether you take a pure compound out of a reagent bottle or if you generate the insoluble combination of ions during a chemical reaction. For example, the solubility rules say that $BaSO_4$ is not soluble in water. This means not only that a pure sample of $BaSO_4$ taken from a reagent bottle will not dissolve in water, but also that if Ba^{2+} ion and SO_4^{2-} ion end up together in the same solution, they will precipitate as $BaSO_4$. If we were to combine barium chloride and sulfuric acid solutions

$$BaCl_2(aq) + H_2SO_4(aq) \rightarrow BaSO_4(s) + 2HCl(aq)$$

then, because barium sulfate is not soluble in water, a precipitate of $BaSO_4(s)$ would form. Because a precipitate of $BaSO_4(s)$ would form no matter what barium compound or what sulfate compound were mixed, we can write the net ionic equation for the reaction as

$$Ba^{2+}(aq) + SO_4^{2-}(aq) \rightarrow BaSO_4(s).$$

Thus if, for example, barium nitrate solution were combined with sodium sulfate solution, a precipitate of $BaSO_4$ would form. Barium sulfate is insoluble in water regardless of its source.

10.   Acids (such as the citric acid found in citrus fruits and the acetic acid found in vinegar) were first noted primarily because of their sour taste. The first bases noted were characterized by their bitter taste and slippery feel on the skin. Acids and bases chemically react with (neutralize) each other forming water: the net ionic equation is

$$H^+(aq) + OH^-(aq) \rightarrow H_2O(l).$$

The *strong* acids and bases fully ionize when they dissolve in water: because these substances fully ionize, they are strong electrolytes. The common strong acids are HCl(hydrochloric), HNO_3(nitric), H_2SO_4(sulfuric), and $HClO_4$(perchloric). The most common strong bases are the alkali metal hydroxides, particularly NaOH(sodium hydroxide) and KOH(potassium hydroxide).

12.   Oxidation–reduction reactions are electron-transfer reactions. Oxidation represents a loss of electrons by an atom, molecule, or ion, whereas reduction is the gain of electrons by such a species. Because an oxidation–reduction process represents the transfer of electrons between species, you can't have one without the other also taking place: the electrons lost by one species must be gained by some other species. An example of a simple oxidation–reduction reaction between a metal and a nonmetal could be the following

$$Mg(s) + F_2(g) \rightarrow MgF_2(s).$$

In this process, Mg atoms lose two electrons each to become Mg^{2+} ions in MgF_2: Mg is oxidized. Each F atom of F_2 gains one electron to become a F^- ion, for a total of two electrons gained for each F_2 molecule: F_2 is reduced.

$$Mg \rightarrow Mg^{2+} + 2e^-$$

$$2(F + e^- \rightarrow F^-)$$

14.   In general, a synthesis reaction represents the reaction of elements or simple compounds to produce more complex substances. There are many examples of synthesis reactions, for example

$$N_2(g) + 3H_2(g) \rightarrow 2NH_3(g)$$

$$NaOH(aq) + CO_2(g) \rightarrow NaHCO_3(s).$$

Decomposition reactions represent the breakdown of a more complex substance into simpler substances. There are many examples of decomposition reactions, for example

$$2H_2O_2(aq) \rightarrow 2H_2O(l) + O_2(g).$$

Synthesis and decomposition reactions are very often also oxidation–reduction reactions, especially if an elemental substance reacts or is generated. It is not necessary, however, for synthesis and decomposition reactions to always involve oxidation–reduction. The reaction between NaOH and CO_2 given as an example of a synthesis reaction does *not* represent oxidation–reduction.

16.   a. $C(s) + O_2(g) \rightarrow CO_2(g)$

      b. $2C(s) + O_2(g) \rightarrow 2CO(g)$

      c. $2Li(l) + 2C(s) \rightarrow Li_2C_2(s)$

      d. $FeO(s) + C(s) \rightarrow Fe(l) + CO(g)$

      e. $C(s) + 2F_2(g) \rightarrow CF_4(g)$

18.   a. $Ba(NO_3)_2(aq) + K_2CrO_4(aq) \rightarrow BaCrO_4(s) + 2KNO_3(aq)$

      b. $NaOH(aq) + CH_3COOH(aq) \rightarrow H_2O(l) + NaCH_3COO(aq)$ (then evaporate the water from the solution)

      c. $AgNO_3(aq) + NaCl(aq) \rightarrow AgCl(s) + NaNO_3(aq)$

      d. $Pb(NO_3)_2(aq) + H_2SO_4(aq) \rightarrow PbSO_4(s) + 2HNO_3(aq)$

      e. $2NaOH(aq) + H_2SO_4(aq) \rightarrow Na_2SO_4(aq) + 2H_2O(l)$ (then evaporate the water from the solution)

      f. $Ba(NO_3)_2(aq) + Na_2CO_3(aq) \rightarrow BaCO_3(s) + 2NaNO_3(aq)$

20.   a. $FeO(s) + 2HNO_3(aq) \rightarrow Fe(NO_3)_2(aq) + H_2O(l)$

         acid–base, double-displacement

      b. $2Mg(s) + 2CO_2(g) + O_2(g) \rightarrow 2MgCO_3(s)$

         synthesis; oxidation–reduction

      c. $2NaOH(s) + CuSO_4(aq) \rightarrow Cu(OH)_2(s) + Na_2SO_4(aq)$

         precipitation, double-displacement

      d. $HI(aq) + KOH(aq) \rightarrow KI(aq) + H_2O(l)$

         acid–base, double–displacement

      e. $C_3H_8(g) + 5O_2(g) \rightarrow 3CO_2(g) + 4H_2O(g)$

         combustion; oxidation–reduction

      f. $Co(NH_3)_6Cl_2(s) \rightarrow CoCl_2(s) + 6NH_3(g)$

         decomposition

      g. $2HCl(aq) + Pb(C_2H_3O_2)_2(aq) \rightarrow 2HC_2H_3O_2(aq) + PbCl_2(s)$

         precipitation, double-displacement

h. $C_{12}H_{22}O_{11}(s) \rightarrow 12C(s) + 11H_2O(g)$

decomposition; oxidation–reduction

i. $2Al(s) + 6HNO_3(aq) \rightarrow 2Al(NO_3)_3(aq) + 3H_2(g)$

oxidation–reduction; single-displacement

j. $4B(s) + 3O_2(g) \rightarrow 2B_2O_3(s)$

synthesis; oxidation–reduction

22.   Specific examples will depend on students' responses. The following are general equations that illustrate each type of reaction:

precipitation: typical when solutions of two ionic solutes are mixed, and one of the new combinations of ions is insoluble.

$$A^+B^-(aq) + C^+D^-(aq) \rightarrow AD(s) + C^+D^-(aq)$$

single displacement: one element replaces a less reactive element from a compound.

$$A(s) + B^+C^-(aq) \rightarrow A^+C^-(aq) + B(s)$$

combustion: a rapid oxidation reaction, most commonly involving $O_2(g)$. Most examples in the text involve the combustion of hydrocarbons or hydrocarbon derivatives.

$$\text{(hydrocarbon or derivative)} + O_2(g) \rightarrow CO_2(g) + H_2O(g)$$

synthesis: elements or simple compounds combine to make more complicated molecules.

$$A(s) + B(s) \rightarrow AB(s)$$

oxidation–reduction: reactions in which electrons are transferred from one species to another. Examples of oxidation–reduction reactions include single-displacement, combustion, synthesis, and decomposition reactions.

decomposition: a compound breaks down into elements and/or simpler compounds.

$$AB(s) \rightarrow A(s) + B(s)$$

acid–base neutralization: a neutralization takes place when a proton from an acid combines with a hydroxide ion from a base to make a water molecule.

24.   a.   no reaction (all combinations are soluble)

b. $Ca^{2+}(aq) + SO_4^{2-}(aq) \rightarrow CaSO_4(s)$

c. $Pb^{2+}(aq) + S^{2-}(aq) \rightarrow PbS(s)$

d. $2Fe^{3+}(aq) + 3CO_3^{2-}(aq) \rightarrow Fe_2(CO_3)_3(s)$

e. $Hg_2^{2+}(aq) + 2Cl^-(aq) \rightarrow Hg_2Cl_2(s)$

f. $Ag^+(aq) + Cl^-(aq) \rightarrow AgCl(s)$

g. $3Ca^{2+}(aq) + 2PO_4^{3-}(aq) \rightarrow Ca_3(PO_4)_2(s)$

Since phosphoric acid is not a very strong acid, a more realistic equation might be

$$3Ca^{2+}(aq) + 2H_3PO_4(aq) \rightarrow Ca_3(PO_4)_2(s) + 6H^+(aq)$$

h.   no reaction (all combinations are soluble)

CHAPTER 8

Chemical Composition

2. The empirical formula is CFH from the structure given. The empirical formula represents the smallest whole number ratio of the number and types of atoms present.

4. The average atomic mass takes into account the various isotopes of an element and the relative abundances in which those isotopes are found.

6.   a. $40.08 \text{ amu Ca} \times \dfrac{1 \text{ Ca atom}}{40.08 \text{ amu}} = 1 \text{ Ca atom}$

      b. $919.5 \text{ amu W} \times \dfrac{1 \text{ W atom}}{183.9 \text{ amu}} = 5 \text{ W atoms}$

      c. $549.4 \text{ amu Mn} \times \dfrac{1 \text{ Mn atom}}{54.94 \text{ amu}} = 10 \text{ Mn atoms}$

      d. $6345 \text{ amu I} \times \dfrac{1 \text{ I atom}}{126.9 \text{ amu}} = 50 \text{ I atoms}$

      e. $2072 \text{ amu} \times \dfrac{1 \text{ Pb atom}}{207.2 \text{ amu}} = 10 \text{ Pb atoms}$

8. One tin atom has a mass of 118.7 amu.

A sample containing 35 tin atoms would weigh: $35 \times \dfrac{118.7 \text{ amu}}{1 \text{ atom}} = 4155 \text{ amu};$

2967.5 amu of tin would represent: $2967.5 \text{ amu} \times \dfrac{1 \text{ tin atom}}{118.7 \text{ amu}} = 25 \text{ tin atoms}.$

10. 26.98 g (1.00 mol)

12. Since 10.09 g of neon represents half the molar mass of neon (20.18 g), then 10.09 g of neon contains

$$\tfrac{1}{2} \times (6.022 \times 10^{23}) = 3.011 \times 10^{23} \text{ neon atoms (0.500 mol)}.$$

Also, 0.500 mol of helium gas would contain the same number of atoms as 0.500 mol of neon gas: this would be

$$\tfrac{1}{2} \times 4.003 \text{ g} = 2.002 \text{ g of helium gas}.$$

14.   The ratio of the atomic mass of Co to the atomic mass of F is (58.93 amu/19.00 amu), and the mass of cobalt is given by

$$57.0 \text{ g} \times \frac{58.93 \text{ amu}}{19.00 \text{ amu}} = 177 \text{ g Co.}$$

16.   mass of a carbon atom $= 4.48 \times 10^{-23} \text{ g} \times \dfrac{12.01 \text{ amu C}}{26.98 \text{ amu Al}} = 1.99 \times 10^{-23} \text{ g}$

18. $0.50 \text{ mol Ne atoms} \times \dfrac{20.18 \text{ g}}{1 \text{ mol}} = 10.09 \text{ g Ne} = 10. \text{ g Ne}$ (two significant figures)

$1 \text{ mol B atoms} \times \dfrac{10.81 \text{ g B}}{1 \text{ mol}} = 10.81 \text{ g B} = 11 \text{ g B}$ (two significant figures)

The neon sample weighs less.

20.   a. $66.50 \text{ g F} \times \dfrac{1 \text{ mol}}{19.00 \text{ g}} = 3.500 \text{ mol of F atoms}$

b. $401.2 \text{ mg Hg} \times \dfrac{1 \text{ mmol}}{200.6 \text{ mg}} = 2.000 \text{ mmol Hg}$ (1 mmol = 1/1000 mol)

c. $84.27 \text{ g Si} \times \dfrac{1 \text{ mol}}{28.09 \text{ g}} = 3.000 \text{ mol Si}$

d. $48.78 \text{ g Pt} \times \dfrac{1 \text{ mol}}{195.1 \text{ g}} = 0.2500 \text{ mol Pt}$

e. $2431 \text{ g Mg} \times \dfrac{1 \text{ mol}}{24.31 \text{ g}} = 100.0 \text{ mol Mg}$

f. $47.97 \text{ g} \times \dfrac{1 \text{ mol}}{95.94 \text{ g}} = 0.5000 \text{ mol Mo}$

22.   a. $0.00552 \text{ mol Ca} \times \dfrac{40.08 \text{ g}}{1 \text{ mol}} = 0.221 \text{ g Ca}$

b. $6.25 \text{ millimol B} \times \dfrac{1 \text{ mol}}{10^{3} \text{ millmol}} \times \dfrac{10.81 \text{ g}}{1 \text{ mol}} = 0.0676 \text{ g B}$

c. $135 \text{ mol Al} \times \dfrac{26.98 \text{ g}}{1 \text{ mol}} = 3.64 \times 10^{3} \text{ g Al}$

d. $1.34 \times 10^{-7} \text{ mol Ba} \times \dfrac{137.3 \text{ g}}{1 \text{ mol}} = 1.84 \times 10^{-5} \text{ g Ba}$

e. $2.79 \text{ mol P} \times \dfrac{30.97 \text{ g}}{1 \text{ mol}} = 86.4 \text{ g P}$

f. $0.0000997 \text{ mol As} \times \dfrac{74.92 \text{ g}}{1 \text{ mol}} = 7.47 \times 10^{-3} \text{ g As}$

24.   a. $125 \text{ Fe atoms} \times \dfrac{55.85 \text{ g Fe}}{6.022 \times 10^{23} \text{ Fe atoms}} = 1.16 \times 10^{-20} \text{ g}$

b. $125 \text{ Fe atoms} \times \dfrac{55.85 \text{ amu}}{1 \text{ Fe atom}} = 6.98 \times 10^{3} \text{ amu}$

c. $125 \text{ g Fe} \times \dfrac{1 \text{ mol Fe}}{55.85 \text{ g Fe}} = 2.24 \text{ mol Fe}$

d. $125 \text{ mol Fe} \times \dfrac{55.85 \text{ g Fe}}{1 \text{ mol Fe}} = 6.98 \times 10^{3} \text{ g Fe}$

e. $125 \text{ g Fe} \times \dfrac{6.022 \times 10^{23} \text{ Fe atoms}}{55.85 \text{ g Fe}} = 1.35 \times 10^{24} \text{ Fe atoms}$

f. $125 \text{ mol Fe} \times \dfrac{6.022 \times 10^{23} \text{ Fe atoms}}{1 \text{ mol Fe}} = 7.53 \times 10^{25} \text{ Fe atoms}$

26.   The molar mass is calculated by summing the individual atomic masses of the atoms in the formula.

28.   a. $KHCO_3$ potassium hydrogen carbonate, potassium bicarbonate

mass of 1 mol K = 39.10 g

mass of 1 mol H = 1.008 g

mass of 1 mol C = 12.01 g

mass of 3 mol O = 3(16.00 g) = 48.00 g

molar mass of $KHCO_3$ = (39.10 + 1.008 + 12.01 + 48.00) = 100.12 g

b. Hg_2Cl_2 mercurous chloride, mercury(I) chloride

mass of 2 mol Hg = 2(200.6 g) = 401.2 g

mass of 2 mol Cl = 2(35.45 g) = 70.90 g

molar mass of Hg_2Cl_2 = (401.2 g + 70.90 g) = 472.1 g

c. H_2O_2 hydrogen peroxide

mass of 2 mol H = 2(1.008 g) = 2.016 g

mass of 2 mol O = 2(16.00 g) = 32.00 g

molar mass of H_2O_2 = (2.016 g + 32.00 g) = 34.02 g

d. $BeCl_2$ beryllium chloride

mass of 1 mol Be = 9.012 g

mass of 2 mol Cl = 2(35.45 g) = 70.90 g

molar mass of $BeCl_2$ = (9.012 g + 70.90 g) = 79.91 g

e. $Al_2(SO_4)_3$ aluminum sulfate

mass of 2 mol Al = 2(26.98 g) = 53.96 g

mass of 3 mol S = 3(32.07 g) = 96.21 g

mass of 12 mol O = 12(16.00 g) = 192.0 g

molar mass of $Al_2(SO_4)_3$ = (53.96 g + 96.21 g + 192.0 g) = 342.2 g

f. $KClO_3$ potassium chlorate

mass of 1 mol K = 39.10 g

mass of 1 mol Cl = 35.45 g

mass of 3 mol O = 3(16.00 g) = 48.00 g

molar mass of $KClO_3$ = 122.55 g

30.   a. $LiClO_4$

mass of 1 mol Li = 6.941 g

mass of 1 mol Cl = 35.45 g

mass of 4 mol O = 4(16.00 g) = 64.00 g

molar mass of $LiClO_4$ = (6.941 g + 35.45 g + 64.00 g) = 106.39 g

b. $NaHSO_4$

mass of 1 mol Na = 22.99 g

mass of 1 mol H = 1.008 g

mass of 1 mol S = 32.07 g = 32.07 g

mass of 4 mol O = 4(16.00 g) = 64.00 g

molar mass of $NaHSO_4$ = (22.99 g + 1.008 g + 32.07 g + 64.00 g) = 120.07 g

c. $MgCO_3$

mass of 1 mol Mg = 24.31 g

mass of 1 mol C = 12.01 g

mass of 3 mol O = 3(16.00 g) = 48.00 g

molar mass of $MgCO_3$ = (24.31 g + 12.01 g + 48.00 g) = 84.32 g

d. $AlBr_3$

mass of 1 mol Al = 26.98 g

mass of 3 mol Br = 3(79.90 g) = 239.7 g

molar mass of $AlBr_3$ = (26.98 g + 239.7 g) = 266.7 g

e. Cr_2S_3

mass of 2 mol Cr = 2(52.00 g) = 104.0 g

mass of 3 mol S = 3(32.07 g) = 96.21 g

molar mass of Cr_2S_3 = (104.0 + 96.21 g) = 200.2 g

32. a. molar mass Al_2O_3 = 101.96 g

$$47.2 \text{ g} \times \frac{1 \text{ mol}}{101.96 \text{ g}} = 0.463 \text{ mol}$$

b. molar mass KBr = 119.00 g

$$1.34 \text{ kg} \times \frac{1000 \text{ g}}{1 \text{ kg}} \times \frac{1 \text{ mol}}{119.00 \text{ g}} = 11.3 \text{ mol}$$

c. molar mass Ge = 72.59 g

$$521 \text{ mg} \times \frac{1 \text{ g}}{1000 \text{ mg}} \times \frac{1 \text{ mol}}{72.59 \text{ g}} = 7.18 \times 10^{-3} \text{ mol}$$

d. molar mass of U = 238.0 g

$$56.2 \text{ μg} \times \frac{1 \text{ g}}{10^6 \text{ μg}} \times \frac{1 \text{ mol}}{238.0 \text{ g}} = 2.36 \times 10^{-7} \text{ mol}$$

e. molar mass of $NaC_2H_3O_2$ = 82.03 g

$$29.7 \text{ g} \times \frac{1 \text{ mol}}{82.03 \text{ g}} = 1.69 \text{ mol} = 0.362 \text{ mol}$$

f. molar mass of SO_3 = 80.07 g

$$1.03 \text{ g} \times \frac{1 \text{ mol}}{80.07 \text{ g}} = 0.0129 \text{ mol}$$

34. a. molar mass of Li_2CO_3 = 73.89 g

$$1.95 \times 10^{-3} \text{ g} \times \frac{1 \text{ mol}}{73.89 \text{ g}} = 2.64 \times 10^{-5} \text{ mol}$$

b. molar mass of $CaCl_2$ = 110.98 g

$$4.23 \text{ kg} \times \frac{1000 \text{ g}}{1 \text{ kg}} \times \frac{1 \text{ mol}}{110.98 \text{ g}} = 38.1 \text{ mol}$$

c. molar mass of $SrCl_2$ = 158.52 g

$$1.23 \text{ mg} \times \frac{1 \text{ g}}{1000 \text{ mg}} \times \frac{1 \text{ mol}}{158.52 \text{ g}} = 7.76 \times 10^{-6} \text{ mol}$$

d. molar mass of $CaSO_4$ = 136.15 g

$$4.75 \text{ g} \times \frac{1 \text{ mol}}{136.15 \text{ g}} = 3.49 \times 10^{-2} \text{ mol}$$

e.   molar mass of NO_2 = 46.01 g

$$96.2 \text{ mg} \times \frac{1 \text{ g}}{1000 \text{ mg}} \times \frac{1 \text{ mol}}{46.01 \text{ g}} = 2.09 \times 10^{-3} \text{ mol}$$

f.   molar mass of Hg_2Cl_2 = 472.1 g

$$12.7 \text{ g} \times \frac{1 \text{ mol}}{472.1 \text{ g}} = 0.0269 \text{ mol}$$

36.   a.   molar mass of H_2S = 34.09 g

$$1.21 \text{ mol} \times \frac{34.09 \text{ g}}{1 \text{ mol}} = 41.2 \text{ g}$$

b.   molar mass of Li_2S = 45.95 g

$$4.22 \times 10^{-3} \text{ mol} \times \frac{45.95 \text{ g}}{1 \text{ mol}} = 0.194 \text{ g}$$

c.   molar mass of $FeCl_3$ = 162.2 g

$$224 \text{ mol} \times \frac{162.2 \text{ g}}{1 \text{ mol}} = 3.63 \times 10^4 \text{ g}$$

d.   molar mass of Na_2CO_3 = 105.99 g

$$7.29 \text{ millmol} \times \frac{1 \text{ mol}}{10^3 \text{ millimol}} \times \frac{105.99 \text{ g}}{1 \text{ mol}} = 0.773 \text{ g}$$

e.   molar mass of $NaC_2H_3O_2$ = 82.03 g

$$8.14 \times 10^3 \text{ mol} \times \frac{82.03 \text{ g}}{1 \text{ mol}} = 6.68 \times 10^5 \text{ g}$$

f.   molar mass of PH_3 = 33.99 g

$$0.00793 \text{ mol} \times \frac{33.99 \text{ g}}{1 \text{ mol}} = 0.270 \text{ g}$$

38.   a.   molar mass C_6H_6 = 78.11 g

$$0.994 \text{ mol} \times \frac{78.11 \text{ g}}{1 \text{ mol}} = 77.6 \text{ g}$$

b.   molar mass CaH_2 = 42.10 g

$$4.21 \text{ mol} \times \frac{42.10 \text{ g}}{1 \text{ mol}} = 177 \text{ g}$$

c.   molar mass H_2O_2 = 34.02 g

$$1.79 \times 10^{-4} \text{ mol} \times \frac{34.02 \text{ g}}{1 \text{ mol}} = 6.09 \times 10^{-3} \text{ g}$$

    d.   molar mass $C_6H_{12}O_6 = 180.16$ g

$$1.22 \text{ mmol} \times \frac{1 \text{ mol}}{10^3 \text{ mmol}} \times \frac{105.99 \text{ g}}{1 \text{ mol}} = 0.220 \text{ g}$$

    e.   molar mass $Sn = 118.7$ g

$$10.6 \text{ mol} \times \frac{118.7 \text{ g}}{1 \text{ mol}} = 1.26 \times 10^3 \text{ g}$$

    f.   molar mass $SrF_2 = 125.62$ g

$$0.000301 \text{ mol} \times \frac{125.62 \text{ g}}{1 \text{ mol}} = 0.0378 \text{ g}$$

40.   a. $6.37 \text{ mol CO} \times \dfrac{6.022 \times 10^{23} \text{ molecules}}{1 \text{ mol}} = 3.84 \times 10^{24} \text{ molecules CO}$

    b.   molar mass of $CO = 28.01$ g

$$6.37 \text{ g} \times \frac{6.022 \times 10^{23} \text{ molecules}}{28.01 \text{ g}} = 1.37 \times 10^{23} \text{ molecules CO}$$

    c.   molar mass of $H_2O = 18.02$ g

$$2.62 \times 10^{-6} \text{ g} \times \frac{6.022 \times 10^{23} \text{ molecules}}{18.02 \text{ g}} = 8.76 \times 10^{16} \text{ molecules } H_2O$$

    d. $2.62 \times 10^{-6} \text{ g} \times \dfrac{6.022 \times 10^{23} \text{ molecules}}{1 \text{ mol}} = 1.58 \times 10^{18} \text{ molec. } H_2O$

    e.   molar mass of $C_6H_6 = 78.11$ g

$$5.23 \text{ g} \times \frac{6.022 \times 10^{23} \text{ molecules}}{78.11 \text{ g}} = 4.03 \times 10^{22} \text{ molecules } C_6H_6$$

42.   a.   molar mass of $Na_2SO_4 = 142.1$ g

$$2.01 \text{ g Na}_2\text{SO}_4 \times \frac{1 \text{ mol Na}_2\text{SO}_4}{142.1 \text{ g}} \times \frac{1 \text{ mol S}}{1 \text{ mol Na}_2\text{SO}_4} = 0.0141 \text{ mol S}$$

    b.   molar mass of $Na_2SO_3 = 126.1$ g

$$2.01 \text{ g Na}_2\text{SO}_3 \times \frac{1 \text{ mol Na}_2\text{SO}_3}{126.1 \text{ g}} \times \frac{1 \text{ mol S}}{1 \text{ mol Na}_2\text{SO}_3} = 0.0159 \text{ mol S}$$

    c.   molar mass of $Na_2S = 78.05$ g

$$2.01 \text{ g Na}_2\text{S} \times \frac{1 \text{ mol Na}_2\text{S}}{78.05 \text{ g}} \times \frac{1 \text{ mol S}}{1 \text{ mol Na}_2\text{S}} = 0.0258 \text{ mol S}$$

    d.   molar mass of $Na_2S_2O_3 = 158.1$ g

$$2.01 \text{ g Na}_2\text{S}_2\text{O}_3 \times \frac{1 \text{ mol Na}_2\text{S}_2\text{O}_3}{158.1 \text{ g}} \times \frac{1 \text{ mol S}}{1 \text{ mol Na}_2\text{S}} = 0.0127 \text{ mol S}$$

44. less than

46. a. mass of Zn present = 65.38 g

    mass of O present = 16.00 g

    molar mass of ZnO = 81.38 g

    $$\%Zn = \frac{65.38 \text{ g Zn}}{81.38 \text{ g}} \times 100 = 80.34\% \text{ Zn}$$

    $$\%O = \frac{16.00 \text{ g O}}{81.38 \text{ g}} \times 100 = 19.66\% \text{ O}$$

    b. mass of Na present = 2(22.99 g) = 45.98 g

    mass of S present = 32.07 g

    molar mass of Na_2S = 78.05 g

    $$\%Na = \frac{45.98 \text{ g Na}}{78.05 \text{ g}} \times 100 = 58.91\% \text{ Na}$$

    $$\%S = \frac{32.07 \text{ g S}}{78.05 \text{ g}} \times 100 = 41.09\% \text{ S}$$

    c. mass of Mg present = 24.31 g

    mass of O present = 2(16.00 g) = 32.00 g

    mass of H present = 2(1.008 g) = 2.016 g

    molar mass of $Mg(OH)_2$ = 58.33 g

    $$\%Mg = \frac{24.31 \text{ g Mg}}{58.33 \text{ g}} \times 100 = 41.68\% \text{ Mg}$$

    $$\%O = \frac{32.00 \text{ g O}}{58.33 \text{ g}} \times 100 = 54.86\% \text{ O}$$

    $$\%H = \frac{2.016 \text{ g H}}{58.33 \text{ g}} \times 100 = 3.456\% \text{ H}$$

    d. mass of H present = 2(1.008 g) = 2.016 g

    mass of O present = 2(16.00 g) = 32.00 g

    molar mass of H_2O_2 = 34.02 g

    $$\%H = \frac{2.016 \text{ g H}}{34.02 \text{ g}} \times 100 = 5.926\% \text{ H}$$

    $$\%O = \frac{32.00 \text{ g O}}{34.02 \text{ g}} \times 100 = 94.06\% \text{ O}$$

e. mass of Ca present = 40.08 g

mass of H present = 2(1.008 g) = 2.016 g

molar mass of CaH_2 = 42.10 g

$$\%Ca = \frac{40.08 \text{ g Ca}}{42.10 \text{ g}} \times 100 = 95.20\% \text{ Ca}$$

$$\%H = \frac{2.016 \text{ g H}}{42.10 \text{ g}} \times 100 = 4.789\% \text{ H}$$

f. mass of K present = 2(39.10 g) = 78.20 g

mass of O present = 16.00 g

molar mass of K_2O = 94.20 g

$$\%K = \frac{78.20 \text{ g K}}{94.20 \text{ g}} \times 100 = 83.01\% \text{ K}$$

$$\%O = \frac{16.00 \text{ g O}}{94.20 \text{ g}} \times 100 = 16.99\% \text{ O}$$

48. a. molar mass of BaO_2 = 169.3 g

$$\% \text{ Ba} = \frac{137.3 \text{ g Ba}}{169.3 \text{ g}} \times 100 = 81.10\% \text{ Ba}$$

b. molar mass of BaO = 153.3 g

$$\% \text{ Ba} = \frac{137.3 \text{ g Ba}}{153.3 \text{ g}} \times 100 = 89.56\% \text{ Ba}$$

c. molar mass of $CoBr_2$ = 218.73 g

$$\% \text{ Co} = \frac{58.93 \text{ g Co}}{218.73 \text{ g}} \times 100 = 26.94\% \text{ Co}$$

d. molar mass of $CoBr_3$ = 298.63 g

$$\% \text{ Co} = \frac{58.93 \text{ g Co}}{298.63 \text{ g}} \times 100 = 19.73\% \text{ Co}$$

e. molar mass of $SnCl_2$ = 189.60 g

$$\% \text{ Sn} = \frac{118.7 \text{ g Sn}}{189.60 \text{ g}} \times 100 = 62.61\% \text{ Sn}$$

f. molar mass of $SnCl_4$ = 260.50 g

$$\% \text{ Sn} = \frac{118.7 \text{ g Sn}}{260.50 \text{ g}} \times 100 = 45.57\% \text{ Sn}$$

g.   molar mass of LiH = 7.949 g

$$\% \, Li = \frac{6.941 \text{ g Li}}{7.949 \text{ g}} \times 100 = 87.32\% \text{ Li}$$

h.   molar mass of AlH_3 = 30.00 g

$$\% \, Al = \frac{26.98 \text{ g Al}}{30.00 \text{ g}} \times 100 = 89.93\% \text{ Al}$$

50.   a.   molar mass of ICl = 162.35 g

$$\%I = \frac{126.9 \text{ g I}}{162.35 \text{ g}} \times 100 = 78.16\% \text{ I}$$

b.   molar mass of N_2O = 44.02 g

$$\%N = \frac{28.02 \text{ g N}}{44.02 \text{ g}} \times 100 = 63.65\% \text{ N}$$

c.   molar mass of NO = 30.01 g

$$\%N = \frac{14.01 \text{ g N}}{30.01 \text{ g}} \times 100 = 46.68\% \text{ N}$$

d.   molar mass of $HgCl_2$ = 271.5 g

$$\%Hg = \frac{200.6 \text{ g Hg}}{271.5 \text{ g}} \times 100 = 73.89\% \text{ Hg}$$

e.   molar mass of Hg_2Cl_2 = 472.1 g

$$\%Hg = \frac{401.2 \text{ g Hg}}{472.1 \text{ g}} \times 100 = 84.98\% \text{ Hg}$$

f.   molar mass of SF_6 = 146.07 g

$$\%S = \frac{32.07 \text{ g S}}{146.07 \text{ g}} \times 100 = 21.96\% \text{ S}$$

g.   molar mass of XeF_2 = 169.3 g

$$\%Xe = \frac{131.3 \text{ g Xe}}{169.3 \text{ g}} \times 100 = 77.55\% \text{ Xe}$$

h.   molar mass of MnO_2 = 86.94 g

$$\%Mn = \frac{54.94 \text{ g Mn}}{86.94 \text{ g}} \times 100 = 63.19\% \text{ Mn}$$

52.   a.   molar mass of $(NH_4)_2S$ = 68.15 g; molar mass of S^{2-} ion = 32.07 g

$$\% \, S^{2-} = \frac{32.07 \text{ g S}^{2-}}{68.15 \text{ g NH}_4\text{S}} \times 100 = 47.06\% \text{ S}^{2-}$$

b. molar mass of $CaCl_2 = 110.98$ g; molar mass of $Cl^- = 35.45$ g

$$\% \ Cl^- = \frac{70.90 \ \text{g} \ Cl^-}{110.98 \ \text{g} \ CaCl_2} \times 100 = 63.89\% \ Cl^-$$

c. molar mass of $BaO = 153.3$ g; molar mass of O^{2-} ion $= 16.00$ g

$$\% \ O^{2-} = \frac{16.00 \ \text{g} \ O^{2-}}{153.3 \ \text{g} \ BaO} \times 100 = 10.44\% \ O^{2-}$$

d. molar mass of $NiSO_4 = 154.76$ g; molar mass of SO_4^{2-} ion $= 96.07$ g

$$\% \ SO_4^{2-} = \frac{96.07 \ \text{g} \ SO_4^{2-}}{154.76 \ \text{g} \ NiSO_4} \times 100 = 62.08\% \ SO_4^{2-}$$

54. The empirical formula indicates the smallest whole number ratio of the number and type of atoms present in a molecule. For example, NO_2 and N_2O_4 both have two oxygen atoms for every nitrogen atom and therefore have the same empirical formula

56. a. yes (each of these has empirical formula CH)

b. no (the number of hydrogen atoms is wrong)

c. yes (both have empirical formula NO_2)

d. no (the number of hydrogen and oxygen atoms is wrong)

58. Assume we have 100.0 g of the compound so that the percentages become masses.

$$11.64 \ \text{g} \ N \times \frac{1 \ \text{mol}}{14.01 \ \text{g}} = 0.8308 \ \text{mol} \ N$$

$$88.36 \ \text{g} \ Cl \times \frac{1 \ \text{mol}}{35.45 \ \text{g}} = 2.493 \ \text{mol} \ Cl$$

Dividing both of these numbers of moles by the smaller number of moles gives

$$\frac{0.8308 \ \text{mol} \ N}{0.8308} = 1.000 \ \text{mol} \ N$$

$$\frac{2.493 \ \text{mol} \ Cl}{0.8308 \ \text{mol}} = 3.001 \ \text{mol} \ Cl$$

The empirical formula is NCl_3.

60. Assume we have 100.0 g of the compound, so that the percentages become masses.

$$78.14 \ \text{g} \ B \times \frac{1 \ \text{mol}}{10.81 \ \text{g}} = 7.228 \ \text{mol} \ B$$

$$21.86 \ \text{g} \ H \times \frac{1 \ \text{mol}}{1.008 \ \text{g}} = 21.69 \ \text{mol} \ H$$

Dividing each number of moles by the smaller number of moles gives

$$\frac{7.228 \text{ mol B}}{7.228 \text{ mol}} = 1.000 \text{ mol B}$$

$$\frac{21.69 \text{ mol H}}{7.228 \text{ mol}} = 3.000 \text{ mol H}$$

The empirical formula is BH_3.

62.   Consider 100.0 g of the compound so that percentages become masses.

$$45.56 \text{ g Sn} \times \frac{1 \text{ mol}}{118.7 \text{ g}} = 0.3838 \text{ mol Sn}$$

$$54.43 \text{ g Cl} \times \frac{1 \text{ mol}}{35.45 \text{ g}} = 1.535 \text{ mol Cl}$$

Dividing each number of moles by the smaller number of moles gives

$$\frac{0.3838 \text{ mol Sn}}{0.3838 \text{ mol}} = 1.000 \text{ mol Sn}$$

$$\frac{1.535 \text{ mol Cl}}{0.3838 \text{ mol}} = 3.999 \text{ mol Cl}$$

The empirical formula is $SnCl_4$.

64.   Consider 100.0 g of the compound.

$$55.06 \text{ g Co} \times \frac{1 \text{ mol}}{58.93 \text{ g}} = 0.9343 \text{ mol Co}$$

If the sulfide of cobalt is 55.06% Co, then it is 44.94% S by mass.

$$44.94 \text{ g S} \times \frac{1 \text{ mol}}{32.07 \text{ g}} = 1.401 \text{ mol S}$$

Dividing each number of moles by the smaller (0.9343 mol Co) gives

$$\frac{0.09343 \text{ mol Co}}{0.9343} = 1.000 \text{ mol Co}$$

$$\frac{1.401 \text{ mol S}}{0.9343 \text{ mol}} = 1.500 \text{ mol S}$$

Multiplying by two, to convert to whole numbers of moles, gives the empirical formula for the compound as Co_2S_3.

66. $2.50 \text{ g Al} \times \dfrac{1 \text{ mol}}{26.98 \text{ g}} = 0.09266 \text{ mol Al}$

$5.28 \text{ g F} \times \dfrac{1 \text{ mol}}{19.00 \text{ g}} = 0.2779 \text{ mol F}$

Dividing each number of moles by the smaller number of moles gives

$$\frac{0.09266 \text{ mol Al}}{0.09266 \text{ mol}} = 1.000 \text{ mol Al}$$

$$\frac{0.2779 \text{ mol F}}{0.09266 \text{ mol}} = 2.999 \text{ mol F}$$

The empirical formula is just AlF_3. Note the similarity between this problem and question 65: they differ in the way the data is given. In question 65, you were given the mass of the product, and first had to calculate how much fluorine had reacted.

68.   Consider 100.0 g of the compound so that percentages become masses.

$$46.46 \text{ g Li} \times \frac{1 \text{ mol}}{6.941 \text{ g}} = 6.694 \text{ mol Li}$$

$$53.54 \text{ g O} \times \frac{1 \text{ mol}}{16.00 \text{ g}} = 3.346 \text{ mol O}$$

Dividing each number of moles by the smaller number of moles gives

$$\frac{6.694 \text{ mol Li}}{3.346 \text{ mol}} = 2.001 \text{ mol Li}$$

$$\frac{3.346 \text{ mol O}}{3.346 \text{ mol}} = 1.000 \text{ mol O}$$

The empirical formula is Li_2O

70.   Consider 100.0 g of the compound.

$$59.78 \text{ g Li} \times \frac{1 \text{ mol}}{6.941 \text{ g}} = 8.613 \text{ mol Li}$$

$$40.22 \text{ g N} \times \frac{1 \text{ mol}}{14.01 \text{ g}} = 2.871 \text{ mol N}$$

Dividing each number of moles by the smaller number of moles (2.871 mol N) gives

$$\frac{8.613 \text{ mol Li}}{2.871 \text{ mol}} = 3.000 \text{ mol Li}$$

$$\frac{2.871 \text{ mol N}}{2.871 \text{ mol}} = 1.000 \text{ mol N}$$

The empirical formula is Li_3N.

72.   Consider 100.0 g of the compound so that percentages become masses.

$$71.06 \text{ g Co} \times \frac{1 \text{ mol}}{58.93 \text{ g}} = 1.206 \text{ mol Co}$$

$$28.94 \text{ g O} \times \frac{1 \text{ mol}}{16.00 \text{ g}} = 1.809 \text{ mol O}$$

Dividing each number of moles by the smaller number of moles gives

$$\frac{1.206 \text{ mol Co}}{1.206 \text{ mol}} = 1.000 \text{ mol Co}$$

$$\frac{1.809 \text{ mol O}}{1.206 \text{ mol}} = 1.500 \text{ mol O}$$

Multiplying these relative numbers of moles by 2 to give whole numbers gives the empirical formula as Co_2O_3

74.   Compound 1: Assume 100.0 g of the compound.

$$22.55 \text{ g P} \times \frac{1 \text{ mol}}{30.97 \text{ g}} = 0.7281 \text{ mol P}$$

$$77.45 \text{ g Cl} \times \frac{1 \text{ mol}}{35.45 \text{ g}} = 2.185 \text{ mol Cl}$$

Dividing each number of moles by the smaller (0.7281 mol P) indicates that the formula of Compound 1 is PCl_3.

Compound 2: Assume 100.0 g of the compound.

$$14.87 \text{ g P} \times \frac{1 \text{ mol}}{30.97 \text{ g}} = 0.4801 \text{ mol P}$$

$$85.13 \text{ g Cl} \times \frac{1 \text{ mol}}{35.45 \text{ g}} = 2.401 \text{ mol Cl}$$

Dividing each number of moles by the smaller (0.4801 mol P) indicates that the formula of Compound 2 is PCl_5.

76.   If only the empirical formula is known, the molar mass of the substance must be determined before the molecular formula can be calculated.

78.   empirical formula mass of CH = 13 g

$$n = \frac{\text{molar mass}}{\text{empirical formula mass}} = \frac{78 \text{ g}}{13 \text{ g}} = 6$$

The molecular formula is $(CH)_6$ or C_6H_6.

80.   empirical formula mass of $C_2H_5O = 46$ g

$$n = \frac{\text{molar mass}}{\text{empirical formula mass}} = \frac{90 \text{ g}}{46 \text{ g}} = \sim 2$$

molecular formula is $(C_2H_5O)_2 = C_4H_{10}O_2$

82.   For NO_2:   molar mass = $14.01 + 2(16.00) = 46.01$ g

$$\%N = \frac{14.01 \text{ g N}}{46.01 \text{ g}} \times 100 = 30.45 \text{ \%N}$$

$$\%O = \frac{2(16.00 \text{ g O})}{46.01 \text{ g}} \times 100 = 69.55 \,\%O$$

For N_2O_4: molar mass = $2(14.01 \text{ g}) + 4(16.00 \text{ g}) = 92.02$ g

$$\%N = \frac{2(14.01 \text{ g N})}{92.02 \text{ g}} \times 100 = 30.45 \,\%N$$

$$\%O = \frac{4(16.00 \text{ g O})}{92.02 \text{ g}} \times 100 = 69.55 \,\%O$$

84.

5.00 g Al	0.185 mol	1.12×10^{23} atoms
0.140 g Fe	0.00250 mol	1.51×10^{21} atoms
2.7×10^2 g Cu	4.3 mol	2.6×10^{24} atoms
0.00250 g Mg	1.03×10^{-4} mol	6.19×10^{19} atoms
0.062 g Na	2.7×10^{-3} mol	1.6×10^{21} atoms
3.95×10^{-18} g U	1.66×10^{-20} mol	1.00×10^4 atoms

86. mass of 2 mol X = $2(41.2 \text{ g}) = 82.4$ g

mass of 1 mol Y = 57.7 g = 57.7 g

mass of 3 mol Z = $3(63.9 \text{ g}) = 191.7$ g

molar mass of X_2YZ_3 = 331.8 g

$$\%X = \frac{82.4 \text{ g}}{331.8 \text{ g}} \times 100 = 24.8 \,\%X$$

$$\% Y = \frac{57.7 \text{ g}}{331.8 \text{ g}} \times 100 = 17.4\% \ Y$$

$$\% Z = \frac{191.7 \text{ g}}{331.8 \text{ g}} \times 100 = 57.8\% \ Z$$

If the molecular formula were actually $X_4Y_2Z_6$, the percentage composition would be the same, and the *relative* mass of each element present would not change. The molecular formula is always a whole number multiple of the empirical formula.

88. For the first compound (*restricted* amount of oxygen)

$$2.118 \text{ g Cu} \times \frac{1 \text{ mol}}{63.55 \text{ g}} = 0.03333 \text{ mol Cu}$$

$$0.2666 \text{ g O} \times \frac{1 \text{ mol}}{16.00 \text{ g}} = 0.01666 \text{ mol O}$$

Since the number of moles of Cu (0.03333 mol) is twice the number of moles of O (0.01666 mol), the empirical formula is Cu_2O.

For the second compound (stream of pure oxygen)

$$2.118 \text{ g Cu} \times \frac{1 \text{ mol}}{63.55 \text{ g}} = 0.03333 \text{ mol Cu}$$

$$0.5332 \text{ g O} \times \frac{1 \text{ mol}}{16.00 \text{ g}} = 0.03333 \text{ mol O}$$

Since the numbers of moles are the same, the empirical formula is CuO.

90. a. molar mass $H_2O = 18.02$ g

$$4.21 \text{ g} \times \frac{1 \text{ mol}}{18.02 \text{ g}} \times \frac{6.022 \times 10^{23} \text{ molecules}}{1 \text{ mol}} = 1.41 \times 10^{23} \text{ molecules}$$

The sample contains 1.41×10^{23} oxygen atoms and $2(1.41 \times 10^{23}) = 2.82 \times 10^{23}$ hydrogen atoms.

b. molar mass $CO_2 = 44.01$ g

$$6.81 \text{ g} \times \frac{1 \text{ mol}}{44.01 \text{ g}} \times \frac{6.022 \times 10^{23} \text{ molecules}}{1 \text{ mol}} = 9.32 \times 10^{22} \text{ molecules}$$

The sample contains 9.32×10^{22} carbon atoms and $2(9.32 \times 10^{22}) = 1.86 \times 10^{23}$ oxygen atoms.

c. molar mass $C_6H_6 = 78.11$ g

$$0.000221 \text{ g} \times \frac{1 \text{ mol}}{78.11 \text{ g}} \times \frac{6.022 \times 10^{23} \text{ molecules}}{1 \text{ mol}} = 1.70 \times 10^{18} \text{ molec.}$$

The sample contains $6(1.70 \times 10^{18}) = 1.02 \times 10^{19}$ atoms of each element.

d. $$2.26 \text{ mol} \times \frac{6.022 \times 10^{23} \text{ molecules}}{1 \text{ mol}} = 1.36 \times 10^{24} \text{ molecules}$$

atoms C $= 12(1.36 \times 10^{24}) = 1.63 \times 10^{25}$ atoms

atoms H $= 22(1.36 \times 10^{24}) = 2.99 \times 10^{25}$ atoms

atoms O $= 11(1.36 \times 10^{24}) = 1.50 \times 10^{25}$ atoms

92. a. molar mass of $C_3O_2 = 3(12.01 \text{ g}) + 2(16.00 \text{ g}) = 68.03$ g

$$\% \text{ C} = \frac{36.03 \text{ g C}}{68.03 \text{ g}} \times 100 = 52.96\% \text{ C}$$

$$7.819 \text{ g C}_3\text{O}_2 \times \frac{52.96 \text{ g C}}{100.0 \text{ g C}_3\text{O}_2} = 4.141 \text{ g C}$$

$$4.141 \text{ g C} \times \frac{6.022 \times 10^{23} \text{ molecules}}{12.01 \text{ g C}} = 2.076 \times 10^{23} \text{ C atoms}$$

b. molar mass of $CO = 12.01 \text{ g} + 16.00 \text{ g} = 28.01$ g

$$\% \text{ C} = \frac{12.01 \text{ g C}}{28.01 \text{ g}} \times 100 = 42.88\% \text{ C}$$

$$1.53 \times 10^{21} \text{ molecules CO} \times \frac{1 \text{ C atom}}{1 \text{ molecule CO}} = 1.53 \times 10^{21} \text{ C atoms}$$

$$1.53 \times 10^{21} \text{ C atoms} \times \frac{12.01 \text{ g C}}{6.022 \times 10^{23} \text{ C atoms}} = 0.0305 \text{ g C}$$

c.   molar mass of C_6H_6O = 6(12.01 g) + 6(1.008 g) + 16.00 g = 94.11 g

$$\% \text{ C} = \frac{72.06 \text{ g C}}{94.11 \text{ g}} \times 100 = 76.57\% \text{ C}$$

$$0.200 \text{ mol } C_6H_6O \times \frac{6 \text{ mol C}}{1 \text{ mol } C_6H_6O} = 1.20 \text{ mol C}$$

$$1.20 \text{ mol C} \times \frac{12.01 \text{ g}}{1 \text{ mol}} = 14.4 \text{ g C}$$

$$14.4 \text{ g C} \times \frac{6.022 \times 10^{23} \text{ C atoms}}{12.01 \text{ g C}} = 7.22 \times 10^{23} \text{ C atoms}$$

94. $$2.24 \text{ g Co} \times \frac{55.85 \text{ g Fe}}{58.93 \text{ g Co}} = 2.12 \text{ g Fe}$$

96. $$5.00 \text{ g Te} \times \frac{200.6 \text{ g Hg}}{127.6 \text{ g Te}} = 7.86 \text{ g Hg}$$

98.   153.8 g CCl_4 = 6.022×10^{23} molecules CCl_4

$$1 \text{ molecule} \times \frac{153.8 \text{ g } CCl_4}{6.022 \times 10^{23} \text{ molecules}} = 2.554 \times 10^{-22} \text{ g}$$

100.   a.   molar mass of $C_2H_5O_2N$ = 2(12.01 g) + 5(1.008 g) + 2(16.00 g) + 14.01 g = 75.07 g

$$5.000 \text{ g} \times \frac{14.01 \text{ g N}}{75.07 \text{ g}} = 0.9331 \text{ g N}$$

b.   molar mass of Mg_3N_2 = 3(24.31 g) + 2(14.01 g) = 100.95 g

$$5.000 \text{ g} \times \frac{28.02 \text{ g N}}{100.95 \text{ g}} = 1.388 \text{ g N}$$

c.   molar mass of $Ca(NO_3)_2$ = 40.08 g + 2(14.01 g) + 6(16.00 g) = 164.10 g

$$5.000 \text{ g} \times \frac{28.02 \text{ g N}}{164.10 \text{ g}} = 0.8537 \text{ g N}$$

d.   molar mass of N_2O_4 = 2(14.01 g) + 4(16.00 g) = 92.02 g

$$5.000 \text{ g} \times \frac{28.02 \text{ g N}}{92.02 \text{ g}} = 1.522 \text{ g N}$$

102. Consider 100.0 g of the compound.

$$16.39 \text{ g Mg} \times \frac{1 \text{ mol}}{24.31 \text{ g}} = 0.6742 \text{ mol Mg}$$

$$18.89 \text{ g N} \times \frac{1 \text{ mol}}{14.01 \text{ g}} = 1.348 \text{ mol N}$$

$$64.72 \text{ g O} \times \frac{1 \text{ mol}}{16.00 \text{ g}} = 4.045 \text{ mol O}$$

Dividing each number of moles by the smallest number of moles

$$\frac{0.6742 \text{ mol Mg}}{0.6742 \text{ mol}} = 1.000 \text{ mol Mg}$$

$$\frac{1.348 \text{ mol N}}{0.6742 \text{ mol}} = 1.999 \text{ mol N}$$

$$\frac{4.045 \text{ mol O}}{0.6742 \text{ mol}} = 5.999 \text{ mol O}$$

The empirical formula is MgN_2O_6 [i.e., $Mg(NO_3)_2$].

104. We use the *average* mass because this average is a *weighted average* and takes into account both the masses and the relative abundances of the various isotopes.

106. $$1.98 \times 10^{13} \text{ amu} \times \frac{1 \text{ Na atom}}{22.99 \text{ amu}} = 8.61 \times 10^{11} \text{ Na atoms}$$

$$3.01 \times 10^{23} \text{ Na atoms} \times \frac{22.99 \text{ amu}}{1 \text{ Na atom}} = 6.92 \times 10^{24} \text{ amu}$$

108. a. $$5.0 \text{ mol K} \times \frac{39.10 \text{ g}}{1 \text{ mol}} = 195 \text{ g} = 2.0 \times 10^2 \text{ g K}$$

   b. $$0.000305 \text{ mol Hg} \times \frac{200.6 \text{ g}}{1 \text{ mol}} = 0.0612 \text{ g Hg}$$

   c. $$2.31 \times 10^{-5} \text{ mol Mn} \times \frac{54.94 \text{ g}}{1 \text{ mol}} = 1.27 \times 10^{-3} \text{ g Mn}$$

   d. $$10.5 \text{ mol P} \times \frac{30.97 \text{ g}}{1 \text{ mol}} = 325 \text{ g P}$$

   e. $$4.9 \times 10^4 \text{ mol Fe} \times \frac{55.85 \text{ g}}{1 \text{ mol}} = 2.7 \times 10^6 \text{ g Fe}$$

   f. $$125 \text{ mol Li} \times \frac{6.941 \text{ g}}{1 \text{ mol}} = 868 \text{ g Li}$$

   g. $$0.01205 \text{ mol F} \times \frac{19.00 \text{ g}}{1 \text{ mol}} = 0.2290 \text{ g F}$$

110. a. mass of 1 mol Fe = 1(55.85 g) = 55.85 g

mass of 1 mol S = 1(32.07 g) = 32.07 g

mass of 4 mol O = 4(16.00 g) = 64.00 g

molar mass of $FeSO_4$ = 151.92 g

b. mass of 1 mol Hg = 1(200.6 g) = 200.6 g

mass of 2 mol I = 2(126.9 g) = 253.8 g

molar mass of HgI_2 =   454.4 g

c. mass of 1 mol Sn = 1(118.7 g) = 118.7 g

mass of 2 mol O = 2(16.00 g) = 32.00 g

molar mass of SnO_2 = 150.7 g

d. mass of 1 mol Co = 1(58.93 g) = 58.93 g

mass of 2 mol Cl = 2(35.45 g) = 70.90 g

molar mass of $CoCl_2$ = 129.83 g

e. mass of 1 mol Cu = 1(63.55 g) = 63.55 g

mass of 2 mol N = 2(14.01 g) = 28.02 g

mass of 6 mol O = 6(16.00 g) = 96.00 g

molar mass of $Cu(NO_3)_2$ = 187.57 g

112. a. molar mass of $(NH_4)_2S$ = 68.15 g

$$21.2 \text{ g} \times \frac{1 \text{ mol}}{68.15 \text{ g}} = 0.311 \text{ mol } (NH_4)_2S$$

b. molar mass of $Ca(NO_3)_2$ = 164.1 g

$$44.3 \text{ g} \times \frac{1 \text{ mol}}{164.1 \text{ g}} = 0.270 \text{ mol } Ca(NO_3)_2$$

c. molar mass of Cl_2O = 86.9 g

$$4.35 \text{ g} \times \frac{1 \text{ mol}}{86.9 \text{ g}} = 0.0501 \text{ mol } Cl_2O$$

d. 1.0 lb = 454 g; molar mass of $FeCl_3$ = 162.2

$$454 \text{ g} \times \frac{1 \text{ mol}}{162.2 \text{ g}} = 2.8 \text{ mol } FeCl_3$$

e. 1.0 kg = 1.0×10^3 g;   molar mass of $FeCl_3$ = 162.2 g

$$1.0 \times 10^3 \text{ g} \times \frac{1 \text{ mol}}{162.2 \text{ g}} = 6.2 \text{ mol } FeCl_3$$

114. a. molar mass of $CuSO_4$ = 159.62 g

$$2.6 \times 10^{-2} \text{ mol} \times \frac{159.62 \text{ g}}{1 \text{ mol}} = 4.2 \text{ g } CuSO_4$$

b. molar mass of C_2F_4 = 100.0 g

$$3.05 \times 10^3 \text{ mol} \times \frac{100.0 \text{ g}}{1 \text{ mol}} = 3.05 \times 10^5 \text{ g } C_2F_4$$

c. 7.83 mmol = 0.00783 mol; molar mass of C_5H_8 = 68.11 g

$$0.00783 \text{ mol} \times \frac{68.11 \text{ g}}{1 \text{ mol}} = 0.533 \text{ g } C_5H_8$$

d. molar mass of $BiCl_3$ = 315.3 g

$$6.30 \text{ mol} \times \frac{315.3 \text{ g}}{1 \text{ mol}} = 1.99 \times 10^3 \text{ g } BiCl_3$$

e. molar mass of $C_{12}H_{22}O_{11}$ = 342.3 g

$$12.2 \text{ mol} \times \frac{342.3 \text{ g}}{1 \text{ mol}} = 4.18 \times 10^3 \text{ g } C_{12}H_{22}O_{11}$$

116. a. molar mass of $C_6H_{12}O_6$ = 180.2 g

$$3.45 \text{ g} \times \frac{6.022 \times 10^{23} \text{ molecules}}{180.2 \text{ g}} = 1.15 \times 10^{22} \text{ molecules } C_6H_{12}O_6$$

b. $$3.45 \text{ mol} \times \frac{6.022 \times 10^{23} \text{ molecules}}{1 \text{ mol}} = 2.08 \times 10^{24} \text{ molecules } C_6H_{12}O_6$$

c. molar mass of ICl_5 = 304.2 g

$$25.0 \text{ g} \times \frac{6.022 \times 10^{23} \text{ molecules}}{304.2 \text{ g}} = 4.95 \times 10^{22} \text{ molecules } ICl_5$$

d. molar mass of B_2H_6 = 27.67 g

$$1.00 \text{ g} \times \frac{6.022 \times 10^{23} \text{ molecules}}{27.67 \text{ g}} = 2.18 \times 10^{22} \text{ molecules } B_2H_6$$

e. 1.05 mmol = 0.00105 mol

$$0.00105 \text{ mol} \times \frac{6.022 \times 10^{23} \text{ formula units}}{1 \text{ mol}} = 6.32 \times 10^{20} \text{ formula units}$$

118. a. mass of Ca present = 3(40.08 g) = 120.24 g

mass of P present = 2(30.97 g) = 61.94 g

mass of O present = 8(16.00 g) = 128.00 g

molar mass of $Ca_3(PO_4)_2$ = 310.18 g

$$\% \text{ Ca} = \frac{120.24 \text{ g Ca}}{310.18 \text{ g}} \times 100 = 38.76\% \text{ Ca}$$

$$\% \text{ P} = \frac{61.94 \text{ g P}}{310.18 \text{ g}} \times 100 = 19.97\% \text{ P}$$

$$\% \text{ O} = \frac{128.00 \text{ g O}}{310.18 \text{ g}} \times 100 = 41.27\% \text{ O}$$

b. mass of Cd present = 112.4 g = 112.4 g

mass of S present = 32.07 g =   32.07 g

mass of O present = 4(16.00 g) = 64.00 g

molar mass of $CdSO_4$ = 208.5 g

$$\% \text{ Cd} = \frac{112.4 \text{ g Cd}}{208.5 \text{ g}} \times 100 = 53.91\% \text{ Cd}$$

$$\% \text{ S} = \frac{32.07 \text{ g S}}{208.5 \text{ g}} \times 100 = 15.38\% \text{ S}$$

$$\% \text{ O} = \frac{64.00 \text{ g O}}{208.5 \text{ g}} \times 100 = 30.70\% \text{ O}$$

c. mass of Fe present = 2(55.85 g) = 111.7 g

mass of S present = 3(32.07 g) = 96.21 g

mass of O present = 12(16.00 g) = 192.0 g

molar mass of $Fe_2(SO_4)_3$ = 399.9 g

$$\% \text{ Fe} = \frac{111.7 \text{ g Fe}}{399.9 \text{ g}} \times 100 = 27.93\% \text{ Fe}$$

$$\% \text{ S} = \frac{96.21 \text{ g S}}{399.9 \text{ g}} \times 100 = 24.06\% \text{ S}$$

$$\% \text{ O} = \frac{192.0 \text{ g O}}{399.9 \text{ g}} \times 100 = 48.01\% \text{ O}$$

d. mass of Mn present = 54.94 g = 54.94 g

mass of Cl present = 2(35.45 g) = 70.90 g

molar mass of $MnCl_2$ = 125.84 g

$$\% \text{ Mn} = \frac{54.94 \text{ g Mn}}{125.84 \text{ g}} \times 100 = 43.66\% \text{ Mn}$$

$$\% \text{ Cl} = \frac{70.90 \text{ g Cl}}{125.84 \text{ g}} \times 100 = 56.34\% \text{ Cl}$$

e. mass of N present = 2(14.01 g) = 28.02 g

mass of H present = 8(1.008 g) = 8.064 g

mass of C present = 12.01 g = 12.01 g

mass of O present = 3(16.00 g) = 48.00 g

molar mass of $(NH_4)_2CO_3$ = 96.09 g

$$\% \text{ N} = \frac{28.02 \text{ g N}}{96.09 \text{ g}} \times 100 = 29.16\% \text{ N}$$

$$\% \text{ H} = \frac{8.064 \text{ g H}}{96.09 \text{ g}} \times 100 = 8.392\% \text{ H}$$

$$\% \text{ C} = \frac{12.01 \text{ g C}}{96.09 \text{ g}} \times 100 = 12.50\% \text{ C}$$

$$\% \text{ O} = \frac{48.00 \text{ g O}}{96.09 \text{ g}} \times 100 = 49.95\% \text{ O}$$

f. mass of Na present = 22.99 g = 22.99 g

mass of H present = 1.008 g = 1.008 g

mass of C present = 12.01 g = 12.01 g

mass of O present = 3(16.00 g) = 48.00 g

molar mass of $NaHCO_3$ = 84.01 g

$$\% \text{ Na} = \frac{22.99 \text{ g Na}}{84.01 \text{ g}} \times 100 = 27.37\% \text{ Na}$$

$$\% \text{ H} = \frac{1.008 \text{ g H}}{84.01 \text{ g}} \times 100 = 1.200\% \text{ H}$$

$$\% \text{ C} = \frac{12.01 \text{ g C}}{84.01 \text{ g}} \times 100 = 14.30\% \text{ C}$$

$$\% \text{ O} = \frac{48.00 \text{ g O}}{84.01 \text{ g}} \times 100 = 57.14\% \text{ O}$$

g. mass of C present = 12.01 g = 12.01 g

mass of O present = 2(16.00 g) = 32.00 g

molar mass of CO_2 = 44.01 g

$$\% \text{ C} = \frac{12.01 \text{ g C}}{44.01 \text{ g}} \times 100 = 27.29\% \text{ C}$$

$$\% \text{ O} = \frac{32.00 \text{ g O}}{44.01 \text{ g}} \times 100 = 72.71\% \text{ O}$$

h.   mass of Ag present = 107.9 g   = 107.9 g

mass of N present = 14.01 g = 14.01 g

mass of O present = 3(16.00 g) = 48.00 g

molar mass of $AgNO_3$ = 169.9 g

$$\% \text{ Ag} = \frac{107.9 \text{ g Ag}}{169.9 \text{ g}} \times 100 = 63.51\% \text{ Ag}$$

$$\% \text{ N} = \frac{14.01 \text{ g N}}{169.9 \text{ g}} \times 100 = 8.246\% \text{ N}$$

$$\% \text{ O} = \frac{48.00 \text{ g O}}{169.9 \text{ g}} \times 100 = 28.25\% \text{ O}$$

120.   a. $$\% \text{ Fe} = \frac{55.85 \text{ g Fe}}{151.92 \text{ g}} \times 100 = 36.76\% \text{ Fe}$$

b. $$\% \text{ Ag} = \frac{215.8 \text{ g Ag}}{231.8 \text{ g}} \times 100 = 93.10\% \text{ Ag}$$

c. $$\% \text{ Sr} = \frac{87.62 \text{ g Sr}}{158.5 \text{ g}} \times 100 = 55.28\% \text{ Sr}$$

d. $$\% \text{ C} = \frac{48.04 \text{ g C}}{86.09 \text{ g}} \times 100 = 55.80\% \text{ C}$$

e. $$\% \text{ C} = \frac{12.01 \text{ g C}}{32.04 \text{ g}} \times 100 = 37.48\% \text{ C}$$

f. $$\% \text{ Al} = \frac{53.96 \text{ g Al}}{101.96 \text{ g}} \times 100 = 52.92\% \text{ Al}$$

g. $$\% \text{ K} = \frac{39.10 \text{ g K}}{106.55 \text{ g}} \times 100 = 36.70\% \text{ K}$$

h. $$\% \text{ K} = \frac{39.10 \text{ g K}}{74.55 \text{ g}} \times 100 = 52.45\% \text{ K}$$

122. $$0.2990 \text{ g C} \times \frac{1 \text{ mol}}{12.01 \text{ g}} = 0.02490 \text{ mol C}$$

$$0.05849 \text{ g H} \times \frac{1 \text{ mol}}{1.008 \text{ g}} = 0.05803 \text{ mol H}$$

$$0.2318 \text{ g N} \times \frac{1 \text{ mol}}{14.01 \text{ g}} = 0.01655 \text{ mol N}$$

$$0.1328 \text{ g O} \times \frac{1 \text{ mol}}{16.00 \text{ g}} = 0.008300 \text{ mol O}$$

Dividing each number of moles by the smallest number of moles (0.008300 mol) gives

$$\frac{0.02490 \text{ mol C}}{0.008300} = 3.000 \text{ mol C} \qquad \frac{0.05803 \text{ mol H}}{0.008300} = 6.992 \text{ mol H}$$

$$\frac{0.01655 \text{ mol N}}{0.008300} = 1.994 \text{ mol N} \qquad \frac{0.008300 \text{ mol O}}{0.008300} = 1.000 \text{ mol O}$$

The empirical formula is $C_3H_7N_2O$.

124.   Mass of oxygen in compound = 4.33 g – 4.01 g = 0.32 g O

$$4.01 \text{ g Hg} \times \frac{1 \text{ mol}}{200.6 \text{ g}} = 0.0200 \text{ mol Hg}$$

$$0.32 \text{ g O} \times \frac{1 \text{ mol}}{16.00 \text{ g}} = 0.020 \text{ mol O}$$

Since the numbers of moles are equal, the empirical formula is HgO.

126.   Assume we have 100.0 g of the compound.

$$65.95 \text{ g Ba} \times \frac{1 \text{ mol}}{137.3 \text{ g}} = 0.4803 \text{ mol Ba}$$

$$34.05 \text{ g Cl} \times \frac{1 \text{ mol}}{35.45 \text{ g}} = 0.9605 \text{ mol Cl}$$

Dividing each of these number of moles by the smaller number gives

$$\frac{0.4803 \text{ mol Ba}}{0.4803 \text{ mol}} = 1.000 \text{ mol Ba} \qquad \frac{0.9605 \text{ mol Cl}}{0.4803 \text{ mol}} = 2.000 \text{ mol Cl}$$

The empirical formula is then $BaCl_2$.

CHAPTER 9

Chemical Quantities

2. The coefficients of the balanced chemical equation for a reaction indicate the *relative numbers of moles* of each reactant that combine during the process, as well as the number of moles of each product formed.

4. Balanced chemical equations tell us in what molar ratios substances combine to form products, not in what mass proportions they combine.

6. a. $(NH_4)_2CO_3(s) \rightarrow 2NH_3(g) + CO_2(g) + H_2O(g)$

   One formula unit of solid ammonium carbonate decomposes to produce two molecules of ammonia gas, one molecule of carbon dioxide gas, and one molecule of water vapor. One mole of solid ammonium carbonate decomposes into two moles of gaseous ammonia, one mole of carbon dioxide gas, and one mole of water vapor.

   b. $6Mg(s) + P_4(s) \rightarrow 2Mg_3P_2(s)$

   Six atoms of magnesium metal react with one molecule of solid phosphorus (P_4) to make two formula units of solid magnesium phosphide. Six moles of magnesium metal react with one mole of phosphorus solid (P_4) to produce two moles of solid magnesium phosphide.

   c. $4Si(s) + S_8(s) \rightarrow 2Si_2S_4(l)$

   Four atoms of solid silicon react with one molecule of solid sulfur (S_8) to form two molecules of liquid disilicon tetrasulfide. Four moles of solid silicon react with one mole of solid sulfur (S_8) to form two moles of liquid disilicon tetrasulfide.

   d. $C_2H_5OH(l) + 3O_2(g) \rightarrow 2CO_2(g) + 3H_2O(g)$

   One molecule of liquid ethanol burns with three molecules of oxygen gas to produce two molecules of carbon dioxide gas and three molecules of water vapor. One mole of liquid ethanol burns with three moles of oxygen gas to produce two moles of gaseous carbon dioxide and three moles of water vapor.

8. Balanced chemical equations tell us in what molar ratios substances combine to form products, not in what mass proportions they combine. How could 2 grams of reactant produce a total of 3 grams of products?

10. $Fe_2O_3(s) + 3H_2SO_4(aq) \rightarrow Fe_2(SO_4)_3(s) + 3H_2O(l)$

   For converting from a given number of moles of iron(III) oxide to the number of moles of sulfuric acid required, the mole ratio is

   $$\left(\frac{3 \text{ mol } H_2SO_4}{1 \text{ mol } Fe_2O_3} \right)$$

For a given number of moles of iron(III) oxide reacting completely, the mole ratios used to calculate the number of moles of each product are

$$\text{For Fe}_2(\text{SO}_4)_3: \left(\frac{1 \text{ mol Fe}_2(\text{SO}_4)_3}{1 \text{ mol Fe}_2\text{O}_3} \right) \qquad \text{For H}_2\text{O}: \left(\frac{3 \text{ mol H}_2\text{O}}{1 \text{ mol Fe}_2\text{O}_3} \right)$$

12.   a. $4\text{Bi}(s) + 3\text{O}_2(g) \rightarrow 2\text{Bi}_2\text{O}_3(s)$

$$0.250 \text{ mol Bi} \times \frac{2 \text{ mol Bi}_2\text{O}_3}{4 \text{ mol Bi}} = 0.125 \text{ mol Bi}_2\text{O}_3$$

       b. $\text{SnO}_2(s) + 2\text{H}_2(g) \rightarrow \text{Sn}(s) + 2\text{H}_2\text{O}(g)$

$$0.250 \text{ mol SnO}_2 \times \frac{1 \text{ mol Sn}}{1 \text{ mol SnO}_2} = 0.250 \text{ mol Sn}$$

$$0.250 \text{ mol SnO}_2 \times \frac{2 \text{ mol H}_2\text{O}}{1 \text{ mol SnO}_2} = 0.500 \text{ mol H}_2\text{O}$$

       c. $\text{SiCl}_4(l) + 2\text{H}_2\text{O}(l) \rightarrow \text{SiO}_2(s) + 4\text{HCl}(g)$

$$0.250 \text{ mol SiCl}_4 \times \frac{1 \text{ mol SiO}_2}{1 \text{ mol SiCl}_4} = 0.250 \text{ mol SiO}_2$$

$$0.250 \text{ mol SiCl}_4 \times \frac{4 \text{ mol HCl}}{1 \text{ mol SiCl}_4} = 1.00 \text{ mol HCl}$$

       d. $2\text{N}_2(g) + 5\text{O}_2(g) + 2\text{H}_2\text{O}(l) \rightarrow 4\text{HNO}_3(aq)$

$$0.250 \text{ mol N}_2 \times \frac{4 \text{ mol HNO}_3}{2 \text{ mol N}_2} = 0.500 \text{ mol HNO}_3$$

14.   a. $\text{C}_5\text{H}_{12}(l) + 8\text{O}_2(g) \rightarrow 5\text{CO}_2(g) + 6\text{H}_2\text{O}(l)$

molar masses: CO_2, 44.01 g; H_2O, 18.02 g

$$0.750 \text{ mol C}_5\text{H}_{12} \times \frac{5 \text{ mol CO}_2}{1 \text{ mol C}_5\text{H}_{12}} = 3.75 \text{ mol CO}_2$$

$$3.75 \text{ mol CO}_2 \times \frac{44.01 \text{ g CO}_2}{1 \text{ mol CO}_2} = 165 \text{ g CO}_2$$

$$0.750 \text{ mol C}_5\text{H}_{12} \times \frac{6 \text{ mol H}_2\text{O}}{1 \text{ mol C}_5\text{H}_{12}} = 4.50 \text{ mol H}_2\text{O}$$

$$4.50 \text{ mol H}_2\text{O} \times \frac{18.02 \text{ g H}_2\text{O}}{1 \text{ mol H}_2\text{O}} = 81.1 \text{ g H}_2\text{O}$$

       b. $2\text{CH}_3\text{OH}(l) + 3\text{O}_2(g) \rightarrow 4\text{H}_2\text{O}(l) + 2\text{CO}_2(g)$

molar masses: H_2O, 18.02 g; CO_2, 44.01 g

$$0.750 \text{ mol CH}_3\text{OH} \times \frac{4 \text{ mol H}_2\text{O}}{2 \text{ mol CH}_3\text{OH}} = 1.50 \text{ mol H}_2\text{O}$$

$$1.50 \text{ mol } H_2O \times \frac{18.02 \text{ g } H_2O}{1 \text{ mol } H_2O} = 27.0 \text{ g } H_2O$$

$$0.750 \text{ mol } CH_3OH \times \frac{2 \text{ mol } CO_2}{2 \text{ mol } CH_3OH} = 0.750 \text{ mol } CO_2$$

$$0.750 \text{ mol } CO_2 \times \frac{44.01 \text{ g } CO_2}{1 \text{ mol } CO_2} = 33.0 \text{ g } CO_2$$

c. $Ba(OH)_2(aq) + H_3PO_4(aq) \rightarrow BaHPO_4(s) + 2H_2O(l)$

molar masses: $BaHPO_4$, 233.3 g; H_2O, 18.02 g

$$0.750 \text{ mol } Ba(OH)_2 \times \frac{1 \text{ mol } BaHPO_4}{1 \text{ mol } Ba(OH)_2} = 0.750 \text{ mol } BaHPO_4$$

$$0.750 \text{ mol } BaHPO_4 \times \frac{233.3 \text{ g } BaHPO_4}{1 \text{ mol } BaHPO_4} = 175 \text{ g } BaHPO_4$$

$$0.750 \text{ mol } Ba(OH)_2 \times \frac{2 \text{ mol } H_2O}{1 \text{ mol } Ba(OH)_2} = 1.50 \text{ mol } H_2O$$

$$1.50 \text{ mol } H_2O \times \frac{18.02 \text{ g } H_2O}{1 \text{ mol } H_2O} = 27.0 \text{ g } H_2O$$

d. $C_6H_{12}O_6(aq) \rightarrow 2C_2H_5OH(aq) + 2CO_2(g)$

molar masses: C_2H_5OH, 46.07 g; CO_2, 44.01 g

$$0.750 \text{ mol } C_6H_{12}O_6 \times \frac{2 \text{ mol } C_2H_5OH}{1 \text{ mol } C_6H_{12}O_6} = 1.50 \text{ mol } C_2H_5OH$$

$$1.50 \text{ mol } C_2H_5OH \times \frac{46.07 \text{ g } C_2H_5OH}{1 \text{ mol } C_2H_5OH} = 69.1 \text{ g } C_2H_5OH$$

$$0.750 \text{ mol } C_6H_{12}O_6 \times \frac{2 \text{ mol } CO_2}{1 \text{ mol } C_6H_{12}O_6} = 1.50 \text{ mol } CO_2$$

$$1.50 \text{ mol } CO_2 \times \frac{44.01 \text{ g } CO_2}{1 \text{ mol } CO_2} = 66.0 \text{ g } CO_2$$

16.   Before doing the calculations, the equations must be *balanced*.

a. $4KO_2(s) + 2H_2O(l) \rightarrow 3O_2(g) + 4KOH(s)$

$$0.625 \text{ mol } KOH \times \frac{3 \text{ mol } O_2}{4 \text{ mol } KOH} = 0.469 \text{ mol } O_2$$

b. $SeO_2(g) + 2H_2Se(g) \rightarrow 3Se(s) + 2H_2O(g)$

$$0.625 \text{ mol } H_2O \times \frac{3 \text{ mol } Se}{2 \text{ mol } H_2O} = 0.938 \text{ mol } Se$$

c. $2CH_3CH_2OH(l) + O_2(g) \rightarrow 2CH_3CHO(aq) + 2H_2O(l)$

$$0.625 \text{ mol } H_2O \times \frac{2 \text{ mol } CH_3CHO}{2 \text{ mol } H_2O} = 0.625 \text{ mol } CH_3CHO$$

d. $Fe_2O_3(s) + 2Al(s) \rightarrow 2Fe(l) + Al_2O_3(s)$

$$0.625 \text{ mol } Al_2O_3 \times \frac{2 \text{ mol } Fe}{1 \text{ mol } Al_2O_3} = 1.25 \text{ mol } Fe$$

18.   Stoichiometry is the process of using a chemical equation to calculate the relative masses of reactants and products involved in a reaction.

20.   a.   molar mass $Ar = 39.95 \text{ g}$

$$72.4 \text{ mg } Ar \times \frac{1 \text{ g}}{1000 \text{ mg}} \times \frac{1 \text{ mol } Ar}{39.95 \text{ g } Ar} = 1.81 \times 10^{-3} \text{ mol } Ar$$

b.   molar mass $CS_2 = 76.15 \text{ g}$

$$52.7 \text{ g } CS_2 \times \frac{1 \text{ mol } CS_2}{76.15 \text{ g } CS_2} = 0.692 \text{ mol } CS_2$$

c.   molar mass $Fe = 55.85 \text{ g}$

$$784 \text{ kg } Fe \times \frac{1000 \text{ g}}{1 \text{ kg}} \times \frac{1 \text{ mol } Fe}{55.85 \text{ g } Fe} = 1.40 \times 10^4 \text{ mol } Fe$$

d.   molar mass $CaCl_2 = 110.98 \text{ g}$

$$0.00104 \text{ g } CaCl_2 \times \frac{1 \text{ mol } CaCl_2}{110.98 \text{ g } CaCl_2} = 9.37 \times 10^{-6} \text{ mol } CaCl_2$$

e.   molar mass $NiS = 90.76 \text{ g}$

$$1.26 \times 10^3 \text{ g } NiS \times \frac{1 \text{ mol } NiS}{90.76 \text{ g } NiS} = 13.9 \text{ mol } NiS$$

22.   a.   molar mass of $C_3H_8 = 44.09 \text{ g}$

$$2.23 \text{ mol } C_3H_8 \times \frac{44.09 \text{ g } C_3H_8}{1 \text{ mol } C_3H_8} = 98.3 \text{ g } C_3H_8$$

b.   molar mass of $Ar = 39.95 \text{ g}$; 9.03 millimol = 0.00903 mol

$$0.00903 \text{ mol } Ar \times \frac{39.95 \text{ g } Ar}{1 \text{ mol } Ar} = 0.361 \text{ g } Ar$$

c.   molar mass of $SiO_2 = 60.09 \text{ g}$

$$5.91 \times 10^6 \text{ mol } SiO_2 \times \frac{60.09 \text{ g } SiO_2}{1 \text{ mol } SiO_2} = 3.55 \times 10^8 \text{ g } SiO_2$$

d.   molar mass of $CuCl_2$ = 134.45 g

$$0.000104 \text{ mol } CuCl_2 \times \frac{134.45 \text{ g } CuCl_2}{1 \text{ mol } CuCl_2} = 0.0140 \text{ g } CuCl_2$$

e.   molar mass of $CuCl$ = 99.00 g

$$0.000104 \text{ mol } CuCl \times \frac{99.00 \text{ g } CuCl}{1 \text{ mol } CuCl} = 0.0103 \text{ g } CuCl$$

24.   Before any calculations are done, the equations must be *balanced*.

a. $2Al(s) + 3Br_2(l) \rightarrow 2AlBr_3(s)$

molar mass Al = 26.98 g

$$0.557 \text{ g Al} \times \frac{1 \text{ mol Al}}{26.98 \text{ g Al}} \times \frac{3 \text{ mol } Br_2}{2 \text{ mol Al}} = 0.0310 \text{ mol } Br_2$$

b. $Hg(s) + 2HClO_4(aq) \rightarrow Hg(ClO_4)_2(aq) + H_2(g)$

molar mass Hg = 200.6 g

$$0.557 \text{ g Hg} \times \frac{1 \text{ mol Hg}}{200.6 \text{ g}} \times \frac{2 \text{ mol } HClO_4}{1 \text{ mol Hg}} = 0.00555 \text{ mol } HClO_4$$

c. $3K(s) + P(s) \rightarrow K_3P(s)$

molar mass K = 39.10 g

$$0.557 \text{ g K} \times \frac{1 \text{ mol K}}{39.10 \text{ g K}} \times \frac{1 \text{ mol P}}{3 \text{ mol K}} = 0.00475 \text{ mol P}$$

d. $CH_4(g) + 4Cl_2(g) \rightarrow CCl_4(l) + 4HCl(g)$

molar mass CH_4 = 16.04 g

$$0.557 \text{ g } CH_4 \times \frac{1 \text{ mol } CH_4}{16.04 \text{ g } CH_4} \times \frac{4 \text{ mol } Cl_2}{1 \text{ mol } CH_4} = 0.139 \text{ mol } Cl_2$$

26.   a. $2BCl_3(s) + 3H_2(g) \rightarrow 2B(s) + 6HCl(g)$

molar masses: BCl_3, 117.16 g; B, 10.81 g; HCl, 36.46 g

$$15.0 \text{ g } BCl_3 \times \frac{1 \text{ mol } BCl_3}{117.16 \text{ g } BCl_3} = 0.128 \text{ mol } BCl_3$$

$$0.128 \text{ mol } BCl_3 \times \frac{2 \text{ mol B}}{2 \text{ mol } BCl_3} \times \frac{10.81 \text{ g B}}{1 \text{ mol B}} = 1.38 \text{ g B}$$

$$0.128 \text{ mol } BCl_3 \times \frac{6 \text{ mol HCl}}{2 \text{ mol } BCl_3} \times \frac{36.46 \text{ g HCl}}{1 \text{ mol HCl}} = 14.0 \text{ g HCl}$$

b. $2Cu_2S(s) + 3O_2(g) \rightarrow 2Cu_2O(s) + 2SO_2(g)$

molar masses: Cu_2S, 159.17 g; Cu_2O, 143.1 g; SO_2, 64.07 g

$$15.0 \text{ g Cu}_2\text{S} \times \frac{1 \text{ mol Cu}_2\text{S}}{159.17 \text{ g Cu}_2\text{S}} = 0.09424 \text{ mol Cu}_2\text{S}$$

$$0.09424 \text{ mol Cu}_2\text{S} \times \frac{2 \text{ mol Cu}_2\text{O}}{2 \text{ mol Cu}_2\text{S}} \times \frac{143.1 \text{ g Cu}_2\text{O}}{1 \text{ mol Cu}_2\text{O}} = 13.5 \text{ g Cu}_2\text{O}$$

$$0.09424 \text{ mol Cu}_2\text{S} \times \frac{2 \text{ mol SO}_2}{2 \text{ mol Cu}_2\text{S}} \times \frac{64.07 \text{ g SO}_2}{1 \text{ mol SO}_2} = 6.04 \text{ g SO}_2$$

c. $2Cu_2O(s) + Cu_2S(s) \rightarrow 6Cu(s) + SO_2(g)$

molar masses: Cu_2S, 159.17 g; Cu, 63.55 g; SO_2, 64.07 g

$$15.0 \text{ g Cu}_2\text{S} \times \frac{1 \text{ mol Cu}_2\text{S}}{159.17 \text{ g Cu}_2\text{S}} = 0.09424 \text{ mol Cu}_2\text{S}$$

$$0.09424 \text{ mol Cu}_2\text{S} \times \frac{6 \text{ mol Cu}}{1 \text{ mol Cu}_2\text{S}} \times \frac{63.55 \text{ g Cu}}{1 \text{ mol Cu}} = 35.9 \text{ g Cu}$$

$$0.09424 \text{ mol Cu}_2\text{S} \times \frac{1 \text{ mol SO}_2}{1 \text{ mol Cu}_2\text{S}} \times \frac{64.07 \text{ g SO}_2}{1 \text{ mol SO}_2} = 6.04 \text{ g SO}_2$$

d. $CaCO_3(s) + SiO_2(s) \rightarrow CaSiO_3(s) + CO_2(g)$

molar masses: SiO_2, 60.09 g; $CaSiO_3$, 116.17 g; CO_2, 44.01 g

$$15.0 \text{ g SiO}_2 \times \frac{1 \text{ mol SiO}_2}{60.09 \text{ g SiO}_2} = 0.2496 \text{ mol SiO}_2$$

$$0.2496 \text{ mol SiO}_2 \times \frac{1 \text{ mol CaSiO}_3}{1 \text{ mol SiO}_2} \times \frac{116.17 \text{ g CaSiO}_3}{1 \text{ mol CaSiO}_3} = 29.0 \text{ g CaSiO}_3$$

$$0.2496 \text{ mol SiO}_2 \times \frac{1 \text{ mol CO}_2}{1 \text{ mol SiO}_2} \times \frac{44.01 \text{ g CO}_2}{1 \text{ mol CO}_2} = 11.0 \text{ g CO}_2$$

28.   The balanced equation for the reaction is:

$CaC_2(s) + 2H_2O(l) \rightarrow C_2H_2(g) + Ca(OH)_2(s)$

molar masses: CaC_2, 64.10 g; C_2H_2, 26.04 g

$$3.75 \text{ g CaC}_2 \times \frac{1 \text{ mol CaC}_2}{64.10 \text{ g CaC}_2} = 0.0585 \text{ mol CaC}_2$$

$$0.0585 \text{ mol CaC}_2 \times \frac{1 \text{ mol C}_2\text{H}_2}{1 \text{ mol CaC}_2} = 0.0585 \text{ mol C}_2\text{H}_2$$

$$0.0585 \text{ mol C}_2\text{H}_2 \times \frac{26.04 \text{ g C}_2\text{H}_2}{1 \text{ mol C}_2\text{H}_2} = 1.52 \text{ g C}_2\text{H}_2$$

30. $2NaHCO_3(s) \rightarrow Na_2CO_3(s) + H_2O(g) + CO_2(g)$

molar masses: $NaHCO_3$, 84.01 g; Na_2CO_3, 106.0 g

$$1.52 \text{ g NaHCO}_3 \times \frac{1 \text{ mol NaHCO}_3}{84.01 \text{ g NaHCO}_3} = 0.01809 \text{ mol NaHCO}_3$$

$$0.01809 \text{ mol NaHCO}_3 \times \frac{1 \text{ mol Na}_2\text{CO}_3}{2 \text{ mol NaHCO}_3} = 0.009047 \text{ mol Na}_2\text{CO}_3$$

$$0.009047 \text{ mol Na}_2\text{CO}_3 \times \frac{106.0 \text{ g Na}_2\text{CO}_3}{1 \text{ mol Na}_2\text{CO}_3} = 0.959 \text{ g Na}_2\text{CO}_3$$

32. $C_6H_{12}O_6(aq) \rightarrow 2C_2H_5OH(aq) + 2CO_2(g)$

molar masses: $C_6H_{12}O_6$, 180.2 g; C_2H_5OH, 46.07 g

$$5.25 \text{ g C}_6\text{H}_{12}\text{O}_6 \times \frac{1 \text{ mol C}_6\text{H}_{12}\text{O}_6}{180.2 \text{ g C}_6\text{H}_{12}\text{O}_6} = 0.02913 \text{ mol C}_6\text{H}_{12}\text{O}_6$$

$$0.02913 \text{ mol C}_6\text{H}_{12}\text{O}_6 \times \frac{2 \text{ mol C}_2\text{H}_5\text{OH}}{1 \text{ mol C}_6\text{H}_{12}\text{O}_6} = 0.5826 \text{ mol C}_2\text{H}_5\text{OH}$$

$$0.5286 \text{ mol C}_2\text{H}_5\text{OH} \times \frac{46.07 \text{ g C}_2\text{H}_5\text{OH}}{1 \text{ mol C}_2\text{H}_5\text{OH}} = 2.68 \text{ g ethyl alcohol}$$

34. $NH_4Cl(s) + NaOH(s) \rightarrow NH_3(g) + NaCl(s) + H_2O(g)$

molar masses: NH_4Cl, 53.49 g; NH_3, 17.03 g

$$1.39 \text{ g NH}_4\text{Cl} \times \frac{1 \text{ mol NH}_4\text{Cl}}{53.49 \text{ g NH}_4\text{Cl}} = 0.02599 \text{ mol NH}_4\text{Cl}$$

$$0.02599 \text{ mol NH}_4\text{Cl} \times \frac{1 \text{ mol NH}_3}{1 \text{ mol NH}_4\text{Cl}} = 0.02599 \text{ mol NH}_3$$

$$0.02599 \text{ mol NH}_3 \times \frac{17.03 \text{ g NH}_3}{1 \text{ mol NH}_3} = 0.443 \text{ g NH}_3$$

36. $4HgS(s) + 4CaO(s) \rightarrow 4Hg(l) + 3CaS(s) + CaSO_4(s)$

molar masses: HgS, 232.7 g Hg, 200.6 g; 10.0 kg = 1.00×10^4 g

$$1.00 \times 10^4 \text{ g HgS} \times \frac{1 \text{ mol HgS}}{232.7 \text{ g HgS}} = 42.97 \text{ mol HgS}$$

$$42.97 \text{ mol HgS} \times \frac{4 \text{ mol Hg}}{4 \text{ mol HgS}} = 42.97 \text{ mol Hg}$$

$$42.97 \text{ mol Hg} \times \frac{200.6 \text{ g Hg}}{1 \text{ mol Hg}} = 8.62 \times 10^3 \text{ g Hg} = 8.62 \text{ kg Hg}$$

38. $C_{12}H_{22}O_{11}(s) \rightarrow 12C(s) + 11H_2O(g)$

molar masses: $C_{12}H_{22}O_{11}$, 342.3 g; C, 12.01

$$1.19 \text{ g C}_{12}\text{H}_{22}\text{O}_{11} \times \frac{1 \text{ mol C}_{12}\text{H}_{22}\text{O}_{11}}{342.3 \text{ g C}_{12}\text{H}_{22}\text{O}_{11}} = 3.476 \times 10^{-3} \text{ mol C}_{12}\text{H}_{22}\text{O}_{11}$$

$$3.476 \times 10^{-3} \text{ mol C}_{12}\text{H}_{22}\text{O}_{11} \times \frac{12 \text{ mol C}}{1 \text{ mol C}_{12}\text{H}_{22}\text{O}_{11}} = 0.04172 \text{ mol C}$$

$$0.04172 \text{ mol C} \times \frac{12.01 \text{ g C}}{1 \text{ mol C}} = 0.501 \text{ g C}$$

40.   The balanced equation is:

$$2\text{C}_8\text{H}_{18} + 25\text{O}_2 \rightarrow 16\text{CO}_2 + 18\text{H}_2\text{O}$$

molar masses: C_8H_{18}, 114.22 g; CO_2, 44.01 g   1 lb of CO_2 = 453.59 g CO_2

$$453.59 \text{ g CO}_2 \times \frac{1 \text{ mol CO}_2}{44.01 \text{ g CO}_2} = 10.31 \text{ mol CO}_2$$

From the balanced chemical equation, we can calculate the number of moles and number of grams of pure octane that would be required to produce 10.31 mol CO_2.

$$10.31 \text{ mol CO}_2 \times \frac{2 \text{ mol C}_8\text{H}_{18}}{16 \text{ mol CO}_2} = 1.288 \text{ mol C}_8\text{H}_{18}$$

$$1.288 \text{ mol C}_8\text{H}_{18} \times \frac{114.22 \text{ g C}_8\text{H}_{18}}{1 \text{ mol C}_8\text{H}_{18}} = 147.2 \text{ g C}_8\text{H}_{18}$$

From the density of C_8H_{18} we can calculate the volume of 147.2 g C_8H_{18}.

$$147.2 \text{ g C}_8\text{H}_{18} \times \frac{1 \text{ mL C}_8\text{H}_{18}}{0.75 \text{ g C}_8\text{H}_{18}} = 196.3 \text{ mL C}_8\text{H}_{18} \ (2.0 \times 10^2 \text{ mL to two significant figures})$$

From the preceding, we know that to travel 1 mile, we need approximately 200 mL of octane

$$\frac{1 \text{ mi}}{196.3 \text{ mL}} \times \frac{1000 \text{ mL}}{1 \text{ L}} \times \frac{3.7854 \text{ L}}{1 \text{ gal}} = \text{approximately 19 mi/gal}$$

42.   To determine the limiting reactant, first calculate the number of moles of each reactant present. Then determine how these numbers of moles correspond to the stoichiometric ratio indicated by the balanced chemical equation for the reaction.

44.   A reactant is present *in excess* if there is more of that reactant present than is needed to combine with the limiting reactant for the process. By definition, the limiting reactant cannot be present in excess. An excess of any reactant does not affect the theoretical yield for a process: the theoretical yield is determined by the limiting reactant.

46.   a. $\text{S}(s) + 2\text{H}_2\text{SO}_4(aq) \rightarrow 3\text{SO}_2(g) + 2\text{H}_2\text{O}(l)$

Molar masses: S, 32.07 g; H_2SO_4, 98.09 g; SO_2, 64.07 g; H_2O, 18.02 g

$$5.00 \text{ g S} \times \frac{1 \text{ mol}}{32.07 \text{ g}} = 0.1559 \text{ mol S}$$

$$5.00 \text{ g H}_2\text{SO}_4 \times \frac{1 \text{ mol}}{98.09 \text{ g}} = 0.05097 \text{ mol H}_2\text{SO}_4$$

According to the balanced chemical equation, we would need twice as much sulfuric acid as sulfur for complete reaction of both reactants. We clearly have much less sulfuric acid present than sulfur: sulfuric acid is the limiting reactant. The calculation of the masses of products produced is based on the number of moles of the sulfuric acid.

$$0.05097 \text{ mol H}_2\text{SO}_4 \times \frac{3 \text{ mol SO}_2}{2 \text{ mol H}_2\text{SO}_4} \times \frac{64.07 \text{ g SO}_2}{1 \text{ mol SO}_2} = 4.90 \text{ g SO}_2$$

$$0.05097 \text{ mol H}_2\text{SO}_4 \times \frac{2 \text{ mol H}_2\text{O}}{2 \text{ mol H}_2\text{SO}_4} \times \frac{18.02 \text{ g H}_2\text{O}}{1 \text{ mol H}_2\text{O}} = 0.918 \text{ g H}_2\text{O}$$

b. $MnO_2(s) + 2H_2SO_4(aq) \rightarrow Mn(SO_4)_2 + 2H_2O(l)$

molar masses: MnO_2, 86.94 g; H_2SO_4 98.09 g; $Mn(SO_4)_2$, 247.1 g; H_2O, 18.02 g

$$5.00 \text{ g MnO}_2 \times \frac{1 \text{ mol}}{86.94 \text{ g}} = 0.05751 \text{ mol MnO}_2$$

$$5.00 \text{ g H}_2\text{SO}_4 \times \frac{1 \text{ mol}}{98.09 \text{ g}} = 0.05097 \text{ mol H}_2\text{SO}_4$$

According to the balanced chemical equation, we would need twice as much sulfuric acid as manganese(IV) oxide for complete reaction of both reactants. We do not have this much sulfuric acid, so sulfuric acid must be the limiting reactant. The amount of each product produced will be based on the sulfuric acid reacting completely.

$$0.05097 \text{ mol H}_2\text{SO}_4 \times \frac{1 \text{ mol Mn(SO}_4)_2}{2 \text{ mol H2SO4}} \times \frac{247.1 \text{ g Mn(SO}_4)_2}{1 \text{ mol Mn(SO}_4)_2} = 6.30 \text{ g Mn(SO}_4)_2$$

$$0.05097 \text{ mol H}_2\text{SO}_4 \times \frac{2 \text{ mol H}_2\text{O}}{2 \text{ mol H}_2\text{SO}_4} \times \frac{18.02 \text{ g H}_2\text{O}}{1 \text{ mol H}_2\text{O}} = 0.918 \text{ g H}_2\text{O}$$

c. $2H_2S(g) + 3O_2(g) \rightarrow 2SO_2(g) + 2H_2O(l)$

Molar masses: H_2S, 34.09 g; O_2, 32.00 g; SO_2, 64.07 g; H_2O, 18.02 g

$$5.00 \text{ g H}_2\text{S} \times \frac{1 \text{ mol}}{34.09 \text{ g}} = 0.1467 \text{ mol H}_2\text{S}$$

$$5.00 \text{ g O}_2 \times \frac{1 \text{ mol}}{32.00 \text{ g}} = 0.1563 \text{ mol O}_2$$

According to the balanced equation, we would need 1.5 times as much O_2 as H_2S for complete reaction of both reactants. We don't have that much O_2, so O_2 must be the limiting reactant that will control the masses of each product produced.

$$0.1563 \text{ mol O}_2 \times \frac{2 \text{ mol SO}_2}{3 \text{ mol O}_2} \times \frac{64.07 \text{ g SO}_2}{1 \text{ mol SO}_2} = 6.67 \text{ g SO}_2$$

$$0.1563 \text{ mol O}_2 \times \frac{2 \text{ mol H}_2\text{O}}{3 \text{ mol O}_2} \times \frac{18.02 \text{ g H}_2\text{O}}{1 \text{ mol H}_2\text{O}} = 1.88 \text{ g H}_2\text{O}$$

d. $3AgNO_3(aq) + Al(s) \rightarrow 3Ag(s) + Al(NO_3)_3(aq)$

Molar masses: $AgNO_3$, 169.9 g; Al, 26.98 g; Ag, 107.9 g; $Al(NO_3)_3$, 213.0 g

$$5.00 \text{ g } AgNO_3 \times \frac{1 \text{ mol}}{169.9 \text{ g}} = 0.02943 \text{ mol } AgNO_3$$

$$5.00 \text{ g Al} \times \frac{1 \text{ mol}}{26.98 \text{ g}} = 0.1853 \text{ mol Al}$$

According to the balanced chemical equation, we would need three moles of $AgNO_3$ for every mole of Al for complete reaction of both reactants. We in fact have fewer moles of $AgNO_3$ than aluminum, so $AgNO_3$ must be the limiting reactant. The amount of product produced is calculated from the number of moles of the limiting reactant present:

$$0.02943 \text{ mol } AgNO_3 \times \frac{3 \text{ mol Ag}}{3 \text{ mol } AgNO_3} \times \frac{107.9 \text{ g Ag}}{1 \text{ mol Ag}} = 3.18 \text{ g Ag}$$

$$0.02943 \text{ mol } AgNO_3 \times \frac{1 \text{ mol } Al(NO_3)_3}{3 \text{ mol } AgNO_3} \times \frac{213.0 \text{ g } Al(NO_3)_3}{1 \text{ mol } Al(NO_3)_3} = 2.09 \text{ g}$$

48.   a. $CS_2(l) + 3O_2(g) \rightarrow CO_2(g) + 2SO_2(g)$

Molar masses: CS_2, 76.15 g; O_2, 32.00 g; CO_2, 44.01 g

$$1.00 \text{ g } CS_2 \times \frac{1 \text{ mol}}{76.15 \text{ g}} = 0.01313 \text{ mol } CS_2$$

$$1.00 \text{ g } O_2 \times \frac{1 \text{ mol}}{32.00 \text{ g}} = 0.03125 \text{ mol } O_2$$

From the balanced chemical equation, we would need three times as much oxygen as carbon disulfide for complete reaction of both reactants. We do not have this much oxygen, and so oxygen must be the limiting reactant.

$$0.03125 \text{ mol } O_2 \times \frac{1 \text{ mol } CO_2}{3 \text{ mol } O_2} \times \frac{44.01 \text{ g } CO_2}{1 \text{ mol } CO_2} = 0.458 \text{ g } CO_2$$

b. $2NH_3(g) + CO_2(g) \rightarrow CN_2H_4O(s) + H_2O(l)$

Molar masses: NH_3, 17.03 g; CO_2, 44.01 g; H_2O, 18.02 g

$$1.00 \text{ g } NH_3 \times \frac{1 \text{ mol}}{17.03 \text{ g}} = 0.05872 \text{ mol } NH_3$$

$$1.00 \text{ g } CO_2 \times \frac{1 \text{ mol}}{44.01 \text{ g}} = 0.02272 \text{ mol } CO_2$$

The balanced chemical equation tells us that we would need twice as many moles of ammonia as carbon dioxide for complete reaction of both reactants. We have *more* than this amount of ammonia present, so the reaction will be limited by the amount of carbon dioxide present.

$$0.02272 \text{ mol CO}_2 \times \frac{1 \text{ mol H}_2\text{O}}{1 \text{ mol CO}_2} \times \frac{18.02 \text{ g H}_2\text{O}}{1 \text{ mol H}_2\text{O}} = 0.409 \text{ g H}_2\text{O}$$

c. $H_2(g) + MnO_2(s) \rightarrow MnO(s) + H_2O(l)$

Molar masses: H_2, 2.016 g; MnO_2, 86.94 g; H_2O, 18.02 g

$$1.00 \text{ g H}_2 \times \frac{1 \text{ mol}}{2.016 \text{ g}} = 0.496 \text{ mol H}_2$$

$$1.00 \text{ g MnO}_2 \times \frac{1 \text{ mol}}{86.94 \text{ g}} = 0.0115 \text{ mol MnO}_2$$

Because the coefficients of both reactants in the balanced chemical equation are the same, we would need equal amounts of both reactants for complete reaction. Therefore, manganese(IV) oxide must be the limiting reactant and controls the amount of product obtained.

$$0.0115 \text{ mol MnO}_2 \times \frac{1 \text{ mol H}_2\text{O}}{1 \text{ mol MnO}_2} \times \frac{18.02 \text{ g H}_2\text{O}}{1 \text{ mol H}_2\text{O}} = 0.207 \text{ g H}_2\text{O}$$

d. $I_2(s) + Cl_2(g) \rightarrow 2ICl(g)$

Molar masses: I_2, 253.8 g; Cl_2, 70.90 g; ICl, 162.35 g

$$1.00 \text{ g I}_2 \times \frac{1 \text{ mol}}{253.8 \text{ g}} = 0.00394 \text{ mol I}_2$$

$$1.00 \text{ g Cl}_2 \times \frac{1 \text{ mol}}{70.90 \text{ g}} = 0.0141 \text{ mol Cl}_2$$

From the balanced chemical equation, we would need equal amounts of I_2 and Cl_2 for complete reaction of both reactants. As we have much less iodine than chlorine, iodine must be the limiting reactant.

$$0.00394 \text{ mol I}_2 \times \frac{2 \text{ mol ICl}}{1 \text{ mol I}_2} \times \frac{162.35 \text{ g ICl}}{1 \text{ mol ICl}} = 1.28 \text{ g ICl}$$

50.   a. $CO(g) + 2H_2(g) \rightarrow CH_3OH(l)$

CO is the limiting reactant; 11.4 mg CH_3OH

b. $2Al(s) + 3I_2(s) \rightarrow 2AlI_3(s)$

I_2 is the limiting reactant; 10.7 mg AlI_3

c. $Ca(OH)_2(aq) + 2HBr(aq) \rightarrow CaBr_2(aq) + 2H_2O(l)$

HBr is the limiting reactant; 12.4 mg $CaBr_2$; 2.23 mg H_2O

d. $2Cr(s) + 2H_3PO_4(aq) \rightarrow 2CrPO_4(s) + 3H_2(g)$

H_3PO_4 is the limiting reactant; 15.0 mg $CrPO_4$; 0.309 mg H_2

52. $CuO(s) + H_2SO_4(aq) \rightarrow CuSO_4(aq) + H_2O(l)$

molar masses: CuO, 79.55 g; H_2SO_4, 98.09 g

$$2.49 \text{ g CuO} \times \frac{1 \text{ mol CuO}}{79.55 \text{ g CuO}} = 0.0313 \text{ mol CuO}$$

$$5.05 \text{ g H}_2\text{SO}_4 \times \frac{1 \text{ mol H}_2\text{SO}_4}{98.09 \text{ g H}_2\text{SO}_4} = 0.0515 \text{ mol H}_2\text{SO}_4$$

Since the reaction is of 1:1 stoichiometry, CuO must be the limiting reactant since it is present in the lesser amount on a molar basis.

54. $4\text{Fe}(s) + 3\text{O}_2(g) \rightarrow 2\text{Fe}_2\text{O}_3(s)$

Molar masses: Fe, 55.85 g; Fe_2O_3, 159.7 g

$$1.25 \text{ g Fe} \times \frac{1 \text{ mol}}{55.85 \text{ g}} = 0.0224 \text{ mol Fe present}$$

Calculate how many mol of O_2 are required to react with this amount of Fe

$$0.0224 \text{ mol Fe} \times \frac{3 \text{ mol O}_2}{4 \text{ mol Fe}} = 0.0168 \text{ mol O}_2$$

Because we have more O_2 than this, Fe must be the limiting reactant.

$$0.0224 \text{ mol Fe} \times \frac{2 \text{ mol Fe}_2\text{O}_3}{4 \text{ mol Fe}} \times \frac{159.7 \text{ g Fe}_2\text{O}_3}{1 \text{ mol Fe}_2\text{O}_3} = 1.79 \text{ g Fe}_2\text{O}_3$$

56. $\text{CaCl}_2(aq) + \text{Na}_2\text{SO}_4(aq) \rightarrow \text{CaSO}_4(s) + 2\text{NaCl}(aq)$

molar masses: CaCl_2, 110.98 g; Na_2SO_4, 142.05 g

$$5.21 \text{ g CaCl}_2 \times \frac{1 \text{ mol CaCl}_2}{110.98 \text{ g CaCl}_2} = 0.0469 \text{ mol CaCl}_2 = 0.0469 \text{ mol Ca}^{2+} \text{ ion}$$

$$4.95 \text{ g Na}_2\text{SO}_4 \times \frac{1 \text{ mol Na}_2\text{SO}_4}{142.05 \text{ g Na}_2\text{SO}_4} = 0.0348 \text{ mol Na}_2\text{SO}_4 = 0.0348 \text{ mol SO}_4^{2-} \text{ ion}$$

Because the balanced chemical equation indicates a 1:1 stoichiometry for the reaction, there is not nearly enough sulfate ion present (0.0348 mol) to precipitate the amount of calcium ion in the sample (0.0469 mol). Sodium sulfate (sulfate ion) is the limiting reactant. Calcium chloride (calcium ion) is present in excess.

58. $\text{SiO}_2(s) + 3\text{C}(s) \rightarrow 2\text{CO}(g) + \text{SiC}(s)$

molar masses: SiO_2, 60.09 g; SiC, 40.10 g; 1.0 kg $= 1.0 \times 10^3$ g

$$1.0 \times 10^3 \text{ g SiO}_2 \times \frac{1 \text{ mol}}{60.09 \text{ g}} = 16.64 \text{ mol SiO}_2$$

From the balanced chemical equation, if 16.64 mol of SiO_2 were to react completely (an excess of carbon is present), then 16.64 mol of SiC should be produced (the coefficients of SiO_2 and SiC are the same).

$$16.64 \text{ mol SiC} \times \frac{40.01 \text{ g}}{1 \text{ mol}} = 6.7 \times 10^2 \text{ g SiC} = 0.67 \text{ kg SiC}$$

60. If the reaction is performed in a solvent, the product may have a substantial solubility in the solvent; the reaction may come to equilibrium before the full yield of product is achieved (see Chapter 16); loss of product may occur through operator error.

62. $2KClO_3(s) \rightarrow 2KCl(s) + 3O_2(g)$

    molar mass: $KClO_3$, 122.55 g; O_2, 32.00 g

    $$4.74 \text{ g } KClO_3 \times \frac{1 \text{ mol } KClO_3}{122.55 \text{ g } KClO_3} = 0.0387 \text{ mol } KClO_3$$

    $$0.0387 \text{ mol } KClO_3 \times \frac{3 \text{ mol } O_2}{2 \text{ mol } KClO_3} = 0.0580 \text{ mol } O_2$$

    $$0.0580 \text{ mol } O_2 \times \frac{32.00 \text{ g } O_2}{1 \text{ mol } O_2} = 1.86 \text{ g } O_2 \text{ theoretical yield}$$

    $$\% \text{ yield} = \frac{1.51 \text{ g actual}}{1.86 \text{ g theoretical}} \times 100 = 81.3\% \text{ of theory}$$

64. $2LiOH(s) + CO_2(g) \rightarrow Li_2CO_3(s) + H_2O(g)$

    molar masses: LiOH, 23.95 g; CO_2, 44.01 g

    $$155 \text{ g LiOH} \times \frac{1 \text{ mol LiOH}}{23.95 \text{ g LiOH}} \times \frac{1 \text{ mol } CO_2}{2 \text{ mol LiOH}} \times \frac{44.01 \text{ g } CO_2}{1 \text{ mol } CO_2} = 142 \text{ g } CO_2$$

    As the cartridge has only absorbed 102 g CO_2 out of a total capacity of 142 g CO_2, the cartridge has absorbed

    $$\frac{102 \text{ g}}{142 \text{ g}} \times 100 = 71.8\% \text{ of its capacity.}$$

66. $Ba^{2+}(aq) + SO_4^{2-}(aq) \rightarrow BaSO_4(s)$

    molar masses: SO_4^{2-}, 96.07 g; $BaCl_2$, 208.2 g; $BaSO_4$, 233.4 g

    $$1.12 \text{ g } SO_4^{2-} \times \frac{1 \text{ mol}}{96.07 \text{ g}} = 0.01166 \text{ mol } SO_4^{2-}$$

    $$5.02 \text{ g } BaCl_2 \times \frac{1 \text{ mol}}{208.2 \text{ g}} = 0.02411 \text{ mol } BaCl_2 = 0.02411 \text{ mol } Ba^{2+}$$

    SO_4^{2-} is the limiting reactant.

    $$0.01166 \text{ mol } SO_4^{2-} \times \frac{1 \text{ mol } BaSO_4}{1 \text{ mol } SO_4^{2-}} \times \frac{233.4 \text{ g } BaSO_4}{1 \text{ mol } BaSO_4} = 2.72 \text{ g } BaSO_4$$

    $$\text{Percent yield} = \frac{\text{actual yield}}{\text{theoretical yield}} \times 100 = \frac{2.02 \text{ g}}{2.72 \text{ g}} \times 100 = 74.3\%$$

68. $NaCl(aq) + NH_3(aq) + H_2O(l) + CO_2(s) \rightarrow NH_4Cl(aq) + NaHCO_3(s)$

    molar masses: NH_3, 17.03 g; CO_2, 44.01 g; $NaHCO_3$, 84.01 g

$$10.0 \text{ g NH}_3 \times \frac{1 \text{ mol}}{17.03 \text{ g}} = 0.5872 \text{ mol NH}_3$$

$$15.0 \text{ g CO}_2 \times \frac{1 \text{ mol}}{44.01 \text{ g}} = 0.3408 \text{ mol CO}_2$$

CO_2 is the limiting reactant.

$$0.3408 \text{ mol CO}_2 \times \frac{1 \text{ mol NaHCO}_3}{1 \text{ mol CO}_2} = 0.3408 \text{ mol NaHCO}_3$$

$$0.3408 \text{ mol NaHCO}_3 \times \frac{84.01 \text{ g}}{1 \text{ mol}} = 28.6 \text{ g NaHCO}_3$$

70. $C_6H_{12}O_6(s) + 6O_2(g) \rightarrow 6CO_2(g) + 6H_2O(g)$

molar masses: glucose, 180.2 g; CO_2, 44.01 g

$$1.00 \text{ g glucose} \times = 5.549 \times 10^{-3} \text{ mol glucose}$$

$$5.549 \times 10^{-3} \text{ mol glucose} \times \frac{6 \text{ mol CO}_2}{1 \text{ mol glucose}} = 3.33 \times 10^{-2} \text{ mol CO}_2$$

$$3.33 \times 10^{-2} \text{ mol CO}_2 \times \frac{44.01 \text{ g}}{1 \text{ mol}} = 1.47 \text{ g CO}_2$$

72. $Ba^{2+}(aq) + SO_4{}^{2-}(aq) \rightarrow BaSO_4(s)$

millimolar ionic masses: Ba^{2+}, 137.3 mg; $SO_4{}^{2-}$, 96.07 mg; $BaCl_2$, 208.2 mg

$$150 \text{ mg SO}_4{}^{2-} \times \frac{1 \text{ mmol}}{96.07 \text{ mg}} = 1.56 \text{ millimol SO}_4{}^{2-}$$

As barium ion and sulfate ion react on a 1:1 stoichiometric basis, then 1.56 millimol of barium ion is needed, which corresponds to 1.56 millimol of $BaCl_2$

$$1.56 \text{ millimol BaCl}_2 \times \frac{208.2 \text{ mg}}{1 \text{ mmol}} = 325 \text{ milligrams BaCl}_2 \text{ needed}$$

74. a. $UO_2(s) + 4HF(aq) \rightarrow UF_4(aq) + 2H_2O(l)$

One molecule (formula unit) of uranium(IV) oxide will combine with four molecules of hydrofluoric acid, producing one uranium(IV) fluoride molecule and two water molecules. One mole of uranium(IV) oxide will combine with four moles of hydrofluoric acid to produce one mole of uranium(IV) fluoride and two moles of water.

b. $2NaC_2H_3O_2(aq) + H_2SO_4(aq) \rightarrow Na_2SO_4(aq) + 2HC_2H_3O_2(aq)$

Two molecules (formula units) of sodium acetate react exactly with one molecule of sulfuric acid, producing one molecule (formula unit) of sodium sulfate and two molecules of acetic acid. Two moles of sodium acetate will combine with one mole of sulfuric acid, producing one mole of sodium sulfate and two moles of acetic acid.

c. $Mg(s) + 2HCl(aq) \rightarrow MgCl_2(aq) + H_2(g)$

One magnesium atom will react with two hydrochloric acid molecules (formula units) to produce one molecule (formula unit) of magnesium chloride and one molecule of hydrogen gas. One mole of magnesium will combine with two moles of hydrochloric acid, producing one mole of magnesium chloride and one mole of gaseous hydrogen.

d. $B_2O_3(s) + 3H_2O(l) \rightarrow 2B(OH)_3(aq)$

One molecule of diboron trioxide will react exactly with three molecules of water, producing two molecules of boron trihydroxide (boric acid). One mole of diboron trioxide will combine with three moles of water to produce two moles of boron trihydroxide (boric acid).

76. For O_2: $\left(\dfrac{5 \text{ mol } O_2}{1 \text{ mol } C_3H_8} \right)$ For CO_2: $\left(\dfrac{3 \text{ mol } CO_2}{1 \text{ mol } C_3H_8} \right)$ For H_2O: $\left(\dfrac{4 \text{ mol } H_2O}{1 \text{ mol } C_3H_8} \right)$

78. a. $NH_3(g) + HCl(g) \rightarrow NH_4Cl(s)$

molar mass of $NH_3 = 17.01$ g

$$1.00 \text{ g } NH_3 \times \frac{1 \text{ mol}}{17.01 \text{ g}} = 0.0588 \text{ mol } NH_3$$

$$0.0588 \text{ mol } NH_3 \times \frac{1 \text{ mol } NH_4Cl}{1 \text{ mol } NH_3} = 0.0588 \text{ mol } NH_4Cl$$

b. $CaO(s) + CO_2(g) \rightarrow CaCO_3(s)$

molar mass $CaO = 56.08$ g

$$1.00 \text{ g } CaO \times \frac{1 \text{ mol}}{56.08 \text{ g}} = 0.0178 \text{ mol } CaO$$

$$0.0178 \text{ mol } CaO \times \frac{1 \text{ mol } CaCO_3}{1 \text{ mol } CaO} = 0.0178 \text{ mol } CaCO_3$$

c. $4Na(s) + O_2(g) \rightarrow 2Na_2O(s)$

molar mass $Na = 22.99$ g

$$1.00 \text{ g } Na \times \frac{1 \text{ mol}}{22.99 \text{ g}} = 0.0435 \text{ mol } Na$$

$$0.0435 \text{ mol } Na \times \frac{2 \text{ mol } Na_2O}{4 \text{ mol } Na} = 0.0217 \text{ mol } Na_2O$$

d. $2P(s) + 3Cl_2(g) \rightarrow 2PCl_3(l)$

molar mass $P = 30.97$ g

$$1.00 \text{ g } P \times \frac{1 \text{ mol}}{30.97 \text{ g}} = 0.0323 \text{ mol } P$$

$$0.0323 \text{ mol } P \times \frac{2 \text{ mol } PCl_3}{2 \text{ mol } P} = 0.0323 \text{ mol } PCl_3$$

80. a. molar mass HNO_3 = 63.0 g

$$5.0 \text{ mol } HNO_3 \times \frac{63.0 \text{ g}}{1 \text{ mol}} = 3.2 \times 10^2 \text{ g } HNO_3$$

b. molar mass Hg = 200.6 g

$$0.000305 \text{ mol } Hg \times \frac{200.6 \text{ g}}{1 \text{ mol}} = 0.0612 \text{ g } Hg$$

c. molar mass K_2CrO_4 = 194.2 g

$$2.31 \times 10^{-5} \text{ mol } K_2CrO_4 \times \frac{194.2 \text{ g}}{1 \text{ mol}} = 4.49 \times 10^{-3} \text{ g } K_2CrO_4$$

d. molar mass $AlCl_3$ = 133.3 g

$$10.5 \text{ mol } AlCl_3 \times \frac{133.3 \text{ g}}{1 \text{ mol}} = 1.40 \times 10^3 \text{ g } AlCl_3$$

e. molar mass SF_6 = 146.1 g

$$4.9 \times 10^4 \text{ mol } SF_6 \times \frac{146.1 \text{ g}}{1 \text{ mol}} = 7.2 \times 10^6 \text{ g } SF_6$$

f. molar mass NH_3 = 17.01 g

$$125 \text{ mol } NH_3 \times \frac{17.01 \text{ g}}{1 \text{ mol}} = 2.13 \times 10^3 \text{ g } NH_3$$

g. molar mass Na_2O_2 = 77.98 g

$$0.01205 \text{ mol } Na_2O_2 \times \frac{77.98 \text{ g}}{1 \text{ mol}} = 0.9397 \text{ g } Na_2O_2$$

82. $2SO_2(g) + O_2(g) \rightarrow 2SO_3(g)$

molar masses: SO_2, 64.07 g; SO_3, 80.07 g; 150 kg = 1.5×10^5 g

$$1.5 \times 10^5 \text{ g } SO_2 \times \frac{1 \text{ mol}}{64.07 \text{ g}} = 2.34 \times 10^3 \text{ mol } SO_2$$

$$2.34 \times 10^3 \text{ mol } SO_2 \times \frac{2 \text{ mol } SO_3}{2 \text{ mol } SO_2} = 2.34 \times 10^3 \text{ mol } SO_3$$

$$2.34 \times 10^3 \text{ mol } SO_3 \times \frac{80.07 \text{ g}}{1 \text{ mol}} = 1.9 \times 10^5 \text{ g } SO_3 = 1.9 \times 10^2 \text{ kg } SO_3$$

84. $2Na_2O_2(s) + 2H_2O(l) \rightarrow 4NaOH(aq) + O_2(g)$

molar masses: Na_2O_2, 77.98 g; O_2, 32.00 g

$$3.25 \text{ g } Na_2O_2 \times \frac{1 \text{ mol}}{77.98 \text{ g}} = 0.0417 \text{ mol } Na_2O_2$$

$$0.0417 \text{ mol } Na_2O_2 \times \frac{1 \text{ mol } O_2}{2 \text{ mol } Na_2O_2} = 0.0209 \text{ mol } O_2$$

$$0.0209 \text{ mol O}_2 \times \frac{32.00 \text{ g}}{1 \text{ mol}} = 0.667 \text{ g O}_2$$

86. $Zn(s) + 2HCl(aq) \rightarrow ZnCl_2(aq) + H_2(g)$

molar masses: Zn, 65.38 g; H_2, 2.016 g

$$2.50 \text{ g Zn} \times \frac{1 \text{ mol}}{65.38 \text{ g}} = 0.03824 \text{ mol Zn}$$

$$0.03824 \text{ mol Zn} \times \frac{1 \text{ mol H}_2}{1 \text{ mol Zn}} = 0.03824 \text{ mol H}_2$$

$$0.03824 \text{ mol H}_2 \times \frac{2.016 \text{ g}}{1 \text{ mol}} = 0.0771 \text{ g H}_2$$

88.   a. $2Na(s) + Br_2(l) \rightarrow 2NaBr(s)$

molar masses: Na, 22.99 g; Br_2, 159.8 g; NaBr, 102.9 g

$$5.0 \text{ g Na} \times \frac{1 \text{ mol}}{22.99 \text{ g}} = 0.2175 \text{ mol Na}$$

$$5.0 \text{ g Br}_2 \times \frac{1 \text{ mol}}{159.8 \text{ g}} = 0.03129 \text{ mol Br}_2$$

Intuitively, we would suspect that Br_2 is the limiting reactant, because there is much less Br_2 than Na on a mole basis. To *prove* that Br_2 is the limiting reactant, the following calculation is needed:

$$0.03129 \text{ mol Br}_2 \times \frac{2 \text{ mol Na}}{1 \text{ mol Br}_2} = 0.06258 \text{ mol Na.}$$

Clearly, there is more Na than this present, so Br_2 limits the reaction extent and the amount of NaBr formed.

$$0.03129 \text{ mol Br}_2 \times \frac{2 \text{ mol NaBr}}{1 \text{ mol Br}_2} = 0.06258 \text{ mol NaBr}$$

$$0.06258 \text{ mol NaBr} \times \frac{102.9 \text{ g}}{1 \text{ mol}} = 6.4 \text{ g NaBr}$$

        b. $Zn(s) + CuSO_4(aq) \rightarrow ZnSO_4(aq) + Cu(s)$

molar masses: Zn, 65.38 g; Cu, 63.55 g; $ZnSO_4$, 161.5 g; $CuSO_4$, 159.6 g

$$5.0 \text{ g Zn} \times \frac{1 \text{ mol}}{65.38 \text{ g}} = 0.07648 \text{ mol Zn}$$

$$5.0 \text{ g CuSO}_4 \times \frac{1 \text{ mol}}{159.6 \text{ g}} = 0.03132 \text{ mol CuSO}_4$$

As the coefficients of Zn and $CuSO_4$ are the *same* in the balanced chemical equation, an equal number of moles of Zn and $CuSO_4$ would be needed for complete reaction. There is less $CuSO_4$ present, so $CuSO_4$ must be the limiting reactant.

$$0.03132 \text{ mol CuSO}_4 \times \frac{1 \text{ mol ZnSO}_4}{1 \text{ mol CuSO}_4} = 0.03132 \text{ mol ZnSO}_4$$

$$0.03132 \text{ mol ZnSO}_4 \times \frac{161.5 \text{ g}}{1 \text{ mol}} = 5.1 \text{ g ZnSO}_4$$

$$0.03132 \text{ mol CuSO}_4 \times \frac{1 \text{ mol Cu}}{1 \text{ mol CuSO}_4} = 0.03132 \text{ mol Cu}$$

$$0.03132 \text{ mol Cu} \times \frac{63.55 \text{ g}}{1 \text{ mol}} = 2.0 \text{ g Cu}$$

c. $NH_4Cl(aq) + NaOH(aq) \rightarrow NH_3(g) + H_2O(l) + NaCl(aq)$

molar masses: NH_4Cl, 53.49 g; NaOH, 40.00 g; NH_3, 17.03 g; H_2O, 18.02 g; NaCl, 58.44 g

$$5.0 \text{ g NH}_4\text{Cl} \times \frac{1 \text{ mol}}{53.49 \text{ g}} = 0.09348 \text{ mol NH}_4\text{Cl}$$

$$5.0 \text{ g NaOH} \times \frac{1 \text{ mol}}{40.00 \text{ g}} = 0.1250 \text{ mol NaOH}$$

As the coefficients of NH_4Cl and NaOH are both *one* in the balanced chemical equation for the reaction, an equal number of moles of NH_4Cl and NaOH would be needed for complete reaction. There is less NH_4Cl present, so NH_4Cl must be the limiting reactant.

As the coefficients of the products in the balanced chemical equation are also all *one*, if 0.09348 mol of NH_4Cl (the limiting reactant) reacts completely, then 0.09348 mol of each product will be formed.

$$0.09348 \text{ mol NH}_3 \times \frac{17.03 \text{ g}}{1 \text{ mol}} = 1.6 \text{ g NH}_3$$

$$0.09348 \text{ mol H}_2\text{O} \times \frac{18.02 \text{ g}}{1 \text{ mol}} = 1.7 \text{ g H}_2\text{O}$$

$$0.09348 \text{ mol NaCl} \times \frac{58.44 \text{ g}}{1 \text{ mol}} = 5.5 \text{ g NaCl}$$

d. $Fe_2O_3(s) + 3CO(g) \rightarrow 2Fe(s) + 3CO_2(g)$

molar masses: Fe_2O_3, 159.7 g; CO, 28.01 g; Fe, 55.85 g; CO_2, 44.01 g

$$5.0 \text{ g Fe}_2\text{O}_3 \times \frac{1 \text{ mol}}{159.7 \text{ g}} = 0.03131 \text{ mol Fe}_2\text{O}_3$$

$$5.0 \text{ g CO} \times \frac{1 \text{ mol}}{28.01 \text{ g}} = 0.1785 \text{ mol CO}$$

Because there is considerably less Fe_2O_3 than CO on a mole basis, let's see if Fe_2O_3 is the limiting reactant.

$$0.03131 \text{ mol Fe}_2\text{O}_3 \times \frac{3 \text{ mol CO}}{1 \text{ mol Fe}_2\text{O}_3} = 0.09393 \text{ mol CO}$$

As there is 0.1785 mol of CO present, but we have determined that only 0.09393 mol CO would be needed to react with all the Fe_2O_3 present, then Fe_2O_3 must be the limiting reactant. CO is present in excess.

$$0.03131 \text{ mol Fe}_2O_3 \times \frac{2 \text{ mol Fe}}{1 \text{ mol Fe}_2O_3} \times \frac{55.85 \text{ g Fe}}{1 \text{ mol Fe}} = 3.5 \text{ g Fe}$$

$$0.03131 \text{ mol Fe}_2O_3 \times \frac{3 \text{ mol CO}_2}{1 \text{ mol Fe}_2O_3} \times \frac{44.01 \text{ g CO}_2}{1 \text{ mol CO}_2} = 4.1 \text{ g CO}_2$$

90. $N_2H_4(l) + O_2(g) \rightarrow N_2(g) + 2H_2O(g)$

molar masses: N_2H_4, 32.05 g; O_2, 32.00 g; N_2, 28.02 g; H_2O, 18.02 g

$$20.0 \text{ g N}_2H_4 \times \frac{1 \text{ mol}}{32.05 \text{ g}} = 0.624 \text{ mol N}_2H_4$$

$$20.0 \text{ g O}_2 \times \frac{1 \text{ mol}}{32.00 \text{ g}} = 0.625 \text{ mol O}_2$$

The two reactants are present in nearly the required ratio for complete reaction (due to the 1:1 stoichiometry of the reaction and the very similar molar masses of the substances). We will consider N_2H_4 as the limiting reactant in the following calculations.

$$0.624 \text{ mol N}_2H_4 \times \frac{1 \text{ mol N}_2}{1 \text{ mol N}_2H_4} \times \frac{28.02 \text{ g N}_2}{1 \text{ mol N}_2} = 17.5 \text{ g N}_2$$

$$0.624 \text{ mol N}_2H_4 \times \frac{2 \text{ mol H}_2O}{1 \text{ mol N}_2H_4} \times \frac{18.02 \text{ g H}_2O}{1 \text{ mol H}_2O} = 22.5 \text{ g H}_2O$$

92. $12.5 \text{ g theory} \times \dfrac{40 \text{ g actual}}{100 \text{ g theory}} = 5.0 \text{ g}$

Chapters 8 and 9

2.   On a microscopic basis, one mole of a substance represents Avogadro's number (6.022×10^{23}) of individual units (atoms or molecules) of the substance. On a macroscopic, more practical basis, one mole of a substance represents the amount of substance present when the molar mass of the substance in grams is taken (for example 12.01 g of carbon will be one mole of carbon). Chemists have chosen these definitions so that there will be a simple relationship between measurable amounts of substances (grams) and the actual number of atoms or molecules present, and so that the number of particles present in samples of *different* substances can easily be compared. For example, it is known that carbon and oxygen react by the reaction

$$C(s) + O_2(g) \rightarrow CO_2(g).$$

Chemists understand this equation to mean that one carbon atom reacts with one oxygen molecule to produce one molecule of carbon dioxide, and also that one mole (12.01 g) of carbon will react with one mole (32.00 g) of oxygen to produce one mole (44.01 g) of carbon dioxide.

4.   The molar mass of a compound is the mass in grams of one mole of the compound (6.022×10^{23} molecules of the compound), and is calculated by summing the average atomic masses of all the atoms present in a molecule of the compound. For example, a molecule of the compound H_3PO_4 contains three hydrogen atoms, one phosphorus atom, and four oxygen atoms: the molar mass is obtained by adding up the average atomic masses of these atoms: molar mass H_3PO_4 = 3(1.008 g) + 1(30.97 g) + 4(16.00 g) = 97.99 g

6.   The empirical formula of a compound represents the lowest ratio of the relative number of atoms of each type present in a molecule of the compound, whereas the molecular formula represents the actual number of atoms of each type present in a real molecule of the compound. For example, both acetylene (molecular formula C_2H_2) and benzene (molecular formula C_6H_6) have the same relative number of carbon and hydrogen atoms (one hydrogen for each carbon atom), and so have the same empirical formula (CH). Once the empirical formula of a compound has been determined, it is also necessary to determine the molar mass of the compound before the actual molecular formula can be calculated. As real molecules cannot contain fractional parts of atoms, the molecular formula is always a whole number multiple of the empirical formula. For the examples above, the molecular formula of acetylene is twice the empirical formula, and the molecular formula of benzene is six times the empirical formula (both factors are integers).

8.   In question 7, suppose we chose to calculate the percentage composition of phosphoric acid, H_3PO_4: 3.086% H, 31.60% P, and 65.31% O. We could convert this percentage composition data into "experimental" data by first choosing a mass of sample to be "analyzed", and then calculating what mass of each element is present in this size sample using the percentage of each element. For example, suppose we choose our sample to have a mass of 2.417 g. Then the masses of H, P, and O present in this sample would be given by the following:

$$\text{g H} = (2.417 \text{ g sample}) \times \frac{3.086 \text{ g H}}{100.0 \text{ g sample}} = 0.07459 \text{ g H}$$

$$g\ P\ = (2.417\ g\ sample) \times \frac{31.60\ g\ P}{100.0\ g\ sample} = 0.7638\ g\ P$$

$$g\ O\ = (2.417\ g\ sample) \times \frac{65.31\ g\ O}{100.0\ g\ sample} = 1.579\ g\ O$$

Note that $(0.07459\ g + 0.7638\ g + 1.579\ g) = 2.41739 = 2.417\ g$.

So our new problem could be worded as follows: "A 2.417 g sample of a compound has been analyzed and was found to contain 0.07459 g H, 0.7638 g of P, and 1.579 g of oxygen. Calculate the empirical formula of the compound".

$$mol\ H = (0.07459\ g\ H) \times \frac{1\ mol\ H}{1.008\ g\ H} = 0.07400\ mol\ H$$

$$mol\ P = (0.7638\ g\ P) \times \frac{1\ mol\ P}{30.97\ g\ P} = 0.02466\ mol\ P$$

$$mol\ O = (1.579\ g\ O) \times \frac{1\ mol\ O}{16.00\ g\ O} = 0.09869\ mol\ O$$

Dividing each of these numbers of moles by the smallest number of moles (0.02466 mol P) gives the following:

$$\frac{0.07400\ mol\ H}{0.02466} = 3.001\ mol\ H$$

$$\frac{0.02466\ mol\ P}{0.02466} = 1.000\ mol\ P$$

$$\frac{0.09869\ mol\ O}{0.02466} = 4.002\ mol\ O$$

The empirical formula is (not surprisingly) just H_3PO_4!

10.   The mole ratios for a reaction are based on the *coefficients* of the balanced chemical equation for the reaction: these coefficients show in what proportions molecules (or moles of molecules) combine. For a given amount of propane, the following mole ratios could be constructed, which would enable you to calculate the number of moles of each product, or of the second reactant, that would be involved.

$$C_3H_8(g) + 5O_2(g) \rightarrow 3CO_2(g) + 4H_2O(g)$$

for O_2: $\dfrac{5\ mol\ O_2}{1\ mol\ C_3H_8}$; $0.55\ mol\ C_3H_8 \times \dfrac{5\ mol\ O_2}{1\ mol\ C_3H_8} = 2.8\ (2.75)\ mol\ O_2$

for CO_2: $\dfrac{3\ mol\ CO_2}{1\ mol\ C_3H_8}$; $0.55\ mol\ C_3H_8 \times \dfrac{3\ mol\ CO_2}{1\ mol\ C_3H_8} = 1.7\ (1.65)\ mol\ CO_2$

for H_2O: $\dfrac{4\ mol\ H_2O}{1\ mol\ C_3H_8}$; $0.55\ mol\ C_3H_8 \times \dfrac{4\ mol\ H_2O}{1\ mol\ C_3H_8} = 2.2\ mol\ H_2O$

12.   Although we can calculate specifically the exact amounts of each reactant needed for a chemical reaction, oftentimes reaction mixtures are prepared using more or less arbitrary amounts of the

reagents. However, regardless of how much of each reagent may be used for a reaction, the substances still react stoichiometrically, according to the mole ratios derived from the balanced chemical equation for the reaction. When arbitrary amounts of reactants are used, there will be one reactant which, stoichiometrically, is present in the least amount. This substance is called the *limiting reactant* for the experiment. It is the limiting reactant that controls how much product is formed, regardless of how much of the other reactants are present. The limiting reactant limits the amount of product that can form in the experiment, because once the limiting reactant has reacted completely, the reaction must stop. We say that the other reactants in the experiment are present in excess, which means that a portion of these reactants will still be present unchanged after the reaction has ended and the limiting reactant has been used up completely.

14.   The *theoretical yield* for an experiment is the mass of product calculated based on the limiting reactant for the experiment being completely consumed. The *actual yield* for an experiment is the mass of product actually collected by the experimenter. Obviously, any experiment is restricted by the skills of the experimenter and by the inherent limitations of the experimental method being used. For these reasons, the actual yield is often *less* than the theoretical yield (most scientific writers report the actual or percentage yield for their experiments as an indication of the usefulness of their experiments). Although one would expect that the actual yield should never be more than the theoretical yield, in real experiments, sometimes this happens: however, an actual yield greater than a theoretical yield is usually taken to mean that something is *wrong* in either the experiment (for example, impurities may be present, or the reaction may not occur as envisioned) or in the calculations.

16.   % element X = $\dfrac{\text{mass of element X in compound}}{\text{molar mass of compound}} \times 100$

    a.   92.26% C   b.   32.37% Na

    c.   15.77% C   d.   20.24% Al

    e.   88.82% Cu   f.   79.89% Cu

    g.   71.06% Co   h.   40.00% C

18.   a.   molar masses: SiC, 40.10 g; $SiCl_4$, 169.9 g

$$12.5 \text{ g SiC} \times \frac{1 \text{ mol}}{40.10 \text{ g}} = 0.3117 \text{ mol SiC}$$

for $SiCl_4$: $0.3117 \text{ mol SiC} \times \dfrac{1 \text{ mol SiCl}_4}{1 \text{ mol SiC}} \times \dfrac{169.9 \text{ g SiCl}_4}{1 \text{ mol SiCl}_4} = 53.0 \text{ g SiCl}_4$

for C: $0.3117 \text{ mol SiC} \times \dfrac{1 \text{ mol C}}{1 \text{ mol SiC}} \times \dfrac{12.01 \text{ g C}}{1 \text{ mol C}} = 3.75 \text{ g C}$

    b.   molar masses: Li_2O, 29.88 g; LiOH, 23.95 g

$$12.5 \text{ g Li}_2\text{O} \times \frac{1 \text{ mol}}{29.88 \text{ g}} = 0.4183 \text{ mol Li}_2\text{O}$$

$$0.4183 \text{ mol Li}_2\text{O} \times \frac{2 \text{ mol LiOH}}{1 \text{ mol Li}_2\text{O}} \times \frac{23.95 \text{ g LiOH}}{1 \text{ mol LiOH}} = 20.0 \text{ g LiOH}$$

c.   molar masses: Na_2O_2, 77.98 g; NaOH, 40.00 g; O_2, 32.00 g

$$12.5 \text{ g} \times \frac{1 \text{ mol}}{77.98 \text{ g}} = 0.1603 \text{ mol } Na_2O_2$$

for NaOH: $0.1603 \text{ mol } Na_2O_2 \times \dfrac{4 \text{ mol NaOH}}{2 \text{ mol } Na_2O_2} \times \dfrac{40.00 \text{ g NaOH}}{1 \text{ mol NaOH}} = 12.8 \text{ g NaOH}$

for O_2: $0.1603 \text{ mol } Na_2O_2 \times \dfrac{1 \text{ mol } O_2}{2 \text{ mol } Na_2O_2} \times \dfrac{32.00 \text{ g } O_2}{1 \text{ mol } O_2} = 2.56 \text{ g } O_2$

d.   molar masses: SnO_2, 150.7 g; Sn, 118.7 g; H_2O, 18.02 g

$$12.5 \text{ g } SnO_2 \times \frac{1 \text{ mol}}{150.7 \text{ g}} = 0.08295 \text{ mol } SnO_2$$

for Sn: $0.08295 \text{ mol } SnO_2 \times \dfrac{1 \text{ mol Sn}}{1 \text{ mol } SnO_2} \times \dfrac{118.7 \text{ g Sn}}{1 \text{ mol Sn}} = 9.84 \text{ g Sn}$

for H_2O: $0.08295 \text{ mol } SnO_2 \times \dfrac{2 \text{ mol } H_2O}{1 \text{ mol } SnO_2} \times \dfrac{18.02 \text{ g } H_2O}{1 \text{ mol } H_2O} = 2.99 \text{ g } H_2O$

20.   molar masses: C, 12.01 g; CO, 28.01 g; CO_2, 44.01 g

$$5.00 \text{ g C} \times \frac{1 \text{ mol C}}{12.01 \text{ g C}} = 0.416 \text{ mol C}$$

for CO: $0.416 \text{ mol C} \times \dfrac{2 \text{ mol CO}}{2 \text{ mol C}} \times \dfrac{28.01 \text{ g CO}}{1 \text{ mol CO}} = 11.7 \text{ g CO}$

for CO_2: $0.416 \text{ mol C} \times \dfrac{1 \text{ mol } CO_2}{1 \text{ mol C}} \times \dfrac{44.01 \text{ g } CO_2}{1 \text{ mol } CO_2} = 18.3 \text{ g } CO_2$

CHAPTER 10

Energy

2. Potential energy is energy due to position or composition. A stone at the top of a hill possesses potential energy since the stone may eventually roll down the hill. A gallon of gasoline possesses potential energy since heat will be released when the gasoline is burned.

4. The total energy of the universe is constant. Energy cannot be created or destroyed, but can only be converted from one form to another.

6. Ball A initially possesses potential energy by virtue of its position at the top of the hill. As Ball A rolls down the hill, its potential energy is converted to kinetic energy and frictional (heat) energy. When Ball A reaches the bottom of the hill and hits Ball B, it transfers its kinetic energy to Ball B. Ball A then has only the potential energy corresponding to its new position.

8. The hot tea is at a higher temperature, which means the particles in the hot tea have higher average kinetic energies. When the tea spills on the skin, energy flows from the hot tea to the skin, until the tea and skin are at the same temperature. This sudden inflow of energy causes the burn.

10. Temperature is the concept by which we express the thermal energy contained in a sample. We cannot measure the motions of the particles/kinetic energy in a sample of matter directly. We know, however, that if two objects are at different temperatures, the one with the higher temperature has molecules that have higher average kinetic energies than the object at the lower temperature.

12. When the chemical system evolves energy, the energy evolved from the reacting chemicals is transferred to the surroundings.

14. exactly equal to

16. internal

18. losing

20. gaining

22. a. $\dfrac{1 \text{ J}}{4.184 \text{ cal}}$

    b. $\dfrac{4.184 \text{ cal}}{1 \text{ J}}$

c. $\dfrac{1\ \text{kcal}}{1000\ \text{cal}}$

d. $\dfrac{1000\ \text{J}}{1\ \text{kJ}}$

24.   6540 J = 6.54 kJ for 10 times more water

26.   a. $8254\ \text{cal} \times \dfrac{1\ \text{kcal}}{1000\ \text{cal}} = 8.254\ \text{kcal}$

b. $41.5\ \text{cal} \times \dfrac{1\ \text{kcal}}{1000\ \text{cal}} = 0.0415\ \text{kcal}$

c. $8.231 \times 10^3 \times \dfrac{1\ \text{kcal}}{1000\ \text{cal}} = 8.231\ \text{kcal}$

d. $752{,}900\ \text{cal} \times \dfrac{1\ \text{kcal}}{1000\ \text{cal}} = 752.9\ \text{kcal}$

28.   a. $243{,}000\ \text{J} \times \dfrac{1\ \text{kJ}}{1000\ \text{J}} = 243\ \text{kJ}$ to 3 significant figures

b. $4.184\ \text{J} \times \dfrac{1\ \text{kJ}}{1000\ \text{J}} = 0.004184\ \text{kJ}$

c. $0.251\ \text{J} \times \dfrac{1\ \text{kJ}}{1000\ \text{J}} = 0.000251\ \text{kJ}$

d. $450.3\ \text{J} \times \dfrac{1\ \text{kJ}}{1000\ \text{J}} = 0.4503\ \text{kJ}$

30.   a. $91.74\ \text{kcal} \times \dfrac{1000\ \text{cal}}{1\ \text{kcal}} = 9.174 \times 10^4\ \text{cal}$

b. $1.781\ \text{kJ} \times \dfrac{1\ \text{kcal}}{4.184\ \text{kJ}} \times \dfrac{1000\ \text{cal}}{1\ \text{kcal}} = 425.7\ \text{cal}$

c. $4.318 \times 10^3\ \text{J} \times \dfrac{1\ \text{cal}}{4.184\ \text{J}} \times \dfrac{1\ \text{kcal}}{1000\ \text{cal}} = 1.032\ \text{kcal}$

d. $9.173 \times 10^4\ \text{cal} \times \dfrac{4.184\ \text{J}}{1\ \text{cal}} \times \dfrac{1\ \text{kJ}}{1000\ \text{J}} = 383.8\ \text{kJ}$

32. $Q = s \times m \times \Delta T$

Specific heat capacity of aluminum is 0.89 J/g°C from Table 10.1.

$Q = (0.89\ \text{J/g°C}) \times (42.7\ \text{g}) \times (15.2°\text{C}) = 5.8 \times 10^2\ \text{J}$ (only two significant figures are justified).

34. $Q = s \times m \times \Delta T$

    Specific heat capacity of mercury is 0.14 J/g°C

    100. J $=$ (0.14 J/g°C) $\times$ 25 g $\times \Delta T$

    $\Delta T = 28.6°C = 29°C$

36. The reaction is exothermic: the chemical reaction liberates heat energy and warms up the beverage.

38. $Q = s \times m \times \Delta T$

    specific heat capacity of water $= 4.184$ J/g°C

    $Q = 4.184$ J/g°C $\times$ 100.0 g $\times$ 35°C $= 1.46 \times 10^4$ J ($\sim$15 kJ to two significant figures)

40. A calorimeter is an insulated device in which reactions are performed and temperature changes measured, enabling the calculation of heat flows. See Figure 10.6

42. a. molar mass of S $= 32.07$ g

    $$1.00 \text{ g S} \times \frac{1 \text{ mol S}}{32.07 \text{ g S}} = 0.0312 \text{ mol S}$$

    From the balanced chemical equation, combustion of 0.0312 mol S would produce 0.0312 mol SO_2

    $$0.0312 \text{ mol} \times \frac{-296 \text{ kJ}}{\text{mol}} = -9.23 \text{ kJ}$$

    b. From the balanced chemical equation, combustion of 0.0312 mol S would produce 0.0312 mol SO_2

    $$0.501 \text{ mol} \times \frac{-296 \text{ kJ}}{\text{mol}} = -148 \text{ kJ}$$

    c. The enthalpy change would be the same in magnitude, but opposite in sign $= +296$ kJ/mol

44. a. molar mass of ethanol $= 46.07$ g; we will assume that 1360 has only 3 significant figures.

    $$-\frac{1360 \text{ kJ}}{1 \text{ mol}} \times \frac{1 \text{ mol}}{46.07 \text{ g}} = -29.5 \text{ kJ/g}$$

    b. Since energy is released by the combustion, ΔH is negative: $\Delta H = -1360$ kJ

    c. In the reaction as written, three moles of water vapor are produced when one mole of ethanol reacts.

    $$\frac{1360 \text{ kJ}}{1 \text{ mol C}_2\text{H}_5\text{OH}} \times \frac{1 \text{ mol C}_2\text{H}_5\text{OH}}{3 \text{ mol H}_2\text{O}} = 453 \text{ kJ/mol H}_2\text{O}$$

46.   The desired equation $2C(s) + O_2(g) \rightarrow 2CO(g)$ can be generated by taking twice the first equation and adding it to the reverse of the second equation:

$$2 \times [C(s) + O_2(g) \rightarrow CO_2(g)] \qquad \Delta H = 2 \times -393 \text{ kJ} = -786 \text{ kJ (equation doubled)}$$

$$2CO_2(g) \rightarrow 2CO(g) + O_2(g) \qquad \Delta H = -(-566 \text{ kJ}) = +566 \text{ kJ (equation reversed)}$$

$$2C(s) + O_2(g) \rightarrow 2CO(g) \qquad \Delta H = (-786) + (+566) = -220 \text{ kJ}$$

48.   The desired equation can be generated as follows:

$$NO(g) + O_3(g) \rightarrow NO_2(g) + O_2(g) \qquad \Delta H = -199 \text{ kJ}$$

$$\tfrac{1}{2} \times [3O_2(g) \rightarrow 2O_3(g)] \qquad \Delta H = \tfrac{1}{2} \times -(-427 \text{ kJ}) = +213.5 \text{ kJ}$$

$$\tfrac{1}{2} \times [2O(g) \rightarrow O_2(g)] \qquad \Delta H = \tfrac{1}{2} \times -(+495 \text{ kJ}) = -247.5 \text{ kJ}$$

$$NO(g) + O(g) \rightarrow NO_2(g) \qquad \Delta H = (-199) + (+213.5) + (-247.5) = -233 \text{ kJ}$$

50.   Once everything in the universe is at the same temperature, no further thermodynamic work can be done. Even though the total energy of the universe will be the same, the energy will have been dispersed evenly making it effectively useless.

52.   Concentrated sources of energy, such as petroleum, are being used so as to disperse the energy they contain, making it unavailable for further use.

54.   Petroleum consists mainly of hydrocarbons, which are molecules containing chains of carbon atoms with hydrogen atoms attached to the chains. The fractions are based on the number of carbon atoms in the chains: for example, gasoline is a mixture of hydrocarbons with 5–10 carbon atoms in the chains, whereas asphalt is a mixture of hydrocarbons with 25 or more carbon atoms in the chains. Different fractions have different physical properties and uses, but all can be combusted to produce energy. See Table 10.3

56.   Tetraethyl lead was used as an additive for gasoline to promote smoother running of engines. It is no longer widely used because of concerns about the lead being released to the environment as the leaded gasoline is burned.

58.   The greenhouse effect is a warming effect due to the presence of gases in the atmosphere which absorb infrared radiation that has reached the earth from the sun, and do not allow it to pass back into space. A limited greenhouse effect is desirable because it moderates the temperature changes in the atmosphere that would otherwise be more drastic between daytime when the sun is shining and nighttime. Having too high a concentration of greenhouse gases, however, will elevate the temperature of the earth too much, affecting climate, crops, the polar ice caps, temperature of the oceans, and so on. Carbon dioxide produced by combustion reactions is our greatest concern as a greenhouse gas.

60.   If a proposed reaction involves either or both of those phenomenon, the reaction will tend to be favorable.

62.   Formation of a solid precipitate represents a concentration of matter.

64.   The molecules in liquid water are moving around freely, and are therefore more "disordered" than when the molecules are held rigidly in a solid lattice in ice. The entropy increases during melting.

66.   a. $462.4 \text{ kJ} \times \dfrac{1 \text{ kcal}}{4.184 \text{ kJ}} = 110.5 \text{ kcal}$

       b. $18.28 \text{ kJ} \times \dfrac{1 \text{ kcal}}{4.184 \text{ kJ}} = 4.369 \text{ kcal}$

       c. $1.014 \text{ kJ} \times \dfrac{1 \text{ kcal}}{4.184 \text{ kJ}} = 0.2424 \text{ kcal}$

       d. $190.5 \text{ kJ} \times \dfrac{1 \text{ kcal}}{4.184 \text{ kJ}} = 45.53 \text{ kcal}$

68.   Temperature increase $= 75.0 - 22.3 = 52.7°C$

      $145 \text{ g} \times 4.184\dfrac{\text{J}}{\text{g °C}} \times 52.7°C \times \dfrac{1 \text{ cal}}{4.184 \text{ J}} = 7641.5 \text{ cal} = 7.65 \text{ kcal}$

70.   From Table 10.1, the specific heat capacity of iron is 0.45 J/g°C.

      $Q = s \times m \times \Delta T$

      $Q = 0.45\dfrac{\text{J}}{\text{g°C}} \times 25.1 \text{ g} \times 17.5°C = 197.7 \text{ J} = 2.0 \times 10^2 \text{ J (two significant figures)}$

72.   2.5 kg water = 2500 g

      Temperature change $= 55.0 - 18.5 = 36.5°C$

      $Q = s \times m \times \Delta T$

      $Q = 4.184 \text{ J/g°C} \times 2500 \text{ g} \times 36.5°C = 3.8 \times 10^5 \text{ J}$

74.   Let T_f represent the final temperature reached by the system.

      For the hot water, heat lost $= 50.0 \text{ g} \times 4.184 \text{ J/g°C} \times (100. - T_f°C)$

      For the cold water, heat gained $= 50.0 \text{ g} \times 4.184 \text{ J/g°C} \times (T_f - 25°C)$

      The heat lost by the hot water must *equal* the heat gained by the cold water; therefore

      $50.0 \text{ g} \times 4.184 \text{ J/g°C} \times (100. - T_f°C) = 50.0 \text{ g} \times 4.184 \text{ J/g°C} \times (T_f - 25°C)$

      Solving this equation for T_f gives $T_f = 62.5°C = 63°C$

76.   9.0 J (It requires twice as much heat to warm a sample of twice the mass over the same temperature interval.)

78. Because, for any substance, $Q = s \times m \times \Delta T$, we can solve this equation for the temperature change, ΔT. The results are tabulated:

Substance	Specific Heat Capacity	Temperature Change
water (l)	4.184 J/g °C	23.9 °C
water (s)	2.03 J/g °C	49.3 °C
water (g)	2.0 J/g °C	50. °C
aluminum	0.89 J/g °C	1.1×10^2 °C
iron	0.45 J/g °C	2.2×10^2 °C
mercury	0.14 J/g °C	7.1×10^2 °C
carbon	0.71 J/g °C	1.4×10^2 °C
silver	0.24 J/g °C	4.2×10^2 °C
gold	0.13 J/g °C	7.7×10^2 °C

80. a. The combustion of gasoline releases heat, so this is an exothermic process.

    b. $H_2O(g) \rightarrow H_2O(l)$; Heat is released when water vapor condenses, so this is an exothermic process.

    c. To convert a solid to a gas, heat must be absorbed, so this is an endothermic process.

    d. Heat must be added (absorbed) in order to break a bond, so this is an endothermic process.

82. Reversing the first equation and dividing by 6 we get

$$\tfrac{3}{6}D \rightarrow \tfrac{3}{6}A + B \qquad\qquad \Delta H = +403 \text{ kJ}/6$$

$$\text{or } \tfrac{1}{2}D \rightarrow \tfrac{1}{2}A + B \qquad\qquad \Delta H = +67.2 \text{ kJ}$$

Dividing the second equation by 2 we get

$$\tfrac{1}{2}E + F \rightarrow \tfrac{1}{2}A \qquad \Delta H = -105.2 \text{ kJ}/2 = -52.6 \text{ kJ}$$

Dividing the third equation by 2 we get

$$\tfrac{1}{2}C \rightarrow \tfrac{1}{2}E + \tfrac{3}{2}D \qquad\qquad \Delta H = +64.8 \text{ kJ}/2 = +32.4 \text{ kJ}$$

Adding these equations together we get

$$\tfrac{1}{2}C + F \rightarrow A + B + D \quad \Delta H = 47.0 \text{ kJ}$$

84. 400 kcal is burned per hour walking 4.0 mph, then the total amount of heat burned while walking at 4.0 mph will be given by

$$Q = 400 \text{ kcal/hr} \times t$$

where t is the amount of time spent walking (in hours). One gram of fat is consumed for every 7.7 kcal of heat. Therefore, one pound of fat requires

$$7.7 \text{ kcal/g} \times 454 \text{ g/lb} = 3500 \text{ kcal/lb}$$

Since we want to lose one pound, $Q = 3500$ kcal and

$$t = \frac{Q}{400 \text{ kcal/hr}} = \frac{3500 \text{ kcal}}{400 \text{ kcal/hr}} = 8.75 \text{ hr} = 9 \text{ hr}$$

CHAPTER 11

Modern Atomic Theory

2.   Rutherford's experiments determined that the atom had a nucleus containing positively-charged particles called protons and neutral particles called neutrons. He established that the nucleus was very small compared to the overall size of the atom. He was not able to determine where the electrons were in the atom or what they were doing.

4.   The different forms of electromagnetic radiation are similar in that they all exhibit the same type of wave-like behavior and are propagated through space at the same speed (the speed of light). The types of electromagnetic radiation differ in their frequency (and wavelength) and in the resulting amount of energy carried per photon.

6.   The *speed* of electromagnetic radiation represents how fast a given wave moves through space. The *frequency* of electromagnetic radiation represents how many complete cycles of the wave pass a given point per second. These two concepts are not the same.

8.   The greenhouse gases do not absorb light in the visible wavelengths, enabling this light to pass through the atmosphere and continue to warm the earth, keeping the earth much warmer than it would be without these gases. The earth, in turn, emits infrared radiation which is absorbed by the greenhouse gases and which is re-emitted in all directions. As we increase our use of fossil fuels, the level of CO_2 in the atmosphere is increasing gradually, but significantly. An increase in the level of CO_2 will warm the earth further, eventually changing the weather patterns on the earth's surface and melting the polar ice caps.

10.   exactly equal to

12.   A photon having an energy corresponding to the energy difference between the two states is emitted by an atom in an excited state when it returns to its ground state.

14.   absorbs

16.   When excited hydrogen atoms emit their excess energy, the photons of radiation emitted are always of exactly the same wavelength and energy. We consider this to mean that the hydrogen atom possesses only certain allowed energy states, and that the photons emitted correspond to the atom changing from one of these allowed energy states to another of the allowed energy state. The energy of the photon emitted corresponds to the energy difference in the allowed states. If the hydrogen atom did not possess discrete energy levels, then we would expect the photons emitted to have random wavelengths and energies.

18.   The energy of an emitted photon is *identical* to the energy change within the atom that gave rise to the emitted photon.

20.   Energy is emitted only at wavelengths corresponding to the specific transitions for the electron among the energy levels of hydrogen.

22.   The electron moves to an orbit farther from the nucleus of the atom.

24.   Bohr's theory *explained* the experimentally *observed* line spectrum of hydrogen *exactly*. Bohr's theory was ultimately discarded because when attempts were made to extend the theory to atoms other than hydrogen, the calculated properties did *not* correspond closely to experimental measurements.

26.   An orbit represents a definite, exact circular pathway around the nucleus in which an electron can be found. An orbital represents a region of space in which there is a high probability of finding the electron.

28.   The firefly analogy is intended to demonstrate the concept of a probability map for electron density. In the wave mechanical model of the atom, we cannot say specifically where the electron is in the atom, we can only say where there is a high probability of finding the electron. The analogy is to imagine a time-exposure photograph of a firefly in a closed room. Most of the time, the firefly will be found near the center of the room.

30.   Pictures we draw to represent orbitals should only be interpreted as probability maps. They are not meant to represent that the electron moves only on the surface of, or within, the region drawn in the picture. As the mathematical probability of finding the electron never actually becomes zero on moving outward from the nucleus, scientists have decided that pictures of orbitals should represent a 90% probability that the electron will be found inside the region depicted in the drawing (for 100% probability, the orbital would have to encompass all space).

32.   The *p* orbitals, in general, have two lobes and are sometimes described as having a "dumbbell" shape. The 2*p* and 3*p* orbitals are similar in shape, and in fact there are three equivalent 2*p* or 3*p* orbitals in the 2*p* or 3*p* subshell. The orbitals differ in size, mean distance from the nucleus, and energy.

34. $n = 1$

36.

Value of n	Possible subshells
1	1*s*
2	2*s*, 2*p*
3	3*s*, 3*p*, 3*d*
4	4*s*, 4*p*, 4*d*, 4*f*

38.   Electrons have an intrinsic spin (they spin on their own axes). Geometrically, there are only two senses possible for spin (clockwise or counter-clockwise). This means only two electrons can occupy an orbital, with the opposite sense or direction of spin. This idea is called the Pauli Exclusion Principle.

40.   increases; as you move out from the nucleus, there is more space and room for more sublevels.

42.   opposite

44.   Choices b and c are possible; choice a is not possible because the *f* subshells do not begin until the $n = 4$ orbit; choice d is not possible because the *p* subshells do not begin until the $n = 2$ orbit.

46.   When a hydrogen atom is in its ground state, the electron is found in the $1s$ orbital. The $1s$ orbital has the lowest energy of all the possible hydrogen orbitals.

48.   The elements in a given vertical column of the periodic table have the same valence electron configuration. Having the same valence electron configuration causes the elements in a given group to have similar chemical properties.

50.   Just count the electrons to get the atomic number of the element.

    a.   silicon

    b.   beryllium

    c.   neon

    d.   argon

52.   Just count the electrons to get the atomic number of the element.

    a.   selenium

    b.   scandium

    c.   sulfur

    d.   iodine

54.   a. $1s(\uparrow\downarrow)$ $2s(\uparrow\downarrow)$ $2p(\uparrow\downarrow)(\uparrow\downarrow)(\uparrow\downarrow)$ $3s(\uparrow\downarrow)$

    b. $1s(\uparrow\downarrow)$ $2s(\uparrow\downarrow)$ $2p(\uparrow\downarrow)(\uparrow\downarrow)(\uparrow\downarrow)$ $3s(\uparrow\downarrow)$ $3p(\uparrow\downarrow)(\uparrow\downarrow)(\uparrow\downarrow)$

    c. $1s(\uparrow\downarrow)$ $2s(\uparrow\ )$

    d. $1s(\uparrow\downarrow)$ $2s(\uparrow\downarrow)$ $2p(\uparrow\downarrow)(\uparrow\downarrow)(\uparrow\downarrow)$ $3s(\uparrow\downarrow)$ $3p(\uparrow\downarrow)(\uparrow\downarrow)(\uparrow\downarrow)$ $4s(\uparrow\downarrow)$
           $3d(\uparrow\downarrow)(\uparrow\downarrow)(\uparrow\downarrow)(\uparrow\downarrow)(\uparrow\downarrow)$ $4p(\uparrow\ )(\uparrow\ )(\uparrow\ )$

56.   Specific answers depend on student choice of elements. Any Group 1 element would have one valence electron. Any Group 3 element would have three valence electrons. Any Group 5 element would have five valence electrons. Any Group 7 element would have seven valence electrons.

58.   The properties of Rb and Sr suggest that they are members of Groups 1 and 2, respectively, and so must be filling the $5s$ orbital. The $5s$ orbital is lower in energy (and fills before) the $4d$ orbitals.

60.   a.   aluminum

    b.   potassium

    c.   bromine

    d.   tin

62.   a. $[\text{Ne}]\ 3s^2\ 3p^3$

    b. $[\text{Ne}]\ 3s^2\ 3p^5$

    c. $[\text{Ne}]\ 3s^2$

    d. $[\text{Ar}]\ 4s^2\ 3d^{10}$

64.   a.   one

       b.   two

       c.   zero

       d.   ten

66.   The *position* of the element (both in terms of vertical column and horizontal row) indicates which set of orbitals is being filled last.

       a. $5f$

       b. $5f$

       c. $4f$

       d. $6p$

68.   [Rn] $7s^2\ 5f^{14}\ 6d^5$

70.   The metallic elements *lose* electrons and form *positive* ions (cations); the nonmetallic elements *gain* electrons and form *negative* ions (anions). Remember that the electron itself is *negatively* charged.

72.   All exist as *diatomic* molecules (F_2, Cl_2, Br_2, I_2); all are *non*metals; all have relatively high electronegativities; all form 1- ions in reacting with metallic elements.

74.   Elements at the *left* of a period (horizontal row) lose electrons more readily; at the left of a period (given principal energy level) the nuclear charge is the smallest and the electrons are least tightly held.

76.   The elements of a given period (horizontal row) have valence electrons in the same principal energy level. Nuclear charge, however, increases across a period going from left to right. Atoms at the left side have smaller nuclear charges and hold onto their valence electrons less tightly.

78.   When substances absorb energy the electrons become excited (move to higher energy levels). Upon returning to the ground state, energy is released, some of which is in the visible spectrum. Since we see colors, this tells us that only *certain wavelengths* of light are released, which means that only *certain transitions* are allowed. This is what is meant by quantized energy levels. If all wavelengths of light were emitted we would see white light.

80.   Ionization energies decrease in going from top to bottom within a vertical group; ionization energies increase in going from left to right within a horizontal period.

       a.   Li

       b.   Ca

       c.   Cl

       d.   S

82. Atomic size increases in going from top to bottom within a vertical group; atomic size decreases in going from left to right within a horizontal period.

    a.   Na

    b.   S

    c.   N

    d.   F

84. speed of light

86. photons

88. quantized

90. orbital

92. transition metal

94. spins

96.   a. $1s^2\,2s^2\,2p^6\,3s^2\,3p^6\,4s^1$ $[Ar]\,4s^1$

        $1s(\uparrow\downarrow)\ 2s(\uparrow\downarrow)\ 2p(\uparrow\downarrow)(\uparrow\downarrow)(\uparrow\downarrow)\ 3s(\uparrow\downarrow)\ 3p(\uparrow\downarrow)(\uparrow\downarrow)(\uparrow\downarrow)\ 4s(\uparrow\ )$

    b. $1s^2\,2s^2\,2p^6\,3s^2\,3p^6\,4s^2\,3d^2$ $[Ar]\,4s^2\,3d^2$

        $1s(\uparrow\downarrow)\ 2s(\uparrow\downarrow)\ 2p(\uparrow\downarrow)(\uparrow\downarrow)(\uparrow\downarrow)\ 3s(\uparrow\downarrow)\ 3p(\uparrow\downarrow)(\uparrow\downarrow)(\uparrow\downarrow)\ 4s(\uparrow\downarrow)$
        $3d(\uparrow\ )(\uparrow\ )(\ )(\ )(\ )$

    c. $1s^2\,2s^2\,2p^6\,3s^2\,3p^2$ $[Ne]\,3s^2\,3p^2$

        $1s(\uparrow\downarrow)\ 2s(\uparrow\downarrow)\ 2p(\uparrow\downarrow)(\uparrow\downarrow)(\uparrow\downarrow)\ 3s(\uparrow\downarrow)\ 3p(\uparrow\ )(\uparrow\ )(\ )$

    d. $1s^2\,2s^2\,2p^6\,3s^2\,3p^6\,4s^2\,3d^6$ $[Ar]\,4s^2\,3d^6$

        $1s(\uparrow\downarrow)\ 2s(\uparrow\downarrow)\ 2p(\uparrow\downarrow)(\uparrow\downarrow)(\uparrow\downarrow)\ 3s(\uparrow\downarrow)\ 3p(\uparrow\downarrow)(\uparrow\downarrow)(\uparrow\downarrow)\ 4s(\uparrow\downarrow)$
        $3d(\uparrow\downarrow)(\uparrow\ )(\uparrow\ )(\uparrow\ )(\uparrow\ )$

    e. $1s^2\,2s^2\,2p^6\,3s^2\,3p^6\,4s^2\,3d^{10}$ $[Ar]\,4s^2\,3d^{10}$

        $1s(\uparrow\downarrow)\ 2s(\uparrow\downarrow)\ 2p(\uparrow\downarrow)(\uparrow\downarrow)(\uparrow\downarrow)\ 3s(\uparrow\downarrow)\ 3p(\uparrow\downarrow)(\uparrow\downarrow)(\uparrow\downarrow)\ 4s(\uparrow\downarrow)$
        $3d(\uparrow\downarrow)(\uparrow\downarrow)(\uparrow\downarrow)(\uparrow\downarrow)(\uparrow\downarrow)$

98.   a. ns^2

    b. $ns^2\,np^5$

    c. $ns^2\,np^4$

    d. ns^1

    e. $ns^2\,np^4$

100.   a. $\lambda = \dfrac{h}{mv}$

$\lambda = \dfrac{6.63 \times 10^{-34}\text{ J s}}{(9.1 \times 10^{-31}\text{kg})[0.90 \times (3.00 \times 10^{8}\text{ m s}^{-1})}$

$\lambda = 2.7 \times 10^{-12}$ m (0.0027 nm)

   b. 4.4×10^{-34} m

   c. 2×10^{-35} m

   The wavelengths for the ball and the person are *infinitesimally small*, whereas the wavelength for the electron is nearly the same order of magnitude as the diameter of a typical atom.

102.   Light is emitted from the hydrogen atom only at certain fixed wavelengths. If the energy levels of hydrogen were *continuous*, a hydrogen atom would emit energy at all possible wavelengths.

104.   The third principal energy level of hydrogen is divided into *three* sublevels (3s, 3p, and 3d); there is a *single* 3s orbital; there is a set of *three* 3p orbitals; there is a set of *five* 3d orbitals. See Figures 11.21-11.24 for the shapes of these orbitals.

106.   Answer depends on student choice of examples.

108.   a. $1s^2\, 2s^2\, 2p^6\, 3s^2\, 3p^6\, 4s^2\, 3d^{10}\, 4p^5$

   b. $1s^2\, 2s^2\, 2p^6\, 3s^2\, 3p^6\, 4s^2\, 3d^{10}\, 4p^6\, 5s^2\, 4d^{10}\, 5p^6$

   c. $1s^2\, 2s^2\, 2p^6\, 3s^2\, 3p^6\, 4s^2\, 3d^{10}\, 4p^6\, 5s^2\, 4d^{10}\, 5p^6\, 6s^2$

   d. $1s^2\, 2s^2\, 2p^6\, 3s^2\, 3p^6\, 4s^2\, 3d^{10}\, 4p^4$

110.   a.   five (2s, 2p)

   b.   seven (3s, 3p)

   c.   one (3s)

   d.   three (3s, 3p)

112.   a.   [Kr] $5s^2\, 4d^2$

   b.   [Kr] $5s^2\, 4d^{10}\, 5p^5$

   c.   [Ar] $4s^2\, 3d^{10}\, 4p^2$

   d.   [Xe] $6s^1$

114.   a.   Se

   b.   Se

   c.   Rb

   d.   V

116.   metals, low; nonmetals, high

118.   Atomic size increases in going from top to bottom within a vertical group; atomic size decreases in going from left to right within a horizontal period.

a.   Ca

b.   P

c.   K

CHAPTER 12

Chemical Bonding

2.   The *bond energy* represents the energy required to break a chemical bond.

4.   A covalent bond represents the *sharing* of pairs of electrons between nuclei.

6.   In H_2 and HF, the bonding is covalent in nature, with an electron pair being shared between the atoms. In H_2, the two atoms are identical (the sharing is equal); in HF, the two atoms are different (the sharing is unequal) and as a result the bond is polar. Both of these are in marked contrast to the situation in NaF: NaF is an ionic compound—an electron has been completely transferred from sodium to fluorine, producing separate ions.

8.   A bond is polar if the centers of positive and negative charge do not coincide at the same point. The bond has a negative end and a positive end. Polar bonds will exist in any molecule with nonidentical bonded atoms (although the molecule, as a whole, may not be polar if the bond dipoles cancel each other). Two simple examples are HF and HCl: in both cases, the negative center of charge is closer to the halogen atom.

10.   The level of polarity in a polar covalent bond is determined by the difference in electronegativity of the atoms in the bond.

12.   a.   I is most electronegative, Rb is least electronegative

   b.   Mg is most electronegative, Ca and Sr have similar electronegativities

   c.   Br is most electronegative, K is least electronegative

14.   Generally, covalent bonds between atoms of *different* elements are *polar*.

   a.   ionic

   b.   polar covalent

   c.   covalent

16.   For a bond to be polar covalent, the atoms involved in the bond must have different electronegativities (must be of different elements).

   a.   nonpolar covalent (atoms of the same element)

   b.   nonpolar covalent (atoms of the same element)

   c.   polar covalent (atoms of different elements)

   d.   polar covalent (atoms of different elements)

18.   The *degree* of polarity of a polar covalent bond is indicated by the magnitude of the difference in electronegativities of the elements involved: the larger the difference in electronegativity, the more polar the bond. Electronegativity differences are given in parentheses below:

    a.   O–Cl (0.5); O–Br(0.7); the O–Br bond is more polar

    b.   N–O (0.5); N–F (1.0); the N–F bond is more polar

    c.   P–S (0.4); P–O (1.4); the P–O bond is more polar

    d.   H–O (1.4); H–N (0.9); the H–O bond is more polar

20.   The greater the electronegativity difference between two atoms, the more ionic will be the bond between those two atoms.

    a.   Ca–Cl

    b.   Ba–Cl

    c.   Fe–I

    d.   Be–F

22.   The presence of strong bond dipoles and a large overall dipole moment in water make it a polar substance overall. Among the properties of water dependent on its dipole moment are its freezing point, melting point, vapor pressure, and its ability to dissolve many substances.

24.   In a diatomic molecule containing two different elements, the more electronegative atom will be the negative end of the molecule, and the *less* electronegative atom will be the positive end.

    a.   H

    b.   Cl

    c.   I

26.   In the figures, the arrow points toward the more electronegative atom.

    a. $\delta+$ S$\rightarrow$O $\delta-$

    b. $\delta+$ S$\rightarrow$N $\delta-$

    c. $\delta+$ S$\rightarrow$F $\delta-$

    d. $\delta+$ S$\rightarrow$Cl $\delta-$

28.   In the figures, the arrow points toward the more electronegative atom.

    a. $\delta+$ H$\rightarrow$C $\delta-$

    b. $\delta+$ N$\rightarrow$O $\delta-$

    c. $\delta+$ S$\rightarrow$N $\delta-$

    d. $\delta+$ C$\rightarrow$N $\delta-$

30.   preceding

32.   Atoms in covalent molecules gain a configuration like that of a noble gas by sharing one or more pairs of electrons between atoms: such shared pairs of electrons "belong" to each of the atoms of the bond at the same time. In ionic bonding, one atom completely gives over one or more electrons to another atom, and the resulting ions behave independently of one another.

34.   a. Br^-, Kr (Br has one electron less than Kr)

        b. Cs^+, Xe (Cs has one electron more than Xe)

        c. P^{3-}, Ar (P has three fewer electrons than Ar)

        d. S^{2-}, Ar (S has two fewer electrons than Ar)

36.   Atoms or ions with the same number of electrons are said to be *isoelectronic*.

        a. F^-, O^{2-}, N^{3-}

        b. Cl^-, S^{2-}, P^{3-}

        c. F^-, O^{2-}, N^{3-}

        d. Br^-, Se^{2-}, As^{3-}

38.   a. $AlBr_3$: Al has three electrons more than a noble gas; Br has one electron less than a noble gas.

        b. Al_2O_3: Al has three electrons more than a noble gas; O has two fewer electrons than a noble gas.

        c.   AlP: Al has three electrons more than a noble gas; P has three fewer electrons than a noble gas.

        d. AlH_3: Al has three electrons more than a noble gas; H has one electron less than a noble gas.

40.   There are many examples possible. Listed below are a few compounds that fit each situation.

        a.   LiF: Li^+, [He]; F^-, [Ne]

        b.   NaF: Na^+, [Ne]; F^-, [Ne]

        c.   LiCl: Li^+, [He]; Cl^-, [Ar]

        d.   NaCl: Na^+, [Ne]; Cl^-, [Ar]

42.   An ionic solid such as NaCl consists of an array of alternating positively– and negatively–charged ions: that is, each positive ion has as its nearest neighbors a group of negative ions, and each negative ion has a group of positive ions surrounding it. In most ionic solids, the ions are packed as tightly as possible.

44.   In forming an anion, an atom gains additional electrons in its outermost (valence) shell. Additional electrons in the valence shell increases the repulsive forces between electrons, so the outermost shell becomes larger to accommodate this.

46.   Relative ionic sizes are given in Figure 12.9. Within a given horizontal row of the periodic chart, negative ions tend to be larger than positive ions because the negative ions contain a larger number of electrons in the valence shell. Within a vertical group of the periodic table, ionic size increases from top to bottom. In general, positive ions are smaller than the atoms they come from, whereas negative ions are larger than the atoms they come from.

    a. F^-

    b. Cl^-

    c.   Ca

    d. I^-

48.   Relative ionic sizes are given in Figure 12.9. Within a given horizontal row of the periodic chart, negative ions tend to be larger than positive ions because the negative ions contain a larger number of electrons in the valence shell. Within a vertical group of the periodic table, ionic size increases from top to bottom. In general, positive ions are smaller than the atoms they come from, whereas negative ions are larger than the atoms they come from.

    a.   I

    b. F^-

    c. F^-

50.   When atoms form covalent bonds, they try to attain a valence electronic configuration similar to that of the following noble gas element. When the elements in the first few horizontal rows of the periodic table form covalent bonds, they will attempt to gain configurations similar to the noble gases helium (2 valence electrons, duet rule), and neon and argon (8 valence electrons, octet rule).

52.   These elements attain a total of eight valence electrons, making the valence electron configurations similar to those of the noble gases Ne and Ar.

54.   When two atoms in a molecule are connected by a triple bond, the atoms share three pairs of electrons (6 electrons) in completing their outermost shells. A simple molecule containing a triple bond is acetylene, C_2H_2 (H:C:::C:H).

56.   The Group in which a representative element is found indicates the number of valence electrons.

    a.   Mg**:**

    b.   :$\ddot{\text{B}}$r.

    c.   :$\ddot{\text{S}}$.

    d.   :$\ddot{\text{S}}$i

58.   a.   each boron provides 3; each oxygen provides 6; total valence electrons = 24

    b.   carbon provides 4; each oxygen provides 6; total valence electrons = 16

c. each carbon provides 4; each hydrogen provides 1; oxygen provides 6; total valence electrons = 20

d. N provides 5; each oxygen provides 6; total valence electrons = 17

60. a. Each hydrogen provides 1 valence electron; total valence electrons = 2

H—H

b. Hydrogen provides 1 valence electron; chlorine provides 7 valence electrons; total valence electrons = 8

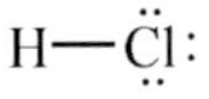

H—C̈l:

c. Carbon provides 4 valence electrons; each fluorine provides 7 valence electrons; total valence electrons = 32

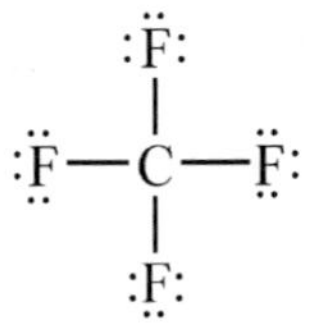

$$
\begin{array}{c}
\quad\ \ :\ddot{F}: \\
\quad\ \ | \\
:\ddot{F}-C-\ddot{F}: \\
\quad\ \ | \\
\quad\ \ :\ddot{F}:
\end{array}
$$

d. Each carbon provides 4 valence electrons; each fluorine provides 7 valence electrons; total valence electrons = 50

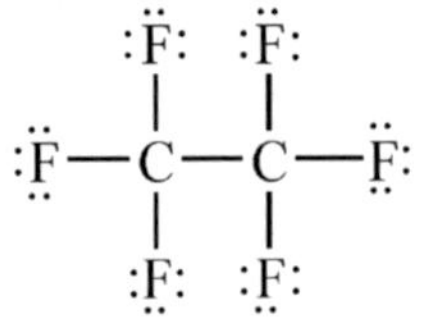

$$
\begin{array}{c}
\quad :\ddot{F}: \ :\ddot{F}: \\
\quad\ | \quad\ | \\
:\ddot{F}-C-C-\ddot{F}: \\
\quad\ | \quad\ | \\
\quad :\ddot{F}: \ :\ddot{F}:
\end{array}
$$

62. a. P provides 5 valence electrons. Each Cl provides 7 valence electrons.
Total valence electrons = 26

$$
\begin{array}{c}
:\ddot{C}l——\ddot{P}——\ddot{C}l: \\
| \\
:\ddot{C}l:
\end{array}
$$

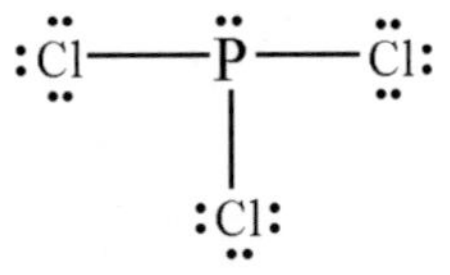

b. C provides 4 valence electrons. Each Cl provides 7 valence electrons. H provides 1 valence electron.
Total valence electrons = 26

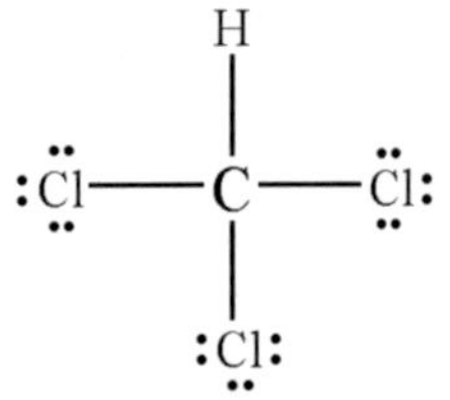

$$
\begin{array}{c}
\quad\quad H \\
\quad\quad | \\
:\ddot{C}l——C——\ddot{C}l: \\
\quad\quad | \\
\quad\quad :\ddot{C}l:
\end{array}
$$

c.   Each C provides 4 valence electrons. Each H provides 1 valence electron. Each Cl provides 7 valence electrons
Total valence electrons = 26

$$
\begin{array}{ccc}
& \text{H} & \text{H} \\
& | & | \\
:\ddot{\text{C}}\text{l}\!-\!\!\!\!&\text{C}\!-\!\text{C}&\!-\!\ddot{\text{C}}\text{l}: \\
& | & | \\
& \text{H} & \text{H}
\end{array}
$$

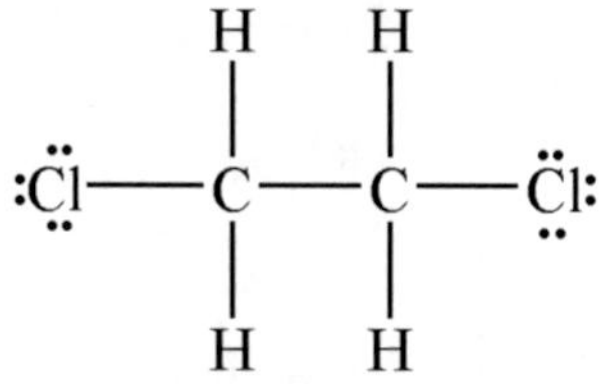

d.   Each N provides 5 valence electrons. Each H provides 1 valence electron.
Total valence electrons = 14

$$
\begin{array}{ccc}
& \ddot{\;} & \ddot{\;} \\
\text{H}\!-\!\!\!\!&\ddot{\text{N}}\!-\!\ddot{\text{N}}&\!-\!\text{H} \\
& | & | \\
& \text{H} & \text{H}
\end{array}
$$

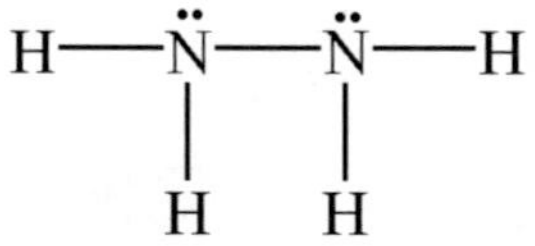

64.   C provides 4 valence electrons. Each oxygen provides 6 valence electrons. Having only 16 total valence electrons requires multiple bonding in the molecule.

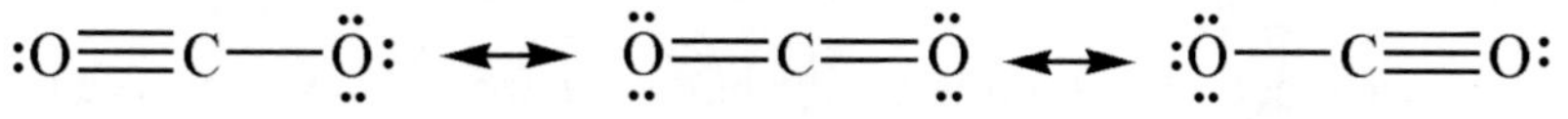

$$:\text{O}\!\equiv\!\text{C}\!-\!\ddot{\underset{..}{\text{O}}}: \;\longleftrightarrow\; \ddot{\underset{..}{\text{O}}}\!=\!\text{C}\!=\!\ddot{\underset{..}{\text{O}}} \;\longleftrightarrow\; :\ddot{\underset{..}{\text{O}}}\!-\!\text{C}\!\equiv\!\text{O}:$$

66.   a.   Cl provides 7 valence electrons. Each O provides 6 valence electrons.   The 1– charge means 1 additional electron. Total valence electrons = 26

$$
\left[
\begin{array}{c}
:\ddot{\text{O}}: \\
| \\
:\ddot{\text{O}}\!-\!\underset{..}{\text{C}}\text{l}\!-\!\ddot{\text{O}}:
\end{array}
\right]^{1-}
$$

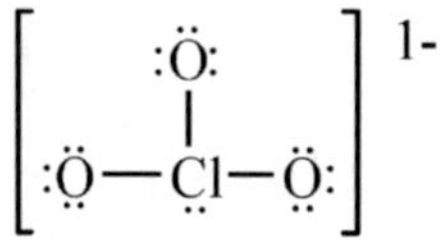

b.   Each O provides 6 valence electrons.   The 2– charge means two additional valence electrons. Total valence electrons = 14

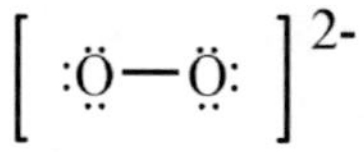

$$
\left[\; :\ddot{\underset{..}{\text{O}}}\!-\!\ddot{\underset{..}{\text{O}}}: \;\right]^{2-}
$$

c.   Each C provides 4 valence electrons. Each H provides 1 valence electron. Each O provides 6 valence electrons.   The 1– charge means 1 additional valence electron. Total valence electrons = 24

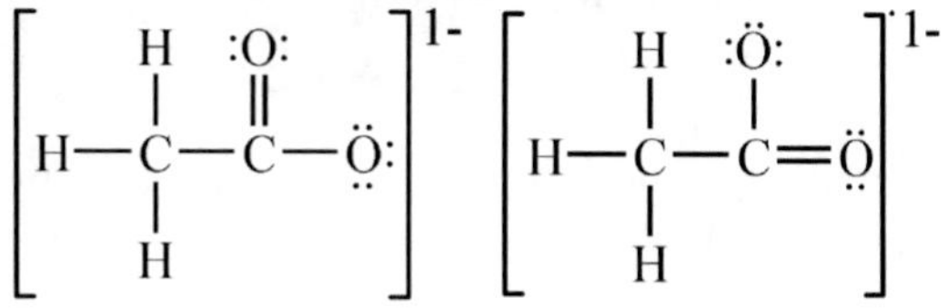

$$
\left[
\begin{array}{ccc}
\text{H} & :\text{O}: & \\
| & \| & \\
\text{H}\!-\!\text{C}\!-\!\text{C}&\!-\!\ddot{\underset{..}{\text{O}}}: \\
| & & \\
\text{H} & &
\end{array}
\right]^{1-}
\left[
\begin{array}{ccc}
\text{H} & :\ddot{\text{O}}: & \\
| & | & \\
\text{H}\!-\!\text{C}\!-\!\text{C}&\!=\!\ddot{\underset{..}{\text{O}}} \\
| & & \\
\text{H} & &
\end{array}
\right]^{1-}
$$

68.   a.   C provides 4 valence electrons. Each O provides 6 valence electrons. The 2– charge means two additional valence electrons.
Total valence electrons = 24

b.   Each H provides 1 valence electron. N provides 5 valence electrons. The 1+ charge means one less valence electron.
Total valence electrons = 8

c.   Cl provides 7 valence electrons. O provides 6 valence electrons. The 1– charge means one additional valence electron. Total valence electrons = 14

70.   The geometric structure of NH_3 is that of a trigonal pyramid. The nitrogen atom of NH_3 is surrounded by four electron pairs (three are bonding, one is a lone pair). The H–N–H bond angle is somewhat less than 109.5° (due to the presence of the lone pair).

72.   The geometric structure of SiF_4 is that of a tetrahedron. The silicon atom of SiF_4 is surrounded by four bonding electron pairs. The F–Si–F bond angle is the characteristic angle of the tetrahedron, 109.5°.

74.   The general molecular structure of a molecule is determined by (1) *how many electron pairs* surround the central atom in the molecule, and (2) which of those electron pairs are used for *bonding* to the other atoms of the molecule. Nonbonding electron pairs on the central atom do, however, cause minor changes in the bond angles, compared to the ideal regular geometric structure.

76.   You will remember from high school geometry, that two points in space are all that is needed to define a straight line. A diatomic molecule represents two points (the nuclei of the atoms) in space.

78.   In NF_3, the nitrogen atom has *four* pairs of valence electrons, whereas in BF_3, there are only *three* pairs of valence electrons around the boron atom. The nonbonding electron pair on nitrogen in NF_3 pushes the three F atoms out of the plane of the N atom.

80. a. four electron pairs in a tetrahedral arrangement with some lone-pair distortion

   b. four electron pairs in a tetrahedral arrangement with some lone-pair distortion

   c. four electron pairs in a tetrahedral arrangement

82. a. trigonal pyramidal (there is a lone pair on N)

   b. trigonal pyramidal (there is a lone pair on As)

   c. non-linear, *V*-shaped (four electron pairs on O, but only two atoms are attached to O)

84. a. basically tetrahedral around the P atom (the hydrogen atoms are attached to two of the oxygen atoms and do not affect greatly the geometrical arrangement of the oxygen atoms around the phosphorus)

   b. tetrahedral (4 electron pairs on Cl, and 4 atoms attached)

   c. trigonal pyramidal (4 electron pairs on S, and 3 atoms attached)

86. a. approximately 109.5° (the molecule is *V*-shaped or nonlinear)

   b. approximately 109.5° (the molecule is trigonal pyramidal)

   c. 109.5°

   d. approximately 120° (the double bond makes the molecule flat)

88. The bond angles would be expected to be 120° around the carbon atoms in the rings. We also expect 120° for the C–N–N and N–N–C bond angles. The double bonds influence the bond angles greatly, with each atom having only three "effective pairs" of electrons around the atom.

90. double

92. The bond with the larger electronegativity difference will be the more polar bond. See Figure 12.3 for electronegativities.

   a. S–F

   b. P–O

   c. C–H

94. The bond energy of a chemical bond is the quantity of energy required to break the bond and separate the atoms.

96. In each case, the element *higher up* within a group on the periodic table has the higher electronegativity.

   a. Be

   b. N

   c. F

98. For a bond to be polar covalent, the atoms involved in the bond must have different electronegativities (must be of different elements).

    a.   polar covalent (different elements)

    b.   *non*polar covalent (two atoms of the same element)

    c.   polar covalent (different elements)

    d.   *non*polar covalent (atoms of the same element)

100. In a diatomic molecule containing two different elements, the more electronegative atom will be the negative end of the molecule, and the *less* electronegative atom will be the positive end.

    a.   oxygen

    b.   bromine

    c.   iodine

102.   a.   Al $1s^2\, 2s^2\, 2p^6\, 3s^2\, 3p^1$

                Al^{3+} $1s^2\, 2s^2\, 2p^6$

                Ne has the same configuration as Al^{3+}.

    b.   Br $1s^2\, 2s^2\, 2p^6\, 3s^2\, 3p^6\, 4s^2\, 3d^{10}\, 4p^5$

                Br^- $1s^2\, 2s^2\, 2p^6\, 3s^2\, 3p^6\, 4s^2\, 3d^{10}\, 4p^6$

                Kr has the same configuration as Br^-.

    c.   Ca $1s^2\, 2s^2\, 2p^6\, 3s^2\, 3p^6\, 4s^2$

                Ca^{2+} $1s^2\, 2s^2\, 2p^6\, 3s^2\, 3p^6$

                Ar has the same configuration as Ca^{2+}.

    d.   Li $1s^2\, 2s^1$

                Li^+ $1s^2$

                He has the same configuration as Li^+.

    e.   F $1s^2\, 2s^2\, 2p^5$

                F^- $1s^2\, 2s^2\, 2p^6$

                Ne has the same configuration as F^-.

104.   a. Na_2Se: Na has one electron more than a noble gas; Se has two electrons fewer than a noble gas.

    b.   RbF: Rb has one electron more than a noble gas; F has one electron less than a noble gas.

    c. K_2Te: K has one electron more than a noble gas; Te has two electrons fewer than a noble gas.

    d.   BaSe: Ba has two electrons more than a noble gas; Se has two electrons fewer than a noble gas.

    e.   KAt: K has one electron more than a noble gas; At has one electron less than a noble gas.

    f.   FrCl: Fr has one electron more than a noble gas; Cl has one electron less than a noble gas.

106.   Relative ionic sizes are indicated in Figure 12.9.

   a. Na^+

   b. Al^{3+}

   c. F^-

   d. Na^+

108.   a.   H provides 1; N provides 5; each O provides 6; total valence electrons = 24

   b.   each H provides 1; S provides 6; each O provides 6; total valence electrons = 32

   c.   each H provides 1; P provides 5; each O provides 6; total valence electrons = 32

   d.   H provides 1; Cl provides 7; each O provides 6; total valence electrons = 32

110.   a. N_2H_4 : Each N provides 5 valence electrons. Each H provides 1 valence electron. Total valence electrons = 14

$$H-\ddot{N}-\ddot{N}-H$$
$$\quad\ |\quad\ |$$
$$\quad\ H\quad\ H$$

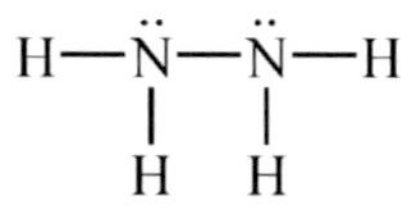

   b. C_2H_6 : Each C provides 4 valence electrons. Each H provides 1 valence electron. Total valence electrons = 14

$$\begin{array}{ccc} H & & H \\ | & & | \\ H-C & - & C-H \\ | & & | \\ H & & H \end{array}$$

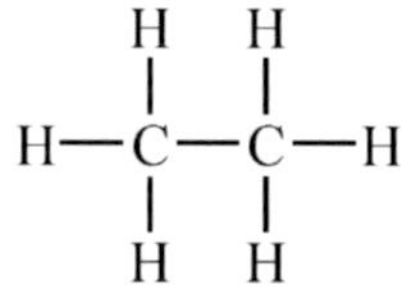

   c. NCl_3 : N provides 5 valence electrons. Each Cl provides 7 valence electrons. Total valence electrons = 26

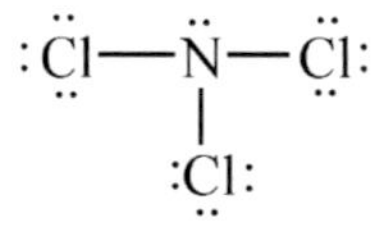

$$:\ddot{Cl}-\ddot{N}-\ddot{Cl}:$$
$$\qquad |$$
$$\qquad :\ddot{Cl}:$$

   d. $SiCl_4$: Si provides 4 valence electrons. Each Cl provides 7 valence electrons. Total valence electrons = 32

$$\qquad :\ddot{Cl}:$$
$$\qquad |$$
$$:\ddot{Cl}-Si-\ddot{Cl}:$$
$$\qquad |$$
$$\qquad :\ddot{Cl}:$$

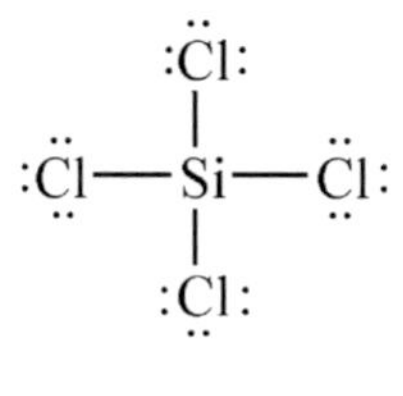

112.   a. NO_3^- : N provides 5 valence electrons. Each O provides 6 valence electrons. The 1– charge means one additional valence electron. Total valence electrons = 24

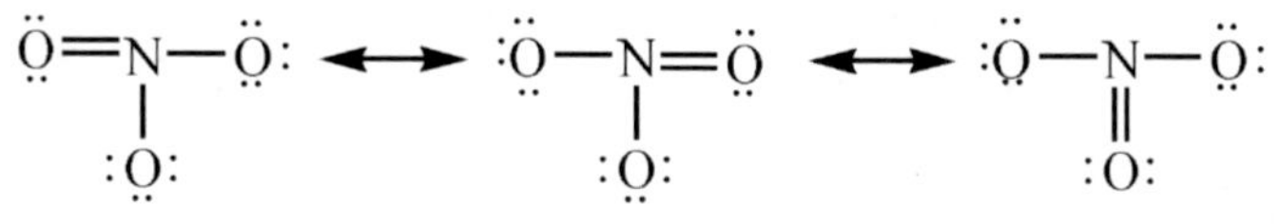

$$\ddot{O}=N-\ddot{O}: \longleftrightarrow :\ddot{O}-N=\ddot{O} \longleftrightarrow :\ddot{O}-N-\ddot{O}:$$
$$\qquad |\qquad\qquad\qquad |\qquad\qquad\qquad ||$$
$$\qquad :\ddot{O}:\qquad\qquad\qquad :\ddot{O}:\qquad\qquad\qquad :\ddot{O}:$$

b.　　CO_3^{2-}: C provides 4 valence electrons. Each O provides 6 valence electrons. The 2– charge means two additional valence electrons. Total valence electrons = 24

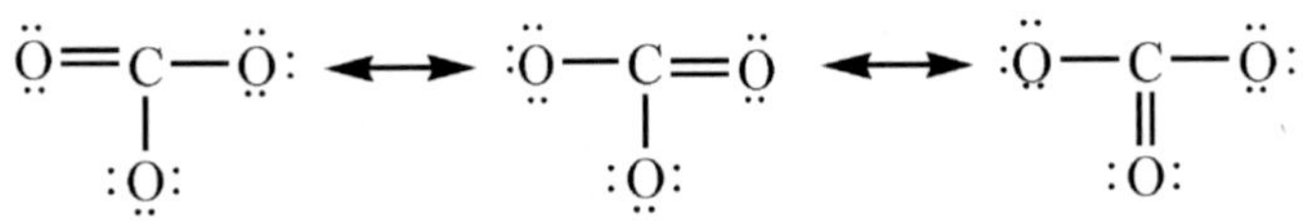

$$\ddot{O}{=}C{-}\ddot{O}\colon \longleftrightarrow \colon\!\ddot{O}{-}C{=}\ddot{O} \longleftrightarrow \colon\!\ddot{O}{-}C{-}\ddot{O}\colon$$
$$\qquad\underset{\ddot{\ddot{O}}\colon}{|} \qquad\qquad \underset{\ddot{\ddot{O}}\colon}{|} \qquad\qquad \underset{\colon\!O\colon}{\|}$$

c.　　NH_4^+: N provides 5 valence electrons. Each H provides 1 valence electron. The 1+ charge means one *less* valence electron. Total valence electrons = 8

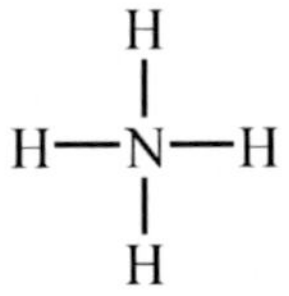

$$\begin{array}{c} H \\ | \\ H{-}N{-}H \\ | \\ H \end{array}$$

114.　a.　　four electron pairs arranged tetrahedrally about C

　　　b.　　four electron pairs arranged tetrahedrally about Ge

　　　c.　　three electron pairs arranged trigonally (planar) around B

116.　a.　　ClO_3^-, trigonal pyramid (lone pair on Cl)

　　　b.　　ClO_2^-, nonlinear (*V*-shaped, two lone pairs on Cl)

　　　c.　　ClO_4^-, tetrahedral (all pairs on Cl are bonding)

118.　a.　　nonlinear (*V*–shaped)

　　　b.　　trigonal planar

　　　c.　　basically trigonal planar around the C (the H is attached to one of the O atoms, and distorts the shape around the carbon only slightly)

　　　d.　　linear

120.　Ionic compounds tend to be hard, crystalline substances with relatively high melting and boiling points. Covalently bonded substances tend to be gases, liquids, or relatively soft solids, with much lower melting and boiling points.

CUMULATIVE REVIEW

Chapters 10–12

2. Temperature is a measure of the random motions of the components of a substance: in other words, temperature is a measure of the average kinetic energy of the particles in a sample. The molecules in warm water must be moving faster than the molecules in cold water (the molecules have the same mass, so if the temperature is higher, the average velocity of the particles must be higher in the warm water). Heat is the energy that flows because of a difference in temperature.

4. Thermodynamics is the study of energy and energy changes. The first law of thermodynamics is the law of conservation of energy: the energy of the universe is constant. Energy cannot be created or destroyed, only transferred from one place to another or from one form to another. The internal energy of a system, E, represents the total of the kinetic and potential energies of all the particles in a system. A flow of heat may be produced when there is a change in internal energy in the system, but it is not correct to say that the system "contains" the heat: part of the internal energy is *converted* to heat energy during the process (under other conditions, the change in internal energy might be expressed as work rather than a heat flow).

6. The enthalpy change represents the heat energy that flows (at constant pressure) on a molar basis when a reaction occurs. The enthalpy change is indeed a state function (which we make great use of in Hess's Law calculations). Enthalpy changes are typically measured in insulated reaction vessels called calorimeters (a simple calorimeter is shown in Figure 10.6 in the text).

8. Consider petroleum. A gallon of gasoline contains concentrated, stored energy. We can use that energy to make our car move, but when we do, the energy stored in the gasoline is dispersed to the environment. Although the energy is still there (it is conserved), it is no longer in a concentrated useful form. So although the energy content of the universe remains constant, the energy that is now stored in concentrated forms in oil, coal, wood, and other sources is gradually being dispersed to the universe where it can do no work.

10. A "driving force" is an effect that tends to make a process occur. Two important driving forces are dispersion of energy during a process or dispersion of matter during a process ("energy spread" and "matter spread"). For example, a log burns in a fireplace because the energy contained in the log is dispersed to the universe when it burns. If we put a teaspoon of sugar into a glass of water, the dissolving of the sugar is a favorable process because the matter of the sugar is dispersed when it dissolves. Entropy is a measure of the randomness or disorder in a system. The entropy of the universe is constant increasing because of "matter spread" and "energy spread". A spontaneous process is one that occurs without outside intervention: the spontaneity of a reaction depends on the energy spread and matter spread if the reaction takes place. A reaction that disperses energy and also disperses matter will always be spontaneous. Reactions that require an input of energy may still be spontaneous if the matter spread is large enough.

12.   molar mass CH_4 = 16.04 g

a. $0.521 \text{ mol} \times -\dfrac{890 \text{ kJ}}{1 \text{ mol}} = -464 \text{ kJ}$

b. $1.25 \text{ g} \times \dfrac{1 \text{ mol}}{16.04 \text{ g}} \times \dfrac{-890 \text{ kJ}}{1 \text{ mol}} = -69.4 \text{ kJ}$

c. $-1250 \text{ kJ} \times \dfrac{1 \text{ mol}}{-890 \text{ kJ}} = 1.40 \text{ mol} (22.5 \text{ g})$

14.   An atom is said to be in its ground state when it is in its lowest possible energy state. When an atom possesses more energy than its ground state energy, the atom is said to be in an excited state. An atom is promoted from its ground state to an excited state by absorbing energy; when the atom returns from an excited state to its ground state it emits the excess energy as electromagnetic radiation. Atoms do not gain or emit radiation randomly, but rather do so only in discrete bundles of radiation called photons. The photons of radiation emitted by atoms are characterized by the wavelength (color) of the radiation: longer wavelength photons carry less energy than shorter wavelength photons. The energy of a photon emitted by an atom corresponds exactly to the difference in energy between two allowed energy states in an atom: thus, we can use an observable phenomenon (emission of light by excited atoms), to gain insight into the energy changes taking place within the atom.

16.   Bohr pictured the electron moving in only certain circular orbits around the nucleus. Each particular orbit (corresponding to a particular distance from the nucleus) had associated with it a particular energy (resulting from the attraction between the nucleus and the electron). When an atom absorbs energy, the electron moves from its ground state in the orbit closest to the nucleus ($n = 1$) to an orbit farther away from the nucleus ($n = 2, 3, 4, ...$). When an excited atom returns to its ground state, corresponding to the electron moving from an outer orbit to the orbit nearest the nucleus, the atom emits the excess energy as radiation. As the Bohr orbits are of fixed distances from the nucleus and from each other, when an electron moves from one fixed orbit to another, the energy change is of a definite amount. This corresponds to a photon being emitted of a particular characteristic wavelength and energy. The original Bohr theory worked very well for hydrogen: Bohr even predicted emission wavelengths for hydrogen that had not yet been seen, but were subsequently found at the exact wavelengths Bohr had calculated. However, when the simple Bohr model for the atom was applied to the emission spectra of other elements, the theory could not predict or explain the observed emission spectra.

18.   The lowest energy hydrogen atomic orbital is called the 1s orbital. The 1s orbital is spherical in shape (that is, the electron density around the nucleus is uniform in all directions from the nucleus). The 1s orbital represents a probability map of electron density around the nucleus for the first principal energy level. The orbital does not have a sharp edge (it appears fuzzy) because the probability of finding the electron does not drop off suddenly with distance from the nucleus. The orbital does not represent just a spherical surface on which the electron moves (this would be similar to Bohr's original theory). When we draw a picture to represent the 1s orbital we are indicating that the probability of finding the electron within this region of space is greater than 90%. We know that the likelihood of finding the electron within this orbital is very high, but we still don't know exactly where in this region the electron is at a given instant in time.

20.   The third principal energy level of hydrogen is divided into three sublevels, the 3s, 3p, and 3d sublevels. The 3s subshell consists of the single 3s orbital: like the other s orbitals, the 3s orbital is spherical in shape. The 3p subshell consists of a set of three equal-energy 3p orbitals: each of these 3p orbitals has the same shape ("dumbbell"), but each of the 3p orbitals is oriented in a different direction in space. The 3d subshell consists of a set of five 3d orbitals: the 3d orbitals have the shapes indicated in Figure 11.28, and are oriented in different directions around the nucleus (students sometimes say that the 3d orbitals have the shape of a 4-leaf clover). The fourth principal energy level of hydrogen is divided into four sublevels, the 4s, 4p, 4d, and 4f orbitals. The 4s subshell consists of the single 4s orbital. The 4p subshell consists of a set of three 4p orbitals. The 4d subshell consists of a set of five 4d orbitals. The shapes of the 4s, 4p, and 4d orbitals are the same as the shapes of the orbitals of the third principal energy level (the orbitals of the fourth principal energy level are larger and further from the nucleus than the orbitals of the third level, however). The fourth principal energy level, because it is further from the nucleus, also contains a 4f subshell, consisting of seven 4f orbitals (the shapes of the 4f orbitals are beyond the scope of this text).

22.   Atoms have a series of principal energy levels symbolized by the letter n. The $n = 1$ level is the closest to the nucleus, and the energies of the levels increase as the value of n increases going out from the nucleus. Each principal energy level is divided into a set of sublevels of different characteristic shapes (designated by the letters s, p, d, and f). Each sublevel is further subdivided into a set of orbitals: each s subshell consists of a single s orbital; each p subshell consists of a set of three p orbitals; each d subshell consists of a set of five d orbitals; etc. A given orbital can be empty or it can contain one or two electrons, but never more than two electrons (if an orbital contains two electrons, then the electrons must have opposite intrinsic spins). The shape we picture for an orbital represents only a probability map for finding electrons: the shape does not represent a trajectory or pathway for electron movements.

24.   The valence electrons are the electrons in an atom's outermost shell. The valence electrons are those most likely to be involved in chemical reactions because they are at the outside edge of the atom.

26.   From the column and row location of an element, you should be able to determine what the valence shell of an element has for its electronic configuration. For example, the element in the third horizontal row, in the second vertical column, has $3s^2$ as its valence configuration. We know that the valence electrons are in the $n = 3$ shell because the element is in the third horizontal row. We know that the valence electrons are s electrons because the first two electrons in a horizontal row are always in an s subshell. We know that there are two electrons because the element is the second element in the horizontal row. As an additional example, the element in the seventh vertical column of the second horizontal row in the periodic table has valence configuration $2s^2 2p^5$.

28.   The ionization energy of an atom represents the energy required to remove an electron from the atom. As one goes from top to bottom in a vertical group in the periodic table, the ionization energies decrease (it becomes easier to remove an electron). As one goes down within a group, the valence electrons are farther and farther from the nucleus and are less tightly held. The ionization energies increase when going from left to right within a horizontal row within the periodic table. The left-hand side of the periodic table is where the metallic elements are found, which lose electrons relatively easily. The right-hand side of the periodic table is where the nonmetallic elements are found: rather than losing electrons, these elements tend to gain electrons. Within a given horizontal row in the periodic table, the valence electrons are all in the

same principal energy shell: however, as you go from left to right in the horizontal row, the nuclear charge that holds onto the electrons is increasing one unit with each successive element, making it that much more difficult to remove an electron. The relative sizes of atoms also vary systematically with the location of an element in the periodic table. Within a given vertical group, the atoms get progressively larger when going from the top of the group to the bottom: the valence electrons of the atoms are in progressively higher principal energy shells (and are progressively further from the nucleus) as we go down in a group. In going from left to right within a horizontal row in the periodic table, the atoms get progressively smaller. Although all the elements in a given horizontal row in the periodic table have their valence electrons in the same principal energy shell, the nuclear charge is progressively increasing from left to right, making the given valence shell progressively smaller as the electrons are drawn more closely to the nucleus.

30.   Ionic bonding results when elements of very different electronegativities react with each other. Typically a metallic element reacts with a nonmetallic element; the metallic element losing electrons and forming positive ions and the nonmetallic element gaining electrons and forming negative ions. Sodium chloride, NaCl, is an example of a typical ionic compound. The aggregate form of such a compound consists of a crystal lattice of alternating positively and negatively charged ions. A given positive ion is attracted by several surrounding negatively charged ions, and a given negative ion is attracted by several surrounding positively charged ions. Similar electrostatic attractions go on in three dimensions throughout the crystal of ionic solid, leading to a very stable system (with very high melting and boiling points, for example). We know that ionic-bonded solids do not conduct electricity in the solid state (because the ions are held tightly in place by all the attractive forces), but such substances are strong electrolytes when melted or when dissolved in water (either process sets the ions free to move around).

32.   Electronegativity represents the relative ability of an atom in a molecule to attract shared electrons towards itself. In order for a bond to be polar, one of the atoms in the bond must attract the shared electron pair towards itself and away from the other atom of the bond: this can only happen if one atom of the bond is more electronegative than the other (that is, that there is a considerable difference in electronegativity for the two atoms of the bond). The larger the difference in electronegativity between two atoms joined in a bond, the more polar is the bond. Specific examples depend on student choice of elements, but in general, a molecule like Cl_2 would be non-polar because both atoms of the bond have the same electronegativity, whereas a molecule like HCl would be polar because there is an electronegativity difference between the two atoms in the bond.

34.   It has been observed over many experiments that when an active metal like sodium or magnesium reacts with a nonmetal, the sodium atoms always form Na^+ ions and the magnesium atoms always form Mg^{2+} ions. It has been further observed that aluminum always forms only the Al^{3+} ion. When nitrogen, oxygen, or fluorine form simple ions, the ions that are formed are always N^{3-}, O^{2-}, and F^-, respectively. Clearly the facts that these elements always form the same ions and that those ions all contain eight electrons in the outermost shell, led scientists to speculate that there must be something fundamentally stable about a species that has eight electrons in its outermost shell (like the noble gas neon). The repeated observation that so many elements, when reacting, tend to attain an electronic configuration that is isoelectronic with a noble gas led chemists to speculate that all elements try to attain such a configuration for their outermost shells. In general, when atoms of a metal react with atoms of a nonmetal, the metal atoms lose electrons until they have the configuration of the preceding noble gas, and the nonmetal atoms gain electrons until they have the configuration of the following noble gas. Covalently and polar covalently bonded molecules also strive to attain pseudo-noble gas electronic configurations. For a covalently

bonded molecule like F_2, in which neither fluorine atom has a greater tendency than the other to gain or lose electrons completely, each F atom provides one electron of the pair of electrons that constitutes the covalent bond. Each F atom feels also the influence of the other F atom's electron in the shared pair, and each F atom effectively fills its outermost shell. Similarly, in polar covalently bonded molecules like HF or HCl, the shared pair of electrons between the atoms effectively completes the outer electron shell of each atom simultaneously to give each atom a noble gas-like electronic configuration.

36.   Bonding between atoms to form a molecule involves only the valence electrons of the atoms (not the inner core electrons). So when we draw the Lewis structure of a molecule, we show only these valence electrons (both bonding valence electrons and nonbonding valence electrons, however). The most important requisite for the formation of a stable compound (which we try to demonstrate when we write Lewis structures) is that each atom of a molecule attains a noble gas electron configuration. When we write Lewis structures, we arrange the bonding and nonbonding valence electrons to try to complete the octet (or duet) for as many atoms as is possible.

38.   Obviously, you could choose practically any molecule for your discussion. Let's illustrate the method for ammonia, NH_3. First count up the total number of valence electrons available in the molecule (without regard to what atom they officially come from); remember that for the representative elements, the number of valence electrons is indicated by what group the element is found in on the periodic table. For NH_3, because nitrogen is in Group 5, one nitrogen atom would contribute five valence electrons. Because hydrogen atoms only have one electron each, the three hydrogen atoms provide an additional three valence electrons, for a total of eight valence electrons overall. Next write down the symbols for the atoms in the molecule, and use one pair of electrons (represented by a line) to form a bond between each pair of bound atoms.

$$H\!-\!N\!-\!H$$
$$|$$
$$H$$

These three bonds use six of the eight valence electrons. Since each hydrogen already has its duet in what we have drawn so far, while the nitrogen atom only has six electrons around it so far, the final two valence electrons must represent a lone pair on the nitrogen.

$$H\!-\!\overset{..}{N}\!-\!H$$
$$|$$
$$H$$

40.   There are several types of exceptions to the octet rule described in the text. The octet rule is really a "rule of thumb" which we apply to molecules unless we have some evidence that a molecule does not follow the rule. There are some common molecules that, from experimental measurements, we know do not follow the octet rule. Boron and beryllium compounds sometimes do not fit the octet rule. For example, in BF_3, the boron atom only has six valence electrons, whereas in BeF_2, the beryllium atom only has four valence electrons. Other molecules that are exceptions to the octet rule include any molecule with an odd number of valence electrons (such as NO or NO_2): you can't get an octet (an even number) of electrons around each atom in a molecule with an odd number of valence electrons. Even the oxygen gas we breathe is an exception to the octet rule: although we can write a Lewis structure for O_2 satisfying the octet rule for each oxygen, we know from experiment that O_2 contains unpaired electrons (which would not be consistent with a structure in which all the electrons were paired up.)

42.

Valence Pairs	Bond Angle	Example(s)
2	180°	BeF_2, BeH_2
3	120°	BCl_3
4	109.5°	CH_4, CCl_4, GeF_4

44. a. $[Kr] 5s^2$

b. $[Ne] 3s^2 3p^1$

c. $[Ne] 3s^2 3p^5$

d. $[Ar] 4s^1$

e. $[Ne] 3s^2 3p^4$

f. $[Ar] 4s^2 3d^{10} 4p^3$

46.

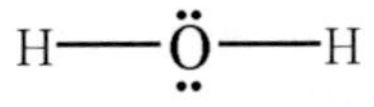 H——Ö——H	4 electron pairs tetrahedrally-oriented on O; non-linear (bent, *V*-shaped) geometry; H–O–H bond angle slightly less than 109.5° because of lone pairs.
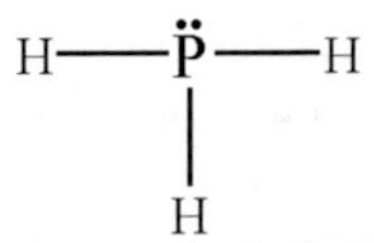 H——P̈——H | H	4 electron pairs tetrahedrally-oriented on P; trigonal pyramidal geometry; H–P–H bond angles slightly less than 109.5° because of lone pair.
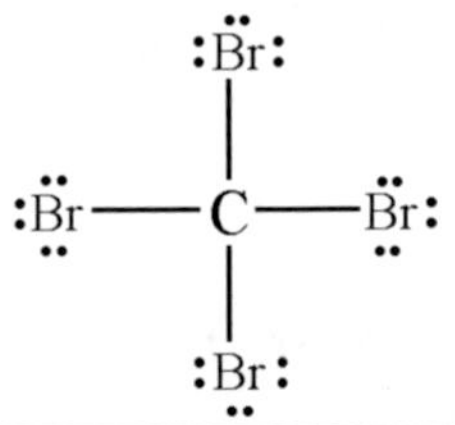 :Br̈: | :Br——C——Br̈: | :Br̈:	4 electron pairs tetrahedrally-oriented on C; overall tetrahedral geometry; Br–C–Br bond angles 109.5°
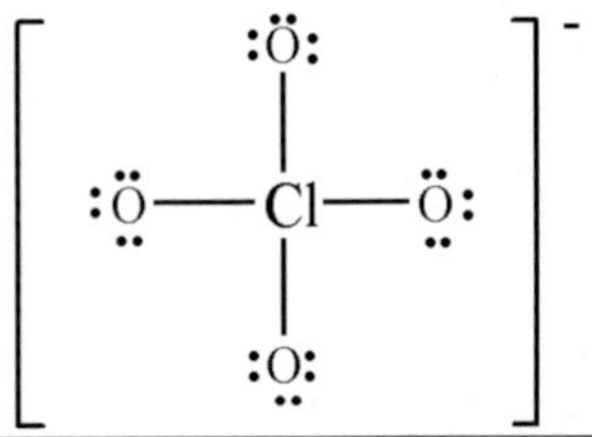 [:Ö: | :Ö——Cl——Ö: | :Ö:]⁻	4 electron pairs tetrahedrally-oriented on Cl; overall tetrahedral geometry; O–Cl–O bond angles 109.5°
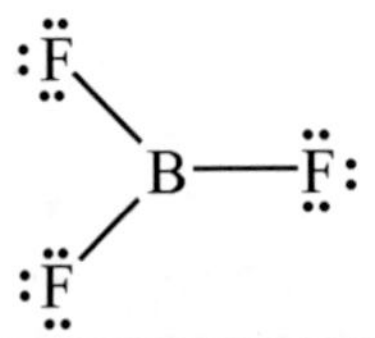 :F̈⟍ B——F̈: :F̈⟋	3 electron pairs trigonally-oriented on B (exception to octet rule); overall trigonal geometry; F–B–F bond angles 120°
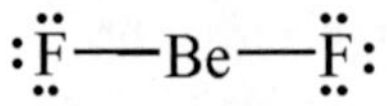 :F̈——Be——F̈:	2 electron pairs linearly-oriented on Be (exception to octet rule); overall linear geometry; F–Be–F bond angle 180°.

CHAPTER 13

Gases

2. Solids and liquids have essentially fixed volumes and are not able to be compressed easily. Gases have volumes that depend on their conditions, and can be compressed or expanded by changes in those conditions. Although the particles of matter in solids are essentially fixed in position (the solid is rigid), the particles in liquids and gases are free to move.

4. Figure 13.2 in the text shows a simple mercury barometer: a tube filled with mercury is inverted over a reservoir (containing mercury) that is open to the atmosphere. When the tube is inverted, the mercury falls to a level at which the pressure of the atmosphere is sufficient to support the column of mercury. One standard atmosphere of pressure is taken to be the pressure capable of supporting a column of mercury to a height of 760.0 mm above the reservoir level.

6. Pressure units include mm Hg, torr, pascals, and psi. The unit "mm Hg" is derived from the barometer, since in a traditional mercury barometer, we measure the height of the mercury column (in millimeters) above the reservoir of mercury.

8. $1.00 \text{ atm} = 760 \text{ torr} = 760 \text{ mm Hg} = 101.325 \text{ kPa} = 14.70 \text{ psi}$

    a. $14.9 \text{ psi} \times \dfrac{1 \text{ atm}}{14.70 \text{ psi}} = 1.01 \text{ atm}$

    b. $795 \text{ torr} \times \dfrac{1 \text{ atm}}{760 \text{ torr}} = 1.05 \text{ atm}$

    c. $743 \text{ mm Hg} \times \dfrac{101.325 \text{ kPa}}{760 \text{ mm Hg}} = 99.1 \text{ kPa}$

    d. $99,436 \text{ Pa} \times \dfrac{1 \text{ kPa}}{1000 \text{ Pa}} = 99.436 \text{ kPa}$

10. $1.00 \text{ atm} = 760 \text{ torr} = 760 \text{ mm Hg} = 101.325 \text{ kPa} = 14.70 \text{ psi}$

    a. $17.3 \text{ psi} \times \dfrac{101.325 \text{ kPa}}{14.70 \text{ psi}} = 119 \text{ kPa}$

    b. $1.15 \text{ atm} \times \dfrac{14.70 \text{ psi}}{1 \text{ atm}} = 16.9 \text{ psi}$

    c. $4.25 \text{ atm} \times \dfrac{760 \text{ mm Hg}}{1 \text{ atm}} = 3.23 \times 10^3 \text{ mm Hg}$

    d. $224 \text{ psi} \times \dfrac{1 \text{ atm}}{14.70 \text{ psi}} = 15.2 \text{ atm}$

12. 1.00 atm $= 760$ torr $= 760$ mm Hg $= 101.325$ kPa $= 14.70$ psi

   a. $6.42 \text{ atm} \times \dfrac{101.325 \text{ kPa}}{1 \text{ atm}} = 651 \text{ kPa}$

   b. $4.21 \text{ atm} \times \dfrac{760 \text{ torr}}{1 \text{ atm}} = 3.20 \times 10^3 \text{ torr}$

   c. $794 \text{ mm Hg} \times \dfrac{1 \text{ atm}}{760 \text{ mm Hg}} = 1.04 \text{ atm}$

   d. $27.2 \text{ psi} \times \dfrac{1 \text{ atm}}{14.70 \text{ psi}} = 1.85 \text{ atm}$

14.   Additional mercury increases the pressure on the gas sample, causing the volume of the gas upon which the pressure is exerted to decrease (Boyle's Law)

16. $PV = k; \quad P_1V_1 = P_2V_2$

18.   a. $P_1 = 1.15 \text{ atm}$ $P_2 = 775 \text{ mm Hg} = 1.020 \text{ atm}$

           $V_1 = 375 \text{ mL}$ $V_2 = ?$

           $V_2 = \dfrac{P_1V_1}{P_2} = \dfrac{(1.15 \text{ atm})(375 \text{ mL})}{(1.020 \text{ atm})} = 423 \text{ mL}$

   b. $P_1 = 1.08 \text{ atm}$ $P_2 = 135 \text{ kPa} = 1.33 \text{ atm}$

           $V_1 = 195 \text{ mL}$ $V_2 = ?$

           $V_2 = \dfrac{P_1V_1}{P_2} = \dfrac{(1.08 \text{ atm})(195 \text{ mL})}{(1.33 \text{ atm})} = 158 \text{ mL}$

   c. $P_1 = 131 \text{ kPa} = 982.6 \text{ mm Hg}$ $P_2 = 765 \text{ mm Hg}$

           $V_1 = 6.75 \text{ L}$ $V_2 = ?$

           $V_2 = \dfrac{P_1V_1}{P_2} = \dfrac{(982.6 \text{ mm Hg})(6.75 \text{ L})}{(765 \text{ mm Hg})} = 8.67 \text{ L}$

20.   a. $P_1 = 755 \text{ mm Hg}$ $P_2 = ?$

           $V_1 = 125 \text{ mL}$ $V_2 = 137 \text{ mL}$

           $P_2 = \dfrac{P_1V_1}{V_2} = \dfrac{(755 \text{ mm Hg})(125 \text{ mL})}{(137 \text{ mL})} = 689 \text{ mm Hg}$

   b. $P_1 = 1.08 \text{ atm}$ $P_2 = ?$

           $V_1 = 331 \text{ mL}$ $V_2 = 299 \text{ mL}$

           $P_2 = \dfrac{P_1V_1}{V_2} = \dfrac{(1.08 \text{ atm})(331 \text{ mL})}{(299 \text{ mL})} = 1.20 \text{ atm}$

c. $P_1 = 789$ mm Hg $P_2 = 135$ kPa $= 1013$ mm Hg

      $V_1 = 3.02$ L $V_2 = ?$

$$V_2 = \frac{P_1 V_1}{P_2} = \frac{(789 \text{ mm Hg})(3.02 \text{ L})}{(1013 \text{ mm Hg})} = 2.35 \text{ L}$$

22. $P_1 = P_1$ $P_2 = 2 \times P_1$

      $V_1 = 1.04$ L $V_2 = ?$ L

$$V_2 = \frac{P_1 V_1}{P_2} = \frac{(P_1)(1.04 \text{ L})}{(2 \times P_1)} = \frac{1.04 \text{ L}}{2} = 0.520 \text{ L}$$

24. $P_2 = \dfrac{P_1 V_1}{V_2} = \dfrac{(1.00 \text{ atm})(27.2 \text{ mL})}{(1.00 \text{ mL})} = 27.2 \text{ atm}$

26.   Charles's Law indicates that an ideal gas decreases by 1/273 of its volume for every degree Celsius its temperature is lowered. This means an ideal gas would approach a volume of zero at –273°C.

28. $V = kT$; $V_1/T_1 = V_2/T_2$

30. $V_1 = 375$ mL $V_2 = ?$ mL

      $T_1 = 78°C = 351$ K $T_2 = 22°C = 295$ K

$$V_2 = \frac{V_1 T_2}{T_1} = \frac{(375 \text{ mL})(295 \text{ K})}{(351 \text{ K})} = 315 \text{ mL}$$

32.   a. $V_1 = 73.5$ mL $V_2 = ?$ L

            $T_1 = 0°C = 273$ K $T_2 = 25°C = 298$ K

$$V_2 = \frac{V_1 T_2}{T_1} = \frac{(73.5 \text{ mL})(298 \text{ K})}{(273 \text{ K})} = 80.2 \text{ mL}$$

        b. $V_1 = 15.2$ L $V_2 = 10.0$ L

            $T_1 = 25°C = 298$ K $T_2 = ?°C$

$$T_2 = \frac{V_2 T_1}{V_1} = \frac{(10.0 \text{ L})(298 \text{ K})}{(15.2 \text{ L})} = 196 \text{ K} = -77°C$$

        c. $V_1 = 1.75$ mL $V_2 = ?$ mL

            $T_1 = 2.3$ K $T_2 = 0°C = 273$ K

$$V_2 = \frac{V_1 T_2}{T_1} = \frac{(1.75 \text{ mL})(273 \text{ K})}{(2.3 \text{ K})} = 208 \text{ mL} \ (2.1 \times 10^2 \text{ mL})$$

34. a. $V_1 = 2.01 \times 10^2$ L $V_2 = 5.00$ L

$T_1 = 1150°C = 1423$ K $T_2 = ?°C$

$$T_2 = \frac{V_2 T_1}{V_1} = \frac{(5.00 \text{ L})(1423 \text{ K})}{(201 \text{ L})} = 35.4 \text{ K} = -238°C$$

b. $V_1 = 44.2$ mL $V_2 = ?$ mL

$T_1 = 298$ K $T_2 = 0$

$$V_2 = \frac{V_1 T_2}{T_1} = \frac{(44.2 \text{ mL})(0 \text{ K})}{(298 \text{ K})} = 0 \text{ mL (0 K is absolute zero)}$$

c. $V_1 = 44.2$ mL $V_2 = ?$ mL

$T_1 = 298$ K $T_2 = 0°C = 273$ K

$$V_2 = \frac{V_1 T_2}{T_1} = \frac{(44.2 \text{ mL})(273 \text{ K})}{(298 \text{ K})} = 40.5 \text{ mL}$$

36. $V_2 = \dfrac{V_1 T_2}{T_1} = \dfrac{(125 \text{ mL})(250 \text{ K})}{(450 \text{ K})} = 69.4 \text{ mL} = 69$ mL to two significant figures

38. $V_2 = \dfrac{V_1 T_2}{T_1}$

Temp, °C	90	80	70	60	50	40	30	20
Volume, mL	124	121	117	113	110	107	103	100

40. $V = an$; $V_1/n_1 = V_2/n_2$

42. $V = an$; $V_1/n_1 = V_2/n_2$

Since 2.08 g of chlorine contains twice the number of moles of gas contained in the 1.04 g sample, the volume of the 2.08 g sample will be twice as large $= 1744$ (1.74×10^3) mL

44. molar mass of Ar $= 39.95$ g

$2.71 \text{ g Ar} \times \dfrac{1 \text{ mol}}{39.95 \text{ g}} = 0.0678 \text{ mol Ar}$

$4.21 \text{ L} \times \dfrac{1.29 \text{ mol}}{0.0678 \text{ mol}} = 80.1 \text{ L}$

46. Real gases most closely approach ideal gas behavior under conditions of relatively high temperatures (0°C or higher) and relatively low pressures (1 atm or lower).

48. For an ideal gas, $PV = nRT$ is true under any conditions. Consider a particular sample of gas (so that n remains constant) at a particular fixed pressure (so that P remains constant also). Suppose that at temperature T_1 the volume of the gas sample is V_1. Then for this set of conditions, the ideal gas equation would be given by

$$PV_1 = nRT_1.$$

If we then change the temperature of the gas sample to a new temperature T_2, the volume of the gas sample changes to a new volume V_2. For this new set of conditions, the ideal gas equation would be given by

$$PV_2 = nRT_2.$$

If we make a ratio of these two expressions for the ideal gas equation for this gas sample, and cancel out terms that are constant for this situation (P, n, and R) we get

$$\frac{PV_1}{PV_2} = \frac{nRT_1}{nRT_2}$$

$$\frac{V_1}{V_2} = \frac{T_1}{T_2}$$

This can be rearranged to the familiar form of Charles's law

$$\frac{V_1}{T_1} = \frac{V_2}{T_2}$$

50. a. $P = 782$ mm Hg $= 1.03$ atm; $T = 27°C = 300$ K

$$V = \frac{nRT}{P} = \frac{(0.210 \text{ mol})(0.08206 \text{ L atm mol}^{-1} \text{ K}^{-1})(300 \text{ K})}{(1.03 \text{ atm})} = 5.02 \text{ L}$$

b. $V = 644$ mL $= 0.644$ L

$$P = \frac{nRT}{V} = \frac{(0.0921 \text{ mol})(0.08206 \text{ L atm mol}^{-1} \text{ K}^{-1})(303 \text{ K})}{(0.644 \text{ L})} = 3.56 \text{ atm}$$

$$= 2.70 \times 10^3 \text{ mm Hg}$$

c. $P = 745$ mm $= 0.980$ atm

$$T = \frac{PV}{nR} = \frac{(0.980 \text{ atm})(11.2 \text{ L})}{(0.401 \text{ mol})(0.08206 \text{ L atm mol}^{-1} \text{ K}^{-1})} = 334 \text{ K}$$

52.   molar mass Ar $= 39.95$ g; $25°C = 298$ K

$$12.2 \text{ g Ar} \times \frac{1 \text{ mol Ar}}{39.95 \text{ g Ar}} = 0.3054 \text{ mol Ar}$$

$$P = \frac{nRT}{V} = \frac{(0.3054 \text{ mol})(0.08206 \text{ L atm mol}^{-1} \text{ K}^{-1})(298 \text{ K})}{(10.0 \text{ L})} = 0.747 \text{ atm}$$

54.   molar mass Ar $= 39.95$ g; 40.0 g $= 1.001$ mol

$$T = \frac{PV}{nR} = \frac{(1.00 \text{ atm})(25.00 \text{ L})}{(1.001 \text{ mol})(0.08206 \text{ L atm mol}^{-1} \text{ K}^{-1})} = 304 \text{ K} = 31°C$$

56.   molar mass Ne = 20.18 g; 25°C = 298 K; 50°C = 323 K

$$1.25 \text{ g Ne} \times \frac{1 \text{ mol}}{20.18 \text{ g}} = 0.06194 \text{ mol}$$

$$P = \frac{nRT}{V} = \frac{(0.06194 \text{ mol})(0.08206 \text{ L atm mol}^{-1} \text{ K}^{-1})(298 \text{ K})}{(10.1 \text{ L})} = 0.150 \text{ atm}$$

$$P = \frac{nRT}{V} = \frac{(0.06194 \text{ mol})(0.08206 \text{ L atm mol}^{-1} \text{ K}^{-1})(323 \text{ K})}{(10.1 \text{ L})} = 0.163 \text{ atm}$$

58.   molar mass O_2 = 32.00 g; 784 mm Hg = 1.032 atm

$$4.25 \text{ g } O_2 \times \frac{1 \text{ mol } O_2}{32.00 \text{ g } O_2} = 0.1328 \text{ mol}$$

$$T = \frac{PV}{nR} = \frac{(1.032 \text{ atm})(2.51 \text{ L})}{(0.1328 \text{ mol})(0.08206 \text{ L atm mol}^{-1} \text{ K}^{-1})} = 238 \text{ K} = -35°C$$

60.   Molar masses: He, 4.003 g; Ar, 39.95 g

$$4.15 \text{ g He} \times \frac{1 \text{ mol He}}{4.003 \text{ g He}} = 1.037 \text{ mol He}$$

$$56.2 \text{ g Ar} \times \frac{1 \text{ mol Ar}}{39.95 \text{ g Ar}} = 1.407 \text{ mol Ar}$$

$$\text{For He, } P = \frac{nRT}{V} = \frac{(1.037 \text{ mol})(0.08206 \text{ L atm mol}^{-1} \text{ K}^{-1})(298 \text{ K})}{(5.00 \text{ L})} = 5.07 \text{ atm}$$

$$\text{For Ar, } P = \frac{nRT}{V} = \frac{(1.407 \text{ mol})(0.08206 \text{ L atm mol}^{-1} \text{ K}^{-1})(303 \text{ K})}{(10.00 \text{ L})} = 3.50 \text{ atm}$$

The helium is at a higher pressure than the argon.

62.   molar mass Ar = 39.95 g; 29°C = 302 K; 42°C = 315 K

$$1.29 \text{ g Ar} \times \frac{1 \text{ mol Ar}}{39.95 \text{ g Ar}} = 0.03329 \text{ mol Ar}$$

$$P = \frac{nRT}{V} = \frac{(0.03329 \text{ mol})(0.08206 \text{ L atm mol}^{-1} \text{ K}^{-1})(302 \text{ K})}{(2.41 \text{ L})} = 0.332 \text{ atm}$$

$$P = \frac{nRT}{V} = \frac{(0.03329 \text{ mol})(0.08206 \text{ L atm mol}^{-1} \text{ K}^{-1})(315 \text{ K})}{(2.41 \text{ L})} = 0.346 \text{ atm}$$

64.   Molar mass of H_2O = 18.02 g; 2.0 mL = 0.0020 L; 225°C = 498 K

$$0.250 \text{ g } H_2O \times \frac{1 \text{ mol } H_2O}{18.02 \text{ g } H_2O} = 0.01387 \text{ mol } H_2O$$

$$P = \frac{nRT}{V} = \frac{(0.01387 \text{ mol})(0.08206 \text{ L atm mol}^{-1} \text{ K}^{-1})(498 \text{ K})}{(0.0020 \text{ L})} = 283 \text{ atm} = 2.8 \times 10^2 \text{ atm}$$

66.   As a gas is bubbled through water, the bubbles of gas become saturated with water vapor, thus forming a gaseous mixture. The total pressure in a sample of gas that has been collected by bubbling through water is made up of two components: the pressure of the gas of interest and the pressure of water vapor. The partial pressure of the gas of interest is then the total pressure of the sample minus the vapor pressure of water.

68.   molar masses: Ne, 20.18 g; Ar, 39.95 g; 27°C = 300 K

$$1.28 \text{ g Ne} \times \frac{1 \text{ mol Ne}}{20.18 \text{ g Ne}} = 0.06343 \text{ mol Ne}$$

$$2.49 \text{ g Ar} \times \frac{1 \text{ mol Ar}}{39.95 \text{ g Ar}} = 0.06233 \text{ mol Ar}$$

$$P_{neon} = \frac{n_{neon}RT}{V} = \frac{(0.06343 \text{ mol})(0.08206 \text{ L atm mol}^{-1} \text{ K}^{-1})(300 \text{ K})}{(9.87 \text{ L})} = 0.1582 \text{ atm}$$

$$P_{argon} = \frac{n_{argon}RT}{V} = \frac{(0.06233 \text{ mol})(0.08206 \text{ L atm mol}^{-1} \text{ K}^{-1})(300 \text{ K})}{(9.87 \text{ L})} = 0.1555 \text{ atm}$$

P_{total} = 0.1582 atm + 0.1555 atm = 0.314 atm

70.   925 mm Hg = 1.217 atm; 26°C = 299 K; molar masses: Ne, 20.18 g; Ar, 39.95 g

$$n = \frac{PV}{RT} = \frac{(1.217 \text{ atm})(3.00 \text{ L})}{(0.08206 \text{ L atm mol}^{-1} \text{ K}^{-1})(299 \text{ K})} = 0.1488 \text{ mol}$$

The number of moles of an ideal gas required to fill a given-sized container to a particular pressure at a particular temperature does not depend on the specific identity of the gas. So 0.1488 mol of Ne gas or 0.1488 mol of Ar gas would give the same pressure in the same flask at the same temperature.

$$\text{mass Ne} = 0.1488 \text{ mol Ne} \times \frac{20.18 \text{ g Ne}}{1 \text{ mol Ne}} = 3.00 \text{ g Ne}$$

$$\text{mass Ar} = 0.1488 \text{ mol Ar} \times \frac{39.95 \text{ g Ar}}{1 \text{ mol Ar}} = 5.94 \text{ g Ar}$$

72.   molar masses: He, 4.003 g; Ar, 39.95 g; 273°C = 546 K

$$1.15 \text{ g He} \times \frac{1 \text{ mol He}}{4.003 \text{ g Ne}} = 0.2873 \text{ mol He}$$

$$2.91 \text{ g Ar} \times \frac{1 \text{ mol Ar}}{39.95 \text{ g Ar}} = 0.07284 \text{ mol Ar}$$

$$P_{helium} = \frac{n_{helium} RT}{V} = \frac{(0.2873 \text{ mol})(0.08206 \text{ L atm mol}^{-1} \text{ K}^{-1})(546 \text{ K})}{(5.25 \text{ L})} = 2.452 \text{ atm}$$

$$P_{argon} = \frac{n_{argon} RT}{V} = \frac{(0.07284 \text{ mol})(0.08206 \text{ L atm mol}^{-1} \text{ K}^{-1})(546 \text{ K})}{(5.25 \text{ L})} = 0.6216 \text{ atm}$$

$$P_{total} = 0.1582 \text{ atm} + 0.1555 \text{ atm} = 3.07 \text{ atm}$$

74.   1.032 atm = 784.3 mm Hg; molar mass of Zn = 65.38 g

$P_{hydrogen}$ = 784.3 mm Hg – 32 mm Hg = 752.3 mm Hg = 0.990 atm

V = 240 mL = 0.240 L; T = 30°C + 273 = 303 K

$$n_{hydrogen} = \frac{PV}{RT} = \frac{(0.990 \text{ atm})(0.240 \text{ L})}{(0.08206 \text{ L atm mol}^{-1} \text{ K}^{-1})(303 \text{ K})} = 0.00956 \text{ mol hydrogen}$$

$$0.00956 \text{ mol H}_2 \times \frac{1 \text{ mol Zn}}{1 \text{ mol H}_2} = 0.00956 \text{ mol of Zn must have reacted}$$

$$0.00956 \text{ mol Zn} \times \frac{65.38 \text{ g Zn}}{1 \text{ mol Zn}} = 0.625 \text{ g Zn must have reacted}$$

76.   A theory is successful if it explains known experimental observations. Theories that have been successful in the past may not be successful in the future (for example, as technology evolves, more sophisticated experiments may be possible in the future).

78.   pressure

80.   no

82.   If the temperature of a sample of gas is increased, the average kinetic energy of the particles of gas increases. This means that the speeds of the particles increase. If the particles have a higher speed, they will hit the walls of the container more frequently and with greater force, thereby increasing the pressure.

84.   Standard Temperature and Pressure, STP = 0°C, 1 atm pressure. These conditions were chosen because they are easy to attain and reproduce *experimentally*. The barometric pressure within a laboratory is likely to be near 1 atm most days, and 0°C can be attained with a simple ice bath.

86.   Molar mass of C = 12.01 g; 25°C = 298 K

$$1.25 \text{ g C} \times \frac{1 \text{ mol}}{12.01 \text{ g}} = 0.1041 \text{ mol C}$$

Since the balanced chemical equation shows a 1:1 stoichiometric relationship between C and O_2, then 0.1041 mol of O_2 will be needed

$$V = \frac{nRT}{P} = \frac{(0.1041 \text{ mol})(0.08206 \text{ L atm mol}^{-1} \text{ K}^{-1})(298 \text{ K})}{(1.02 \text{ atm})} = 2.50 \text{ L } O_2$$

88. Molar mass of Mg = 24.31 g; STP: 1.00 atm, 273 K

$$1.02 \text{ g Mg} \times \frac{1 \text{ mol}}{24.31 \text{ g}} = 0.0420 \text{ mol Mg}$$

As the coefficients for Mg and Cl_2 in the balanced equation are the same, for 0.0420 mol of Mg reacting we will need 0.0420 mol of Cl_2.

$$V = 0.0420 \text{ mol } Cl_2 \times \frac{22.4 \text{ L}}{1 \text{ mol}} = 0.941 \text{ L } Cl_2 \text{ at STP.}$$

90. molar mass CaC_2 = 64.10 g; 25°C = 298 K

$$2.49 \text{ g } CaC_2 \times \frac{1 \text{ mol}}{64.10 \text{ g}} = 0.03885 \text{ mol } CaC_2$$

From the balanced chemical equation for the reaction, 0.03885 mol of CaC_2 reacting completely would generate 0.03885 mol of acetylene, C_2H_2

$$V = \frac{nRT}{P} = \frac{(0.03885 \text{ mol})(0.08206 \text{ L atm mol}^{-1} \text{ K}^{-1})(298 \text{ K})}{(1.01 \text{ atm})} = 0.941 \text{ L}$$

$$V = \frac{nRT}{P} = \frac{(0.03885 \text{ mol})(0.08206 \text{ L atm mol}^{-1} \text{ K}^{-1})(273 \text{ K})}{(1.00 \text{ atm})} = 0.870 \text{ L at STP}$$

92. Molar mass of Mg_3N_2 = 100.95 g; T = 24°C = 297 K; P = 752 mm Hg = 0.989 atm

$$10.3 \text{ g } Mg_3N_2 \times \frac{1 \text{ mol}}{100.95 \text{ g}} = 0.102 \text{ mol } Mg_3N_2$$

From the balanced chemical equation, the amount of NH_3 produced will be

$$0.102 \text{ mol } Mg_3N_2 \times \frac{2 \text{ mol } NH_3}{1 \text{ mol } Mg_3N_2} = 0.204 \text{ mol } NH_3$$

$$V = \frac{nRT}{P} = \frac{(0.204 \text{ mol})(0.08206 \text{ L atm mol}^{-1} \text{ K}^{-1})(297 \text{ K})}{(0.989 \text{ atm})} = 5.03 \text{ L}$$

This assumes that the ammonia was collected dry.

94. Molar masses: O_2, 32.00 g; N_2, 28.02 g; T = 35°C = 308 K; P = 755 mm Hg = 0.993 atm

$$26.2 \text{ g } O_2 \times \frac{1 \text{ mol } O_2}{32.00 \text{ g } O_2} = 0.819 \text{ mol } O_2$$

$$35.1 \text{ g N}_2 \times \frac{1 \text{ mol N}_2}{28.02 \text{ g N}_2} = 1.25 \text{ mol N}_2$$

total moles $= 0.819 \text{ mol} + 1.25 \text{ mol} = 2.07 \text{ mol}$

$$V = \frac{nRT}{P} = \frac{(2.07 \text{ mol})(0.08206 \text{ L atm mol}^{-1} \text{ K}^{-1})(308 \text{ K})}{(0.993 \text{ atm})} = 52.7 \text{ L}$$

96.   molar masses: He, 4.003 g; Ar, 39.95 g

$$5.02 \text{ g He} \times \frac{1 \text{ mol He}}{4.003 \text{ g He}} = 1.254 \text{ mol He}$$

$$1.254 \text{ mol He} \times \frac{22.4 \text{ L}}{1 \text{ mol}} = 28.1 \text{ L}$$

$$42.1 \text{ g Ar} \times \frac{1 \text{ mol Ar}}{39.95 \text{ g Ar}} = 1.054 \text{ mol Ar}$$

$$1.054 \text{ mol Ar} \times \frac{22.4 \text{ L}}{1 \text{ mol}} = 23.6 \text{ L}$$

98.   Molar masses: He, 4.003 g; Ne, 20.18 g

$$6.25 \text{ g He} \times \frac{1 \text{ mol He}}{4.003 \text{ g He}} = 1.561 \text{ mol He}$$

$$4.97 \text{ g Ne} \times \frac{1 \text{ mol Ne}}{20.18 \text{ g Ne}} = 0.2463 \text{ mol Ne}$$

$n_{\text{total}} = 1.561 \text{ mol} + 0.2463 \text{ mol} = 1.807 \text{ mol}$

As 1 mol of an ideal gas occupies 22.4 L at STP, the volume is given by

$$1.807 \text{ mol} \times \frac{22.4 \text{ L}}{1 \text{ mol}} = 40.48 \text{ L} = 40.5 \text{ L}.$$

The partial pressure of a given gas in a mixture will be proportional to what *fraction* of the total number of moles of gas the given gas represents

$$P_{\text{He}} = \frac{1.561 \text{ mol He}}{1.807 \text{ mol total}} \times 1.00 \text{ atm} = 0.8639 \text{ atm} = 0.864 \text{ atm}$$

$$P_{\text{Ne}} = \frac{0.2463 \text{ mol Ne}}{1.807 \text{ mol total}} \times 1.00 \text{ atm} = 0.1363 \text{ atm} = 0.136 \text{ atm}$$

100. $2C_2H_2(g) + 5O_2(g) \rightarrow 2H_2O(g) + 4CO_2(g)$

molar mass $C_2H_2 = 26.04 \text{ g}$

$$1.00 \text{ g C}_2\text{H}_2 \times \frac{1 \text{ mol}}{26.04 \text{ g}} = 0.0384 \text{ mol C}_2\text{H}_2$$

From the balanced chemical equation, $2 \times 0.0384 = 0.0768$ mol of CO_2 will be produced.

$$0.0768 \text{ mol } CO_2 \times \frac{22.4 \text{ L}}{1 \text{ mol}} = 1.72 \text{ L at STP}$$

102.   125 mL = 0.125 L

$$0.125 \text{ L} \times \frac{1 \text{ mol}}{22.4 \text{ L}} = 0.00558 \text{ mol } H_2$$

From the balanced chemical equation, one mole of zinc is required for each mole of hydrogen produced. Therefore, 0.00558 mol of Zn will be required.

$$0.00558 \text{ mol Zn} \times \frac{65.38 \text{ g Zn}}{1 \text{ mol}} = 0.365 \text{ g Zn}$$

104.   twice

106.   a. $PV = k; \; P_1V_1 = P_2V_2$

       b. $V = kT; \; V_1/T_1 = V_2/T_2$

       c. $V = an; \; V_1/n_1 = V_2/n_2$

       d. $PV = nRT$

       e. $P_1V_1/T_1 = P_2V_2/T_2$

108.   First determine what volume the helium in the tank would have if it were at a pressure of 755 mm Hg (corresponding to the pressure the gas will have in the balloons).

8.40 atm = 6384 mm Hg

$$V_2 = (25.2 \text{ L}) \times \frac{6384 \text{ mm Hg}}{755 \text{ mm Hg}} = 213 \text{ L}$$

Allowing for the fact that 25.2 L of He will have to remain in the tank, this leaves $213 - 25.2 = 187.8$ L of He for filling the balloons.

$$187.8 \text{ L He} \times \frac{1 \text{ balloon}}{1.50 \text{ L He}} = 125 \text{ balloons}$$

110.   According to the balanced chemical equation, when 1 mol of $(NH_4)_2CO_3$ reacts, a total of 4 moles of gaseous substances is produced.

molar mass $(NH_4)_2CO_3 = 96.09$ g; 453 °C = 726 K

$$52.0 \text{ g} \times \frac{1 \text{ mol}}{96.09 \text{ g}} = 0.541 \text{ mol}$$

As 0.541 mol of $(NH_4)_2CO_3$ reacts, $4(0.541) = 2.16$ mol of gaseous products result.

$$V = \frac{nRT}{P} = \frac{(2.16 \text{ mol})(0.08206 \text{ L atm mol}^{-1} \text{ K}^{-1})(726 \text{ K})}{(1.04 \text{ atm})} = 124 \text{ L}$$

112. $CaCO_3(s) + 2H^+(aq) \rightarrow Ca^{2+}(aq) + H_2O(l) + CO_2(g)$

molar mass $CaCO_3$ = 100.1 g; 60°C + 273 = 333 K

$$10.0 \text{ g } CaCO_3 \times \frac{1 \text{ mol}}{100.1 \text{ g}} = 0.0999 \text{ mol } CaCO_3 = 0.0999 \text{ mol } CO_2 \text{ also}$$

$P_{\text{carbon dioxide}} = P_{\text{total}} - P_{\text{water vapor}}$

$P_{\text{carbon dioxide}} = 774 \text{ mm Hg} - 149.4 \text{ mm Hg} = 624.6 \text{ mm Hg} = 0.822 \text{ atm}$

$$V_{wet} = \frac{nRT}{P} = \frac{(0.0999 \text{ mol})(0.08206 \text{ L atm mol}^{-1} \text{ K}^{-1})(333 \text{ K})}{(0.822 \text{ atm})} = 3.32 \text{ L wet } CO_2$$

$$V_{dry} = 3.32 \text{ L} \times \frac{624.6 \text{ mm Hg}}{774 \text{ mm Hg}} = 2.68 \text{ L}$$

114. $2KClO_3(s) \rightarrow 2KCl(s) + 3O_2(g)$

molar mass $KClO_3$ = 122.6 g; 25°C + 273 = 298 K; 630. torr = 0.829 atm

$$50.0 \text{ g } KClO_3 \times \frac{1 \text{ mol } KClO_3}{122.6 \text{ g } KClO_3} = 0.408 \text{ mol } KClO_3$$

$$0.408 \text{ mol } KClO_3 \times \frac{3 \text{ mol } O_2}{2 \text{ mol } KClO_3} = 0.612 \text{ mol } O_2$$

$$V = \frac{nRT}{P} = \frac{(0.612 \text{ mol})(0.08206 \text{ L atm mol}^{-1} \text{ K}^{-1})(298 \text{ K})}{(0.829 \text{ atm})} = 18.1 \text{ L } O_2$$

116.   a. $752 \text{ mm Hg} \times \dfrac{101,325 \text{ Pa}}{760 \text{ mm Hg}} = 1.00 \times 10^5 \text{ Pa}$

b. $458 \text{ kPa} \times \dfrac{1 \text{ atm}}{101.325 \text{ kPa}} = 4.52 \text{ atm}$

c. $1.43 \text{ atm} \times \dfrac{760 \text{ mm Hg}}{1 \text{ atm}} = 1.09 \times 10^3 \text{ mm Hg}$

d.   842 torr = 842 mm Hg

118.   a. $645 \text{ mm Hg} \times \dfrac{101,325 \text{ Pa}}{760 \text{ mm Hg}} = 8.60 \times 10^4 \text{ Pa}$

b. $221 \text{ kPa} = 221 \times 10^3 \text{ Pa} = 2.21 \times 10^5 \text{ Pa}$

c. $0.876 \text{ atm} \times \dfrac{101,325 \text{ Pa}}{1 \text{ atm}} = 8.88 \times 10^4 \text{ Pa}$

d. $32 \text{ torr} \times \dfrac{101,325 \text{ Pa}}{760 \text{ torr}} = 4.3 \times 10^3 \text{ Pa}$

120.   a.   1.00 mm Hg = 1.00 torr

$$V = 255 \text{ mL} \times \frac{1.00 \text{ torr}}{2.00 \text{ torr}} = 128 \text{ mL}$$

b.   1.0 atm = 101.325 kPa

$$V = 1.3 \text{ L} \times \frac{1.0 \text{ kPa}}{101.325 \text{ kPa}} = 1.3 \times 10^{-2} \text{ L}$$

c.   1.0 mm Hg = 0.133 kPa

$$V = 1.3 \text{ L} \times \frac{1.0 \text{ kPa}}{0.133 \text{ kPa}} = 9.8 \text{ L}$$

122. $1.52 \text{ L} = 1.52 \times 10^3 \text{ mL}$

$$755 \text{ mm Hg} \times \frac{1.52 \times 10^3 \text{ mL}}{450 \text{ mL}} = 2.55 \times 10^3 \text{ mm Hg}$$

124.   a. $74°C + 273 = 347 \text{ K}; -74°C + 273 = 199 \text{ K}$

$$100. \text{ mL} \times \frac{199 \text{ K}}{347 \text{ K}} = 57.3 \text{ mL}$$

b. $100°C + 273 = 373 \text{ K}$

$$373 \text{ K} \times \frac{600 \text{ mL}}{500 \text{ mL}} = 448 \text{ K } (175°C)$$

c.   zero (the volume of any gas sample becomes zero at 0 K)

126. $12°C + 273 = 285 \text{ K}; 192°C + 273 = 465 \text{ K}$

$$75.2 \text{ mL} \times \frac{465 \text{ K}}{285 \text{ K}} = 123 \text{ mL}$$

128.   For a given gas, the number of moles present in a sample is directly proportional to the mass of the sample. The problem therefore can be solved even though the gas is not identified (so that its molar mass is not known).

$$23.2 \text{ g} \times \frac{10.4 \text{ L}}{93.2 \text{ L}} = 2.59 \text{ g}$$

130.   a. $V = 21.2 \text{ mL} = 0.0212 \text{ L}$

$$T = \frac{PV}{nR} = \frac{(1.034 \text{ atm})(0.0212 \text{ L})}{(0.00432 \text{ mol})(0.08206 \text{ L atm mol}^{-1} \text{ K}^{-1})} = 61.8 \text{ K}$$

b. $V = 1.73 \text{ mL} = 0.00173 \text{ L}$

$$P = \frac{nRT}{V} = \frac{(0.000115 \text{ mol})(0.08206 \text{ L atm mol}^{-1} \text{ K}^{-1})(182 \text{ K})}{(0.00173 \text{ L})} = 0.993 \text{ atm}$$

c. $P = 1.23$ mm Hg $= 0.00162$ atm; $T = 152°C + 273 = 425$ K

$$V = \frac{nRT}{P} = \frac{(0.773 \text{ mol})(0.08206 \text{ L atm mol}^{-1} \text{ K}^{-1})(425 \text{ K})}{(0.00162 \text{ atm})} = 1.66 \times 10^4 \text{ L}$$

132. $27°C + 273 = 300$ K

The number of moles of gas it takes to fill the 100. L tanks to 120 atm at 27°C is independent of the identity of the gas.

$$n = \frac{PV}{RT} = \frac{(120 \text{ atm})(100. \text{ L})}{(0.08206 \text{ L atm mol}^{-1} \text{ K}^{-1})(300 \text{ K})} = = 487 \text{ mol}$$

487 mol of *any* gas will fill the tanks to the required specifications.

molar masses: CH_4, 16.0 g; N_2, 28.0 g; CO_2, 44.0 g

for CH_4: (487 mol)(16.0 g/mol) = 7792 g = 7.79 kg CH_4

for N_2: (487 mol)(28.0 g/mol) = 13,636 g = 13.6 kg N_2

for CO_2: (487 mol)(44.0 g/mol) = 21,428 g = 21.4 kg CO_2

134.   molar mass of O_2 = 32.00 g; 55 mg = 0.055 g

$$n = 0.055 \text{ g} \times \frac{1 \text{ mol } O_2}{32.00 \text{ g } O_2} = 0.0017 \text{ mol}$$

$V = 100.$ mL $= 0.100$ L; $T = 26°C + 273 = 299$ K

$$P = \frac{nRT}{V} = \frac{(0.0017 \text{ mol})(0.08206 \text{ L atm mol}^{-1} \text{ K}^{-1})(299 \text{ K})}{(0.100 \text{ L})} = 0.42 \text{ atm}$$

136. $P_1 = 1.13$ atm $P_2 = 1.89$ atm

$V_1 = 100$ mL $= 0.100$ L $V_2 = 500$ mL $= 0.500$ L

$T_1 = 300$ K $T_2 = ?$

$$T_2 = \frac{T_1 P_2 V_2}{P_1 V_1} = \frac{(300 \text{ K})(1.89 \text{ atm})(0.500 \text{ L})}{(1.13 \text{ atm})(0.100 \text{ L})} = 2.51 \times 10^3 \text{ K}$$

Note that the calculation could have been carried through with the two volumes expressed in milliliters because the universal gas constant does not appear explicitly in this form of the ideal gas equation.

138.   molar masses: N_2, 28.02 g; He, 4.003 g; STP: 1.00 atm, 273 K

$$12.1 \text{ g } N_2 \times \frac{1 \text{ mol } N_2}{28.02 \text{ g } N_2} = 0.432 \text{ mol } N_2$$

$$4.05 \text{ g He} \times \frac{1 \text{ mol He}}{4.003 \text{ g He}} = 1.01 \text{ mol He}$$

Total moles of gas = 0.432 mol + 1.01 mol = 1.44 mol

$$V = \frac{nRT}{P} = \frac{(1.44 \text{ mol})(0.08206 \text{ L atm mol}^{-1} \text{ K}^{-1})(273 \text{ K})}{(1.00 \text{ atm})} = 32.3 \text{ L}$$

140. $N_2(g) + 3H_2(g) \rightarrow 2NH_3(g)$

molar mass of NH_3 = 17.03 g; 11°C + 273 = 284 K

$$5.00 \text{ g NH}_3 \times \frac{1 \text{ mol NH}_3}{17.03 \text{ g NH}_3} = 0.294 \text{ mol NH}_3 \text{ to be produced}$$

$$0.294 \text{ mol NH}_3 \times \frac{1 \text{ mol N}_2}{2 \text{ mol NH}_3} = 0.147 \text{ mol N}_2 \text{ required}$$

$$0.294 \text{ mol NH}_3 \times \frac{3 \text{ mol H}_2}{2 \text{ mol NH}_3} = 0.441 \text{ mol H}_2 \text{ required}$$

$$V_{nitrogen} = \frac{nRT}{P} = \frac{(0.147 \text{ mol})(0.08206 \text{ L atm mol}^{-1} \text{ K}^{-1})(284 \text{ K})}{(0.998 \text{ atm})} = 3.43 \text{ L N}_2$$

$$V_{hydrogen} = \frac{nRT}{P} = \frac{(0.441 \text{ mol})(0.08206 \text{ L atm mol}^{-1} \text{ K}^{-1})(284 \text{ K})}{(0.998 \text{ atm})} = 10.3 \text{ L H}_2$$

142. $2Cu_2S(s) + 3O_2(g) \rightarrow 2Cu_2O(s) + 2SO_2(g)$

molar mass Cu_2S = 159.2 g; 27.5°C + 273 = 301 K

$$25 \text{ g Cu}_2\text{S} \times \frac{1 \text{ mol Cu}_2\text{S}}{159.2 \text{ g Cu}_2\text{S}} = 0.1570 \text{ mol Cu}_2\text{S}$$

$$0.1570 \text{ mol Cu}_2\text{S} \times \frac{3 \text{ mol O}_2}{2 \text{ mol Cu}_2\text{S}} = 0.2355 \text{ mol O}_2$$

$$V_{oxygen} = \frac{nRT}{P} = \frac{(0.2355 \text{ mol})(0.08206 \text{ L atm mol}^{-1} \text{ K}^{-1})(301 \text{ K})}{(0.998 \text{ atm})} = 5.8 \text{ L O}_2$$

$$0.1570 \text{ mol Cu}_2\text{S} \times \frac{2 \text{ mol SO}_2}{2 \text{ mol Cu}_2\text{S}} = 0.1570 \text{ mol SO}_2$$

$$V_{sulfur \, dioxide} = \frac{nRT}{P} = \frac{(0.1570 \text{ mol})(0.08206 \text{ L atm mol}^{-1} \text{ K}^{-1})(301 \text{ K})}{(0.998 \text{ atm})} = 3.9 \text{ L SO}_2$$

144.   One mole of any ideal gas occupies 22.4 L at STP.

$$35 \text{ mol N}_2 \times \frac{22.4 \text{ L}}{1 \text{ mol}} = 7.8 \times 10^2 \text{ L}$$

146.   molar masses: He, 4.003 g; Ar, 39.95 g; Ne, 20.18 g

$$5.0 \text{ g He} \times \frac{1 \text{ mol He}}{4.003 \text{ g He}} = 1.249 \text{ mol He}$$

$$1.0 \text{ g Ar} \times \frac{1 \text{ mol Ar}}{39.95 \text{ g Ar}} = 0.02503 \text{ mol Ar}$$

$$3.5 \text{ g Ne} \times \frac{1 \text{ mol Ne}}{20.18 \text{ g Ne}} = 0.1734 \text{ mol Ne}$$

Total moles of gas $= 1.249 + 0.02503 + 0.1734 = 1.447$ mol

22.4 L is the volume occupied by one mole of any ideal gas at STP. This would apply even if the gas sample is a *mixture* of individual gases.

$$1.447 \text{ mol} \times \frac{22.4 \text{ L}}{1 \text{ mol}} = 32 \text{ L total volume for the mixture}$$

The *partial pressure* of each individual gas in the mixture will be related to what *fraction* on a mole basis each gas represents in the mixture.

$$P_{He} = 1.00 \text{ atm} \times \frac{1.249 \text{ mol He}}{1.447 \text{ mol total}} = 0.86 \text{ atm}$$

$$P_{Ar} = 1.00 \text{ atm} \times \frac{0.02503 \text{ mol Ar}}{1.447 \text{ mol total}} = 0.017 \text{ atm}$$

$$P_{Ne} = 1.00 \text{ atm} \times \frac{0.1734 \text{ mol Ne}}{1.447 \text{ mol total}} = 0.12 \text{ atm}$$

148.   The solution is only 50% H_2O_2. Therefore 125 g solution = 62.5 g H_2O_2

molar mass of $H_2O_2 = 34.02$ g; $T = 27°C = 300$ K; $P = 764$ mm Hg $= 1.01$ atm

$$62.5 \text{ g } H_2O_2 \times \frac{1 \text{ mol}}{34.02 \text{ g}} = 1.84 \text{ mol } H_2O_2$$

$$1.84 \text{ mol } H_2O_2 \times \frac{1 \text{ mol } O_2}{2 \text{ mol } H_2O_2} = 0.920 \text{ mol } O_2$$

$$V = \frac{nRT}{P} = \frac{(0.920 \text{ mol})(0.08206 \text{ L atm mol}^{-1} \text{ K}^{-1})(300 \text{ K})}{(1.01 \text{ atm})} = 22.4 \text{ L}$$

CHAPTER 14

Liquids and Solids

2. Liquids and solids are *less* compressible than are gases.

4. Since it requires so much more energy to vaporize water than to melt ice, this suggests that the gaseous state is significantly different from the liquid state, but that the liquid and solid state are relatively similar.

6. See Figure 14.2.

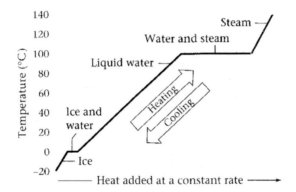

8. When a solid is heated, the molecules begin to vibrate/move more quickly. When enough energy has been added to overcome the intermolecular forces that hold the molecules in a crystal lattice, the solid melts. As the liquid is heated, the molecules begin to move more quickly and more randomly. When enough energy has been added, molecules having sufficient kinetic energy will begin to escape from the surface of the liquid. Once the pressure of vapor coming from the liquid is equal to the pressure above the liquid, the liquid boils. Only intermolecular forces need to be overcome in this process: no chemical bonds are broken.

10. Intramolecular; intermolecular

12. The molar heat of fusion of a substance represents the quantity of energy that must be applied to melt one mole of the substance.

14. a. More energy is required to separate the atoms of the liquid into the freely-moving and widely-separated atoms of the vapor/gas.

    b. $1.00 \text{ g Al} \times \dfrac{1 \text{ mol Al}}{26.98 \text{ g Al}} \times \dfrac{293.4 \text{ kJ}}{1 \text{ mol Al}} = 10.9 \text{ kJ}$

c. $5.00 \text{ g Al} \times \dfrac{1 \text{ mol Al}}{26.98 \text{ g Al}} \times \dfrac{-10.79 \text{ kJ}}{1 \text{ mol Al}} = -2.00 \text{ kJ (heat is evolved)}$

d. $0.105 \text{ mol Al} \times \dfrac{10.79 \text{ kJ}}{1 \text{ mol Al}} = 1.13 \text{ kJ}$

16.   molar mass Ag = 107.9 g

melt: $12.5 \text{ g Ag} \times \dfrac{1 \text{ mol Ag}}{107.9 \text{ g Ag}} \times \dfrac{11.3 \text{ kJ}}{1 \text{ mol Al}} = 1.31 \text{ kJ}$

condense: $4.59 \text{ g Ag} \times \dfrac{1 \text{ mol Ag}}{107.9 \text{ g Ag}} \times \dfrac{-250. \text{ kJ}}{1 \text{ mol Ag}} = -10.6 \text{ kJ (heat is evolved)}$

18.   The *molar* heat of fusion of aluminum is the heat required to melt 1 mol.

$\dfrac{113 \text{ J}}{1.00 \text{ g Na}} \times \dfrac{22.99 \text{ g Na}}{1 \text{ mol Na}} = 2598 \text{ J/mol} = 2.60 \text{ kJ/mol}$

20.   Dipole-dipole forces get *weaker* as the distance between the dipoles increases.

22.   Water molecules are able to form strong *hydrogen bonds* with each other. These bonds are an especially strong form of dipole-dipole forces and are only possible when hydrogen atoms are bonded to the most electronegative elements (N, O, and F). The particularly strong intermolecular forces in H_2O require much higher temperatures (higher energies) to be overcome in order to permit the liquid to boil. We take the fact that water has a much higher boiling point than the other hydrogen compounds of the Group 6 elements as proof that a special force is at play in water (hydrogen bonding).

24.   London dispersion forces are instantaneous dipole forces that arise when the electron cloud of an atom is momentarily distorted by a nearby dipole, temporarily separating the centers of positive and negative charge in the atom.

26.   a.   London dispersion forces (non polar molecules)

        b.   hydrogen bonding (H bonded to N); London dispersion forces

        c.   London dispersion forces (nonpolar molecules)

        d.   dipole-dipole forces (polar molecules); London dispersion forces

28.   An increase in the heat of fusion is observed for an increase in the size of the halogen atom involved (the electron cloud of a larger atom is more easily polarized by an approaching dipole, thus giving larger London dispersion forces).

30.   For a homogeneous mixture to be able to form at all, the forces between molecules of the two substances being mixed must be at least *comparable in magnitude* to the intermolecular forces within each *separate* substance. Apparently in the case of a water-ethanol mixture, the forces that exist when water and ethanol are mixed are stronger than water-water or ethanol-ethanol forces in the separate substances. This allows ethanol and water molecules to approach each other more closely in the mixture than either substance's molecules could approach a like molecule in separate substances. There is strong hydrogen bonding in both ethanol and water.

32.   Vapor pressure is the pressure of vapor present *at equilibrium* above a liquid in a sealed container at a particular temperature. When a liquid is placed in a closed container, molecules of the liquid evaporate freely into the empty space above the liquid. As the number of molecules present in the vapor state increases with time, vapor molecules begin to rejoin the liquid state (condense). Eventually a dynamic equilibrium is reached between evaporation and condensation in which the net number of molecules present in the vapor phase becomes *constant* with time.

34.   A liquid is injected at the bottom of the column of mercury and rises to the surface of the mercury, where the liquid evaporates into the vacuum above the mercury column. As the liquid evaporates, the pressure of vapor increases in the space above the mercury, and presses down on the mercury. The level of mercury, therefore, drops, and the amount by which the mercury level drops (in mm Hg) is equivalent to the vapor pressure of the liquid.

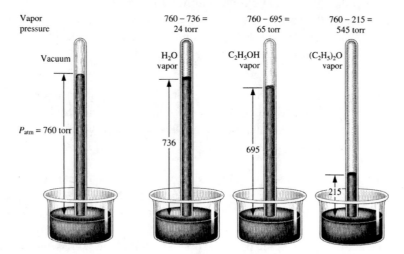

In the picture, the left tube represents a barometer—a tube of mercury inverted into a dish of mercury, with a vacuum above the mercury column: the height of the mercury column represents the pressure of the atmosphere. In the remaining 3 tubes, liquids of different volatilities are admitted to the bottom of the tube of mercury: they rise through the mercury and evaporate into the vacuum above the column of mercury. As the pressure of vapor builds up above the mercury column, the height of the mercury in the tube drops. Note that diethyl ether, $(C_2H_5)_2O$, shows the highest vapor pressure because it is the most volatile of the three liquids.

36.   a.   HF: Although both substances are capable of hydrogen bonding, water has two O–H bonds that can be involved in hydrogen bonding versus only one F–H bond in HF.

        b. CH_3OCH_3: As there is no H attached to the O atom, no hydrogen bonding can exist. Moreover, as there is no hydrogen bonding possible, the molecule should be relatively more volatile than CH_3CH_2OH even though it contains the same number of atoms of each element.

        c. CH_3SH: Hydrogen bonding is not as important for a S–H bond (because S has a lower electronegativity than O). As there is little hydrogen bonding, the molecule is relatively more volatile than CH_3OH.

38.   Both substances have the same molar mass. However, ethyl alcohol contains a hydrogen atom directly bonded to an oxygen atom. Therefore, hydrogen bonding can exist in ethyl alcohol, whereas only weak dipole-dipole forces can exist in dimethyl ether. Dimethyl ether is more volatile; ethyl alcohol has a higher boiling point.

40. *Ionic* solids have as their fundamental particles positive and negative *ions*; a simple example is sodium chloride, in which Na^+ and Cl^- ions are held together by strong electrostatic forces.

    Molecular solids have molecules as their fundamental particles, with the molecules being held together in the crystal by dipole-dipole forces, hydrogen bonding forces, or London dispersion forces (depending on the identity of the substance); simple examples of molecular solids include ice (H_2O) and ordinary table sugar (sucrose).

    Atomic solids have simple atoms as their fundamental particles, with the atoms being held together in the crystal either by covalent bonding (as in graphite or diamond) or by metallic bonding (as in copper or other metals).

42. The interparticle forces in ionic solids (the ionic bond) are much stronger than the interparticle forces in molecular solids (dipole-dipole forces, London forces, etc.). The difference in intermolecular forces is most clearly shown in the great differences in melting points and boiling points between ionic and molecular solids. For example, table salt and ordinary sugar are both crystalline solids that appear very similar. Yet sugar can be melted easily in a saucepan during the making of candy, whereas even the full heat of a stove will not melt salt.

44. Sodium chloride is an ionic substance in which a crystal lattice of alternating positive and negative ions holds the substance together with very strong forces that are difficult to overcome. Sucrose is a molecular substance in which the molecules are held together in the solid by dipole-dipole (and H-bonding) forces which are weaker than the ionic forces.

46. In liquid hydrogen, the only intermolecular forces are weak London dispersion forces. In ethyl alcohol and water we have hydrogen bonding possible, but the hydrogen bonding forces are weaker in ethyl alcohol because of the influence of the remainder of the molecule. In sucrose, we also have hydrogen bonding possible, but now at several places in the molecule, leading to stronger forces. In calcium chloride, we have an ionic crystal lattice with even stronger forces between the particles.

48. Although ions exist in the solid, liquid, or dissolved states, in the solid state the ions are rigidly held in place in the crystal lattice and cannot *move* so as to conduct an electrical current.

50. Nitinol is an alloy of nickel and titanium. When nickel and titanium are heated to a sufficiently high temperature during the production of Nitinol, the atoms arrange themselves in a compact and regular pattern of the atoms.

52. j

54. f

56. d

58. a

60. l

62. Diethyl ether has the larger vapor pressure. No hydrogen bonding is possible because the O atom does not have a hydrogen atom attached. Hydrogen bonding can occur *only* when a hydrogen atom is *directly* attached to a strongly electronegative atom (such as N, O, or F). Hydrogen bonding *is* possible in 1-butanol (1-butanol contains an ÷OH group).

64. a. H_2: London dispersion forces are the only intermolecular forces present in these nonpolar molecules; typically London forces become larger with increasing atomic size (as the atoms become bigger, the edge of the electron cloud lies farther from the nucleus and becomes more easily distorted).

   b. Xe: Only the relatively weak London forces could exist in a crystal of Xe atoms, whereas in NaCl strong ionic forces exist. In diamond, strong covalent bonding exists between carbon atoms.

   c. Cl_2 :Only London forces exist among such nonpolar molecules. London forces become larger with increasing atomic size.

66. Steel is a general term applied to alloys consisting primarily of iron, but with small amounts of other substances added. Whereas pure iron itself is relatively soft, malleable, and ductile, steels are typically much stronger and harder, and much less subject to damage.

68. Water is the solvent in which cellular processes take place in living creatures. Water in the oceans moderates the Earth's temperature. Water is used in industry as a cooling agent. Water serves as a means of transportation on the Earth's oceans. The liquid range is 0°C to 100°C at 1 atm pressure.

70. At higher altitudes, the boiling points of liquids, such as water, are lower because there is a lower atmospheric pressure above the liquid. The temperature at which food cooks is determined by the temperature to which the water in the food can be heated before it escapes as steam. Thus, food cooks at a lower temperature at high elevations where the boiling point of water is lowered.

72. Heat of fusion (melt); heat of vaporization (boil).

   The heat of vaporization is always larger, because virtually all of the intermolecular forces must be overcome to form a gas. In a liquid, considerable intermolecular forces remain. Thus going from a solid to liquid requires less energy than going from the liquid to the gas.

74. Dipole-dipole interactions are typically about 1% as strong as a covalent bond. Dipole-dipole interactions represent electrostatic attractions between portions of molecules that carry only a *partial* positive or negative charge. Such forces require the molecules that are interacting to come *near* enough to each other.

76. London dispersion forces are relatively weak forces that arise among noble gas atoms and in nonpolar molecules. London forces are due to *instantaneous dipoles* that develop when one atom (or molecule) momentarily distorts the electron cloud of another atom (or molecule). London forces are typically weaker than either permanent dipole-dipole forces or covalent bonds.

78. For every mole of liquid water that evaporates, several kilojoules of heat must be absorbed to provide kinetic energy to overcome attractive forces among the molecules. This heat is absorbed by the water from its surroundings.

80. In NH_3, strong hydrogen bonding can exist. In CH_4, because the molecule is nonpolar, only the relatively weak London dispersion forces exist.

82. In a crystal of ice, strong *hydrogen bonding* forces are present, whereas in the crystal of a nonpolar substance like oxygen, only the much weaker *London* forces exist.

84. Ice floats on liquid water; water expands when it is frozen

86.   Although they are at the same *temperature*, steam at 100°C contains a larger amount of *energy* than hot water, equal to the heat of vaporization of water.

88.   Hydrogen bonding is a special case of dipole-dipole interactions that occur among molecules containing hydrogen atoms bonded to highly electronegative atoms such as fluorine, oxygen, or nitrogen. The bonds are very polar, and the small size of the hydrogen atom (compared to other atoms) allows the dipoles to approach each other very closely. Examples: H_2O, NH_3, HF, etc.

90.   Evaporation and condensation are opposite processes. Evaporation is an endothermic process, condensation is an exothermic process. Evaporation requires an input of energy to provide the increased kinetic energy possessed by the molecules when they are in the gaseous state. Evaporation occurs when the molecules in a liquid are moving fast enough and randomly enough that molecules are able to escape from the surface of the liquid and

CHAPTER 15

Solutions

2.   A heterogeneous mixture does not have a uniform composition: the composition varies in different places within the mixture. Examples of non–homogeneous mixtures include salad dressing (mixture of oil, vinegar, water, herbs, and spices) and granite (combination of minerals).

4.   solid

6.   "Like dissolves like." The hydrocarbons in oil have intermolecular forces that are very different from those in water, and so the oil spreads out rather than dissolving in the water.

8.   Carbon dioxide is somewhat soluble in water, especially if pressurized (otherwise, the soda you may be drinking while studying Chemistry would be "flat"). Carbon dioxide's solubility in water is approximately 1.5 g/L at 25°C under a pressure of approximately 1 atm. Although the carbon dioxide molecule overall is non-polar, that is because the two individual C–O bond dipoles cancel each other due to the linearity of the molecule. However these bond dipoles are able to interact with water, making CO_2 more soluble in water than non-polar molecules such as O_2 or N_2 that do not possess individual bond dipoles.

10.   unsaturated

12.   large

14.   100.0

16.   6.11 mg = 0.00611 g

a. $\dfrac{0.00611 \text{ g } CaCl_2}{(0.00611 \text{ g } CaCl_2 + 5.25 \text{ g water})} \times 100 = 0.116\% \, CaCl_2$

b. $\dfrac{0.00611 \text{ g } CaCl_2}{(0.00611 \text{ g } CaCl_2 + 52.5 \text{ g water})} \times 100 = 0.0116\% \, CaCl_2$

c. $\dfrac{6.11 \text{ g } CaCl_2}{(6.11 \text{ g } CaCl_2 + 52.5 \text{ g water})} \times 100 = 10.4\% \, CaCl_2$

d. $\dfrac{6.11 \text{ kg } CaCl_2}{(6.11 \text{ kg } CaCl_2 + 52.5 \text{ kg water})} \times 100 = 10.4\% \, CaCl_2$

18.   a. $525 \text{ g solution} \times \dfrac{3.91 \text{ g } FeCl_3}{100. \text{g solution}} = 20.5 \text{ g } FeCl_3$

525 g solution – 20.5 g $FeCl_3$ = 504.5 g water (505 g water)

b. $225 \text{ g solution} \times \dfrac{11.9 \text{ g sucrose}}{100. \text{ g solution}} = 26.8 \text{ g sucrose}$

   $225 \text{ g solution} - 26.8 \text{ g sucrose} = 198.2 \text{ g water (198 g water)}$

c. $1.45 \text{ kg} = 1.45 \times 10^3 \text{ g}$

   $1.45 \times 10^3 \text{ g solution} \times \dfrac{12.5 \text{ g NaCl}}{100. \text{ g solution}} = 181.3 \text{ g NaCl (181 g NaCl)}$

   $1.45 \times 10^3 \text{ g solution} - 181.3 \text{ g NaCl} = 1268.7 \text{ g water } (1.27 \times 10^3 \text{ g water})$

d. $635 \text{ g solution} \times \dfrac{15.1 \text{ g KNO}_3}{100. \text{ g solution}} = 95.9 \text{ g KNO}_3$

   $635 \text{ g solution} - 95.9 \text{ g KNO}_3 = 539.1 \text{ g water (539 g water)}$

20.   Percent means "per hundred". So the percentages in Question 19 represent the number of grams of the particular element present in 100. g of the alloy. Since 1.00 kg represents ten times the mass of 100. g, we would need 957 g Fe, 26.9 g C, and 16.5 g Cr to prepare 1.00 kg of the alloy.

22. $\dfrac{67.1 \text{ g CaCl}_2}{(67.1 \text{ g CaCl}_2 + 275 \text{ g water})} \times 100 = 19.6\% \text{ CaCl}_2$

24.   To say that the solution is 6.25% KBr by mass, means that 100. g of the solution will contain 6.25 g KBr.

   $125 \text{ g solution} \times \dfrac{6.25 \text{ g KBr}}{100. \text{ g solution}} = 7.81 \text{ g KBr}$

26.   molar mass $O_2 = 32.00$ g

   $1.00 \text{ g O}_2 \times \dfrac{1 \text{ mol}}{32.00 \text{ g}} = 0.03125 \text{ mol O}$

   from the balanced chemical equation, it will take $2(0.03125) = 0.0625$ mol H_2O_2 to produce this quantity of oxygen.

   molar mass $H_2O_2 = 34.02$ g

   $0.0625 \text{ mol H}_2\text{O}_2 \times \dfrac{34.02 \text{ g H}_2\text{O}_2}{1 \text{ mol H}_2\text{O}_2} = 2.13 \text{ g H}_2\text{O}_2$

   $2.13 \text{ g H}_2\text{O}_2 \times \dfrac{100. \text{ g solution}}{3 \text{ g H}_2\text{O}_2} = \text{approximately 71 g}$

28. $1000 \text{ g} \times \dfrac{0.95 \text{ g stablizer}}{100. \text{ g}} = 9.5 \text{ g}$

30.   0.110 mol; 0.220 mol

32.   The molarity represents the number of moles of solute per liter of solution: choice b is the only scenario that fulfills this definition.

34. Molarity $= \dfrac{\text{moles of solute}}{\text{liters of solution}}$

    a. 225 mL = 0.225 L

    $$M = \frac{0.754 \text{ mol KNO}_3}{0.225 \text{ L}} = 3.35 \ M$$

    b. 10.2 mL = 0.0102 L

    $$M = \frac{0.0105 \text{ mol CaCl}_2}{0.0102 \text{ L}} = 1.03 \ M$$

    c. $M = \dfrac{3.15 \text{ mol NaCl}}{5.00 \text{ L}} = 0.630 \ M$

    d. 100. mL = 0.100 L

    $$M = \frac{0.499 \text{ mol NaBr}}{0.100 \text{ L}} = 4.99 \ M$$

36. Molarity $= \dfrac{\text{moles of solute}}{\text{liters of solution}}$; molar mass of $CaCl_2$ = 110.98 g; 125 mL = 0.125 L

    a. $5.59 \text{ g CaCl}_2 \times \dfrac{1 \text{ mol CaCl}_2}{110.98 \text{ g CaCl}_2} = 0.05037 \text{ mol CaCl}_2$

    $$M = \frac{0.05037 \text{ mol}}{0.125 \text{ L}} = 0.403 \ M$$

    b. $2.34 \text{ g CaCl}_2 \times \dfrac{1 \text{ mol CaCl}_2}{110.98 \text{ g CaCl}_2} = 0.02108 \text{ mol CaCl}_2$

    $$M = \frac{0.02108 \text{ mol}}{0.125 \text{ L}} = 0.169 \ M$$

    c. $8.73 \text{ g CaCl}_2 \times \dfrac{1 \text{ mol CaCl}_2}{110.98 \text{ g CaCl}_2} = 0.07866 \text{ mol CaCl}_2$

    $$M = \frac{0.07866 \text{ mol}}{0.125 \text{ L}} = 0.629 \ M$$

    d. $11.5 \text{ g CaCl}_2 \times \dfrac{1 \text{ mol CaCl}_2}{110.98 \text{ g CaCl}_2} = 0.1036 \text{ mol CaCl}_2$

    $$M = \frac{0.1036 \text{ mol}}{0.125 \text{ L}} = 0.829 \ M$$

38. molar mass of KBr = 119.0 g; 135 mL = 0.135 L

    $$0.135 \text{ L} \times \frac{0.251 \text{ mol}}{1 \text{ L}} \times \frac{119.0 \text{ g}}{1 \text{ mol}} = 4.03 \text{ g KBr}$$

40. molar mass of I_2 = 253.8 g; 225 mL = 0.225 L

$$5.15 \text{ g } I_2 \times \frac{1 \text{ mol}}{253.8 \text{ g}} = 0.0203 \text{ mol } I_2$$

$$M = \frac{0.0203 \text{ mol } I_2}{0.225 \text{ L solution}} = 0.0902 \ M$$

42. molar mass of KNO_3 = 101.11 g; 25.0 mL = 0.0250 L

$$1.21 \text{ g } KNO_3 \times \frac{1 \text{ mol } KNO_3}{101.11 \text{ g}} = 0.01197 \text{ mol } KNO_3$$

$$M = \frac{0.01197 \text{ mol } KNO_3}{0.0250 \text{ L solution}} = 0.479 \ M$$

44. a. 12.5 mL = 0.0125 L

$$0.0125 \text{ L solution} \times \frac{0.104 \text{ mol HCl}}{1.00 \text{ L solution}} = 0.00130 \text{ mol HCl}$$

b. 27.3 mL = 0.0273 L

$$0.0273 \text{ L solution} \times \frac{0.223 \text{ mol NaOH}}{1.00 \text{ L solution}} = 0.00609 \text{ mol NaOH}$$

c. 36.8 mL = 0.0368 L

$$0.0368 \text{ L solution} \times \frac{0.501 \text{ mol } HNO_3}{1.00 \text{ L solution}} = 0.0184 \text{ mol } HNO_3$$

d. 47.5 mL = 0.0475 L

$$0.0475 \text{ L solution} \times \frac{0.749 \text{ mol KOH}}{1.00 \text{ L solution}} = 0.0356 \text{ mol KOH}$$

46. a. molar mass of $CaCl_2$ = 110.98 g; 17.8 mL = 0.0178 L

$$0.0178 \text{ L solution} \times \frac{0.119 \text{ mol } CaCl_2}{1 \text{ L solution}} \times \frac{110.98 \text{ g } CaCl_2}{1 \text{ mol } CaCl_2} = 0.235 \text{ g } CaCl_2$$

b. molar mass of KCl = 74.55 g; 27.6 mL = 0.0276 L

$$0.0276 \text{ L solution} \times \frac{0.288 \text{ mol KCl}}{1 \text{ L solution}} \times \frac{74.55 \text{ g KCl}}{1 \text{ mol KCl}} = 0.593 \text{ g KCl}$$

c. molar mass of $FeCl_3$ = 162.2 g; 35.4 mL = 0.0354 L

$$0.0354 \text{ L solution} \times \frac{0.399 \text{ mol } FeCl_3}{1 \text{ L solution}} \times \frac{162.2 \text{ g } FeCl_3}{1 \text{ mol } FeCl_3} = 2.29 \text{ g } FeCl_3$$

d. molar mass KNO_3 = 101.11 g; 46.1 mL = 0.0461 L

$$0.0461 \text{ L solution} \times \frac{0.559 \text{ mol } KNO_3}{1 \text{ L solution}} \times \frac{101.11 \text{ g } KNO_3}{1 \text{ mol } KNO_3} = 2.61 \text{ g } KNO_3$$

48.　　molar mass of KBr = 119.0 g; 225 mL = 0.225 L

$$0.225 \text{ L solution} \times \frac{0.355 \text{ mol KBr}}{1 \text{ L solution}} \times \frac{119.0 \text{ g KBr}}{1 \text{ mol KBr}} = 9.51 \text{ g KBr}$$

50.　　a.　　10.2 mL = 0.0102 L

$$0.0102 \text{ L} \times \frac{0.451 \text{ mol AlCl}_3}{1.00 \text{ L}} \times \frac{1 \text{ mol Al}^{3+}}{1 \text{ mol AlCl}_3} = 4.60 \times 10^{-3} \text{ mol Al}^{3+}$$

$$0.0102 \text{ L} \times \frac{0.451 \text{ mol AlCl}_3}{1.00 \text{ L}} \times \frac{3 \text{ mol Cl}^-}{1 \text{ mol AlCl}_3} = 1.38 \times 10^{-2} \text{ mol Cl}^-$$

　　　　b.　　$$5.51 \text{ L} \times \frac{0.103 \text{ mol Na}_3\text{PO}_4}{1.00 \text{ L}} \times \frac{3 \text{ mol Na}^+}{1 \text{ mol Na}_3\text{PO}_4} = 1.70 \text{ mol Na}^+$$

$$5.51 \text{ L} \times \frac{0.103 \text{ mol Na}_3\text{PO}_4}{1.00 \text{ L}} \times \frac{1 \text{ mol PO}_4^{3-}}{1 \text{ mol Na}_3\text{PO}_4} = 0.568 \text{ mol PO}_4^{3-}$$

　　　　c.　　1.75 mL = 0.00175 L

$$0.00175 \text{ L} \times \frac{1.25 \text{ mol CuCl}_2}{1.00 \text{ L}} \times \frac{1 \text{ mol Cu}^{2+}}{1 \text{ mol CuCl}_2} = 2.19 \times 10^{-3} \text{ mol Cu}^{2+}$$

$$0.00175 \text{ L} \times \frac{1.25 \text{ mol CuCl}_2}{1.00 \text{ L}} \times \frac{2 \text{ mol Cl}^-}{1 \text{ mol CuCl}_2} = 4.38 \times 10^{-3} \text{ mol Cl}^-$$

　　　　d.　　25.2 mL = 0.0252 L

$$0.0252 \text{ L} \times \frac{0.00157 \text{ mol Ca(OH)}_2}{1.00 \text{ L}} \times \frac{1 \text{ mol Ca}^{2+}}{1 \text{ mol Ca(OH)}_2} = 3.96 \times 10^{-5} \text{ mol Ca}^{2+}$$

$$0.0252 \text{ L} \times \frac{0.00157 \text{ mol Ca(OH)}_2}{1.00 \text{ L}} \times \frac{2 \text{ mol OH}^-}{1 \text{ mol Ca(OH)}_2} = 7.91 \times 10^{-5} \text{ mol OH}^-$$

52.　　Molar mass of Na$_2$CO$_3$ = 106.0 g; 250 mL = 0.250 L

$$0.250 \text{ L} \times \frac{0.0500 \text{ mol Na}_2\text{CO}_3}{1.00 \text{ L}} \times \frac{106.\text{g}}{1 \text{ mol}} = 1.33 \text{ g Na}_2\text{CO}_3$$

54.　　half

56.　　$$M_1 \times V_1 = M_2 \times V_2$$

　　　　a.　　$M_1 = 0.251 \, M$　　　　　　　　　　　$M_2 = ?$

　　　　　　$V_1 = 10.0 \text{ mL}$　　　　　　　　　　　$V_2 = (10.0 + 25.0) = 35.0 \text{ mL}$

$$M_2 = \frac{(0.251 \, M)(10.0 \text{ mL})}{(35.0 \text{ mL})} = 0.0717 \, M$$

b. $M_1 = 3.00\ M$ $M_2 = ?$

$V_1 = 125\ mL$ $V_2 = (125 + 97.5) = 222.5\ mL$

$$M_2 = \frac{(3.00\ M)(125\ mL)}{(222.5\ mL)} = 1.69\ M$$

c. $M_1 = 0.851\ M$ $M_2 = ?$

$V_1 = 25.0\ mL$ $V_2 = 500.\ mL$

$$M_2 = \frac{(0.851\ M)(25\ mL)}{(500.\ mL)} = 0.0426\ M$$

d. $M_1 = 1.25\ M$ $M_2 = ?$

$V_1 = 25.0\ mL$ $V_2 = 50.0\ mL$

$$M_2 = \frac{(1.25\ M)(25\ mL)}{(50.0\ mL)} = 0.625\ M$$

58. $M_1 = 19.4\ M$ $M_2 = 3.00\ M$

$V_1 = ?\ mL$ $V_2 = 3.50\ L$

$$M_1 = \frac{(3.00\ M)(3.50\ mL)}{(19.4\ M)} = 0.541\ L\ (541\ mL)$$

60. $M_1 \times V_1 = M_2 \times V_2$

$M_1 = 1.01\ M$ $M_2 = 0.150\ M$

$V_1 = ?\ mL$ $V_2 = 325\ mL$

$$M_2 = \frac{(0.150\ M)(325\ mL)}{(1.01\ M)} = 48.3\ mL$$

Dilute 48.3 mL of the 1.01 M solution to a final volume of 325 mL.

62. $$\frac{(100.\ mL)(1.25\ M)}{(12.1\ M)} = 10.3\ mL$$

64. $Na_2CO_3(aq) + CaCl_2(aq) \rightarrow CaCO_3(s) + 2NaCl(s)$

mmol Ca^{2+} ion: $37.2\ mL \times \dfrac{0.105\ mmol\ Ca^{2+}}{1.00\ mL} = 3.91\ mmol\ Ca^{2+}$

From the balanced chemical equation, 3.91 mmol CO_3^{2} will be needed to precipitate this quantity of Ca^{2+} ion.

$3.91\ mmol\ CO_3^{2} \times \dfrac{1.00\ mL}{0.125\ mmol} = 31.2\ mL$

66.   molar mass $Na_2C_2O_4 = 134.0$ g   37.5 mL = 0.0375 L

moles Ca^{2+} ion $= 0.0375$ L $\times \dfrac{0.104 \text{ mol Ca}^{2+}}{1.00 \text{ L}} = 0.00390$ mol Ca^{2+} ion

$Ca^{2+}(aq) + C_2O_4^{2-}(aq) \rightarrow CaC_2O_4(s)$

As the precipitation reaction is of 1:1 stoichiometry, then 0.00390 mol of $C_2O_4^{2-}$ ion is needed. Moreover, each formula unit of $Na_2C_2O_4$ contains one $C_2O_4^{2-}$ ion, so 0.00390 mol of $Na_2C_2O_4$ is required.

0.00390 mol $Na_2C_2O_4 \times \dfrac{134.0 \text{ g}}{1 \text{ mol}} = 0.523$ g $Na_2C_2O_4$ required

68.   10.0 mL = 0.0100 L

0.0100 L $\times \dfrac{0.250 \text{ mol AlCl}_3}{1.00 \text{ L}} = 2.50 \times 10^{-3}$ mol $AlCl_3$

$AlCl_3(aq) + 3NaOH(s) \rightarrow Al(OH)_3(s) + 3NaCl(aq)$

2.50×10^{-3} mol $AlCl_3 \times \dfrac{3 \text{ mol NaOH}}{1 \text{ mol AlCl}_3} = 7.50 \times 10^{-3}$ mol NaOH

molar mass NaOH = 40.00 g

7.50×10^{-3} mol NaOH $\times \dfrac{40.00 \text{ g NaOH}}{1 \text{ mol}} = 0.300$ g NaOH

70. $NaOH(aq) + HCl(aq) \rightarrow H_2O(l) + NaCl(aq)$

125 mL = 0.125 L

0.125 L $\times \dfrac{3.01 \text{ mol NaOH}}{1 \text{ L}} = 0.3763$ mol NaOH

0.3763 mol NaOH $\times \dfrac{1 \text{ mol HCl}}{1 \text{ mol NaOH}} = 0.3763$ mol HCl

0.3763 mol HCl $\times \dfrac{1 \text{ L solution}}{0.995 \text{ mol HCl}} = 0.378$ L = 378 mL

72.   7.2 mL = 0.0072 L

0.0072 L $\times \dfrac{2.5 \times 10^{-3} \text{ mol NaOH}}{1.00 \text{ L}} = 1.8 \times 10^{-5}$ mol NaOH

$H^+(aq) + OH^-(aq) \rightarrow H_2O(l)$

1.8×10^{-5} mol $OH^- \times \dfrac{1 \text{ mol H}^+}{1 \text{ mol OH}^-} = 1.8 \times 10^{-5}$ mol H^+

100 mL = 0.100 L

$M = \dfrac{1.8 \times 10^{-5} \text{ mol H}^+}{0.100 \text{ L}} = 1.8 \times 10^{-4} \ M \ H^+(aq)$

74. Experimentally, neutralization reactions are usually performed with volumetric glassware that is calibrated in milliliters rather than liters. For convenience in calculations for such reactions, the arithmetic is often performed in terms of *milli*liters and *milli*moles, rather than in liters and moles: 1 mmol = 0.001 mol. Note that the number of moles of solute per liter of solution, the molarity, is numerically equivalent to the number of *milli*moles of solute per *milli*liter of solution.

   a. $HNO_3(aq) + NaOH(aq) \rightarrow NaNO_3(aq) + H_2O(l)$

   $$12.7 \text{ mL} \times \frac{0.501 \text{ mmol}}{1.00 \text{ mL}} = 6.36 \text{ mmol NaOH present in the sample}$$

   $$6.36 \text{ mmol NaOH} \times \frac{1 \text{ mmol HNO}_3}{1 \text{ mmol NaOH}} = 6.36 \text{ mmol HNO}_3 \text{ required to react}$$

   $$6.36 \text{ mmol HNO}_3 \times \frac{1.00 \text{ mL}}{0.101 \text{ mmol HNO}_3} = 63.0 \text{ mL HNO}_3 \text{ required}$$

   b. $2HNO_3(aq) + Ba(OH)_2 \rightarrow Ba(NO_3)_2 + 2H_2O(l)$

   $$24.9 \text{ mL} \times \frac{0.00491 \text{ mmol}}{1.00 \text{ mL}} = 0.122 \text{ mmol Ba(OH)}_2 \text{ present in sample}$$

   $$0.122 \text{ mmol Ba(OH)}_2 \times \frac{2 \text{ mmol HNO}_3}{1 \text{ mmol Ba(OH)}_2} = 0.244 \text{ mmol HNO}_3 \text{ required}$$

   $$0.244 \text{ mmol HNO}_3 \times \frac{1.00 \text{ mL}}{0.101 \text{ mmol HNO}_3} = 2.42 \text{ mL HNO}_3 \text{ is required}$$

   c. $HNO_3(aq) + NH_3(aq) \rightarrow NH_4NO_3(aq)$

   $$49.1 \text{ mL} \times \frac{0.103 \text{ mmol}}{1.00 \text{ mL}} = 5.06 \text{ mmol NH}_3 \text{ present in the sample}$$

   $$5.06 \text{ mmol NH}_3 \times \frac{1 \text{ mmol HNO}_3}{1 \text{ mmol NH}_3} = 5.06 \text{ mmol HNO}_3 \text{ required}$$

   $$5.06 \text{ mmol HNO}_3 \times \frac{1.00 \text{ mL}}{0.101 \text{ mmol HNO}_3} = 50.1 \text{ mL HNO}_3 \text{ required}$$

   d. $KOH(aq) + HNO_3(aq) \rightarrow KNO_3(aq) + H_2O(l)$

   $$1.21 \text{ L} \times \frac{0.102 \text{ mol}}{1.00 \text{ L}} = 0.123 \text{ mol KOH present in the sample}$$

   $$0.123 \text{ mol KOH} \times \frac{1 \text{ mol HNO}_3}{1 \text{ mol KOH}} = 0.123 \text{ mol HNO}_3 \text{ required}$$

   $$0.123 \text{ mol HNO}_3 \times \frac{1.00 \text{ L}}{0.101 \text{ mol HNO}_3} = 1.22 \text{ L HNO}_3 \text{ required}$$

76. 1 normal

78. 1.53 equivalents OH⁻ ion are needed to react with 1.53 equivalents of H⁺ ion. By *definition*, one equivalent of OH⁻ ion exactly neutralizes one equivalent of H⁺ ion.

80. $N = \dfrac{\text{number of equivalents of solute}}{\text{number of liters of solution}}$

a.   equivalent weight NaOH = molar mass NaOH = 40.00 g

$$0.113 \text{ g NaOH} \times \frac{1 \text{ equiv NaOH}}{40.00 \text{ g}} = 2.83 \times 10^{-3} \text{ equiv NaOH}$$

10.2 mL = 0.0102 L

$$N = \frac{2.83 \times 10^{-3} \text{ equiv}}{0.0102 \text{ L}} = 0.277 \ N$$

b.   equivalent weight $Ca(OH)_2$ $\dfrac{\text{molar mass}}{2} = \dfrac{74.10 \text{ g}}{2} = 37.05$ g

$$12.5 \text{ mg} \times \frac{1 \text{ g}}{10^3 \text{ mg}} \times \frac{1 \text{ equiv}}{37.05 \text{ g}} = 3.37 \times 10^{-4} \text{ equiv } Ca(OH)_2$$

100. mL = 0.100 L

$$N = \frac{3.37 \times 10^{-4} \text{ equiv}}{0.100 \text{ L}} = 3.37 \times 10^{-3} \ N$$

c.   equivalent weight $H_2SO_4 = \dfrac{\text{molar mass}}{2} = \dfrac{98.09 \text{ g}}{2} = 49.05$ g

$$12.4 \text{ g} \times \frac{1 \text{ equiv}}{49.05 \text{ g}} = 0.253 \text{ equiv } H_2SO_4$$

155 mL = 0.155 L

$$N = \frac{0.253 \text{ equiv}}{0.155 \text{ L}} = 1.63 \ N$$

82.   a. $0.134 \ M \text{ NaOH} \times \dfrac{1 \text{ equiv NaOH}}{1 \text{ mol NaOH}} = 0.134 \ N \text{ NaOH}$

b. $0.00521 \ M \, Ca(OH)_2 \times \dfrac{2 \text{ equiv } Ca(OH)_2}{1 \text{ mol } Ca(OH)_2} = 0.0104 \ N \, Ca(OH)_2$

c. $4.42 \ M \, H_3PO_4 \times \dfrac{3 \text{ equiv } H_3PO_4}{1 \text{ mol } H_3PO_4} = 13.3 \ N \, H_3PO_4$

84.   Molar mass of $Ca(OH)_2 = 74.10$ g

$$5.21 \text{ mg } Ca(OH)_2 \times \frac{1 \text{ g}}{10^3 \text{ mg}} \times \frac{1 \text{ mol}}{74.10 \text{ g}} = 7.03 \times 10^{-5} \text{ mol } Ca(OH)_2$$

1000. mL = 1.000 L (volumetric flask volume: 4 significant figures).

$$M = \frac{7.03 \times 10^{-5}\ \text{mol}}{1.000\ L} = 7.03 \times 10^{-5}\ M\ Ca(OH)_2$$

$$N = 7.03 \times 10^{-5}\ M\ Ca(OH)_2 \times \frac{2\ \text{equiv}\ Ca(OH)_2}{1\ \text{mol}\ Ca(OH)_2} = 1.41 \times 10^{-4}\ N\ Ca(OH)_2$$

86. $H_2SO_4(aq) + 2NaOH(aq) \rightarrow Na_2SO_4(aq) + 2H_2O(l)$

$N_{acid} \times V_{acid} = N_{base} \times V_{base}$

$(0.104\ N)(V_{acid}) = (0.152\ N)(15.2\ \text{mL})$

$V_{acid} = 22.2\ \text{mL}$

The 0.104 *M* sulfuric acid solution is *twice as concentrated* as the 0.104 *N* sulfuric acid solution (1 mole = 2 equivalents), so half as much will be required to neutralize the same quantity of NaOH = 11.1 mL

88. $2NaOH(aq) + H_2SO_4(aq) \rightarrow Na_2SO_4(aq) + 2\ H_2O(l)$

$$27.34\ \text{mL NaOH} \times \frac{0.1021\ \text{mmol}}{1.00\ \text{mL}} = 2.791\ \text{mmol NaOH}$$

$$2.791\ \text{mmol NaOH} \times \frac{1\ \text{mmol}\ H_2SO4}{2\ \text{mmol NaOH}} = 1.396\ \text{mmol}\ H_2SO_4$$

$$M = \frac{1.396\ \text{mmol}\ H_2SO4}{25.00\ \text{mL}} = 0.05583\ M\ H_2SO_4 = 0.1117\ N\ H_2SO_4$$

90.   Molarity is defined as the number of moles of solute contained in 1 liter of *total* solution volume (solute plus solvent after mixing). In the first case, where 50. g of NaCl is dissolved in 1.0 L of water, the total volume after mixing is *not* known and the molarity cannot be calculated. In the second example, the final volume after mixing is known and the molarity can be calculated simply.

92. $$75\ \text{g solution} \times \frac{25\ \text{g NaCl}}{100.\ \text{g solution}} = 18.75\ \text{g NaCl}$$

$$\text{new}\ \% = \frac{18.75\ \text{g NaCl}}{575\ \text{g solution}} \times 100 = 3.26 = 3.3\ \%$$

94.   molar mass $NaHCO_3$ = 84.01 g; 25.2 mL = 0.0252 L

$NaHCO_3(s) + HCl(aq) \rightarrow NaCl(aq) + H_2O(l)$

$$\text{mol HCl} = \text{mol}\ NaHCO_3\ \text{required} = 0.0252\ L \times \frac{6.01\ \text{mol HCl}}{1.00\ L} = 0.151\ \text{mol}$$

$$0.151\ \text{mol} \times \frac{84.01\ \text{g}}{1\ \text{mol}} = 12.7\ \text{g}\ NaHCO_3\ \text{required}$$

96.   molar mass H_2O = 18.0 g

1.0 L water = 1.0×10^3 mL water $\cong 1.0 \times 10^3$ g water

1.0×10^3 g $H_2O \times \dfrac{1 \text{ mol } H_2O}{18.0 \text{ g } H_2O} = 56$ mol H_2O

98.   500 mL HCl solution = 0.500 L HCl solution

0.500 L solution $\times \dfrac{0.100 \text{ mol HCl}}{1.00 \text{ L solution}} = 0.0500$ mol HCl

0.0500 mol HCl $\times \dfrac{22.4 \text{ L}}{1 \text{ mol}} = 1.12$ L HCl gas at STP

100.   10.0 g HCl $\times \dfrac{100. \text{ g solution}}{33.1 \text{ g HCl}} = 30.21$ g solution

30.21 g solution $\times \dfrac{1.00 \text{ mL solution}}{1.147 \text{ g solution}} = 26.3$ mL solution

102.   molar mass $CaCl_2$ = 111.0 g

14.2 g $CaCl_2 \times \dfrac{1 \text{ mol } CaCl_2}{111.0 \text{ g } CaCl_2} = 0.128$ mol $CaCl_2$

50.0 mL = 0.0500 L

$M = \dfrac{0.128 \text{ mol } CaCl_2}{0.0500 \text{ L}} = 2.56 \ M$

104.   a. $\dfrac{5.0 \text{ g } KNO_3}{(5.0 \text{ g } KNO_3 + 75 \text{ g } H_2O)} \times 100 = 6.3\% \ KNO_3$

b.   2.5 mg = 0.0025 g

$\dfrac{0.0025 \text{ g } KNO_3}{(0.0025 \text{ g } KNO_3 + 1.0 \text{ g } H_2O)} \times 100 = 0.25\% \ KNO_3$

c. $\dfrac{11 \text{ g } KNO_3}{(11 \text{ g } KNO_3 + 89 \text{ g } H_2O)} \times 100 = 11\% \ KNO_3$

d. $\dfrac{11 \text{ g } KNO_3}{(11 \text{ g } KNO_3 + 49 \text{ g } H_2O)} \times 100 = 18\% \ KNO_3$

106. $$\%C = \frac{5.0 \text{ g C}}{(5.0 \text{ g C} + 1.5 \text{ g Ni} + 100. \text{ g Fe})} \times 100 = 4.7\% \text{ C}$$

$$\%Ni = \frac{1.5 \text{ g Ni}}{(5.0 \text{ g C} + 1.5 \text{ g Ni} + 100. \text{ g Fe})} \times 100 = 1.4\% \text{ Ni}$$

$$\%Fe = \frac{100. \text{ g Fe}}{(5.0 \text{ g C} + 1.5 \text{ g Ni} + 100. \text{ g Fe})} \times 100 = 93.9\% \text{ Fe}$$

108. To say that the solution is 5.5% by mass Na_2CO_3 means that 5.5 g of Na_2CO_3 are contained in every 100 g of the solution.

$$500. \text{ g solution} \times \frac{5.5 \text{ g Na}_2\text{CO}_3}{100. \text{ g solution}} = 28 \text{ g Na}_2\text{CO}_3$$

110. For NaCl: $\quad 125 \text{ g solution} \times \dfrac{7.5 \text{ g NaCl}}{100. \text{ g solution}} = 9.4 \text{ g NaCl}$

For KBr: $\quad 125 \text{ g solution} \times \dfrac{2.5 \text{ g KBr}}{100. \text{ g solution}} = 3.1 \text{ g KBr}$

112. a. $\quad 25 \text{ mL} = 0.025 \text{ L}$

$$M = \frac{0.10 \text{ mol CaCl}_2}{0.025 \text{ L solution}} = 4.0 \text{ M}$$

b. $\quad M = \dfrac{2.5 \text{ mol KBr}}{2.5 \text{ L solution}} = 1.0 \text{ M}$

c. $\quad 755 \text{ mL} = 0.755 \text{ L}$

$$M = \frac{0.55 \text{ mol NaNO}_3}{0.755 \text{ L solution}} = 0.73 \text{ M}$$

d. $\quad M = \dfrac{4.5 \text{ mol Na}_2\text{SO}_4}{1.25 \text{ L solution}} = 3.6 \text{ M}$

114. molar mass $C_{12}H_{22}O_{11} = 342.3$ g; 450. mL = 0.450 L

$$125 \text{ g C}_{12}\text{H}_{22}\text{O}_{11} \times \frac{1 \text{ mol}}{342.3 \text{ g}} = 0.3652 \text{ mol C}_{12}\text{H}_{22}\text{O}_{11}$$

$$M = \frac{0.3652 \text{ mol}}{0.450 \text{ L solution}} = 0.812 \text{ M}$$

116.   molar mass NaCl = 58.44 g

$$1.5 \text{ g NaCl} \times \frac{1 \text{ mol}}{58.44 \text{ g}} = 0.0257 \text{ mol NaCl}$$

$$M = \frac{0.0257 \text{ mol NaCl}}{1.00 \text{ L solution}} = 0.026 \, M$$

118.   a. $4.25 \text{ L solution} \times \dfrac{0.105 \text{ mol KCl}}{1.00 \text{ L solution}} = 0.446 \text{ mol KCl}$

molar mass KCl = 74.6 g

$$0.446 \text{ mol KCl} \times \frac{74.6 \text{ g KCl}}{1 \text{ mol KCl}} = 33.3 \text{ g KCl}$$

b.   15.1 mL = 0.0151 L

$$0.0151 \text{ L solution} \times \frac{0.225 \text{ mol NaNO}_3}{1.00 \text{ L solution}} = 3.40 \times 10^{-3} \text{ mol NaNO}_3$$

molar mass $NaNO_3$ = 85.00 g

$$3.40 \times 10^{-3} \text{ mol} \times \frac{85.00 \text{ g NaNO}_3}{1 \text{ mol NaNO}_3} = 0.289 \text{ g NaNO}_3$$

c.   25 mL = 0.025 L

$$0.025 \text{ L solution} \times \frac{3.0 \text{ mol HCl}}{1.00 \text{ L solution}} = 0.075 \text{ mol HCl}$$

molar mass HCl = 36.46 g

$$0.075 \text{ mol HCl} \times \frac{36.46 \text{ g HCl}}{1 \text{ mol HCl}} = 2.7 \text{ g HCl}$$

d.   100. mL = 0.100 L

$$0.100 \text{ L solution} \times \frac{0.505 \text{ mol H}_2\text{SO}_4}{1.00 \text{ L solution}} = 0.0505 \text{ mol H}_2\text{SO}_4$$

molar mass H_2SO_4 = 98.09 g

$$0.0505 \text{ mol H}_2\text{SO}_4 \times \frac{98.09 \text{ g H}_2\text{SO}_4}{1 \text{ mol H}_2\text{SO}_4} = 4.95 \text{ g H}_2\text{SO}_4$$

120.   a. $1.25 \text{ L} \times \dfrac{0.250 \text{ mol Na}_3\text{PO}_4}{1.00 \text{ L}} = 0.3125 \text{ mol Na}_3\text{PO}_4$

$$0.3125 \text{ mol Na}_3\text{PO}_4 \times \frac{3 \text{ mol Na}^+}{1 \text{ mol Na}_3\text{PO}_4} = 0.938 \text{ mol Na}^+$$

$$0.3125 \text{ mol Na}_3\text{PO}_4 \times \frac{1 \text{ mol PO}_4^-}{1 \text{ mol Na}_3\text{PO}_4} = 0.313 \text{ mol PO}_4^{3-}$$

b. $3.5 \text{ mL} = 0.0035 \text{ L}$

$$0.0035 \text{ L} \times \frac{6.0 \text{ mol } H_2SO_4}{1.00 \text{ L}} = 0.021 \text{ mol } H_2SO_4$$

$$0.021 \text{ mol } H_2SO_4 \times \frac{2 \text{ mol } H^+}{1 \text{ mol } H_2SO_4} = 0.042 \text{ mol } H^+$$

$$0.021 \text{ mol } H_2SO_4 \times \frac{1 \text{ mol } SO_4^{2-}}{1 \text{ mol } H_2SO_4} = 0.021 \text{ mol } SO_4^{2-}$$

c. $25 \text{ mL} = 0.025 \text{ L}$

$$0.025 \text{ L} \times \frac{0.15 \text{ mol } AlCl_3}{1.00 \text{ L}} = 0.00375 \text{ mol } AlCl_3$$

$$0.00375 \text{ mol } AlCl_3 \times \frac{1 \text{ mol } Al^{3+}}{1 \text{ mol } AlCl_3} = 0.0038 \text{ mol } Al^{3+}$$

$$0.00375 \text{ mol } AlCl_3 \times \frac{1 \text{ mol } Cl^-}{1 \text{ mol } AlCl_3} = 0.011 \text{ mol } Cl^-$$

d. $$1.50 \text{ L} \times \frac{1.25 \text{ mol } BaCl_2}{1.00 \text{ L}} = 1.875 \text{ mol } BaCl_2$$

$$1.875 \text{ mol } BaCl_2 \times \frac{1 \text{ mol } Ba^{2+}}{1 \text{ mol } BaCl_2} = 1.88 \text{ mol } Ba^{2+}$$

$$1.875 \text{ mol } BaCl_2 \times \frac{2 \text{ mol } Cl^-}{1 \text{ mol } BaCl_2} = 3.75 \text{ mol } Cl^-$$

122. $M_1 \times V_1 = M_2 \times V_2$

a. $M_1 = 0.200 \ M$ $M_2 = ?$

$V_1 = 125 \text{ mL}$ $V_2 = 125 + 150. = 275 \text{ mL}$

$$M_2 = \frac{(0.200 \ M)(125 \text{ mL})}{(275 \text{ mL})} = 0.0909 \ M$$

b. $M_1 = 0.250 \ M$ $M_2 = ?$

$V_1 = 155 \text{ mL}$ $V_2 = 155 + 150. = 305 \text{ mL}$

$$M_2 = \frac{(0.250 \ M)(155 \text{ mL})}{(305 \text{ mL})} = 0.127 \ M$$

c. $M_1 = 0.250 \ M$ $M_2 = ?$

$V_1 = 0.500 \text{ L} = 500. \text{ mL}$ $V_2 = 500. + 150. = 650. \text{ mL}$

$$M_2 = \frac{(0.250 \ M)(500. \text{ mL})}{(650 \text{ mL})} = 0.192 \ M$$

d. $M_1 = 18.0\ M$ $M_2 = ?$

         $V_1 = 15\ mL$ $V_2 = 15 + 150. = 165\ mL$

$$M_2 = \frac{(18.0\ M)(15\ mL)}{(165\ mL)} = 1.6\ M$$

124. $M_1 \times V_1 = M_2 \times V_2$

         $M_1 = 5.4\ M$ $M_2 = ?$

         $V_1 = 50.\ mL$ $V_2 = 300.\ mL$

$$M_2 = \frac{(5.4\ M)(50.\ mL)}{(300.\ mL)} = 0.90\ M$$

126. $25.0\ mL = 0.0250\ L$

$$0.0250\ L\ NiCl_2\ solution \times \frac{0.20\ mol\ NiCl_2}{1.00\ L\ NiCl_2\ \ solution} = 0.00500\ mol\ NiCl_2$$

$$0.00500\ mol\ NiCl_2 \times \frac{1\ mol\ Na_2S}{1\ mol\ NiCl_2} = 0.00500\ mol\ Na_2S$$

$$0.00500\ mol\ Na_2S \times \frac{1.00\ L\ Na_2S\ solution}{0.10\ mol\ Na_2S} = 0.050\ L = 50.\ mL\ Na_2S\ solution$$

128. $HNO_3(aq) + NaOH(aq) \rightarrow NaNO_3(aq) + H_2O(l)$

      $35.0\ mL = 0.0350\ L$

$$0.0350\ L \times \frac{0.150\ mol\ NaOH}{1.00\ L} = 5.25 \times 10^{-3}\ mol\ NaOH$$

$$5.25 \times 10^{-3}\ mol\ NaOH \times \frac{1\ mol\ HNO_3}{1\ mol\ NaOH} = 5.25 \times 10^{-3}\ mol\ HNO_3$$

$$5.25 \times 10^{-3}\ mol\ HNO_3 \times \frac{1.00\ L}{0.150\ mol\ HNO_3} = 0.0350\ L = 35.0\ mL\ HNO_3$$

130.   a.   equivalent weight HCl = molar mass HCl = 36.46 g; 500. mL = 0.500 L

$$15.0\ g\ HCl \times \frac{1\ equiv\ HCl}{36.46\ g\ HCl} = 0.411\ equiv\ HCl$$

$$N = \frac{0.411\ equiv}{0.500\ L} = 0.822\ N$$

b.   equivalent weight $H_2SO_4 = \dfrac{\text{molar mass}}{2} = \dfrac{98.09 \text{ g}}{2} = 49.05$ g; $250.$ mL $= 0.250$ L

$$49.0 \text{ g } H_2SO_4 \times \dfrac{1 \text{ equiv } H_2SO_4}{49.05 \text{ g } H_2SO_4} = 0.999 \text{ equiv } H_2SO_4$$

$$N = \dfrac{0.999 \text{ equiv}}{0.250 \text{ L}} = 4.00 \; N$$

c.   equivalent weight $H_3PO_4 = \dfrac{\text{molar mass}}{3} = \dfrac{98.0 \text{ g}}{3} = 32.67$ g; $100.$ mL $= 0.100$ L

$$10.0 \text{ g } H_3PO_4 \times \dfrac{1 \text{ equiv } H_3PO_4}{32.67 \text{ g } H_3PO_4} = 0.3061 \text{ equiv } H_3PO_4$$

$$N = \dfrac{0.3061 \text{ equiv}}{0.100 \text{ L}} = 3.06 \; N$$

132.   molar mass $NaH_2PO_4 = 120.0$ g; $500.$ mL $= 0.500$ L

$$5.0 \text{ g } NaH_2PO_4 \times \dfrac{1 \text{ mol } NaH_2PO_4}{120.0 \text{ g } NaH_2PO_4} = 0.04167 \text{ mol } NaH_2PO_4$$

$$M = \dfrac{0.04167 \text{ mol}}{0.500 \text{ L}} = 0.08333 \; M \, NaH_2PO_4 = 0.083 \; M \, NaH_2PO_4$$

$$0.08333 \; M \, NaH_2PO_4 \times \dfrac{2 \text{ equiv } NaH_2PO_4}{1 \text{ mol } NaH_2PO_4} = 0.1667 \; N \, NaH_2PO_4 = 0.17 \; N \, NaH_2PO_4$$

134. $N_{acid} \times V_{acid} = N_{base} \times V_{base}$

$N_{acid} \times (10.0 \text{ mL}) = (3.5 \times 10^{-2} \; N)(27.5 \text{ mL})$

$N_{acid} = 9.6 \times 10^{-2} \; N \, HNO_3$

Chapters 13–15

2. The pressure of the atmosphere represents the mass of the gases in the atmosphere pressing down on the surface of the earth. The device most commonly used to measure the pressure of the atmosphere is the mercury barometer shown in Figure 13.2 in the text.

A simple experiment to demonstrate the pressure of the atmosphere is shown in Figure 13.1 in the text. Some water is added to a metal can, and the can heated until the water boils (boiling represents when the pressure of the vapor coming from the water is equal to the atmospheric pressure). The can is then stoppered. As the steam in the can cools, it condenses to liquid water, which lowers the pressure of gas inside the can. The pressure of the atmosphere outside the can is then much larger than the pressure inside the can, and the can collapses.

4. In simple terms, Boyle's law states that the volume of a gas sample will decrease if you squeeze harder on it. Imagine squeezing hard on a tennis ball with your hand: the ball collapses as the gas inside is forced into a smaller volume by your hand. Of course, to be perfectly correct, the temperature and amount of gas (moles) must remain the same as you adjust the pressure for Boyle's law to hold true. There are two mathematical statements of Boyle's law you should remember. The first is

$$P \times V = \text{constant},$$

which basically is the definition of Boyle's law (in order for the product $(P \times V)$ to remain constant, if one of these terms increases the other must decrease). The second formula is the one more commonly used in solving problems,

$$P_1 \times V_1 = P_2 \times V_2.$$

With this second formulation, we can determine pressure-volume information about a given sample under two sets of conditions. These two mathematical formulas are just two different ways of saying the same thing: if the pressure on a sample of gas is increased, the volume of the sample of gas will decrease. A graph of Boyle's law data is given as Figure 13.5: this type of graph $(xy = k)$ is known to mathematicians as a hyperbola.

6. Charles's law simply says that if you heat a sample of gas, the volume of the sample will increase. That is, when the temperature of a gas is increased, the volume of the gas also increases (assuming the pressure and amount of gas remains the same). Charles's law is a direct proportionality when the temperature is expressed in kelvins (if you increase T, this increases V), whereas Boyle's law is an inverse proportionality (if you increase P, this decreases V). There are two mathematical statements of Charles's law with which you should be familiar. The first statement is:

$$V = kT.$$

This is simply a definition (the volume of a gas sample is directly related to its Kelvin temperature: if you increase the temperature, the volume increases). The working formulation of Charles's law we use in problem solving is given as:

$$\frac{V_1}{T_1} = \frac{V_2}{T_2}$$

With this formulation, we can determine volume-temperature information for a given gas sample under two sets of conditions. Charles's law only holds true if the amount of gas remains the same (obviously the volume of a gas sample would increase if there were more gas present) and also if the pressure remains the same (a change in pressure also changes the volume of a gas sample).

8. Avogadro's law tells us that, with all other things being equal, two moles of gas are twice as big as one mole of gas! That is, the volume of a sample of gas is directly proportional to the number of moles or molecules of gas present (at constant temperature and pressure). If we want to compare the volumes of two samples of the same gas as an indication of the amount of gas present in the samples, we would have to make certain that the two samples of gas are at the same pressure and temperature: the volume of a sample of gas would vary with either temperature or pressure, or both. Avogadro's law holds true for comparing gas samples that are under the same conditions. Avogadro's law is a direct proportionality: the greater the number of gas molecules you have in a sample, the larger the sample's volume will be.

10. The "partial" pressure of an individual gas in a mixture of gases represents the pressure the gas would have in the same container at the same temperature if it were the only gas present. The total pressure in a mixture of gases is the sum of the individual partial pressures of the gases present in the mixture. Because the partial pressures of the gases in a mixture are additive (i.e., the total pressure is the sum of the partial pressures), this suggests that the total pressure in a container is a function only of the number of molecules present in the same, and not of the identity of the molecules or any other property of the molecules (such as their inherent atomic size).

12. The main postulates of the kinetic-molecular theory for gases are as follows: (a) gases consist of tiny particles (atoms or molecules), and the size of these particles is negligible compared to the bulk volume of a gas sample; (b) the particles in a gas are in constant random motion, colliding with each other and with the walls of the container; (c) the particles in a gas sample do not exert any attractive or repulsive forces on one another; (d) the average kinetic energy of the particles in a sample of gas is directly related to the absolute temperature of the gas sample. The pressure exerted by a gas is a result of the molecules colliding with (and pushing on) the walls of the container. The pressure increases with temperature because at a higher temperature, the molecules are moving faster and hit the walls of the container with greater force. A gas fills whatever volume is available to it because the molecules in a gas are in constant random motion: if the motion of the molecules is random, they eventually will move out into whatever volume is available until the distribution of molecules is uniform. At constant pressure, the volume of a gas sample increases as the temperature is increased because with each collision having greater force, the container must expand so that the molecules (and therefore the collisions) are farther apart if the pressure is to remain constant.

14. Solids and liquids are much more condensed states of matter than are gases: the molecules are much closer together in solids and liquids and interact with each other to a much greater extent. Solids and liquids have much greater densities than do gases, and are much less compressible, because there is so little room between the molecules in the solid and liquid states (solids and liquids effectively have native volumes of their own, and their volumes are not affected nearly as much by the temperature or pressure). Although solids are more rigid than liquids, the solid and liquid state have much more in common with each other than either of these states has with the gaseous state. We know this is true because it typically only takes a few kilojoules of energy to

melt 1 mol of a solid (not much change has to take place in the molecules), whereas it may take 10 times more energy to vaporize a liquid (as there is a great change between the liquid and gaseous states).

16.   The normal boiling point of water, that is, water's boiling point at a pressure of exactly 760 mm Hg, is 100°C (you will recall that the boiling point of water was used to set one of the reference temperatures of the Celsius temperature scale). Water remains at 100°C while boiling, until all the water has boiled away, because the additional heat energy being added to the sample is used to overcome attractive forces among the water molecules as they go from the condensed, liquid state to the gaseous state. The normal (760 mm Hg) freezing point of water is exactly 0°C (again, this property of water was used as one of the reference points for the Celsius temperature scale). A cooling curve for water is given in Figure 14.2. Notice how the curve shows that the amount of heat needed to boil the sample is much larger than the amount needed to melt the sample.

18.   Dipole-dipole forces are a type of intermolecular force that can exist between molecules with permanent dipole moments. Molecules with permanent dipole moments try to orient themselves so that the positive end of one polar molecule can attract the negative end of another polar molecule. Dipole-dipole forces are not nearly as strong as ionic or covalent bonding forces (only about 1% as strong as covalent bonding forces) because electrostatic attraction is related to the magnitude of the charges of the attracting species. As polar molecules have only a "partial" charge at each end of the dipole, the magnitude of the attractive force is not as large. The strength of such forces also drops rapidly as molecules become farther apart and is important only in the solid and liquid states (such forces are negligible in the gaseous state because the molecules are too far apart). Hydrogen bonding is an especially strong sort of dipole-dipole attractive force that can exist when hydrogen atoms are directly bonded to the most strongly electronegative atoms (N, O, and F). Because the hydrogen atom is so small, dipoles involving N–H, O–H, and F–H bonds can approach each other much more closely than can dipoles involving other atoms. As the magnitude of dipole-dipole forces is dependent on distance, unusually strong attractive forces can exist in such molecules. We take the fact that the boiling point of water is higher than that of the other covalent hydrogen compounds of the Group 6 elements as evidence for the special strength of hydrogen bonding (it takes more energy to vaporize water because of the extra strong forces holding together the molecules in the liquid state).

20.   Vaporization of a liquid requires an input of energy because the intermolecular forces that hold the molecules together in the liquid state must be overcome. The high heat of vaporization of water is essential to life on Earth because much of the excess energy striking the Earth from the sun is dissipated in vaporizing water. Condensation is the opposite process to vaporization; that is, condensation refers to the process by which molecules in the vapor state form a liquid. In a closed container containing a liquid and some empty space above the liquid, an equilibrium is set up between vaporization and condensation. The liquid in such a sealed container never completely evaporates: when the liquid is first placed in the container, the liquid phase begins to evaporate into the empty space. As the number of molecules in the vapor phase begins to get large, however, some of these molecules begin to re-enter the liquid phase. Eventually, every time a molecule of liquid somewhere in the container enters the vapor phase, somewhere else in the container a molecule of vapor re-enters the liquid. There is no further net change in the amount of liquid phase (although molecules are continually moving between the liquid and vapor phases). The pressure of the vapor in such an equilibrium situation is characteristic for the liquid at each particular temperature (for example, the vapor pressures of water are tabulated at different temperatures in Table 13.2). A simple experiment to determine vapor pressure is shown in Figure 14.10. Samples of a liquid are injected into a sealed tube containing mercury; because mercury is so dense, the liquids float to the top of the mercury where they evaporate. As the vapor pressures

of the liquids develop to the saturation point, the level of mercury in the tube changes as an index of the magnitude of the vapor pressures. Typically, liquids with strong intermolecular forces have small vapor pressures (they have more difficulty in evaporating) than do liquids with very weak intermolecular forces: for example, the components of gasoline (weak forces) have much higher vapor pressures, and evaporate more easily than does water (strong forces).

22.   The simple model we use to explain many properties of metallic elements is called the electron sea model. In this model we picture a regular lattice array of metal cations in sort of a "sea" of mobile valence electrons. The electrons can move easily to conduct heat or electricity through the metal; and the lattice of cations can be deformed fairly easily, allowing the metal to be hammered into a sheet or stretched to make a wire. An alloy contains a mixture of elements, which overall has metallic properties. Substitutional alloys consist of a host metal in which some of the atoms in the metal's crystalline structure are replaced by atoms of other metallic elements of comparable size to the atoms of the host metal. For example, sterling silver consists of an alloy in which approximately 7% of the silver atoms have been replaced by copper atoms. Brass and pewter are also substitutional alloys. An interstitial alloy is formed when other smaller atoms enter the interstices (holes) between atoms in the host metal's crystal structure. Steel is an interstitial alloy in which typically carbon atoms enter the interstices of a crystal of iron atoms. The presence of the interstitial carbon atoms markedly changes the properties of the iron, making it much harder, more malleable, and more ductile. Depending on the amount of carbon introduced into the iron crystals, the properties of the resulting steel can be carefully controlled.

24.   A saturated solution is one that contains as much solute as can dissolve at a particular temperature. To say that a solution is saturated does not necessarily mean that the solute is present at a high concentration. For example, magnesium hydroxide only dissolves to a very small extent before the solution is saturated, whereas it takes a great deal of sugar to form a saturated solution (and the saturated solution is extremely concentrated). A saturated solution is one which is in equilibrium with undissolved solute: as molecules of solute dissolve from the solid in one place in the solution, dissolved molecules rejoin the solid phase in another place in the solution. As with the development of vapor pressure above a liquid (see Question 20 above), formation of a solution reaches a state of dynamic equilibrium: once the rates of dissolving and "undissolving" become equal, there will be no further net change in the concentration of the solution and the solution will be saturated.

26.   Adding more solvent to a solution so as to dilute the solution *does not change* the number of moles of solute present, but only changes the volume in which the solute is dispersed. If we are using the molarity of the solution to describe its concentration, the number of liters is changed when we add solvent, and the number of moles per liter (the molarity) changes, but the actual number of moles of solute does not change. For example, 125 mL of 0.551 M NaCl contains 68.9 millimol of NaCl. The solution will still contain 68.9 millimol of NaCl after the 250 mL of water is added to it, only now the 68.9 millimol of NaCl will be dispersed in a total volume of 375 mL. This gives the new molarity as 68.9 mmol/375 mL = 0.184 M. The volume and the concentration have changed, but the number of moles of solute in the solution has not changed.

28. $P_1 \times V_1 = P_2 \times V_2$

a.
$$V_2 = \frac{P_1 \times V_1}{P_2} = \frac{125 \text{ mL} \times 755 \text{ mm Hg}}{899 \text{ mm Hg}} = 105 \text{ mL}$$

b.
$$P_2 = \frac{P_1 \times V_1}{V_2} = \frac{455 \text{ mL} \times 755 \text{ mm Hg}}{327 \text{ mL}} = 1.05 \times 10^3 \text{ mm Hg}$$

30. a. $PV = nRT$; molar mass He = 4.003 g; 25°C = 298 K

$$1.15 \text{ g He} \times \frac{1 \text{ mol}}{4.003 \text{ g}} = 0.2873 \text{ mol He}$$

$$V = \frac{nRT}{P} = \frac{(0.2873 \text{ mol})(0.08206 \text{ L-atm/mol-K})(298 \text{ K})}{(1.01 \text{ atm})} = 6.96 \text{ L}$$

  b. molar masses: H$_2$, 2.016 g; He, 4.003 g; 0°C = 273 K

$$2.27 \text{ g H}_2 \times \frac{1 \text{ mol H}_2}{2.016 \text{ g H}_2} = 1.126 \text{ mol H}_2$$

$$1.03 \text{ g He} \times \frac{1 \text{ mol He}}{4.003 \text{ g He}} = 0.2573 \text{ mol He}$$

$$P_{H_2} = \frac{nRT}{V} = \frac{(1.126 \text{ mol H}_2)(0.08206 \text{ L-atm/mol-K})(273 \text{ K})}{(5.00 \text{ L})} = 5.05 \text{ atm}$$

$$P_{He} = \frac{nRT}{V} = \frac{(0.2573 \text{ mol He})(0.08206 \text{ L-atm/mol-K})(273 \text{ K})}{(5.00 \text{ L})} = 1.15 \text{ atm}$$

  c. molar mass of Ar = 39.95 g; 27°C = 300 K

$$42.5 \text{ g Ar} \times \frac{1 \text{ mol Ar}}{39.95 \text{ g Ar}} = 1.064 \text{ mol Ar}$$

$$P = \frac{nRT}{V} = \frac{(1.064 \text{ mol Ar})(0.08206 \text{ L-atm/mol-K})(300 \text{ K})}{(9.97 \text{ L})} = 2.63 \text{ atm}$$

32. molar masses: CaCO$_3$, 100.09 g; CO$_2$, 44.01 g

$$1.25 \text{ g CaCO}_3 \times \frac{1 \text{ mol CaCO}_3}{100.09 \text{ g}} = 0.01249 \text{ mol CaCO}_3$$

$$0.01249 \text{ mol CaCO}_3 \times \frac{1 \text{ mol CO}_2}{1 \text{ mol CaCO}_3} = 0.01249 \text{ mol CO}_2$$

$$0.01249 \text{ mol CO}_2 \times \frac{44.01 \text{ g CO}_2}{1 \text{ mol CO}_2} = 0.550 \text{ g CO}_2$$

$$0.01249 \text{ mol CO}_2 \times \frac{22.4 \text{ L}}{1 \text{ mol}} = 0.280 \text{ L CO}_2 \text{ at STP}$$

34. a. mass of solution = 2.05 g NaCl + 19.2 g water = 21.25 g solution

$$\frac{2.05 \text{ g NaCl}}{21.25 \text{ g solution}} \times 100 = 9.65\% \text{ NaCl}$$

b. $26.2 \text{ g solution} \times \dfrac{10.5 \text{ g CaCl}_2}{100 \text{ g solution}} = 2.75 \text{ g CaCl}_2$

c. $225 \text{ g solution} \times \dfrac{5.05 \text{ g NaCl}}{100 \text{ g solution}} = 11.4 \text{ g NaCl required}$

36. $M_1 \times V_1 = M_2 \times V_2$

a. $M_2 = \dfrac{(12.5 \text{ mL})(1.515 \, M)}{(12.5 + 25 \text{ mL})} = 0.505 \, (0.51) \, M$

b. $M_2 = \dfrac{(75.0 \text{ mL})(0.252 \, M)}{(225 \text{ mL})} = 0.0840 \, M$

c. $M_2 = \dfrac{(52.1 \text{ mL})(0.751 \, M)}{(52.1 + 250. \text{ mL})} = 0.130 \, M$

38. a. $125 \text{ mL solution} \times \dfrac{1.84 \text{ g solution}}{1 \text{ mL solution}} = 230. \text{ g solution}$

$230. \text{ g solution} \times \dfrac{98.3 \text{ g H}_2\text{SO}_4}{1 \text{ g solution}} = 226 \text{ g H}_2\text{SO}_4$

b. The concentrated solution contains 226 g of H_2SO_4 (molar mass 98.09 g) in 125 mL (0.125 L) of solution

$226 \text{ g H}_2\text{SO}_4 \times \dfrac{1 \text{ mol H}_2\text{SO}_4}{98.09 \text{ g H}_2\text{SO}_4} = 2.304 \text{ mol H}_2\text{SO}_4$

$M = \dfrac{2.304 \text{ mol H}_2\text{SO}_4}{0.125 \text{ L solution}} = 18.4 \, M$

c. $M_1 \times V_1 = M_2 \times V_2$

$M_2 = \dfrac{(0.125 \text{ L})(18.4 \, M)}{3.01 \text{ L}} = 0.764 \, M$

d. $\dfrac{0.764 \text{ mol}}{1 \text{ L}} \times \dfrac{2 \text{ equivalents}}{1 \text{ mol}} = 1.53 \, N$

e. $\text{mmol NaOH} = 45.3 \text{ mL} \times \dfrac{0.532 \text{ mmol NaOH}}{1 \text{ mL}} = 24.10 \text{ mmol}$

$H_2SO_4 + 2NaOH \rightarrow Na_2SO_4 + 2H_2O$

$\text{mmol H}_2\text{SO}_4 \text{ required} = 24.10 \text{ mmol NaOH} \times \dfrac{1 \text{ mmol H}_2\text{SO}_4}{2 \text{ mmol NaOH}} = 12.05 \text{ mmol H}_2\text{SO}_4$

$12.05 \text{ mmol H}_2\text{SO}_4 \times \dfrac{1 \text{ mL solution}}{0.764 \text{ mmol H}_2\text{SO}_4} = 15.8 \text{ mL of the sulfuric acid solution.}$

CHAPTER 16

Acids and Bases

2. $HCl(g) \xrightarrow{H_2O} H^+(aq) + Cl^-(aq)$

    $NaOH(s) \xrightarrow{H_2O} Na^+(aq) + OH^-(aq)$

4. Conjugate acid–base pairs differ from each other by one proton (one hydrogen ion, H^+). For example, CH_3COOH (acetic acid), differs from its conjugate base, CH_3COO^- (acetate ion), by a single H^+ ion.

    $CH_3COOH(aq) \rightleftharpoons CH_3COO^-(aq) + H^+(aq)$

6. In addition to sodium bicarbonate, the gum also contains citric acid and malic acid. When the gum is exposed to moisture in the mouth, the bicarbonate ion behaves as a *base* and reacts with hydrogen ion from the acids: $H^+(aq) + HCO_3^-(aq) \rightarrow H_2O(l) + CO_2(g)$

8. a. a conjugate pair: the two species differ by one proton

    b. a conjugate pair: the two species differ by one proton

    c. a conjugate pair: the two species differ by one proton

    d. not a conjugate pair

    H_2O, OH^-

    OH^-, O^{2-}

10. a. $NH_3(aq)(\text{base}) + H_2O(l)(\text{acid}) \rightleftharpoons NH_4^+(aq)(\text{acid}) + OH^-(aq)(\text{base})$

    b. $NH_4^+(aq)(\text{acid}) + H_2O(l)(\text{base}) \rightleftharpoons NH_3(aq)(\text{base}) + H_3O^+(aq)(\text{acid})$

    c. $NH_2^-(aq)(\text{base}) + H_2O(l)(\text{acid}) \rightleftharpoons NH_3(aq)(\text{acid}) + OH^-(aq)(\text{base})$

12. The conjugate *acid* of the species indicated would have *one additional proton*:

    a. $HClO$

    b. HCl

    c. $HClO_3$

    d. $HClO_4$

14. The conjugate *bases* of the species indicated would have *one less proton*:

    a. BrO^-

    b. HSO_3^-

    c. SO_3^{2-}

    d. CH_3NH_2

16.   a. $O^{2-}(aq) + H_2O(l) \rightleftharpoons OH^-(aq) + OH^-(aq)$

       b. $NH_3(aq) + H_2O(l) \rightleftharpoons NH_4^+(aq) + OH^-(aq)$

       c. $HSO_4^-(aq) + H_2O(l) \rightleftharpoons SO_4^{2-}(aq) + H_3O^+(aq)$

       d. $HNO_2(aq) + H_2O(l) \rightleftharpoons NO_2^-(aq) + H_3O^+(aq)$

18.   To say that an acid is *weak* in aqueous solution means that the acid does not easily transfer protons to water (and does not fully ionize). If an acid does not lose protons easily, then the acid's anion must be a strong attractor of protons (good at holding on to protons).

20.   A strong acid is one that loses its protons easily and fully ionizes in water; this means that the acid's conjugate base must be poor at attracting and holding on to protons, and is therefore a relatively weak base. A weak acid is one that resists loss of its protons and does not ionize well in water; this means that the acid's conjugate base attracts and holds onto protons tightly and is a relatively strong base.

22. H_2SO_4 (sulfuric): $H_2SO_4 + H_2O \rightarrow HSO_4^- + H_3O^+$

       HCl (hydrochloric): $HCl + H_2O \rightarrow Cl^- + H_3O^+$

       HNO_3 (nitric): $HNO_3 + H_2O \rightarrow NO_3^- + H_3O^+$

       $HClO_4$ (perchloric): $HClO_4 + H_2O \rightarrow ClO_4^- + H_3O^+$

24.   An oxyacid is an acid containing a particular element which is bonded to one or more oxygen atoms. HNO_3, H_2SO_4, $HClO_4$ are oxyacids. HCl, HF, HBr are not oxyacids.

26.   Salicylic acid is a monoprotic acid: only the hydrogen of the carboxyl group ionizes.

28.   For example, HCO_3^- can behave as an acid if it reacts with something that more strongly gains protons than does HCO_3^- itself. For example, HCO_3^- would behave as an acid when reacting with hydroxide ion (a much stronger base).

       $HCO_3^-(aq) + OH^-(aq) \rightarrow CO_3^{2-}(aq) + H_2O(l)$.

       On the other hand, HCO_3^- would behave as a base when reacted with something that more readily loses protons than does HCO_3^- itself. For example, HCO_3^- would behave as a base when reacting with hydrochloric acid (a much stronger acid).

       $HCO_3^-(aq) + HCl(aq) \rightarrow H_2CO_3(aq) + Cl^-(aq)$

       For $H_2PO_4^-$, similar equations can be written:

       $H_2PO_4^-(aq) + OH^-(aq) \rightarrow HPO_4^{2-}(aq) + H_2O(l)$

       $H_2PO_4^-(aq) + H_3O^+(aq) \rightarrow H_3PO_4(aq) + H_2O(l)$

30.   The hydrogen ion concentration and the hydroxide ion concentration of water are *not* independent: they are related by the equilibrium

$$H_2O(l) \rightleftharpoons H^+(aq) + OH^-(aq)$$

for which $K_w = [H^+][OH^-] = 1.0 \times 10^{-14}$ at 25°C.

If the concentration of one of these ions is increased by addition of a reagent producing H^+ or OH^-, then the concentration of the complementary ion will have to decrease so that the value of K_w will hold true. So if an acid is added to a solution, the concentration of hydroxide ion in the solution will decrease to a lower value. Similarly, if a base is added to a solution, then the concentration of hydrogen ion will have to decrease to a lower value.

32. $K_w = [H^+][OH^-] = 1.0 \times 10^{-14}$ at 25°C

   a. $[H^+] = \dfrac{1.0 \times 10^{-14}}{3.44 \times 10^{-1}\,M} = 2.9 \times 10^{-14}\,M$; solution is basic

   b. $[H^+] = \dfrac{1.0 \times 10^{-14}}{9.79 \times 10^{-11}\,M} = 1.0 \times 10^{-4}\,M$; solution is acidic

   c. $[H^+] = \dfrac{1.0 \times 10^{-14}}{4.89 \times 10^{-6}\,M} = 2.0 \times 10^{-9}\,M$; solution is basic

   d. $[H^+] = \dfrac{1.0 \times 10^{-14}}{3.78 \times 10^{-7}\,M} = 2.6 \times 10^{-8}\,M$; solution is basic

34. $K_w = [H^+][OH^-] = 1.0 \times 10^{-14}$ at 25°C

   a. $[OH^-] = \dfrac{1.0 \times 10^{-14}}{1.02 \times 10^{-7}\,M} = 9.8 \times 10^{-8}\,M$; solution is acidic

   b. $[OH^-] = \dfrac{1.0 \times 10^{-14}}{9.77 \times 10^{-8}\,M} = 1.02 \times 10^{-7}\,M\,(1.0 \times 10^{-7}\,M)$; solution is slightly basic

   c. $[OH^-] = \dfrac{1.0 \times 10^{-14}}{3.41 \times 10^{-3}\,M} = 2.9 \times 10^{-12}\,M$; solution is acidic

   d. $[OH^-] = \dfrac{1.0 \times 10^{-14}}{4.79 \times 10^{-11}\,M} = 2.1 \times 10^{-4}\,M$; solution is basic

36.   a. $[OH^-] = 6.03 \times 10^{-4}\,M$ is more basic

       b. $[OH^-] = 4.21 \times 10^{-6}\,M$ is more basic

       c. $[OH^-] = 8.04 \times 10^{-4}\,M$ is more basic

38.   Answer depends on student choice.

40.   pH 1–2, deep red; pH 4, purple; pH 8, blue; pH 11, green

42. $pH = -\log[H^+]$

    a. $pH = -\log[9.35 \times 10^{-2}\ M] = 1.029$; solution is acidic

    b. $pH = -\log[3.75 \times 10^{-4}\ M] = 3.426$; solution is acidic

    c. $pH = -\log[8.36 \times 10^{-6}\ M] = 5.078$; solution is acidic

    d. $pH = -\log[5.42 \times 10^{-8}\ M] = 7.266$; solution is basic

44. $pOH = -\log[OH^-]$ $pH = 14.00 - pOH$

    a. $pOH = -\log[8.63 \times 10^{-3}\ M] = 2.064$

        $pH = 14.00 - 2.064 = 11.936 = 11.94$; solution is basic

    b. $pOH = -\log[7.44 \times 10^{-6}\ M] = 5.128$

        $pH = 14.00 - 5.128 = 8.872 = 8.87$; solution is basic

    c. $pOH = -\log[9.35 \times 10^{-9}\ M] = 8.029$

        $pH = 14.00 - 8.029 = 5.971 = 5.97$; solution is acidic

    d. $pOH = -\log[1.21 \times 10^{-11}\ M] = 10.917$

        $pH = 14.00 - 10.917 = 3.083 = 3.08$; solution is acidic

46. $pOH = 14.00 - pH$

    a. $pOH = 14.00 - 9.78 = 4.22$; solution is basic

    b. $pOH = 14.00 - 4.01 = 9.99$; solution is acidic

    c. $pOH = 14.00 - 2.79 = 11.21$; solution is acidic

    d. $pOH = 14.00 - 11.21 = 2.79$; solution is basic

48.   a. $pH = -\log[1.91 \times 10^{-2}\ M] = 1.719$; solution is acidic

$$[OH^-] = \frac{1.0 \times 10^{-14}}{1.91 \times 10^{-2}\ M} = 5.2 \times 10^{-13}\ M$$

    b. $pH = -\log[4.83 \times 10^{-7}\ M] = 6.316$; solution is acidic

$$[OH^-] = \frac{1.0 \times 10^{-14}}{4.83 \times 10^{-7}\ M} = 2.1 \times 10^{-8}\ M$$

    c. $pH = -\log[8.92 \times 10^{-11}\ M] = 10.050$; solution is basic

$$[OH^-] = \frac{1.0 \times 10^{-14}}{8.92 \times 10^{-11}\ M} = 1.1 \times 10^{-4}\ M$$

    d. $pH = -\log[6.14 \times 10^{-5}\ M] = 4.212$; solution is acidic

$$[OH^-] = \frac{1.0 \times 10^{-14}}{6.14 \times 10^{-5}\ M} = 1.6 \times 10^{-10}\ M$$

50. $[H^+] = \{inv\}\{log\}[-pH]$ or 10^{-pH}

    a. $[H^+] = \{inv\}\{log\}[-11.21] = 6.2 \times 10^{-12}\ M$

    b. $[H^+] = \{inv\}\{log\}[-4.39] = 4.1 \times 10^{-5}\ M$

    c. $[H^+] = \{inv\}\{log\}[-7.44] = 3.6 \times 10^{-8}\ M$

    d. $[H^+] = \{inv\}\{log\}[-1.38] = 4.2 \times 10^{-2}\ M$

52. $pH + pOH = 14.00$ $[H^+] = \{inv\}\{log\}[-pH]$ or 10^{-pH}

    a. $pH = 14.00 - 4.99 = 9.01$

             $[H^+] = \{inv\}\{log\}[-9.01] = 9.8 \times 10^{-10}\ M$

    b. $[H^+] = \{inv\}\{log\}[-7.74] = 1.8 \times 10^{-8}\ M$

    c. $pH = 14.00 - 10.74 = 3.26$

             $[H^+] = \{inv\}\{log\}[-3.26] = 5.5 \times 10^{-4}\ M$

    d. $[H^+] = \{inv\}\{log\}[-2.25] = 5.6 \times 10^{-3}\ M$

54.   a. $pH = -\log[4.39 \times 10^{-6}\ M] = 5.358$

    b. $pH = 14.00 - pOH = 14.00 - 10.36 = 3.64$

    c. $pOH = -\log[9.37 \times 10^{-9}\ M] = 8.028$ $pH = 14.00 - 8.028 = 5.97$

    d. $pH = -\log[3.31 \times 10^{-1}\ M] = 0.480$

56.   The solution contains water molecules, H_3O^+ ions (protons), and NO_3^- ions. Because HNO_3 is a strong acid, which is completely ionized in water, there are no HNO_3 molecules present.

58.   a. HNO_3 is a strong acid and completely ionized so $[H^+] = 1.21 \times 10^{-3}\ M$ and $pH = 2.917$.

    b. $HClO_4$ is a strong acid and completely ionized so $[H^+] = 0.000199\ M$ and $pH = 3.701$.

    c. HCl is a strong acid and completely ionized so $[H^+] = 5.01 \times 10^{-5}\ M$ and $pH = 4.300$.

    d. HBr is a strong acid and completely ionized so $[H^+] = 0.00104\ M$ and $pH = 2.983$.

60.   A buffered solution consists of a mixture of a weak acid and its conjugate base; one example of a buffered solution is a mixture of acetic acid (CH_3COOH) and sodium acetate ($NaCH_3COO$).

62.   The weak acid component of a buffered solution is capable of reacting with added strong base. For example, using the buffered solution given as an example in Question 60, acetic acid would consume added sodium hydroxide as follows:

    $CH_3COOH(aq) + NaOH(aq) \rightarrow NaCH_3COO(aq) + H_2O(l)$.

Acetic acid *neutralizes* the added NaOH and prevents it from having much effect on the overall pH of the solution.

64.   HCl: $H_3O^+ + C_2H_3O_2^- \rightarrow HC_2H_3O_2 + H_2O$

       NaOH: $OH^- + HC_2H_3O_2 \rightarrow C_2H_3O_2^- + H_2O$

66.   a.   NaOH is completely ionized, so $[OH^-] = 0.10\ M$.

$pOH = -\log[0.10] = 1.00$

$pH = 14.00 - 1.00 = 13.00$

    b.   KOH is completely ionized, so $[OH^-] = 2.0 \times 10^{-4}\ M$.

$pOH = -\log[2.0 \times 10^{-4}] = 3.70$

$pH = 14.00 - 3.70 = 10.30$

    c.   CsOH is completely ionized, so $[OH^-] = 6.2 \times 10^{-3}\ M$.

$pOH = -\log[6.2 \times 10^{-3}] = 2.21$

$pH = 14.00 - 2.21 = 11.79$

    d.   NaOH is completely ionized, so $[OH^-] = 0.0001\ M$.

$pOH = -\log[0.0001] = 4.0$

$pH = 14.00 - 4.0 = 10.0$

68.   b, c, and d

70.   a, c, and e represent strong acids; b and d are typical weak acids.

72.   Ordinarily in calculating the pH of strong acid solutions, the major contribution to the concentration of hydrogen ion present is from the dissolved strong acid; we ordinarily neglect the small amount of hydrogen ion present in such solutions due to the ionization of water. With $1.0 \times 10^{-7}\ M$ HCl solution, however, the amount of hydrogen ion present due to the ionization of *water* is *comparable* to that present due to the addition of *acid* (HCl) and must be considered in the calculation of pH.

74.   accepts

76.   base

78.   carboxyl (–COOH) $CH_3COOH + H_2O \rightleftharpoons C_2H_3O_2^- + H_3O^+$

80. 1.0×10^{-14}

82.   higher

84.   pH

86.   weak acid

88.   a. H_2O and OH^- represent a conjugate acid–base pair (H_2O is the acid, having one more proton than the base, OH^-).

    b. H_2SO_4 and SO_4^{2-} are *not* a conjugate acid–base pair (they differ by *two* protons). The conjugate base of H_2SO_4 is HSO_4^-; the conjugate acid of SO_4^{2-} is also HSO_4^-.

c. H_3PO_4 and $H_2PO_4^-$ represent a conjugate acid–base pair (H_3PO_4 is the acid, having one more proton than the base $H_2PO_4^-$).

d. $HC_2H_3O_2$ and $C_2H_3O_2^-$ represent a conjugate acid–base pair ($HC_2H_3O_2$ is the acid, having one more proton than the base $C_2H_3O_2^-$).

90. The conjugate *acid* of the species indicated would have *one additional proton*:

   a. NH_4^+

   b. NH_3

   c. H_3O^+

   d. H_2O

92. When an acid ionizes in water, a proton is released to the water as an H_3O^+ ion:

   a. $CH_3CH_2COOH + H_2O \rightleftharpoons CH_3CH_2COO^- + H_3O^+$

   b. $NH_4^+ + H_2O \rightleftharpoons NH_3 + H_3O^+$

   c. $H_2SO_4 + H_2O \rightarrow HSO_4^- + H_3O^+$

   d. $H_3PO_4 + H_2O \rightleftharpoons H_2PO_4^- + H_3O^+$

94. $K_w = [H^+][OH^-] = 1.0 \times 10^{-14}$ at 25°C

   a. $[H^+] = \dfrac{1.0 \times 10^{-14}}{4.22 \times 10^{-3}\ M} = 2.4 \times 10^{-12}\ M$; solution is basic

   b. $[H^+] = \dfrac{1.0 \times 10^{-14}}{1.01 \times 10^{-13}\ M} = 9.9 \times 10^{-2}\ M$; solution is acidic

   c. $[H^+] = \dfrac{1.0 \times 10^{-14}}{3.05 \times 10^{-7}\ M} = 3.3 \times 10^{-8}\ M$; solution is basic

   d. $[H^+] = \dfrac{1.0 \times 10^{-14}}{6.02 \times 10^{-6}\ M} = 1.7 \times 10^{-9}\ M$; solution is basic

96. a. $[OH^-] = 0.0000032\ M$ is more basic

   b. $[OH^-] = 1.54 \times 10^{-8}\ M$ is more basic

   c. $[OH^-] = 4.02 \times 10^{-7}\ M$ is more basic

98. $pOH = -\log[OH^-]$ $pH = 14.00 - pOH$

   a. $pOH = -\log[1.4 \times 10^{-6}\ M] = 5.85$; $pH = 14.00 - 5.85 = 8.15$; solution is basic

   b. $pOH = -\log[9.35 \times 10^{-9}\ M] = 8.029 = 8.03$; $pH = 14.00 - 8.029 = 5.97$; solution is acidic

   c. $pOH = -\log[2.21 \times 10^{-1}\ M] = 0.656 = 0.66$; $pH = 14.00 - 0.656 = 13.34$; solution is basic

   d. $pOH = -\log[7.98 \times 10^{-12}\ M] = 11.10$; $pH = 14.00 - 11.098 = 2.90$; solution is acidic

100.   a. $[OH^-] = \dfrac{1.0 \times 10^{-14}}{5.72 \times 10^{-4} \ M} = 1.75 \times 10^{-11} \ M = 1.8 \times 10^{-11} \ M$

            $pOH = -\log[1.75 \times 10^{-11} \ M] = 10.76$

            $pH = 14.00 - 10.76 = 3.24$

    b. $[H^+] = \dfrac{1.0 \times 10^{-14}}{8.91 \times 10^{-5} \ M} = 1.12 \times 10^{-10} \ M = 1.1 \times 10^{-10} \ M$

            $pH = -\log[1.12 \times 10^{-10} \ M] = 9.95$

            $pOH = 14.00 - 9.95 = 4.05$

    c. $[OH^-] = \dfrac{1.0 \times 10^{-14}}{2.87 \times 10^{-12} \ M} = 3.48 \times 10^{-3} \ M = 3.5 \times 10^{-3} \ M$

            $pOH = -\log[3.48 \times 10^{-3} \ M] = 2.46$

            $pH = 14.00 - 2.46 = 11.54$

    d. $[H^+] = \dfrac{1.0 \times 10^{-14}}{7.22 \times 10^{-8} \ M} = 1.39 \times 10^{-7} \ M = 1.4 \times 10^{-7} \ M$

            $pH = -\log[1.39 \times \times 10^{-7} \ M] = 6.86$

            $pOH = 14.00 - 6.86 = 7.14$

102. $pH = 14.00 - pOH$ $[H^+] = \{inv\}\{\log\}[-pH]$ or 10^{-pH}

    a. $[H^+] = \{inv\}\{\log\}[-5.41] = 3.9 \times 10^{-6} \ M$

    b. $pH = 14.00 - 12.04 = 1.96$ $[H^+] = \{inv\}\{\log\}[-1.96] = 1.1 \times 10^{-2} \ M$

    c. $[H^+] = \{inv\}\{\log\}[-11.91] = 1.2 \times 10^{-12} \ M$

    d. $pH = 14.00 - 3.89 = 10.11$ $[H^+] = \{inv\}\{\log\}[-10.11] = 7.8 \times 10^{-11} \ M$

104.   a. $HClO_4$ is a strong acid and completely ionized so $[H^+] = 1.4 \times 10^{-3} \ M$ and $pH = 2.85$.

    b. HCl is a strong acid and completely ionized so $[H^+] = 3.0 \times 10^{-5} \ M$ and $pH = 4.52$.

    c. HNO_3 is a strong acid and completely ionized so $[H^+] = 5.0 \times 10^{-2} \ M$ and $pH = 1.30$.

    d. HCl is a strong acid and completely ionized so $[H^+] = 0.0010 \ M$ and $pH = 3.00$.

CHAPTER 17

Equilibrium

2. Four C–H bonds in the CH_4 molecule and four Cl–Cl bonds in the four Cl_2 molecules must be broken. Four C–Cl bonds in CCl_4 and four H–Cl bonds in the four HCl molecules must form.

4. The symbol E_a represents the *activation energy* of the reaction. The activation energy is the minimum energy two colliding molecules must possess in order for the collision to result in reaction. If molecules do not possess energies equal to or greater than E_a, a collision between these molecules will not result in a reaction.

6. Enzymes are biochemical catalysts that accelerate the complicated biochemical reactions in cells that would ordinarily be too slow to sustain life at normal body temperatures.

8. A state of equilibrium is attained when two opposing processes are exactly balanced so there is no further observable net change in the system.

10. Chemical equilibrium occurs when two *opposing* chemical reactions reach the *same speed* in a closed system. When a state of chemical equilibrium has been reached, the concentrations of reactants and products present in the system remain *constant* with time, and the reaction appears to "stop." A chemical reaction that reaches a state of equilibrium is indicated by using a double arrow ($\rightleftharpoons$). The points of the double arrow point in opposite directions, to indicate that two opposite processes are going on.

12. The two curves come together when a state of chemical equilibrium has been reached, after which point, the forward and reverse reactions are occurring at the same rate so that there is no further net change in concentration.

14. The equilibrium constant is a *ratio* of concentration of products to concentration of reactants, with all concentrations measured at equilibrium. Depending on the amount of reactant present at the beginning of an experiment, there may be different absolute amounts of reactants and products present at equilibrium, but the *ratio* will always be the same for a given reaction at a given temperature. For example, the ratios (4/2) and (6/3) are different absolutely in terms of the numbers involved, but each of these ratios has the *value* of 2.

16. a. $K = \dfrac{[H_2O][CO]}{[H_2][CO_2]}$

    b. $K = \dfrac{[NO]^4}{[N_2O]^2[O_2]}$

    c. $K = \dfrac{[CH_3OH]}{[CO][H_2]^2}$

18.   a. $K = \dfrac{[CH_3OH]}{[CO][H_2]^2}$

      b. $K = \dfrac{[NO]^2[O_2]}{[NO_2]^2}$

      c. $K = \dfrac{[PBr_3]^4}{[P_4][Br_2]^6}$

20. $COCl_2(g) \rightleftharpoons CO(g) + Cl_2(g)$

$$K = \frac{[CO][Cl_2]}{[COCl_2]} = \frac{[0.0345\ M][0.0219\ M]}{[0.00103\ M]} = 0.734$$

22. $2N_2O(g) + O_2(g) \rightleftharpoons 4NO(g)$

$$K = \frac{[NO]^4}{[N_2O]^2[O_2]} = \frac{[0.00341\ M]^4}{[0.0293\ M]^2[0.0325\ M]} = 4.85 \times 10^{-6}$$

24.   Equilibrium constants represent ratios of the *concentrations* of products and reactants present at the point of equilibrium. The *concentration* of a pure solid or of a pure liquid is constant and is determined by the density of the solid or liquid. For example, suppose you had a liter of water. Within that liter of water are 55.5 mol of water (the number of moles of water that is contained in one liter of water *does not vary*).

26.   a. $K = \dfrac{[H_2]}{[H_2O]}$

      b. $K = \dfrac{1}{[O_2]^3}$

      c. $K = \dfrac{[HCl]^4}{[CH_4][Cl_2]^4}$

28.   a. $K = \dfrac{[S_2Cl_2(g)]}{[CS_2(g)][Cl_2(g)]^3}$

      b. $K = \dfrac{1}{[Xe(g)][F_2(g)]^3}$

      c. $K = \dfrac{1}{[O_2(g)]^3}$

30.   When an additional amount of one of the reactants is added to an equilibrium system, the system shifts to the right and adjusts so as to consume some of the added reactant. This results in a net *increase* in the amount of product, compared to the equilibrium system before the additional reactant was added, and so the amount of $CO_2(g)$ in the system will be higher than if the additional $CO(g)$ had not been added. The numerical *value* of the equilibrium constant does *not*

change when a reactant is added: the concentrations of all reactants and products adjust until the correct value of K is once again achieved.

32.   If heat is applied to an endothermic reaction (i.e., the temperature is raised), the equilibrium is shifted to the right. More product will be present at equilibrium than if the temperature had not been increased. The value of K increases.

34.   a.   shifts right (system reacts to the right to get rid of excess fluorine)

b.   no change (P is in the *solid* state)

c.   shifts left (system reacts to get rid of excess PF_3)

36.   a.   no change (B is solid)

b.   shift right (system reacts to replace removed C)

c.   shift left (system reacts by shifting in direction of fewer mol of gas)

d.   shift right (the reaction is endothermic as written)

38.   An increase in temperature (by adding heat) favors the forward reaction for endothermic reactions such as this example.

40.   For an *endo*thermic reaction, an increase in temperature will shift the position of equilibrium to the right (toward products).

42. $CO(g) + 2H_2(g) \rightleftharpoons CH_3OH(l)$

add additional $CO(g)$ or $H_2(g)$: the system will react in the forward direction to remove the excess

decrease the volume of the system: the system will react in the direction of fewer moles of gas

44.   A small equilibrium constant implies that not much product forms before equilibrium is reached. The reaction would not be a good source of the products unless Le Châtelier's principle can be used to force the reaction to the right.

46. $K = \dfrac{[SO_3][NO]}{[SO_2][NO_2]} = \dfrac{[4.99\times10^{-5}\,M][6.31\times10^{-7}\,M]}{[2.11\times10^{-2}\,M][1.73\times10^{-3}\,M]} = 8.63\times10^{-7}$

48. $K = 5.21\times10^{-3} = \dfrac{[CO][H_2O]}{[CO_2][H_2]} = \dfrac{[4.73\times10^{-3}\,M][5.21\times10^{-3}\,M]}{[3.99\times10^{-2}\,M][H_2]}$

$[H_2] = 0.119\,M$

50. $K = 2.4\times10^{-3} = \dfrac{[H_2]^2[O_2]}{[H_2O]^2} = \dfrac{[1.9\times10^{-2}]^2[O_2]}{[1.1\times10^{-1}]^2}$

$[O_2] = 8.0\times10^{-2}\,M$

52. $K = 8.1\times10^{-3} = \dfrac{[NO_2]^2}{[N_2O_4]} = \dfrac{[0.0021\,M]^2}{[N_2O_4]}$

$[N_2O_4] = 5.4\times10^{-4}\,M$

54.   solubility product, K_{sp}

56.   Stirring or grinding the solute increases the speed with which the solute dissolves, but the ultimate *amount* of solute that dissolves is fixed by the equilibrium constant for the dissolving process, K_{sp}, which changes only with temperature. Therefore only the temperature will affect the solubility.

58.   a. $Bi_2S_3(s) \rightleftharpoons 2Bi^{3+}(aq) + 3S^{2-}(aq)$ $K_{sp} = [Bi^{3+}(aq)]^2[S^{2-}(aq)]^3$

    b. $Ca(OH)_2(s) \rightleftharpoons Ca^{2+}(aq) + 2OH^-(aq)$ $K_{sp} = [Ca^{2+}(aq)][OH^-(aq)]^2$

    c. $Co(OH)_3(s) \rightleftharpoons Co^{3+}(aq) + 3OH^-(aq)$ $K_{sp} = [Co^{3+}(aq)][OH^-(aq)]^3$

    d. $Cu_2S(s) \rightleftharpoons 2Cu^+(aq) + S^{2-}(aq)$ $K_{sp} = [Cu^+(aq)]^2[S^{2-}(aq)]$

60. $MgCO_3(s) \rightleftharpoons Mg^{2+}(aq) + CO_3^{2-}(aq)$

    Molar mass $MgCO_3 = 84.32$ g

    Let x represent the solubility of $MgCO_3$ in mol/L. Then $[CO_3^{2-}] = x$ and $[Mg^{2+}] = x$ from the stoichiometry of the equation.

    $K_{sp} = [Mg^{2+}][CO_3^{2-}] = 3.5 \times 10^{-8} = (x)(x) = x^2$

    then the molar solubility of $MgCO_3 = x = 1.87 \times 10^{-4}\ M\,(1.9 \times 10^{-4}\ M)$

    $1.87 \times 10^{-4}\ \dfrac{mol}{L} \times \dfrac{84.32\ g}{1\ mol} = 0.016\,g/L$

62. $Ni(OH)_2(s) \rightleftharpoons Ni^{2+}(aq) + 2OH^-(aq)$

    molar mass $Ni(OH)_2 = 92.71$ g

    let x represent the molar solubility of $Ni(OH)_2$: then $[Ni^{2+}] = x$ and $[OH^-] = 2x$.

    $K_{sp} = [Ni^{2+}][OH^-]^2 = 2.0 \times 10^{-15} = [x][2x]^2 = 4x^3$

    then the molar solubility of $Ni(OH)_2 = x = 7.9 \times 10^{-6}\ M$

    gram solubility $= 7.98 \times 10^{-6}\ \dfrac{mol}{L} \times \dfrac{92.71\ g}{1\ mol} = 7.4 \times 10^{-4}\ g/L$

64. $CaSO_4(s) \rightleftharpoons Ca^{2+}(aq) + SO_4^{2-}(aq)$

    molar mass $CaSO_4 = 136.15$ g

    $2.05\ \dfrac{g}{L} \times \dfrac{1\ mol}{136.15\ g} = 1.506 \times 10^{-2}\ M$

    If $CaSO_4$ dissolves to the extent of $1.506 \times 10^{-2}\ M$, then $[Ca^{2+}]$ will be $1.506 \times 10^{-2}\ M$ and $[SO_4^{2-}]$ will be $1.506 \times 10^{-2}\ M$ also.

    $K_{sp} = [Ca^{2+}][SO_4^{2-}] = [1.506 \times 10^{-2}\ M][\ 1.506 \times 10^{-2}\ M] = 2.27 \times 10^{-4}$

66. $Cr(OH)_3(s) \rightleftharpoons Cr^{3+}(aq) + 3OH^-(aq)$

If $Cr(OH)_3$ dissolves to the extent of 8.21×10^{-5} M, then $[Cr^{3+}]$ will be 8.21×10^{-5} M and $[OH^-]$ will be $3(8.21 \times 10^{-5}$ $M)$ in a saturated solution.

$K_{sp} = [Cr^{3+}][OH^-]^3 = [8.21 \times 10^{-5}\ M][\ 8.21 \times 10^{-5}\ M]^3 = 1.23 \times 10^{-15}$

68. $PbCl_2(s) \rightleftharpoons Pb^{2+}(aq) + 2Cl^-(aq)$

$K_{sp} = [Pb^{2+}][Cl^-]^2$

If $PbCl_2$ dissolves to the extent of 3.6×10^{-2} M, then $[Pb^{2+}] = 3.6 \times 10^{-2}$ M and $[Cl^-] = 2 \times (3.6 \times 10^{-2}) = 7.2 \times 10^{-2}$ M.

$K_{sp} = (3.6 \times 10^{-2}\ M)(7.2 \times 10^{-2}\ M)^2 = 1.9 \times 10^{-4}$

molar mass $PbCl_2 = 278.1$ g

$$\frac{3.6 \times 10^{-2}\ mol}{1L} \times \frac{278.1g}{1mol} = 10.\ g/L$$

70. $Fe(OH)_3(s) \rightleftharpoons Fe^{3+}(aq) + 3OH^-(aq)$

$K_{sp} = [Fe^{3+}][OH^-]^3 = 4 \times 10^{-38}$

Let x represent the number of moles of $Fe(OH)_3$ that dissolve per liter; then $[Fe^{3+}] = x$.

The amount of hydroxide ion that would be produced by the dissolving of the $Fe(OH)_3$ would then be $3x$, but pure water itself contains hydroxide ion at the concentration of 1.0×10^{-7} M (see Chapter 17). The total concentration of hydroxide ion is then $[OH^-] = (3x + 1.0 \times 10^{-7})$. As x must be a very small number [because $Fe(OH)_3$ is not very soluble], we can save ourselves a lot of arithmetic if we use the approximation that

$(3x + 1.0 \times 10^{-7}\ M) = 1.0 \times 10^{-7}$

$K_{sp} = [x][1.0 \times 10^{-7}]^3 = 4 \times 10^{-38}$

$x = 4 \times 10^{-17}$ M

molar mass $Fe(OH)_3 = 106.9$ g

$$\frac{4 \times 10^{-17}\ mol}{1\ L} \times \frac{106.9\ g}{1\ mol} = 4 \times 10^{-15}\ g/L$$

72. An increase in temperature increases the fraction of molecules that possess sufficient energy for a collision to result in a reaction.

74. catalyst

76. constant

78. When we say that a chemical equilibrium is *dynamic*, we are recognizing the fact that even though the reaction has appeared macroscopically to have stopped, on a microscopic basis the forward and reverse reactions are still taking place, at the same speed.

80. heterogeneous

82.   position

84.   Heat is considered a *product* of an exothermic process. Adding a product to a system in equilibrium causes the reverse reaction to occur (producing additional reactants).

86.   An equilibrium reaction may come to many *positions* of equilibrium, but at each possible position of equilibrium, the numerical value of the equilibrium constant is fulfilled. If different amounts of reactant are taken in different experiments, the *absolute amounts* of reactant and product present at the point of equilibrium reached will differ from one experiment to another, but the *ratio* that defines the equilibrium constant will be the same.

88. $PCl_5(g) \rightleftharpoons PCl_3(g) + Cl_2(g)$

$$K = \frac{[PCl_3][Cl_2]}{[PCl_5]} = 4.5 \times 10^{-3}$$

The concentration of PCl_5 is to be twice the concentration of PCl_3: $[PCl_5] = 2 \times [PCl_3]$

$$K = \frac{[PCl_3][Cl_2]}{2 \times [PCl_3]} = 4.5 \times 10^{-3}$$

$$K = \frac{[Cl_2]}{2} = 4.5 \times 10^{-3} \quad \text{and} \quad [Cl_2] = 9.0 \times 10^{-3} \, M$$

90.   As all of the metal carbonates indicated have the metal ion in the +2 oxidation state, we can illustrate the calculations for a general metal carbonate, MCO_3:

$$MCO_3(s) \rightleftharpoons M^{2+}(aq) + CO_3^{2-}(aq) \qquad\qquad K_{sp} = [M^{2+}(aq)][CO_3^{2-}(aq)]$$

If we then let x represent the number of moles of MCO_3 that dissolve per liter, then $[M^{2+}(aq)] = x$ and $[CO_3^{2-}(aq)] = x$ also because the reaction is of 1:1 stoichiometry. Therefore,

$K_{sp} = [M^{2+}(aq)][CO_3^{2-}(aq)] = x^2$ for each salt. Solving for x gives the following results.

$[BaCO_3] = x = 7.1 \times 10^{-5} \, M$

$[CdCO_3] = x = 2.3 \times 10^{-6} \, M$

$[CaCO_3] = x = 5.3 \times 10^{-5} \, M$

$[CoCO_3] = x = 3.9 \times 10^{-7} \, M$

92.   Although a small solubility product generally implies a small solubility, comparisons of solubility based directly on K_{sp} values are only valid if the salts produce the same numbers of positive and negative ions per formula when they dissolve. For example, one can compare the solubilities of $AgCl(s)$ and $NiS(s)$ directly using K_{sp}, because each salt produces one positive and one negative ion per formula when dissolved. One could not directly compare $AgCl(s)$ with a salt such as $Ca_3(PO_4)_2$, however.

94.   At higher temperatures, the average kinetic energy of the reactant molecules is larger. At higher temperatures, the probability that a collision between molecules will be energetic enough for reaction to take place is larger. On a molecular basis, a higher temperature means a given molecule will be moving faster.

96. a. $$K = \dfrac{[HBr]^2}{[H_2][Br_2]}$$

    b. $$K = \dfrac{[H_2S]^2}{[H_2]^2[S_2]}$$

    c. $$K = \dfrac{[HCN]^2}{[H_2][C_2N_2]}$$

98. $$K = \dfrac{[Br]^2}{[Br_2]} = \dfrac{[0.034\,M]2}{[0.97\,M]} = 1.2 \times 10^{-3}$$

100. a. $$K = \dfrac{1}{[O_2]^3}$$

    b. $$K = \dfrac{1}{[NH_3][HCl]}$$

    c. $$K = \dfrac{1}{[O_2]}$$

102. An *exo*thermic reaction is one that liberates heat energy. Increasing the temperature (adding heat) for such a reaction is fighting against the reaction's own tendency to liberate heat. The net effect of raising the temperature will be a shift to the left to decrease the amount of product. If it is desired to increase the amount of product in an exothermic reaction, heat must be *removed* from the system. Changing the temperature *does* change the numerical value of the equilibrium constant for a reaction.

104. The reaction is *exo*thermic as written. An increase in temperature (addition of heat) will shift the reaction to the left (toward reactants).

106. $$K = \dfrac{[NH_3]^2}{[N_2][H_2]^3} = 1.3 \times 10^{-2} = \dfrac{[NH_3]^2}{[0.1M][0.1M]^3}$$

    $[NH_3]^2 = 1.3 \times 10^{-6}$

    $[NH_3] = 1.1 \times 10^{-3}\,M$

108. a. $Cu(OH)_2(s) \rightleftharpoons Cu^{2+}(aq) + 2OH^-(aq)$

    $K_{sp} = [Cu^{2+}][OH^-]^2$

    b. $Cr(OH)_3(s) \rightleftharpoons Cr^{3+}(aq) + 3OH^-(aq)$

    $K_{sp} = [Cr^{3+}][OH^-]^3$

    c. $Ba(OH)_2(s) \rightleftharpoons Ba^{2+}(aq) + 2OH^-(aq)$

    $K_{sp} = [Ba^{2+}][OH^-]^2$

    d. $Sn(OH)_2(s) \rightleftharpoons Sn^{2+}(aq) + 2OH^-(aq)$

    $K_{sp} = [Sn^{2+}][OH^-]^2$

110.   molar mass AgCl = 143.4 g

$$9.0 \times 10^{-4} \text{ g AgCl/L} \times \frac{1 \text{ mol AgCl}}{143.4 \text{ g AgCl}} = 6.28 \times 10^{-6} \text{ mol AgCl/L}$$

$\text{AgCl}(s) \rightleftharpoons \text{Ag}^+(aq) + \text{Cl}^-(aq)$

$K_{sp} = [\text{Ag}^+][\text{Cl}^-] = (6.28 \times 10^{-6} \, M)(6.28 \times 10^{-6} \, M) = 3.9 \times 10^{-11}$

112.   molar mass Ni(OH)$_2$ = 92.71 g

$$\frac{0.14 \text{ g Ni(OH)}_2}{1 \text{ L}} \times \frac{1 \text{ mol}}{92.71 \text{ g Ni(OH)}_2} = 1.510 \times 10^{-3} \, M$$

$\text{Ni(OH)}_2(s) \rightleftharpoons \text{Ni}^{2+}(aq) + 2\text{OH}^-(aq)$

$K_{sp} = [\text{Ni}^{2+}][\text{OH}^-]^2$

If $1.510 \times 10^{-3} \, M$ of Ni(OH)$_2$ dissolves, then $[\text{Ni}^{2+}] = 1.510 \times 10^{-3} \, M$ and $[\text{OH}^-] = 2 \times (1.510 \times 10^{-3} \, M) = 3.020 \times 10^{-3} \, M$.

$K_{sp} = (1.510 \times 10^{-3} \, M)(3.020 \times 10^{-3} \, M)^2 = 1.4 \times 10^{-8}$

114.   The activation energy is the minimum energy two colliding molecules must possess in order for the collision to result in reaction. If molecules do not possess energies equal to or greater than E_a, a collision between these molecules will not result in a reaction.

116.   Once a system has reached equilibrium the net concentration of product no longer increases because molecules of product already present react to form the original reactants. This is not to say that the *same* product molecules are necessarily always present.

118.   a. $K = [\text{H}_2\text{O}(g)][\text{CO}_2(g)]$

        b. $K = [\text{CO}_2]$

        c. $K = \dfrac{1}{[\text{O}_2]^3}$

CUMULATIVE REVIEW

Chapters 16 and 17

2. A conjugate acid–base pair consists of two species related to each other by donation or acceptance of a single proton, H^+. An acid has one more H^+ than its conjugate base; a base has one less H^+ than its conjugate acid.

    Brønsted-Lowry acids:

    $$HCl(aq) + H_2O(l) \rightarrow Cl^-(aq) + H_3O^+(aq)$$

    $$H_2SO_4(aq) + H_2O(l) \rightarrow HSO_4^-(aq) + H_3O^+(aq)$$

    $$H_3PO_4(aq) + H_2O(l) \rightleftharpoons H_2PO_4^-(aq) + H_3O^+(aq)$$

    $$NH_4^+(aq) + H_2O(l) \rightleftharpoons NH_3(aq) + H_3O^+(aq)$$

    Brønsted-Lowry bases:

    $$NH_3(aq) + H_2O(l) \rightleftharpoons NH_4^+(aq) + OH^-(aq)$$

    $$HCO_3^-(aq) + H_2O(l) \rightleftharpoons H_2CO_3(aq) + OH^-(aq)$$

    $$NH_2^-(aq) + H_2O(l) \rightarrow NH_3(aq) + OH^-(aq)$$

    $$H_2PO_4^-(aq) + H_2O(l) \rightleftharpoons H_3PO_4(aq) + OH^-(aq)$$

4. The strength of an acid is a direct result of the position of the acid's ionization equilibrium. Strong acids are those whose ionization equilibrium positions lie far to the right, whereas weak acids are those whose equilibrium positions lie only slightly to the right. For example, HCl, HNO_3, and $HClO_4$ are all strong acids, which means they are completely ionized in aqueous solution (the position of equilibrium is very far to the right):

    $$HCl(aq) + H_2O(l) \rightarrow Cl^-(aq) + H_3O^+(aq)$$

    $$HNO_3(aq) + H_2O(l) \rightarrow NO_3^-(aq) + H_3O^+(aq)$$

    $$HClO_4(aq) + H_2O(l) \rightarrow ClO_4^-(aq) + H_3O^+(aq)$$

    As these are very strong acids, we know their anions (Cl^-, NO_3^-, ClO_4^-) must be very weak bases, and that solutions of the sodium salts of these anions would *not* be appreciably basic. As these acids have a strong tendency to lose protons, there is very little tendency for the anions (bases) to gain protons.

6. The pH of a solution is defined as the negative of the base 10 logarithm of the hydrogen ion concentration in the solution; that is

    $$pH = -\log_{10}[H^+].$$

    As in pure water, the amount of $H^+(aq)$ ion present is equal to the amount of $OH^-(aq)$ ion, we say that pure water is *neutral*. As $[H^+] = 1.0 \times 10^{-7}$ M in pure water, this means that the pH of pure water is $-\log[1.0 \times 10^{-7}\ M] = 7.00$. Solutions in which the hydrogen ion concentration is greater than 1.0×10^{-7} M (pH < 7.00) are *acidic*; solutions in which the hydrogen ion concentration is less than $1.0 \times 10^{-7}\ M$ (pH > 7.00) are *basic*. The pH scale is logarithmic. When the pH changes by one unit, this corresponds to a change in the hydrogen ion concentration by a factor of *ten*.

In some instances, it may be more convenient to speak directly about the hydroxide ion concentration present in a solution, and so an analogous logarithmic expression is defined for the hydroxide ion concentration:

$$pOH = -\log_{10}[OH^-].$$

The concentrations of hydrogen ion and hydroxide ion in water (and in aqueous solutions) are *not* independent of one another, but rather are related by the dissociation equilibrium constant for water,

$$K_w = [H^+][OH^-] = 1.0 \times 10^{-14} \text{ at } 25°C.$$

From this constant it is obvious that pH + pOH = 14.00 for water (or an aqueous solution) at 25°C.

8.   Chemists envision that a reaction can only take place between molecules if the molecules physically *collide* with each other. Furthermore, when molecules collide, the molecules must collide with enough force for the reaction to be successful (there must be enough energy to break bonds in the reactants), and the colliding molecules must be positioned with the correct relative orientation for the products (or intermediates) to form. Reactions tend to be faster if higher concentrations are used for the reaction; because, if there are more molecules present per unit volume there will be more collisions between molecules in a given time period. Reactions are faster at higher temperatures because at higher temperatures the reactant molecules have a higher average kinetic energy, and the number of molecules that will collide with sufficient force to break bonds increases.

10.   Chemists define equilibrium as the exact balancing of two exactly opposing processes. When a chemical reaction is begun by combining pure reactants, the only process possible initially is

reactants → products

However, for many reactions, as the concentration of product molecules increases, it becomes more likely that product molecules will collide and react with each other

products → reactants

giving back molecules of the original reactants. At some point in the process the rates of the forward and reverse reactions become equal, and the system attains chemical equilibrium. To an outside observer, the system appears to have stopped reacting. On a microscopic basis, though, both the forward and reverse processes are still going on: every time additional molecules of the product form, however, somewhere else in the system molecules of product react to give back molecules of reactant.

Once the point is reached that product molecules are reacting at the same speed at which they are forming, there is no further net change in concentration. A graph showing how the rates of the forward and reverse reactions change with time is given in the text as Figure 17.8. At the start of the reaction, the rate of the forward reaction is at its maximum, whereas the rate of the reverse reaction is zero. As the reaction proceeds, the rate of the forward reaction gradually decreases as the concentration of reactants decreases, whereas the rate of the reverse reaction increases as the concentration of products increases. Once the two rates have become equal, the reaction has reached a state of equilibrium.

12.   The equilibrium constant for a reaction is a *ratio* of the concentration of products present at the point of equilibrium to the concentration of reactants still present. A *ratio* means that we have one number divided by another number (for example, the density of a substance is the ratio of a substance's mass to its volume). As the equilibrium constant is a ratio, there are an infinite number of sets of data that can give the same ratio: for example, the ratios 8/4, 6/3, 100/50 all have the same value, 2. The actual concentrations of products and reactants will differ from one experiment to another involving a particular chemical reaction, but the ratio of the amount of product to reactant at equilibrium should be the same for each experiment.

Consider this simple example: suppose we have a reaction for which $K = 4$, and we begin this reaction with 100 reactant molecules. At the point of equilibrium, there should be 80 molecules of product and 20 molecules of reactant remaining ($80/20 = 4$). Suppose we perform another experiment involving the same reaction, only this time we begin the experiment with 500 molecules of reactant. This time, at the point of equilibrium, there will be 400 molecules of product present and 100 molecules of reactant remaining ($400/100 = 4$). As we began the two experiments with different numbers of reactant molecules, it's not troubling that there are different absolute numbers of product and reactant molecules present at equilibrium; however, the ratio, K, is the same for both experiments. We say that these two experiments represent two different positions of equilibrium: an equilibrium position corresponds to a particular set of experimental equilibrium concentrations that fulfill the value of the equilibrium constant. Any experiment that is performed with a different amount of starting material will come to its own unique equilibrium position, but the equilibrium constant ratio, K, will be the same for a given reaction regardless of the starting amounts taken.

14.   Your paraphrase of Le Châtelier's principle should go something like this: "when you make any change to a system in equilibrium, this throws the system temporarily out of equilibrium, and the system responds by reacting in whichever direction will be able to reach a new position of equilibrium". There are various changes that can be made to a system in equilibrium. Following are examples:

a.   the concentration of one of the reactants is increased.

Consider the reaction: $2SO_2(g) + O_2(g) \rightleftharpoons 2SO_3(g)$

Suppose the reactants have already reacted and a position of equilibrium has been reached that fulfills the value of K for the reaction. At this point there will be present particular amounts of each reactant and of product. Suppose then one additional mole of O_2 is added to the system from outside. At the instant the additional O_2 is added, the system will not be in equilibrium: there will be too much O_2 present in the system to be compatible with the amounts of SO_2 and SO_3 present. The system will respond by reacting to get rid of some of the excess O_2 until the value of the ratio K is again fulfilled. If the system reacts to get rid of the excess of O_2, additional product SO_3 will form. The net result is more SO_3 produced than if the change had not been made.

b.   The concentration of one of the products is decreased by selectively removing it from the system.

Consider the reaction: $CH_3COOH + CH_3OH \rightleftharpoons H_2O + CH_3COOCH_3$

This reaction is typical of many reactions involving organic chemical substances, in which two organic molecules react to form a larger molecule, with a molecule of water split out during the combination. This type of reaction on its own tends to come to equilibrium with only part of the starting materials being converted to the desired organic product (which effectively would leave the experimenter with a mixture of materials). A technique that is used by organic chemists to increase the effective yield of the desired organic product is to *separate* the two products (if the products are separated, they cannot react to give back the reactants). One method used is to add a drying agent to the mixture: such a drying agent chemically or physically absorbs the water from the system, removing it from equilibrium. If the water is removed, the reverse reaction cannot take place, and the reaction proceeds to a greater extent in the forward direction than if the drying agent had not been added. In other situations, an experimenter may separate the products of the reaction by distillation (if the boiling points make this possible): again, if the products have been separated, then the reverse reaction will not be possible, and the forward reaction will occur to a greater extent.

c.   The reaction system is compressed to a smaller volume.

Consider the example: $3H_2(g) + N_2(g) \rightleftharpoons 2NH_3(g)$

For equilibria involving gases, when the volume of the reaction system is compressed suddenly, the pressure in the system increases. However, if the reacting system can relieve some of this increased pressure by reacting, it will do so. This will happen by the reaction occurring in whichever direction will give the smaller number of moles of gas (if the number of moles of gas is decreased in a particular volume, the pressure will decrease).

For the reaction above, there are two moles of the gas on the right side of the equation, but there is a total of four moles on the left side. If this system at equilibrium were to be suddenly compressed to a smaller volume, the reaction would proceed further to the right (in favor of more ammonia being produced).

d.   The temperature is increased for an endothermic reaction.

Consider the reaction: $2NaHCO_3 + heat \rightleftharpoons Na_2CO_3 + H_2O + CO_2$

Although a change in temperature actually does change the *value* of the equilibrium constant, we can simplify reactions involving temperature changes by treating heat energy as if it were a chemical substance: for this endothermic reaction, heat is one of the reactants. As we saw in the example in part (a) of this question, increasing the concentration of one of the reactants for a system at equilibrium causes the reaction to proceed further to the right, forming additional product. Similarly for the endothermic reaction given above, increasing the temperature causes the reaction to proceed further in the direction of products than if no change had been made. It is as if there were too much "heat" to be compatible with the amount of substances present. The substances react to get rid of some of the energy.

e.   the temperature is decreased for an exothermic process.

Consider the reaction: $PCl_3 + Cl_2 \rightleftharpoons PCl_5 + heat$

As discussed in part (d) above, although changing the temperature at which a reaction is performed does change the numerical value of K, we can simplify our discussion of this reaction by treating heat energy as if it were a chemical substance. Heat is a product of this reaction. If we are going to lower the temperature of this reaction system, the only way to accomplish this is to remove energy from the system. Lowering the temperature of the system is really working with this system in its attempt to release heat energy. So lowering the temperature should favor the production of more product than if no change were made.

16.   Specific answer depends on student choice of examples. In general, for a weak acid, HA, and a weak base, B:

$$HA + H_2O \rightleftharpoons H_3O^+ + A^- \qquad\qquad B + H_2O \rightleftharpoons HB^+ + OH^-$$

18.   a. $NH_3(aq)(base) + H_2O(l)(acid) \rightleftharpoons NH_4^+(aq)(acid) + OH^-(aq)(base)$

   b. $H_2SO_4(aq)(acid) + H_2O(l)(base) \rightleftharpoons HSO_4^-(aq)(base) + H_3O^+(aq)(acid)$

   c. $O^{2-}(s)(base) + H_2O(l)(acid) \rightleftharpoons OH^-(aq)(acid) + OH^-(aq)(base)$

   d. $NH_2^-(aq)(base) + H_2O(l)(acid) \rightleftharpoons NH_3(aq)(acid) + OH^-(aq)(base)$

   e. $H_2PO_4^-(aq)(acid) + OH^-(aq)(base) \rightleftharpoons HPO_4^{2-}(aq)(base) + H_2O(l)(acid)$

20.   a. HNO_3 is a strong acid, so $[H^+] = 0.00141\ M$

   $pH = -\log(0.00141) = 2.851$

   $pOH = 14.00 - 2.851 = 11.15$

   b.   NaOH is a strong base, so $[OH^-] = 2.13 \times 10^{-3}\ M$

   $pOH = -\log(2.13 \times 10^{-3}) = 2.672$

   $pH = 14.00 - 2.672 = 11.33$

   c.   HCl is a strong acid, so $[H^+] = 0.00515\ M$

   $pH = -\log(0.00515) = 2.288$

   $pOH = 14.00 - 2.288 = 11.71$

   d. $Ca(OH)_2$ is a strong, but not very soluble base. Each formula unit of $Ca(OH)_2$ produces two formula units of OH^- ion.

   $[OH^-] = 2 \times 5.65 \times 10^{-5}\ M = 1.13 \times 10^{-4}\ M$

   $pOH = -\log(1.13 \times 10^{-4}) = 3.947$

   $pH = 14.00 - 3.947 = 10.05$

22. $Br_2(g) + Cl_2(g) \rightleftharpoons 2BrCl(g)$

$$K = \frac{[BrCl(g)]^2}{[Br_2][Cl_2]} = \frac{[4.9 \times 10^{-4}]^2}{[7.2 \times 10^{-8}][4.3 \times 10^{-6}]} = 7.8 \times 10^5$$

24. $MgCO_3 \rightleftharpoons Mg^{2+}(aq) + CO_3^{2-}(aq)$ \qquad\qquad molar mass of $MgCO_3 = 84.32$ g

$K_{sp} = [Mg^{2+}][CO_2^{2-}]$

let x represent the number of moles of $MgCO_3$ that dissolve per liter. Then $[Mg^{2+}] = x$ and $[CO_3^{2-}] = x$ also

$K_{sp} = [x][x] = x^2 = 6.82 \times 10^{-6}$

$x = [MgCO_3] = 2.61 \times 10^{-3}\ M$

$$\frac{2.61 \times 10^{-3}\ \text{mol}}{1\ L} \times \frac{84.32\ \text{g}}{1\ \text{mol}} = 0.220\ \text{g/L}$$

CHAPTER 18

Oxidation–Reduction Reactions/Electrochemistry

2. Oxidation can be defined as the loss of electrons by an atom, molecule, or ion. Oxidation may also be defined as an increase in oxidation state for an element, but because elements can only increase their oxidation states by losing electrons, the two definitions are equivalent. The following equation shows the oxidation of copper metal to copper(II) ion

$$Cu \rightarrow Cu^{2+} + 2e^-$$

Reduction can be defined as the gaining of electrons by an atom, molecule, or ion. Reduction may also be defined as a decrease in oxidation state for an element, but naturally such a decrease takes place by the gaining of electrons (so the two definitions are equivalent). The following equation shows the reduction of sulfur atoms to sulfide ion.

$$S + 2e^- \rightarrow S^{2-}$$

4. Each of these reactions involves one or more *free* elements on one side of the equation; on the other side of the equation, however, the element(s) is(are) *combined* in a compound. This is a clear sign that an oxidation–reduction process is taking place.

   a. boron is oxidized; oxygen is reduced

   b. nitrogen is oxidized; oxygen is reduced

   c. carbon is oxidized; hydrogen is reduced

   d. magnesium is oxidized; copper is reduced

6. Each of these reactions involves one or more *free* elements on one side of the equation; on the other side of the equation, however, the element(s) is(are) *combined* in a compound. This is a clear sign that an oxidation–reduction process is taking place.

   a. sulfur is being oxidized, oxygen is being reduced

   b. phosphorus is being oxidized, oxygen is being reduced

   c. hydrogen is being oxidized, carbon is being reduced

   d. boron is being oxidized, hydrogen is being reduced.

8. Oxidation numbers represent a "relative charge" one atom has compared to another in a compound. In an element, all the atoms are equivalent.

10. Fluorine is always assigned a negative oxidation state (−1) because all other elements are less electronegative. The other halogens are *usually* assigned an oxidation state of −1 in compounds. In interhalogen compounds such as ClF, fluorine is assigned oxidation state −1 (F is more electronegative than Cl). Chlorine, therefore, must be assigned a +1 oxidation state in this instance.

12.   Oxidation states represent a bookkeeping method to assign electrons in a molecule or ion. For an ion with an overall net charge, the sum of the oxidation states in the ion must equal the charge on the ion. So in the PO_4^{3-} ion, the sum of all the oxidation states must be –3.

14.   The rules for assigning oxidation states are given in Section 18.2 of the text. The rule that applies for each element in the following answers is given in parentheses after the element and its oxidation state.

    a.   Cr, +3 (Rule 6); Cl, –1 (Rule 5)

    b.   Ni, +2 (Rules 6, 2); O, –2 (Rule 3); H, +1 (Rule 4)

    c.   H, +1 (Rule 4); S, –2 (Rule 5)

    d.   C, +4 (Rule 6); S, –2 (Rule 5)

16.   a.   0 (Rule 1)

    b.   –3 (using Rule 4 for H)

    c.   +4 (using Rule 3 for O)

    d.   +5 (using Rule 3 for O and Rule 2 for Na)

18.   a.   +2 (using Rule 5 for Cl)

    b.   +7 (using Rule 3 for O and Rule 2 for K)

    c.   +4 (using Rule 3 for O)

    d.   +3 (realizing that the acetate ion has 1– charge and apply Rule 6)

20.   The rules for assigning oxidation states are given in Section 18.2 of the text. The rule that applies for each element in the following answers is given in parentheses after the element and its oxidation state.

    a.   Ca, +2 (Rule 6); O, –2 (Rule 3)

    b.   Al, +3 (Rules 6 and 2); O, –2 (Rule 3)

    c.   P, +3 (Rule 6); F, –1 (Rule 5)

    d.   P, +5 (Rule 6); O, –2 (Rule 3)

22.   The rules for assigning oxidation states are given in Section 18.2 of the text. The rule that applies for each element in the following answers is given in parentheses after the element and its oxidation state.

    a.   H, +1 (Rule 4); S, +6 (Rule 7); O, –2 (Rule 3)

    b.   Mn, +7 (Rule 7); O, –2 (Rule 3)

    c.   Cl, +5 (Rule 7); O, –2 (Rule 3)

    d.   Br, +7 (Rule 7; O, –2 (Rule 3)

24.   Electrons are negative; when an atom gains electrons, it gains one negative charge for each electron gained. For example, in the reduction reaction $Cl + e^- \rightarrow Cl^-$, the oxidation state of chlorine decreases from 0 to –1 as the electron is gained.

26.   Answer depends on student example chosen.

28. An antioxidant is a substance that prevents oxidation of some molecule(s) in the body. It is not certain how all antioxidants work, but one example is in preventing oxygen molecules and other substances from stripping electrons from cell membranes, leaving them vulnerable to destruction by the immune system.

30. a. $2Al(s) + 3S(s) \rightarrow Al_2S_3(s)$

   aluminum is being oxidized, sulfur is being reduced

   b. $CH_4(g) + 2O_2(g) \rightarrow CO_2(g) + 2H_2O(g)$

   carbon is being oxidized, oxygen is being reduced

   c. $2Fe_2O_3(s) + 3C(s) \rightarrow 3CO_2(g) + 4Fe(s, l)$

   carbon is being oxidized, iron is being reduced

   d. $K_2Cr_2O_7(aq) + 14HCl(aq) \rightarrow 2KCl(aq) + 2CrCl_3(s) + 7H_2O(l) + 3Cl_2(g)$

   chlorine is being oxidized, chromium is being reduced

32. a. $4KClO_3(s) + C_6H_{12}O_6(s) \rightarrow 4KCl(s) + 6H_2O(l) + 6CO_2(g)$

   carbon is being oxidized, chlorine is being reduced

   b. $2C_8H_{18}(l) + 25O_2(g) \rightarrow 16CO_2(g) + 18H_2O(l)$

   carbon is being oxidized, oxygen is being reduced

   c. $PCl_3(g) + Cl_2(g) \rightarrow PCl_5(g)$

   phosphorus is being oxidized, chlorine is being reduced

   d. $Ca(s) + H_2(g) \rightarrow CaH_2(g)$

   calcium is being oxidized, hydrogen is being reduced

34. Iron is reduced [+3 in $Fe_2O_3(s)$, 0 in $Fe(l)$]; carbon is oxidized [+2 in $CO(g)$, +4 in $CO_2(g)$]. $Fe_2O_3(s)$ is the oxidizing agent; $CO(g)$ is the reducing agent.

36. a. chlorine is being reduced, iodine is being oxidized; chlorine is the oxidizing agent, iodide ion is the reducing agent

   b. iron is being reduced, iodine is being oxidized; iron(III) is the oxidizing agent, iodide ion is the reducing agent

   c. copper is being reduced, iodine is being oxidized; copper(II) is the oxidizing agent, iodide ion is the reducing agent

38. Oxidation–reduction reactions are often more complicated than "regular" reactions; frequently the coefficients necessary to balance the number of electrons transferred come out to be large numbers. We also have to make certain that we account for the electrons being transferred.

40. Under ordinary conditions it is impossible to have "free" electrons that are not part of some atom, ion, or molecule. For this reason, the total number of electrons lost by the species being oxidized must equal the total number of electrons gained by the species being reduced.

42.   a. $Cl^-(aq) \rightarrow Cl_2(g) + 2e^-$

balance chlorine: $\mathbf{2}Cl^-(aq) \rightarrow Cl_2(g)$

balance charge: $2Cl^-(aq) \rightarrow Cl_2(g) + \mathbf{2}e^-$

balanced half-reaction: $2Cl^-(aq) \rightarrow Cl_2(g) + 2e^-$

    b. $Fe^{2+}(aq) \rightarrow Fe^{3+}(aq) + e^-$

    c. $Fe(s) \rightarrow Fe^{3+}(aq) + 3e^-$

    d. $Cu^{2+}(aq) + e^- \rightarrow Cu^+(aq)$

44.   a. $O_2(g) \rightarrow H_2O(l)$

balance oxygen: $O_2 \rightarrow 2H_2O$

balance hydrogen: $4H^+ + O_2 \rightarrow 2H_2O$

balance charge: $4e^- + 4H^+ + O_2 \rightarrow 2H_2O$

balanced half-reaction: $4e^- + 4H^+(aq) + O_2(g) \rightarrow 2H_2O(l)$

    b. $SO_4{}^{2-}(aq) \rightarrow H_2SO_3(aq)$

balance oxygen: $SO_4{}^{2-} \rightarrow H_2SO_3 + H_2O$

balance hydrogen: $4H^+ + SO_4{}^{2-} \rightarrow H_2SO_3 + H_2O$

balance charge: $2e^- + 4H^+ + SO_4{}^{2-} \rightarrow H_2SO_3 + H_2O$

balanced half-reaction: $2e^- + 4H^+(aq) + SO_4{}^{2-}(aq) \rightarrow H_2SO_3(aq) + H_2O(l)$

    c. $H_2O_2(aq) \rightarrow H_2O(l)$

balance oxygen : $H_2O_2 \rightarrow 2H_2O$

balance hydrogen : $2H^+ + H_2O_2 \rightarrow 2H_2O$

balance charge : $2e^- + 2H^+ + H_2O_2 \rightarrow 2H_2O$

balanced half-reaction: $2e^- + 2H^+(aq) + H_2O_2(aq) \rightarrow 2H_2O(l)$

    d. $NO_2{}^-(aq) \rightarrow NO_3{}^-(aq)$

balance oxygen : $H_2O + NO_2{}^- \rightarrow NO_3{}^-$

balance hydrogen: $H_2O + NO_2{}^- \rightarrow NO_3{}^- + 2H^+$

balance charge: $H_2O + NO_2{}^- \rightarrow NO_3{}^- + 2H^+ + 2e^-$

balanced half-reaction: $H_2O(l) + NO_2{}^-(aq) \rightarrow NO_3{}^-(aq) + 2H^+(aq) + 2e^-$

46.   For simplicity, the physical states of the substances have been omitted until the final balanced equation is given.

    a. $Al(s) + H^+(aq) \rightarrow Al^{3+}(aq) + H_2(g)$

$Al \rightarrow Al^{3+}$

Balance charge: $Al \rightarrow Al^{3+} + \mathbf{3}e^-$

$H^+ \rightarrow H_2$

Balance hydrogen: $\mathbf{2H^+} \rightarrow H_2$

Balance charge: $\mathbf{2e^-} + 2H^+ \rightarrow H_2$

Combine half–reactions:

$3 \times (\mathbf{2e^-} + 2H^+ \rightarrow H_2)$

$2 \times (Al \rightarrow Al^{3+} + \mathbf{3e^-})$

$2Al(s) + 6H^+(aq) \rightarrow 2Al^{3+}(aq) + 3H_2(g)$

b. $S^{2-}(aq) + NO_3^-(g) \rightarrow S(s) + NO(g)$

$S^{2-} \rightarrow S$

Balance charge: $S^{2-} \rightarrow S + \mathbf{2e^-}$

$NO_3^- \rightarrow NO$

Balance oxygen: $NO_3^- \rightarrow NO + 2H_2O$

Balance hydrogen: $\mathbf{4H^+} + NO_3^- \rightarrow NO + 2H_2O$

Balance charge: $\mathbf{3e^-} + 4H^+ + NO_3^- \rightarrow NO + 2H_2O$

Combine half–reactions:

$3 \times (S^{2-} \rightarrow S + 2e^-)$

$2 \times (3e^- + 4H^+ + NO_3^- \rightarrow NO + 2H_2O)$

$8H^+ + 3S^{2-}(aq) + 2NO_3^-(g) \rightarrow 3S(s) + 2NO(g) + 4H_2O$

c. $I_2(aq) + Cl_2(aq) \rightarrow IO_3^-(aq) + HCl(g)$

$I_2 \rightarrow IO_3^-$

Balance iodine: $I_2 \rightarrow \mathbf{2IO_3^-}$

Balance oxygen: $\mathbf{6H_2O} + I_2 \rightarrow IO_3^-$

Balance hydrogen: $6H_2O + I_2 \rightarrow IO_3^- + \mathbf{12H^+}$

Balance charge: $6H_2O + I_2 \rightarrow IO_3^- + 12H^+ + \mathbf{10e^-}$

$Cl_2 \rightarrow HCl$

Balance chlorine: $Cl_2 \rightarrow \mathbf{2HCl}$

Balance hydrogen: $\mathbf{2H^+} + Cl_2 \rightarrow 2HCl$

Balance charge: $\mathbf{2e^-} + 2H^+ + Cl_2 \rightarrow 2HCl$

Combine half–reactions:

$5 \times (2e^- + 2H^+ + Cl_2 \rightarrow 2HCl)$

$6H_2O + I_2 \rightarrow IO_3^- + 12H^+ + 10e^-$

$6H_2O(l) + 2I_2(aq) + 5Cl_2(aq) \rightarrow 2IO_3^-(aq) + 10HCl(g) + 2H^+(aq)$

d. $AsO_4^-(aq) + S^{2-}(aq) \rightarrow AsO_3^-(s) + S(s)$

$AsO_4^- \rightarrow AsO_3^-$

Balance oxygen: $AsO_4^- \rightarrow AsO_3^- + \mathbf{H_2O}$

Balance hydrogen: $\mathbf{2H^+} + AsO_4^- \rightarrow AsO_3^- + H_2O$

Balance charge: $\mathbf{2e^-} + 2H^+ + AsO_4^- \rightarrow AsO_3^- + H_2O$

$S^{2-} \rightarrow S$

Balance charge: $S^{2-} \rightarrow S + \mathbf{2e^-}$

$2H^+(aq) + AsO_4^-(aq) + S^{2-}(aq) \rightarrow AsO_3^-(s) + S(s) + H_2O(l)$

48. $Cu(s) + 2HNO_3(aq) + 2H^+(aq) \rightarrow Cu^{2+}(aq) + 2NO_2(g) + 2H_2O(l)$

$Mg(s) + 2HNO_3(aq) \rightarrow Mg(NO_3)_2(aq) + H_2(g)$

50.   A salt bridge typically consists of a U–shaped tube filled with an inert electrolyte (one involving ions that are not part of the oxidation–reduction reaction). A salt bridge is used to complete the electrical circuit in a cell. Any method that allows transfer of charge without allowing bulk mixing of the solutions may be used (another common method is to set up one half–cell in a porous cup, which is then placed in the beaker containing the second half–cell).

52.   Reduction takes place at the cathode and oxidation takes place at the anode.

54.   A diagram of the cell is shown below:

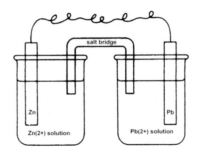

$Pb^{2+}(aq)$ ion is reduced; $Zn(s)$ is oxidized.

The reaction at the anode is $Zn(s) \rightarrow Zn^{2+}(aq) + 2e^-$.

The reaction at the cathode is $Pb^{2+}(aq) + 2e^- \rightarrow Pb(s)$

56. $Cd + 2OH^- \rightarrow Cd(OH)_2 + 2e^-$ (oxidation)

$NiO_2 + 2H_2O + 2e^- \rightarrow Ni(OH)_2 + 2OH^-$ (reduction)

58.   Aluminum is a very reactive metal when freshly isolated in the pure state. However, on standing for even a relatively short period of time, aluminum metal forms a thin coating of Al_2O_3 on its surface from reaction with atmospheric oxygen. This coating of Al_2O_3 is much less reactive than the metal and serves to protect the surface of the metal from further attack.

60.   Chromium protects stainless steel by forming a thin coating of chromium oxide on the surface of the steel, which prevents oxidation of the iron in the steel.

62.   The main recharging reaction for the lead storage battery is

$$2PbSO_4(s) + 2H_2O(l) \rightarrow Pb(s) + PbO_2(s) + 2H_2SO_4(aq).$$

A major side reaction is the electrolysis of water

$$2H_2O(l) \rightarrow 2H_2(g) + O_2(g).$$

This results in production of an explosive mixture of hydrogen and oxygen, which accounts for many accidents in recharging of such batteries.

64.   The balanced equation is $2H_2O(l) \rightarrow 2H_2(g) + O_2(g)$. Oxygen is oxidized (going from –2 oxidation state in water to zero oxidation state in the free element). Hydrogen is reduced (going from +1 oxidation state in water to zero oxidation state in the free element). Heat is produced by burning the hydrogen gas produced by the electrolysis: since energy must be applied to water to electrolyze it, energy is released when hydrogen gas produced by the electrolysis and oxygen gas combine to form water in the fireplace.

66.   loss; oxidation state

68.   electronegative

70.   An *oxidizing agent* is an atom, molecule, or ion that causes the oxidation of another species. During this process, the oxidizing agent is reduced.

72.   lose

74.   separate from

76.   oxidation

78.   An electrolysis reaction results when an electrical current from an outside source is used to cause an otherwise nonspontaneous reaction to occur. An example is the electrolysis of water: $2H_2O(l) \rightarrow 2H_2(g) + O_2(g)$; this reaction only takes place if an electrical current of sufficient voltage is passed through the water.

80.   hydrogen; oxygen

82.   oxidation

84.   a. $4Fe(s) + 3O_2(g) \rightarrow 2Fe_2O_3(s)$

            iron is oxidized; oxygen is reduced

       b. $2Al(s) + 3Cl_2(g) \rightarrow 2AlCl_3(s)$

            aluminum is oxidized; chlorine is reduced

       c. $6Mg(s) + P_4(s) \rightarrow 2Mg_3P_2(s)$

            magnesium is oxidized; phosphorus is reduced

86.   a.   aluminum is oxidized; hydrogen is reduced

       b.   hydrogen is reduced; iodine is oxidized

       c.   copper is oxidized; hydrogen is reduced

88.   a. $C_3H_8(g) + 5O_2(g) \rightarrow 3CO_2(g) + 4H_2O(g)$

        b. $CO(g) + 2H_2(g) \rightarrow CH_3OH(l)$

        c. $SnO_2(s) + 2C(s) \rightarrow Sn(s) + 2CO(g)$

        d. $C_2H_5OH(l) + 3O_2(g) \rightarrow 2CO_2(g) + 3H_2O(g)$

90.   Each of these reactions involves a *metallic* element in the form of the *free* element on one side of the equation; on the other side of the equation, the metallic element is *combined* in an ionic compound. If a metallic element goes from the free metal to the ionic form, the metal is oxidized (loses electrons).

        a.   sodium is oxidized; oxygen is reduced

        b.   iron is oxidized; hydrogen is reduced

        c.   oxygen (O^{2-}) is oxidized; aluminum (Al^{3+}) is reduced (this reaction is the reverse of the type discussed above)

        d.   magnesium is oxidized; nitrogen is reduced

92.   The rules for assigning oxidation states are given in Section 18.2 of the text. The rule that applies for each element in the following answers is given in parentheses after the element and its oxidation state.

        a.   H +1 (Rule 4); N –3 (Rule 6)

        b.   C +2 (Rule 6); O –2 (Rule 3)

        c.   C +4 (Rule 6); O –2 (Rule 3)

        d.   N +3 (Rule 6); F –1 (Rule 5)

94.   The rules for assigning oxidation states are given in Section 18.2 of the text. The rule that applies for each element is that given in parentheses after the element and its oxidation state.

        a.   Mn +4 (Rule 6); O –2 (Rule 3)

        b.   Ba +2 (Rule 2); Cr +6 (Rule 6); O –2 (Rule 3)

        c.   H +1 (Rule 4); S +4 (Rule 6); O –2 (Rule 3)

        d.   Ca +2 (Rule 2); P +5 (Rule 6); O –2 (Rule 3)

96.   The rules for assigning oxidation states are given in Section 18.2 of the text. The rule that applies for each element is that given in parentheses after the element and its oxidation state.

        a.   Bi +3 (Rule 7); O –2 (Rule 3)

        b.   P +5 (Rule 7); O –2 (Rule 3)

        c.   N +3 (Rule 7); O –2 (Rule 3)

        d.   Hg +1 (Rule 7)

98.   a. $2B_2O_3(s) + 6Cl_2(g) \rightarrow 4BCl_3(l) + 3O_2(g)$

                  oxygen is oxidized (–2 to 0); chlorine is reduced (0 to –1)

b. $GeH_4(g) + O_2(g) \rightarrow Ge(s) + 2H_2O(g)$

germanium is oxidized (-4 to 0); oxygen is reduced (0 to -2)

c. $C_2H_4(g) + Cl_2(g) \rightarrow C_2H_4Cl_2(l)$

carbon is oxidized -2 to -1); chlorine is reduced (0 to -1)

d. $O_2(g) + 2F_2(g) \rightarrow 2OF_2(g)$

oxygen is oxidized (0 to $+2$); fluorine is reduced (0 to -1)

100. a. $SiO_2(s) \rightarrow Si(s)$

Balance oxygen: $SiO_2(s) \rightarrow Si(s) + \mathbf{2H_2O}(l)$

Balance hydrogen: $SiO_2(s) + \mathbf{4H^+}(aq) \rightarrow Si(s) + 2H_2O(l)$

Balance charge: $SiO_2(s) + 4H^+(aq) + \mathbf{4e^-} \rightarrow Si(s) + 2H_2O(l)$

Balanced half–reaction: $SiO_2(s) + 4H^+(aq) + 4e^- \rightarrow Si(s) + 2H_2O(l)$

b. $S(s) \rightarrow H_2S(g)$

Balance hydrogen: $S(s) + \mathbf{2H^+}(aq) \rightarrow H_2S(g)$

Balance charge: $S(s) + 2H^+(aq) + \mathbf{2e^-} \rightarrow H_2S(g)$

Balanced half–reaction: $S(s) + 2H^+(aq) + 2e^- \rightarrow H_2S(g)$

c. $NO_3^-(aq) \rightarrow HNO_2(aq)$

Balance oxygen: $NO_3^-(aq) \rightarrow HNO_2(aq) + \mathbf{H_2O}(l)$

Balance hydrogen: $NO_3^-(aq) + \mathbf{3H^+}(aq) \rightarrow HNO_2(aq) + H_2O(l)$

Balance charge: $NO_3^-(aq) + 3H^+(aq) + \mathbf{2e^-} \rightarrow HNO_2(aq) + H_2O(l)$

Balanced half–reaction: $NO_3^-(aq) + 3H^+(aq) + 2e^- \rightarrow HNO_2(aq) + H_2O(l)$

d. $NO_3^-(aq) \rightarrow NO(g)$

Balance oxygen: $NO_3^-(aq) \rightarrow NO(g) + \mathbf{2H_2O}(l)$

Balance hydrogen: $NO_3^-(aq) + \mathbf{4H^+}(aq) \rightarrow NO(g) + 2H_2O(l)$

Balance charge: $NO_3^-(aq) + 4H^+(aq) + \mathbf{3e^-} \rightarrow NO(g) + 2H_2O(l)$

Balanced half–reaction: $NO_3^-(aq) + 4H^+(aq) + 3e^- \rightarrow NO(g) + 2H_2O(l)$

102. For simplicity, the physical states of the substances have been omitted until the final balanced equation is given.

For the reduction of the permanganate ion, MnO_4^-, in acid solution, the half–reaction is always the *same*:

$MnO_4^- \rightarrow Mn^{2+}$

Balance oxygen: $MnO_4^- \rightarrow Mn^{2+} + \mathbf{4H_2O}$

Balance hydrogen: $\mathbf{8H^+} + MnO_4^- \rightarrow Mn^{2+} + 4H_2O$

Balance charge: $8H^+ + MnO_4^- + \mathbf{5e^-} \rightarrow Mn^{2+} + 4H_2O$

a. $C_2O_4^{2-} \rightarrow CO_2$

Balance carbon: $C_2O_4^{2-} \rightarrow \mathbf{2}CO_2$

Balance charge: $C_2O_4^{2-} \rightarrow \mathbf{2}CO_2 + \mathbf{2e^-}$

Combine half–reactions:

$5 \times (C_2O_4^{2-} \rightarrow \mathbf{2}CO_2 + 2e^-)$

$2 \times (8H^+ + MnO_4^- + 5e^- \rightarrow Mn^{2+} + 4H_2O)$

$16H^+(aq) + 2MnO_4^-(aq) + 5C_2O_4^{2-}(aq) \rightarrow 2Mn^{2+}(aq) + 8H_2O(l) + 10CO_2(g)$

b. $Fe^{2+} \rightarrow Fe^{3+}$

Balance charge: $Fe^{2+} \rightarrow Fe^{3+} + \mathbf{e^-}$

Combine half–reactions:

$5 \times (Fe^{2+} \rightarrow Fe^{3+} + e^-)$

$8H^+ + MnO_4^- + 5e^- \rightarrow Mn^{2+} + 4H_2O$

$8H^+(aq) + MnO_4^-(aq) + 5Fe^{2+}(aq) \rightarrow Mn^{2+}(aq) + 4H_2O(l) + 5Fe^{3+}(aq)$

c. $Cl^- \rightarrow Cl_2$

Balance chlorine: $\mathbf{2}Cl^- \rightarrow Cl_2$

Balance charge: $2Cl^- \rightarrow Cl_2 + \mathbf{2e^-}$

Combine half–reactions:

$5 \times (2Cl^- \rightarrow Cl_2 + 2e^-)$

$2 \times (8H^+ + MnO_4^- + 5e^- \rightarrow Mn^{2+} + 4H_2O)$

$16H^+(aq) + 2MnO_4^-(aq) + 10Cl^-(aq) \rightarrow 2Mn^{2+}(aq) + 8H_2O(l) + 5Cl_2(g)$

104. A galvanic cell is a battery. A spontaneous oxidation reduction reaction is separated physically into the two half-reactions, and the electrons being transferred between the two half-cells are made available as an electrical current.

CHAPTER 19

Radioactivity and Nuclear Energy

2. The radius of a typical atomic nucleus is on the order of 10^{-13} cm, which is about one hundred thousand times smaller than the radius of an atom overall.

4. The mass number represents the total number of protons and neutrons in a nucleus.

6. The atomic number (Z) is written in such formulas as a left subscript, whereas the mass number (A) is written as a left superscript. That is, the general symbol for a nuclide is $_Z^A X$. As an example, consider the isotope of oxygen with 8 protons and 8 neutrons: its symbol would be $_8^{16}O$.

8. The symbol $_{-1}^0 e$ refers to a beta particle (an electron): the particle has mass number zero and charge 1–.

10. Emission of a neutron, $_0^1 n$, does not change the atomic number of the parent nucleus, but causes the mass number of the parent nucleus to decrease by one unit.

12. Gamma rays are high energy photons of electromagnetic radiation. Gamma rays are not considered to be particles. When a nucleus produces only gamma radiation, the atomic number and mass number of the nucleus do not change. Gamma rays represent the energy changes associated with transitions and rearrangement of the particles within the nucleus.

14. Electron capture occurs when one of the inner orbital electrons is pulled into and becomes part of the nucleus.

16. The fact that the average atomic mass of potassium is only slightly above 39 amu reflects the fact that the isotope of mass number 39 predominates.

isotope	number of neutrons
$_{19}^{39}K$	20 neutrons
$_{19}^{40}K$	21 neutrons
$_{19}^{41}K$	22 neutrons

18. The approximate atomic molar mass could be calculated as follows:

$0.79(24) + 0.10(25) + 0.11(26) = 24.3$.

This is *only* an approximation because the mass numbers, rather than the actual isotopic masses, were used. The fact that the approximate mass calculated is slightly above 24 shows that the isotope of mass number 24 predominates.

20. a. electron

   b. positron

    c.   neutron

    d.   proton

22.   a. $^{23}_{12}\text{Mg}$

       b. $^{5}_{3}\text{Li}$

       c. $^{4}_{2}\text{He}$

24.   a. $^{218}_{86}\text{Rn}$

       b. $^{0}_{+1}\text{e}$ (positron)

       c. $^{137}_{56}\text{Ba}$

26.   a. $^{234}_{92}\text{U} \rightarrow {}^{4}_{2}\text{He} + {}^{230}_{90}\text{Th}$

       b. $^{222}_{86}\text{Rn} \rightarrow {}^{4}_{2}\text{He} + {}^{218}_{84}\text{Po}$

       c. $^{162}_{75}\text{Re} \rightarrow {}^{4}_{2}\text{He} + {}^{158}_{73}\text{Ta}$

28.   a. $^{212}_{82}\text{Pb} \rightarrow {}^{0}_{-1}\text{e} + {}^{212}_{83}\text{Bi}$

       b. $^{212}_{81}\text{Tl} \rightarrow {}^{0}_{-1}\text{e} + {}^{212}_{82}\text{Pb}$

       c. $^{228}_{88}\text{Ra} \rightarrow {}^{0}_{-1}\text{e} + {}^{228}_{89}\text{Ac}$

30.   In a nuclear bombardment process, a target nucleus is bombarded with high-energy particles (typically subatomic particles or small atoms) from a particle accelerator. This may result in the transmutation of the target nucleus into some other element. For example, nitrogen-14 may be transmuted into oxygen-17 by bombardment with alpha particles. There is often considerable repulsion between the target nucleus and the particles being used for bombardment (especially if the bombarding particle is positively charged like the target nucleus). Using accelerators to increases the kinetic energy of the bombarding particles can overcome this repulsion.

32. $^{24}_{12}\text{Mg} + {}^{2}_{1}\text{H} \rightarrow {}^{22}_{11}\text{Na} + {}^{4}_{2}\text{He}$

34.   The half-life of a nucleus is the time required for one-half of the original sample of nuclei to decay. A given isotope of an element always has the same half-life, although different isotopes of the same element may have greatly different half-lives. Nuclei of different elements typically have different half-lives.

36. $^{226}_{88}\text{Ra}$ is the most stable (longest half-life); $^{224}_{88}\text{Ra}$ is the "hottest" (shortest half-life)

38.   With a half-life of 2.6 hours, strontium-87 is the hottest; with a half-life of 45.1 days, iron-59 is the most stable to decay.

40. Half-life, 1.5 min; let x represent the starting amount of isotope

time, min	0	1.5	3.0	4.5	6.0
mass	x	$\frac{1}{2}x$	$\frac{1}{4}x$	$\frac{1}{8}x$	$\frac{1}{16}x$

After six minutes (four half-lives), $\frac{1}{16}$ of the original Co-62 sample $[(\frac{1}{2})^4]$ will remain.

42. For an administered dose of 100 µg, 0.39 µg remains after 2 days. The fraction remaining is $0.39/100 = 0.0039$; on a percentage basis, less than 0.4% of the original radioisotope remains.

44. Carbon-14 is produced in the upper atmosphere by the bombardment of ordinary nitrogen with neutrons from space:

$$^{14}_{7}\text{N} + ^{1}_{0}\text{n} \rightarrow ^{14}_{6}\text{C} + ^{1}_{1}\text{H}$$

46. We assume that the concentration of C-14 in the atmosphere is effectively constant. A living organism is constantly replenishing C-14 either through the processes of metabolism (sugars ingested in foods contain C-14), or photosynthesis (carbon dioxide contains C-14). When a plant dies, it can no longer replenish, and as the C-14 undergoes radioactive decay, its amount decreases with time.

48. 1 day is about 13 half-lives for $^{18}_{9}\text{F}$. If we begin with 6.02×10^{23} atoms (1 mol), then after 13 half-lives, 7.4×10^{19} atoms of $^{18}_{9}\text{F}$ will remain.

50. fission, fusion, fusion, fission

52. $^{1}_{0}\text{n} + ^{235}_{92}\text{U} \rightarrow ^{142}_{56}\text{Ba} + ^{91}_{36}\text{Kr} + 3^{1}_{0}\text{n}$ is one possibility.

54. A critical mass of a fissionable material is the amount needed to provide a high enough internal neutron flux to sustain the chain reaction (enough neutrons are produced to cause the continuous fission of further material). A sample with less than a critical mass is still radioactive, but cannot sustain a chain reaction.

56. An actual nuclear explosion, of the type produced by a nuclear weapon, cannot occur in a nuclear reactor because the concentration of the fissionable materials is not sufficient to form a supercritical mass. However, since many reactors are cooled by water, which can decompose into hydrogen and oxygen gases, a *chemical* explosion is possible that could scatter the radioactive material used in the reactor.

58. Some advantages: fuel available domestically, relatively "clean," does not produce greenhouse gases that fossil fuel plants produce. Some disadvantages: safety, waste disposal, cost.

60. In one type of fusion reactor, two $^{2}_{1}\text{H}$ atoms are fused to produce $^{4}_{2}\text{He}$. Because the hydrogen nuclei are positively charged, extremely high energies (temperatures of 40 million K) are needed to overcome the repulsion between the nuclei as they are shot into each other.

62.   In the theory of stellar nucleosynthesis, it is considered that the nucleus began as a cloud of neutrons which exploded (the Big Bang). After this initial explosion, neutrons were thought to have decomposed into protons and electrons

$$\begin{smallmatrix}1\\0\end{smallmatrix}n \rightarrow \begin{smallmatrix}1\\1\end{smallmatrix}H + \begin{smallmatrix}0\\-1\end{smallmatrix}e$$

The products of this decomposition were then thought to have combined to form large clouds of hydrogen atoms. As the hydrogen clouds became larger, gravitational forces caused these clouds to contract and heat up. Eventually the clouds of hydrogen were so dense and so hot that fusion of hydrogen nuclei into helium nuclei took place, with a great release of energy. When the tendency for the hydrogen clouds to expand from the heat of fusion was counter-balanced by the gravitational forces of the cloud, a small star had formed. In addition to the fusion of hydrogen nuclei into helium mentioned already, as the star's hydrogen supply is exhausted, the helium present in the star also begins to undergo fusion into nuclei of other elements.

64.   Somatic damage is directly to the organism itself, causing nearly immediate sickness or death to the organism. Genetic damage is to the genetic machinery of the organism, which will be manifested in future generations of offspring.

66.   Gamma rays penetrate long distances, but seldom cause ionization of biological molecules. Alpha particles, because they are much heavier although less penetrating, are very effective at ionizing biological molecules and leave a dense trail of damage in the organism. Isotopes that release alpha particles can be ingested or breathed into the body where the damage from the alpha particles will be more acute.

68.   Nuclear waste may remain radioactive for thousands of years, and much of it is chemically poisonous as well as radioactive. Most reactor waste is still in "temporary storage." Various suggestions have been made for a more permanent solution, such as casting the spent fuel into glass bricks to contain it, and then storing the bricks in corrosion-proof metal containers deep underground. No agreement on a permanent solution to the disposal of nuclear waste has yet been reached.

70.   radioactive

72.   mass

74.   neutron; proton

76.   radioactive decay

78.   mass number

80.   transuranium

82.   half-life

84.   radiotracers

86.   chain

88.   breeder

90. 4.5×10^{9} dollars (\$4.5 billion)

92. 3.5×10^{-11} J/atom; 8.9×10^{10} J/g

94. $^{90}_{40}\text{Zr}$, $^{91}_{40}\text{Zr}$, $^{92}_{40}\text{Zr}$, $^{94}_{40}\text{Zr}$, and $^{96}_{40}\text{Zr}$

96. $^{27}_{13}\text{Al}$ (13 protons, 14 neutrons)

    $^{28}_{13}\text{Al}$ (13 protons, 15 neutrons)

    $^{29}_{13}\text{Al}$ (13 protons, 16 neutrons)

98. a. $^{0}_{-1}\text{e}$

    b. $^{74}_{34}\text{Se}$

    c. $^{240}_{92}\text{U}$

100. $^{9}_{4}\text{Be} + ^{4}_{2}\text{He} \rightarrow ^{12}_{6}\text{C} + ^{1}_{0}\text{n}$

102. $^{238}_{92}\text{U} + ^{1}_{0}\text{n} \rightarrow ^{239}_{92}\text{U}$

    $^{239}_{92}\text{U} \rightarrow ^{239}_{93}\text{Np} + ^{0}_{-1}\text{e}$

    $^{239}_{93}\text{Np} \rightarrow ^{239}_{94}\text{Pu} + ^{0}_{-1}\text{e}$

CHAPTER 20

Organic Chemistry

2.	Carbon has only four valence electrons and can only make 4 bonds to other atoms.

4.	A triple bond represents the sharing of three pairs of electrons between two bonded atoms. The sharing of three pairs imparts a linear geometry in the region of the triple bond. The simplest example of an organic molecule containing a triple bond is acetylene, $H-C\equiv C-H$.

6.	$$\ddot{O}=C=\ddot{O} \qquad\qquad C\equiv\ddot{O}$$

8.	Molecules a and c contain only carbon–carbon single bonds and are therefore saturated.

10.	In an alkane, carbons atoms make 4 separate bonds to adjacent atoms, with these bonds having the tetrahedral arrangement predicted by the VSEPR theory. With all bond angles on the order of 109.5°, the molecule cannot be linear (180°).

12.	The general formula for the alkanes is C_nH_{2n+2}.

	a.	$2(4) + 2 = 10$

	b.	$2(6) + 2 = 14$

	c.	$2(13) + 2 = 28$

	d.	$2(17) + 2 = 36$

14.	a.	pentane	$CH_3-CH_2-CH_2-CH_2-CH_3$

	b.	undecane	$CH_3-CH_2-CH_2-CH_2-CH_2-CH_2-CH_2-CH_2-CH_2-CH_2-CH_3$

	c.	nonane	$CH_3-CH_2-CH_2-CH_2-CH_2-CH_2-CH_2-CH_2-CH_3$

	d.	heptane	$CH_3-CH_2-CH_2-CH_2-CH_2-CH_2-CH_3$

16.	A branched alkane contains one or more shorter carbon atom chains, attached to the side of the main (longest) carbon atom chain. The simplest branched alkane is 2-methylpropane.

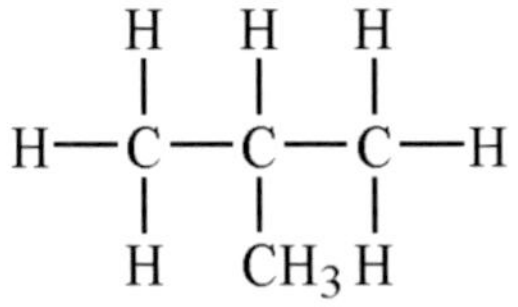

213

18.   Carbon skeletons are shown.

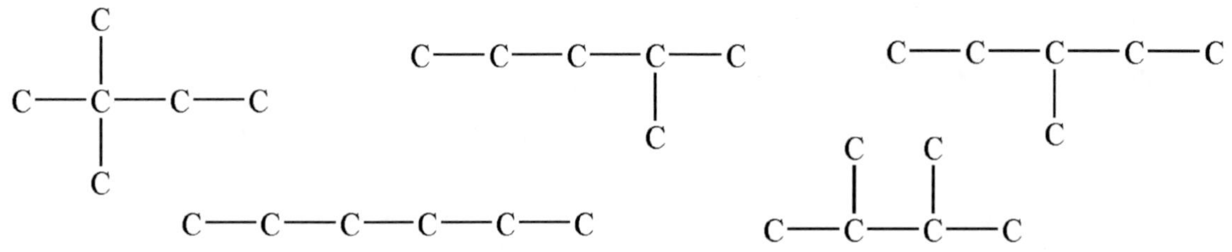

20.   The root name is derived from the number of carbon atoms in the *longest continuous chain* of carbon atoms.

22.   The numbers indicate to which carbon of the longest continuous chain of carbon atoms the substituents are attached. The longest continuous chain is numbered from the end closest to the first substituent so as to give the lowest possible locator numbers.

24.   Multiple substituents are listed in alphabetical order, disregarding any prefix.

26.   Look for the *longest* continuous chain of carbon atoms.

    a.   2,3,4-trimethylpentane

    b.   2,3-dimethylpentane

    c.   3,4-dimethylhexane

    d.   4,5-dimethyloctane

28.   a.

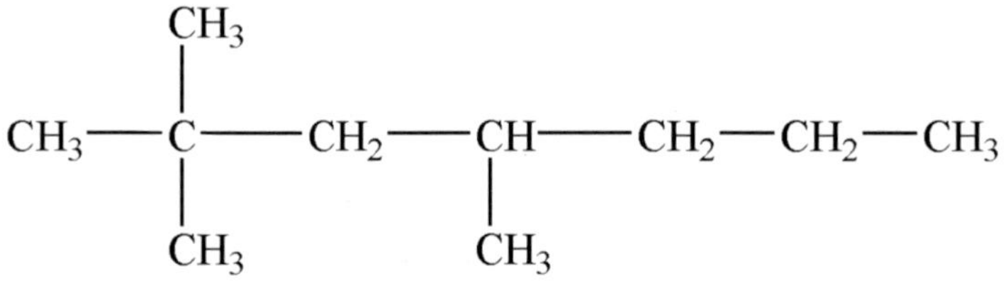

    b.

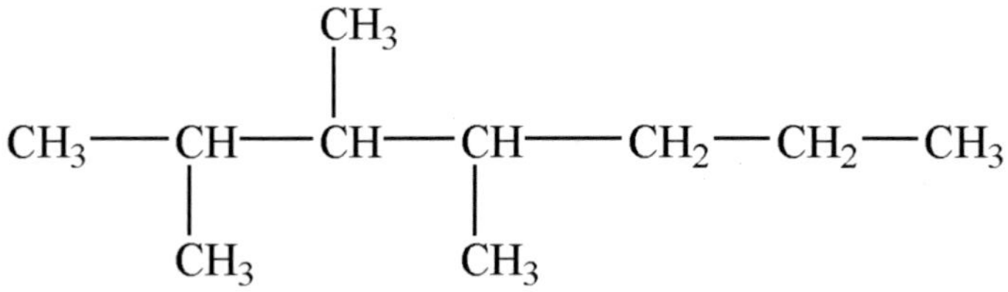

    c.

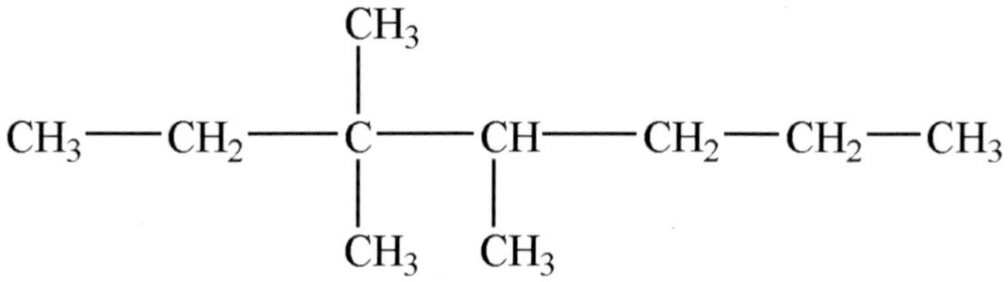

    d.

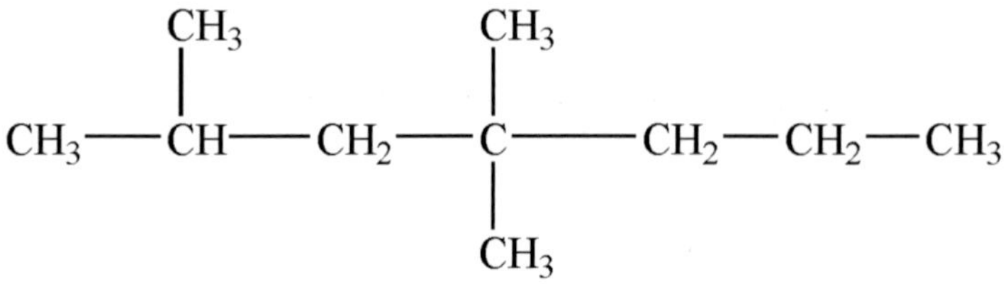

30. | C atoms | Use |
        |---------|-----|
        | C_5–C_{12} | gasoline |
        | C_{10}–C_{18} | kerosene, jet fuel |
        | C_{15}–C_{25} | diesel fuel, heating oil, lubrication |
        | C_{25}– | asphalt |

32.   Tetraethyl lead was added to gasolines to prevent "knocking" of high efficiency automobile engines. The use of tetraethyl lead is being phased out because of the danger to the environment posed by the lead in this substance.

34.   The combustion of alkanes has been used as a source of heat, light, and mechanical energy.

$$C_3H_8(g) + 5O_2(g) \rightarrow 3CO_2(g) + 4H_2O(g) + heat$$

36.   When an alkane molecule is *dehydrogenated*, a double bond is introduced into the molecule, converting it to an alk*ene*. The simplest example is for the dehydrogenation of ethane, to produce ethene (ethylene): CH_3–CH_3 $\xrightarrow{\text{dehydrogenation}}$ $CH_2{=}CH_2 + H_2$

38.   a. $2C_6H_{14}(l) + 19O_2(g) \rightarrow 12CO_2(g) + 14H_2O(g)$

        b. $CH_4(g) + Cl_2(g) \rightarrow CH_3Cl(l) + HCl(g)$

        c. $CHCl_3(l) + Cl_2(g) \rightarrow CCl_4(l) + HCl(g)$

40.   An alkyne is a hydrocarbon containing a carbon-carbon triple bond. The general formula is C_nH_{2n-2}.

42.   The location of a double or triple bond in the longest chain of an alkene or alkyne is indicated by giving the *number* of the lowest number carbon atom involved in the double or triple bond.

44.   Hydrogenation converts unsaturated compounds to saturated (or less unsaturated) compounds. In the case of a liquid vegetable oil, this is likely to convert the oil to a solid.

$$C_2H_4(g) + H_2(g) \rightarrow C_2H_6(g)$$

46.   a.   5,5-dichloro-3,4-dimethyl-1-pentene

        b.   4,5-dichloro-2-hexene (look for the *longest* chain)

        c.   2,2,5-trimethyl-3-heptene

        d.   5-methyl-1-hexyne

48.   Shown are carbon skeletons:

C≡C—C—C—C—C   C—C≡C—C—C—C   C—C—C≡C—C—C

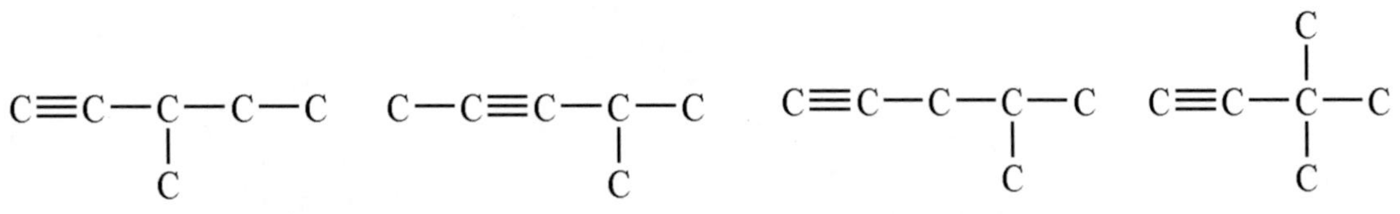

C≡C—C—C—C   C—C≡C—C—C   C≡C—C—C—C   C≡C—C—C
     | | | |
     C   C   C   C

50.   For benzene, a *set* of equivalent Lewis structures can be drawn, differing only in the *location* of the three double bonds in the ring. Experimentally, however, benzene does not demonstrate the chemical properties expected for molecules having *any* double bonds. We say that the "extra" electrons that would go into making the second bond of the three double bonds are delocalized around the entire benzene ring; this delocalization of the electrons explains benzene's unique properties.

52.   When named as a substituent, the benzene ring is called the *phenyl* group. Two examples are:

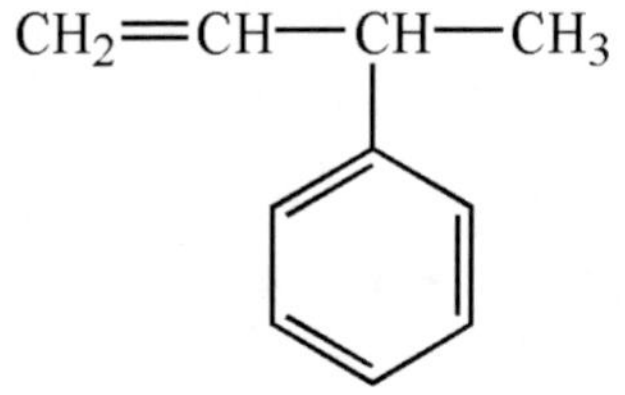

$$CH_2\!\!=\!\!CH\!\!-\!\!CH\!\!-\!\!CH_3 \qquad\qquad CH_3\!\!-\!\!CH\!\!-\!\!CH_2\!\!-\!\!CH_2\!\!-\!\!CH_2\!\!-\!\!CH_3$$

3-phenyl-1-butene	2-phenylhexane

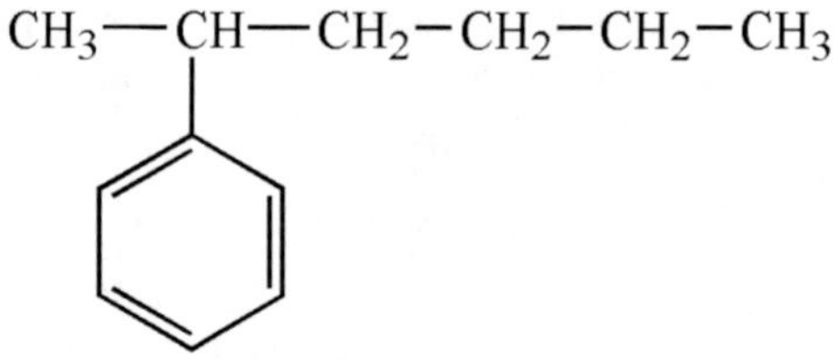

54.   *ortho*– refers to adjacent substituents (1,2–); *meta*– refers to two substituents with one unsubstituted carbon atom between them (1,3–); *para*– refers to two substituents with two unsubstituted carbon atoms between them (1,4–).

56.   a.   3,4-dibromo-1-methylbenzene, 3,4-dibromotoluene

       b.   naphthalene

       c.   3-methylphenol; 3-hydroxytoluene

       d.   1,4-dinitrobenzene, *p*-dinitrobenzene

58.   a.   carboxylic (organic) acids

       b.   aldehydes

       c.   ketones

       d.   alcohols

60.   Primary alcohols have *one* hydrocarbon fragment (alkyl group) bonded to the carbon atom where the –OH group is attached. Secondary alcohols have *two* such alkyl groups attached, and tertiary alcohols contain *three* such alkyl groups. Examples are:

ethanol (primary)

$$CH_3\!\!-\!\!CH_2\!\!-\!\!OH$$

2-propanol (secondary)

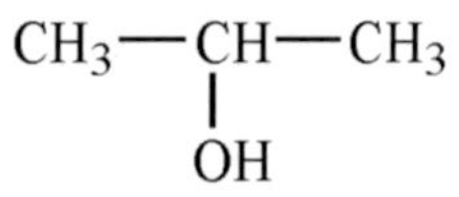

$$CH_3\!\!-\!\!CH\!\!-\!\!CH_3$$
$$\;\;\;\;\;\;\;|$$
$$\;\;\;\;\;OH$$

2-methyl-2-propanol (tertiary)

$$CH_3-\underset{\underset{OH}{|}}{\overset{\overset{CH_3}{|}}{C}}-CH_3$$

62.   Specific examples will depend on students' choice. Below are examples for alcohols with five carbon atoms.

primary   (1-pentanol)

$$CH_3-CH_2-CH_2-CH_2-CH_2-OH$$

secondary   (2-pentanol)

$$CH_3-CH_2-CH_2-\underset{\underset{OH}{|}}{CH}-CH_3$$

tertiary   (2-methyl-2-butanol)

$$CH_3-\underset{\underset{OH}{|}}{\overset{\overset{CH_3}{|}}{C}}-CH_2-CH_3$$

64.   The reaction is

$$C_6H_{12}O_6 \xrightarrow{\text{yeast}} 2CH_3-CH_2-OH + 2CO_2$$

The yeast necessary for the fermentation process are killed if the concentration of ethanol is over 13%. More concentrated ethanol solutions are most commonly made by distillation.

66.   methanol (CH_3OH) - starting material for synthesis of acetic acid and many plastics

ethylene glycol (CH_2OH-CH_2OH) - automobile antifreeze

isopropyl alcohol (2-propanol, $CH_3-CH(OH)-CH_3$) - rubbing alcohol

68.   Aldehydes and ketones both contain the carbonyl group C=O.

$$\diagdown\hspace{-0.3em}\diagup C=O$$

Aldehydes and ketones differ in the *location* of the carbonyl function: aldehydes contain the carbonyl group at the end of a hydrocarbon chain (the carbon atom of the carbonyl group is bonded only to at most one other carbon atom); the carbonyl group of ketones represents one of the interior carbon atoms of a chain (the carbon atom of the carbonyl group is bonded to two other carbon atoms).

70.   The specific answers depend on your choice of alcohols. Here are representative reactions involving general primary and secondary alcohols:

$$R-CH_2-OH \xrightarrow{\text{mild oxidation}} R-CHO$$

$$R-CHOH-R' \xrightarrow{\text{mild oxidation}} R-C(=O)-R'$$

72.   In addition to their systematic names (based on the hydrocarbon root, with the ending –*one*), ketones can also be named by naming the groups attached to either side of the carbonyl carbon as alkyl groups, followed by the word "ketone". Examples are:

$CH_3–C(=O)–CH_2CH_3$ methyl ethyl ketone (2-butanone, butanone)

$CH_3CH_2–C(=O)–CH_2CH_3$ diethyl ketone (3-pentanone)

74.   The structures are:

a.

b.

c.

d.

76.   Carboxylic acids are typically *weak* acids.

$CH_3–CH_2–COOH(aq) \rightleftarrows H^+(aq) + CH_3–CH_2–COO^-(aq)$

78.   a. $CH_3—CH_2—CH_2—CHO$

b. $CH_3—CH_2—COOH$

c.

80.   Acetylsalicylic acid is synthesized from salicylic acid (behaving as an alcohol through its –OH group) and acetic acid.

82.   The structures are:

a.

b.

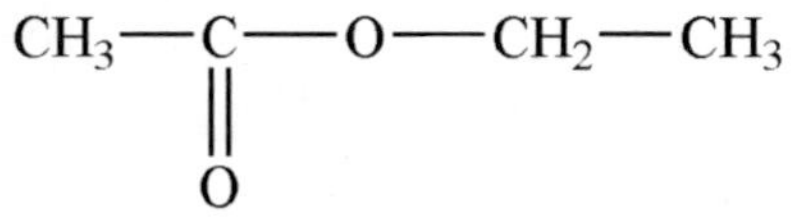

$$CH_3-\underset{\underset{O}{\|}}{C}-O-CH_2-CH_3$$

c.

COOH

Cl

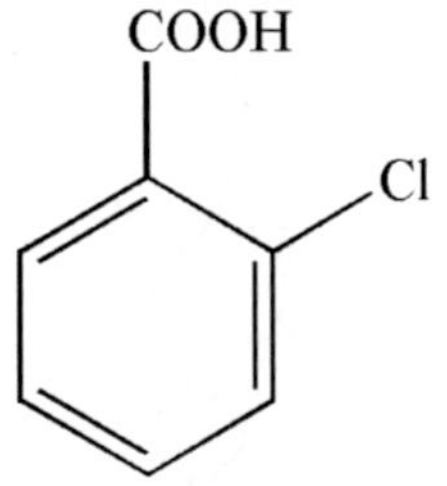

d.

$$CH_3-\underset{\underset{}{|}}{\overset{\overset{Cl}{|}}{CH}}-\underset{\underset{CH_3}{|}}{\overset{\overset{CH_3}{|}}{C}}-COOH$$

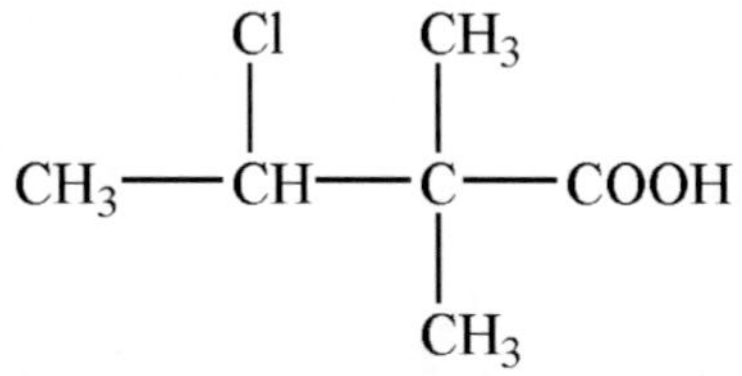

84.   In addition polymerization, the monomer units simply add together to form the polymer, with no other products. Polyethylene and polytetrafluoroethylene (Teflon) are common examples.

86.   Kevlar is a *co*-polymer since two different types of monomers combine to generate the polymer chain.

88.   The structures are:

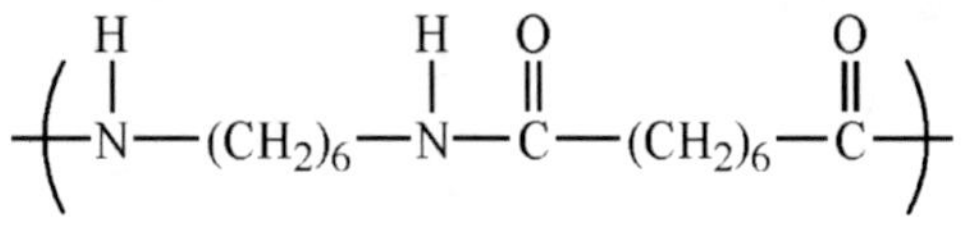

$$\left(\!\!\begin{array}{c}\overset{H}{\underset{|}{N}}-(CH_2)_6-\overset{H}{\underset{|}{N}}-\overset{O}{\overset{\|}{C}}-(CH_2)_6-\overset{O}{\overset{\|}{C}}\end{array}\!\!\right)$$

nylon

$$\left(\!\!\begin{array}{c}O-CH_2-CH_2-O-\overset{O}{\overset{\|}{C}}-\bigcirc-\overset{O}{\overset{\|}{C}}\end{array}\!\!\right)$$

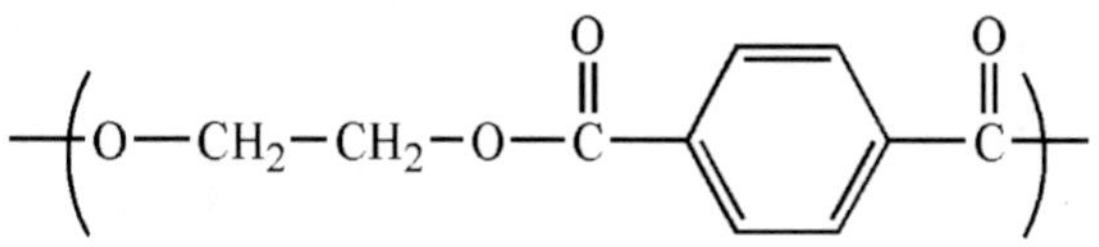

dacron

90.   unsaturated

92.   straight-chain or normal

94.   -*ane*

96.   number

98.   anti-knocking

100.   substitution

102.   hydrogenation

104.   functional

106.   carbon monoxide

108.   carbonyl

110. carboxyl

112. addition

114. Structures depend on student choices.

116. a.   2-chlorobutane

     b.   1,2-dibromoethane

     c.   triiodomethane (common name: iodoform)

     d.   2,3,4-trichloropentane

     e.   2,2-dichloro-4-isopropylheptane

118. a.

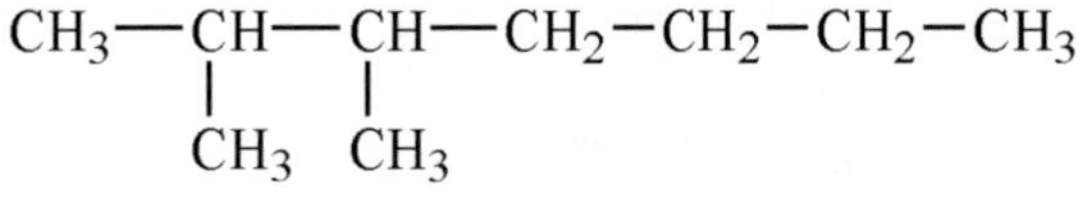

$$CH_3—CH—CH—CH_2—CH_2—CH_2—CH_3$$
$$\qquad\quad | \qquad\ |$$
$$\qquad\quad CH_3\ \ CH_3$$

     b.

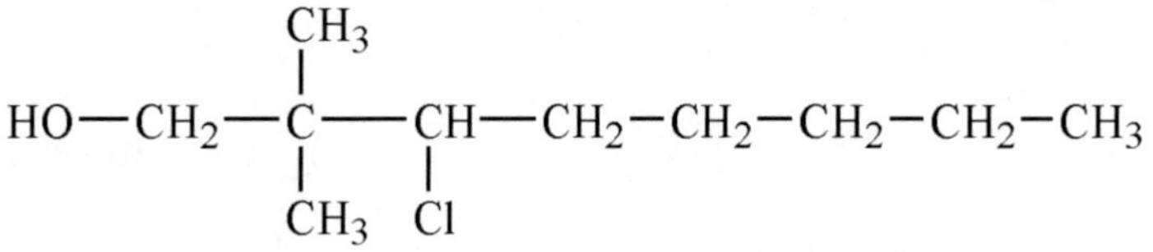

$$\qquad\qquad\qquad CH_3$$
$$\qquad\qquad\qquad\ |$$
$$HO—CH_2—C—CH—CH_2—CH_2—CH_2—CH_2—CH_3$$
$$\qquad\qquad\ \ |\qquad\ |$$
$$\qquad\qquad\ \ CH_3\ \ Cl$$

     c.

$$CH_2{=}C—CH_2—CH_2—CH_2—CH_3$$
$$\qquad\ |$$
$$\qquad\ Cl$$

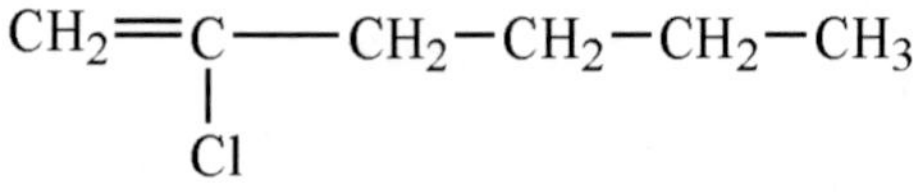

     d. $Cl—CH_2—CH{=}CH—CH_2—CH_2—CH_3$

     e.

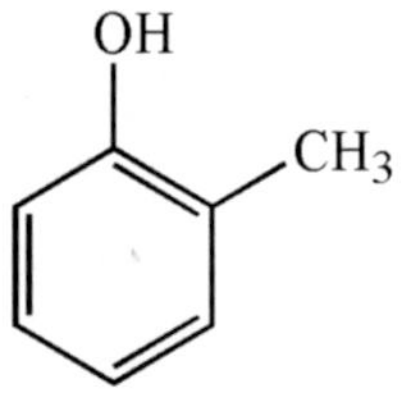

120. primary

$$CH_3—CH_2—CH_2—CH_2—CH_2—CH_2—OH$$

secondary

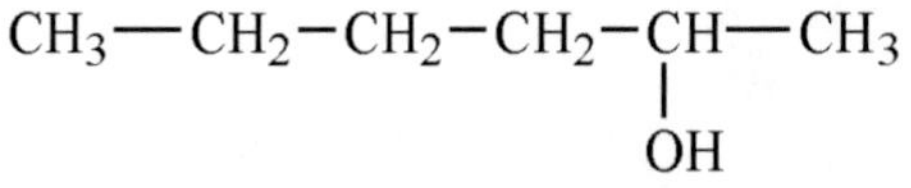

$$CH_3—CH_2—CH_2—CH_2—CH—CH_3$$
$$\qquad\qquad\qquad\qquad\qquad |$$
$$\qquad\qquad\qquad\qquad\qquad OH$$

tertiary

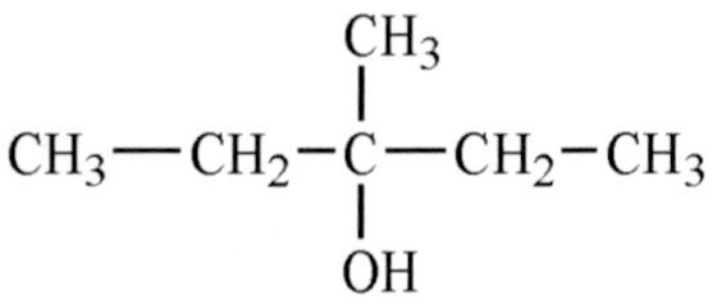

$$\qquad\qquad\quad CH_3$$
$$\qquad\qquad\quad\ |$$
$$CH_3—CH_2—C—CH_2—CH_3$$
$$\qquad\qquad\ |$$
$$\qquad\qquad\ OH$$

122. 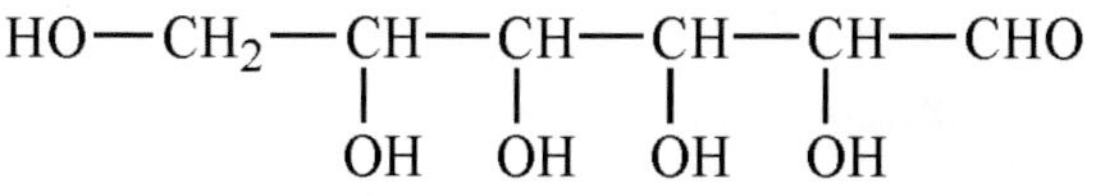
$$HO-CH_2-CH-CH-CH-CH-CHO$$
with OH, OH, OH, OH below

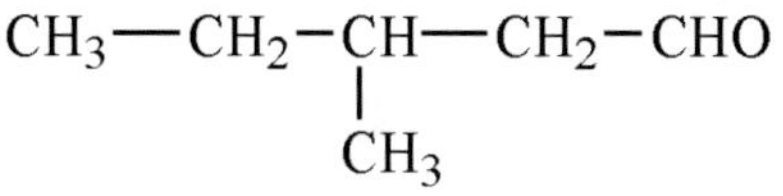

124. a. 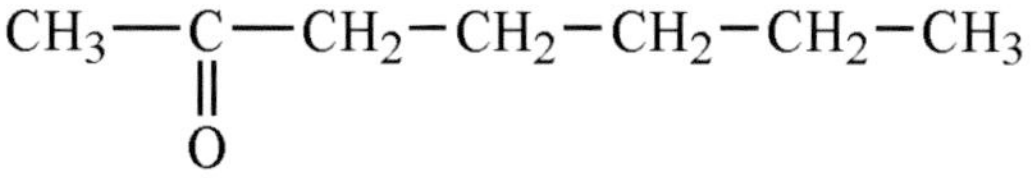
$$CH_3-C-CH_2-CH_2-CH_2-CH_2-CH_3$$
$$\overset{\|}{O}$$

b.
$$CH_3-CH_2-CH-CH_2-CHO$$
$$\underset{CH_3}{|}$$

c.
$$CH_3-CH_2-CH_2-CH-CH_2-OH$$
$$\underset{CH_3}{|}$$

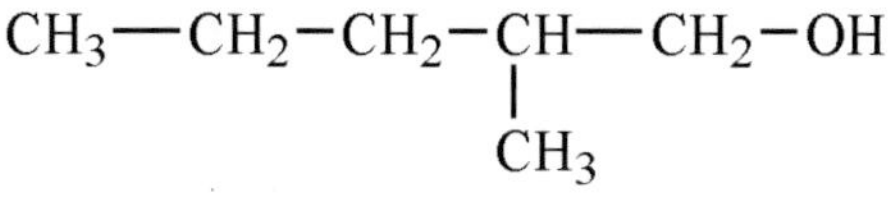

d. 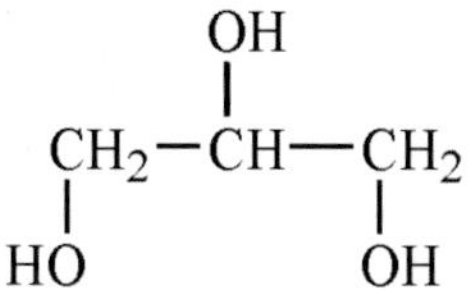
$$\overset{OH}{\overset{|}{CH_2-CH-CH_2}}$$
$$\underset{HO\qquad\quad OH}{}$$

e. 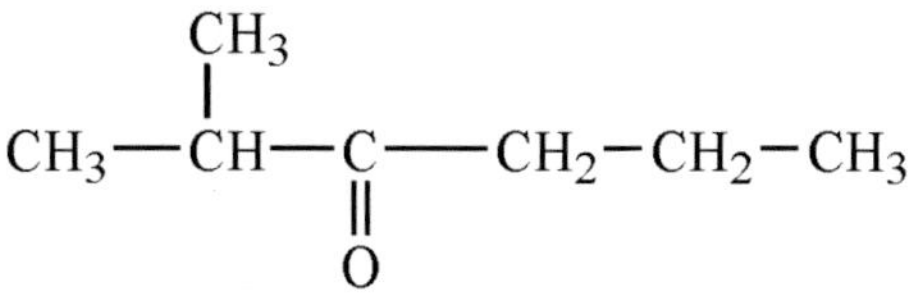
$$\overset{CH_3}{\overset{|}{CH_3-CH-C-CH_2-CH_2-CH_3}}$$
$$\underset{O}{\overset{\|}{}}$$

126. 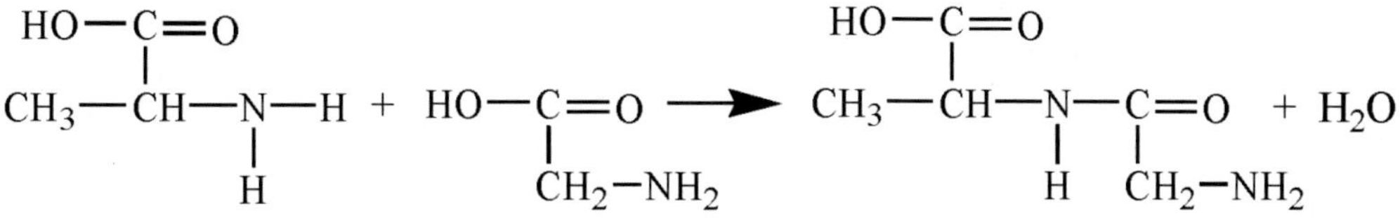
$$\overset{HO-C=O}{\underset{CH_3-CH-N-H}{|}} + \overset{HO-C=O}{\underset{CH_2-NH_2}{|}} \longrightarrow \overset{HO-C=O}{\underset{CH_3-CH-N-C=O}{|}} + H_2O$$
with H below N on left; H and CH₂—NH₂ below on right

128. a. $CH_3-CH_2-CH_2-CH_2-CH_2-CH_2-CH_2-CH_3$

b. $CH_3-CH_2-CH_2-CH_2-CH_2-CH_3$

c. $CH_3-CH_2-CH_2-CH_3$

d. $CH_3-CH_2-CH_2-CH_2-CH_3$

130. a.   2,3-dimethylbutane

b.   3,3-diethylpentane

c.   2,3,3-trimethylhexane

d.   2,3,4,5,6-pentamethylheptane

132. a. $CH_3Cl(g)$

b. $H_2(g)$

c. $HCl(g)$

134. $CH\equiv C-CH_2-CH_2-CH_2-CH_2-CH_2-CH_3$ 1-octyne

$CH_3-C\equiv C-CH_2-CH_2-CH_2-CH_2-CH_3$ 2-octyne

$$CH_3-CH_2-C{\equiv}C-CH_2-CH_2-CH_2-CH_3 \qquad \text{3-octyne}$$

$$CH_3-CH_2-CH_2-C{\equiv}C-CH_2-CH_2-CH_3 \qquad \text{4-octyne}$$

136. a. carboxylic acid

 b. ketone

 c. ester

 d. alcohol (phenol)

138. a. 3-methylpentanal

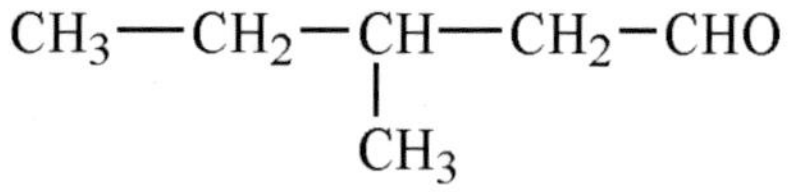

 b. 3-methyl-2-pentanone

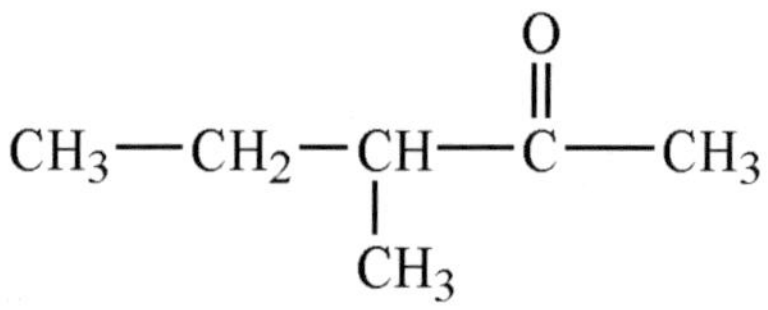

 c. methyl phenyl ketone

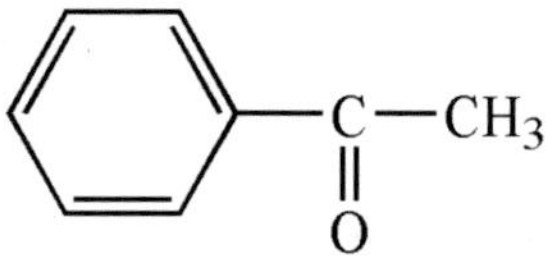

 d. 2-hydroxybutanal

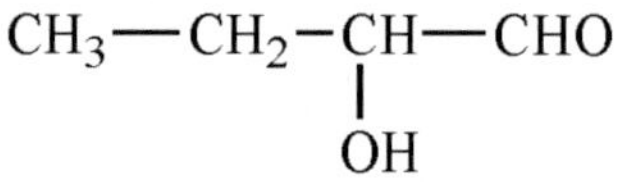

 e. propanal

$$CH_3-CH_2-CHO$$

140. a.

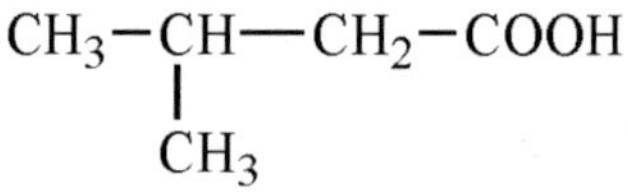

 b.

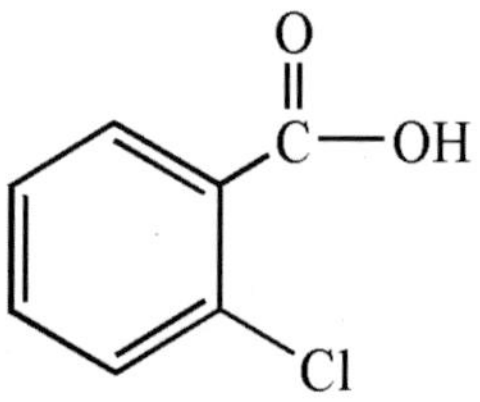

 c. $CH_3-CH_2-CH_2-CH_2-CH_2-COOH$

 d. CH_3-COOH

CHAPTER 21

Biochemistry

2.   Trace elements are those elements present in the body in only very small amounts, but which are essential to many biochemical processes in the body.

4.   Fibrous proteins provide structural integrity and strength for many types of tissue and are the main components of muscle, hair, and cartilage. Globular proteins are the "worker" molecules of the body, performing such functions as transporting oxygen throughout the body, catalyzing many of the reactions in the body, fighting infections, and transporting electrons during the metabolism of nutrients.

6.   All α-amino acids have the general structure

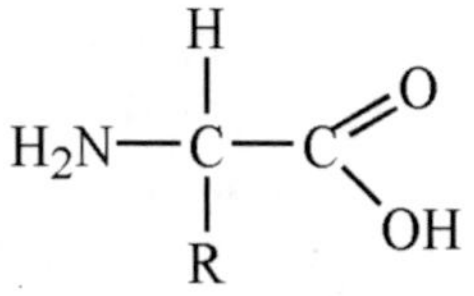

The essential amino acids used by the body to construct proteins differ in the structure of the "R-group". Figure 21-2 shows the essential amino acids and their specific R-groups. Some amino acids contain R-groups that are non-polar in nature, while other amino acids contain R-groups that are very polar and which may be capable of hydrogen bonding. Proteins with a preponderance of non-polar R groups would tend to be insoluble in water while proteins with a high content of polar R-groups would tend to be soluble in water.

8.   The amino acid will be hydrophilic if the R group is polar, and hydrophobic if the R group is nonpolar. Serine is a good example of an amino acid in which the R group is polar. Leucine is a good example of an amino acid with a nonpolar R group.

10.   There are six tripeptides possible.

cys-ala-phe   ala-cys-phe   phe-ala-cys

cys-phe-ala   ala-phe-cys   phe-cys-ala

12.   The primary structure of a protein is the specific *sequence* of amino acids in the peptide chain. Adjacent amino acids are connected to each other by peptide (amide) linkages.

14.   Long, thin, resilient proteins, such as hair, typically contain elongated, elastic alpha-helical protein molecules. Other proteins, such as silk, which in bulk form sheets or plates, typically contain protein molecules having the beta pleated sheet secondary structure. Proteins that do not have a structural function in the body, such as hemoglobin, typically have a globular structure.

16.   Silk consists of a sheet structure where the individual chains of amino acids are lined up lengthwise next to each other to form the sheet.

18. A disulfide linkage represents a S–S bond between two sulfur-containing amino acids in a peptide chain. It is the amino acid cysteine that forms such linkages. The presence of disulfide linkages produces bends and folds in the peptide chain and contributes greatly to the tertiary structure of a protein.

20. Oxygen is transported by the protein *hemoglobin*.

22. Ferritin helps to store iron in the liver, spleen, and bone marrow (the Latin root *ferr-* in the name implies iron).

24. Amino acids contain both a weak-acid and a weak-base group, and thus they can neutralize both bases and acids, respectively.

26. When we say that an enzyme is selective for a particular substrate, we mean that the enzyme will catalyze the reactions of that molecule and that molecule only.

28. The lock-and-key model for enzymes indicates that the structures of an enzyme and its substrate must be *complementary*, so that the substrate can approach and attach itself along the length of the enzyme at the enzyme's active sites. A given enzyme is intended to act upon a particular substrate: the substrate attaches itself to the enzyme, is acted upon, and then moves away from the enzyme. If a different molecule has a similar structure to the substrate, this other molecule may also be capable of attaching itself to the enzyme. But since this molecule is not the enzyme's proper substrate, the enzyme may not be able to act upon the molecule, and the molecule may remain attached to the enzyme preventing proper substrate molecules from approaching the enzyme (irreversible inhibition). If the enzyme cannot act upon its proper substrate, then the enzyme is said to be inhibited. Irreversible inhibition might be a desirable feature in an antibiotic, which would bind to the enzymes of a bacteria and prevent the bacteria from reproducing, thereby preventing or curing an infection.

30. Sugars contain an aldehyde or ketone functional group (carbonyl group), as well as several –OH groups (hydroxyl group).

32. A pentose sugar is a carbohydrate containing five (*pent-*) carbon atoms in the chain. The pentose ribose is shown below.

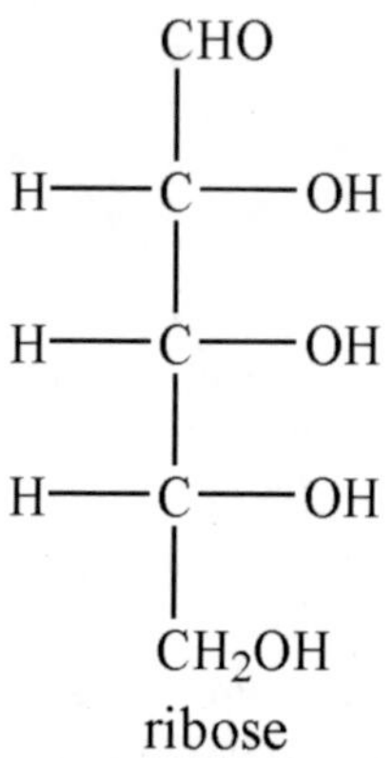

$$\begin{array}{c}
\text{CHO} \\
| \\
\text{H}\!-\!\text{C}\!-\!\text{OH} \\
| \\
\text{H}\!-\!\text{C}\!-\!\text{OH} \\
| \\
\text{H}\!-\!\text{C}\!-\!\text{OH} \\
| \\
\text{CH}_2\text{OH}
\end{array}$$

ribose

34. Starch is the form in which glucose is stored by plants for later use as cellular fuel. Cellulose is used by plants as their major structural component. Although starch and cellulose are both polymers of glucose, the linkage between adjacent glucose units differs in the two polysaccharides. Humans do not possess the enzyme needed to hydrolyze the linkage in cellulose.

36. ribose (aldopentose); arabinose (aldopentose); ribulose (ketopentose); glucose (aldohexose); mannose (aldohexose); galactose (aldohexose); fructose (ketohexose).

38. DNA nucleotides consist of a nitrogen-containing base, a pentose, and a phosphate group.

40. Uracil (RNA only); cytosine (DNA, RNA); thymine (DNA only); adenine (DNA, RNA); guanine (DNA, RNA)

42. An overall DNA molecule consists of two chains of nucleotides, with the organic bases on the nucleotides arranged in complementary pairs (cytosine with guanine, and adenine with thymine). The structures and properties of the organic bases are such that these pairs fit together well and allow the two chains of nucleotides to form the double helix structure. When DNA replicates, it is assumed the double helix unwinds, and then new molecules of the organic bases come in and pair up with their respective partner on the separated nucleotide chains, thereby replicating the original structure. See Figure 21.20

44. Lipids are a group of substances defined in terms of their solubility characteristics: lipids are typically oily, greasy substances that are not very soluble in water.

46. A triglyceride typically consists of a glycerol backbone, to which three separate fatty acid molecules are attached by ester linkages.

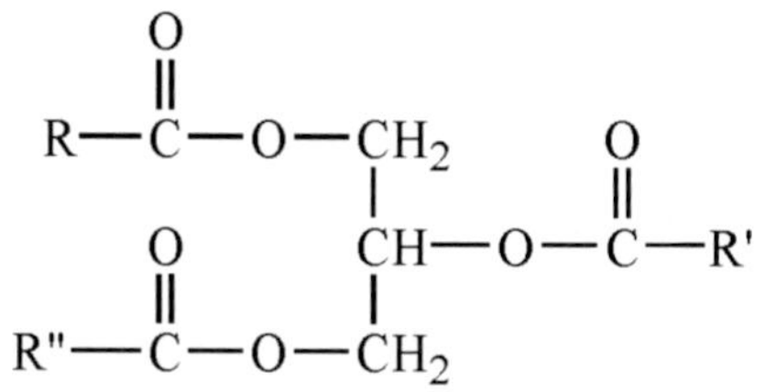

48. "Soaps" are the salts of long-chain organic acids ("fatty acids"), most commonly either the sodium or potassium salt. Soaps are prepared by treating a fat or oil (a triglyceride) with a strong base such as NaOH or KOH. This breaks the ester linkages in the triglyceride, releasing three fatty acid anions and glycerol.

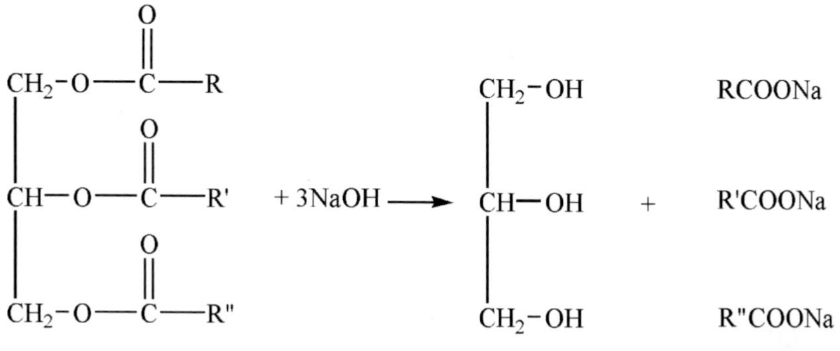

50. Soaps have both a nonpolar nature (due to the long chain of the fatty acid) and an ionic nature (due to the charge on the carboxyl group). In water, soap anions form aggregates called micelles, in which the water-repelling hydrocarbon chains are oriented towards the interior of the aggregate, with the ionic, water-attracting carboxyl groups oriented towards the outside. Most dirt has a greasy nature. A soap micelle is able to interact with a grease molecule, pulling the grease molecule into the hydrocarbon interior of the micelle. When the clothing is rinsed, the micelle containing the grease is washed away. See Figures 21.22 and 21.23.

52.   Cholesterol is the naturally occurring steroid from which the body synthesizes other needed steroids. As cholesterol is insoluble in water, it is thought that having too large a concentration of this substance in the bloodstream may lead to its deposition and build up on the walls of blood vessels, causing their eventual blockage.

54.   The bile acids are synthesized from cholesterol in the liver and are stored in the gall bladder. Bile acids such as cholic acid act as emulsifying agents for lipids and aid in their digestion.

56.   i

58.   m

60.   u

62.   f

64.   g

66.   r

68.   p

70.   o

72.   b

74.   d

76.   a

78.   nucleotides

80.   ester

82.   thymine, guanine

84.   transfer, messenger

86.   lipids

88.   unsaturated, saturated

90.   ionic, nonpolar

92.   fatty (long chain)

94.   progesterone

96.   The primary structure of a protein refers to the specific identity and ordering of amino acids in a protein's polypeptide chain. The primary structure is sometimes referred to as the protein's amino acid *sequence*.

98.   tendons, bone (with mineral constituents), skin, cartilage, hair, fingernails.

100.   Proteins contain both acidic (–COOH) and basic (–NH$_2$) groups in their side chains, which can neutralize both acids and bases.

102.   pentoses (5 carbons); hexoses (6 carbons); trioses (3 carbons)

104.   In a strand of DNA, the phosphate group and the sugar molecule of adjacent nucleotides become bound to each other. The chain-portion of the DNA molecule, therefore, consists of alternating phosphate groups and sugar molecules. The nitrogen bases are found protruding from the side of this phosphate-sugar chain, bonded to the sugar molecules.

106.   Phospholipids are esters of glycerol. Two fatty acids are bonded to the –OH groups of the glycerol backbone, with the third –OH group of glycerol bonded to a phosphate group. Having the two fatty acids, but also the polar phosphate group, makes the phospholipid lecithin a good emulsifying agent.

Introductory Chemistry: A Foundation, Introductory Chemistry, Basic Chemistry

SEVENTH EDITION

Steven S. Zumdahl
University of Illinois Urbana-Champaign

Donald J. DeCoste
University of Illinois Urbana-Champaign

Written by

Donald J. DeCoste

BROOKS/COLE
CENGAGE Learning

Australia • Brazil • Japan • Korea • Mexico • Singapore • Spain • United Kingdom • United States

Contents

Preface

You are probably asking yourself, "What can I do to help me learn chemistry?" This is a question many students ask when they first begin a chemistry course. The complete answer to this question is not simple, but there are some things you can do to help make your study of chemistry successful.

First, read the textbook assignment at least twice, once before you go to class (so that you will receive maximum benefit from each lecture) and once after going to class (so that you can slowly and carefully review the main points of the lecture). Second, keep up with the homework assignments. Don't wait until the day before the exam to start attempting to solve practice problems. Solving chemistry problems takes time, thought and practice. You will need to work steadily to become a good problem-solver.

This *Study Guide* can provide additional help. The **Chapter Discussion** summarizes important concepts from the chapter. The **Chapter Discussion** is not a rewrite of the chapter nor is it all-inclusive. However, it provides additional explanations for concepts that students generally find particularly difficult.

The **Learning Review** provides problems in addition to those in the text. Each one has a worked-out solution in **Answers to Learning Review**. Try to arrive at your own solution first, and then check your answer. Looking at the solutions before you try your hand at the problem will not benefit you. One of the main goals of studying chemistry is to become better at problem solving. Looking at the solutions, even if helps you understand them in the short term, defeats the purpose of the problem-solving exercise and is not the same thing as coming up with the solutions in the first place.

Take advantage of the resources available to you – your instructor, your textbook, this *Study Guide* and your own personal effort and abilities – and you will get the most out of your chemistry course. Have a good semester!

D.J.D.

CHAPTER 1

Chemistry: An Introduction

Introduction

Your study of chemistry will require work on your part. Use all of the resources available to you so that you can get the most out of your effort. The textbook should be your primary resource, but do not hesitate to turn to this *Study Guide* for additional help.

This chapter introduces you to how scientists solve problems. Learning how to solve problems is an important part of any chemistry course. Problem solving means more than just calculating a numerical answer. It also includes sifting through the given information, deciding which pieces of information are useful, and finally selecting an approach that will solve the problem. The problem-solving skills you develop will be useful to you throughout your life.

Studying Chemistry

What does it mean to know chemistry? And what makes chemistry courses among the most difficult courses you take? We asked these questions of students at the University of Illinois at the beginning of the academic year over several years. While not all of the answers are the same, the spirit of the answers is quite consistent. To many of the students, "knowing chemistry" means knowing a bunch of disparate, unrelated and often counterintuitive, facts, equations and constants. Knowing chemistry also means solving problems. These problems are usually math based, and are solved by plugging the right numbers into the right equations. These understandings (or, rather, misunderstandings) of chemistry may help to explain some of the difficulty with chemistry courses. It is much harder to memorize a large number of facts than to apply a set of comprehensive tools with which you are familiar.

So what can be done about the problems with learning chemistry? Solving the problems may seem far-fetched, at least initially. One of the reasons that chemistry is difficult is because of the way students try to make it easier. To illustrate what we mean, read this passage below. Does it sound like you?

> You attend all of the lectures and studiously take notes on everything the professor writes on the board. You become distracted when the professor seems to go on a tangent or derives an equation that could just be memorized. You dislike it when the professor follows a line of thought that proves to be incorrect just to make a point.

> You generally do all of the assigned homework questions. You usually go straight to the problems and try to do them with minimal reading of the text. This usually consists of trying a problem. If you have difficulty, you go to a section in the chapter looking for an example problem. When you do read the text, you generally pay little attention to the graphs and figures, and rarely write questions about what you have read. Sometimes you do the problems with the *Solutions Manual* open; but you only take a small peek, because once you see how to set up the problem you can usually solve it. You can answer most of the "what" questions, but have difficulty with the "why" questions. You have become adept at using units to solve problems you really do not understand.

How many of these characteristics come close to describing you? While no one student is exactly like the student described, all of the students we have talked to share some of these characteristics. In fact, many of these qualities are admirable. For example, the described student goes to all the lectures, and does all the homework. In fact, some students matching the description above do well in their chemistry courses. So what is the problem?

This kind of success in chemistry often comes with much unnecessary frustration. Worse yet, many students have so much difficulty they either drop the course, or end up doing quite poorly. Many of the latter students spend more and more time studying while getting less and less out of it.

Sadly, there is a cyclical pattern that we have seen for good, hard-working students who end up doing poorly. They see chemistry as unrelated facts, and so they study for it as though for a memorization challenge. They see the material as counterintuitive, so it doesn't stick. They do not think of chemistry as being about concepts, so they don't recognize patterns. By using shortcuts, mnemonic devices, and memorized algorithms, they actually make chemistry more difficult because when they come across a problem they have not seen, they have no idea what to do with it. They are not used to trial and error, and are unfamiliar with the idea of making mistakes as a way of learning. Thus, they learn less. The more difficult the material becomes, the more they study (assuming they do not give up). But they do not necessarily study more effectively.

When you understand chemistry, you can solve unique problems by applying fundamental ideas, not by using memorized solutions, or plugging numbers into an equation. In fact, the following tenets can and should assist the chemistry student:

1. **Chemistry content should make sense.** Many of our students have stated that when answering a question, they think about what makes sense, and then say the opposite. Because, after all, this is chemistry and "the answer is always the opposite of what you think it should be." One of the goals of learning chemistry is to be able to understand, explain and predict real phenomena in the real world. You should strive for an understanding of the connectedness of the ideas; you should not just memorize equations and methods for solving problems. The ideas and concepts support each other and are consistent. Make sure to understand it this way.

2. **Explaining is different from knowing or remembering, and formulas and equations are not explanatory devices.** For example, claiming "elements want to have an electron configuration like Noble gases" may help you figure out that oxygen has a 2− charge as an ion, but it does not explain why. Remembering the equation $PV = nRT$ does not mean you have a good understanding of the gas laws.

3. **Scientists use models to try to better understand and explain concepts and ideas.** These models are not reality but a way of simplifying our ideas. What you need to do is to understand the models – do not merely memorize the premises of a model, but understand the significance and limitations of the model. Albert Einstein once said "Explanations should be as simple as possible, but not simpler." This is a good way of thinking about models – we want to maximize understanding and minimize complexity. Science is about making observations and using these to derive models, which are further refined by new observations. The observations we make and the questions we want to answer guide our development of the model. For example, when discussing gas laws we generally think of gases as consisting of indestructible particles – no protons, electrons or neutrons exist in this model. Is this wrong? Yes and no. While atoms do consist of subatomic particles, these particles do not serve to increase our understanding of gas laws. Thinking of gases this way does not mean we are saying there are no subatomic particles, only that the model disregards them. If a model is not the absolute truth, why do we bother studying it at all? Unfortunately, we must develop simplified models because we would otherwise find the innumerable bits of information overwhelming. Models only become more complicated when we try to answer more questions. Our goal is to keep the model as simple as possible and answer as many questions as possible. When we find ourselves with too many questions we cannot answer, the model is refined and expanded or even disregarded. And it is acceptable that the model is not the absolute truth. As long as you know that, and as long as you have an

understanding of the limitations of models, then understanding, the kinetic molecular theory, for example, goes beyond memorization. Instead, you can understand the premises, why they make sense, how they are simplified, what their limitations are, and their significance.

In order to understand chemistry, you need to take an active role in your own learning. You have undoubtedly heard countless times from your parents and teachers that you are responsible for your own learning. But what does that mean in practice? You already go to class, do your homework, and study for quizzes and exams. What else can you do to take responsibility? One of the best ways is to constantly ask questions – while you are reading a text, attending a lecture, doing homework problems, reviewing your notes, or studying with friends. You should consistently ask "Why?" and "What does this mean?" and "What are the implications?"

When you are in a lecture, listen intently to the proofs and derivations. Understand where the knowledge comes from as well as its implications and limits. Ask questions of the professor or at the very least, write questions to yourself during lecture. You can think about these, and ask the professor, a teaching assistant or friends, later.

When reading your text, do not read it as a novel. Be critical. Write down questions, look at the graphs and figures, and understand what they are telling you. You have heard the phrase "a picture is worth a thousand words" – it's true about graphs and figures, too. There is a lot of information and you should extract and understand as much of it as possible. One goal of a text is to provide a source of detailed information and to slowly develop ideas. You are doing a disservice to yourself if you do not read it thoroughly and repeatedly; and, you make learning chemistry more difficult.

In doing homework, use the *Solutions Manual* sparingly because the crucial part of the problems is setting them up. Many students view homework as an exercise in answering questions rather than practice for future problem solving. Getting a correct answer does not necessarily confer understanding. Chemistry problems are not meant to be answered quickly and easily, but often require a lot of thought and trial and error. Think about what the problem is asking. Draw a picture. Do not just go directly to an equation, but think about what you have and where you are trying to go. Do not be afraid to make a mistake or to go down an incorrect pathway. Many times you will learn from this. Obviously you have a limited amount of time, and you cannot spend too much time on any single problem. But students find that something interesting happens when they do problems this way. The problems seem to get easier and the students find they can actually do fewer problems with more understanding.

The Active Learning Questions at the end of each chapter are conceptually based questions that work well as discussion questions with a group of students. If your instructor does not assign these, consider getting together with a group of classmates and using these questions to see how well you understand the material in each chapter. While all of the questions work well, Active Learning Questions 10, 12, and 13 focus on the scientific method and you are strongly encouraged to answer these.

Learning Review

1.   Explain why chemistry is important to you, even if your career is far removed from the sciences.

2.   Aside from helping you to get a good grade in chemistry, of what use are the problem-solving skills you will learn?

3.   Imagine that you are a scientist exploring life on the newly discovered planet, Cryon. Cryon is cold, and is perpetually covered with snow on one side. While exploring the snowy side of Cryon you repeatedly observe that all the birds have white feathers. You hypothesize that *all* the birds on Cryon have white feathers. Being a good scientist, you:

   a.   Declare that all birds on Cryon must be white, since all the ones on the snowy side are white.

    b.   Test your hypothesis about all birds on Cryon being white by observing a bird color on the non-snow-covered part of the planet as well as the snowy side.

    c.   Elevate your hypothesis about white birds to a natural law which states that all life forms on cold planets that are covered with snow on one side are white.

Answers to Learning Review

1.   Chemistry will have a different impact on the career of each individual, but even if your career is far removed from the sciences, chemistry plays an important role in our everyday lives. We depend on the science of chemistry to provide us with a better standard of living.

2.   Problem solving skills can be used throughout your life. Many situations require you to think logically, to propose hypothetical solutions, and to choose the most reasonable one. Chemistry can help develop logical thinking skills.

3.   You, as the scientist in this problem, have made some observations. But your information is not complete. You have no information about the color of birds on the other side of Cryon. A good scientist would test the hypothesis about bird color by collecting more data. It would not be appropriate to elevate the hypothesis to a natural law until the hypothesis was more thoroughly tested. Choice c is not correct, so the correct answer is b.

CHAPTER 2

Measurements and Calculations

Introduction

Chemistry is a science that requires observation of the world around us and measurements of the phenomena we observe. In this chapter you will learn how to record your observations and how to perform calculations with measured values. Scientific measurements are usually made using the metric system or the International System. You will need to become familiar with these systems of measurement and know the magnitude of each of the major units.

Chapter Discussion

Significant Figures

Measurement is an important part of science, and an understanding of uncertainty is an important part of measurement. Science is often thought of (incorrectly) as a body of unchanging absolute truths, which makes the concept of uncertainty seem odd. But you should realize that uncertainty is always a factor in any measurement except for exact counting. For measurements you will be taking in the lab, there is always one (and only one) uncertain digit which we can reasonably estimate. Imagine, for example, measuring water in a beaker as shown below.

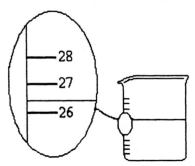

Using this beaker, we know that there is more than 26 mL of water and less than 27 mL of water. To report "26 mL" or "27 mL" would be imprecise. Now imagine if we used a beaker as shown below.

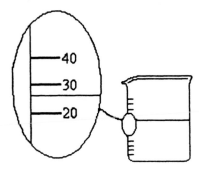

In this case we would report an answer to the ones place – the most accurate we can be without overstating our certainty. In this case, the water appears just over the halfway point between "20" and "30", so "26" is a reasonable estimate. Note that we would not call this an exact measurement. The actual amount of water may be 25 mL or even 27 mL. Unless the glassware is marked with more precision, we generally assume our uncertainty is ±1 for the digit that we estimate.

Look back to the first beaker. We can make a reasonable estimate to the tenths place in this case. The water level appears to be just under halfway between the two graduations, so we might report 26.4 mL. In this case, we can only assume that the actual amount of water is between 26.3 and 26.5 mL. Therefore, we cannot report an answer of 26.42 mL, since this would imply we knew the volume was between 26.41 and 26.43 mL (again, this assumes the glassware does not have a precision associated with it). What if we wanted to measure water to the hundredths place? We would need glassware with graduations as shown in the beaker below.

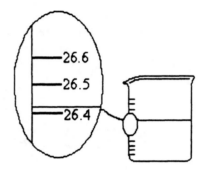

In this case, 26.42 mL is a reasonable estimate for the volume of water, although you might think it is 26.41 or 26.43. Again, realize that we never get an exact measurement. Even if the water level seemed to be right on the 26.4 graduation, we would report 26.40 mL, but we cannot report "exactly 26.4 mL". Reporting "exactly 26.4 mL" implies 26.4 with an infinite number of zeros (26.400000000 etc.). In terms of measurement, 26.42 is not the same as 26.420 (although your calculator treats them as the same). The only way to get an exact number is to count it. For example, there are five beans on a table.

Thus, the glassware determines the precision, which affects the number of digits you can report in a measurement. These digits are what's known as significant figures, and they include all measured digits, and the single estimated digit. Our three measurements in this example, along with the number of significant figures, are:

Beaker 1	26.2 mL	3 significant figures
Beaker 2	26 mL	2 significant figures
Beaker 3	26.42 mL	4 significant figures

Now, what happens if we add the water from each of these figures together? How can we report the results? Mathematically, we have:

26.4 mL

26   mL

+ 26.42 mL

78.82 mL

However, we should realize that we have some uncertain digits in the solution. That is, the above procedure implies that the first measurement is 26.40, and the second is 26.00. However, we know we cannot claim that reasonably. A better representation for this addition is

$$
\begin{array}{r}
26.4?\ \text{mL} \\
26.??\ \text{mL} \\
+\ \underline{26.42\ \text{mL}} \\
78.??\ \text{mL}
\end{array}
$$

Note in the hundredths we are adding a 2 to two unknown digits. What is "2 + ? + ?"? The answer has to be we don't know! In this case, we only know the sum to the ones place, so we can only report it as such. So do we report it as 78? 79? Because the sum of the numbers is 78.82, we round up to 79. We can also justify this by recalling the uncertainty of the added numbers. Let's assume two extreme cases. In the first case, assume we estimated too high for all three measurements (that is, assume there was actually less water than we thought). In the second case, assume we estimated too low for all three measurements. Remember that we assume we can be off by ±1 in the last digit. The range for the total amount of water in each case is shown below:

$$
\begin{array}{rr}
26.3\ \text{mL} \qquad\qquad & 26.5\ \text{mL} \\
25\quad\ \text{mL} \qquad\qquad & 27\quad\ \text{mL} \\
+\ \underline{26.41\ \text{mL}} \qquad\qquad & +\ \underline{26.43\ \text{mL}} \\
77.71\ \text{mL} \qquad\qquad & 79.93\ \text{mL}
\end{array}
$$

The maximum range of volume should be between 77.71 mL and 79.93 mL. Since we can only report the answer to the ones place, the range should be between 78 mL and 80. mL. Therefore, a reported answer of 79 mL (with a range of ±1) is reasonable.

After studying about measurement and significant figures, you should be able to answer the following questions:

1.   Why do we care about significant figures? What is the point of determining which figures are significant? That is, what is the practical application?

2.   Why is it that there is always one uncertain digit? Why can't we just measure more accurately? Why is there just one uncertain digit in the reported answer?

3.   Make sense of the rules for which zeros are significant. Be able to explain them (not just recite) to a classmate or instructor. (One way to understand these is to relate the concept of significant figures to scientific notation).

Dimensional Analysis

When multiplying numbers in dimensional analysis, we are really just multiplying fractions. Remember, when multiplying fractions, multiply all of the numbers in the numerator first, then multiply all of the numbers in the denominator. The last step is to divide the numerator product by the denominator product.

For example, to find the product of $\dfrac{1}{3}$ and $\dfrac{2}{5}$ we can write the expression in one of two ways:

$$
\frac{1}{3} \times \frac{2}{5} \quad \text{or} \quad \left(\frac{1}{3}\right)\left(\frac{2}{5}\right)
$$

We then solve the problem using the following method:

$$\left(\frac{1}{3}\right)\left(\frac{2}{5}\right) = \frac{(1\times2)}{(3\times5)} = \frac{2}{15} = 0.133$$

Whenever we see the same number in both the numerator and denominator, they cancel out (to equal 1).

$$\left(\frac{1}{\cancel{3}}\right)\left(\frac{\cancel{3}}{5}\right) = \frac{1}{5} = 0.20$$

If the number we are analyzing is a whole number, remember that this really means that the number is over 1 (whole number in the numerator, 1 in the denominator). For example, the number 4 really means $\frac{4}{1}$.

When multiplying units, use the same principle that you use for multiplying fractions. If one unit is in the numerator and the identical unit is in the denominator, they cancel each other out. Any remaining units are evaluated for the answer.

$$\left(\frac{\cancel{centimeter}}{1}\right)\left(\frac{meter}{\cancel{centimeter}}\right) = \frac{meter}{1} = meter$$

You can also multiply several units together at once using the same principle as for fractions.

$$\left(\frac{\cancel{centimeter}}{sec\,ond}\right)\left(\frac{\cancel{meter}}{\cancel{centimeter}}\right)\left(\frac{\cancel{kilometer}}{\cancel{meter}}\right)\left(\frac{megameter}{\cancel{kilometer}}\right) = \frac{megameter}{sec\,ond}$$

It is very important to note that if a unit appears once in the numerator but more than once in the denominator, we can only cancel out one of the unit expressions in the denominator. Think of this concept in terms of fractions. If there was the number 4 in the numerator and two 4s in the denominator of different fractions, we would only cancel out one of the 4s on the bottom, not both.

$$\left(\frac{\cancel{4}}{5}\right)\left(\frac{3}{\cancel{4}}\right)\left(\frac{1}{4}\right) = \frac{(3\times1)}{(5\times4)} = \frac{3}{20} = 0.15$$

Let's look at an example with exponents. Consider multiplying the following units.

$$\left(\frac{ki\log ram}{sec\,ond}\right)^2\left(\frac{meter}{ki\log ram}\right)^2\left(\frac{second}{meter}\right) =$$

The squared factor is equivalent to multiplying the fraction by itself.

$$\left(\frac{ki\log ram}{sec\,ond}\right)\left(\frac{ki\log ram}{sec\,ond}\right)\left(\frac{meter}{ki\log ram}\right)\left(\frac{meter}{ki\log ram}\right)\left(\frac{second}{meter}\right) =$$

Now we can evaluate the expression by canceling out units.

$$\left(\frac{\cancel{kilogram}}{sec\,ond}\right)\left(\frac{\cancel{kilogram}}{\cancel{second}}\right)\left(\frac{meter}{\cancel{kilogram}}\right)\left(\frac{\cancel{meter}}{\cancel{kilogram}}\right)\left(\frac{\cancel{second}}{\cancel{meter}}\right) = \frac{meter}{sec\,ond}$$

A Warning About Dimensional Analysis

Dimensional analysis is a double-edged sword. It is extremely useful and quite dangerous. It is dangerous because it can allow you to solve problems you do not understand. For example, consider the following problem:

> There are 2 igals in 1 odonku, and 6 odonkus in 4 falgers. If you have 3 igals, how many falgers is this?

We can solve this simply using dimensional analysis:

$$3 \text{ igals} \times \left(\frac{1 \text{ odonku}}{2 \text{ igals}} \right) \times \left(\frac{4 \text{ falgers}}{6 \text{ odonkus}} \right) = 1 \text{ falger}$$

Therefore, the answer is 1 falger. The questions to ask are "What is an igal?", "What is an odonku?", "What is a falger?", "What is the point of this problem?" Even though you can solve this problem, the solution is absolutely meaningless. Avoid solving problems without understanding them. Even if you can solve without understanding on some occasions, many of the problems in chemistry require an understanding of underlying principles, and it is good practice to start understanding early on. Dimensional analysis is a good tool for unit conversion, but you should never use it to try to replace understanding a problem.

Active Learning Questions

The Active Learning Questions at the end of each chapter are conceptually based questions that work well as discussion questions with a group of students. If your instructor does not assign these, consider getting together with a group of classmates and using these questions to see how well you understand the material in each chapter. While all of the questions work well, Active Learning Questions 4, 15, 19 and 20 focus on uncertainty in measurement, question 18 is a challenging conceptual problem dealing with density, and question 21 asks you to derive a new temperature scale. You are strongly encouraged to answer these.

Learning Review

1.   To express each of the following numbers in scientific notation, would you move the decimal point to the right or to the left? Would the power of 10 be positive or would it be negative (have a minus sign)?

   a.   0.001362

   b.   146,218

   c.   342.016

   d.   0.986

   e.   18.8

2.   Complete the table below and convert the numbers to scientific notation.

		coefficient		exponent
a.	0.00602	6.02	×	_____
b.	60,000	6	×	_____
c.	49	_____	×	10^1
d.	1.002	1.002	×	_____

3.   Convert the numbers below to scientific notation.

   a.   1,999,945

   b.   650,700

   c.   0.1109

   d.   545

   e.   0.0068

   f.   0.042001

   g.   1.2

   h.   13.921

4.   To express the following numbers in decimal notation, would you move the decimal point to the right or to the left? How many places?

   a. 1.02×10^3

   b. 4.1×10^{-6}

   c. 5×10^5

   d. 4.31×10^2

   e. 9.31×10^{-2}

5.   Convert the numbers below to decimal notation.

   a. 4.91×10^{10}

   b. 5.42×10^{-6}

   c. 2.07×10^3

   d. 1.009×10^{-4}

   e. 9.2×10^1

   f. 4.395×10^5

   g. 7.03×10^{-2}

6.   How can you convert −1235.1 to scientific notation?

7.   Which quantity in each pair is larger?

   a.   1 meter or 1 milliliter

   b.   10 seconds or 1 microsecond

   c.   1 cm or 1 mm

   d.   1 kilogram or 1 decigram

8.   Which quantity in each pair is larger?

   a.   1 mile or 1 kilometer

   b.   1 liter or 1 cubic meter

   c.   1 kilogram or 1 pound

     d.   1 quart or 1 milliliter

     e.   1 micrometer or 12 inches

9.   What metric or SI unit would you be likely to use in place of the English units given below?

     a.   Bathroom scales commonly provide weight in pounds.

     b.   A convenient way to purchase small quantities of milk is by the quart.

     c.   A cheesecake recipe calls for 1 teaspoon of vanilla extract.

     d.   Carpeting is usually priced by the square yard.

     e.   "An ounce of prevention is worth a pound of cure."

10.   What number would you record for each of the following measurements?

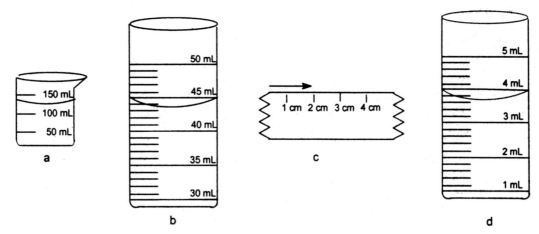

11.   How many significant figures are in each of the following numbers?

     a.   100

     b.   1180.3

     c.   0.00198

     d.   1.001

     e.   67,342

     f.   0.0103

     g. 4.10×10^4

12.   Express the results of each calculation to the correct number of significant figures.

     a. 1.8×2.93

     b.   0.002/0.041

     c. 0.00031×4.030

     d.   495.0/390

     e. 5024×19.2

     f. $91.3 \times 2.10 \times 7.7$

     g. $8.003 \times 4.93/61.05$

13. Round off the following numbers to the number of significant figures indicated.

	number	number of significant figures
a.	0.58333333	4
b.	451.0324	3
c.	942.359	4
d.	0.0090060	2
e.	6.8	1
f.	1346	3
g.	490,000.423	6
h.	0.06295	3

14. For each of the quantities below, give a conversion factor that will cancel the given units, and produce a number that has the desired units. For example:

$$8.6 \, \cancel{g} \times \frac{1 \text{ kg}}{1000 \, \cancel{g}} =$$

a.	10.6 m ×		$\dfrac{\text{cm}}{\text{m}}$
b.	0.98 L ×		$\dfrac{\text{qt}}{\text{L}}$
c.	18.98 cm ×		$\dfrac{\text{in}}{\text{cm}}$
d.	0.5 yd ×		$\dfrac{\text{m}}{\text{yd}}$
e.	25.6 kg ×		$\dfrac{\text{lb}}{\text{kg}}$

15. Perform the following conversions:

   a. 5.43 kg to g

   b. 65.5 in to cm

   c. 0.62 L to ft^3

   d. 111.3 g to lb

   e. 40.0 qt to L

   f. 2.83 g to lb

   g. 0.21 cm to in

16.   Fill in the important reference temperatures on each of the temperature scales.

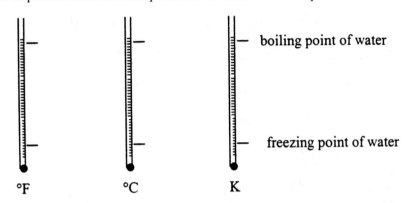

17.   How many degrees are there between the freezing point and the boiling point of water on the Fahrenheit and on the Celsius scales?

Also:

a.   Calculate the ratio of the number of degrees Fahrenheit to the number of degrees Celsius between the freezing and boiling points of water.

b.   Calculate the ratio of the number of degrees Celsius to the number of degrees Kelvin between the freezing and boiling points of water.

c.   Calculate the ratio of the number of degrees Fahrenheit to the number of degrees Kelvin between the freezing and boiling points of water.

18.   Comfortable room temperature for houses is 75 °F. What is this on the Celsius scale?

19.   Ethyl alcohol boils at 78.0 °C. What is this on the Fahrenheit scale?

20.   In some parts of the Midwest, temperatures may drop as low as −22 °F in winter. What is this on the Kelvin scale?

21.   Perform the temperature conversions below.

a.   180 °F to °C

b.   −10.8 °C to K

c.   244 K to °C

d.   25.1 °F to °C

22.   Fill in the missing quantities in the table below.

substance	density (g/mL)	mass	volume
seawater	1.025	52.6 g	_____
diamond	_____	2.13 g	0.65 mL
beeswax	0.96	125.5 g	_____
oak wood	_____	4.63 g	6173.3 mL

Answers to Learning Review

1. To convert to scientific notation for numbers which are greater than 0 but less than 1, move the decimal point to the *right*. For numbers which are greater than 1, move the decimal point to the *left*. Make sure that your final answer has only 1 number to the left of the decimal point.

   a. right   0.001362   power of ten: negative

   b. left   146218   power of ten: positive

   c. left   342.016   power of ten: positive

   d. right   0.986   power of ten: negative

   e. left   18.8   power of ten: positive

2. Remember that numbers written in scientific notation are divided into two parts. The coefficient on the left is a small number between one and ten, and the exponent on the right is ten raised to some power.

		coefficient		exponent
a.	0.00602	6.02	×	10^{-3}
b.	60,000	6	×	10^4
c.	49	4.9	×	10^1
d.	1.002	1.002	×	10^0

3. The answer for g, 1.2×10^0, means that we do not need to move the decimal point of the coefficient. 1.2×10^0 is the same as writing 1.2.

   a. 1.999945×10^6

   b. 6.507×10^5

   c. 1.109×10^{-1}

   d. 5.45×10^2

   e. 6.8×10^{-3}

   f. 4.2001×10^{-2}

   g. 1.2×10^0

   h. 1.3921×10^1

4. When converting from scientific notation to decimal, look first at the exponent. If the exponent is positive (has no negative sign) move the decimal point to the right. If the exponent is negative, move the decimal point to the left.

   a.   right   1020

   b.   left   0.0000041

    c.   right 500,000

    d.   right 431

    e.   left   0.0931

5.   A large number such as 49,100,000,000 has only three significant figures. The trailing zeros are not significant because there is no decimal point at the end.

    a.   49,100,000,000

    b.   0.00000542

    c.   2070

    d.   0.0001009

    e.   92

    f.   439,500

    g.   0.0703

6.   This number is different from others we have seen. It is smaller than one, and also smaller than zero. You can convert these numbers to scientific notation in much the same way as you convert numbers which are greater than one. First, move the decimal point to the left as you normally would.

$$-1235.1$$

Then, count the number of times the decimal point was moved and add the correct exponent.

$$1.2351 \times 10^3$$

Just keep the minus sign in front of the entire number.

$$-1.2351 \times 10^3$$

The minus sign goes in front of 1.235 because this number is less than zero. The exponent is negative only for numbers that are between 0 and 1.

7.   To work this problem, you need to have learned the SI prefixes and how they modify the size of the base unit.

    a.   meter is larger than millimeter

    b.   10 seconds is larger than 1 microsecond

    c.   1 Mm is larger than 1 cm

    d.   1 kilogram is larger than 1 decigram

8.   This problem asks about the relationship between English units and SI units. You need to know the relative sizes of English and SI units.

    a.   1 mile is larger than 1 kilometer

    b.   1 cubic meter is larger than 1 liter

    c.   1 kilogram is larger than 1 pound.

    d.   1 quart is larger than 1 milliliter

    e.   12 inches is larger than 1 micrometer

9.   a.   kilograms

    b.   liter

    c.   milliliter

    d.   square meter (m^2)

    e.   "A gram of prevention is worth a kilogram of cure."

10.   a.   This measuring device is a beaker. Each division represents 50 mL. The volume of liquid in the beaker is somewhere between 100 mL and 150 mL. We estimate that the volume is 120 mL.

    b.   This measuring device is a graduated cylinder. The numbers tell us that each major graduation is 5 mL, so each of the smaller lines must be 1 mL. We can accurately measure the volume to the nearest 1 mL. The volume in this cylinder is between 43 and 44 mL. We estimate the volume to be 43.5 mL.

    c.   The length of the arrow lies between 1 cm and 2 cm. We estimate that the arrow lies 0.9 of the way between the two marks. So the reported measurement would be 1.9 cm.

    d.   This graduated cylinder has major divisions of 1 mL. The smaller marks represent 0.2 mL. The liquid lies between 3.6 and 3.8 mL. We estimate that the volume is about a quarter (0.05) of the way between the two marks, so the volume would be reported as 3.65 mL.

11.   Remember that all nonzero numbers count as significant figures, and zeros in the middle of a number are always significant. Zeros to the right of some nonzero numbers are only significant if they are followed by a decimal point.

    a.   1

    b.   5

    c.   3

    d.   4

    e.   5

    f.   3

    g.   3

12.   For problems involving multiplication and division, your answer should have the same number of decimal points as the measurement with the least number of significant figures. For problems involving addition and subtraction, your answer should have the same number of significant figures as the measurement with the least number of digits to the right of the decimal point.

    a.   5.3

    b.   0.05

    c.   0.0012

    d.   1.3

e. 96,500

f. 1500

g. 0.646

13. You can answer problems such as 13(g) by putting the decimal point at the end to show that all 6 digits are significant, or use scientific notation with a coefficient that contains 6 digits.

a. 0.5833

b. 451

c. 942.4

d. 0.0090

e. 7

f. 1350

g. 490,000. or 4.90000×10^5

h. 0.0630

14. To answer this question, you need to have the common equivalencies and know how to write them as a unit factor.

a. $10.6 \text{ m} \times \dfrac{100 \text{ cm}}{1 \text{ m}}$

b. $0.98 \text{ L} \times \dfrac{1.06 \text{ qt}}{1 \text{ L}}$

c. $18.98 \text{ cm} \times \dfrac{1 \text{ in}}{2.54 \text{ cm}}$

d. $0.5 \text{ yd} \times \dfrac{1 \text{ m}}{1.094 \text{ yd}}$

e. $25.6 \text{ kg} \times \dfrac{1000 \text{ g}}{1 \text{ Kg}}$

15. a. $5.43 \text{ kg} \times \dfrac{1000 \text{ g}}{1 \text{ kg}} = 5430 \text{ g}$

b. $65.5 \text{ in} \times \dfrac{2.54 \text{ cm}}{1 \text{ in}} = 166 \text{ cm}$

c. $0.62 \text{ L} \times \dfrac{1 \text{ ft}^3}{28.32 \text{ L}} = 0.022 \text{ ft}^3$

d. $111.3 \text{ g} \times \dfrac{1 \text{ lb}}{453.6 \text{ g}} = 0.2454 \text{ lb}$

e. $40.0 \text{ qt} \times \dfrac{1 \text{ L}}{1.06 \text{ qt}} = 38 \text{ L}$

f. $2.83 \text{ g} \times \dfrac{1 \text{ lb}}{453.6 \text{ g}} = 6.24 \times 10^{-3} \text{ lb}$

g. $0.21 \text{ cm} \times \dfrac{1 \text{ in}}{2.54 \text{ cm}} = 0.083 \text{ in}$

16.

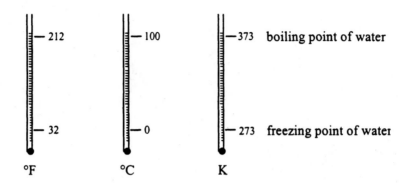

17.   There are 180 degrees between the freezing and boiling points of water on the Fahrenheit scale, and 100 degrees on the Celsius scale.

a. $\dfrac{°F}{°C} = \dfrac{180}{100} = 1.80$

b. $\dfrac{°C}{K} = \dfrac{100}{100} = 1$

c. $\dfrac{°F}{K} = \dfrac{180}{100} = 1.80$

18.   We want to convert from degrees Fahrenheit to degrees Celsius.

$T_{°F} = 75$

We can use the formula below to calculate degrees Celsius.

$T_{°C} = \dfrac{T_{°F} - 32}{1.80} = \dfrac{75 - 32}{1.80}$

$T_{°C} = 24$

75 degrees Fahrenheit is equivalent to 24 degrees Celsius.

19.   We want to convert from degrees Celsius to degrees Fahrenheit.

$T_{°C} = 78.0$

We can use the formula below to calculate degrees Fahrenheit.

$T_{°F} = 1.80 \, (T_{°C}) + 32$

$T_{°F} = 1.80(78.0) + 32$

$T_{°F} = 172$

78.0 degrees Celsius is equivalent to 172 degrees Fahrenheit.

20.   We want to convert from degrees Fahrenheit to Kelvin.

$T_{°F} = -22$

We do not have a formula to directly convert degrees Fahrenheit to Kelvins, but we can convert from degrees Fahrenheit to degrees Celsius, then from degrees Celsius to Kelvins.

Convert $T_{°F}$ to $T_{°C}$ first.

$$T_{°C} = \frac{T_{°F} - 32}{1.80}$$

$$T_{°C} = \frac{-22 - 32}{1.80}$$

$T_{°C} = -30.$

Now, calculate Kelvins.

$T_K = T_{°C} + 273$

$T_K = -30. + 273$

$T_K = 243$

21.   a. $T_{°F} = 180$

$$T°C = \frac{T_{°F} - 32}{1.80}$$

$$T_{°C} = \frac{180 - 32}{1.80}$$

$T_{°C} = 82$

b. $T_{°C} = -10.8$

$T_K = T_{°C} + 273$

$T_K = -10.8 + 273$

$T_K = 262$

c. $T_K = 244$

$T_K = T_{°C} + 273$

Rearrange this equation to isolate $T_{°C}$.

$T_{°C} = T_K - 273$

$T_{°C} = 244 - 273$

$T_{°C} = -29$

d. $T_{°F} = 25.1$

$$T_{°C} = \frac{T_{°F} - 32}{1.80} = \frac{25.1 - 32}{1.80}$$

$T_{°C} = -3.8$

20

22. $\text{density} = \dfrac{\text{mass}}{\text{volume}}$

substance	density	mass	volume
seawater	1.025 g/mL	52.6 g	51.3 mL
diamond	3.3 g/mL	2.13 g	0.65 mL
beeswax	0.96 g/mL	125.5 g	130 mL
oak wood	0.750 g/mL	4.63 g	6173.3 mL

CHAPTER 3

Matter

Introduction

This chapter provides you with a basic foundation of facts and concepts about matter you will need throughout your chemistry course. There are fewer mathematical calculations in this chapter than in other chapters you will study.

Pay careful attention to Section 3.2 (Physical and Chemical Properties and Changes) and 3.4 (Mixtures and Pure Substances) in your textbook. The concepts in these sections often seem confusing when you are first introduced to them. Look carefully at the examples in your text, which will help you distinguish between physical and chemical changes and between mixtures and pure substances.

Chapter Discussion

Take the opportunity while studying this chapter to get used to thinking microscopically; that is, at a molecular level. One of the most difficult aspects of learning chemistry is that we see on a large scale (a macroscopic level) but the chemical changes and physical processes occur at a molecular level (microscopic level). You are expected to be able to relate the two of these. See Figure 3.2 in your text for the difference between these two perspectives. Atoms and molecules will be formally introduced in Chapter 4, but it is a good idea to start thinking microscopically now.

For example, understanding the difference between physical changes and chemical changes requires thinking at a molecular level. In Section 3.2 of your text, the phrase "change in composition" is used to denote a chemical change. But what does this mean? Steam appears to us to be vastly different from ice. Do they have different compositions? To understand this, we need to know what the term "composition" means. For a chemist, composition of a substance has to do with the makeup of the molecules. Thus, heating ice until it melts and heating water until it boils does not change the molecules. The substance is still made of water molecules, each with 2 atoms of hydrogen and 1 atom of oxygen, and symbolized H_2O. Note that in Figure 3.2 ice, liquid water, and steam are all made of H_2O molecules. Thus, melting, freezing, boiling and condensing are all physical processes – the molecules are left unchanged.

If water underwent a chemical change, however, its composition (molecular makeup) would change. The bonds holding the hydrogen and the oxygen atoms together in a water molecule would break, and new bonds would form, making hydrogen gas (H_2) and oxygen gas (O_2). We can visualize this chemical change with the following representation:

Water (H_2O) has a different composition from a mixture of hydrogen and oxygen (H_2 and O_2) and different chemical properties. For example, putting a lit match to a mixture of hydrogen and oxygen can result in a loud explosion (do not try this), but putting a lit match to water results in a wet match.

Therefore, making sense of chemical and physical changes is difficult without a molecular perspective. The same is true with the concepts of elements, mixtures and compounds. Don't merely memorize the text definitions for these concepts, but understand the differences among each of these (including heterogeneous and homogeneous mixtures). One of the best ways to achieve this understanding is to make sketches of these at a molecular level.

For example, answer the following questions (think about these before reading on).

1.   Which best represents a homogeneous mixture of an element and a compound?

2.   Which best represents a gaseous compound?

3.   Which best represents a solid element?

4.   Which best represents a heterogeneous mixture of two elements?

5.   What would you term the choice not chosen in 1-4?

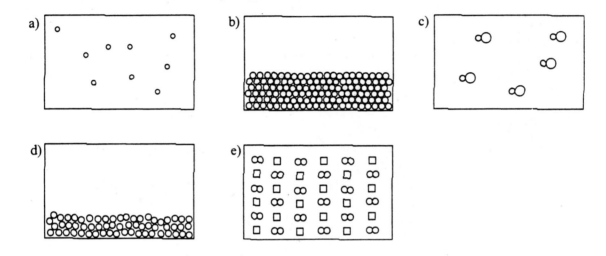

The answers are "e", "c", "b", "d" and "a gaseous element". Notice that a compound differs from an element in that a compound is made of at least 2 different types of atoms.

You should be able to draw molecular-level sketches of any possible combinations of elements, compounds, mixtures (homogeneous and heterogeneous), gases, liquids and solids. For example, sketch a homogeneous mixture of a gaseous element in a liquid compound.

You should also be able to answer the following questions:

1.   What is wrong with the term "heterogeneous compound?" What about "homogeneous compound?"

2.   Sketch molecular-level diagrams to make sense of Figure 3.9 and Figure 3.10.

Active Learning Questions

The Active Learning Questions at the end of each chapter are conceptually based questions that work well as discussion questions with a group of students. If your instructor does not assign these, consider getting together with a group of classmates and using these questions to see how well you understand the material in each chapter. While all of the questions work well, Active Learning Questions 13 and 14 are visual problems to test your understanding of the terms *atomic element, molecular element, compound, gas,* and *solid*. You are strongly encouraged to answer these.

Learning Review

1. Which of the properties below are physical properties, and which are chemical properties?

    a. Oxygen atoms can combine with hydrogen atoms to form water molecules.

    b. Ethyl alcohol boils at 78°C.

    c. Liquid oxygen is pale blue in color.

2. Which of the changes below are physical changes, and which are chemical changes?

    a. A copper strip is hammered flat to make a bracelet.

    b. Copper and sulfur react to form a new substance, copper(I) sulfide.

    c. Liquid water freezes at 273 K.

    d. Oxygen gas condenses to a liquid at −183°C.

    e. You prepare a 3-minute egg for breakfast.

3. Which of the symbols below represent elements, and which represent compounds?

    a. S

    b. H_2O

    c. C

    d. N_2O_5

    e. NaOH

4. Are the properties below physical or chemical properties?

    a. Temperature at which a solid is converted to a liquid

    b. Odor

    c. Temperature at which a compound breaks down into its elements

    d. Oxygen reacts with a substance to produce energy

5. Which of the substances below are mixtures, and which are pure substances?

    a. Gasoline

    b. Table sugar (sucrose)

    c. Garden soil

    d. Sterling silver necklace

6. Which of the mixtures is homogeneous and which is heterogeneous?

    a. Sweetened hot tea

    b. Plastic bag filled with leaves and grass clippings

    c. A weak solution of rubbing alcohol in water

    d. Devil's food cake mix

7. Describe how you can separate a mixture by filtration.

8.   What type of mixture is best separated by filtration: a homogeneous mixture or a heterogeneous mixture?

9.   Describe how you would separate the following mixtures.

    a.   Sand from gravel

    b.   Salt from sand

    c.   Sugar from water

10.   Label each part of the distillation apparatus below.

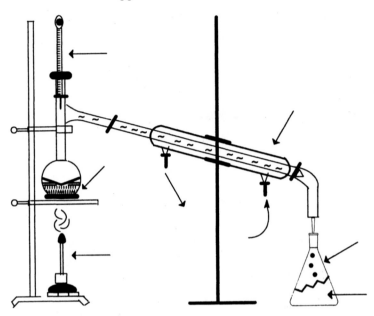

Answers to Learning Review

1.   a.   Oxygen can combine with hydrogen to produce a new substance, water. Because oxygen and hydrogen have the potential to combine to form a new substance, this is an example of a chemical property.

    b.   Observing ethyl alcohol boiling does not destroy or change the ethyl alcohol molecules. Therefore, boiling point is a physical property.

    c.   Observing the color of a substance does not change its composition. The pale blue color of liquid oxygen is a physical property.

2.   a.   When a copper strip is hammered into a bracelet, the shape of the copper is changed, but not the composition. This is a physical change.

    b.   The new substance, copper sulfide, is a black solid which does not have any of the characteristics of copper metal or yellow elemental sulfur. This is a chemical change.

    c.   When liquid water freezes to become solid ice, the molecules are still those of water. No change in composition has occurred. This is a physical change.

    d.   Liquid oxygen molecules become solid oxygen molecules at $-183°C$. This is a physical change.

    e.   Cooking an egg causes changes to the egg's composition. Heating changes the structure of large egg proteins, causing them to form solids. This is a chemical change.

3.   a.   S is the symbol for the element sulfur.

    b. H_2O has two kinds of atoms, O and H. It is a compound.

    c.   C is the symbol for the element carbon.

    d. N_2O_5 has two kinds of atoms, N and O. It is a compound.

    e.   NaOH has three kinds of atoms, Na, O and H. It is a compound.

4.   a.   Physical property, because a melted substance has the same composition as a solid substance.

    b.   Physical property, because observing the odor of a substance does not change the composition of the substance.

    c.   Chemical property, because the temperature which causes a substance to break down into elements causes destruction of the substance.

    d.   Chemical property, because oxygen reaction with a substance describes a chemical change occurring.

5.   a.   Gasoline is a mixture of complex carbon-containing molecules, detergents and additives.

    b.   Table sugar is a pure substance. It contains only sucrose molecules.

    c.   Garden soil is a mixture. It contains sand, water, clay, dead plant leaves and other components.

    d.   Sterling silver is made from 93 percent silver and 7 percent copper by mass. It is a mixture.

6.   a.   Sweetened tea is a homogeneous mixture. When sugar is added to hot tea, it dissolves. All of the tea is equally sweetened.

    b.   A bag full of leaves and grass clippings is a heterogeneous mixture. Some parts of the bag will contain more leaves than grass, and other parts will contain more grass than leaves.

    c.   Rubbing alcohol and water mix freely with each other. The molecules of one completely disperse in molecules of the other. This produces a homogeneous solution.

    d.   A devil's food cake mix is a homogeneous mixture. There are no lumps (usually) of sugar, or clumps of flour. All of the ingredients are distributed equally throughout the mix.

7.   Separating mixtures by filtration depends upon a difference in physical properties of the mixture. Pour the mixture onto a mesh. One common mesh is filter paper, which is made from a mesh of cellulose fibers. The liquid in the mixture can pass through the cellulose fibers into a container below. The particles remain behind, trapped in the fibers of the mesh.

8.   Filtration can separate a heterogeneous mixture which contains a liquid and a solid component.

9.   a.   Sand and gravel can be separated by filtration. Use a mesh which allows the sand particles to pass through, but retains the gravel, for example, a piece of wire screen.

b.   A salt and sand mixture can be separated by adding water and filtering. The salt will dissolve in the water, while the sand will not. By filtering the sand and salt water mixture, the pure sand remains behind, while the salt passes through the mesh with the water.

c.   Sugar and water cannot be separated by filtration because the sugar molecules dissolve in the water and will pass through a mesh. They can, however, be separated by distillation. Heat the mixture until the water boils (at 100 °C) and is converted to steam. The sugar has a higher boiling point than water does and is not vaporized. The steam rises in the distillation apparatus and can be captured and recondensed to liquid water. The sugar remains behind in the distilling flask.

10.

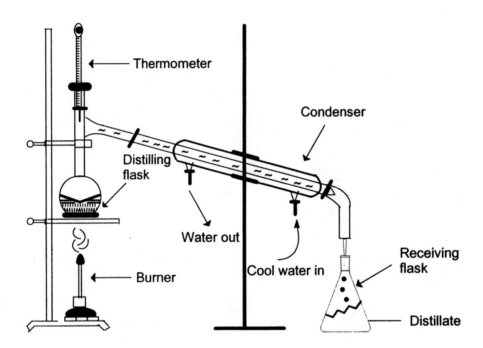

CHAPTER 4

Chemical Foundations: Elements, Atoms and Ions

Introduction

In Chapter 4 you are introduced to the names and symbols of the common elements and ions. Make sure you learn the names and symbols now. Most of the chemistry covered in subsequent chapters depends upon knowledge of these names and symbols.

The remainder of the chapter covers the categories of elements, which are organized into the periodic table, and the formation of ions from atoms.

Chapter Discussion

Models of the Atom

This chapter is the first of many chapters in which theories (models) play a big role. It is crucial to examine these models and understand their significance and limitations. You should develop questions and observations about what the models help us to understand and what the models do not answer. For example, in this chapter you should do this for both Dalton's model, and for the more modern view of the structure of the atom.

The reason to make a model more complicated than Dalton's model arose from such questions that Dalton's model could not answer.

Look at the following questions concerning Dalton's model. Can it explain the following?

1. When you pour water on a table, the water molecules seem to "stick" together as the water forms drops. How can the molecules "stick" together?

2. Compounds that consist solely of oxygen atoms include the oxygen we breathe (symbolized as O_2) and ozone (symbolized as O_3). How can oxygen atoms form diatomic (2-atom) or triatomic (3-atom) molecules? Why are other molecules with only oxygen unstable?

3. Chlorine naturally exists as a yellow-green gas. Nitrogen naturally exists as a colorless gas. Iron naturally exits as a solid. How can these different properties be explained?

Realize that Dalton's simple model cannot account for the observations made above. We know, then, that Dalton's model is incomplete. However, Dalton's model is still useful (for example, when we study gas laws in Chapter 13, we will use it almost exclusively). It is important to understand not only what the model tells us, but what it doesn't answer.

The next models of the atoms began incorporating the subatomic particles protons, neutrons and electrons. But these improvements do not answer all of our questions. For example, in Section 4.6 you will find the question "If all atoms are composed of these same components, why do different atoms have different chemical properties?" This requires a more modern view of the structure of the atom.

Even this modern view of the atom, as presented in this chapter (and expanded upon in Chapter 11), brings up questions. Consider the following:

> Opposite charges are said to attract one another, and like charges are said to repel. If this is the case, why do the electrons not fall into the nucleus?

> What holds the protons together in the nucleus?

The simple models that are discussed in Chapter 4, while more complicated than Dalton's model (and while they can answer more questions than Dalton's model), cannot answer these questions.

And even though Dalton's model is quite simple, and brings about many questions, we still use it frequently. Look back, for example, at the molecular level drawings in Chapter 3 (and these drawings throughout the text). They use Dalton's model because it conveys all of the useful information. Chemical formulas in the next section emphasize once again that all models are simplifications and will fail at some point.

Chemical Formulas

A chemical formula symbolizes the composition of a molecule. For example, we can sketch a molecule of water as

In chemistry, we call water H_2O, which conveys that there are two hydrogen atoms joined with one oxygen atom in a water molecule. Note, though, that the formula H_2O does not tell us that the order of atoms is HOH. In most cases, the formula just tells you which elements, and how many atoms of each, are in the molecule. So how do we know the structure? Sometimes formulas will convey structure. Also, we will study how to determine the structure from a formula in more detail in Chapter 12.

To test your understanding of this idea, which of the following sketches do you think best represents "$2NH_3$"? Think about this before reading on.

The correct answer is "c". The ammonia molecule (NH_3) has one nitrogen atom and 3 hydrogen atoms bonded together. The "2" in front of the "NH_3" just means we have 2 of these molecules. We will see this idea again in Chapter 6 – the "2" is called a coefficient, and the "3" is a subscript. We can examine this idea further by looking at Figure 4.15 in your text. Notice how a chemical equation (which we will study in more detail in Chapter 6) can be symbolized with a molecular perspective (which, incidentally, uses Dalton's model). You can symbolize the chemical reaction shown in Figure 4.15 as

$$2H_2O \rightarrow 2H_2 + O_2$$

Make sense of these symbols and how they relate to the molecular level representation and you are in good shape for understanding Chapter 6 (which is crucial for understanding the remaining chapters, especially Chapters 7, 8 and 9).

The Periodic Table

This chapter also introduces you to the periodic table which will be studied in more detail in Chapter 11. For now you should realize that the periodic table was constructed to minimize confusion and memorization in favor of understanding and explanation, so use it this way. The elements in the table are not arranged alphabetically or chronologically according to discovery, but according to the number of protons. The elements in the same vertical column have chemical similarities which you will study later. But you should realize now that you can determine the most stable charge of many of the ions made from atoms.

For example, look at the sample problems in Section 4.11 of your text. Notice that the most stable ionic charge for Na and Li is 1+, and both are in the same column of the periodic table. The most stable charge for Mg and Ca as ions? Each stable ion has a charge of 2+, each of these is in the same column, and they are one column from Li and Na. Find other examples of this, and realize that the periodic table is loaded with such patterns. Now is the time to begin your appreciation of the table, which provides many answers. Use the periodic table as the valuable resource that it is.

Active Learning Questions

The Active Learning Questions at the end of each chapter are conceptually based questions that work well as discussion questions with a group of students. If your instructor does not assign these, consider getting together with a group of classmates and using these questions to see how well you understand the material in each chapter. While all of the questions work well for these, Active Learning Questions 1-4 are multiple choice questions in which you are to choose the best response and justify your answer. These types of questions often cause good discussions and you are strongly encouraged to answer these.

Learning Review

1.   This review question can help you to determine your progress with the material in Chapter 4. You should be able to answer each of the questions below for the common elements listed in Table 4.3 of the textbook. Answer each question below for the element symbolized by Br.

   a.   What is the name of the element?

   b.   In which group of the periodic table is it found?

   c.   What is its family name?

   d.   When found in nature uncombined with other elements, what is its state?

   e.   At room temperature, what is its physical state: solid, liquid or gas?

   f.   What is the name and charge of the ion it forms?

   g.   How many neutrons are found in this isotope, $^{80}_{35}\text{Br}$?

2.   Which of the ten most abundant elements (determined by mass percent) on earth are not found in large amounts in the human body?

3.   Match the elements below with the correct description.

   oxygen   most abundant element on earth

   silicon   most abundant element in the human body

   carbon   trace element in human body

   titanium   25.7 percent of mass on earth

   hydrogen   these three elements makeup 93 percent of mass in the human body

   molybdenum   less than 1 percent of the mass on earth

4.   Write symbols for the following elements.

   a.   arsenic

   b.   fluorine

   c.   magnesium

   d.   iron

   e.   neon

   f.   lead

   g.   potassium

   h.   chromium

   i.   nitrogen

   j.   calcium

5.   Which of the common elements in Table 4.3 of your textbook have a one-letter symbol?

6.   Some of the element symbols are not related to the modern name of the element. What are the elements represented by the following element symbols?

   a.   W

   b.   Hg

   c.   Cu

   d.   K

   e.   Fe

   f.   Pb

   g.   Sb

   h.   Na

7.   Match the element name with the correct element symbol.

   cadmium   Cl

   carbon   Cr

   calcium   C

   chlorine   Co

   cobalt   Cu

   copper   Cd

   chromium   Ca

8. Match the element symbol with the correct element name.

   Na   silver

   Sr   sulfur

   S   sodium

   Ag   silicon

   Si   strontium

9. Describe the main parts of Dalton's atomic theory.

10. How does Dalton's atomic theory relate to the law of constant composition?

11. Dalton's model became more widely accepted when the existence of NO, NO_2, and N_2O became known. What aspect of Dalton's model allowed Dalton to predict the existence of these compounds?

12. Write chemical formulas for the following compounds.

    a.   Ethyl alcohol, which contains 2 carbon atoms, 6 hydrogen atoms, and 1 oxygen atom

    b.   A compound that contains 1 atom of magnesium and 2 atoms of bromine

    c.   A compound that contains 4 atoms of phosphorus and 10 atoms of oxygen

    d.   A compound that contains 1 atom of arsenic and 3 atoms of hydrogen

13. What is the *total* number of atoms found in each of the following compounds? What is the total number of elements found in each?

    a.   KOH

    b. N_2O_3

    c. CCl_4

    d. H_2O_2

    e. Na_3PO_4

14. A physicist named J.J. Thomson showed that all atoms can be made to emit tiny particles that are repelled by the negative pole of an electric field. This evidence pointed to the existence of which subatomic particle?

    a.   proton

    b.   neutron

    c.   electron

    d.   nucleus

    e.   isotope

15.   Match the scientist(s) with the discovery.

Ernest Rutherford   demonstrated the existence of electrons

J. J. Thomson   demonstrated the existence of neutrons

Lord Kelvin   developed the plum pudding model of the atom

Rutherford & Chadwick   developed the nuclear atom model from gold foil experiments

16.   Label the parts of the experimental apparatus used to develop the model of the nuclear atom.

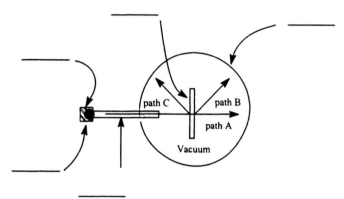

17.   In the gold foil experiment, how did Rutherford interpret each of the following observations?

a.   Most of the α-particles traveled unimpeded through the foil.

b.   Some of the α-particles were deflected slightly from the straight path when they entered the foil.

c.   A few of the α-particles bounced back when they entered the foil.

18.   Fill in the missing relative masses and relative charges for each of the subatomic particles.

		Relative mass	**Relative charge**
a.	Electron	_____	1 –
b.	Proton	_____	_____
c.	Neutron	1839	_____

19.   Is the following statement true or false? An isotope of sodium could contain 12 protons, 12 neutrons and 11 electrons.

20.   Label the parts of the symbol below.

_____ A

    X _____

_____ Z

21.   Write the symbols for the isotopes below in $_Z^A X$ notation.

a.   An isotope of hydrogen has an atomic number of 1 and a mass number of 3.

b.   An isotope of chlorine has an atomic number of 17 and a mass number of 37.

c.   An isotope of oxygen has 8 protons and 10 neutrons.

    d.   An isotope of uranium has 92 electrons and 143 neutrons.

    e.   An isotope of sulfur has an atomic number of 16 and 16 neutrons.

22.   An isotope of titanium contains 24 neutrons and has a mass number of 46.

    a.   How many protons does it contain?

    b.   How many electrons does it contain?

23.   Aluminum-29 has an atomic number of 13.

    a.   What is its mass number?

    b.   How many neutrons does it have?

24.   Match the group name on the left with an element found in that group.

halogen	Ca
transition metal	Ne
alkali metal	Fe
alkaline earth metal	K
Noble gas	F

25.   Fill in the boxes of the periodic table with element symbols for each of the families below. The number at the top of each box represents atomic number.

    a. halogens   **b. alkaline earth metals**

    c. noble gases   **d. alkali metals**

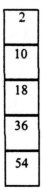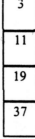

26.   Which of the following elements are nonmetals?

   a.   Al

   b.   C

   c.   Cr

   d.   P

   e.   Br

   f.   I

27.   Some of the elements along the jagged line on the right side of the periodic table have properties of both metals and nonmetals. Fill in the elemental symbols for these metalloids.

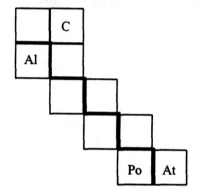

28.   Some elements exist in nature as diatomic molecules. Which of the elements below will be found as diatomic molecules?

   a.   Ar

   b.   O

   c.   K

   d.   F

   e.   S

   f.   N

   g.   H

   h.   Cl

29.   At room temperature, what is the physical state (solid, liquid or gas) of each of the elements that naturally form diatomic molecules?

30.   Which of the elements below are always found in nature as individual atoms?

   a.   carbon

   b.   krypton

   c.   magnesium

   d.   chlorine

   e.   helium

   f.   neon

g.   aluminum

h.   sulfur

31.   Fill in the name of the correct element next to its description at 25°C.

a.   Liquid metal   _____

b.   Yellow green gas   _____

c.   Colorless gas   _____

d.   A 2-carat diamond   _____

e.   A reddish brown liquid _____

f.   Dark purple solid   _____

32.   Balance the equations for the formation of cations from neutral atoms.

a. $Ca \rightarrow$ _____   +   _____

b. $K \rightarrow$ _____   +   _____

c. $Sr \rightarrow$ _____   +   _____

d. $Rb \rightarrow$ _____   +   _____

33.   Balance the equations for the reactions of cations with electrons.

a. Mg^{2+} +   _____ $\rightarrow$ _____

b. Li^{+} +   _____ $\rightarrow$ _____

c. $2H^{+}$ +   _____ $\rightarrow$ _____

d. Na^{+} +   _____ $\rightarrow$ _____

34.   Fill in the correct number of protons for either the element or the ion in the table below.

element	protons	electrons	ion	protons	electrons
potassium	19	19	_____	_____	_____
oxygen	_____	_____	_____	8	10
bromine	35	_____	_____		36
strontium	_____	38	_____	38	_____
aluminum	13	_____	_____	_____	10

35.   You wish to find out whether the compound MgF_2 is composed of ions. What test could you perform to help you make a decision?

36. a. Which diagram represents a solid NaCl crystal?

   b. Which diagram represents NaCl dissolved in water?

   c. Which form of NaCl – solid or aqueous solution – allows free movement of ions?

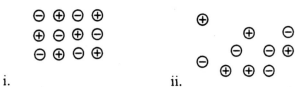

   i.   ii.

37. How many of each ion is needed to form a neutral compound?

   a. Ca^{2+} and F^-

   b. Mg^{2+} and O^{2-}

   c. Na^+ and S^{2-}

   d. Li^+ and I^-

   e. Sr^{2+} and Cl^-

   f. K^+ and P^{3-}

   g. Na^+ and N^{3-}

   h. Na^+ and N^{3-}

38. What is *wrong* with the formulas below? Write the correct formula for each.

   a. $AlCl_2$

   b. NaO

   c. Mg_2P

   d. CaI_3

   e. LiN_3

   f. KS

Answers to Learning Review

1. a. bromine

   b. group 7

   c. halogens

   d. Br_2

   e. liquid

   f. bromide ion, Br^-

   g. 45

2. Silicon, aluminum and iron are found in large amounts on earth, but in small amounts in the human body.

3.   Note that some of the elements are found in more than one category.

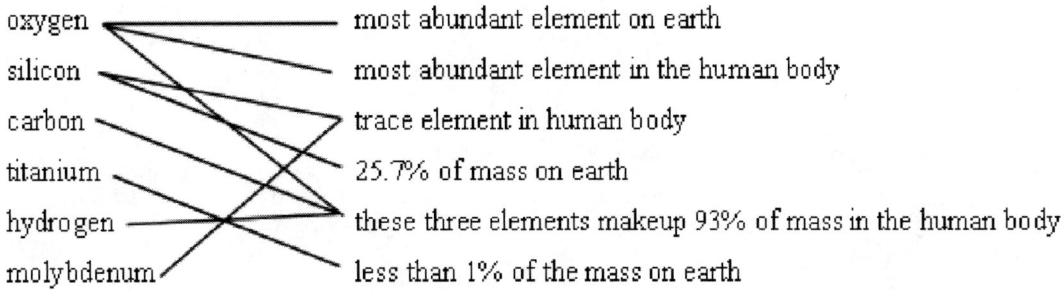

oxygen —————————————— most abundant element on earth

silicon ————————————— most abundant element in the human body

carbon ————————————— trace element in human body

titanium ————————————— 25.7% of mass on earth

hydrogen ————————————— these three elements makeup 93% of mass in the human body

molybdenum ————————————— less than 1% of the mass on earth

4.   a.   As

      b.   F

      c.   Mg

      d.   Fe

      e.   Ne

      f.   Pb

      g.   K

      h.   Cr

      i.   N

      j.   Ca

5.   Boron, carbon, fluorine, iodine, nitrogen, oxygen, phosphorous, potassium, sulfur, tungsten and uranium all have one-letter symbols.

6.   a.   tungsten

      b.   mercury

      c.   copper

      d.   potassium

      e.   iron

      f.   lead

      g.   antimony

      h.   sodium

7. There are quite a few elements whose symbols begin with the letter "c". The symbols for these elements are therefore similar to each other.

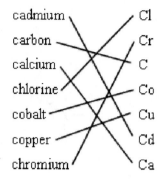

8.

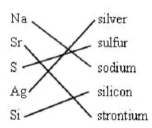

9. Dalton's atomic theory states that all elements are made of atoms. For any one element, all the atoms are the same (Dalton didn't know about isotopes). Different elements are made from different kinds of atoms. Atoms from different elements can combine to make compounds. Each compound always has the same relative numbers and kinds of atoms. Chemical reactions do not cause new elements to form.

10. The law of constant composition states that compounds always have the same proportions of each element by mass. Dalton's model states that compounds always have the same relative numbers and kinds of atoms. If compounds always have the same relative number of atoms, they will also have a constant proportion by mass. For example, the compound carbon dioxide always has 1 carbon atom for two oxygen atoms. The ratio of the mass of a carbon atom to the mass of two oxygen atoms also stays constant for molecules of carbon dioxide. This relationship was predicted by Dalton's model.

11. Dalton's model states that atoms from different elements can combine to produce compounds and that each compound always has the same relative numbers and kinds of atoms. Dalton predicted that different compounds would be found that were made of the same kinds of atoms, but combined in different numbers. The discovery of NO, NO_2, and N_2O confirmed Dalton's prediction and supported his model.

12. a. C_2H_6O

    b. $MgBr_2$

    c. P_4O_{10}

    d. AsH_3

13.   Remember that when an element symbol has no subscript, only 1 atom of that element is present. Subscript numbers always refer to the element to the *left* of the subscript number.

   a.   There are 3 atoms total and 3 different elements.

   b.   There are 5 atoms total and 2 different elements.

   c.   There are 5 atoms total and 2 different elements.

   d.   There are 4 atoms total and 2 different elements.

   e.   There are 8 atoms total and 3 different elements.

14.   Because the particles were repelled by the negative pole, it was believed that the particles were negatively charged because like charges repel each other. The electron is a subatomic particle with a negative charge, so the correct answer is c.

15.

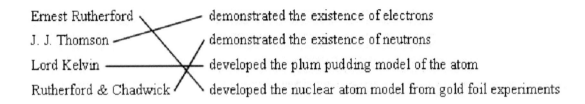

16.

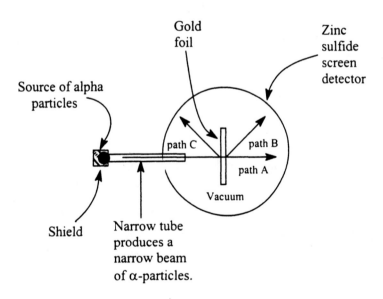

17.   a.   An atom consists mostly of empty space.

   b.   α-particles have a positive charge, because they contain 2 protons. When a moving α-particle travels close to the nucleus of an atom which itself contains protons, the α-particle is deflected from its path because two areas of positive charge repel each other.

   c.   Some of the α-particles scored a direct hit and bounced straight back. The particle that the α-particle hit must be an area within the atom that is very massive for the heavy α-particle to bounce straight back.

18.

		Relative mass	Relative charge
a.	Electron	1	1 −
b.	Proton	1836	1 +
c.	Neutron	1839	0

19.   Isotopes of all atoms have the same number of protons as they do electrons. All sodium isotopes have 11 protons and 11 electrons. So the answer is false.

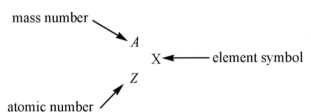

mass number

A

X ◄——— element symbol

Z

20.   atomic number

21.   a. ^3_1H

b. $^{37}_{17}\text{Cl}$

c. $^{18}_8\text{O}$

d. $^{235}_{92}\text{U}$

e. $^{32}_{16}\text{S}$

22.   a.   The mass number provides the number of protons plus the number of neutrons. If the number of neutrons is 24, then the number of protons is 46 minus 24, or 22 protons.

b.   The number of protons always equals the number of electrons, so there are 22 electrons in this isotope.

23.   a.   When isotopes are designated with the element name followed by a number, as in aluminum-29, the number is the mass number.

b.   Aluminum-29 has 16 neutrons.

24.

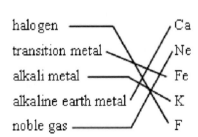

halogen
transition metal
alkali metal
alkaline earth metal
noble gas

Ca
Ne
Fe
K
F

25.

a.   halogens

9 F
17 Cl
35 Br
53 I

b.   alkaline earth metals

12 Mg
20 Ca
38 Sr
56 Ba

c.   noble gases

2 He
10 Ne
18 Ar
36 Kr
54 Xe

d.   alkali metals

3 Li
11 Na
19 K
37 Rb

26.   C, P, Br and I are nonmetals. The nonmetals are found to the right of the jagged line on the right side of the periodic table.

27.

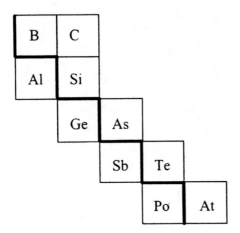

28.   b.   Oxygen is found in nature as O_2 molecules.

        d.   Fluorine is found in nature as F_2 molecules.

        f.   Nitrogen is found in nature as N_2 molecules.

        g.   Hydrogen is found in nature as H_2 molecules.

        h.   Chlorine is found in nature as Cl_2 molecules.

29.   Most of the diatomic molecules, H_2, N_2, O_2, F_2, Cl_2, are gases at room temperature. Br_2 is a reddish-brown liquid: I_2 is a dark purple solid.

30.   a.   Carbon is usually found combined with other elements such as hydrogen.

        b.   Krypton is always found as individual krypton atoms.

        c.   Magnesium is usually found combined with other elements.

        d.   Chlorine is found as either Cl_2, or combined with other elements.

        e.   Helium is always found as individual helium atoms.

        f.   Neon is always found as individual neon atoms.

        g.   Aluminum is usually found combined with other elements.

        h.   Sulfur is usually found as S_8 molecules or combined with other elements.

31.   Only a few of the elements have unique properties, but there are many elements which could be described as colorless gases, or as shiny metals.

        a.   Liquid metal   mercury

        b.   Yellow green gas   chlorine

        c.   Colorless gas   Many elements fit this description: oxygen, hydrogen, etc.

        d.   A 2 carat diamond   carbon

        e.   A reddish brown liquid   bromine

        f.   Dark purple solid   iodine

32.   Cations have lost one or more electrons and the number of electrons lost always equals the charge on the cation.

        a. $Ca \rightarrow Ca^{2+} + 2e^-$

        b. $K \rightarrow K^+ + e^-$

        c. $Sr \rightarrow Sr^{2+} + 2e^-$

        d. $Rb \rightarrow Rb^+ + e^-$

33.   Cations will react with electrons to form neutral atoms.

        a. $Mg^{2+} + 2e^- \rightarrow Mg$

        b. $Li^+ + e^- \rightarrow Li$

c. $2H^+ + 2e^- \rightarrow H_2$

d. $Na^+ + e^- \rightarrow Na$

34.   The number of protons does not change when neutral atoms form ions, but the number of electrons either increases or decreases.

element	protons	electrons	ion	protons	electrons
potassium	19	19	potassium	19	18
oxygen	8	8	oxide	8	10
bromine	35	35	bromide	35	36
strontium	38	38	strontium	38	36
aluminum	13	13	aluminum	13	10

35.   You can place some solid MgF_2 in water. If the solid MgF_2 contains Mg^{2+} ions and F^- ions, when the compound dissolves in water an aqueous solution of Mg^{2+} and F^- ions will form. Test whether or not a solution of MgF_2 will conduct an electrical current by immersing electrodes in the solution. If the solution allows current to flow and a bulb to shine, there is evidence that ions are in solution, free to move around, and able to conduct an electrical current.

36.   a.   A solid NaCl crystal is an ordered rigid structure, structure i.

        b.   Ions are pulled away from the orderly crystal by water molecules, as in structure ii.

        c.   Ions in water are free to move around and are not packed close together. Those in a solid are ordered, and packed close together so that each anion is surrounded by cations.

37.   A neutral compound has no electrical charge.

        a.   1 calcium and 2 fluoride ions CaF_2

        b.   1 magnesium and 1 oxide ion MgO

        c.   2 sodium and 1 sulfide ion Na_2S

        d.   1 lithium and 1 iodide ion LiI

        e.   2 strontium and 2 chloride ions $SrCl_2$

        f.   3 potassium and 1 phosphide ion K_2P

        g.   3 sodium and 1 nitride ion Na_3N

38.   a.   Aluminum forms ions with a 3+ charge and chlorine forms ions with a 1– charge. Three chlorine ions will combine with one aluminum ion to form $AlCl_3$.

        b.   Sodium forms ions with a 1+ charge and oxygen forms ions with a 2– charge. Two sodium ions will combine with one oxide to form Na_2O.

        c.   Magnesium forms ions with a 2+ charge and phosphorus forms ions with a 3– charge. Three magnesium ions will combine with two phosphide ions to form Mg_3P_2.

d.   Calcium forms ions with a 2+ charge and iodine forms ions with a 1– charge. One calcium ion will combine with two iodide ions to form CaI_2.

e.   Lithium forms ions with a 1+ charge and nitrogen forms ions with a 3– charge. Three lithium ions will combine with one nitride ion to form Li_3N.

f.   Potassium forms ions with a 1+ charge and sulfur forms ions with a 2– charge. Two potassium ions will combine with one sulfide ion to form K_2S.

CHAPTER 5

Nomenclature

Introduction

In this chapter, you will learn how to name ions and compounds. You will be asked to learn rules for naming ions and compounds and you will need to memorize some names. Many of the problems at the end of this chapter have as their goal the application of the rules you will learn. Work on the naming problems until you have developed your skill at naming chemical compounds.

Chapter Discussion

Many students look at nomenclature as memorizing the names of a seemingly endless list of chemicals, but there are systematic rules for naming compounds. By knowing only a few rules you can name almost any compound you will encounter in introductory chemistry.

For example, all of the charges for the common simple cations and anions in Table 5.1 of your text come from the placement on the periodic table (see Chapter 4 if this is unfamiliar to you).

Also, look at Table 5.2, the "common type II cations." What is the difference here? The difference is that these ions come from transition metals (not from the alkali or alkaline earth metals in the first two columns of the periodic table). These ions can have more than one stable charge, so we have to specify which ion we are talking about. The Roman numeral is the charge, not the subscript. Therefore, the formula Fe_2O_3 should be read as "iron(III) oxide." Make sure to prove to yourself that it is indeed iron(III); that is Fe^{3+}.

Notice that this requirement is different from NaCl. The name "sodium (I) chloride" is not so much wrong as it is redundant. The most stable charge for the sodium ion in a compound is 1+ and the most stable charge for the chloride ion in a compound is 1−. Therefore, the only possible formula for "sodium chloride" is NaCl. However, the name "iron oxide" is incomplete, because it could be referring to Fe_2O_3 [iron(III) oxide] or FeO [iron(II) oxide]. We only use Roman numerals when we have to for clarity's sake.

The same goes for prefixes. There is no reason to call $CaCl_2$ "calcium dichloride" because $CaCl_2$ is the only stable formula for an ionic compound made of calcium and chloride ions. Therefore, we can simply say calcium chloride and everyone knows to expect $CaCl_2$. However, we cannot use the name carbon oxide because these are both nonmetals, meaning the compound is not made up of ions. There is no way to deduce from the name carbon oxide to know the formula (although we do know the compound is made from carbon and oxygen). Therefore, we have to specify carbon monoxide (CO) or carbon dioxide (CO_2), for example. The only way to make sure you can name compounds is to practice. Being able to name compounds requires you to have some rules memorized, but it also requires you to understand these rules.

Active Learning Questions

The Active Learning Questions at the end of each chapter are conceptually based questions that work well as discussion questions with a group of students. If your instructor does not assign these, consider getting together with a group of classmates and using these questions to see how well you understand the material in each chapter. You are strongly encouraged to answer these to make sure you understand the reasons for the rules of naming compounds. The rules are systematic and logical, and answering these questions will help you to see this.

Learning Review

1. Name the cations and anions below.

    a. Cl^-

    b. Mg^{2+}

    c. Li^+

    d. Ba^{2+}

    e. N^{3-}

    f. O^{2-}

    g. F^-

2. Name the following Type I binary compounds.

    a. KF

    b. CaS

    c. NaI

    d. Li_3N

    e. HCl

    f. Al_2O_3

    g. AgCl

    h. MgF_2

3. The following elements can all form more than one cation. How many cations form and what is the charge on each of them?

    a. Cu

    b. Fe

    c. Sn

    d. Hg

    e. Pb

4. Name the following Type II binary compounds.

    a. $FeCl_3$

    b. PbO_2

    c. CoI_2

    d. SnF_2

    e. Fe_2S_3

    f. Hg_2Br_2

5.   Name each of the compounds below.

    a. $CaBr_2$

    b.   PbS

    c.   AlP

    d.   FeS

    e.   CoO

    f. $MgCl_2$

6.   Each of the compounds below has an *incorrect* name. Name each one correctly.

    a.   KBr   potassium(I) bromide

    b. Cu_2O cupric oxide

    c. PbS_2 lead(IV) sulfide(II)

    d. Na_3P sodium(III) phosphide

    e. $FeCl_3$ iron chloride

7.   Name the following Type III binary compounds.

    a. PCl_5

    b. CCl_4

    c. N_2O_3

    d. S_2F_{10}

    e. SO_2

    f.   CO

8.   Name the following Type I, Type II and Type III compounds.

    a.   KI

    b. NO_2

    c. $FeCl_2$

    d. Al_2O_3

    e. Cl_2O_7

    f.   CaS

9.   What are the names of the polyatomic ions below?

    a. HCO_3^-

    b. OH^-

    c. NH_4^+

    d. NO_2^-

    e. SO_4^{2-}

    f. CrO_4^{2-}

10.   The compounds below all contain polyatomic ions. Name each one.

  a. K_2SO_4

  b. $Fe(OH)_3$

  c. NH_4NO_3

  d. $Al_2(Cr_2O_7)_3$

  e. $Ca(CN)_2$

  f. $Mg_2(PO_4)_2$

  g. $NaMnO_4$

  h. $Cu(ClO_3)_2$

  i. $PbCO_3$

11.   Check your knowledge of the common acids by naming the acids below.

  a. H_2SO_4

  b. HCN

  c. HBr

  d. HNO_3

  e. H_2S

  f. $HC_2H_3O_2$

12.   From their names, write formulas for the compounds below.

  a.   aluminum chloride

  b.   cobalt(III) permanganate

  c.   dinitrogen trioxide

  d.   sulfur dioxide

  e.   calcium nitrate

  f.   silver chloride

  g.   iron(II) acetate

  h.   tin(IV) chlorite

  i.   sodium sulfate

  j.   lithium hydrogen carbonate

  k.   mercury(II) dichromate

Answers to Learning Review

1.   The ions in this problem are all monatomic ions. The cations all have the same name as the element, while the anions all end in –ide.

   a.   chloride

   b.   magnesium

   c.   lithium

   d.   barium

   e.   nitride

   f.   oxide

   g.   fluoride

2.   Type I binary compounds form between a metal and a nonmetal.

   a.   potassium fluoride

   b.   calcium sulfide

   c.   sodium iodide

   d.   lithium nitride

   e.   hydrogen chloride

   f.   aluminum oxide

   g.   silver chloride

   h.   magnesium fluoride

3.   Notice that these are all transition metal ions.

   a. Cu^+ Cu^{2+}

   b. Fe^{2+} Fe^{3+}

   c. Sn^{2+} Sn^{4+}

   d. Hg_2^{2+} Hg^{2+}

   e. Pb^{2+} Pb^{4+}

4.   Type II binary compounds form between a metal which forms more than one cation and a nonmetal.

   a.   iron(III) chloride

   b.   lead(IV) oxide

   c.   cobalt(II) iodide

   d.   tin(II) iodide

   e.   iron(III) sulfide

   f.   mercury(I) bromide

5.   The compounds are mixed Type I and Type II binary compounds.

     a.   calcium bromide

     b.   lead(II) sulfide

     c.   aluminum phosphide

     d.   iron(II) sulfide

     e.   cobalt(II) oxide

     f.   magnesium chloride

6.   a.   Potassium only forms cations with 1+ charge, so potassium(I) bromide should be potassium bromide.

     b.   The formula Cu_2O shows copper with a 1+ charge, which is named the copper(I), or cuprous ion. The correct name for this formula is copper(I) oxide, or cuprous oxide.

     c.   The formula PbS_2 tells us that the charge on the lead ion is 4+, so the first part of the name, lead(IV) is correct. The sulfide ion has a 2– charge, but we do not use Roman numerals after the anion name. So the correct name for this compound is lead(IV) sulfide.

     d.   Sodium only forms cations with 1+ charge, so sodium(III) phosphide should be sodium phosphide.

     e.   The formula $FeCl_3$ tells us that iron has a 3+ charge. Because iron forms cations with more than one charge, the correct name would be iron(III) chloride.

7.   Type III binary compounds form between nonmetals. The prefix which indicates 10 atoms is *deca-*. This prefix is used in problem 7d.

     a.   phosphorus pentachloride

     b.   carbon tetrachloride

     c.   dinitrogen trioxide

     d.   disulfur decafluoride

     e.   sulfur dioxide

     f.   carbon monoxide

8.   The compounds are a mixture of Type I, Type II and Type III compounds.

     a.   potassium iodide

     b.   nitrogen dioxide

     c.   iron(II) chloride

     d.   aluminum oxide

     e.   dichlorine heptoxide

     f.   calcium sulfide

9.   If you have trouble naming these ions, go back and review the names again. You will need these names throughout your chemistry career.

a.   bicarbonate

b.   hydroxide

c.   ammonium

d.   nitrite

e.   sulfate

f.   chromate

10.   a.   potassium sulfate

b.   iron(III) hydroxide

c.   ammonium nitrate

d.   aluminum dichromate

e.   calcium cyanide

f.   magnesium phosphate

g.   sodium permanganate

h.   copper(II) chlorate

i.   lead(II) carbonate

11.   a.   sulfuric acid

b.   hydrocyanic acid

c.   hydrobromic acid

d.   nitric acid

e.   hydrosulfuric acid

f.   acetic acid

12.   a. $AlCl_3$

b. $Co(MnO_4)_3$

c. N_2O_3

d. SO_2

e. $Ca(NO_3)_2$

f. $AgCl$

g. $Fe(C_2H_3O_2)_2$

h. $Sn(ClO_2)_4$

i. Na_2SO_4

j. $LiHCO_3$

k. $HgCr_2O_7$

CHAPTER 6

Chemical Reactions: An Introduction

Introduction

Knowing how to write chemical equations and how to interpret what they mean is an important part of chemistry. If you have learned the symbols for the elements, and can write the formulas of compounds from their names, then learning to write chemical equations will be easier. The Answers to Learning Review (#5) discusses the logic used when balancing a chemical equation by trial and error. If you are having trouble balancing equations, go over the steps used to balance the equations in the Answers to Learning Review.

Chapter Discussion

You have already seen a molecular-level representation of a balanced chemical equation in Chapter 4 (see Figure 4.15). Another such representation of a different chemical equation can be seen in Figure 6.4.

Remember that the point of a chemical equation is to use symbols to show what happens during the chemical reaction. Therefore, when you are first learning to balance chemical equations, it is a good idea to think at the molecular level to make sure you are balancing the equation and not changing the composition of a reactant or a product. Learn to relate the words to the representation (molecular-level perspective) to the symbols (the coefficients, subscripts, and atomic symbols).

For example, consider the statement:

"hydrogen gas reacts with oxygen gas to produce water vapor"

We would like to write this reaction as an equation in terms of the symbols for the elements. What is the advantage to this? First, it is generally easier to write, once you understand the language. But more importantly, using the symbols allows us to balance the equation, which means we are able to determine the relative amounts of the reactants we need (in this case hydrogen gas and oxygen gas) along with the relative amount of product produced (in this case, the water).

First, look at the reaction statement in terms of a molecular-level sketch. Of course, we have to know the formulas for hydrogen gas, oxygen gas, and water, and how to sketch them. Recall that hydrogen and oxygen gases are diatomic (two atoms per molecule) and that the water molecule consists of two hydrogen atoms and one oxygen atom. We can sketch a representation of the reaction as follows:

While this picture conveys what occurs, it is not balanced. That is, it does not give us information about the relative amounts of reactants and products. Notice, for example, that there are two oxygen atoms on the left side of the equation, and only one oxygen atom on the right side. As you know, this reaction cannot occur as drawn.

Because oxygen gas is diatomic and water consists of only one oxygen atom, a diatomic oxygen molecule can produce two molecules of water.

However, one hydrogen molecule can only produce one molecule of water. To produce two molecules of water would require two molecules of hydrogen gas.

This equation is now balanced. All atoms are accounted for on each side of the equation, which is the same as saying that all atoms are conserved.

Now we are ready to think about this sketch in terms of chemical symbols. We have four atoms of hydrogen on each side of the equation, and two atoms of oxygen, but we also want to convey that hydrogen gas is reacting with oxygen gas to form water. In fact, now that we have balanced our equation, we can be more specific about the amounts and state the reaction as:

> "Two molecules of hydrogen gas react with one molecule of oxygen gas to produce two molecules of water."

We can symbolize the diatomic hydrogen gas as H_2, the diatomic oxygen gas as O_2, and water as H_2O. We have balanced the equation with our molecular level sketches, so now we can add these numbers to our equation to get:

$$2H_2\,(g) + O_2\,(g) \rightarrow 2H_2O\,(l)$$

Note there is a 2:1:2 ratio of molecules, just as we determined with the molecular level sketches (we generally do not include the "1" in front of a molecule – it is assumed). These numbers are called the coefficients and represent the ratio of molecules (reactants and products) in the equation. Recall from Chapter 4 that the subscripts in the molecules tell us how many atoms of a particular element are in one molecule.

One common mistake made when first balancing equations is to change subscripts. For example, if we look at the unbalanced equation

$$H_2\,(g) + O_2\,(g) \rightarrow H_2O\,(l)$$

it may seem reasonable to balance this equation by adding another oxygen atom to the water molecule to get

$$2H_2\,(g) + O_2\,(g) \rightarrow 2H_2O_2\,(l)$$

What is wrong with this? Think back to our molecular-level drawings, and how you would sketch H_2O compared to H_2O_2. They are different molecules with different chemical properties. Changing the subscript changes the identity of the chemical. In this case, for example, H_2O_2 is hydrogen peroxide, which is quite different from water. The goal to balancing a chemical equation is not just to make sure there are the same numbers of each type of atom on both sides of the equation, but to balance the equation that is given to you. In this case, we wanted to balance the equation that represented the production of water, not hydrogen peroxide.

For another example, answer the following question (think about it before reading on).

> The reaction of an element X (Δ) with element Y (O) is represented in the following diagram. Which of the equations best describes this reaction?

a. $3X + 8Y \rightarrow X_3Y_8$

b. $3X + 6Y \rightarrow X_3Y_6$

c. $X + 2Y \rightarrow XY_2$

d. $3 + 8Y \rightarrow 3XY_2 + 2Y$

e. $X + 4Y \rightarrow XY_2$

The correct answer is "c". Choices "a" and "b" give the wrong products. The product formed should be symbolized as XY_2 from the molecular drawing. Choices "c", "d", and "e" have this as a product, but choice "e" is not balanced. So what is wrong with choice "d"? Many students choose this because it correctly gives the number of Xs and Ys on the reactant side, and shows that there are 2 Ys left over when the reaction is completed. So why is it incorrect?

First of all, the chemicals on the right side of the equation are the products, that is, they are produced in the reaction. If choice "d" is correct, Ys were produced in this reaction, but Ys were left over – not made. Also, the fact that we started with 3 Xs and 8 Ys is not relevant in this case. The balanced equation does not (repeat – does **not**) tell us how much of each chemical we have, but it gives us a ratio of the amounts that react or are produced. Think of it in terms of a recipe. A recipe is written to tell you how much of each ingredient is needed to react with the others in order to make a certain amount of product. It does not tell you how much of each ingredient you happen to have in your kitchen. Thus, choice "c" tells us what is actually reacting; that is, for every one X, two Ys react to form one XY_2.

Could we symbolize the reaction the following way?

$$2X + 4Y \rightarrow 2XY_2$$

Yes we could. However, we generally reduce all of the coefficients to the least common whole numbers for the sake of simplicity. This practice brings up an important point: the value of an individual coefficient is not important; what is important is the ratio between the coefficients.

Suppose, for example, you want a recipe for chocolate chip cookies, and you are told that you will need flour, sugar, eggs, baking soda, salt, and one egg. Telling you that you need one egg is not very helpful since you don't know the amounts of the other ingredients, nor do you know how many cookies it will make. And realize that even if you are told all of the amounts, you can change them to make the number of cookies you want. Thus, it is not the actual numbers that are important as much as the ratio.

For example, recall the balanced equation

$$2H_2 + O_2 \rightarrow 2H_2O$$

This equation can be read as

"Two molecules of diatomic hydrogen react with one molecule of diatomic oxygen to produce 2 molecules of water."

or

"Two dozen molecules of diatomic hydrogen react with one dozen molecules of diatomic oxygen to produce two dozen molecules of water."

or

"Two hundred molecules of diatomic hydrogen react with 100 molecules of diatomic oxygen to produce 200 molecules of water"

In fact, there is an infinite number of possibilities, as long as the ratio of number of molecules of H_2, O_2 and H_2O is 2:1:2, respectively.

Again, the individual coefficient is not important. It is the ratio between reactants and products that is important.

Finally, while you are first balancing equations you may wish to use molecular level drawings, but you should eventually be able to write an equation (and balance it) using symbols directly from the words. There are many examples of these types of questions at the end of Chapter 6 in your text.

Active Learning Questions

The Active Learning Questions at the end of each chapter are conceptually based questions that work well as discussion questions with a group of students. If your instructor does not assign these, consider getting together with a group of classmates and using these questions to see how well you understand the material in each chapter. While all of the questions work well for these, Active Learning Questions 3, 10, 12 and 14 will specifically test your understanding of the significance of a balanced chemical equation (and the mole ratio). You are strongly encouraged to answer these.

Learning Review

1.   Which of the following indicates that a chemical reaction has occurred?

   a.   Liquid water boils to produce steam.

   b.   Burning firewood gives off heat.

   c.   Mixing two colorless liquids produces a bright yellow solid.

   d.   Solid $NaHCO_3$ dissolves in water.

2.   Why is it important that chemical equations be balanced?

3.   Count the number of each kind of atom on both sides of the equation and decide which reactions are balanced, and which are not.

   a. $H_2 + Br_2 \rightarrow HBr$

   b. $KClO_3 \rightarrow KCl + O_2$

   c. $2NaOH + CO_2 \rightarrow Na_2CO_3 + H_2O$

   d. $C_2H_5OH + 3O_2 \rightarrow 2CO_2 + 3H_2O$

   e. $3Cu + HNO_3 \rightarrow 3Cu(NO_3)_2 + NO + H_2O$

4.   Use the following word descriptions to write *unbalanced* chemical equations showing the formulas of reactants and products. Make sure you include the physical states of reactants and products.

   a.   Solid iron metal reacts with oxygen in the atmosphere to form rust, iron(III) oxide.

   b.   Solid magnesium metal reacts with aqueous hydrochloric acid to produce hydrogen gas and an aqueous solution of magnesium chloride.

   c.   Solid silver oxide decomposes upon heating to produce solid silver metal and oxygen gas.

   d.   Aqueous sodium hydroxide reacts with aqueous nitric acid to produce aqueous sodium nitrate and liquid water.

5.   Balance these chemical equations. Check your work by counting the number of each kind of atom on both sides of the equation.

     a. $KOH(aq) + H_2S(aq) \rightarrow K_2S(aq) + H_2O(l)$

     b. $HNO_2(aq) \rightarrow N_2O_3(g) + H_2O(aq)$

     c. $NaOH(aq) + H_2SO_4(aq) \rightarrow Na_2SO_4(aq) + H_2O(l)$

     d. $(NH_4)_2S(aq) + Pb(NO_3)_2(aq) \rightarrow PbS(s) + NH_4NO_3(aq)$

     e. $Al(s) + O_2(g) \rightarrow Al_2O_3(s)$

6.   Balance these chemical equations.

     a. $SO_2(g) + O_2(g) \rightarrow SO_3(g)$

     b. $C_4H_{10}(g) + O_2(g) \rightarrow CO_2(g) + H_2O(g)$

     c. $Fe_2O_3(s) + C(s) \rightarrow Fe(s) + CO_2(g)$

     d. $TiCl_4(l) + H_2O(l) \rightarrow TiO_2(s) + HCl(aq)$

7.   Balance these chemical equations.

     a. $KI(aq) + Br_2(l) \rightarrow KBr(aq) + I_2(s)$

     b. $PbO_2(s) \rightarrow PbO(s) + O_2(g)$

     c. $Fe(OH)_3(s) + H_2SO_4(aq) \rightarrow Fe_2(SO_4)_3(s) + H_2O(l)$

     d. $K_3PO_4(aq) + BaCl_2(aq) \rightarrow KCl(aq) + Ba_3(PO_4)_2(s)$

Answers to Learning Review

1.   a.   Boiling represents a physical change, not a chemical reaction.

     b.   Heat production is an indication of a chemical reaction.

     c.   A color change and the production of a solid (a new substance) are both indications of a chemical reaction.

     d.   No chemical reaction has occurred. Solid $NaHCO_3$ dissolves into ions in water. The ions are so small they cannot be seen but the identity of the compound does not change.

2.   When a chemical reaction occurs, atoms are neither created nor destroyed. The atoms are only rearranged to produce new molecules. Therefore it is important that the same kinds and numbers of atoms be present on both sides of a chemical equation.

3.   a.

        $H_2 + Br_2 \rightarrow HBr$
          2 H   1 H
          2 Br   1 Br   unbalanced

     b.

        $KClO_3 \rightarrow KCl + O_2$
          1 K   1 K
          1 Cl   1 Cl
          3 O   2 O   unbalanced

c.

$$2NaOH + CO_2 \rightarrow Na_2CO_3 + H_2O$$

2 Na	2 Na
2 O	1 C
2 H	3 O
1 C	2 H
2 O	1 O

The **total** number of atoms of each kind is

2 Na	2 Na	
4 O	4 O	
2 H	2 H	
1 C	1 C	balanced

d.

$$C_2H_5OH + 3O_2 \rightarrow 2CO_2 + 3H_2O$$

2 C	2 C
(5 + 1) H	(2 × 2) O
1 O	(3 × 2) H
(3 × 2) O	3 O

The **total** number of atoms of each kind is

2 C	2 C	
6 H	6 H	
7 O	7 O	balanced

e.

$$3Cu + HNO_3 \rightarrow 3Cu(NO_3)_2 + NO + H_2O$$

3 Cu	3 Cu
1 H	(3 × 2) O
1 N	2 N
3 O	1 N
	1 O
	2 H
	1 O

The **total** number of atoms of each kind is

3 Cu	3 Cu	
1 H	2 H	
1 N	3 N	
3 O	8 O	unbalanced

4.   This problem requires that you be able to write formulas from word descriptions. Do not forget to include the physical state of both products and reactants.

a. $Fe(s) + O_2(g) \rightarrow Fe_2O_3(s)$

b. $Mg(s) + HCl(aq) \rightarrow H_2(g) + MgCl_2(aq)$

c. $Ag_2O(s) \rightarrow Ag(s) + O_2(g)$

d. $NaOH(aq) + HNO_3(aq) \rightarrow NaNO_3(aq) + H_2O(l)$

5.   a.   First, find the most complex formula. KOH contains three different kinds of atoms, so begin by adjusting the coefficients of the atoms in KOH. There are two potassium atoms on the right and only one on the left. Adjust potassium by increasing the coefficient of KOH from one to two.

$$2KOH(aq) + H_2S(aq) \rightarrow K_2S(aq) + H_2O(l)$$

2 K	2 K
2 O	1 O
4 H	2 H
1 S	1 S

Now, K and S are balanced, but oxygen and hydrogen are not. There are four hydrogen and two oxygen atoms on the left, but only two hydrogen and two oxygen atoms on the right. If we adjust the coefficient of water to two, oxygen and hydrogen are the same on each side and the equation is balanced.

$$2KOH(aq) + H_2S(aq) \rightarrow K_2S(aq) + 2H_2O(l)$$

2 K	2 K
2 O	2 O
4 H	4 H
1 S	1 S

b.   Because HNO_2 is the most complex molecule, begin by adjusting the number of nitrogen atoms on both sides of the equation. There are two on the right, but only one on the left. Increase the coefficient of HNO_2 to two. Hydrogen and oxygen are the same on each side, and the equation is balanced.

$$2HNO_2(aq) \rightarrow N_2O_3(g) + H_2O(aq)$$

2 H	2 H
2 N	2 N
4 O	4 O

c.   Either NaOH or H_2SO_4 is a good place to begin balancing. Let's start by adjusting the number of sodium ions. Put a coefficient of two in front of NaOH.

$$2NaOH(aq) + H_2SO_4(aq) \rightarrow Na_2SO_4(aq) + H_2O(l)$$

2 Na	2 Na
6 O	5 O
4 H	2 H
1 S	1 S

There is one sulfur atom on each side, but the left side now has four hydrogen and six oxygen atoms, while the right side has only five oxygen atoms and two hydrogen atoms. The right side can be adjusted by placing a coefficient of two in front of H_2O. The equation is now balanced.

d. Begin by adjusting the ammonium ion and the nitrate ion by putting a coefficient of two in front of $NH_4NO_3(aq)$. The equation is now balanced.

$$(NH_4)_2S(aq) + Pb(NO_3)_2(aq) \rightarrow PbS(s) + 2\ NH_4NO_3(aq)$$

4 N	4 N
8 H	8 H
1 S	1 S
1 Pb	1 Pb
6 O	6 O

e. The numbers of aluminum atoms and oxygen atoms on the left are less than on the right. Begin by increasing the coefficient of aluminum to two. Aluminum is now balanced on both sides.

$$2Al(s) + O_2(g) \rightarrow Al_2O_3(s)$$

2 Al	2 Al
2 O	3 O

Aluminum is balanced, but oxygen is not. There are three oxygen atoms on the right, and two on the left. We cannot use a coefficient on the left to produce three oxygen atoms so that the left and right balance. But, we can put a coefficient of two in front of Al_2O_3 to make six oxygen atoms. A coefficient of three on the left adjusts the oxygen atoms on the left to six.

$$2Al(s) + 3O_2(g) \rightarrow 2Al_2O_3(s)$$

2 Al	4 Al
6 O	6 O

There are now four aluminum atoms on the right, and two on the left, so increase the coefficient of aluminum on the left to four. The equation is now balanced.

$$4Al(s) + 3O_2(g) \rightarrow 2Al_2O_3(s)$$

4 Al	4 Al
6 O	6 O

6. a. $2SO_2(g) + O_2(g) \rightarrow 2SO_3(g)$

b. $2C_4H_{10}(g) + 13O_2(g) \rightarrow 8CO_2(g) + 10H_2O(g)$

c. $2Fe_2O_3(s) + 3C(s) \rightarrow 4Fe(s) + 3CO_2(g)$

d. $TiCl_4(l) + 2H_2O(l) \rightarrow TiO_2(s) + 4HCl(aq)$

7. a. $2KI(aq) + Br_2(l) \rightarrow 2KBr(aq) + I_2(s)$

b. $2PbO_2(s) \rightarrow 2PbO(s) + O_2(g)$

c. $2Fe(OH)_3(s) + 3H_2SO_4(aq) \rightarrow Fe_2(SO_4)_3(s) + 6H_2O(l)$

d. $2K_3PO_4(aq) + 3BaCl_2(aq) \rightarrow 6KCl(aq) + Ba_3(PO_4)_2(s)$

CHAPTER 7

Reactions in Aqueous Solutions

Introduction

Water is a good solvent in the chemical laboratory because many compounds are soluble in water. There are many chemical reactions that occur in water and you will study some of them in this chapter. To predict what will happen when two compounds that are dissolved in water are mixed, you will need to learn some rules. These rules will help you predict what kinds of compounds are soluble in water, and what kinds of products are formed.

Water is also an important part of our environment, and many common reactions take place in water. For example, the rusting of iron takes place in water. For these reasons, a whole chapter is devoted to what happens when substances are added to water.

There are many different chemical reactions. When you first look at the equation for a reaction, it often looks completely new and unfamiliar. After you learn the material in this chapter, you will be able to classify many of the new reactions you come across into one or more basic categories. Categorizing a reaction is important. By fitting a reaction into a specific familiar category, you automatically know some things about that reaction, even if you have never seen that specific reaction before.

Chapter Discussion

Precipitation Reactions

When you mix an aqueous solution of lead(II) nitrate with an aqueous solution of potassium iodide (both solutions are colorless), beautiful yellow crystals are produced in a clear solution. What is the formula for these crystals? What is occurring in this reaction? This type of reaction is called a precipitation reaction, and the solid formed is termed the precipitate. Let's think about what is going on.

By now, you should be able to write the left side of the chemical equation (the reactant side) from the names given. Try to do this before reading on.

Since lead(II) has a 2+ charge and nitrate has a 1− charge, the formula for lead(II) nitrate is $Pb(NO_3)_2$. The potassium ion has a charge of 1+, and the iodide ion has a charge of 1−. So the formula for potassium iodide is KI. Thus, the reactant side of the chemical equation is

$$Pb(NO_3)_2(aq) + KI(aq) \rightarrow$$

But what are the products? To understand this, let's think about what the reactants look like. The reactants are both aqueous solutions of ionic compounds (also known as salts). An aqueous solution of an ionic compound will consist of the ions floating separately in solution. Thus, we can visualize the reactants as

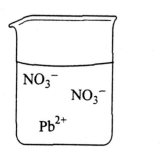 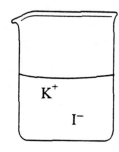

When these solutions are mixed together, the four ions Pb^{2+}, NO_3^-, K^+, I^- are all in solution. Therefore, there are four possibilities for products. Try to predict the formulas for these products before reading on.

Recall that ions of opposite charges will have attraction for one another, and that a molecule will be neutral overall. Therefore, we have the following four possibilities for products:

$$Pb(NO_3)_2, \ KI, \ PbI_2, \ KNO_3$$

We can eliminate the first two possibilities listed above because they are the original reactants. That is, since we know these exist as ions in solution, neither of these two will re-form simply by mixing with the other solution. Therefore, we know that the possible products are the last two possibilities, and we can write the equation as

$$Pb(NO_3)_2\ (aq) + KI\ (aq) \rightarrow PbI_2 + KNO_3$$

As a side note, notice that the subscripts are not necessarily the same on each side. For example, many students make the mistake of writing this equation as (WARNING – THE FOLLOWING CHEMICAL EQUATION IS INCORRECT)

$$Pb(NO_3)_2\ (aq) + KI\ (aq) \rightarrow PbI + K(NO_3)_2$$

Make sure you understand why this is NOT correct. There is no reason that just because a reactant consists of two nitrates (for example) the product must also. This is one reason why it is a good idea to think about the reactants as separate ions when balancing a precipitation reaction.

The correct balanced equation is

$$Pb(NO_3)_2\ (aq) + 2KI\ (aq) \rightarrow PbI_2 + 2KNO_3$$

The equation above is what is known as a molecular equation because it shows the complete formulas for all the reactants and products. Note that in this case we have not included phases for the products because we are still not sure which is the solid.

How can we tell which of the two products is the solid? There are a few ways of doing this.

1.   We can know something about the possible products. For example, by mixing the solutions, a yellow solid was noted. A chemist would know (or could look up) properties of lead(II) iodide and potassium nitrate to see if either was an insoluble yellow solid. In this case, lead(II) iodide is a yellow insoluble solid.

2.   We could experiment some more. For example, suppose we mix an aqueous solution of sodium nitrate with an aqueous solution of potassium chloride. In this case, the possible products would be sodium chloride and potassium nitrate (make sure you understand why). However, upon mixing, there is no reaction. Therefore, we know potassium nitrate is not a yellow, insoluble solid.

3.   We can use the solubility rules (see Table 7.1 in your text). These rules came about by performing similar experiments as described in #2 above. Ask your instructor if you need to memorize these. Even if you do not, make sure you know how to use them. For example, make

sure you understand how these rules allow you to determine that the solid in the above example is lead(II) iodide. In this case, solubility Rule #1 (Table 7.1 in your text) tells us that most nitrate salts are soluble, and rule #2 tells us most salts of K^+ are soluble. Therefore, potassium nitrate is expected to be soluble, so the solid that formed must be lead(II) iodide.

So, where are we with our equation? We now know the identity of the solid, so we can write

$$Pb(NO_3)_2(aq) + 2KI(aq) \rightarrow PbI_2(s) + 2KNO_3(aq)$$

Again, this is the molecular equation, but in this case we have noted the phase of each reactant and product. However, there are other ways we can represent this equation.

Recall that by writing KI (aq), for example, we are stating that the potassium iodide exists in solution as potassium and iodide ions. Thus, we can write the equation as:

$$Pb^{2+}(aq) + 2NO_3^-(aq) + 2K^+(aq) + 2I^-(aq) \rightarrow PbI_2(s) + 2K^+(aq) + 2NO_3^-(aq)$$

This representation more clearly conveys what is occurring in solution. Note that the subscripts that told us how many of a certain ion are present are now coefficients; so we write

$$2NO_3^-(aq)$$

not

$$(NO_3)_2^-(aq)$$

Also, note that the solid is written as a molecule. We call the resulting equation the complete ionic equation because it contains all of the ions that are in solution. It is a rather long way to represent the equation, however, and note that not all of the ions participate. That is, the potassium and nitrate ions do not "do" anything in the reaction (they are called spectator ions). To simplify the equation, we can consider only the species that are actually involved in the reaction, and thus we write

$$Pb^{2+}(aq) + 2I^-(aq) \rightarrow PbI_2(s)$$

This is called the net ionic equation. Your text contains many other examples of net ionic equations in Sections 7.2 and 7.3.

Here are some problems you should be able to answer:

1.   Use molecular-level drawings to show what is meant by the terms "strong electrolyte," "insoluble" and "precipitation reaction."

2.   If spectator ions do not participate in the reaction, why are they in solution?

3.   Mixing an aqueous solution of sodium chloride with an aqueous solution of potassium nitrate is not a chemical reaction. Why not?

Acid–Base Reactions

The acid–base reactions considered in the text are similar to precipitation reactions in that the products can be determined by switching ions. The acid–base reactions are simpler, however, because in all cases that we will consider, one of the products is water.

For example, if we mix hydrochloric acid with an aqueous solution of sodium hydroxide, we get sodium chloride and water as shown in the equation

$$HCl(aq) + NaOH(aq) \rightarrow NaCl(aq) + H_2O(l)$$

The complete ionic equation is

$$H^+(aq) + Cl^-(aq) + Na^+(aq) + OH^-(aq) \rightarrow Na^+(aq) + Cl^-(aq) + H_2O(l)$$

And the net ionic equation is

$$H^+(aq) + OH^-(aq) \rightarrow H_2O(l)$$

The equation above is also the net ionic equation for all acid–base reactions we will consider.

Classifying Chemical Reactions

Sections 7.6 and 7.7 provide an excellent discussion of classifying chemical reactions. Make sense of Figure 7.12. For example, why are combustion, synthesis and decomposition reactions all oxidation–reduction reactions? Realize that although there are a seemingly infinite number of actual reactions, there are only a few types of reactions. In the same way we dealt with nomenclature – having a systematic approach to looking at chemical reactions means we can know a lot about them without an overabundance of memorization.

Active Learning Questions

The Active Learning Questions at the end of each chapter are conceptually based questions that work well as discussion questions with a group of students. If your instructor does not assign these, consider getting together with a group of classmates and using these questions to see how well you understand the material in each chapter. While all of the questions work well for these, Active Learning Question 1 focuses on how to determine the products of a precipitation reaction, and questions 15-17 are visual problems to help you "see" what a solution looks like at a molecular level. You are strongly encouraged to answer these.

Learning Review

1.   Which one of the following does **not** tend to drive a reaction to produce products?

       a.   formation of a gas

       b.   transfer of electrons

       c.   color change

       d.   formation of water

       e.   formation of a solid

2.   Write the formulas for the ions that are formed when these ionic compounds are dissolved in water. How many of each kind of ion are produced for each molecule dissolved?

       a. $(NH_4)_2SO_4$

       b. KNO_3

       c. $Na_2Cr_2O_7$

       d. $MgCl_2$

       e. Li_3PO_4

       f. $Al(NO_3)_3$

3. When predicting a product for a reaction between two ionic compounds, we can always eliminate some of the ion pairs as possible products. Give a reason for eliminating each of the pairs as a product of the reaction below.

    $$AgNO_3 + Na_3PO_4 \rightarrow$$

    a. Ag^+, Na^+

    b. Na^+, NO_3^-

    c. NO_3^-, PO_3^{3-}

4. Use the solubility rules to predict the water solubility of each of the following compounds.

    a. Na_2S b. $PbCl_2$

    c. K_2SO_4 d. $(NH_4)_2CrO_4$

    e. $Pb(OH)_2$ f. $Ca(NO_3)_2$

    g. $Ba_3(PO_4)_2$ h. $ZnCl_2$

5. For each word description, write the balanced molecular equation and identify the product of the reaction.

    a. Aqueous solutions of sodium sulfate and lead(II) nitrate are mixed.
        One of the products is a white solid.

    b. Aqueous solutions of potassium hydroxide and nickel(II) chloride are mixed.
        One of the products is a green solid.

    c. Aqueous solutions of potassium sulfide and zinc nitrate are mixed.
        A pale yellow solid is produced.

    d. Aqueous solutions of silver nitrate and ammonium phosphate are mixed.
        A white solid is produced.

6. For each of the balanced equations below, write the complete ionic equation.

    a. $3CaCl_2(aq) + 2Na_3PO_4(aq) \rightarrow Ca_3(PO_4)_2(s) + 6NaCl(aq)$

    b. $Cu(NO_3)_2(aq) + K_2S(aq) \rightarrow CuS(s) + 2KNO_3(aq)$

    c. $2AgNO_3(aq) + K_2SO_4(aq) \rightarrow Ag_2SO_4(s) + 2KNO_3(aq)$

7. Complete and balance the equations below and identify the spectator ions.

    a. $Ca(NO_3)_2(aq) + K_2SO_4(aq) \rightarrow$

    b. $(NH_4)_2CO_3(aq) + CuCl_2(aq) \rightarrow$

    c. $NaOH(aq) + Pb(NO_3)_2(aq) \rightarrow$

    d. $Na_2S(aq) + Zn(NO_3)_2(aq) \rightarrow$

    e. $CoCl_2(aq) + Ca(OH)_2(aq) \rightarrow$

8. Write the net ionic equation for each reaction.

    a. $K_2CO_3(aq) + CaCl_2(aq) \rightarrow CaCO_3(s) + 2KCl(aq)$

    b. $Pb(NO_3)_2(aq) + (NH_4)_2S(aq) \rightarrow 2NH_4NO_3(aq) + PbS(s)$

    c. $2LiCl(aq) + 2Hg_2(NO_3)_2(aq) \rightarrow Hg_2Cl_2(s) + 2LiNO_3(aq)$

    d. $2NaOH(aq) + MgCl_2(aq) \rightarrow Mg(OH)_2(s) + 2NaCl(aq)$

9. What salts in aqueous solutions could you mix together to produce the solids below?

    a. $Zn(OH)_2$

    b. $Ba_3(PO_4)_2$

    c. $PbCl_2$

    d. $CaSO_4$

    e. $CoCO_3$

    f. Ag_2SO_4

10. Which of the substances below are strong acids, which are strong bases, and which are neither of these?

    a. HNO_3

    b. $C_2H_4O_2$

    c. H_2SO_4

    d. HCl

    e. $NaCl$

    f. K_2SO_4

11. Write complete ionic equations for the reactions below.

    a. Sodium hydroxide reacts with sulfuric acid.

    b. Hydrochloric acid reacts with potassium hydroxide.

    c. Nitric acid reacts with sodium hydroxide.

12. Write net ionic equations for each reaction in Problem 11.

13. Which of the reactions below are acid/base reactions?

    a. $K_2SO_4(aq) + Pb(NO_3)(aq) \rightarrow PbSO_4(s) + 2KNO_3(aq)$

    b. $KOH(aq) + HNO_3(aq) \rightarrow KNO_3(aq) + H_2O(l)$

    c. $H_2SO_4(aq) + 2NaOH(aq) \rightarrow Na_2SO_4(aq) + 2H_2O(l)$

    d. $Na_2CO_3(aq) + CoCl_2(aq) \rightarrow CoCO_3(s) + 2NaCl(aq)$

14. How many electrons do the elements below either gain or lose? For example, potassium atoms lose one electron.

$$K \rightarrow K^+ + e^-$$

    a. Br_2

    b. Mg

    c. H_2

    d. Al

    e. O_2

    f. S

15.   Show how the ions below can gain or lose electrons to form atoms or molecules. For example, a sodium ion gains one electron to form an atom of sodium.

$$Na^+ + e^- \rightarrow Na$$

a. $2Cl^-$ b. K^+

c. $4P^{3+}$ d. Ca^{2+}

e. $2I^-$ f. Al^{3+}

16.   For each reaction below, write equations showing the gain and loss of electrons.

a. $Cu(s) + 2AgNO_3(aq) \rightarrow 2Ag(s) + Cu(NO_3)_2(aq)$

b. $2HCl(aq) + Zn(s) \rightarrow H_2(g) + ZnCl_2(aq)$

c. $2NaBr(aq) + Cl_2(g) \rightarrow 2NaCl(aq) + Br_2(g)$

d. $2Hg(l) + O_2(g) \rightarrow 2HgO(s)$

17.   Classify the reactions below as a precipitation reaction, an acid–base reaction, or an oxidation–reduction reaction.

a. $2NaCl(s) + Br_2(l) \rightarrow 2NaBr(s) + Cl_2(g)$

b. $Na_2SO_4(aq) + Pb(NO_3)_2(aq) \rightarrow PbSO_4(s) + 2NaNO_3(aq)$

c. $2NaOH(aq) + H_2SO_4(aq) \rightarrow 2H_2O(l) + Na_2SO_4(aq)$

d. $2AgNO_3(aq) + Fe(s) \rightarrow Fe(NO_3)_2(aq) + 2Ag(s)$

e. $2KOH(aq) + ZnCl_2(aq) \rightarrow Zn(OH)_2(s) + 2KCl(aq)$

18.   Classify the reactions below as combustion, synthesis or decomposition reactions.

a. $N_2(g) + 3H_2(g) \rightarrow 2NH_3(g)$

b. $C_7H_{16}(g) + 11O_2(g) \rightarrow 7CO_2(g) + 8H_2O(g)$

c. $16Cu(s) + S_8(s) \rightarrow 8Cu_2S(s)$

d. $2NaNO_3(s) \rightarrow 2NaNO_2(s) + O_2(g)$

e. $SO_3(g) + H_2O(l) \rightarrow H_2SO_4(l)$

19.   Write balanced equations for each of the word descriptions. Classify each reaction as precipitation, oxidation–reduction or acid–base.

a.   Ethyl alcohol, a gasoline additive, burns in the presence of oxygen gas to produce carbon dioxide and water vapor.

b.   Aqueous solutions of ammonium sulfide and lead nitrate are mixed to produce solid lead sulfide and aqueous ammonium nitrate.

c.   Aluminum metal reacts with oxygen to produce solid aluminum oxide.

d.   Sodium metal reacts with liquid water to produce aqueous sodium hydroxide and hydrogen gas.

e.   Aqueous solutions of potassium hydroxide and nitric acid are mixed to produce aqueous potassium nitrate and liquid water.

f.   Aqueous solutions of sodium phosphate and aqueous sodium nitrate.

Answers to Learning Review

1. Only "c," color change, does not tend to make a reaction occur.

2.
   a. $2NH_4^+$ $1SO_4^{2-}$
   b. $1K^+$ $1NO_3^-$
   c. $2Na^+$ $1Cr_2O_7^{2-}$
   d. $1Mg^{2+}$ $2Cl^-$
   e. $3Li^+$ $1PO_4^{3-}$
   f. $1Al^{3+}$ $3NO_3^-$

3.
   a. Both Ag^+ and Na^+ are cations. Both an anion and a cation are needed.
   b. $NaNO_3$ is soluble in water, and so it exists in solution as Na^+ ions and NO_3^- ions.
   c. Both NO_3^- and PO_4^{3-} are anions. An anion and a cation are needed to form a neutral product.

4.
   a. water soluble (rule 2)
   b. not soluble (rule 3)
   c. water soluble (rule 2)
   d. water soluble (rule 2)
   e. not soluble (rule 5)
   f. water soluble (rule 1)
   g. not soluble (rule 6)
   h. water soluble (rule 3)

5.
   a. $Na_2SO_4(aq) + Pb(NO_3)_2(aq) \rightarrow PbSO_4(s) + 2NaNO_3(aq)$
      The product is lead(II) sulfate.
   b. $NiCl_2(aq) + 2KOH(aq) \rightarrow Ni(OH)_2(s) + 2KCl(aq)$
      The product is nickel(II) hydroxide.
   c. $K_2S(aq) + Zn(NO_3)_2(aq) \rightarrow ZnS(s) + 2KNO_3(aq)$
      The product is zinc sulfide.
   d. $3AgNO_3(aq) + (NH_4)_3PO_4(aq) \rightarrow Ag_3PO_4(s) + 3NH_4NO_3(aq)$
      The product is silver phosphate.

6.
   a. $3Ca^{2+} + 6Cl^- + 6Na^+ + 2PO_4^{3-} \rightarrow Ca_3(PO_4)_2(s) + 6Na^+ + 6Cl^-$
   b. $Cu^{2+} + 2NO_3^- + 2K^+ + S^{2-} \rightarrow CuS(s) + 2K^+ + 2NO_3^-$
   c. $2Ag^+ + 2NO_3^- + 2K^+ + SO_4^{2-} \rightarrow Ag_2SO_4(s) + 2K^+ + 2NO_3^-$

7.   a. $Ca(NO_3)_2(aq) + K_2SO_4(aq) \rightarrow CaSO_4(s) + 2KNO_3(aq)$
            K^+ and NO_3^- are the spectator ions.

      b. $(NH_4)_2CO_3(aq) + CuCl_2(aq) \rightarrow CuCO_3(s) + 2NH_4Cl(aq)$
            NH_4^+ and Cl^- are the spectator ions.

      c. $2NaOH(aq) + Pb(NO_3)_2(aq) \rightarrow Pb(OH)_2(s) + 2NaNO_3(aq)$
            Na^+ and NO_3^- are the spectator ions.

      d. $Na_2S(aq) + Zn(NO_3)_2(aq) \rightarrow ZnS(s) + 2NaNO_3(aq)$
            Na^+ and NO_3^- are the spectator ions.

      e. $CoCl_2(aq) + Ca(OH)_2(aq) \rightarrow Co(OH)_2(s) + CaCl_2(aq)$
            Ca^{2+} and Cl^- are the spectator ions.

8.   a. $Ca^{2+} + CO_3^{2-} \rightarrow CaCO_3(s)$

      b. $Pb^{2+} + S^{2-} \rightarrow PbS(s)$

      c. $Hg_2^{2+} + 2Cl^- \rightarrow Hg_2Cl_2(s)$

      d. $Mg^{2+} + 2OH^- \rightarrow Mg(OH)_2(s)$

9.   It is possible to produce the solids below from several different soluble salts, so your answer could be correct, but not be listed as the answer below. If your answer does not match the one below, use the solubility rules to help determine whether the aqueous salt solutions you chose would be soluble in water, and whether an exchange of anions would produce the desired insoluble salt.

      a. $Zn(NO_3)_2$ and $NaOH$

      b. $Ba(NO_3)_2$ and K_3PO_4

      c. $Pb(NO_3)_2$ and $NaCl$

      d. $CaCl_2$ and $(NH_4)_2SO_4$

      e. $Co(NO_3)_2$ and Na_2CO_3

      f. $AgNO_3$ and K_2SO_4

10.   a. HNO_3 is a strong acid.

      b. $C_2H_4O_2$ is a weak acid, so the correct answer is neither of these.

      c. H_2SO_4 is a strong acid.

      d.   HCl is a strong acid.

      e.   NaCl is a salt produced when HCl and NaOH react, so it is neither a strong acid nor a strong base.

      f. K_2SO_4 is a salt produced when H_2SO_4 and KOH react, so it is neither a strong acid nor a strong base.

11.   a. $2Na^+ + 2OH^- + 2H^+ + SO_4^{2-} \rightarrow 2Na^+ + SO_4^{2-} + 2H_2O(l)$

      b. $K^+ + OH^- + H^+ + Cl^- \rightarrow K^+ + Cl^- + H_2O(l)$

      c. $Na^+ + OH^- + H^+ + NO_3^- \rightarrow Na^+ + NO_3^- + H_2O(l)$

12.   a. $H^+ + OH^- \rightarrow H_2O(l)$

       b. $H^+ + OH^- \rightarrow H_2O(l)$

       c. $H^+ + OH^- \rightarrow H_2O(l)$

13.   a.   This is a precipitation reaction.

       b.   This is an acid–base reaction. The products are water and the salt KNO_3.

       c.   This is an acid–base reaction. The products are water and the salt Na_2SO_4.

       d.   This is a precipitation reaction.

14.   When atoms or molecules lose electrons, a positively charged cation is produced. When electrons are gained, then a negatively charged anion is produced. You can show how electrons are gained or lost by adding electrons to either the right side or the left side of an equation.

       a. $Br_2 + 2e^- \rightarrow 2Br^-$ b. $Mg \rightarrow Mg^{2+} + 2e^-$

       c. $H_2 \rightarrow 2H^+ + 2e^-$ d. $Al \rightarrow Al^{3+} + 3e^-$

       e. $O_2 + 4e^- \rightarrow 2O^{2-}$ f. $S + 2e^- \rightarrow S^{2-}$

15.   Ions can either gain or lose electrons to become neutral atoms or molecules. You can show whether the ions must lose or gain electrons by adding electrons to either the right side or the left side of an equation.

       a. $2Cl^- \rightarrow Cl_2 + 2e^-$ b. $K^+ + e^- \rightarrow K$

       c. $4P^{3-} \rightarrow P_4 + 12e^-$ d. $Ca^{2+} + 2e^- \rightarrow Ca$

       e. $2I^- \rightarrow I_2 + 2e^-$ f. $Al^{3+} + 3e^- \rightarrow Al$

16.   When presented with a reaction where electrons are transferred, it is possible to extract the parts of the reaction where electrons are lost and where electrons are gained and to write each part separately. Notice that the number of electrons lost is equal to the number gained.

       a. $Cu \rightarrow Cu^{2+} + 2e^-$ 2 electrons are lost
             $2Ag^+ + 2e^- \rightarrow 2Ag$ 2 electrons are gained
       b. $Zn \rightarrow Zn^{2+} + 2e^-$ 2 electrons are lost
             $2H^+ + 2e^- \rightarrow H_2$ 2 electrons are gained
       c. $2Br^- \rightarrow Br_2 + 2e^-$ 2 electrons are lost
             $Cl_2 + 2e^- \rightarrow H_2$ 2 electrons are gained
       d. $2Hg \rightarrow 2Hg^{2+} + 4e^-$ 4 electrons are lost
             $O_2 + 4e^- \rightarrow 2O^{2-}$ 4 electrons are gained

17.   a.   In this reaction, two chloride ions lose electrons to become a chlorine molecule, and a bromine molecule gains two electrons to become two bromide ions. This is an oxidation–reduction reaction. Because the chloride ion paired with sodium is exchanged for a bromide ion, this kind of reaction is often called a replacement reaction.

       b.   Two aqueous solutions containing ionic compounds react and one of the products is the ionic solid $PbSO_4$. This is a precipitation reaction.

       c.   The base NaOH reacts with the acid H_2SO_4 to produce water. This is an acid–base reaction.

d.   In this reaction, two Ag^+ ions gain two electrons to become two atoms of silver, and an atom of iron loses two electrons to become an Fe^{2+} ion. This is an oxidation–reduction reaction. Because the silver ion paired with the nitrate ion is exchanged for an iron ion, this kind of reaction is called a replacement reaction.

e.   Two aqueous solutions containing ionic compounds react and one of the products is the ionic solid $Zn(OH)_2$. This is an example of a precipitation reaction.

18. a.   Molecular nitrogen and molecular hydrogen react to produce a larger molecule, ammonia. This is a synthesis reaction.

b.   A molecule that is composed of carbon and hydrogen reacts with oxygen gas. The products are carbon dioxide and water. Reactions that have oxygen as a reactant are members of a sub-class of oxidation–reduction reactions called combustion reactions.

c.   Elemental copper reacts with elemental sulfur. A compound containing both elements is the product. This is a synthesis reaction.

d.   Solid sodium nitrate is converted to two simpler molecules, sodium nitrite and molecular oxygen. This is an example of a decomposition reaction.

e.   In this reaction, two small molecules combine to produce one larger molecule. This is an example of a synthesis reaction.

19. a. $C_2H_5OH(l) + 3O_2(g) \rightarrow 2CO_2(g) + 3H_2O(l)$

A molecule reacts with oxygen gas. Because this reaction has oxygen as a reactant, it is an oxidation–reduction reaction.

b. $(NH_4)_2S(aq) + Pb(NO_3)_2(aq) \rightarrow PbS(s) + 2NH_4NO_3(aq)$
Two aqueous solutions are mixed to produce a solid product (precipitation reaction).

c. $4Al(s) + 3O_2(g) \rightarrow 2Al_2O_3(s)$

Elemental aluminum loses 3 electrons to become Al^{3+} and molecular oxygen gains 2 electrons to become O^{2-}. This is an oxidation–reduction reaction.

d. $2Na(s) + 2H_2O(l) \rightarrow 2NaOH(aq) + H_2(g)$

Sodium metal loses an electron to become Na^+ and two hydrogen ions gain an electron to become hydrogen gas. This is an oxidation–reduction reaction.

e. $KOH(aq) + HNO_3(aq) \rightarrow KNO_3(aq) + H_2O(l)$

Aqueous solutions of the base KOH and the acid HNO_3 are mixed to produce liquid water. This is an acid–base reaction.

f. $Na_3PO_4(aq) + 3AgNO_3(aq) \rightarrow Ag_3PO_4(s) + 3NaNO_3(aq)$

Two aqueous solutions are mixed. The product is a solid, Ag_3PO_4. This is a precipitation reaction.

CHAPTER 8

Chemical Composition

Introduction

Before beginning a project of any kind, it is always important to know the quantity of material needed. It is usually possible to count the number of individual items you will need. In chemistry, it is difficult to count the number of atoms or molecules needed, because the individual particles are too small, and there are too many of them. This chapter will show you how you can "count" the number of particles by weighing them.

Chapter Discussion

The Mole

One crucial concept in this chapter is the mole. Make sure you understand why it is so important. There are two main ideas you need to consider:

1. We can count objects by weighing a sample of the objects provided we know the average mass of the object.

2. Relative masses of two or more different objects stay the same but can be expressed in larger units if we have the same number of objects.

Section 8.1 in your text provides a very good discussion of this first point. Make sure to read this. Talk to an instructor if you have difficulty with it. Let's look at the second point more carefully.

Suppose we have two blocks: a red block and a yellow block. The red block weighs 1 ounce, and the yellow block weighs 4 ounces. Now suppose we have 16 of each type of block. What is the mass of each sample? The sample of red blocks weighs 16 ounces and the sample of yellow blocks weighs 64 ounces. But note that 16 ounces is also 1 pound, thus 64 ounces is 4 pounds. Note the relative masses of the blocks:

	1 block	16 blocks
red	1 ounce	1 pound
yellow	4 ounces	4 pounds

The relative masses stay the same (1:4) but the units are changed. Why is this important?

Recall from Chapter 4 that the periodic table gives us the relative masses of the elements. But what are the units of these? Actually, there need not be any unit at all, or the units could be anything; that is, the table gives us relative masses, much like the 1:4 ratio we see in the examples with the blocks. A better question to ask is what units would be useful for us? The standard unit of mass that we will use is the gram. The average hydrogen atom, for example, has a mass of 1.66057×10^{-24} g. This mass is much too small for us to work with. We would like to keep the relative mass of hydrogen at 1.008 (as it is on the periodic table) but in units of grams. How many hydrogen atoms are there in a 1.008 g sample of hydrogen?

$$1.008 \text{ g H} \times \left(\frac{1 \text{ atom H}}{1.66057 \times 10^{-24} \text{ g H}} \right) = 6.022 \times 10^{23} \text{ H atoms}$$

Thus, if we have 6.022×10^{23} atoms of hydrogen the sample will have a mass of 1.008 g. Along the same lines, if we have 6.022×10^{23} atoms of carbon, the sample will have a mass of 12.01 g. If we have 6.022×10^{23} atoms of oxygen, the sample will have a mass of 16.00 g. That is, 6.022×10^{23}, which is called a mole, is the number which converts the units on the periodic table (called amu or atomic mass units) to grams.

The mole is just a number (like a dozen is 12), and it allows us to convert between how many atoms (or molecules) we have, and the mass of the sample. In the example with the blocks, this number was 16 (to convert ounces to grams). To convert amu to grams, we use the mole.

Learning to Solve Problems

Section 8.4 in the text discusses *conceptual problem solving*. It's a general approach to solving quantitative problems. You should ask and answer the questions "Where are we going?" (that is, what are we trying to solve?), "What do we know?" (this includes constants, equations and other given information), and "How do we get there?" (how do we set up the problem?). When first encountering a new problem it is tempting to look at the solution, memorize it, and then use this specific solution for a different but similar problem. We strongly advise against this method because it often does not work and it also keeps you from really understanding the problem and the solution. Instead, the conceptual problem solving approach is a systematic way to think about all of the problems you will see in the text. The solutions to the example problems throughout the text will use this approach. At first, read through these solutions and make sure that you understand them. As you continue in your studies, cover up the solutions to the example problems and try to solve them on your own. Then, compare your solutions with the ones in the text. The eventual goal is for you to be able to solve these completely on your own.

Formulas and Mass Percent

Would you say ammonia (NH_3) is mostly nitrogen or mostly hydrogen? Your answer depends on if you are looking at the number of atoms or the mass of the atoms. In terms of numbers of atoms, ammonia is ¾ hydrogen (there are four atoms making up an ammonia molecule, and three of them are hydrogen). But it is often important to know the composition by mass of a compound. Chemists have instruments that give them percent by mass data, and they use it to determine the formulas of compounds. How can we do the same?

Suppose we have 1.0 mole of ammonia molecules. The molar mass of ammonia (NH_3) is 17.034 g (N = 14.01 g/mol and H = 1.008 g/mol, thus the molar mass of NH_3 is 14.01 + 3(1.008) = 17.034 g). How much of this mass is hydrogen? How much of this mass is nitrogen?

Since there are three hydrogen atoms per ammonia molecule, there are three moles of hydrogen atoms per mole of ammonia molecules. Thus, the total mass of hydrogen should be 3(1.008) or 3.024 g. Thus, there is 14.01 g of nitrogen. The mass percent of each element is:

$$\text{Hydrogen: } \frac{3.024 \text{ g}}{17.034 \text{ g}} \times 100\% = 17.75\% \text{ hydrogen by mass}$$

$$\text{Nitrogen: } \frac{14.01 \text{ g}}{17.034 \text{ g}} \times 100\% = 82.25\% \text{ nitrogen by mass}$$

Note that even though there are more hydrogen atoms than nitrogen atoms, the percent by mass of hydrogen in this case is lower than that of nitrogen.

Try the following example before reading on:

What is the mass percent of hydrogen and of nitrogen for the compound N_2H_6?

To solve this problem, you can find the molar mass of the compound, which is 34.068, and the total mass of hydrogen (6.048 g) and nitrogen (28.02 g). If you are having difficulty getting these numbers, read through your text or talk with your instructor.

Thus, the mass percent of each element is:

$$\text{Hydrogen: } \frac{6.028 \text{ g}}{34.068 \text{ g}} \times 100\% = 17.75\% \text{ hydrogen by mass}$$

$$\text{Nitrogen: } \frac{28.02 \text{ g}}{34.068 \text{ g}} \times 100\% = 82.25\% \text{ nitrogen by mass}$$

Why is this significant? Note that the percentages are the same percent by mass as ammonia (NH_3). Chemists generally use percent by mass data to determine the formula of a compound. But what if we know a compound is 17.75 percent hydrogen by mass and 82.25 percent nitrogen by mass? Is the formula NH_3? Or N_2H_6? Actually, you should prove to yourself that any formula that has 3 times as many hydrogen atoms as nitrogen atoms (N_xH_{3x}) will be 17.75 percent hydrogen and 82.25 percent nitrogen by mass. So what are we to do?

We need to know the molar mass of a compound to know the actual formula for the compound (the molecular formula). Given just the percent by mass data allows us only to determine the ratio of atoms in the molecule (in this case 1:3), which determines the empirical formula. Let's consider another example.

A compound consisting of carbon, hydrogen and oxygen is 40.00% carbon by mass, and 6.71% hydrogen by mass. What is the empirical formula of the compound?

In this case, we are given the percent by mass data and are asked to determine the formula for the compound. How should we think about this?

We are looking for the formula (empirical) of this compound. Recall that the formula gives us the ratio of atoms in the compound. The general formula for this compound is $C_xH_yO_z$. Here x, y, and z represent the number of atoms in one molecule of the compound (or, in the case of the empirical formula, the lowest whole number ratio). Our problem, then, is to determine x, y and z. Thus, we have been given mass percent data for the atoms and need to determine the number of atoms. In essence, we will have to change a mass to a number. How do we do this? We know, for example, that 1 mole (6.022×10^{23}) of carbon atoms has a mass of 12.01 g. Thus, we will use the molar mass of the atoms to make this conversion.

Before we go on, notice that we have done quite a bit of thinking about this problem before doing any calculations, and that's generally a good approach with chemistry problems. Think about the setup of the problem before worrying about the specifics. Do not immediately try to plug numbers into a given equation. Think about the problem first.

Now we know that we will need to convert the mass data to numbers using the mole. But what is the mass of carbon? Hydrogen? Oxygen? We are only given the mass percent data. This requires us to think about what is meant by mass percent.

Stating that the compound is 40.00% carbon by mass means that for every 100.00 g of compound, 40.00 g is carbon.

It is not stating that we have 40.00 g of carbon necessarily, but that 40.00 g out of every 100.00 g of compound is carbon (if we had 200.00 g of compound, we would have 80.00 g of carbon). Since we are only trying to determine the number ratio for the atoms, we only need to know the mass ratio, not the actual masses. The easiest way to do this is to just assume we have 100.00 g of the compound (we could assume *any* mass here; make sure you understand why). Therefore, the masses of the atoms are:

mass of carbon:	40.00 g
mass of hydrogen:	6.71 g
mass of oxygen:	53.29 g

Note that these masses add up to 100.00 g (which is how we can determine the value for oxygen). Now we can convert these masses to numbers (moles) by using the molar masses of each element. Do this before reading on.

The mole ratios you should have calculated are:

moles of carbon:	3.33
moles of hydrogen:	6.66
moles of oxygen:	3.33

If you cannot get these numbers, review this step in your text, work with a friend or see your instructor.

We now have the mole ratios. Does this mean the empirical formula is $C_{3.33}H_{6.66}O_{3.33}$? No. We must represent the formulas with whole numbers (we cannot have fractions of atoms). However, 3.33:6.66:3.33 can be written as 1:2:1. Since we used mass ratio data, we calculated atom ratio data. That is, we do not actually have 3.33 moles of carbon (or 2 moles for that matter) but we have a 1:2:1 ratio of atoms of carbon, hydrogen and oxygen, respectively. We can write the empirical formula as:

$$C_1H_2O_1$$

Of course, $C_1H_2O_1$ is not necessarily the actual (molecular) formula of the compound. You should prove to yourself, for example, that the formula $C_2H_4O_2$ has the same mass percent of each atom as $C_1H_2O_1$. To determine the actual formula we would need to know the molar mass of the compound.

For example, if we are told that the molar mass of this compound is about 180 g/mol, how do we determine the molecular formula? We know that the answer has to follow the general formula $C_xH_{2x}O_x$. Recall that the molar mass is the sum of the masses of the atoms. Thus, $180 = 12.01(x) + 1.008(2x) + 16.00(x)$, or $180 = 30.026x$. Solving for x, we get 6. The molecular formula is $C_6H_{12}O_6$.

Again, note the amount of thought that went into solving this problem. Do not expect to simply plug numbers into equations. By thinking about the underlying concepts involved, you will find that you can solve quite difficult and novel problems. This is a major goal.

Active Learning Questions

The Active Learning Questions at the end of each chapter are conceptually based questions that work well as discussion questions with a group of students. If your instructor does not assign these, consider getting together with a group of classmates and using these questions to see how well you understand the material in each chapter. While all of the questions work well for these, Active Learning Questions 1 and 13 ask you to consider the significance of the mole concept, and question 21 is a particularly challenging conceptual problem dealing with percent composition. You are strongly encouraged to answer these.

Learning Review

1. A hardware store employee determined that the average mass of a certain size nail was 2.35 g.

    a. How many nails are there in 1057.5 g nails?

    b. If a customer needs 1,500 nails, what mass of nails should the employee weigh out?

2. Ten individual screws have masses of 10.23 g, 10.19 g, 10.24 g, 10.23 g, 10.26 g, 10.23 g, 10.28 g, 10.30 g, 10.25 g, and 10.26 g. What is the average mass of the screws?

3. The average mass of a hydrogen atom is 1.008 amu. How many hydrogen atoms are there in a sample that has a mass of 25,527.6 amu?

4. The average mass of a sodium atom is 22.99 amu. What is the mass in amu of a sample of sodium atoms that contains 3.29×10^3 sodium atoms?

5. A sample with a mass of 4.100×10^5 amu is 25.00 percent carbon, and 75.00 percent hydrogen by mass. How many atoms of carbon and hydrogen are in the sample? The average mass of a carbon atom is 12.01 amu and of a hydrogen atom is 1.008 amu.

6. The average mass of a neon atom is 20.18 amu.

    a. How many grams of neon are found in a mole of neon?

    b. How many atoms of neon are in a mole of neon?

7. What is the value of Avogadro's number and how is it defined?

8. Use the average mass values found inside the front cover of your textbook to solve the problems below.

    a. A helium balloon contains 5.38×10^{22} helium atoms. How many grams of helium are in the balloon?

    b. A piece of iron was found to contain 3.25 mol Fe. How many grams are in the sample?

    c. A sample of liquid bromine contains 65.00 g Br atoms. How many bromine atoms are in the sample?

    d. A sample of zinc contains 0.78 mol Zn. How many zinc atoms are in this sample?

9. What is meant by the term "molar mass"?

10. Calculate the molar mass of the following substances.

    a. Fe_2O_3

    b. NH_3

    c. C_2H_5OH

    d. CO_2

    e. N_2O_5

11. Calculate the molar mass of these ionic compounds.

    a. HCl

    b. $MgBr_2$

    c. $Pb(OH)_2$

    d. $Cu(NO_3)_2$

e.   KCl

f. Na_2SO_4

12.   Acetone, which has a formula of C_3H_6O, is used as a solvent in some fingernail polish removers. How many moles of acetone are in 5.00 g of acetone?

13.   How many grams of potassium sulfate are in 0.623 mol potassium sulfate?

14.   Calculate the mass fraction of nitrogen in N_2O_5.

15.   Calculate the mass percent of each element in the following substances.

a. CH_3NH_2

b. H_2SO_4

16.   Explain the difference between the empirical formula and the molecular formula of a compound.

17.   The molecular formula of the gas acetylene is C_2H_2. What is the empirical formula?

18.   When 2.500 g of an oxide of mercury, Hg_xO_y, is decomposed into its elements by heating, 2.405 g of mercury is produced. Calculate the empirical formula for this compound.

19.   A compound was analyzed and found to obtain only carbon, hydrogen and chlorine. A 6.380 g sample of the compound contained 2.927 g carbon and 0.5729 g hydrogen. What is the empirical formula of the compound?

20.   The compound benzamide has the following percent composition. What is the empirical formula?

$$C = 69.40\% \quad H = 5.825\% \quad N = 11.57\% \quad O = 13.21\%$$

21.   The empirical formula for a compound used (in the past) as a green paint pigment is $C_2H_3As_3Cu_2O_8$. The molar mass is 1013.71 g. What is the molecular formula?

22.   A sugar that is broken down by the body to produce energy has the following percent composition:

$$C = 39.99\% \quad H = 6.713\% \quad O = 53.29\%$$

The molar mass is 210.18 g. What is the molecular formula?

Answers to the Learning Review

1.   a.   This problem relies on the principle of counting by weighing. The question "how many nails?" can be answered because we are given the average mass of one nail.

$$\frac{1 \text{ nail}}{2.35 \text{ g}} \times 1057.5 \text{ g} = 450. \text{ nails}$$

b.   If we know the mass of 1 nail equals 2.35 g, then the mass of 1500. nails is a multiple of 2.35 g.

$$\frac{2.35 \text{ g}}{1 \text{ nail}} \times 1500. \text{ nails} = 3530 \text{ g}$$

2. Average mass can be determined by adding the masses of each individual screw, then dividing by the number of screws measured.

$$10.23 \text{ g} + 10.19 \text{ g} + 10.24 \text{ g} + 10.23 \text{ g} + 10.26 \text{ g} + 10.23 \text{ g} +$$
$$10.28 \text{ g} + 10.30 \text{ g} + 10.25 \text{ g} + 10.26 \text{ g} = 102.47 \text{ g}$$

The total mass of all 10 screws is 102.47 g.

$$\frac{102.47 \text{ g}}{10 \text{ screws}} = 10.25 \text{ g/screw}$$

The average mass of a screw is 10.25 g.

3. This problem is an example of counting by weighing. We are given the average mass of one hydrogen atom, and asked for the number of hydrogen atoms in some other mass of hydrogen.

$$\frac{1 \text{ hydrogen atom}}{1.008 \text{ amu}} \times 25{,}527.6 \text{ amu} = 25{,}330 \text{ hydrogen atoms}$$

4. If we know the average mass of an atom, we can calculate the mass of any quantity of atoms.

$$\frac{22.99 \text{ amu}}{1 \text{ sodium atom}} \times 3.29 \times 10^3 \text{ sodium atoms} = 75{,}600 \text{ amu}$$

5. The total mass of the sample is 4.100×10^5 amu. Of this mass, 25.00 percent comes from carbon atoms. So the mass contributed by carbon is:

$$4.100 \times 10^5 \text{ amu} \times 0.2500 = 1.025 \times 10^5 \text{ amu}$$

The mass contributed by hydrogen is the original mass minus the mass contributed by carbon:

$$4.100 \times 10^5 \text{ amu} - 1.025 \times 10^5 \text{ amu} = 3.075 \times 10^5 \text{ amu}$$

Now that we know the total mass of each kind of atom, we can use the average mass of one atom to count the number of atoms present.

$$\frac{1 \text{ hydrogen atom}}{1.008 \text{ amu}} \times 3.075 \times 10^5 \text{ amu} = 3.051 \times 10^5 \text{ hydrogen atoms}$$

$$\frac{1 \text{ carbon atom}}{12.01 \text{ amu}} \times 1.025 \times 10^5 \text{ amu} = 8.535 \times 10^3 \text{ carbon atoms}$$

6. a. A mole of any element always contains a mass in grams equal to the average atomic mass of that element. So there are 20.18 g Ne in 1 mol Ne.

    b. A mole of atoms of any element always contains 6.022×10^{23} atoms.

7. Avogadro's number is the number equal to the number of atoms in 12.01 grams of carbon. Chemists have accurately determined this number to be 6.022×10^{23} atoms.

8. These problems use conversions between moles and grams, or between moles and number of atoms. For each element, you must write a different conversion factor for moles to grams depending upon the average mass for that element.

   a. This problem requires first determining the moles of He, and then converting moles to grams.

   $$5.38 \times 10^{22} \text{ He atoms} \times \frac{1 \text{ mol He}}{6.022 \times 10^{23} \text{ He atoms}} \times \frac{4.003 \text{ g He}}{1 \text{ mol He}} = 0.357 \text{ g He}$$

   b. $3.25 \text{ mol Fe} \times \dfrac{55.85 \text{ g Fe}}{1 \text{ mol Fe}} = 182 \text{ g Fe}$

   c. This is a two-step problem, requiring that you first calculate the number of moles of Br, then the number of Br atoms.

   $$65.00 \text{ g Br} \times \frac{1 \text{ mol Br}}{79.90 \text{ g Br}} \times \frac{6.022 \times 10^{23} \text{ Br atoms}}{1 \text{ mol Br}} = 4.899 \times 10^{23} \text{ Br atoms}$$

   d. $0.78 \text{ mol Zn} \times \dfrac{6.022 \times 10^{23} \text{ Zn atoms}}{1 \text{ mol Zn}} = 4.7 \times 10^{23} \text{ Zn atoms}$

9. Molar mass is the number of grams found in one mole of a substance. The molar mass is calculated by adding together the masses of each atom in the substance.

10. a. Fe_2O_3 contains 2 Fe atoms and 3 O atoms.

   $(2 \times 55.85 \text{ g Fe}) + (3 \times 16.00 \text{ g O}) = 159.7 \text{ g}$

   b. NH_3 contains 1 nitrogen atom and 3 hydrogen atoms.

   $(1 \times 14.01 \text{ g N}) + (3 \times 1.008 \text{ g H}) = 17.03 \text{ g}$

   c. C_2H_5OH contains 2 C atoms, 6 H atoms and 1 O atom.

   $(2 \times 12.01 \text{ g C}) + (6 \times 1.008 \text{ g H}) + (1 \times 16.00 \text{ g O}) = 46.07 \text{ g}$

   d. CO_2 contains 1 C atom and 2 O atoms.

   $(1 \times 12.01 \text{ g C}) + (2 \times 16.00 \text{ g O}) = 44.01 \text{ g}$

   e. N_2O_5 contains 2 N atoms and 5 O atoms

   $(2 \times 14.02 \text{ g N}) + (5 \times 16.00 \text{ g O}) = 108.0 \text{ g}$

11. a. $1.008 \text{ g H} + 35.45 \text{ g Cl} = 36.46 \text{ g}$

   b. $24.31 \text{ g Mg} + (2 \times 79.90 \text{ g Br}) = 184.1 \text{ g}$

   c. $207.19 \text{ g Pb} + (2 \times 16.00 \text{ g O}) + (2 \times 1.008 \text{ H}) = 241.2 \text{ g}$

   d. $63.55 \text{ g Cu} + (2 \times 14.01 \text{ g N}) + (6 \times 16.00 \text{ g O}) = 187.6 \text{ g}$

   e. $39.10 \text{ g K} + 35.45 \text{ g Cl} = 74.55 \text{ g}$

   f. $(2 \times 22.99 \text{ g Na}) + 32.07 \text{ g S} + (4 \times 16 \text{ g O}) = 142.1 \text{ g}$

12. To solve this problem, we need to know how many grams of acetone are in one mole of acetone. The number of grams of acetone equal to one mole of acetone is the molar mass.

$$\text{molar mass acetone} = (3 \times 12.01 \text{ g}) + (6 \times 1.008 \text{ g}) + 16.00 \text{ g} = 58.08 \text{ g}$$

$$5.00 \text{ g acetone} \times \frac{1 \text{ mol acetone}}{58.08 \text{ g acetone}} = 0.0861 \text{ mol acetone}$$

13. $\text{molar mass } K_2SO_4 = (2 \times 39.10 \text{ g}) + 32.07 \text{ g} + (4 \times 16.00 \text{ g}) = 174.3 \text{ g}$

$$0.623 \text{ mol } K_2SO_4 \times \frac{174.3 \text{ g } K_2SO_4}{1 \text{ mol } K_2SO_4} = 109 \text{ g } K_2SO_4$$

14. Mass fraction is equal to the mass of the desired element – in this case nitrogen – divided by the molar mass.

$$\frac{28.02 \text{ g N}}{108.0 \text{ g total}} = 0.2594$$

15. a. molar mass of CH_3NH_2 is $12.01 \text{ g C} + (5 \times 1.008 \text{ g H}) + 14.01 \text{ g N} = 31.06 \text{ g total}$

$$\frac{12.01 \text{ g C}}{31.06 \text{ g total}} \times 100 = 38.67\% \text{ C}$$

$$\frac{5.040 \text{ g H}}{31.06 \text{ g total}} \times 100 = 16.23\% \text{ H}$$

$$\frac{14.01 \text{ g N}}{31.06 \text{ g total}} \times 100 = 45.11\% \text{ N}$$

   b. molar mass of H_2SO_4 is $(2 \times 1.008 \text{ g H}) + 32.07 \text{ g S} + (4 \times 16.00 \text{ g O}) = 98.09 \text{ g total}$

$$\frac{2.016 \text{ g H}}{98.09 \text{ g total}} \times 100 = 2.055\% \text{ H}$$

$$\frac{32.07 \text{ g S}}{98.09 \text{ g total}} \times 100 = 32.69\% \text{ S}$$

$$\frac{64.00 \text{ g O}}{98.09 \text{ g total}} \times 100 = 65.25\% \text{ O}$$

16. The empirical formula gives only the relative number of atoms, or a ratio of each kind of atom. The molecular formula tells you exactly how many of each kind of atom are present in the molecule.

17. For every two atoms of carbon in acetylene there are two atoms of hydrogen. The ratio of carbon atoms to hydrogen atoms is 1:1. So, the empirical formula of acetylene is CH.

18. Since we know that the mercury and oxygen combined weighed 2.500 g before the reaction took place, and that the mass of the mercury is 2.405 g, then the mass of oxygen must be 2.500 − 2.405 = 0.095 g. We can now convert grams of mercury and grams of oxygen to moles, using the atomic masses of these elements.

$$Hg_xO_y \quad \longrightarrow \quad x\,Hg \quad + \quad y\,O$$
$$2.500\ g \qquad\qquad 2.405\ g \qquad\ ?\ g$$

$$2.405\ g\ Hg \times \frac{1\ mol\ Hg}{200.59\ g\ Hg} = 0.01199\ mol\ Hg$$

$$0.095\ g\ O \times \frac{1\ mol\ O}{16.00\ g\ O} = 0.0059\ mol\ O$$

The ratio of mercury atoms to oxygen atoms is, $\dfrac{0.01199}{0.0059} = 2.03$ to 1.

So, there are twice as many Hg atoms as O atoms, and the empirical formula is Hg_2O.

19. When 6.380 g of a compound that contained only carbon, hydrogen and chlorine was analyzed, it was found to contain 2.927 g carbon and 0.5729 g hydrogen. The mass of chlorine must be equal to the total mass minus the mass of carbon plus hydrogen.

$$mass\ of\ chlorine = 6.380 - (2.927\ g\ C + 0.5729\ g\ H) = 2.880\ g$$

The moles of each kind of atom are determined from the average atomic mass.

$$2.927\ g\ C \times \frac{1\ mol\ C}{12.01\ g\ C} = 0.2437\ mol\ C$$

$$0.5729\ g\ H \times \frac{1\ mol\ H}{1.008\ g\ H} = 0.5684\ mol\ H$$

$$2.880\ g\ Cl \times \frac{1\ mol\ Cl}{35.45\ g\ Cl} = 0.08124\ mol\ Cl$$

Express the mole ratios in whole numbers by dividing each number of moles by the smallest number of moles.

$$\frac{0.2437\ mol\ C}{0.08124} = 3.000\ mol\ C$$

$$\frac{0.5684\ mol\ H}{0.08124} = 7.000\ mol\ H$$

$$\frac{0.08124\ mol\ Cl}{0.08124} = 1.000\ mol\ Cl$$

The empirical formula is C_3H_7Cl.

20. This problem provides only percent composition data for the compound benzamide. It does not provide an analysis in grams for each of the elements present. We need to know how many grams of each element are present in a sample of benzamide so we can calculate the moles of each element. We can convert percent composition data to grams of each element. Assume that

we have 100.0 g of benzamide. Of that sample, 69.40 percent is carbon. For a 100.0 g sample, 69.40 g are carbon, 5.825 g are hydrogen, 11.57 g are nitrogen and 13.21 g are oxygen. We can calculate the number of moles of each element.

$$69.40 \text{ g C} \times \frac{1 \text{ mol C}}{12.01 \text{ g C}} = 5.779 \text{ mol C}$$

$$5.825 \text{ g H} \times \frac{1 \text{ mol H}}{1.008 \text{ g H}} = 5.779 \text{ mol H}$$

$$11.57 \text{ g N} \times \frac{1 \text{ mol N}}{14.01 \text{ g N}} = 0.8258 \text{ mol N}$$

$$13.21 \text{ g O} \times \frac{1 \text{ mol O}}{16.00 \text{ g O}} = 0.8256 \text{ mol O}$$

Now, divide each number of moles by the smallest number of moles to convert the number of moles to whole numbers.

$$\frac{5.779 \text{ mol C}}{0.08256} = 7.000 \text{ mol C}$$

$$\frac{5.779 \text{ mol H}}{0.08256} = 7.000 \text{ mol H}$$

$$\frac{0.08258 \text{ mol N}}{0.08256} = 1.000 \text{ mol N}$$

$$\frac{0.8256 \text{ mol O}}{0.08256} = 1.000 \text{ mol O}$$

The empirical formula is C_7H_7NO.

21.   If you are given both the molar mass and the empirical formula, determining the molecular formula is straightforward. If we multiply all of the atoms in the empirical formula by some number, we will have a correct molecular formula. So the molecular formula is a multiple of the empirical formula. We can determine what this multiple is by comparing the molar mass of the molecular formula with the molar mass of the empirical formula.

$$\text{molar mass empirical formula} = (2 \times 12.01 \text{ g C}) + (3 \times 1.008 \text{ g H}) +$$
$$(3 \times 74.92 \text{ g As}) + (2 \times 63.55 \text{ g Cu}) + (8 \times 16.00 \text{ g O}) = 506.9 \text{ g}$$

The molar mass of the empirical formula is 506.9 g, and we know that the molar mass of the molecular formula is 1013.7 g. There are two empirical formulas in the molecular formula.

$$\frac{1013.7 \text{ g in molecular formula}}{506.9 \text{ g in empirical formula}} = 2.000$$

So, the molecular formula is two times the empirical formula. The molecular formula is $2(C_2H_3As_3Cu_2O_8)$ or $C_4H_6As_6Cu_4O_{16}$.

22.   In this problem, we are asked to find the molecular formula given the molar mass and the percent composition. To determine the molecular formula, we must first find the empirical formula.

$$39.99 \text{ g C} \times \frac{1 \text{ mol C}}{12.01 \text{ g C}} = 3.330 \text{ mol C}$$

$$6.713 \text{ g H} \times \frac{1 \text{ mol H}}{1.008 \text{ g H}} = 6.660 \text{ mol H}$$

$$53.29 \text{ g O} \times \frac{1 \text{ mol O}}{16.00 \text{ g O}} = 3.331 \text{ mol O}$$

Divide each molar quantity by the smallest number of moles to convert the number of moles to a whole number.

$$\frac{3.330 \text{ mol C}}{3.330} = 1.000$$

$$\frac{6.660 \text{ mol H}}{3.330} = 2.000$$

$$\frac{3.331 \text{ mol O}}{3.330} = 1.000$$

The empirical formula is CH_2O. The molar mass of the molecule is 210.18 g. So we need to know the molar mass of the empirical formula.

The molar mass empirical formula = 12.01 g C + (2 × 1.008 g H) + 16.00 g O = 30.03 g

How many empirical formulas are there in one molecular formula? We can tell by dividing the molar mass of the molecular formula by the molar mass of the empirical formula.

$$\frac{210.18 \text{ g in molecular formula}}{30.03 \text{ g in empirical formula}} = 6.999$$

The molecular formula is 7 times the empirical formula.

$$\text{molecular formula} = 7 \times (CH_2O) \text{ or } C_7H_{14}O_7$$

CHAPTER 9

Chemical Quantities

Introduction

In this chapter you will perform many chemical calculations, all of which are based on fundamental principles, such as balanced equations. A balanced equation can provide more information than is apparent at first glance. You can use a balanced equation to help answer such questions as "How much is produced?" and "How much would be needed to make this amount?" Only a balanced equation will provide correct answers to these questions.

Often, when two reactants are mixed together, one of them will run out before the other one is all used up. In this situation, the amount of product you can make will be limited by the reactant that is first used up. The balanced equation will help you determine which reactant runs out, and how much product you can make.

Chapter Discussion

A main point of this chapter is that you can calculate the mass of reactant needed or mass of product formed given the mass of one or more reactants or products (this is called stoichiometry). Realize that there is really nothing new in this chapter, but you are expected to put together what you have learned in the last few chapters. For example, you need to know how to balance an equation and what it means; you need to understand the mole concept; you need to be able to calculate molar masses of molecules. If you are having difficulty with any of these concepts, make sure to get help (and re-read these chapters) or you will find this chapter to be quite difficult.

Also, make sure not to get lost in the math with stoichiometry problems. By now you should be used to thinking about these problems at a molecular level. Make sure you understand what you are solving for and how you are getting there. Look back to the percent by mass problem at the end of the Chapter Discussion for Chapter 8 in this *Study Guide*. Remember that dimensional analysis doesn't help if you don't understand the problem. In other words, a shortcut is not faster if you get lost along the way.

In the text "maps" are frequently used to show how to solve these problems. Don't merely memorize these, but make sure to understand the thinking behind them. Note that the balanced equation is always a part of any of these maps; make sure you understand why.

One way to make sense of stoichiometry is to first consider a molecular-level sketch of a reaction. For example, consider the following problem, and answer it before you read on.

> The equation for a reaction is $2S + 3O_2 \rightarrow 2SO_3$. Consider the mixture of S and O_2 in a closed container as illustrated below:
>
> 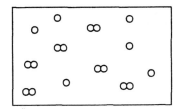   ← This represents the entire container.
>
> Sketch a molecular-level representation of the product mixture.

In order to answer this question we need to take note of two things:

1.   The number of molecules of each reactant given.

2.   The ratio of the reactants that are needed.

The first piece of information is given in the problem; that is, there are six molecules of each reactant given. The second piece of information comes from the balanced equation; that is, for every two molecules of sulfur (S), three molecules of oxygen (O_2) are needed – or, for every two moles of sulfur (S), three moles of oxygen (O_2) are needed.

We can visualize this ratio by circling the reactants that react with each other as shown below:

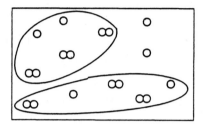

The reactants produce the compound sulfur trioxide (SO_3) and we can represent the product mixture (including any leftover reactant) as:

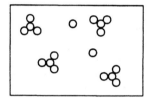

We can see that four molecules of SO_3 are produced, and two atoms of S are leftover (unreacted). Make sure to understand this problem because it covers the basic concepts of stoichiometry. It even considers limiting reactants, which many students find to be the most difficult section of this chapter. The rest of stoichiometry has to do with the math (mass-mole conversions, essentially), and we will consider this briefly later.

While sketching these pictures is a good way of thinking about the problems initially, it is rather inefficient to solve all problems this way and you will eventually want to formalize the solution a bit more. Before reading on, though, make sure to understand this example. See Section 9.4 (The Concept of Limiting Reactants) in your text for an extended discussion and another example of using molecular-level pictures to understand the concept of limiting reactants.

Formalizing a Solution

Let's consider the same problem, but different (and perhaps more efficient) ways of solving it. Recall the problem:

You react 6 moles of S with 6 moles of O_2 according to the equation:

$$2S + 3O_2 \rightarrow 2SO_3$$

Calculate the number of moles of SO_3 produced and the number of moles of leftover reactant.

Solution I

One way to solve this problem is to determine the number of moles of product formed if each reactant reacted completely. That is, change the given problem to two separate problems:

1. How many moles of SO_3 could be produced from 6 moles of S and excess O_2?

2. How many moles of SO_3 could be produced from 6 moles of O_2 and excess S?

To answer this question we still need to know (as with the molecular-level sketch solution earlier) the number of moles we have (given in the problem) and the ratio from the balanced equation. Answer the two questions above before reading on.

From six moles of S, we can produce six moles of SO_3. There are a few ways to solve this: with ratios, dimensional analysis or even by inspection (the mole ratio between S and SO_3 is 2:2 or 1:1, thus for every 6 moles of S reacted, 6 moles of SO_3 will be produced).

From six moles of O_2, we can produce four moles of SO_3. Again, solve this using ratios or dimensional analysis. For example:

$$6 \text{ moles } O_2 \times \left(\frac{2 \text{ moles } SO_3}{3 \text{ moles } O_2} \right) = 4 \text{ moles } SO_3$$

So now we have 2 answers. That is, we have calculated 6 moles SO_3 and 4 moles SO_3. We know from our molecular-level sketch that the answer is 4 moles. Note that it is NOT 10 moles – we do NOT simply add up the answers. Why not? Let's make sense of this.

Realize what these two answers represent. They are the maximum amount of product that could be produced if the given reactant is used up completely. The answer must be the smaller number (four moles in this case) because there is not enough O_2 to form six moles of SO_3. Once four moles of SO_3 are produced, there is no O_2 left, thus no more SO_3 can be produced. We now know, then, that four moles of SO_3 can be produced, and that O_2 is the limiting reactant; that is, the reactant that limits the reaction is the one that runs out first.

So if all of the O_2 is used up, how much of the S is used? How much of the S is leftover? We can answer these questions similarly to the previous question. We know that all six moles of O_2 are reacted. How many moles of sulfur (S) would the reaction require? Recall that the ratio between S and O_2 is 2:3 (from the balanced equation). Thus, we get

$$6 \text{ moles } O_2 \times \left(\frac{2 \text{ moles } SO_3}{3 \text{ moles } O_2} \right) = 4 \text{ moles } S$$

What do the four moles sulfur (S) represent? The four moles represent the S that is required to react with the six moles of O_2. We initially had six moles of sulfur, and four moles of S were reacted. So how many moles are left? Two moles of sulfur, just as we saw with our molecular-level sketches. This method is one way of formalizing this problem – calculate the moles of product formed if each reactant went to completion, and decide which reactant is limiting.

Solution II

There is another way we can solve this problem: by comparing what we are given to what is needed for a complete reaction. For example, recall the problem:

You react 6 moles of S with 6 moles of O_2 according to the equation

$$2S + 3O_2 \rightarrow 2SO_3$$

Calculate the number of moles of SO_3 produced and the number of moles of leftover reactant.

We know that we have 6 moles of S and 6 moles of O_2. Can we determine which reactant is limiting without solving for the product twice?

We need to calculate the moles of each reactant needed to react with the moles of the other reactant that we are given. For example, we know that we have six moles of sulfur. How many moles of oxygen would be required to react completely with these six moles? Try this before reading on.

You should be able to calculate that nine moles of oxygen (O_2) are needed to react with six moles of sulfur (S). Use the mole ratio given in the balanced equation to do so. If you are still having difficulty doing this, you need to talk with your instructor.

We know from the last solution (Solution I) that four moles of S are required to react with 6 moles of O_2. We can present this information in the following table:

	moles sulfur (S)	*moles oxygen (O_2)*
have	6 moles S	6 moles O_2
need	4 moles S	9 moles O_2

Note that we have more moles of sulfur than we need, and fewer moles of O_2 than we need. Thus, O_2 must be the limiting reactant (the reactant that runs out first). We will therefore use the oxygen data to calculate the moles of product (SO_3) formed. That is:

$$6 \text{ moles } O_2 \times \left(\frac{2 \text{ moles } SO_3}{3 \text{ moles } O_2} \right) = 4 \text{ moles } SO_3$$

Also, we can see from the table above that we have six moles of sulfur and need four moles of sulfur, thus two moles of sulfur are leftover. This solution also agrees with our previous solution. It also agrees with our next solution, as we shall see.

Solution III

Another way of thinking about this problem is to set up a table which includes all of the information shown in Solution I and Solution II. For example, consider the following:

	2S	+	$3O_2$	→	$2SO_3$
Initial	6		6		0
Change	– ?		– ?		+ ?
End	?		?		?

Note that the six moles of each reactant (and no product initially) are represented in the "Initial" row. The "Change" row represents how much of each chemical reacts or is produced. The "End" row represents what constitutes the final reaction mixture.

Because we are assuming that the reaction runs to completion, we know that one (or possibly both) of the values for sulfur or oxygen must be zero (0) in the end row; that is, we "run out" of one (or possibly both) of the reactants. But which one? We can decide this by realizing a crucial point:

The change row ratio has to be the same as the ratio of the coefficients in the balanced equation.

Make sure you understand this. The balanced equation represents the ratio of the reactants that react and the products that are formed; the change row represents the same thing.

Let's look, then, at the two possibilities:

	2S	+	3O$_2$	→	2SO$_3$
Initial	6		6		0
Change	−6		−9		+6
End	0		−3		6

	2S	+	3O$_2$	→	2SO$_3$
Initial	6		6		0
Change	−4		−6		+4
End	2		0		4

In the first table, we are assuming that all of the sulfur is reacted, and in the second example we are assuming that all of the oxygen is used. We have already looked at other solutions to this problem so we know that the answers to the second table are correct. But we can see why sulfur is not limiting by looking at the first table. For all of the sulfur to react, we need three more moles of oxygen than we have. We cannot end up with a negative amount of oxygen so the first table must be incorrect.

Using a table is convenient in that all of the possible information is displayed; we now know which reactant is limiting, how much of the excess reactant is leftover, and how much product is formed. It also emphasizes an understanding of what a balanced equation means because we have to use the ratio for the balanced equation in the "change" row.

Stoichiometry Problems with Masses

Once you understand the concepts of stoichiometry, the rest is math. Most typical problems will give you mass data of reactants, for example, and ask for the mass of products formed. As an example, consider the following problem:

> Hydrogen gas (H_2) reacts with oxygen gas (O_2) to form water (H_2O). If you react 10.0 g of hydrogen gas with 10.0 g of oxygen gas, what mass of water can be produced? How much of which reactant is left over?

Try to solve this problem before reading on. Remember, think about the problem before merely plugging numbers into an equation.

One way to start is to determine the balanced equation for the reaction. We know that we will need to know the mole ratio of the reactants and products to solve this problem.

You should get: $2H_2 + O_2 \rightarrow 2H_2O$ as the balanced equation.

This equation tells us that for every two moles of hydrogen gas, we need one mole of oxygen gas to make two moles of water. We need to know how many moles of each reactant we have. How do we do this? By now you should know how to convert from grams to moles. In this case, you should be able to calculate the following values:

moles H_2 : 4.96 moles

moles O_2 : 0.313 moles

If you are having difficulty getting these numbers, review molar mass in Chapter 8 of your text or talk with an instructor.

Now that we know the number of moles of each reactant, we can solve the questions that were asked in the problem. You should be able to calculate the following:

mass of water formed: 11.3 g

mass hydrogen left over: 8.74 g

If you are having difficulty with this, review the various solutions to the previous problem in this *Study Guide*.

Active Learning Questions

The Active Learning Questions at the end of each chapter are conceptually based questions that work well as discussion questions with a group of students. If your instructor does not assign these, consider getting together with a group of classmates and using these questions to see how well you understand the material in each chapter. While all of the questions work well for these, Active Learning Questions 3, 4 and 21 are visual problems dealing with the concept of limiting reactants, questions 7, 8, 15, 16 and 20 are multiple choice questions that will cause a great deal of discussion, and question 18 asks you to explain a graph that should help you come to a stronger understanding of mole ratios. You are strongly encouraged to answer these.

Learning Review

1. Rewrite the equation below in terms of moles of reactants and products.

$$6.022 \times 10^{23} \text{ molecules } H_2(g) + 6.022 \times 10^{23} \text{ molecules } I_2(g) \rightarrow 1.204 \times 10^{24} \text{ molecules } HI(g)$$

2. How many moles of hydrogen gas could be produced from 0.8 mol sodium and an excess of water? Solve this problem by writing the equation using moles and by using the mole ratio for sodium and hydrogen.

$$2Na(s) + 2H_2O(l) \rightarrow 2NaOH(aq) + H_2(g)$$

3. How many moles of aluminum oxide could be produced from 0.12 mol Al?

$$4Al(s) + 3O_2(g) \rightarrow 2Al_2O_3(s)$$

4. How many moles of zinc chloride would be formed by the reaction of 1.38 mol Zn with HCl?

$$Zn(s) + 2HCl(aq) \rightarrow ZnCl_2(aq) + H_2(g)$$

5. Solid silver carbonate decomposes to produce silver metal, oxygen gas and carbon dioxide.

   a. Write a balanced chemical equation for this reaction.

   b. What mass of silver will be produced by the decomposition of 6.32 g silver carbonate?

6. When aqueous solutions of sodium sulfate and lead(II) nitrate are mixed, a solid white precipitate is formed. How much solid lead(II) sulfate could be produced from 12.0 g Na_2SO_4 if $Pb(NO_3)_2$ is in excess?

$$Na_2SO_4(aq) + Pb(NO_3)_2(aq) \rightarrow PbSO_4(s) + 2NaNO_3(aq)$$

7. Hydrogen gas and chlorine gas will combine to produce gaseous hydrogen chloride. How many molecules of hydrogen chloride can be produced from 20.1 g hydrogen gas and excess chlorine gas?

8. Some lightweight backpacking stoves use kerosene as a fuel. Kerosene is composed of carbon and hydrogen, and although it is a mixture of molecules, we can represent the formula of kerosene as $C_{11}H_{24}$. When a kerosene stove is lit, the fuel reacts with oxygen in the air to produce

carbon dioxide gas and water vapor. If it takes 15 g of kerosene to fry a trout for dinner, how many grams of water are produced?

$$C_{11}H_{24}(l) + 17O_2(g) \rightarrow 11CO_2(g) + 12H_2O(g)$$

9.   You are trying to prepare six copies of a three-page report. If you have on hand six copies of pages one and two, and four copies of page three.

    a.   How many complete reports can you produce?

    b.   Which page limits the number of complete reports you can produce?

10.   Manganese(IV) oxide reacts with hydrochloric acid to produce chlorine gas, manganese(II) chloride and water.

$$MnO_2(s) + 4HCl(aq) \rightarrow Cl_2(g) + MnCl_2(aq) + 2H_2O(l)$$

    a.   When 10.2 g MnO_2 react with 18.3 g HCl, which is the limiting reactant?

    b.   What mass of chlorine gas can be produced?

    c.   How many molecules of water can be produced?

11.   The acid-base reaction between phosphoric acid and magnesium hydroxide produces solid magnesium phosphate and liquid water. If 121.0 g of phosphoric acid reacts with 89.70 g magnesium hydroxide, how many grams of magnesium phosphate will be produced?

12.   If 85.6 g of potassium iodide reacts with 2.41×10^{24} molecules of chlorine gas, how many grams of iodine can be produced?

$$Cl_2(g) + 2KI(s) \rightarrow 2KCl(s) + I_2(s)$$

13.   Aqueous sodium iodide reacts with aqueous lead(II) nitrate to produce the yellow precipitate lead(II) iodide and aqueous sodium nitrate.

    a.   What is the theoretical yield of lead iodide if 125.5 g of sodium iodide reacts with 205.6 g of lead nitrate?

    b.   If the actual yield from this reaction is 197.5 g lead iodide, what is the percent yield?

Answers to Learning Review

1. 6.022×10^{23} molecules is equivalent to 1 mol of molecules and 1.204×10^{24} molecules is equivalent to $2(6.022 \times 10^{23}$ molecules), so the equation can be rewritten as:

$$1 \text{ mol } H_2(g) + 1 \text{ mol } I_2(g) \rightarrow 2 \text{ mol } HI(g)$$

2.   The balanced equation tells us that two moles of sodium react with two moles of water to form two moles of sodium hydroxide and four moles of hydrogen. By using mole ratios determined from the balanced equation, we can calculate the number of moles of reactants required and products produced from 0.8 mol sodium.

$$0.8 \text{ mol Na} \times \frac{2 \text{ mol } H_2O}{2 \text{ mol Na}} = 0.8 \text{ mol } H_2O \qquad \text{0.8 mol sodium requires 0.8 mol } H_2O.$$

$$0.8 \text{ mol Na} \times \frac{2 \text{ mol NaOH}}{2 \text{ mol Na}} = 0.8 \text{ mol NaOH} \qquad \text{0.8 mol Na produces 0.8 mol NaOH.}$$

$$0.8 \text{ mol Na} \times \frac{1 \text{ mol } H_2}{2 \text{ mol Na}} = 0.4 \text{ mol } H_2 \qquad \text{0.8 mol Na produces 0.4 mol } H_2.$$

We can write the molar values we have calculated in equation form.

$$0.8 \text{ mol Na}(s) + 0.8 \text{ mol } H_2O(l) \rightarrow 0.8 \text{ mol NaOH}(aq) + 0.4 \text{ mol } H_2(g)$$

3.   First, make sure the equation is balanced. You should always determine whether or not an equation is balanced, and balance it if necessary. To solve this problem, we need to know the mole ratio for aluminum and aluminum oxide. The mole ratio represents the relationship between the mol of substance given in the problem and the mol of the desired substance, and is taken directly from the balanced equation. The mole ratio for aluminum oxide and aluminum is.

$$\frac{2 \text{ mol } Al_2O_3}{4 \text{ mol Al}}$$

$$0.12 \text{ mol Al} \times \frac{2 \text{ mol } Al_2O_3}{4 \text{ mol Al}} = 0.060 \text{ mol } Al_2O_3$$

4.   First, make sure the equation is balanced. The mole ratio for zinc and zinc chloride is taken from the balanced equation and is.

$$\frac{1 \text{ mol } ZnCl_2}{1 \text{ mol Zn}}$$

$$1.38 \text{ mol Zn} \times \frac{1 \text{ mol } ZnCl_2}{1 \text{ mol Zn}} = 1.38 \text{ mol } ZnCl_2$$

Because there is a 1:1 mole ratio of $ZnCl_2$ to Zn, the number of moles of zinc equals the moles of zinc chloride produced.

5.   a.   First, write the formulas for reactants and products. Include the physical states. Then, balance the equation.

$$2Ag_2CO_3(s) \rightarrow 4Ag(s) + O_2(g) + 2CO_2(g)$$

     b.   It is <u>not</u> possible to solve this problem by converting directly from grams of Ag_2CO_3 to grams of Ag. However, the balanced equation tells us the relationship between Ag_2CO_3 and Ag in moles. If we can convert grams of Ag_2CO_3 to moles, we can use the mole ratio to tell us how many moles of Ag are produced. To convert grams of Ag_2CO_3 to moles, you can produce a conversion factor from the equivalence statement that relates number of moles to molar mass. The correct conversion factor is:

$$\frac{1 \text{ mol } Ag_2CO_3}{275.75 \text{ g } Ag_2CO_3}$$

$$6.32 \text{ g } Ag_2CO_3 \times \frac{1 \text{ mol } Ag_2CO_3}{275.75 \text{ g } Ag_2CO_3} = 0.0229 \text{ mol } Ag_2CO_3$$

Now, we can use the mole ratio for Ag_2CO_3 and Ag to calculate the moles of Ag.

$$0.0229 \text{ mol Ag}_2CO_3 \times \frac{4 \text{ mol Ag}}{2 \text{ mol Ag}_2CO_3} = 0.0458 \text{ mol Ag}$$

We now know the moles of Ag, but we want to know the grams of Ag. The conversion factor below, which is derived from the molar mass of silver, will allow us to calculate grams.

$$\frac{107.87 \text{ g Ag}}{1 \text{ mol Ag}}$$

$$0.0458 \text{ mol Ag} \times \frac{107.87 \text{ g Ag}}{1 \text{ mol Ag}} = 4.94 \text{ g Ag}$$

If we string together all the parts of this problem, we can see that the overall strategy is to convert grams to moles using the molar mass, then moles to moles using the mole ratio, and moles to mass using the molar mass.

$$6.32 \text{ g Ag2CO3} \times \frac{1 \text{ mol Ag}_2CO_3}{175.75 \text{ g Ag}_2CO_3} \times \frac{4 \text{ mol Ag}}{2 \text{ mol Ag}_2CO_3} \times \frac{107.87 \text{ g Ag}}{1 \text{ mol Ag}} = 4.94 \text{ g Ag}$$

↑	↑	↑	↑	↑
grams of reactant	molar mass of reactant	mole ratio	molar mass of product	grams of product

6.   This question provides us with grams of reactant and asks for grams of product. Because we are told that $Pb(NO_3)_2$ is in excess, the limiting reactant must be Na_2SO_4. The amount of precipitate that can be formed is determined by the amount of Na_2SO_4 to grams $PbSO_4$. We must first calculate the moles of Na_2SO_4, then use the mole ratio derived from the balanced equation to tell us how many moles of $PbSO_4$ are produced, and finally, we can use the molar mass of $PbSO_4$ to calculate the grams of $PbSO_4$.

$$12.0 \text{ g Na}_2SO_4 \times \frac{1 \text{ mol Na}_2SO_4}{142.05 \text{ g Na}_2SO_4} \times \frac{1 \text{ mol PbSO}_4}{1 \text{ mol Na}_2SO_4} \times \frac{303.27 \text{ g PbSO}_4}{1 \text{ mol PbSO}_4} = 25.6 \text{ g PbSO}_4$$

7.   First, write the balanced equation for this reaction.

$$H_2(g) + Cl_2(g) \rightarrow 2HCl(g)$$

This problem gives us grams of hydrogen and asks for molecules of hydrogen chloride. There is no way to convert grams of hydrogen directly to molecules of hydrogen chloride. However, we can convert grams of hydrogen to moles of hydrogen using the molar mass of hydrogen gas. The balanced equation provides a mole ratio so that we can calculate the moles of hydrogen chloride. Converting from moles to molecules can be done because we know that 1 mole of hydrogen chloride equals 6.022×10^{23} molecules of hydrogen chloride.

$$20.1 \text{ g H}_2 \times \frac{1 \text{ mol H}_2}{2.016 \text{ g H}_2} \times \frac{2 \text{ mol HCl}}{1 \text{ mol H}_2} \times \frac{6.022 \times 10^{23} \text{ molecules HCl}}{1 \text{ mol HCl}}$$
$$= 1.20 \times 10^{25} \text{ molecules}$$

8.   We are given grams of kerosene and asked for grams of water vapor. Because we cannot convert directly between grams of kerosene and grams of water, we first convert grams of kerosene to moles of kerosene using the molar mass of kerosene. Then, use the mole ratio of kerosene and water from the balanced equation to determine the moles of water vapor. The molar mass of water will allow us to convert moles to grams of water.

$$15 \text{ g C}_{11}\text{H}_{24} \times \frac{1 \text{ mol C}_{11}\text{H}_{24}}{156.30 \text{ g C}_{11}\text{H}_{24}} \times \frac{12 \text{ mol H}_2\text{O}}{1 \text{ mol C}_{11}\text{H}_{24}} \times \frac{18.02 \text{ g H}_2\text{O}}{1 \text{ mol H}_2\text{O}} = 21 \text{ g H}_2\text{O}$$

9.   a.   You can prepare 4 complete copies. Copies 4 and 5 would lack page 3.

       b.   Page 3 limits the number of complete reports that can be produced.

10.   a.   By looking at the grams of MnO_2 and the grams of HCl, it is impossible to tell which is the limiting reactant. It is possible to compare moles of reactants because we know the mole ratio of reactants from the balanced equation. So, calculate the number of moles of each reactant. Then determine how many moles of product could be produced from each of the two reactants. The reactant that allows the fewest number of moles of product is the limiting reactant.

$$10.2 \text{ g MnO}_2 \times \frac{1 \text{ mol MnO}_2}{86.94 \text{ g MnO}_2} \times \frac{1 \text{ mol Cl}_2}{1 \text{ mol MnO}_2} = 0.117 \text{ mol Cl}_2$$

$$18.3 \text{ g HCl} \times \frac{1 \text{ mol HCl}}{36.46 \text{ g HCl}} \times \frac{1 \text{ mol Cl}_2}{4 \text{ mol HCl}} = 0.125 \text{ mol Cl}_2$$

       From 10.2 MnO_2, 0.117 mol Cl_2 can be produced, and from 18.3 g HCl, 0.125 mol Cl_2 can be produced. So the limiting reactant is MnO_2.

       b.   We already know that the most chlorine we can make is 0.117 mol. To convert from moles to grams, use the molar mass of a chlorine molecule.

$$0.117 \text{ mol Cl}_2 \times \frac{70.90 \text{ g Cl}_2}{1 \text{ mol Cl}_2} = 8.30 \text{ g Cl}_2$$

       c.   The limiting reactant is manganese(IV) oxide so we need to calculate the moles of water that can be produced from 10.2 g MnO_2. By using the mole ratio from the balanced equation we can calculate the moles of water. To convert from moles of water to the number of molecules, use Avogadro's number as a conversion factor.

$$10.2 \text{ g MnO}_2 \times \frac{1 \text{ mol MnO}_2}{86.94 \text{ g MnO}_2} \times \frac{2 \text{ mol H}_2\text{O}}{1 \text{ mol MnO}_2} \times \frac{6.022 \times 10^{23} \text{ molecules H}_2\text{O}}{1 \text{ mol H}_2\text{O}}$$
$$= 1.41 \times 10^{23} \text{ molecules H}_2\text{O}$$

11.   First, write the balanced equation for this reaction.

$$2H_3PO_4(aq) + 3Mg(OH)_2(s) \rightarrow Mg_3(PO_4)_2(s) + 6H_2O(l)$$

       When the mass is given for two reactants, and you are asked to determine the quantity of product which can be produced, you must first determine which reactant is limiting. Determine how many moles of product would be produced from each reactant. The reactant that will produce the fewest number of moles of product is the limiting reactant.

$$121.0 \text{ g H}_3\text{PO}_4 \times \frac{1 \text{ mol H}_3\text{PO}_4}{97.99 \text{ g H}_3\text{PO}_4} \times \frac{1 \text{ mol Mg}_3(\text{PO}_4)_2}{2 \text{ mol H}_3\text{PO}_4} = 0.6174 \text{ mol Mg}_3(\text{PO}_4)_2$$

$$89.70 \text{ g Mg(OH)}_2 \times \frac{1 \text{ mol Mg(OH)}_2}{58.33 \text{ g Mg(OH)}_2} \times \frac{1 \text{ mol Mg}_3(\text{PO}_4)_2}{3 \text{ mol Mg(OH)}_2} = 0.5126 \text{ mol Mg}_3(\text{PO}_4)_2$$

In this reaction, the $Mg(OH)_2$ is the limiting reactant. We now know how many moles of $Mg_3(PO_4)_2$ are produced, but we want to know the number of grams. Use the molar mass of $Mg(PO_4)_2$ to convert from moles of grams.

$$0.5126 \text{ mol Mg}_3(\text{PO4})_2 \times \frac{262.87 \text{ g Mg}_3(\text{PO4})_2}{1 \text{ mol Mg}_3(\text{PO4})_2} = 134.7 \text{ g Mg}_3(\text{PO4})_2$$

12. In this problem we are given quantities of two reactants, one expressed in grams and the other in molecules. Before we can calculate grams of product, we need to know which reactant limits the amount of product that can be produced. Convert the grams of KI to moles using the molar mass of KI and calculate the moles of I_2 from the mole ratio.

$$85.6 \text{ g KI} \times \frac{1 \text{ mol KI}}{166.0 \text{ g KI}} \times \frac{1 \text{ mol I}_2}{2 \text{ mol KI}} = 0.258 \text{ mol I}_2$$

The quantity of the other reactant, Cl_2, is given in molecules, not grams. We can convert molecules of Cl_2 to moles of Cl_2 using Avogadro's number. $1 \text{ mol Cl}_2 = 6.022 \times 10^{23}$ molecules Cl_2.

$$2.41 \times 10^{24} \text{ molecules Cl}_2 \times \frac{1 \text{ mol Cl}_2}{6.022 \times 10^{23} \text{ molecules Cl}_2} = 4.00 \text{ mol Cl}_2$$

So 2.41×10^{24} molecules is equivalent to 4.00 moles of Cl_2. Now we can find the moles of I_2 that can be produced from 4.00 moles of Cl_2.

$$4.00 \text{ mol Cl}_2 \times \frac{1 \text{ mol I}_2}{1 \text{ mol Cl}_2} = 4.00 \text{ mol I}_2$$

KI limits the amount of I_2 that can be produced, so it is the limiting reactant. We can calculate the grams of I_2 using the molar mass of I_2.

$$0.258 \text{ mol I}_2 \times \frac{253.8 \text{ g I}_2}{1 \text{ mol I}_2} = 65.5 \text{ g Cl}_2$$

13. a. First, balance the equation.

$$2 \text{ NaI} + \text{Pb(NO}_3)_2 \rightarrow \text{PbI}_2 + 2 \text{ NaNO}_3$$

This problem first asks for the theoretical yield of PbI_2 when two quantities of reactants are mixed. Before we can calculate the amount of product, we need to know which reactant is limiting. Use the molar mass for each product and the mole ratio for the balanced equation to calculate the moles of PbI_2 that could be produced.

$$125.5 \text{ g NaI} \times \frac{1 \text{ mol NaI}}{149.89 \text{ g NaI}} \times \frac{1 \text{ mol PbI}_2}{2 \text{ mol NaI}} = 0.4186 \text{ mol PbI}_2$$

$$205.6 \text{ g Pb(NO}_3)_2 \times \frac{1 \text{ mol Pb(NO}_3)_2}{331.22 \text{ g Pb(NO}_3)_2} \times \frac{1 \text{ mol PbI}_2}{1 \text{ mol Pb(NO}_3)_2} = 0.6207 \text{ mol PbI}_2$$

The limiting reactant is NaI. Now we can answer the question about theoretical yield. Theoretical is the amount of product we calculate can be produced, that is, 0.4186 mol PbI_2. In real life, the actual yield might be less than the calculated yield. The theoretical yield of PbI_2 can be calculated from the number of moles of PbI_2 if we know the molar mass.

$$0.4186 \text{ mol PbI}_2 \times \frac{461.00 \text{ g PbI}_2}{1 \text{ mol PbI}_2} = 193.0 \text{ g PbI}_2$$

b.   In part a we calculated the theoretical yield of lead(II) iodide, which is 193.0 g. We are told that the actual yield from this reaction was found to be 164.5 g. The percent yield is equal to the actual yield divided by the theoretical yield, multiplied by 100 percent. So the percent yield of lead(II) iodide is

$$\frac{164.5 \text{ g PbI}_2}{193.0 \text{ g PbI}_2} \times 100\% = 85.23\%$$

CHAPTER 10

Energy

Introduction

Chemistry is about matter and its changes. As part of all chemical reactions, energy (in the form of heat) is either released or required. Even though energy is converted from one form to another as a chemical reaction proceeds, the total amount of energy in the universe is constant (this is known as the law of conservation of energy). In this chapter you will learn about the nature of energy and energy sources, discover how we can predict whether or not a reaction will be spontaneous, and calculate the amount of energy needed to heat water and other substances.

Chapter Discussion

Energy is defined as the ability to do work or produce heat. For example, imagine that we move a chair across a room. We do work on the chair because we need to exert a force to get the chair to move, and we move it over a certain distance (work is defined as a force acting over a distance). The heavier the chair, the more force required, so the more work is done (or the more energy is required). The farther we move the chair (the larger the distance), the more work is done, and the more energy is required. Heat is flow of energy due to a temperature difference. Although we often talk of heat as though it were a substance ("Close the window, you are letting the heat out."), heat is not a "thing."

Another useful way of thinking about energy is the following:

Energy is what is required in order to resist a natural tendency.

For example, consider holding a bowling ball above your head. You are not moving the ball so there is no work. But obviously you get tired after awhile, so it feels as though you are exerting energy. How can this be? The natural tendency of the bowling ball is to fall to the ground (due to gravity). By keeping the ball from falling, you are making the ball resist its natural tendency and you are exerting energy. The same goes if you are holding a string connected to a helium balloon. The natural tendency of the balloon is to float away, and by holding the string, you are keeping the balloon from doing so. This action, too, requires energy.

In discussing energy, you also need to keep in mind the distinction between potential energy and kinetic energy. The "ball on a hill" example given in the text is a good one to read and understand, but it is a non-chemical example. When thinking about chemistry, keep in mind that the potential energy of a chemical system is stored in the bonds (you will learn more about chemical bonds in Chapter 12, but it is enough for now to know that chemical bond is a force that holds atoms together in a molecule). In order to break apart a molecule, energy is required to break the bonds. As bonds re-form when new molecules are made, energy is released in the form of heat (as kinetic energy).

Let's look at the reaction for combustion of methane, which occurs in a Bunsen burner:

$$CH_4(g) + 2O_2(g) \rightarrow CO_2(g) + H_2O(l)$$

In this case, more energy is released when the bonds form CO_2 and H_2O than is required to break the bonds in CH_4 and O_2. Thus, this reaction is exothermic and we report the heat with a negative sign (in this case ($\Delta H = -891$ kJ/mol). See Figure 10.5 in your text for a potential energy diagram of this reaction. It would be a good idea to see if you can draw a similar diagram for an endothermic reaction.

You should also be able to differentiate between heat and temperature. Specifically, make sure you understand that heat and temperature are not the same. Temperature is a measure of the random motions of the particles that make up a substance. The concept of specific heat capacity helps us see this difference. You have seen that different substances change temperatures differently when the same amount of heat is transferred. For example, if you are making soup on the stove and are stirring with a metal spoon, you notice that the spoon gets hot rather quickly. A wooden spoon does not get nearly so hot, even though the amount of heat in the soup is the same. Why is this? Different substances, due to their composition, react to heat differently. We quantify this property with the specific heat capacity, which is defined as the amount of energy required to change the temperature of one gram of the substance by one Celsius degree. See Table 10.1 in your text for a list of specific heat capacities, and notice that the heat capacities of metals are lower than water. The temperature of a given mass of metal will increase much more than the temperature of the same mass of water when the same amount of heat is transferred to each. Practice doing problems dealing with specific heat capacities to make sure you can either use heat capacities to calculate temperature differences, or that you can calculate heat capacities and determine the substance that is being heated or cooled.

You will also be expected to calculate the heat (enthalpy) or a reaction from known heats of related reactions. You can do this using Hess's law, which works because energy is a state function. Make sure you understand how Hess's law uses the idea of energy as a state function (in other words, the law relies on the existence of the first law of thermodynamics – make sure you know why).

While energy is conserved (that is, the quantity stays the same), the quality of energy is constantly decreasing. That is, the amount of usefulness of a sample of energy decreases as the energy is used. The example used in your text is gasoline. A sample of gasoline can be thought of as concentrated energy (potential energy); however, as you drive the car, heat is released to the road and the air. While the amount of energy in the universe is the same before and after you drive your car, the usefulness of that energy has decreased. Natural processes always occur in a way that increases the "spreading" of energy, and thus decreases the usefulness of the energy. We call this concept entropy, a measure of disorder. For a process to be spontaneous, the entropy of the universe must increase.

Active Learning Questions

The Active Learning Questions at the end of each chapter are conceptually based questions that work well as discussion questions with a group of students. If your instructor does not assign these, consider getting together with a group of classmates and using these questions to see how well you understand the material in each chapter. While all of the questions work well, Active Learning Questions 2 and 3 help differentiate between the terms *endothermic* and *exothermic*, questions 9-12 focus on energy as a driving force, and questions 16 and 17 test your understanding of heat capacity. You are strongly encouraged to answer these.

Learning Review

1.   Explain the difference between *kinetic energy* and *potential energy*.

2.   Why isn't all energy available as work?

3.   The law of conservation of energy means that energy is a state function. Explain why.

4.   Explain differences among heat, temperature and thermal energy.

5.   Provide a molecular-level explanation of why the temperatures of a cold soft drink and a hot coffee in the same room will eventually be the same.

6. In which case is more heat involved: mixing 100.0-g samples of 90 °C water and 80 °C water or mixing 100.0-g samples of 60 °C water and 10 °C water? Assume no heat is lost to the environment.

7. What is meant by potential energy in a chemical reaction? Where is it located?

8. Are the following processes exothermic or endothermic?

 a. When solid KBr is dissolved in water, the solution gets colder.

 b. Natural gas (CH_4) is burned in a furnace.

 c. When concentrated sulfuric acid is added to water, the solution gets very hot.

 d. Water is boiled in a tea kettle.

9. In thermodynamics, the chemist takes the system's point of view. What does this statement mean?

10. A gas absorbs 45 kJ of heat and does 29 kJ of work. Calculate ΔE.

11. Convert the energy values below to the desired units:

 a. 45.8 cal to J

 b. 0.561 cal to J

 c. 5.96 J to cal

 d. 76 J to cal

12. Calculate the number of calories required to change the temperature of each of the quantities of water below.

 a. 100.1 g of water from 6°C to 25°C

 b. 2.32 g of water from 36°F to 42°F

 c. 40 g of water by 12°C

 d. 16.9 g of water from 75.0°C to 80.0°C

13. How much energy (in joules) is required to raise the temperature of 25.2 g of solid carbon rod from 25°C to 50.°C? The specific heat capacity of solid carbon is 0.71 J/g°C.

14. How much energy (in calories) is required to raise the temperature of 10. g steam from 122.2°C to 130.4°C? The specific heat capacity of water(g) is 2.0 J/g°C.

15. How much of a temperature change would occur if 2736.8 J of energy were applied to a piece of iron bar weighing 450.5 g? The specific heat capacity of solid iron is 0.45 J/g°C.

16. What is the mass in grams of a piece of aluminum wire if a change in temperature of 5.67°C required 8.53 J? The specific heat capacity of solid aluminum is 0.89 J/g°C.

17. What is the specific heat capacity of ethyl alcohol if 1972.4 J of energy is necessary to raise the temperature of 53.4 g ethyl alcohol by 15.2°C?

18. Calculate the enthalpy change when 1.00 g of methane is burned in excess oxygen according to the reaction $CH_4(g) + 2O_2(g) \rightarrow CO_2(g) + H_2O(l)$ ($\Delta H = -891$ kJ/mol).

19. Given the following data:

$$C_2H_2(g) + \tfrac{5}{2} O_2(g) \rightarrow 2CO_2(g) + H_2O(l) \qquad \Delta H = -1300. \text{ kJ/mol}$$

$$C(s) + O_2(g) \rightarrow CO_2(g) \qquad \Delta H = -394 \text{ kJ/mol}$$

$$H_2(g) + \tfrac{1}{2} O_2(g) \rightarrow H_2O(l) \qquad \Delta H = -286 \text{ kJ/mol}$$

calculate ΔH for the reaction

$$2C(s) + H_2(g) \rightarrow C_2H_2(g)$$

20. What is the difference between the *quality* of energy and the *quantity* of energy? Which is decreasing?

21. Which energy sources used in the United States have declined the most in the last 150 years? Which have increased the most?

22. Why can't the first law of thermodynamics explain why a ball doesn't spontaneously roll up a hill?

23. Exothermic reactions have a driving force. Nevertheless, water melting into a liquid is endothermic and this process occurs at room temperature. Explain why.

Answers to Learning Review

1. Kinetic energy is the energy of motion. Potential energy is the energy of position.

2. Some energy is given off in other forms such as heat or light.

3. Because energy is conserved in any process, the pathway of the process does not matter. This statement means that energy is a state function.

4. Heat is a flow of energy due to a temperature difference; temperature is a measure of the average kinetic energy of a substance; thermal energy comes from the random motion of the components of the system.

5. Temperature is a measure of the average kinetic energy of the samples. The "coffee particles" (mostly water molecules) are of higher average kinetic energy than the "air particles" (a mixture of mostly nitrogen and oxygen molecules) in the room, which are of higher energy than the "soft drink particles" (mostly water molecules). At the coffee-air interface a collision of higher-energy coffee particles and air particles results in energy being transferred from the coffee to the room. Transfer also occurs from air to soft drink because air particles are of higher energy than the soft drink particles (due to the temperature difference). The energy transfers result in the eventual average kinetic energies of each sample being equal, which means the temperatures are equal. Because the volume of air is so large (the system is open), no noticeable temperature change of the air will result.

6. There is more heat involved in mixing 100.0-g samples of 60 °C and 10 °C water because there is a large temperature difference (and heat is a flow of energy due to a temperature difference).

7. The potential energy is the energy available to do work. Potential energy in a chemical reaction is stored in the chemical bonds.

8.   a.   endothermic

       b.   exothermic

       c.   exothermic

       d.   endothermic

9.   The chemist chooses the sign based on whether energy flows from the system (negative sign) or into the system (positive sign).

10. $\Delta E = q + w = 45 \text{ kJ} + (-29 \text{ kJ}) = 16 \text{ kJ}$

11.   Converting calories to joules or joules to calories requires knowing that 1 cal = 4.184 J.

       a. $45.8 \text{ cal} \times \dfrac{4.184 \text{ J}}{1 \text{ cal}} = 192 \text{ J}$

       b. $0.561 \text{ cal} \times \dfrac{4.184 \text{ J}}{1 \text{ cal}} = 2.35 \text{ J}$

       c. $5.96 \text{ J} \times \dfrac{1 \text{ cal}}{4.184 \text{ J}} = 1.42 \text{ cal}$

       d. $76 \text{ J} \times \dfrac{1 \text{ cal}}{4.184 \text{ J}} = 18 \text{ cal}$

12.   These problems ask you to calculate the calories required to heat a quantity of water. One calorie is defined as the amount of heat required to raise the temperature of 1 gram of water by 1 degree Celsius. To solve these problems, you need to multiply the number of grams of water to be heated by the number of degrees Celsius change in the temperature of the water.

       a. $100.1 \text{ g water} \times 19°C \times \dfrac{1 \text{ cal}}{\text{g water} \times °C} = 1900 \text{ cal}$

       b.   The initial and final temperatures of water are given in °F. We must convert to °C before solving the problem.

            Initial temperature:

$$T_{°C} = \frac{(T_{°F} - 32)}{1.80}$$

$$T_{°C} = \frac{(36 - 32)}{1.80}$$

$$T_{°C} = 2.2$$

            Final temperature:

$$T_{°C} = \frac{(T_{°F} - 32)}{1.80}$$

$$T_{°C} = \frac{(42 - 32)}{1.80}$$

$$T_{°C} = 5.6$$

Temperature change:

$$5.6°C - 2.2°C = 3.4°C$$

Solution: $2.32 \text{ g water} \times 3.3°C \times \dfrac{1 \text{ cal}}{\text{g water} \times °C} = 7.9 \text{ cal}$

c. $40. \text{ g water} \times 12°C \times \dfrac{1 \text{ cal}}{\text{g water} \times °C} = 480 \text{ cal}$

d. $16.9 \text{ g water} \times 5.0°C \times \dfrac{1 \text{ cal}}{\text{g water} \times °C} = 85 \text{ cal}$

13.   In this problem we want to calculate the heat energy needed to raise the temperature of a substance other than water. To do this, we need to know the specific heat capacity of the substance. The specific heat capacity tells us the amount of heat energy required to change the temperature of 1 gram of a substance by 1 degree Celsius. Every substance has its own specific heat capacity. That of solid carbon is 0.71 J/g°C.

If it takes 0.71 J to raise the temperature of 1 gram of carbon 1 degree Celsius, then it will take $0.71 \text{ J} \times 25.2$ to raise 25.2 g carbon by 1 degree Celsius. We wish to raise the temperature of the carbon rod by 25°C, not 1°C. We will need 25 times the heat energy needed to raise the temperature of 25.2 g carbon by 1 degree Celsius.

$$\text{Joules} = \dfrac{0.71 \text{ J}}{\text{g carbon} \times °C} \times 25.2 \text{ g carbon} \times 25°C$$

The joules required to raise the temperature of 25.2 g carbon by 25°C = 450 J.

14.   When you are given the number of grams of a substance, a change in temperature in degrees Celsius and the specific heat capacity for that substance, and are asked to calculate the heat energy required, you can use the formula $Q = s \times m \times \Delta T$. The specific heat capacity is s, m equals the mass in grams, ΔT is the change in temperature in degrees Celsius, and Q is the heat energy required. We can solve this problem with the formula, although we will need to convert Q from joules to calories, since calories are asked for.

$$Q = s \times m \times \Delta T$$

$$Q = \dfrac{2.0 \text{ J}}{\text{g water}(g) \times °C} \times 10. \text{ g water}(g) \times 8.2 \text{ }°C$$

$$Q = 160 \text{ J}$$

The answer should be expressed in calories:

$$160 \text{ J} \times \dfrac{1 \text{ cal}}{4.184 \text{ J}} = 38 \text{ cal}$$

15. In this problem, we are given Q, the heat energy in joules; m, the mass in grams of a piece of iron; and s, the specific heat capacity of iron. We are asked for ΔT, the change in temperature. If we rearrange the equation $Q = s \times m \times \Delta T$, we can solve for ΔT.

Divide both sides by ΔT.

$$\frac{Q}{\Delta T} = s \times m$$

Now, divide both sides by Q (same as multiplying by $\frac{1}{Q}$).

$$\frac{Q}{\Delta T} \times \frac{1}{Q} = \frac{s \times m}{Q}$$

We now have $1/\Delta T$ (the inverse of ΔT) isolated on one side of the equation.

$$\frac{1}{\Delta T} = \frac{s \times m}{Q}$$

Invert both sides of the equation.

$$\frac{\Delta T}{1} = \frac{Q}{s \times m}$$

$$\frac{\Delta T}{1} = \Delta T = \frac{Q}{s \times m}$$

Now, find ΔT.

$$\Delta T = \frac{2736.8 \text{ J}}{\dfrac{0.45 \text{ J}}{\text{g }^\circ\text{C}} \times 450.5 \text{ g}}$$

$$\Delta T = 14^\circ\text{C}$$

16. In this problem we are asked to solve for mass, m. We are given ΔT, Q, and s. We can rearrange the equation as illustrated below.

Divide both sides of the equation by m.

$$\frac{Q}{m} = \frac{s \times m \times \Delta T}{m}$$

Divide both sides of the equation by Q.

$$\frac{Q}{m} \times \frac{1}{Q} = s \times \Delta T \times \frac{1}{Q}$$

$$\frac{1}{m} = \frac{s \times \Delta T}{Q}$$

Invert both sides of the equation.

$$\frac{m}{1} = m = \frac{Q}{s \times \Delta T}$$

Now, find m.

$$m = \frac{8.53 \text{ J}}{\dfrac{0.89 \text{ J}}{g \times °C} \times 5.67 °C}$$

$$m = 1.7 \text{ g}$$

17. We are asked to find the specific heat capacity, s, when given ΔT, Q, and m. Rearrange the equation to isolate s on one side of the equation.

$$s = \frac{Q}{m \times \Delta T}$$

Now, substitute values into the equation.

$$s = \frac{1972.4 \text{ J}}{54 \text{ g} \times 15.2 °C} = 2.43 \text{ J/g}°C.$$

The specific heat capacity of ethyl alcohol is 2.43 J/g°C.

18. $1.00 \text{ g CH}_4 \times \dfrac{1 \text{ mol CH}_4}{16.04 \text{ g CH}_4} \times \dfrac{-891 \text{ kJ}}{1 \text{ mol CH}_4} = -55.5 \text{ kJ}$

19. $2C(s) + 2O_2(g) \rightarrow 2CO_2(g)$ $\qquad\qquad$ $\Delta H = 2(-394 \text{ kJ/mol})$

$H_2(g) + \frac{1}{2} O_2(g) \rightarrow H_2O(l)$ $\qquad\qquad$ $\Delta H = -286 \text{ kJ/mol}$

$2CO_2(g) + H_2O(l) \rightarrow C_2H_2(g) + \frac{5}{2} O_2(g)$ $\qquad$ $\Delta H = -(-1,300. \text{ kJ/mol})$

$2C(s) + H_2(g) \rightarrow C_2H_2(g)$ $\qquad\qquad$ $\Delta H = 226 \text{ kJ/mol}$

20. The quality of energy tells us the form of the energy (potential or kinetic). The quantity of energy tells us how much. The total amount (or quantity) is conserved. However, when potential energy is converted to kinetic energy, we say the quality is decreasing.

21. Wood has decreased the most. Nuclear and petroleum/natural gas have increased the most (see Figure 10.7).

22. The first law of thermodynamics tells us the total amount of energy is constant. It does not tell us anything about the direction of energy transfer.

23. The energy of the surroundings is used to melt solid water. The temperature of the water will eventually reach that of the room, and room temperature is higher than the melting point of water. In addition, liquid water has greater entropy than solid water, so entropy is the driving force in this process.

CHAPTER 11

Modern Atomic Theory

Introduction

It is difficult to create a mental image of atoms because we can't see them. Scientists have produced models that account for the behavior of atoms by making observations about the properties of atoms. So we know quite a bit about these tiny particles that make up matter even though we cannot see them. In this chapter you will learn how chemists believe atoms are structured.

Chapter Discussion

This is yet another chapter in which models play a significant role. Recall that we like models to be simple, but we also need models to explain the questions we want to answer. For example, Dalton's model of the atom has the advantage of being quite simple and it is useful when considering molecular-level views of solids, liquids and gases, as well as in representing chemical equations. However, it cannot explain fundamental questions such as why atoms stick together to form molecules. Scientists such as Thomson and Rutherford expanded the model of the atom to include subatomic particles. Their model is more complicated than Dalton's, as it begins to explain chemical reactivity (electrons are involved) and formulas for ionic compounds. But questions still abound. For example, why are there similarities in reactivities of elements (periodic trends)?

To begin our understanding of modern atomic theory, let's first discuss some observations. For example, you have undoubtedly seen a fireworks display, either in person or on television. Where do the colors come from? How do we get so many different colors? It turns out that different salts, when heated, give off different colors. For example, copper(II) chloride is a characteristic green color and lithium chloride is red. But why?

To answer these questions, let's consider a light bulb, and why we see white light from it. The light that we see is part of a spectrum of electromagnetic radiation, which includes x-rays, ultraviolet rays, visible light, microwaves and others. (see Section 11.1 in your text). A light bulb lights up because a thin filament in the bulb is heated (electric current is sent through the thin filament) and this heat (energy) is released as light. Realize that energy is related to the wavelength of electromagnetic radiation and the wavelength (if visible) is related to color. Because the wire in the light bulb is heated, energy of all wavelengths is emitted, and therefore wavelengths of all colors are emitted. When all of the colors of visible light are mixed, the result is white light.

So what about our fireworks? We know that electrons and protons attract each other, so that electrons want to be close to the nucleus. We will include energy levels into our model of the structure of the atom. Light is given off because when the salts are heated, the electrons become excited and move to a higher energy level. When the sample is heated, these electrons are moved further from the nucleus, but will go back to their original state. When the electrons return to their original (ground) state, energy is released, sometimes in the form of visible light. It is quite significant that the light is not white, but has a characteristic color associated with each different salt. This must mean that not all wavelengths of light are present when a metallic salt (such as copper(II) chloride) is heated. In other words, the electrons cannot go to any excited state and then return to any other state. If this occurred, all wavelengths of light would be emitted and the light would be white. It must mean that the electrons can only go to certain energy levels. This property would account for only certain colors being emitted.

This discovery is a surprising and non-intuitive result. Energy levels in an atom are quantized – that is, only certain levels are possible. For example, electrons can exist at one level or another level, but not in between the levels. The first person who tried to make sense of this idea was Neils Bohr. He assumed a planetary-type model in which the electrons would orbit the nucleus much like we envision the planets orbiting the sun. That is, the electrons had known, predictable pathways. It is important to realize that this model is fundamentally incorrect. It assumes we know where the electrons are and we know where they are going. The model we accept today just is not that simple. It turns out that we simply do not know how the electron travels.

The next step in trying to make sense of atomic structure was to consider the electron as moving like a wave (as in electromagnetic radiation). While the specifics of this property are beyond a first-year chemistry course, consider the following implications: 1) waves have a probability function associated with them; 2) waves can add up and cancel each other, thus we can get regions of high and low probability (and even zero probability of finding an electron). The firefly analogy in your text (Section 11.4) is a good one to read and understand in terms of how to think about electrons in an atom. Realize that the "size" or radius of an atom is arbitrary, and that we usually consider 90 percent of the probability of finding an electron to be the orbital (an unfortunate term that does not mean to suggest that the electron orbits the nucleus).

In considering the firefly analogy, a spherical pattern of a firefly makes sense, and is analogous to the *s* orbitals. But what about the *p* and *d* orbitals? The shapes of these orbitals are not intuitive but have been mathematically determined. It is not expected that you look at the shape of a *p* orbital, for example, and say "Of course that's the probability region of finding the electrons!" You would have no way of predicting this exact shape. Realize though that, like we could expect, the higher the energy level, the more complex and large the orbitals become. Realize as well that orbitals are not physical things but regions of probability.

The periodic table is considered in more detail in this chapter. Make sure to use it as a resource, not just another thing to memorize. The text provides an excellent discussion of this concept, and you should be able to answer the following:

1.   How are electron configurations consistent with the placement on the table? You don't have to memorize all configurations but should be able to quickly tell the configuration from the table.

2.   In Chapter 4 we saw <u>what</u> the most stable charges were for many ions. Now you should be able to explain <u>why</u>.

3.   Explain (don't just state) the trends of atomic radii and ionization energy and explain how they are related to one another.

Active Learning Questions

The Active Learning Questions at the end of each chapter are conceptually based questions that work well as discussion questions with a group of students. If your instructor does not assign these, consider getting together with a group of classmates and using these questions to see how well you understand the material in each chapter. While all of the questions work well, Active Learning Questions 12-14 test your understanding of ionization energy trends on the periodic table, and questions 15 and 16 focus on the significance of the term *quantized*. You are strongly encouraged to answer these.

Learning Review

1. Which of the following represents the wavelength of electromagnetic radiation?

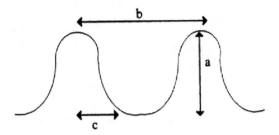

2. How does a microwave oven warm food?

3. Which has the shorter wavelength, ultraviolet light or infrared light? See Figure 11.3 in your textbook for help with electromagnetic radiation.

4. Light can be thought of as waves of energy. There is also evidence that light exists in another form. What is the other form?

5. What is meant by the terms "ground state" and "excited state" of an atom?

6. A sample of helium atoms absorbs energy. Will the photons of light emitted by the helium atoms be found at all wavelengths? Explain your answer.

7. Which energy level represents the ground state?

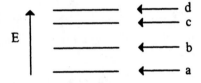

8. Which quantum has the greatest energy?

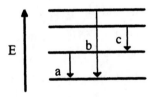

9. What does the Bohr model of the atom say about electron movement?

10. What characteristics of light led de Broglie and Schrödinger to formulate a new model of the atom?

11. Which of the following statements about the wave mechanical model of the atom are true, and which are false?

    a. The probability of finding an electron is the same in any location within an orbital.

    b. An electron will probably spend most of its time close to the nucleus.

    c. Electrons travel in circular orbits around the nucleus.

12. Which of the following statements about an orbital are true and which are false?

    a.   An electron will be found inside an orbital 90 percent of the time.

    b.   An electron travels around the surface of an orbital.

    c.   An electron cannot be found outside an orbital.

13. Consider the third principal energy level of hydrogen.

    a.   How many sublevels are found in this level?

    b.   How many orbitals are found in the $3d$ sublevel?

    c.   Which shape represents a $3p$ orbital?

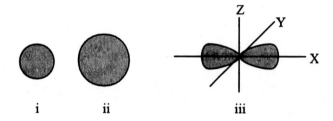

    i   ii   iii

14. How many sublevels do you think would be found in the n=5 principal energy level?

15. What is meant by each part of the orbital symbol $4p_x^1$?

16. How many electrons can occupy an orbital?

17. How does each column of the periodic table relate to electron configuration?

Use a periodic table such as the one found inside the front cover of your textbook to help answer questions 18, 19 and 20.

18. a.   Write the complete electron configuration and the complete orbital diagram for aluminum.

     b.   How many valence electrons and how many core electrons does aluminum have?

19. How many valence electrons are found in the elements beryllium, magnesium, calcium and strontium?

20. Write an electron configuration and box diagram for the elements below.

    a.   vanadium

    b.   copper

    c.   bromine

    d.   tin

21. How does each row of the periodic table relate to electron configuration?

22. What is characteristic of the electron configuration of the Noble gases?

23. Which orbitals are filling in the lanthanide series elements?

24.   Decide whether the elements below are representative elements or transition metals.

    a.   Ar

    b.   Fe

    c.   N

    d.   Sr

25.   Which element in each pair would have a lower ionization energy?

    a.   F and C

    b.   O and As

    c.   Ca and Br

    d.   Li and Rb

    e.   Ne and Rn

    f.   Sr and Br

26.   Which element in each pair would have the smaller atomic size?

    a.   Ne and Xe

    b.   In and I

    c.   Na and Cs

    d.   F and Sr

    e.   Ba and Bi

    f.   Cl and Al

Answers to Learning Review

1.   Wavelength is the distance from crest to crest, or trough to trough, so the correct answer is b.

2.   The kind of electromagnetic radiation generated by the oven – microwave radiation – is of the right frequency to be absorbed by water in food. As the water molecules in food absorb microwave energy, their movement increases. The extra energy is transferred to other molecules in the food when they collide with the water molecules, so heat is transferred from rapidly moving water molecules to other molecules, causing the food to heat up.

3.   Infrared light has a wavelength of 10^{-4} meters and ultraviolet light has a wavelength of around 10^{-8} meters, so ultraviolet light has a shorter wavelength than infrared light.

4.   There is evidence that light consists of packets of energy called photons.

5.   The lowest possible energy state of an atom is the ground state. When an atom has absorbed excess energy it is in an excited state.

6.   When helium atoms absorb energy, some of the electrons move from the ground state to an excited state. When helium atoms lose this excess energy they will often emit light. The light is not of just any wavelength. Only certain wavelengths, corresponding to the differences in energy, are allowed.

7.   The energy level marked "a" is the ground state because it is the level with the lowest amount of energy.

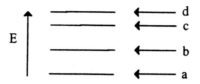

8.   The quantum marked by b has the highest amount of energy because this excited state has more energy than the excited states below it.

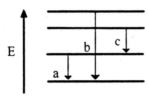

9.   Bohr's model said that electrons move in circular orbits around the nucleus. Each circular orbit represents an excited state farther from the nucleus.

10.   The fact that light could act both as a wave and as a particle led de Broglie and Schrödinger to suggest that an electron might also exhibit characteristics of both waves and particles. When Schrödinger used these ideas to analyze the problem mathematically, the wave mechanical model of the atom was the result.

11.   a.   The probability of finding an electron within an orbital is 90 percent, but some locations within the orbital shape are more likely to contain an electron at any given time than are others. So this statement is false.

       b.   The electron does tend to spend most of its time around the nucleus. This statement is true.

       c.   Bohr thought that electrons traveled in circular orbits around the nucleus, but the current model says that electrons are found in orbitals. We do not know their exact paths. This statement is false.

12.   a.   The orbital shape represents a probability cloud. It is true that an electron will be found within the orbital 90 percent of the time.

       b.   The orbital marks the area of 90 percent probability. It does not mark the surface on which the electron travels. This statement is false.

       c.   Ten percent of the time, an electron will be found outside the orbital. This statement is false.

13.   a.   The third principal energy level, n=3, contains 3 sublevels.

       b.   There are five orbitals in the 3*d* sublevel.

       c.   i and ii represent *s* orbitals. iii is a *p* orbital.

14.   Each principal energy level has n sublevels, so the fifth principal energy level, n=5, would have 5 sublevels.

15.   Four is the principal energy level, p is the sublevel type, x is the specific orbital within the p sublevel, and the superscript 1 says that there is one electron in the orbital.

16.   Each orbital can hold two electrons.

17.   The period or row number indicates which s and p orbitals are being filled for elements in that row. For example, antimony, which is in row 5, has filled its $5s$ orbitals, $4d$ orbitals and is filling $5p$ orbitals.

18.   a. $1s^2 2s^2 2p^6 3s^2 3p^1$

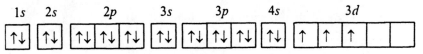

        b.   Aluminum has three valence electrons and 10 core electrons.

19.   Each of these elements has two valence electrons.

20.   a. $1s^2 2s^2 2p^6 3s^2 3p^6 4s^2 3d^3$

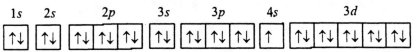

        b. $1s^2 2s^2 2p^6 3s^2 3p^6 4s^1 3d^{10}$ or $[Ar]4s^1 3d^{10}$

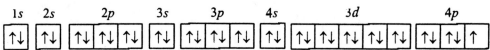

        Note that copper does not completely fill $4s$ before filling $3d$.

        c. $1s^2 2s^2 2p^6 3s^2 3p^6 4s^2 3d^{10} 4p^5$ or $[Ar]4s^2 3d^{10} 4p^5$

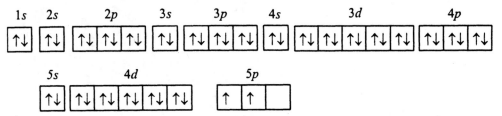

        d. $1s^2 2s^2 2p^6 3s^2 3p^6 4s^2 3d^{10} 4p^6 5s^2 4d^{10} 5p^2$

21.   The group number on the top of each column of the periodic table is the same as the sum of $ns + np$ electrons for the highest principal energy level and is equal to the number of valence electrons for that element. For example, sulfur is in group 6 and its electron configuration is $1s^2 2s^2 2p^6 3s^2 3p^4$. The sum $ns + np$ for n=3 is 6, which is the same as the group number. Sulfur has 6 valence electrons, $3s^2$ and $3p^4$.

22.   The *s* and *p* orbitals for the principal energy level, which is the same as the row number, are full. That is, all the *s* and *p* orbitals contain a maximum of two electrons for a total of eight electrons.

23.   In the lanthanide series elements, the 4*f* orbitals are filling.

24.   a.   Representative element (Noble gas)

b.   Transition metal

c.   Representative element

d.   Representative element (alkaline earth metal)

25.   a.   Carbon would have a lower ionization energy than fluorine.

b.   Arsenic would have a lower ionization energy than oxygen.

c.   Calcium would have a lower ionization energy than bromine.

d.   Rubidium would have a lower ionization energy than lithium.

e.   Radon would have a lower ionization energy than neon.

f.   Strontium would have a lower ionization energy than bromine.

26.   a.   Neon would have a smaller atomic size than xenon.

b.   Iodine would have a smaller atomic size than indium.

c.   Sodium would have a smaller atomic size than cesium.

d.   Fluorine would have a smaller atomic size than strontium.

e.   Bismuth would have a smaller atomic size than barium.

f.   Chlorine would have a smaller atomic size than aluminum.

CHAPTER 12

Chemical Bonding

Introduction

There are 116 elements now known, which seems like a lot of elements, yet the elements can combine to produce a far greater number of different molecules. One of the most important substances in our environment, water, is made from two hydrogen atoms and one oxygen atom that have bonded together. Understanding how and why the elements combine is a fundamental chemical concept that helps chemists predict the structures and properties of new molecules.

Chapter Discussion

Why do atoms bond to form molecules? How do atoms bond to form molecules? These are questions that Dalton's model could not address. But after studying Chapter 11 in your text, we are ready to address them.

Let's first consider a very simple molecule, H_2. Why does H_2 exist? Why is it more stable than individual H atoms? Perhaps the simplest way to begin thinking about this concept is to realize that a hydrogen atom consists of an electron and a proton. The electron from one hydrogen atom could be attracted to the proton of another hydrogen atom if the atoms were close enough together. There is always potential attraction between atoms because of this. The model that we will use in this chapter requires that we consider the orbital theory from Chapter 11. Imagine two hydrogen atoms as represented in Figure 12.1 of your text. The first picture has the hydrogen atoms very far apart. The attraction of one atom to another (electron to proton) is negligible. But what about when these atoms are brought closer together? Electrons, which are negatively charged, will be attracted to a positive proton. Therefore, it makes sense that the electrons will spend most of the time between the two protons. This is not to say that the electrons are always there (recall from Chapter 11 that we cannot say for certain where the electrons are and how they move), but we can predict that the negatively charged electrons will be most attracted to the region between the two positively charged protons.

We want to maximize this attraction, and Figure 12.1(b) shows that the molecule is most stable when the hydrogen atoms are close together. How close will the atoms become? While the electrons are attracted to the protons, the protons repel each other. So there is a limit to how close the atoms will be in the molecule.

The H_2 molecule is said to have a perfectly covalent bond. The electrons are shared between the atoms equally (each hydrogen has the same attraction for the electrons) and the electrons are lower in energy (better off) when part of the molecule than as individual atoms.

This is a simple view of covalent molecules that does not answer questions such as "Why doesn't H_3 or He_2 exist?" We can hypothesize that certain numbers of electrons will be too repulsive to allow for a stable molecule, but this model does not help us to predict which molecules will be stable and which will not. We will discuss this further with Lewis structures. For now, realize that we can state that by sharing electrons, each hydrogen in the molecule can be said to have two electrons. And by having two electrons, the outer energy level (the first energy level in this case) is complete, like the stable Noble gas helium. And because it is the electron structure that is responsible for chemical activity, the H_2 molecule should be stable. This statement does not mean that a filled energy level causes stability, but it appears to be related to stability. Like all models, this model is a simplification, but it is a good way to first start thinking about molecules.

We have considered a molecule with two of the same atoms. What about the other end of the spectrum? That is, what about a molecule with two very different atoms? For example, what about sodium chloride (NaCl)? At first, it seems reasonable to think of this molecule in the same way as we did with H_2. That is, there should be attraction between these atoms because of the attraction between the electrons and protons. Thus, we might be tempted to represent the molecule in the same way as we did H_2. However, in the case of H_2, the hydrogen atoms exhibited equal attraction for the electrons. This situation does not exist between sodium and chlorine. It turns out that chlorine has a much greater attraction for electrons than does sodium (we will consider why later). Instead of the electrons being shared between the atoms, ions are formed. An electron will be transferred from the sodium atom to the chlorine atom. We should represent the sodium chloride molecule like Figure 12.4(c) in your text. This arrangement is known as an ionic bond.

These cases (H_2 and NaCl) are two extremes. In the first case, electrons were perfectly shared and in the second case, an electron was transferred from one atom to another. But what about intermediate cases? For example, consider the CO (carbon monoxide) molecule. While these atoms will not share electrons equally, the difference in their attraction for electrons is not so great that an electron would be transferred. In this case, oxygen has more attraction for the electrons than carbon. There is therefore a greater probability of finding an electron nearer the oxygen than the carbon. This scenario can be represented as in Figure 12.4(b) of your text. Note that this molecule has partial positive and partial negative regions (not as extreme as ions, but not perfectly covalent either). We call this setup a dipole moment, and the bond is considered polar covalent. Covalent because electrons are shared, but polar because the sharing is unequal and leads to partial charges.

It is best to think of bonding as a continuum, not as three distinct types. That is, the more alike the atoms are with respect to their attraction for electrons, the more covalent the bond is; the more different they are, the more ionic the bond is. This spectrum is represented in Table 12.1 of your text.

These ideas bring about another trend called electronegativity, which is the attraction an atom in a molecule feels for a shared electron. It is discussed in detail in Section 12.2 of your text. As with atomic radii and ionization energy trends from Chapter 11, make sure to understand these trends, not merely memorize them.

Now that we have a better understanding of chemical bonds, we can go on to other questions. For example, can we predict that H_2O is a stable molecule? Of course, we know that water (H_2O) is stable, but can our model support this? And can it lead us to better understand the properties of water? The answer to both of these questions is yes.

The Localized Electron Model

At this point we would like to show how the electrons (outer shell or valence electrons) are arranged in the molecule, and to describe the geometry of the molecules (which is an important function of the properties of the molecule).

To do this we will use a very simple model, called the localized electron model. This model, like all models, is a simplification, but it serves to answer our questions, make correct predictions, and is relatively simple to use. In this model, we assume that we know where the electrons in a molecule are located. Recall that we predict the electrons in a covalent bond will spend a great deal of time between atoms. Therefore, we assume that the electrons are fixed (localized) between the atoms. Again, these are simplifications, but they serve our purposes. Also, we assume that electrons will be shared in a molecule such that the individual atoms have eight electrons (known as the octet rule), with the exception of hydrogen, which will have two electrons. There are some exceptions to this model (as always), but these general guidelines work surprisingly well.

Sections 12.6 and 12.7 provide good guidelines for drawing Lewis structures, which show how the valence electrons are distributed in the molecule. There are also many examples of these structures, along with notable exceptions, so we will not belabor the point here. Becoming proficient at drawing Lewis structures requires practice. But make sure you also understand what the Lewis structures represent (as described above).

From Lewis structures we can determine the geometry of the molecules using the VSEPR model. Again, this model is quite simple, but works well. The basic premise is that the electron pairs (both bonding and lone pairs) repel each other, and the geometry is a direct result of minimizing the repulsions between electron pairs. Table 12.4 gives a nice overview of these geometries, along with example molecules.

You must draw the Lewis structure before you can determine the geometry of the molecule because the lone pairs do affect the geometry. For example, note in Table 12.4 the molecules BF_3 and NH_3. Both of these molecules seem similar from their formulas. However, they have different geometries because they have different Lewis structures.

Active Learning Questions

The Active Learning Questions at the end of each chapter are conceptually based questions that work well as discussion questions with a group of students. If your instructor does not assign these, consider getting together with a group of classmates and using these questions to see how well you understand the material in each chapter. While all of the questions work well, Active Learning Question 6 has you relate the trends of *electronegativity*, *atomic radius*, and *ionization energy*, question 13 has you consider the significance of the concept of electronegativity, and question 18 focuses on the formulas and shapes of molecules. You are strongly encouraged to answer these.

Learning Review

1. What are the two kinds of bonds that can form between atoms?

2. What kind of bond forms between

    a. two identical atoms?

    b. a metal and a nonmetal?

3. What is meant by a polar covalent bond?

4. Which of the choices has an ionic bond?

    a. CO

    b. $CaBr_2$

    c. HBr

    d. Cl_2

5. Arrange the following atoms based on electronegativity. Put the most electronegative atom on the right and the least electronegative atom on the left.

    P   Al   Cl   Mg

6. Which bond is the most polar? Which bond is the least polar?

    a. P–Cl

    b. H–H

     c.   N–H

     d.   C–F

7.   Write electron configurations for both reactants and products for the reactions below.

     a. $Mg + Cl_2 \rightarrow Mg^{2+} + 2Cl^-$

     b. $2Li + S \rightarrow 2LI^+ + S^{2-}$

8.   When two nitrogen atoms combine to form a nitrogen molecule, how many electrons are shared to give each atom a complete octet?

9.   How many electrons do each of the atoms below need to gain, lose or share to achieve a Noble gas valence electron configuration?

     a.   S

     b.   Mg

     c.   C

10.   In which of the atom/ion pairs is the ion smaller than the atom?

     a. S/S^{2-}

     b. Ca/Ca^{2+}

     c. Li/Li^{2+}

     d. I/I^-

11.   Draw Lewis structures for these ionic compounds.

     a.   MgS

     b. Na_2O

12.   Write valence electron configurations for the following atoms.

     a.   B

     b.   Sr

     c.   Kr

     d.   Cl

13.   Draw Lewis structures for the molecules and ions below.

     a. H_2S

     b.   HCCH

     c. $PO_4{}^{3-}$

     d.   HI

     e. PCl_3

14.   Some molecules have Lewis structures that violate the octet rule. Draw a probable Lewis structure for BeI_2.

15.   Use the VSEPR model to determine the molecular structure of each of the molecules below.

     a. SbF_3

     b. BH_3

c.   SiH$_4$

d.

$$\begin{array}{c} H \\ \diagdown \\ \diagup \\ H \end{array} C = O$$

Answers to Learning Review

1.   When atoms combine they form either ionic bonds or covalent bonds. In an ionic bond, electrons are completely transferred. In a covalent bond, electrons are shared between atoms. Ionic bonds usually form when a metal and a nonmetal react. Covalent bonds usually form when two nonmetals react.

2.   a.   When two identical atoms bond, a nonpolar covalent bond forms.

        b.   When a metal and a nonmetal bond, an ionic bond forms.

3.   Electrons shared between two atoms are not always shared equally. Sometimes, the electrons are attracted to one of the atoms more than the other. The atom in a bond that attracts the electron pair will have an extra electron part of the time and so bear a partial negative charge. The atom that does not strongly attract the electron pair it shares will be electron-deficient part of the time and so bears a positive charge. The kind of covalent bond where the electrons are not shared equally is called a polar covalent bond.

4.   Ionic bonds are formed when a metal loses an electron to a nonmetal. Among these choices, the only bond between a metal and a nonmetal is the bond formed between calcium and bromine to form calcium bromide. So the correct answer is b.

5.   Elements on the right side of the periodic table have higher electronegativity values than do elements on the left side of the periodic table. The atom with the highest electronegativity would be Cl, because it is in the upper right hand corner of the periodic table; then P, then Al, and Mg, on the left side of the periodic table, is the lowest.

        Mg   Al   P   Cl

6.   To determine the polarity of a bond, subtract the electronegativity of the least electronegative atom from the electronegativity of the most electronegative atom. The largest difference is the most polar bond and the smallest difference is the least polar bond.

        a.   P is 2.1 while Cl is 3.0. The difference is 0.9.

        b.   Both H atoms are 2.1. The difference is 0.0.

        c.   N is 3.0 while H is 2.1. The difference is 0.9.

        d.   C is 2.5 while F is 4.0. The difference is 1.5.

        The most polar of these bonds is the C—F bond, because the difference in electronegativities is the highest (1.5). The least polar bond is that which is formed between two hydrogen atoms. The difference in electronegativities is 0, which means that this bond is completely nonpolar.

7.   a. $Mg + Cl_2 \rightarrow Mg^{2+} + 2Cl^-$

                 $1s^2 2s^2 2p^6 3s^2 + 1s^2 2s^2 2p^6 3s^2 3p^5 \rightarrow 1s^2 2s^2 2p^6 + 2(1s^2 2s^2 2p^6 3s^2 3p^6)$

     b. $2Li + S \rightarrow 2Li^+ + S^{2-}$

                 $2(1s^2 2s^1) + 1s^2 2s^2 2p^6 3s^2 3p^4 \rightarrow 2(1s^2) + 1s^2 2s^2 2p^6 3s^2 3p^6$

8.   Nitrogen is in Group 5 of the periodic table, which means that it has five valence electrons. Most elements obey the octet rule when they bond with other atoms, so a nitrogen molecule should be composed of two nitrogen atoms each with a complete octet. When two nitrogen atoms bond, they can only achieve an octet by sharing six electrons, three from each nitrogen atom. So in a nitrogen molecule, each nitrogen atom has two valence electrons of its own and shares six with another nitrogen atom.

9.   a.   Sulfur is in Group 6 of the periodic table so it has six valence electrons. Sulfur needs two more electrons to fill its valence shell. Sulfur often gains two electrons to become a sulfide ion, S^{2-}. The sulfide ion has the same electron configuration as argon.

     b.   Magnesium is in Group 2 of the periodic table, and has two valence electrons. Magnesium atoms lose two electrons to form the Mg^{2+} ion. The magnesium ion has the same electron configuration as neon.

     c.   Carbon is in Group 4 of the periodic table so it has four valence electrons. Each carbon atom will share four valence electrons with other atoms. When a carbon atom shares four electrons with other atoms, it has the same electron configuration as neon.

10.   a.   The sulfide ion has gained two electrons so it is larger than the sulfur atom.

      b.   The calcium ion has lost two electrons so it is smaller than the calcium atom.

      c.   The lithium ion has lost one electron so it is smaller than the lithium atom.

      d.   The iodide ion has gained one electron so it is larger than the iodine atom.

11.   a.   In ionic compounds, the electrons lost from the metal are transferred to the nonmetal so that each atom can achieve a Noble gas configuration.

$$Mg^{2+} \qquad \overset{\cdot\cdot}{\underset{\cdot\cdot}{:S:}}^{2-}$$

      b.   Two sodium atoms each lose one electron to an oxygen atom so that all three atoms achieve a noble gas configuration.

$$Na^+ \qquad \overset{\cdot\cdot}{\underset{\cdot\cdot}{:O:}}^{2-} \qquad Na^+$$

12.   a.   B $2s^1 2p^1$

      b.   Sr $5s^2$

      c.   Kr $4s^2 4p^6$

      d.   Cl $3s^2 3p^5$

13.   a.   Step 1. Find the total number of valence electrons in all the atoms. There are eight valence electrons in a molecule of H_2S. Six come from sulfur and one each from hydrogen.

Step 2. Begin distributing the available valence electrons by putting a pair of electrons between each atom. An electron pair is often symbolized with a line.

$$H\!-\!S\!-\!H$$

Step 3. We have used up four of the available electrons. There are four more to distribute. Each of the two hydrogen atoms is satisfied, so the four extra electrons must appear as unshared pairs on the sulfur atom.

$$H\!-\!\ddot{\underset{..}{S}}\!-\!H$$

Now all atoms satisfy either the octet or the duet rule.

   b.   Step 1. The total number of valence electrons for two carbon atoms and two hydrogen atoms is 10, four from each carbon atom and one each from the hydrogen atoms.

Step 2. Arrange the electron pairs between atoms.

$$H\!-\!C\!-\!C\!-\!H$$

Step 3. There are now four electrons left. If we distribute two around each carbon atom we have:

$$H\!-\!\ddot{C}\!-\!\ddot{C}\!-\!H$$

The carbon atoms do not fulfill the octet rule and we have run out of electrons. Some of the atoms must share more than one pair of electrons in order for the octet rule to be satisfied. We cannot share more electrons between the carbon and the hydrogen atoms because hydrogen already satisfies the duet rule. So the electrons must be shared between the two carbon atoms. Let's begin by sharing one more pair of electrons. The result is:

$$H\!-\!C\!=\!C\!-\!H$$

We have two electrons left.

$$H\!-\!\dot{C}\!=\!\dot{C}\!-\!H$$

Carbon is still not satisfied. Let's share another electron pair between the two carbon atoms.

$$H\!-\!C\!\equiv\!C\!-\!H$$

Now, all of the valence electrons are used and both hydrogen and carbon are satisfied.

   c.   Step 1. The phosphate ion, PO_4^{3-}, has a total of 32 valence electrons: 24 from the oxygen atoms, five from phosphorus, and three extra electrons because of the 3^- charge on the phosphate ion.

Step 2. Distribute pairs of electrons among the atoms.

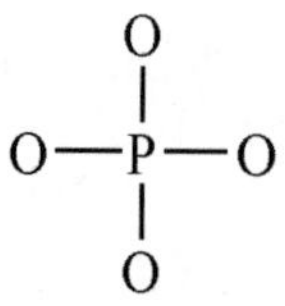

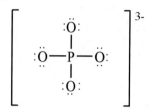

Step 3. There are 24 electrons left. Begin arranging the electrons around the atoms to satisfy the octet rule for all the atoms. Three unshared pairs of electrons surround each oxygen atom. The complete Lewis structure is:

$$\left[\begin{array}{c} :\ddot{O}: \\ | \\ :\ddot{O}-P-\ddot{O}: \\ | \\ :\ddot{O}: \end{array} \right]^{3-}$$

.

d. Step 1. HI has a total of eight valence electrons.

Step 2. Arrange an electron pair between the two atoms.

H—I

Step 3. Now, hydrogen is satisfied and there are six electrons left. Arrange the remaining electron pairs around the iodine atom.

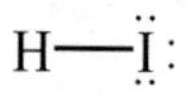

H—İ:

e. Step 1. Phosphorus trichloride has a total of 26 valence electrons.

Step 2. Arrange electron pairs among the atoms.

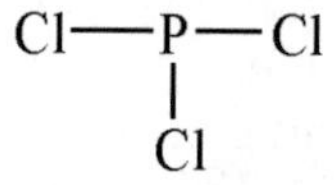

Cl—P—Cl
|
Cl

Step 3. There are 20 electrons left. Then, arrange the electrons around each atom until each has eight electrons. Three unshared pairs surround each chlorine atom, and the phosphorus atom has one unshared pair.

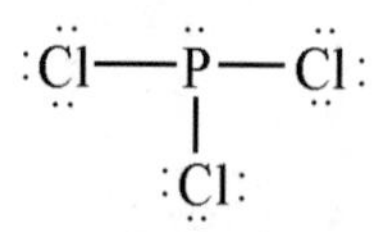

:Cl—P̈—Cl:
|
:Cl:

14. Step 1. Add together the valence electrons contributed by each atom in the compound. Each iodide has seven, and beryllium has two, for a total of 16 valence electrons.

Step 2. Arrange the electrons in pairs between the atoms.

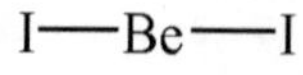

I—Be—I

Step 3. This leaves 12 electrons to distribute as unshared pairs. The iodide atoms obey the octet rule, but beryllium atoms often do not. Beryllium is electron-deficient and will have only four valence electrons.

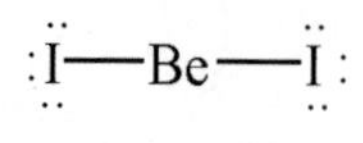

:Ï—Be—Ï:

15. a. Step 1. Draw the Lewis structure for the molecule. Antimony has five valence electrons and fluorine has seven. Antimony can share an electron pair with each of the three fluorine atoms, so the Lewis structure looks like:

Step 2. Count the electron pairs and arrange them so that they are as far apart as possible. When three pairs of electrons are shared and there is one pair left which is not shared, we can arrange the electrons in a tetrahedron.

Step 3. Determine the positions of the atoms using the electron pairs as a guide. The fluorine atoms will occupy the corners of a tetrahedron. The lone pair of electrons on the antimony atom will occupy the fourth corner of the tetrahedron.

Step 4. Determine the molecular structure using the positions of the atoms. In this molecule there are three atoms surrounding antimony, and each one is located in the corner of a tetrahedron. Because only three corners of the tetrahedron are occupied by atoms, this molecular shape is a trigonal pyramid.

b. Step 1. The Lewis structure of boron trihydride is

$$H-B-H$$
(with H on top)

Boron has three valence electrons and shares electrons with three hydrogen atoms. Note that boron is an exception to the octet rule.

Step 2. The three pairs of electrons spread themselves out as far as possible to form a trigonal planar shape.

Step 3. The three hydrogen atoms occupy the corners of a triangle.

Step 4. This molecular structure is called trigonal planar. The bond angle is 120°.

c. Step 1. Silicon has four valence electrons and each of the hydrogen atoms has one. Silicon can share electron pairs with each of the four hydrogen atoms so the Lewis structure looks like:

Step 2. When four pairs of electrons are shared, the VSEPR model predicts that they will spread apart to form a tetrahedron.

Step 3. There are four hydrogen atoms bonded to a central silicon atom. The four hydrogen atoms will occupy the four corners of a tetrahedron.

Step 4. The molecular structure of this molecule will be a tetrahedron. The bond angle is 109.5°.

$$\overset{\displaystyle H}{\underset{\displaystyle H}{\overset{|}{\underset{|}{Si}}}}\quad 109.5^{\circ}$$

d. Step 1. The Lewis structure for this molecule shows that there is a carbon-oxygen double bond.

$$H-\overset{\overset{\displaystyle \cdot\cdot O\cdot\cdot}{\|}}{C}-H$$

Step 2. The three effective pairs of electrons spread themselves out as far as possible to form a trigonal planar shape.

Step 3. The two hydrogen atoms and the oxygen atom occupy the corners of a triangle.

Step 4. This molecular structure is trigonal planar. The bond angle around the center atom is 120°.

$$\underset{\displaystyle H\qquad H}{\overset{\displaystyle \cdot\cdot O\cdot}{\overset{\|}{C}}}\quad 120^{\circ}$$

CHAPTER 13

Gases

Introduction

We live in a gaseous environment. The air we breathe is a mixture of gases. Yet gases are not as conspicuous as liquids and solids are, and it is easy to overlook their significance. Understanding why gases behave as they do can help us understand everyday occurrences such as "low pressure systems" in our weather and the apparent decrease of the amount of air in car tires in cold weather. This chapter focuses on how gases behave under various circumstances, and why they behave as they do.

Chapter Discussion

One of the best by-products of studying gas laws is achieving a greater understanding of the concept of models, and getting a better feel for scientific thinking. As with most scientific endeavors, one of the goals is to be able to explain real phenomena; for example, explaining how a hot-air balloon works, or why our ears "pop" when flying in an airplane. Observations are made, and when they appear to be consistent, they are termed laws (for example, Boyle's law). It is important to understand that these laws tell us "what" (for example, the pressure of a gas is inversely proportional to its volume if the amount of gas and temperature are held constant), but do not tell us "why." Models (or theories) are developed to explain the "why." In the case of gases, the kinetic molecular theory is offered as an explanation. Remember, though, that models are not reality; they include simplifications.

Sections 13.2, 13.3, and 13.4 give us observations that, for the most part, consist of facts. For example, place a balloon filled with air in the freezer and it will shrink. Temperature and volume of a gas are directly related, as long as pressure and amount of gas remain constant (as the temperature decreases, the volume decreases). These observations should not be surprising to you, but they are presented in these sections as mathematical expressions.

There is no need to memorize all of these relationships because we bring them all together in the ideal gas equation:

$$PV = nRT$$

This equation brings together all of the gas laws discussed in Chapter 13. There are quite a few example problems in Sections 13.1-13.5. After reading these sections and working on the examples, you should be able to show how all of the other gas laws (Boyle's law, etc.) can be derived from the ideal gas law equation. Pay attention to what is constant and why – and you only need to know this one equation.

For example, consider Charles's law. This law states that the volume of a gas is directly dependent on the temperature of the gas (in Kelvin), provided that the amount of gas and pressure are held constant. Thus, V and T are changing, and P and n are constant (as is R, of course, as always). Let's rearrange the ideal gas law equation so that the factors that can change are on one side, and the factors that are constant are on the other:

$$\frac{V}{T} = \frac{nR}{P} = \text{constant}$$

Because R, P, and n are all constant, the factor "$\dfrac{nR}{P}$" must be constant as well. Therefore, we can write this as:

$$\frac{V}{T} = \frac{nR}{P} = \text{constant}$$

or

$$\frac{V}{T} = \text{constant}$$

This shows us that the ratio "$\dfrac{V}{T}$" is a constant, as long as P and n are held constant (and the temperature is in Kelvin). We can rewrite this as

$$\frac{V_1}{T_1} = \frac{V_2}{T_2} \, ,$$

which is the mathematical representation of Charles's law that you will find in Section 13.3 of your text. You should spend some time and derive the other laws using this same approach.

These relationships explain what happens, but not why. To explain why, we need to consider a model of gases. Section 13.6 in your text discusses Dalton's law of partial pressures. Read through this section and understand that this law is an observation; it is a fact. The text also discusses that this law tells us two important things about gases that are important enough to repeat here:

1.   The volume of the individual gas particle must not be very important.

2.   The forces among the particles must not be very important.

Make sure to understand how Dalton's law of partial pressures tells us this. Discuss it with friends or an instructor. These conclusions lead us to our model, the kinetic molecular theory (KMT).

The KMT is discussed in Section 13.8. Notice that two of the premises come from the above conclusions, which come from observations. This is how model development works. We make observations and use the significance of these observations to develop a model. For example, consider two of the assumptions in the KMT:

1.   The volume (size) of the individual particles can be assumed to be zero.

2.   The particles are assumed not to attract or to repel each other.

Note how these two premises are actually "ideal" cases that come from Dalton's law of partial pressures. That is, Dalton's law of partial pressures leads us to believe that the volume of gas particles is not important, nor are the forces among these particles. In the KMT, we assume that not only are these factors not important, they are non-existent. Why do we do this? Because it is easier; it makes for a simpler model. And recall, our goal is to make the model as simple as we can, as long as it explains the observations that we want it to explain.

You should strive to understand the significance of the KMT. Read through Sections 13.8 and 13.9 and make sure that you can <u>explain</u> the relationships among pressure, volume, amount of gas and temperature.

Active Learning Questions

The Active Learning Questions at the end of each chapter are conceptually based questions that work well as discussion questions with a group of students. If your instructor does not assign these, consider getting together with a group of classmates and using these questions to see how well you understand the material in each chapter. While all of the questions work well, Active Learning Questions 3, 6, and 11 focus on familiar phenomena for you to explain, question 20 relies on your ability to estimate and calculate, and question 22 is a challenging conceptual problem testing your understanding of the relationship between pressure and volume of a gas. You are strongly encouraged to answer these.

Learning Review

1.   Gas in compressed gas cylinders is usually under a great deal of pressure. If the gas in a particular cylinder has a pressure of 2,500 psi, how many torr is this?

2.   Convert each of the units of pressure below.

    a.   0.408 atm to torr

    b.   68,471 Pa to mm Hg

    c.   50.9 psi to atm

3.   The relationship observed by Boyle between volume and pressure is:

    a.   linear

    b.   proportional

    c.   inversely proportional

    d.   no relationship

4.   Examine the cylinder with a moveable piston. If the piston moves downward, causing the volume of the gas to decrease, will the pressure of the gas become larger or smaller?

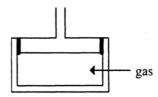

5.   A sample of nitrogen gas at 2.4 atm has a volume of 50.3 L. If the pressure is decreased to 1.9 atm, will the new volume be greater or smaller? What is the new volume?

6.   Absolute zero is the temperature at which gases have zero volume. But zero volume has never been measured in the laboratory. So how do we know at what temperature the volume of a gas equals zero? Be as specific as possible.

7.   Which of the following equations cannot be derived from Charles's law, $V = bT$?

    a. $\dfrac{V}{T} = b$ b. $\dfrac{V_1}{T_1} = \dfrac{V_2}{T_2}$

    c. $\dfrac{V_1}{T_1} + \dfrac{V_2}{T_2} = b$ d. $\dfrac{3V}{3T} = b$

8.   A container with a moveable piston contains 0.89 L methane gas at 100.5 °C. If the temperature of the gas rises by 11.3 °C, what is the new volume of the gas?

9.   Avogadro's law describes the relationship between the amount (number of moles) of a gas and the volume of the gas. Under what conditions of temperature and pressure is Avogadro's law true?

10.   Where does the universal gas constant, R, come from?

11.   Use the ideal gas law to solve the problems below.

   a.   A sample of chlorine gas at 543 torr has a volume of 21.6 L. If the temperature of the chlorine is 0°C, how many moles of chlorine gas are present?

   b.   Poisonous carbon monoxide gas is a product of the internal combustion engine. If 1.2 mol of CO at 11°C and 102 mm Hg are present in a container, what will be the volume of the CO gas?

   c.   A 0.45 mol sample of a gas has a pressure of 299 torr at 300.°C and a volume of 53.8 L. At the same temperature and pressure, the volume of the gas is decreased to 39.7 L. How many moles of gas are present after the volume has changed?

12.   Which statements about Dalton's law of partial pressure are true and which are false?

   a.   The total pressure (P_{TOTAL}) of a mixture of gases is independent of the sizes of the gas particles.

   b.   Attractive forces between gas particles are important in determining P_{TOTAL}.

   c.   For ideal gases, P_{TOTAL} depends solely on the total number of moles of gas, for any temperature and volume.

13.   Assume that a sample of humid air contains only nitrogen gas, oxygen gas and water vapor. If the atmospheric pressure is 745 mm Hg and the partial pressure of N_2 is 566 mm Hg and of oxygen is 140. mm Hg, what is the partial pressure of water vapor in the air?

14.   A 7.5 L mixture of gases is produced by mixing 4.0 L of N_2 at 450 torr, 3.5 L of O_2 at 252 torr, and 0.21 L of CO_2 at 150 torr. If the temperature is held constant at 65°C, what is the total pressure of the mixture?

15.   Explain the difference between a law and a model.

16.   Which statements about the Kinetic Molecular Theory are true, and which are false?

   a.   The postulates of the Kinetic Molecular Theory are true for all gases, at all temperatures and pressures.

   b.   Gas particles are assumed to either attract or repel each other.

   c.   The distance between individual gas particles is much greater than the volume of an individual gas particle.

   d.   As the Kelvin temperature of a gas increases, the average kinetic energy increases.

17.   According to the Kinetic Molecular Theory, what are we measuring when we measure the temperature of a gas?

18. Carbon dioxide is produced during the combustion of liquid propane fuel in the following reaction:

$$C_3H_8 + 5O_2 \rightarrow 3CO_2 + 4H_2O$$

If 5.0 kg of propane are burned at 1.000 atm pressure and 400.°C, what volume of CO_2 gas is produced?

19. A sample of fluorine gas has a volume of 19.9 L at STP. How many moles of fluorine are in the sample?

Answers to Learning Review

1. There is no conversion factor directly between psi and torr. However, we can convert psi to atm and atm to torr.

$$2500 \text{ psi} \times \frac{1.000 \text{ atm}}{14.69 \text{ psi}} \times \frac{760.00 \text{ torr}}{1.000 \text{ atm}} = 1.3 \times 10^5 \text{ torr}$$

2. a. $0.408 \text{ atm} \times \dfrac{760.0 \text{ torr}}{1.000 \text{ atm}} = 310. \text{ torr}$

   b. $68{,}471 \text{ Pa} \times \dfrac{1.000 \text{ atm}}{101{,}325 \text{ Pa}} \times \dfrac{760.0 \text{ mm Hg}}{1.000 \text{ atm}} = 513.6 \text{ mm Hg}$

   c. $50.9 \text{ psi} \times \dfrac{1.000 \text{ atm}}{14.69 \text{ psi}} = 3.46 \text{ atm}$

3. Boyle observed that as the volume increased, the pressure decreased. Pressure and volume are inversely proportional. The correct answer is c.

4. If the volume of gas inside the cylinder becomes smaller, then the pressure of the gas will become larger.

5. This problem provides pressure and volume data. Boyle's law relates pressure to volume. We can use $P_1V_1 = P_2V_2$, which is one way of writing Boyle's law, to solve this problem. In this equation, P_1 and V_1 represent initial, or starting, conditions. P_2 and V_2 represent final or changed conditions. We know that 2.4 atm is the initial pressure, (P_1) and 50.3 L is the initial volume (V_1). Pressure has changed so P_2 is 1.9 atm, and we are asked for the new volume, V_2. First, will the new volume be larger or smaller? The pressure decreases from 2.4 atm to 1.9 atm. There is an inverse relationship between temperature and pressure, so if the pressure decreases, we would expect the volume to increase.

Rearrange the equation to isolate V_2 on one side.

$$P_1V_1 = P_2V_2$$

$$V_1 \times \frac{P_1}{P_2} = V_2 \times \frac{P_2}{P_2}$$

$$V_2 = V_1 \times \frac{P_1}{P_2}$$

Now, substitute values into the equation.

$$V_2 = 50.3 \text{ L} \times \frac{2.4 \text{ atm}}{1.9 \text{ atm}}$$

$$V_2 = 64 \text{ L N}_2$$

This answer makes sense. The pressure has decreased from 2.4 atm to 1.9 atm so we would expect the volume to increase. The volume has in fact increased from 50.3 L to 64 L. There is an inverse relationship between pressure and volume.

6.   We can measure the volume of a gas at various temperatures, some of which are very cold, but not quite absolute zero. We can then plot on a graph each temperature and volume pair.

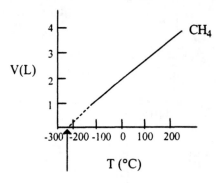

Although we cannot measure the volume of a gas at $-273.2°C$, we can determine at what temperature the volume would be zero by drawing a continuation of the straight line of the graph and noting where the temperature axis hits the line. This calculation has been done for many different gases and the result is always the same; the temperature at which the volume of a gas would be zero is $-273.2°C$.

7.   a.   Charles's law can be written as $V = bT$, where V is volume, T is temperature and b is a constant. We can rearrange the equation by dividing both sides by T.

$$\frac{V}{T} = b \times \frac{T}{T}$$

$$b = \frac{V}{T}$$

So, $\dfrac{V}{T} = b$ can be derived from Charles's law.

b.   If $\dfrac{V_1}{T_1} = b$ and $\dfrac{V_2}{T_2} = b$, then it is also true that $\dfrac{V_1}{T_1} = \dfrac{V_2}{T_2}$, so this relationship can also be derived from $V = bT$.

c.   We know that $\dfrac{V_1}{T_1} = b$ and that $\dfrac{V_2}{T_2} = b$. We also know that $\dfrac{V_1}{T_1} = \dfrac{V_2}{T_2}$, but we cannot add $\dfrac{V_1}{T_1}$ and $\dfrac{V_2}{T_2}$ together to equal the constant b. So this relationship cannot be derived from $V = bT$.

d. By multiplying temperature and volume by the same value, we are not changing the equation, because $\dfrac{3V}{3T}$ and $\dfrac{V}{T}$ are both equal to the constant b.

$$\frac{3V}{3T} = b = \frac{V}{T}$$

so this relationship can also be derived from $V = \dfrac{b}{T}$.

8. This problem provides temperature and volume data and asks about the volume of methane gas when the temperature changes. We can use Charles's law to solve the problem. One form of Charles's law is

$$\frac{V_1}{T_1} = \frac{V_2}{T_2}$$

The initial volume of methane is 0.89 L and the initial temperature is 100.5°C. The rise in temperature is 11.3°C, so the final temperature is the sum of 100.5°C plus 11.3°C, or 111.8°C. The unknown quantity is the final volume, V_2. Rearrange the equation to isolate V_2 on one side.

$$\frac{V_1}{T_1} = \frac{V_2}{T_2}$$

$$V_1 \times \frac{T_2}{T_1} = V_2 \times \frac{T_2}{T_2}$$

$$V_2 = V_1 \times \frac{T_2}{T_1}$$

Because both the initial and final temperatures are given in °C, we must convert to Kelvin.

initial temperature (T_1)

$T_K = T_{°C} + 273$

$T_K = 100.5 + 273$

$T_K = 374$

final temperature (T_2)

$T_K = 111.8 + 273$

$T_K = 385$

Now, substitute values into the equation.

$$V_2 = 0.89 \text{ L methane} \times \frac{385 \text{ K}}{374 \text{ K}}$$

$$V_2 = 0.92 \text{ L methane}$$

This answer makes sense. The temperature has increased, so the volume should also increase. There is a direct relationship between the temperature in Kelvin of a gas and its volume.

9.   Avogadro's law, which expresses a relationship between the volume of a gas and the number of moles of that gas, is true only when the gas temperature and pressure are constant.

10.   When the three laws that relate volume to pressure, to temperature and to the number of moles are combined, the constants that are present in each individual law are combined into one constant, called R, the universal gas constant. When volume is expressed in liters, pressure in atmospheres and temperature in Kelvin, R has units of L·atm/K·mol and a value of 0.08206 L atm/K mol.

11.   The ideal gas law can be expressed as $PV = nRT$. Remember that temperature must be expressed in Kelvin, pressure in atmospheres, and volume in liters. If any of the quantities given in the problem are expressed in other units, we must convert before we can use the ideal gas law.

     a.   This problem provides the pressure of chlorine gas in torr and the temperature in °C. Before we proceed let's convert torr to atmosphere and °C to K.

$$543 \text{ torr} \times \frac{1.000 \text{ atm}}{760.0 \text{ torr}} = 0.714 \text{ atm}$$

$$T_K = T_{°C} + 273$$

$$T_K = 0 + 273$$

$$T_K = 273$$

     We are provided with pressure, volume, and temperature data and we are asked for the number of moles. Rearrange the ideal gas law equation to isolate n on one side.

$$PV = nRT$$

$$\frac{PV}{RT} = n \times \frac{RT}{RT}$$

$$n = \frac{PV}{RT}$$

     Now, substitute values into the equation.

$$n = \frac{(0.714 \text{ atm})(21.6 \text{ L Cl}_2)}{(0.08206 \text{ L atm/K mol})(273 \text{ K})}$$

$$n = 0.688 \text{ mol Cl}_2$$

     b.   This problem asks us to calculate the volume of carbon monoxide gas, CO, given temperature, pressure and the number of moles of gas. The pressure of CO is given in mm Hg and temperature in °C. Before we proceed, we need to convert mm Hg to atmospheres and °C to K.

$$102 \text{ mm Hg} \times \frac{1.000 \text{ atm}}{760.0 \text{ mm Hg}} = 0.134 \text{ atm}$$

$$T_K = T_{°C} + 273$$

$$T_K = 11 + 273$$

$$T_K = 284$$

We can use the ideal gas law to solve this problem because we are provided with temperature, pressure and the number of moles of gas. Rearrange the ideal gas law to isolate V on one side.

$$PV = nRT$$

$$V \times \frac{P}{P} = \frac{nRT}{P}$$

$$V = \frac{nRT}{P}$$

Now, substitute values into the equation.

$$V = \frac{(1.2 \text{ mol})(0.08206 \text{ L atm/mol K})(284 \text{ K})}{(0.134 \text{ atm})}$$

$$V = 210 \text{ L CO}$$

c.   In this problem we are provided with information about two different gases. The information about the first gas is complete. That is, we know the number of moles, the temperature, the volume and the pressure of the gas. We know the temperature, the volume and pressure of the second gas and are asked to calculate the number of moles, n. We could use Avogadro's law, which relates volume and moles, to solve this problem but we are asked to use the ideal gas law. Because we know the temperature and the volume and the pressure of the second gas, we can use the ideal gas law to calculate the number of moles. First, convert pressure, which is given in torr, to atm, and temperature, which is given in °C, to K.

$$299 \text{ torr} \times \frac{1.000 \text{ atm}}{760.0 \text{ torr}} = 0.393 \text{ atm}$$

$$T_K = T_{°C} + 273$$

$$T_K = 300. + 273$$

$$T_K = 573$$

Rearrange the ideal gas law to isolate n on one side.

$$PV = nRT$$

$$\frac{PV}{RT} = n \times \frac{RT}{RT}$$

$$n = \frac{PV}{RT}$$

Now, substitute values into the equation.

$$n = \frac{(0.393 \text{ atm})(39.7 \text{ L})}{(0.08206 \text{ L atm/mol K})(573 \text{ K})}$$

$$n = 0.332 \text{ mol}$$

12. a. The total pressure (P_{TOTAL}) depends only on the total quantity of gas, not on the kind and size of the particles. So this statement is true.

  b. Because P_{TOTAL} does not depend on the identity of the gas particles but only on the quantity of particles. This statement is false.

  c. The pressure of a single gas or a mixture of gases depends on the number of moles, and also the temperature and volume. A mixture of gases follows the ideal gas law, just as a single gas does. So this statement is false.

13. P_{TOTAL} represents the pressure exerted by the gases in the atmosphere, which in this case is equal to 745 mm Hg, P_{TOTAL} equals $P_{OXYGEN} + P_{NITROGEN} + P_{WATER\ VAPOR}$. The two major components of air are nitrogen and oxygen. If $P_{NITROGEN}$ equals 566 mm Hg and P_{OXYGEN} equals 140. mm Hg, then we can use the following equation to calculate $P_{WATER\ VAPOR}$.

$$P_{TOTAL} = P_{OXYGEN} + P_{NITROGEN} + P_{WATER\ VAPOR}$$

Rearrange the equation to isolate $P_{WATER\ VAPOR}$ on one side.

$$P_{WATER\ VAPOR} = P_{TOTAL} - (P_{OXYGEN} + P_{NITROGEN})$$

Now, substitute values into the equation.

$$P_{WATER\ VAPOR} = 745 \text{ mm Hg} - (140. \text{ mm Hg} + 566 \text{ Hg})$$

$$P_{WATER\ VAPOR} = 39 \text{ mm Hg.}$$

14. We are asked to calculate P_{TOTAL} for a mixture of three gases. To determine P_{TOTAL}, we need to know the partial pressure of each individual gas. Calculating the partial pressure of any gas by using the ideal gas law requires us to know the number of moles, n, of that gas. So we need to find a way to calculate n.

We are given the initial volume of each gas, the initial pressure, and the initial temperature, so we can use the ideal gas law to find the number of moles. Because the number of moles of each gas does not change when the gases are mixed together, we can use the value of n we calculated for each gas before they are mixed together to calculate the partial pressure of each gas under the conditions present when the gases are mixed. Because pressure is given in torr, and temperature in °C, convert to atmospheres and Kelvin before proceeding.

The temperature is held constant at 65 °C, so convert to atmospheres and Kelvin before proceeding.

$$T_K = T_{°C} + 273$$

$$T_K = 65 + 273$$

$$T_K = 338$$

For nitrogen:

$$450 \text{ torr} \times \frac{1.000 \text{ atm}}{760.0 \text{ torr}} = 0.59 \text{ atm}$$

$$n_{N_2} = \frac{(0.59 \text{ atm})(4.0 \text{ L N}_2)}{(0.08206 \text{ L atm/mol K})(338 \text{ K})} = 0.085 \text{ mol N}_2$$

For oxygen:

$$252 \text{ torr} \times \frac{1.000 \text{ atm}}{760.0 \text{ torr}} = 0.332 \text{ atm}$$

$$n_{O_2} = \frac{(0.332 \text{ atm})(3.5 \text{ L } O_2)}{(0.08206 \text{ L atm/mol K})(338 \text{ K})} = 0.042 \text{ mol } O_2$$

For carbon dioxide:

$$150 \text{ torr} \times \frac{1.000 \text{ atm}}{760.0 \text{ torr}} = 0.197 \text{ atm}$$

$$n_{CO_2} = \frac{(0.197 \text{ atm})(0.21 \text{ L } CO_2)}{(0.08206 \text{ L atm/mol K})(338 \text{ K})} = 1.5 \times 10^{-3} \text{ mol } CO_2$$

So now we know the number of moles of each gas. We can use the ideal gas law to calculate the partial pressure of each gas. We will need to use the volume of the gas **mixture**, not the volume of each individual gas. Use the ideal gas law with P isolated on one side.

$$P = \frac{nRT}{V}$$

$$P_{N_2} = \frac{(0.085 \text{ mol } N_2)(0.08206 \text{ L atm/mol K})(338 \text{ K})}{7.5 \text{ L}} = 0.31 \text{ atm}$$

$$P_{O_2} = \frac{(0.042 \text{ mol } O_2)(0.08206 \text{ L atm/mol K})(338 \text{ K})}{7.5 \text{ L}} = 0.16 \text{ atm}$$

$$P_{CO_2} = \frac{(1.5 \times 10^{-3} \text{ mol } CO_2)(0.08206 \text{ L atm/mol K})(338 \text{ K})}{7.5 \text{ L}} = 5.5 \times 10^{-3} \text{ atm}$$

The total pressure, P_{TOTAL}, can be calculated from

$$P_{TOTAL} = 0.31 \text{ atm} + 0.16 \text{ atm} + 5.5 \times 10^{-3} \text{ atm}$$

$$P_{TOTAL} = 0.48 \text{ atm}$$

15. A law is a generalization about behavior that has been drawn from repeated observation about nature. A model is a theory that attempts to explain why a certain behavior is observed.

16. a. False. Gases obey the postulates of the Kinetic Molecular Theory best at high temperatures and/or high pressures. When these conditions are not met, gases can exhibit other kinds of behavior.

    b. False. In postulate four of the Kinetic Molecular Theory it is assumed that gas particles neither attract nor repel each other.

    c. True. In postulate two of the Kinetic Molecular Theory, it is assumed that individual gas particles are very small compared to the distances between the particles.

    d. True. The kinetic energy of a gas is proportional to the Kelvin temperature.

17. When we measure the temperature of a gas, we are actually measuring how fast the gas particles are moving. Postulate five of the Kinetic Molecular Theory results from the observation that as the temperature of a gas increases, the movement of gas particles increases.

18.   This problem provides the pressure, the temperature and the quantity in kg of a sample of propane gas. We are asked to find the volume of another gas, carbon dioxide, produced when propane burns. We know some information about carbon dioxide: we know that the pressure is 1 atm and the temperature is 400°C. If we knew the number of moles of carbon dioxide, we could use the ideal gas law to calculate the volume of carbon dioxide.

$$PV = nRT$$

$$?\qquad ?$$

We know the mass of propane that reacts to form CO_2, and we have a balanced equation, so we can calculate the moles of carbon dioxide using the mole ratio from the balanced equation. But first, let's calculate the number of moles of propane that are equivalent to 5.0 kg of propane.

$$5.0 \text{ kg C}_3\text{H}_8 \ \times \ \frac{1000 \text{ g C}_3\text{H}_8}{1 \text{ kg C}_3\text{H}_8} \times \frac{1 \text{ mol C}_3\text{H}_8}{44.09 \text{ g C}_3\text{H}_8} = 110 \text{ mol C}_3\text{H}_8$$

Now that we know the number of moles of propane, we can use the mole ratio to calculate the moles of CO_2 that would be produced. The balanced equation tells us that every mole of C_3H_8 produces 3 moles of CO_2 so the correct mole ratio is $\dfrac{3 \text{ mol CO}_2}{1 \text{ mol C}_3\text{H}_8}$

$$110 \text{ mol C}_3\text{H}_8 \ \times \ \frac{3 \text{ mol CO}_2}{1 \text{ mol C}_3\text{H}_8} = 330 \text{ mol CO}_2$$

Now we know the number of moles of CO_2, the pressure and the temperature, so we can use the ideal gas law to calculate the volume. First, isolate V on one side.

$$PV = nRT$$

$$\frac{P}{P} \times V = \frac{nRT}{P}$$

$$V = \frac{nRT}{P}$$

Because the temperature is given in °C, we must convert to Kelvin.

$$T_K = T_{°C} + 273$$

$$T_K = 400. + 273$$

$$T_K = 673 \text{ K}$$

Now, substitute values into the equation.

$$V = \frac{(330 \text{ mol C}_3\text{H}_8)(0.08206 \text{ L atm/mol K})(673 \text{ K})}{(1.0 \text{ atm})}$$

$$V = 1.8 \times 10^4 \text{ L CO}_2$$

19. We can solve this problem two ways. In the first method, we can use the ideal gas law because we know the volume, the temperature and the pressure. Rearrange the equation to isolate moles on one side.

$$PV = nRT$$

$$\frac{PV}{RT} = n \times \frac{RT}{RT}$$

$$n = \frac{PV}{RT}$$

The fluorine gas is at STP, which means that the temperature is 0 °C and the pressure is 1 atm. We need to convert °C to Kelvin before we proceed.

$$T_K = 0 + 273$$

$$T_K = 273$$

Now, substitute values into the equation.

$$n_{F_2} = \frac{(1.0 \text{ atm})(19.9 \text{ L})}{(0.08206 \text{ L atm/mol K})(273 \text{ K})}$$

$$n_{F_2} = 0.888 \text{ mol}$$

In the second method we can use the conversion of 1 mol of an ideal gas = 22.4 liters of gas. This conversion works only if the gas is at STP. In this problem we are told that the temperature and pressure are at STP.

$$19.9 \text{ L F}_2 \times \frac{1.00 \text{ mol F}_2}{22.4 \text{ L F}_2} = 0.888 \text{ mol F}_2$$

Both methods gave the same answer, but we can only use the second method when the temperature is 0°C (273 K) and the pressure is 1.00 atmosphere.

CHAPTER 14

Liquids and Solids

Introduction

This chapter discusses the properties of liquids and solids. You will learn what makes the particles in solids stay together and why some liquids boil at higher temperatures than others. One liquid of particular importance is water. Liquid water is one of the most important parts of our environment, and we routinely use water to dissolve many kinds of substances. As we will see, water has some unusual properties.

Chapter Discussion

Why is it that when we constantly apply heat to ice it eventually melts to form liquid water? And why does this water, when heated, eventually form steam? Also, how can it be that different chemicals are different phases at the same temperature? For example, sodium chloride is a solid, water is a liquid, and nitrogen is a gas, all at normal room temperature conditions. These are the types of questions that you should be able to answer by studying Chapter 14 in your text.

The bonds that we discussed in Chapter 12 were intramolecular bonds. That is, these were forces that held atoms together in a molecule. We now want to consider intermolecular bonds, or bonds that occur among molecules to form a solid or a liquid. Figure 14.1 provides a microscopic representation of a solid, liquid and gas.

Recall from our discussion of the VSEPR model (Chapter 12) that water is a bent or v-shaped molecule, and is therefore polar. In other words, there are regions of partial positive and negative charges in a water molecule, and these opposite charges provide the force that holds these molecules together (see Figures 14.4, 14.5, and 14.6 in your text). This attraction is termed dipole-dipole attraction. For molecules such as water, which has hydrogen bonded to oxygen (very electronegative – see Chapter 12), these dipole-dipole attractions are particularly strong and called hydrogen bonding. Hydrogen bonding accounts for some of the quite unusual properties of water. For example, because these intermolecular bonds are rather strong, water is a liquid at room conditions (water is a rather small and relatively lightweight molecule, and its boiling point is quite high for its molar mass and size).

So why does ice turn to water which turns to steam as we heat our sample? We know that temperature is a measure of kinetic energy (see Chapter 10) and an increase in kinetic energy will cause the molecules to move more quickly. The more movement, the more disorder. Look again at Figure 14.1 and note that solids are more ordered than liquids, which are more ordered than gases.

So this concept provides us with a way of thinking about phase changes. But what about the fact that some chemicals are solids, some are liquids, and some are gases at the same room conditions? This question can also be answered with our model of intermolecular forces.

Consider, for example, nitrogen gas (N_2). Draw the Lewis structure for N_2 and convince yourself that it is a non-polar molecule and because of this there should be no permanent dipole-dipole interactions. Because there seems to be no strong force holding these molecules together, it should make sense that N_2 is a gas. In fact, it is not obvious that one N_2 molecule would have any attraction for another N_2 molecule.

However, we know that N_2 can be a liquid if we get the temperature low enough (you may have seen or heard of liquid nitrogen before). There must be intermolecular attractions of some sort among all molecules. These forces are called London dispersion forces and come about from a random uneven distribution of electrons around the nucleus (see Figure 14.8). As the temperature is lowered the molecules slow down. If they are slowed down enough (liquid nitrogen is very cold) the molecules have enough attraction to come together to form a liquid.

Look at Figure 14.8 and think about this question: "Will a molecule with more electrons have a greater or smaller chance of having an uneven distribution of electrons?" Think about this before reading on.

The more electrons there are, the greater the chance that there will be an uneven distribution of electrons. The more electrons, the greater number of ways there are to be unevenly distributed. As a simple example, consider the following: if there were only two electrons in a diatomic molecule, the electrons can be evenly distributed or both could be on one side of the molecule. But with 10 electrons there are many more ways for uneven distribution (six on one side, four on the other; seven and three) and many combinations of these. This factor should lead us to believe that the more electrons a molecule has, the stronger the London dispersion forces will be (the greater the uneven distribution, the stronger the attraction).

Consider, for example, I_2, Br_2, and Cl_2. Each is non-polar and therefore relies only on London dispersion forces for intermolecular attractions. Thus, the type of attraction for each is the same. But I_2 has the most electrons and Cl_2 has the least. We would predict, then, that I_2 molecules would exhibit the most attraction for one another, and Cl_2 would exhibit the least. As it turns out, I_2 is a solid, Br_2 is a liquid, and Cl_2 is a gas all at room conditions. While our simple model could not predict that I_2 should be a solid, it is rewarding to note that we can predict the order of attraction.

You should be able to answer the following questions after studying Chapter 14:

1.   Why is sodium chloride a solid with such a high melting point?

2.   Why is water a liquid but methane (CH_4) a gas at room conditions?

Active Learning Questions

The Active Learning Questions at the end of each chapter are conceptually based questions that work well as discussion questions with a group of students. If your instructor does not assign these, consider getting together with a group of classmates and using these questions to see how well you understand the material in each chapter. While all of the questions work well, Active Learning Question 14 has you consider the difference between *intramolecular* and *intermolecular* forces, question 15 asks you to relate the shape of a molecule (water) to its properties, and questions 18 and 19 have you consider the term *molecule* in more depth. You are strongly encouraged to answer these.

Learning Review

1.   Why does ice float on the surface of liquid water?

2.   Which of the following statements about water are true, and which are false?

  a.   At 0°C water can be either a solid or a liquid.

  b.   The normal boiling point of water is 97.5°C at 1 atm pressure.

  c.   Forces between water molecules are called intramolecular forces.

3.   Why does it take more energy to convert liquid water to steam than it does to convert ice to liquid water?

4.   How much energy is required when 15.0 g of liquid water at 75°C is heated to 100.°C and then converted to steam at 100.°C? The molar heat of vaporization for liquid water is 40.6 kJ/mol and the specific heat capacity of liquid water is 4.18 J/g°C.

5.   How much energy is required to convert 6.0 g liquid water to steam at 100°C?

6.   Which bond is stronger, a covalent bond or a hydrogen bond?

7.   Draw a diagram showing how three NH_3 molecules can form hydrogen bonds.

8.   Why does water, H_2O, boil at a higher temperature than H_2S?

9.   Explain how London dispersion forces form between two molecules of argon.

10.   Match the following terms with the correct definition.

Terms	**Definitions**
a. condensation	the pressure exerted by a liquid at equilibrium with its vapor
b. vapor pressure	a balance between two opposite processes
c. vaporization	vapor molecules form a liquid
d. equilibrium	a liquid becomes a gas

11.   Which of the molecules in each pair would have the greater vapor pressure? To help you determine which of these molecules is polar, review Sections 12.2 and 12.3 of your textbook.

   a. CH_4, CH_3OH

   b. H_2O, H_2S

12.   Name the three types of crystalline solids and give an example of each.

13.   What intermolecular force is responsible for holding each of the following compounds together in the solid state?

   a.   KCl

   b.   HF

   c. $SiCl_4$

14.   Mixtures of metallic elements form alloys. What are the two kinds of alloys, and how do they differ from each other?

Answers to Learning Review

1.   Ice is less dense than the water, so it floats on the surface. The density of ice (solid water) is less than the density of liquid water because water expands as it freezes. This fact means that ice has the same mass as water but occupies a greater volume. Using the formula density = mass/volume, as the volume becomes greater, the density is less.

2.   a.   The normal freezing point of water is 0°C. Both liquids and solids can exist at the same time at the normal freezing point of a liquid. This statement is true.

   b.   The normal boiling point of water is 100°C at 1 atm pressure, not 97.5°C. This statement is false.

   c.   Forces between water molecules are called intermolecular forces. Forces between atoms of a single water molecule are called intramolecular forces. This statement is false.

3.   Converting ice to liquid water involves overcoming relatively few intermolecular forces because the molecules in both solid and liquid water are close together, so there is relatively little disruption when the change from solid to liquid occurs. However, going from liquid water to steam requires overcoming the intermolecular forces between water molecules, so a great amount of energy is required. The water molecules in steam are very far apart compared to water molecules in the liquid state.

4.   In this problem, there are two changes occurring. Each change must be considered separately when calculating the overall amount of energy needed. In the first change, we heat the liquid water from 75°C to 100°C. This conversion requires the use of the specific heat capacity for water along with the equation below.

Energy required = specific heat capacity × mass × temperature change

$$Q = c \times m \times \Delta T$$

We are given the specific heat capacity for liquid water, the mass of water, and we can calculate the change in temperature. If the final temperature is 100°C and the beginning temperature is 75°C, then the change in temperature, ΔT, must be 25°C.

Now substitute into the equation.

$$Q = c \times m \times \Delta T$$

$$Q = 4.18 \text{ J/g°C} \times 15.0 \text{ g water} \times 25°C$$

$$Q = 1{,}600 \text{ J}$$

In the second change, liquid water at 100°C is converted to steam at 100.°C. We are going from the liquid state to a gas, but the temperature remains 100°C. To calculate the amount of energy needed during this change, we can use the molar heat of vaporization for water as a conversion factor.

molar heat of vaporization = 40.6 kJ/mol H_2O

This conversion factor requires us to know the number of moles of steam. The problem tells us we have 15.0 g steam. We can calculate the number of moles from the molar mass of water.

$$15.0 \text{ g } H_2O \times \frac{1 \text{ mol } H_2O}{18.02 \text{ g } H_2O} = 0.832 \text{ mol } H_2O$$

Now, use the molar heat of vaporization as a conversion.

$$0.832 \text{ mol } H_2O \times \frac{40.6 \text{ kJ}}{1 \text{ mol } H_2O} = 33.8 \text{ kJ}$$

To convert 15.0 g liquid water from 75°C to 100°C requires 1,600 J and to convert 15.0 g liquid water at 100°C to a gas requires 33.8 kJ. To determine the total amount of energy required, we can add together the two quantities of energy. However, the units do not match. One quantity is given in Joules and the other in kiloJoules. Let's convert J to kJ.

$$1600 \text{ J} \times \frac{1 \text{ kJ}}{1000 \text{ J}} = 1.6 \text{ kJ}$$

The total amount of energy required is 1.6 kJ plus 33.8 kJ, which is equal to 35.4 kJ.

5.   We want to know how much energy is needed to convert water at 100°C to steam at 100°C. We can use the molar heat of vaporization of water as a conversion factor after we convert grams of water to moles of water.

$$6.0 \text{ g water} \times \frac{1 \text{ mol water}}{18.02 \text{ g water}} = 0.33 \text{ mol water}$$

Now, use the molar heat of vaporization to convert mol water to kiloJoules.

$$0.33 \text{ mol water} \times \frac{40.6 \text{ kJ}}{1 \text{ mol water}} = 13 \text{ kJ}$$

The amount of energy required to convert 6.0 g water at 100°C to steam at 100°C is 13 kJ.

6.   Hydrogen bonds are very strong dipole-dipole forces that occur between molecules that contain a hydrogen atom bonded to either a nitrogen atom, an oxygen atom or a fluorine atom. Even relatively strong hydrogen bonds are only 1 percent as strong as covalent bonds. Covalent bonds are much stronger than hydrogen bonds.

7.   Ammonia molecules can form hydrogen bonds because there is a hydrogen atom bonded to a strongly electronegative nitrogen atom, producing a strong dipole.

8.   Both H_2O and H_2S contain two hydrogen atoms. The difference between the two molecules is the central atom, oxygen or sulfur. Oxygen is an electronegative atom, while sulfur is not very electronegative. Water molecules can form strong hydrogen bonds because the O–H bond is very polar. The difference in electronegativity between oxygen and hydrogen is large. A great deal of heat energy is required to break apart the hydrogen bonds between water molecules so that the molecules can enter the vapor phase. The S–H bond in H_2S is not very polar because the difference in electronegativity between hydrogen and sulfur is small. No hydrogen bonds form between H_2S molecules, so less heat energy is required to boil liquid H_2S.

9.   The weak intermolecular forces are called London dispersion forces. They are weaker than hydrogen bonds or dipole-dipole interactions. We normally assume that the electrons in atoms such as argon are distributed somewhat evenly around the atom. However, we cannot predict the path an electron will take as it moves around the atom. Sometimes, more electrons are momentarily found on one side of an argon atom. This causes a small and temporary dipole. This temporary dipole can induce a dipole on an atom that may be nearby. The negative side of one argon atom is attracted to the positive side of another argon atom. These attractive forces between atoms are weak, and they do not last long. As the electrons move, the force dissipates.

10. a. condensation: vapor molecules form a liquid

   b. vapor pressure: the pressure exerted by a vapor in equilibrium with its liquid

   c. vaporization: a liquid becomes a gas

   d. equilibrium: a balance between two opposite processes

11. Two factors determine the relative vapor pressure of any two liquids: the molecular weights and the intermolecular forces.

   a. CH_3OH has a higher molecular weight (32.0 g/mol) than CH_4, which has a molecular weight of 16.0 g/mol. In a molecule of CH_3OH, a hydrogen atom is bonded to an electronegative oxygen atom. When hydrogen atoms are bonded to electronegative atoms such as oxygen, hydrogen bonds can form among molecules. CH_3OH molecules are attracted to each other by hydrogen bonds. CH_4 molecules contain only carbon-hydrogen bonds. Carbon is not as electronegative as atoms such as oxygen, so molecules of CH_4 are not very polar. There are no hydrogen bonds between CH_4 molecules. The intermolecular forces will be weak London dispersion forces. So the vapor pressure of CH_4 will be higher than CH_3OH.

   b. H_2S has a higher molecular weight (34.0 g/mol) than H_2O (18.0 g/mol). Purely on the basis of molecular weight, H_2S would have a lower vapor pressure than water. However, intermolecular forces are also important in determining vapor pressure. Water molecules form relatively strong hydrogen bonds, while H_2S does not. Because of the lack of strong intermolecular forces, H_2S has a higher vapor pressure than H_2O.

12. The three types of crystalline solids are ionic solids, molecular solids and atomic solids. An ionic solid exists as a collection of cations and anions held together by the attractive forces between the ions. An example is the salt potassium chloride. Molecular solids consist of molecules. There are no ions present. An example is table sugar, or sucrose. An atomic solid is made from individual atoms, all the same type. Pure copper metal is an example of an atomic solid.

13. a. KCl consists of potassium ions and chloride ions. The ions are held together in solid KCl by the forces that exist between the oppositely charged ions.

   b. When hydrogen is bonded to electronegative fluorine atoms to produce molecules of hydrogen fluoride, hydrogen bonds can form between molecules. The fluorine atom bears a partial negative charge, while the hydrogen atom bears a partial positive charge.

   c. $SiCl_4$ contains only silicon-chlorine bonds. This molecule will not form intermolecular hydrogen bonds because hydrogen bonding only occurs when hydrogen bonds to electronegative atoms such as oxygen, nitrogen or fluorine. Also, this molecule is not polar because it is a balanced molecule. There are no partially positive or negative ends. So there are no hydrogen bonds and no dipole-dipole attractions among $SiCl_4$ molecules, but London dispersion forces cause weak attractive forces between the molecules.

14. An alloy is a substance that contains a mixture of elements and has metallic properties. There are two basic kinds of alloys. Substitutional alloys have some of the metal atoms replaced with other metal atoms that are approximately the same size. Interstitial alloys have some of the small spaces between metal atoms filled with atoms smaller than the metal atoms.

CHAPTER 15

Solutions

Introduction

It is important to know how much solid is dissolved in a liquid. Telling someone that you added a little sugar to their iced tea does not give them much of a clue about how sweet the tea will be. A little sugar to you might mean a lot of sugar to someone else. In this chapter you will learn ways to express concentration so that you know just how much dissolved solid is present in a given volume of liquid.

Chapter Discussion

Many common ionic and nonionic substances dissolve in water. When an ionic substance dissolves, it breaks apart into ions. For example, when potassium sulfate, K_2SO_4, dissolves, it forms K^+ and SO_4^{2-} ions. To understand why a crystal of potassium sulfate breaks apart into ions, we need to consider the nature of the water molecule. Water molecules are polar; that is, one end of the molecule has a partial positive charge, and the other end has a partial negative charge. The positive potassium ion is attracted to the partial negative charge on the water molecule, and the negative sulfate ion is attracted to the partial positive charge on the water molecule. The K_2SO_4 crystal is pulled apart by the polarity of the water molecule. Ions in solution are surrounded by oppositely charged ends of water molecules.

Nonionic compounds such as ethyl alcohol (C_2H_5OH) also dissolve in water. The O–H of ethyl alcohol is polar, just as the O–H on the water molecule is. This property means that alcohol molecules have a negative end and a positive end just as water molecules do. Alcohol molecules are attracted by water molecules and are dissolved in them. Molecules that are not water-soluble do not have positive or negative ends to be attracted to water.

One way of describing the composition of a solution is mass percent. The mass percent of a solution is the mass of solute dissolved by the total mass of the solute plus solvent, multiplied by 100 percent.

$$\text{mass percent} = \left(\frac{\text{mass of solute}}{\text{mass of solution}} \right) \times 100\%$$

However, the mass percent of a solution is inconvenient to use when the solvent itself is liquid. It is much more convenient to measure the volume of a liquid than it is to measure its mass. The most often used indication of the amount of solute in a given volume of solution is molarity. Molarity is equal to the number of moles of solute per volume of solution.

$$\text{Molarity} = \left(\frac{\text{moles of solute}}{\text{liters of solution}} \right)$$

Molarity is often abbreviated as $M = \text{mol/L}$.

When the molarity of a solution is calculated, it is assumed that the solute is in the form it would be in before it dissolved. One mole of Na_2SO_4 when added to water produces two moles of Na^+ ions and one mole of SO_4^{2-} ions.

$$1.0 \text{ mol } Na_2SO_4 \rightarrow 2.0 \text{ mol } Na^+ + 1.0 \text{ mol } SO_4^{2-}$$

Compounds that do not form ions have the same molar concentration before and after they dissolve in water. Sucrose, table sugar, dissolves in water but does not form ions. So 1 mol of sucrose in 1 liter of solution produces a 1 *M* solution of sucrose.

Dilution is the process of adding more solvent to a solution. When we prepare a dilute solution, we are measuring the quality of a stock solution (relatively highly concentrated solution) and adding it to water. The amount of solute in the measured portion of stock solution is the same as the amount of solute in the more dilute solution. The only thing that has changed is the volume of the solution. We have decreased the concentration of the solution by increasing the volume, but the amount of solute stays the same.

In Chapter 9, you learned to solve stoichiometry problems. From the balanced equation you could answer questions about the quantity of reactant required or the quantity of product produced. The same principles are used here, but the reactions occur in solution. In Chapter 9 we used molar mass to convert mass to moles. Here, we use molarity to convert volume of solution to moles. Use the steps in Section 15.6 of your text.

Active Learning Questions

The Active Learning Questions at the end of each chapter are conceptually based questions that work well as discussion questions with a group of students. If your instructor does not assign these, consider getting together with a group of classmates and using these questions to see how well you understand the material in each chapter. While all of the questions work well, Active Learning Questions 4, 5 and 6 are multiple choice questions in which choosing the best answers will cause considerable discussion, question 9 requires you to understand an equation to solve dilution problems, question 12 has you draw a molecular-level diagram to make sure you understand the math in solution stoichiometry problems, and questions 13 and 14 are visual problems that test your conceptual understanding of concentration and solution stoichiometry. You are strongly encouraged to answer these.

Learning Review

1. 150 mL of ethyl alcohol is mixed with 1 L of water. Which is the solute, ethyl alcohol or water?

2. Which of the molecules below would you predict is soluble in water?

    a. CH_2-OH
       |
       $CH-OH$
       |
       CH_2-OH

    b. $CH_3-CH_2-CH_3$

    c. K_2SO_4

3. Three solutions are prepared by mixing the quantities of sodium chloride given below in a volume of 500 mL of solution. Which solution is the most concentrated?

    a. 55 g NaCl in 500 mL solution

    b. 127 g NaCl in 500 mL solution

    c. 105 g NaCl in 500 mL solution

4. A student stirred 5.0 g of table sugar into 250. g of hot coffee. What is the mass percent of sugar in the coffee?

5.   Calculate mass percents for the solutions below.

    a.   6.5 g KOH in 250. g water

    b.   0.40 g baking soda in 2,000.0 g flour

    c.   150. g acetone in 438 g water

6.   A solution of HCl in water is 0.15 M. How many mol/L of HCl are present?

7.   You dissolve 150.5 g of NaOH in water. The final volume of the solution is 3.8 L. What is the molarity of the solution?

8.   Calculate the molarity of each of the solutions below.

    a.   0.62 g $AgNO_3$ in a final volume of 1.5 L solution

    b.   10.6 g NaCl in a final volume of 286 mL solution

    c.   152 g $Ca(NO_3)_2$ in a final volume of 0.92 L solution

9.   You have 2.5 L of a solution of KI in water with a concentration of 0.15 M. How many grams of KI are in the solution?

10.   What is the concentration of each ion in the following solutions?

    a.   2.0 M H_2SO_4

    b.   0.6 M Na_3PO_4

    c.   1.5 M $AlCl_3$

11.   How many moles of KCl are present in 1.5 L of a 0.48 M solution of KCl in water?

12.   How many grams of NaOH are needed to make 1.50 L of a 0.650 M NaOH solution?

13.   How many grams of K_2SO_4 are needed to make 250 mL of a 0.150 M K_2SO_4 solution?

14.   Sodium fluoride is added to many water supplies to prevent tooth decay. How many grams of NaF must be added to a water supply so that 2.0×10^6 L of water contain 3.0×10^{-6} M NaF?

15.   What volume of 12 M HCl solution is needed to make 2.5 L of 1.0 M HCl?

16.   What volume of 18 M H_2SO_4 stock solution is needed to make 1,855 mL of 0.65 M H_2SO_4?

17.   If 2.5 L of solution contains 0.10 M $CaCl_2$, how many grams of Na_3PO_4 are needed to exactly precipitate all of the calcium as $Ca_3(PO_4)_2$?

18.   How many grams of $Fe(OH)_3$ can be produced by the addition of 0.25 moles of $FeCl_3$ to 1.2 L of a 0.85 M NaOH solution?

19.   What volume of 0.15 M NaOH solution will react completely with 150 mL of 0.25 M HCl?

20.   For each of the strong acids and strong bases below, give the number of equivalents present in 1 mole, and the equivalent weight of each.

Material	molar mass	equivalents	equivalent weight
1.0 mol HCl	36.46		
1.0 mol H_2SO_4	98.08		
1.0 mol KOH	56.11		

21.   If 5.6 grams of phosphoric acid, H_3PO_4, are added to water so that the final volume is 125 mL, what is the normality of the solution?

Answers to Learning Review

1.   Ethyl alcohol is the solute. Water is the solvent, because it is present in the larger amount.

2.   a.   This molecule contains three polar O–H bonds. Each of these O–H bonds can form hydrogen bonds with water. This molecule is soluble in water.

    b.   This molecule has no polar bonds. There is no part of the molecule that will interact with polar water molecules. This molecule is not soluble in water.

    c.   Potassium sulfate is an ionic compound. Many ionic compounds dissolve in water because the charged ions are pulled from the crystal by the polar water molecules. This molecule is soluble in water.

3.   Solution b, 127 g NaCl per 500 mL solution, is the most concentrated because the amount of solute per amount of solution is the greatest.

4.   The mass percent of a solution can be calculated by

$$\text{mass percent} = \left(\frac{\text{mass of solute}}{\text{mass of solution}} \right) \times 100\%$$

The mass of solute is 5.0 g sugar; and the mass of the solution is the mass of solute plus the mass of the solvent, 5.0 g sugar plus 250. g coffee equals 255 g solution. The mass percent sugar is

$$\frac{5.0 \text{ g sugar}}{255 \text{ g solution}} \times 100\% = 2.0\% \text{ sugar}$$

5.   a.   The mass of solute is 6.5 g KOH and the mass of solution is 6.5 g KOH plus 250. g water, which is 257 g. The mass percent is

$$\frac{\text{mass of solute}}{\text{mass of solution}} \times 100\% = \frac{6.5 \text{ g KOH}}{257 \text{ g solution}} \times 100\% = 2.5\% \text{ KOH}$$

    b.   The mass of solute is 0.40 g and the mass of solution is 0.40 g baking soda plus 2,000.0 g flour, which is equal to 2,000.4 g. The mass percent is

$$\frac{0.40 \text{ g baking soda}}{2000.4 \text{ g solution}} \times 100\% = 0.02\% \text{ baking soda}$$

    c.   The mass of solute is 150. g acetone and the mass of solution is 150. g of acetone plus 438 g water, which is 588 g. The mass percent is:

$$\frac{150. \text{ g acetone}}{588 \text{ g solution}} \times 100\% = 25.5\% \text{ acetone}$$

6.   The definition of molarity, M, is moles solute/liter solution. An HCl solution that is 0.15 M would contain 0.15 mol HCl/liter solution.

$$0.15 \ M \text{ HCl} = \frac{0.15 \text{ mol HCl}}{\text{L}}$$

7. The molarity of a solution is equal to the moles solute/liter solution. In this problem we have 150.5 g solute, NaOH. We do not know the number of moles. Using the molar mass for NaOH, we can calculate the number of moles.

$$150.5 \text{ g NaOH} \times \frac{1 \text{ mol NaOH}}{40.00 \text{ g NaOH}} = 3.763 \text{ mol NaOH}$$

Now, we can find the molarity.

$$M = \frac{\text{moles solute}}{\text{liters solution}}$$

$$M = \frac{3.763 \text{ mol NaOH}}{3.8 \text{ L}} = 0.99 \, M \text{ NaOH}$$

8. a. First, calculate the moles of $AgNO_3$.

$$0.62 \text{ g AgNO}_3 \times \frac{1 \text{ mol AgNO}_3}{169.91 \text{ g AgNO}_3} = 0.0036 \text{ mol AgNO}_3$$

Now, calculate the molarity.

$$M = \frac{0.0036 \text{ mol AgNO}_3}{1.5 \text{ L}}$$

$$M = 2.4 \times 10^{-3} \, M \text{ AgNO}_3$$

b. First, calculate the moles of NaCl.

$$10.6 \text{ g NaCl} \times \frac{1 \text{ mol NaCl}}{58.44 \text{ g NaCl}} = 0.181 \text{ mol NaCl}$$

The volume of the solution is given in milliliters. We need to know the number of liters.

$$286 \text{ mL solution} \times \frac{1 \text{ L solution}}{1000 \text{ mL solution}} = 0.286 \text{ L solution}$$

Now, calculate the molarity.

$$M = \frac{0.181 \text{ mol NaCl}}{0.286 \text{ L solution}}$$

$$M = 0.633 \, M \text{ NaCl}$$

c. First, calculate the moles of $Ca(NO_3)_2$

$$152 \text{ g Ca(NO}_3)_2 \times \frac{1 \text{ mol Ca(NO}_3)_2}{164.10 \text{ g Ca(NO}_3)_2} = 0.926 \text{ mol Ca(NO}_3)_2$$

Now, calculate the molarity.

$$M = \frac{0.926 \text{ mol Ca(NO}_3)_2}{0.92 \text{ L}}$$

$$M = 1.0 \, M \text{ Ca(NO}_3)_2$$

9. This problem gives us the number of liters of solution and the molar concentration of the solution. From the definition of molarity, moles solute/liter solution, we can calculate the number of moles of solute, KI.

$$2.5 \text{ L solution} \times \frac{0.15 \text{ mol KI}}{\text{L solution}} = 0.38 \text{ mol KI}$$

Now use the molar mass of KI to calculate the grams of KI.

$$0.38 \text{ mol KI} \times \frac{166.0 \text{ g KI}}{1 \text{ mol KI}} = 63 \text{ g KI}$$

10. a. Sulfuric acid produces 2 moles of hydrogen ions and 1 mole of sulfate ions for each mole of sulfuric acid.

$$1 \text{ mol H}_2\text{SO}_4(aq) \rightarrow 2 \text{ mol H}^+(aq) + 1 \text{ mol SO}_4^{2-}(aq)$$

A 2.0 M solution of sulfuric acid would contain 2(2.0 mol H$^+$) per liter, or 4.0 M H$^+$ total, and 2(1.0 mol SO$_4^{2-}$) per liter, or 2.0 M SO$_4^{2-}$.

   b. Sodium phosphate produces three moles of sodium ions for each mole of sodium phosphate, and one mole of phosphate ions for each mole of sodium phosphate.

$$1 \text{ mol Na}_3\text{PO}_4(aq) \rightarrow 3 \text{ mol Na}^+(aq) + 1 \text{ mol PO}_4^{3-}(aq)$$

A 0.6 M solution of sodium phosphate would contain 3(0.6 mol Na$^+$) per liter, or 1.8 M Na$^+$, and 1(0.6 mol PO$_4^{3-}$) per liter, or 0.6 M PO$_4^{3-}$.

   c. Aluminum chloride produces one mole of aluminum ions for each mole of aluminum chloride, and three moles of chloride ions for each mole of aluminum chloride.

$$1 \text{ mol AlCl}_3(aq) \rightarrow 1 \text{ mol Al}^{3+}(aq) + 3 \text{ mol Cl}^-(aq)$$

A 1.5 M solution of aluminum chloride would contain 1(1.5 mol Al^{3+}) per liter, or 1.5 M Al^{3+}, and 3(1.5 mol Cl$^-$) per liter, or 4.5 M Cl$^-$.

11. We are given the concentration and the volume of a solution containing KCl and water, and are asked for the number of moles of solute, KCl. The number of moles of KCl can be calculated from the definition of molarity, moles solute/liter solution.

$$1.5 \text{ L solution} \times \frac{0.48 \text{ mol KCl}}{\text{L solution}} = 0.72 \text{ mol KCl}$$

12. We are given the concentration of a solution containing NaOH and water. We are asked for the number of grams of NaOH needed to make 1.50 L of solution. The number of moles of NaOH can be calculated from the definition of molarity – moles solute per liter of solution. The grams of NaOH can be calculated using the molar mass of NaOH.

$$1.50 \text{ L solution} \times \frac{0.650 \text{ mol NaOH}}{\text{L solution}} \times \frac{40.00 \text{ g NaOH}}{\text{mol NaOH}} = 39.0 \text{ g NaOH}$$

13. We are given the concentration of a solution containing K_2SO_4 and water. We are asked for the number of grams of K_2SO_4 needed to make 250 mL of solution. The number of moles of K_2SO_4 can be calculated from the definition of molarity. The grams of K_2SO_4 can be calculated using the molar mass of K_2SO_4. We will need to convert the given units of volume, milliliters, to liters.

$$250 \text{ mL solution} \times \frac{1 \text{ L solution}}{1000 \text{ mL solution}} \times \frac{0.150 \text{ mol } K_2SO_4}{\text{L solution}} \times \frac{174.27 \text{ g } K_2SO_4}{\text{mol } K_2SO_4} = 6.5 \text{ g } K_2SO_4$$

14. We are given the concentration of a solution containing NaF and water. We are asked for the number of grams of NaF needed to make 2.0×10^6 L of solution. The number of moles of NaF can be calculated from the definition of molarity. The grams of NaF can be calculated from the molar mass of NaF.

$$2.0 \times 10^6 \text{ L solution} \times \frac{3.0 \times 10^{-6} \text{ mol NaF}}{\text{L solution}} \times \frac{41.99 \text{ g NaF}}{\text{mol NaF}} = 2.5 \times 10^2 \text{ g NaF}$$

15. In this problem we are asked to calculate how much of a concentrated stock solution, which is 12 M HCl, is needed to prepare a dilute HCl solution. We will need to know how many moles of HCl are present in 2.5 L of 1.0 M HCl, that is, in the dilute solution. Then we need to find a volume of the concentrated solution that contains this same number of moles. We can use this procedure because the number of moles of solute in the dilute solution is the same as the number of moles of solute in the volume of stock solution. Only the volume of water changes. First, find the number of moles of HCl that will be present in the dilute solution by multiplying the volume by the molarity.

$$2.5 \text{ L solution} \times \frac{1.0 \text{ mol HCl}}{\text{L solution}} = 2.5 \text{ mol HCl}$$

So the dilute solution will contain 2.5 mol HCl, and the volume of stock solution we need will also contain 2.5 mol HCl. The volume of stock solution multiplied by the molarity of the stock solution equals the number of moles of HCl that will be in the dilute solution.

$$\text{volume of stock soluton} \times \frac{\text{mol HCl in stock solution}}{\text{L stock solution}} = \text{mol HCl in dilute solution}$$

Now, substitute values into the equation.

$$V \times \frac{12 \text{ mol HCl}}{\text{L solution}} = 2.5 \text{ mol HCl}$$

Rearrange the equation to isolate V on one side.

$$V = \frac{2.5 \text{ mol HCl}}{12 \text{ mol HCl/L solution}}$$

$$V = 0.21 \text{ L HCl}$$

So to make 2.5 L of 1.0 M HCl, use 0.21 L of 12 M HCl, and add enough water to bring the total volume to 2.5 L.

A different way to approach this problem is to use the formula

$$M_1 \times V_1 = M_2 \times V_2$$

M_1 represents the molarity of the stock solution; V_1, the volume of the stock solution needed; M_2, the molarity of the dilute solution we wish to make; and V_2, the volume of the dilute solution. In this case we want to know the volume of stock solution needed, so isolate V_1 on one side of the equation by dividing both sides by M_1.

$$M_1 \times V_1 = M_2 \times V_2$$

$$\frac{M_1}{M_1} \times V_1 = V_2 \times \frac{M_2}{M_1}$$

$$V_1 = V_2 \times \frac{M_2}{M_1}$$

Now, substitute values into the equation.

$$V_1 = 2.5 \text{ L} \times \frac{1.0\ M}{12\ M}$$

$$V_1 = 0.21 \text{ L}$$

The answer to this problem is the same either way we solve it.

16.   We want to know how much concentrated stock solution is needed to make 1,855 mL of 0.65 M H_2SO_4. We can use the formula:

$$M_1 \times V_1 = M_2 \times V_2$$

M_1 is the molarity of the stock solution, V_1 is the volume of the stock solution, M_2 is the molarity of the dilute solution, and V_2 is the volume of the dilute solution. We want to know how much stock solution is needed, so we isolate V_1 on one side of the equation.

$$V_1 = V_2 \times \frac{M_2}{M_1}$$

The volume of the dilute solution, V_2, is given in milliliters. We will need to convert milliliters to liters.

$$1855 \text{ mL} \times \frac{1 \text{ L}}{1000 \text{ mL}} = 1.855 \text{ L}$$

Now, substitute values into the equation.

$$V_1 = 1.855 \text{ L} \times \frac{0.65\ M\ H_2SO_4}{18\ M\ H_2SO_4}$$

$$V_1 = 0.067 \text{ L}$$

So, 0.067 L of 18 M H_2SO_4 diluted to 1.855 L would produce a 0.65 M H_2SO_4 solution.

17.   In this problem a solution of $CaCl_2$ is mixed with a solution of Na_3PO_4. A reaction occurs. We are asked for the number of grams of Na_3PO_4 that will react with the $CaCl_2$. Section 15.6 of your textbook gives five steps for solving problems like this one, so let's follow those same steps here.

Step 1: First, write the balanced molecular equation for this reaction. Because this is a reaction between ionic compounds, we also should write the net ionic equation. The balanced molecular equation is:

$$3CaCl_2(aq) + 2Na_3PO_4(aq) \rightarrow Ca_3(PO_4)_2(s) + 6NaCl(aq)$$

The net ionic equation is the solid product, $Ca_3(PO_4)_2$, and the ions that react to form the solid product.

$$3Ca^{2+}(aq) + 2PO_4^{3-}(aq) \rightarrow Ca_3(PO_4)_2(s)$$

Step 2: We need to add just enough PO_4^{3-} to react with all the Ca^{2+}. We need to know how many moles of Ca^{2+} there are in the $CaCl_2$ solution. From the volume and the molarity of the $CaCl_2$ solution, we can calculate the number of moles of Ca^{2+}.

$$V \times M = \text{mol } CaCl_2$$

$$2.5 \text{ L } CaCl_2 \text{ solution} \times \frac{0.10 \text{ mol } CaCl_2}{\text{L } CaCl_2 \text{ solution}} = 0.25 \text{ mol } CaCl_2$$

Each mole of $CaCl_2$ produces one mole of Ca^{2+}.

$$0.25 \text{ mol } CaCl_2 \times \frac{1 \text{ mol } Ca^{2+}}{1 \text{ mol } CaCl_2} = 0.25 \text{ mol } Ca^{2+}$$

Step 3: In this problem Ca^{2+} is limiting. We must add just enough PO_4^{3-} to react with all the Ca^{2+}.

Step 4: We need to know how many moles of PO_4^{3-} will react with 0.25 mol Ca^{2+}. We can use the mole ratio from the balanced equation to calculate the moles of PO_4^{3-} that are needed.

$$0.25 \text{ mol } Ca^{2+} \times \frac{2 \text{ mol } PO_4^{3-}}{3 \text{ mol } Ca^{2+}} = 0.17 \text{ mol } PO_4^{3-}$$

So 0.17 mol PO_4^{3-} will react with 0.25 mol Ca^{2+}.

Step 5: We are asked for grams of Na_3PO_4, not moles of PO_4^{3-}, so convert moles of PO_4^{3-} to grams of Na_3PO_4. Each mole of Na_3PO_4 contains one mole of PO_4^{3-} ions. We can use the molar mass of Na_3PO_4 to convert from moles Na_3PO_4 to grams Na_3PO_4.

$$0.17 \text{ mol } PO_4^{3-} \times \frac{1 \text{ mol } Na_3PO_4}{1 \text{ mol } PO_4^{3-}} \times \frac{163.94 \text{ g } Na_3PO_4}{1 \text{ mol } Na_3PO_4} = 28 \text{ g } Na_3PO_4$$

18. We want to know how many grams of product, $Fe(OH)_3$, can be produced when two aqueous solutions are mixed together.

Step 1: Write and balance the equation for this reaction.

$$FeCl_3(aq) + 3NaOH(aq) \rightarrow Fe(OH)_3(s) + 3NaCl(aq)$$

From the balanced equation, write the net ionic equation.

$$Fe^{3+}(aq) + 3OH^-(aq) \rightarrow Fe(OH)_3(s)$$

Step 2: We need to know the number of moles of reactant present in each solution. The solution of $FeCl_3$ contains 0.25 mol $FeCl_3$, and each mole of $FeCl_3$ contains one mole of Fe^{3+}.

$$0.25 \text{ mol } FeCl3 \times \frac{1 \text{ mol } Fe^{3+}}{1 \text{ mol } FeCl_3} = 0.25 \text{ mol } Fe^{3+}$$

We need to know the number of moles of OH^- that are present.

$$V \times M = \text{moles NaOH}$$

$$1.2 \text{ L NaOH solution} \times \frac{0.85 \text{ mol NaOH}}{\text{L NaOH solution}} = 1.0 \text{ mol NaOH}$$

Each mole of NaOH contains one mole of OH^-.

$$1.0 \text{ mol NaOH} \times \frac{1 \text{ mol } OH^-}{1 \text{ mol NaOH}} = 1.0 \text{ mol } OH^-$$

Step 3: 0.25 mol Fe^{3+} is mixed with 1.0 mol OH^-. Because each mole of Fe^{3+} requires three moles of OH^-, 0.25 mol Fe^{3+} requires 3(0.25 mol OH^-) or 0.75 mol OH^-. Because we have 1.0 mol OH^-, the amount of product that forms is limited by the amount of Fe^{3+}.

Step 4: From the mole ratio, each mole of Fe^{3+} produces one mole of $Fe(OH)_3$.

$$0.25 \text{ mol } Fe^{3+} \times \frac{1 \text{ mol } Fe(OH)_3}{1 \text{ mol } Fe^{3+}} = 0.25 \text{ mol } Fe(OH)_3$$

Step 5: We want to know the number of grams of $Fe(OH)_3$, so use the molar mass of $Fe(OH)_3$ to convert from moles to grams.

$$0.25 \text{ mol } Fe(OH)_3 \times \frac{106.87 \text{ g } Fe(OH)_3}{1 \text{ mol } Fe(OH)_3} = 27 \text{ g } Fe(OH)_3$$

19. In this problem we are mixing a solution of HCl of known volume and molarity with a solution of NaOH of known molarity and an unknown volume. We are asked to determine the volume of NaOH that will react with the HCl. We can follow the same steps we have used previously.

Step 1: Write the balanced equation for this reaction.

$$\text{NaOH}(aq) + \text{HCl }(aq) \rightarrow \text{NaCl}(aq) + H_2O(l)$$

Now, write the net ionic equation.

$$H^+(aq) + OH^-(aq) \rightarrow H_2O(l)$$

Step 2: Calculate the moles of HCl using the formula $V \times M = \text{moles}$.

$$150 \text{ mL} \times \frac{1 \text{ L HCl}}{1000 \text{ mL}} \times \frac{0.25 \text{ mol } H^+}{\text{L HCl}} = 0.038 \text{ mol } H^+$$

Step 3: This problem requires mixing just enough OH^- to react with all the H^+ which is present. The moles of H^+ determine how much OH^- is to be added. The H^+ ions are limiting.

Step 4: From the net ionic equation we can determine how many moles of OH^- are needed to react with all the H^+.

$$0.038 \text{ mol } H^+ \times \frac{1 \text{ mol } OH^-}{1 \text{ mol } H^+} = 0.038 \text{ mol } OH^-$$

Step 5: We now know the moles of OH^- and the molarity. We can use the formula $V \times M$ equals moles to calculate the volume of NaOH. Rearrange the equation to isolate V on one side.

$$V \times \frac{M}{M} = \frac{\text{moles}}{M}$$

$$V = \frac{moles}{M}$$

Now, substitute values into the equation.

$$V = \frac{0.038 \text{ mol OH}^-}{0.15 \text{ mol NaOH/L NaOH}}$$

$$V = 0.25 \text{ L NaOH}$$

So, 0.25 L of 0.15 M NaOH will completely react with 150 mL of 0.25 M HCl.

20.

Material	molar mass	equivalents	equivalent weight
1.0 mol HCl	36.46	1	36.46
1.0 mol H$_2$SO$_4$	98.08	2	49.05
1.0 mol KOH	56.11	1	56.11

21.   We want to calculate the normality of a solution of phosphoric acid in water. To do so, we need to know the number of equivalents of phosphoric acid present in 5.6 g phosphoric acid. The equivalent weight of phosphoric acid is:

$$\text{equivalent weight H}_3\text{PO}_4 = \frac{\text{molar mass H}_3\text{PO}_4}{3}$$

$$\text{equivalent weight H}_3\text{PO}_4 = \frac{97.99 \text{ g}}{3}$$

$$\text{equivalent weight H}_3\text{PO}_4 = 32.66 \text{ g}$$

We can now calculate the equivalents of H$_3$PO$_4$ present in 5.6 g H$_3$PO$_4$.

$$5.6 \text{ g H}_3\text{PO}_4 \times \frac{1 \text{ equiv H}_3\text{PO}_4}{32.66 \text{ g H}_3\text{PO}_4} = 0.17 \text{ equiv H}_3\text{PO}_4$$

The definition of normality is $N = \dfrac{\text{equiv}}{\text{L}}$. We can use this equation to calculate the normality of the H$_3$PO$_4$ solution.

$$N = \frac{0.17 \text{ equiv H}_3\text{PO}_4}{125 \text{ mL}} \times \frac{1000 \text{ mL}}{1 \text{ L}} = \frac{1.36 \text{ equiv H}_3\text{PO}_4}{\text{L}}$$

This solution is 1.36 N H$_3$PO$_4$.

CHAPTER 16

Acids and Bases

Introduction

In this chapter you will learn about the properties of acids and bases. You know about some of the properties of acids already. Solutions such as lemon juice and vinegar contain acids, and their sour taste is from the acid each contains. You will learn how to determine the properties of acids and how to measure the acidity of a solution.

Chapter Discussion

Arrhenius proposed that an acid was anything that produced hydrogen ions in solution, and a base was anything that produced hydroxide ions. Scientists discovered that this definition was too restrictive and that there were other bases besides hydroxide ions. Brønsted and Lowry proposed a much broader definition: that an acid was a proton (hydrogen ion) donor and a base was a proton acceptor.

The general reaction for an acid acting in water is given by the following equation:

$$HA\ (aq) + H_2O\ (l) \rightleftharpoons H_3O^+\ (aq) + A^-\ (aq)$$

The protonated water (H_3O^+) is called the hydronium ion and is the conjugate acid of H_2O. It acts as a base to the acid HA. The remaining part of the acid (A^-) is called the conjugate base.

The reaction of an acid and water is a reversible reaction (see Chapter 17). The proton can be attached to the water molecule or to the conjugate base. The relative attractions of H_2O and A^- for the proton determine whether HA or H_3O^+ predominates. If A^- attracts the proton more strongly that water, the equilibrium lies to the left and there is relatively little H_3O^+. The acid HA is said to be a weak acid. If the water attracts the proton more strongly than does A^-, the equilibrium lies to the right and HA is a strong acid because virtually all of the protons have dissociated from HA.

The hydrogen ion concentration of a solution is represented by very small numbers. Using scientific notation is a good way to represent small numbers, but calculating and using the pH of a solution is another easy way to represent small numbers. Taking the p of any number means we take the logarithm (log) of that number, and multiply the result by -1.

$$pN = (-1) \times \log N$$

When we find the pH of a solution, we take the log of the hydrogen ion concentration in mol/L and multiply by -1.

A log scale can also be used to express hydroxide ion concentration. So pOH is calculated the same way as pH, except we take the log of the hydroxide ion concentration in mol/L and multiply by -1.

$[H^+]$ and $[OH^-]$ are related to each other through the equilibrium expression for the dissociation of water, and the ion product constant K_w (at 25°C).

$$[H^+][OH^-] = K_w = 1.0 \times 10^{-14}$$

If we take the p ($-\log$) of each of the parts of this equation we have:

$$pH + pOH = 14.00$$

For any aqueous solution at 25°C, the sum of pH and pOH will always equal 14. If we know the pH, we can easily find the pOH and vice versa.

A buffered solution resists large changes in pH even when strong acid or strong base is added. The addition of even small amounts of strong acid or base can greatly lower or raise the pH of a nonbuffered solution. Living systems contain many different kinds of buffers to help keep fluids and tissues at the correct pH, even under stressful conditions.

Active Learning Questions

The Active Learning Questions at the end of each chapter are conceptually based questions that work well as discussion questions with a group of students. If your instructor does not assign these, consider getting together with a group of classmates and using these questions to see how well you understand the material in each chapter. While all of the questions work well, Active Learning Questions 6 asks you to draw molecular-level pictures of weak and strong acids and relate these to the strengths of the conjugate bases, questions 10 through 12 focus on buffered solutions, and questions 14 and 15 test your conceptual understanding of the concept of pH. You are strongly encouraged to answer these.

Learning Review

1.   Explain the differences between the Arrhenius concept of an acid and a base, and the concept of Brønsted and Lowry.

2.   For the reaction of perbromic acid with water:

$$HBrO_4(aq) + H_2O(l) \rightarrow H_3O^+(aq) + BrO_4^-(aq)$$

   a.   Which two substances are an acid-conjugate base pair?

   b.   Which two substances are a base-conjugate acid pair?

3.   Write equations to show what happens when each of the acids below reacts with water.

   a. H_2S

   b. HNO_2

4.   Show how acetic acid ($HC_2H_3O_2$) reacts with water by drawing Lewis structures for water and its conjugate acid.

5.   When formic acid, HCOOH, is mixed with water, the resulting solution weakly conducts an electric current.

   a.   Is formic acid a strong or a weak acid?

   b.   Toward which side of the reaction does the equilibrium lie?

   c.   Which species is the stronger base, H_2O or $HCOO^-$?

6.   Which of the acids below are strong acids and which are weak acids?

   a.   HF

   b. H_2SO_4

   c. $HC_2H_3O_2$

   d. $HClO_4$

7.   The expression for the dissociation of water is $K_w = [H^+][OH^-]$. Why does liquid water not appear in this expression?

8. All the aqueous solutions below are at a temperature of 25°C.

    a. What is the $[H^+]$ of a solution for which $[OH^-] = 1.5 \times 10^{-6} M$?

    b. What is the $[H^+]$ of a solution for which $[OH^-] = 6.3 \times 10^{-3} M$?

    c. What is the $[OH^-]$ of a solution for which $[H^+] = 3.25 \times 10^{-1} M$?

9. What is the $[H^+]$ of a 0.1 M solution of NaOH in water at 25°C?

10. What is the pH of each of the solutions below?

    a. A solution in which $[H^+] = 3.0 \times 10^{-3} M$

    b. A solution in which $[H^+] = 5.2 \times 10^{-6} M$

    c. A solution in which $[OH^-] = 1.4 \times 10^{-1} M$

11. What is the pOH of each solution below?

    a. $[OH^-] = 4.89 \times 10^{-10} M$

    b. $[OH^-] = 3.2 \times 10^{-5} M$

    c. $[H^+] = 1.6 \times 10^{-8} M$

12. For any solution, what is the relationship between pH and pOH?

13. The pH of lemon juice is 2.1. What is the pOH?

14. The pOH of black coffee is 9.0. What is the pH?

15. Calculate the $[H^+]$ or $[OH^-]$ for the solutions below.

    a. Milk has a pH of 6.9. What is the $[H^+]$?

    b. Oven cleaner has a pH of 13.4. What is the $[OH^-]$?

    c. A phosphate-containing detergent has a pOH of 4.7. What is the $[OH^-]$?

16. What is the pH of each of the following solutions?

    a. 0.02 M HCl

    b. $3.5 \times 10^{-3} M$ HNO$_3$

17. HCl is added to a solution containing H_2CO_3 and $NaHCO_3$.

    a. Use an equation to show what would happen to the hydrogen ions from the HCl.

    b. Why would the pH of this solution not change drastically when the HCl is added?

Answers to Learning Review

1. Arrhenius's model of acids and bases proposes that acids produce hydrogen ions in aqueous solution, while bases produce hydroxide ions. The Brønsted-Lowry model of acids and bases proposes that acids are proton donors, while bases are proton acceptors.

2. a.   For the reaction of perbromic acid with water, perbromic acid/perbromate ($HBrO_4/BrO_4^-$) is the acid-conjugate base pair.

    b.   Water/hydronium ion (H_2O/H_3O^+) is the base-conjugate acid pair.

3. One model of an acid postulates that acids donate protons in aqueous solutions. The proton acceptor is the base, water. In aqueous solutions, acids donate protons to the base water to form the hydronium ion and the conjugate base.

    a. $H_2S(aq) + H_2O(l) \rightarrow HS^-(aq) + H_3O^+(aq)$

    b. $HNO_2(aq) + H_2O(l) \rightarrow NO_2^-(aq) + H_3O^+(aq)$

4.

5. a.   When formic acid is mixed with water, a weak electric current is generated. An electrical current requires ions. We know that only a few ions are in this solution because the current is weak. So formic acid is a weak acid.

    b.   Because there are only a few formate and hydronium ions formed, the equilibrium lies toward the left, that is, toward undissociated formic acid.

    c.   A base can be defined as a proton acceptor. The formate ion has a stronger attraction for hydrogen ions than water does because most of the formic acid is undissociated. The formate ion has pulled the hydrogen ion away from the hydronium ion so $HCOO^-$ is a stronger base than water is.

6. The common strong acids are HCl, HNO_3, H_2SO_4 and $HClO_4$. So, b (H_2SO_4) and d ($HClO_4$) are strong acids. HF and $HC_2H_3O_2$ are weak acids.

7. The concentration of liquid water does not appear in the expression for the dissociation of water because the concentration of water changes very little when dissociation occurs. The concentration of water is considered a constant.

8. a.   The product of $[H^+][OH^-]$ is always equal to 1.0×10^{-14}.

    $$K_w = 1.0 \times 10^{-14} = [H^+][OH^-]$$

    When we are given either $[H^+]$ or $[OH^-]$, we can calculate the other if we remember that K_w is equal to 1.0×10^{-14}. In this problem, we know that $[OH^-] = 1.5 \times 10^{-6} M$ and we want to know $[H^+]$. Rearrange the equation to isolate $[H^+]$ on one side by dividing both sides by $[OH^-]$.

    $$K_w = [H^+][OH^-]$$

Divide both sides by [OH⁻].

$$\frac{K_w}{[OH^-]} = \frac{[H^+][OH^-]}{[OH^-]}$$

$$[H^+] = \frac{K_w}{[OH^-]}$$

Substitute values into the equation.

$$[H^+] = \frac{1.0 \times 10^{-14}}{1.5 \times 10^{-6}}$$

$$[H^+] = 6.7 \times 10^{-9}\, M$$

b. We are given [OH⁻] and asked for [H⁺]. We can use the K_w expression to find [H⁺]. Rearrange the equation to isolate [H⁺] on one side.

$$K_w = [H^+][OH^-]$$

$$\frac{K_w}{[OH^-]} = \frac{[H^+][OH^-]}{[OH^-]}$$

$$[H^+] = \frac{K_w}{[OH^-]}$$

Substitute values into the equation.

$$[H^+] = \frac{1.0 \times 10^{-14}}{6.3 \times 10^{-3}}$$

$$[H^+] = 1.6 \times 10^{-12}\, M$$

c. We are given [H⁺] and asked for [OH⁻]. Use the K_w expression to find [OH⁻]. Rearrange the K_w expression to isolate [OH⁻] on one side by dividing both sides by [H⁺].

$$K_w = [H^+][OH^-]$$

$$\frac{K_w}{[H^+]} = \frac{[H^+][OH^-]}{[H^+]}$$

$$[OH^-] = \frac{K_w}{[H^+]}$$

Now, substitute values into the equation.

$$[OH^-] = \frac{1.0 \times 10^{-14}}{3.25 \times 10^{-1}} = 3.08 \times 10^{-14}\, M$$

9. When NaOH dissolves in water, each mole of NaOH forms a mole of Na^+ ions and a mole of OH⁻ ions. A solution that is 0.1 M NaOH is also 0.1 M OH⁻. We can use the K_w expression to find [H⁺].

$$K_w = [H^+][OH^-]$$

Rearrange the equation to isolate $[H^+]$ on one side.

$$\frac{K_w}{[OH^-]} = \frac{[H^+][OH^-]}{[OH^-]}$$

$$[H^+] = \frac{K_w}{[OH^-]}$$

Substitute values into the equation and find $[H^+]$.

$$[H^+] = \frac{1.0 \times 10^{-14}}{0.1}$$

$$[H^+] = 1 \times 10^{-13} \, M$$

The amount of H^+ is very small compared with the amount of OH^-.

10.   The pH scale is a way to write very small numbers in a more convenient form.
So pH $= -\log[H^+]$.

   a.   2.52

   a.   5.28

   b.   We are given $[OH^-]$ and are asked for pH. We must find $[H^+]$ before we can find the pH. Use the K_w expression to find $[H^+]$.

$$K_w = [H^+][OH^-]$$

$$[H^+] = \frac{K_w}{[OH^-]}$$

$$[H^+] = \frac{1.0 \times 10^{-14}}{1.4 \times 10^{-1}} = 7.14 \times 10^{-14}$$

Now that we know $[H^+]$, we can find the pH. The pH of a solution that contains $1.4 \times 10^{-1} \, M \, OH^-$ is 13.15.

11.   a.   The pOH of a solution is equal to $-\log [OH^-]$. The pOH of a solution that contains $4.89 \times 10^{-10} \, M \, OH^-$ is 9.311.

   b.   The pOH of a solution is equal to $-\log [OH^-]$. The result is 4.49. The pOH of a solution that contains $3.2 \times 10^{-5} \, M \, OH^-$ is 4.49.

   c.   To find the pOH of this solution, we must find the OH^- concentration. Use the K_w expression to find $[OH^-]$.

$$K_w = [H^+][OH^-]$$

$$[OH^-] = \frac{K_w}{[H^+]}$$

$$[OH^-] = \frac{1.0 \times 10^{-14}}{1.6 \times 10^{-8}} = 6.3 \times 10^{-7} \, M$$

The concentration of OH^- is $6.3 \times 10^{-7} \, M$. The pOH of a solution that contains $1.6 \times 10^{-8} \, M \, H^+$ is 6.20.

12.   For all solutions, the sum of pH and pOH must equal 14.00. This relationship is derived from the K_w expression, $[H^+][OH^-] = 1.0 \times 10^{-14}$. If we know either the pH or the pOH, we can find the other using this relationship. For example, if the pH of a solution is 4.5, then the pOH is 14.00 minus 4.5, which equals 9.5.

13.   If we know either the pH of a solution or the pOH, we can calculate the other. pH and pOH are related by the expression:

$$pH + pOH = 14.00$$

This equation is derived from

$$[H^+][OH^-] = K_w = 1.0 \times 10^{-14}$$

If the pH of lemon juice is 2.1, then the pOH is:

$$pOH = 14.00 - pH$$

$$pOH = 11.9$$

14.   pOH and pH are related to each other by the equation:

$$pH + pOH = 14$$

If the pOH of black coffee is 9.0, then the pH is:

$$pH = 14.00 - pOH$$

$$pH = 5.0$$

15.   a.   We want to find $[H^+]$ of milk, and the pH of milk is 6.9. To find the pH of milk from $[H^+]$, we take minus the log of $[H^+]$, so to find $[H^+]$ from pH we must go backward and undo the log of $[H^+]$. We can do this by finding the inverse log of $-pH$.

$$[H^+] = \text{inverse log}(-pH)$$

$$[H^+] = \text{inverse log}(-6.9) = 1 \times 10^{-7} M$$

        b.   We want to find the $[OH^-]$ of oven cleaner, which has a pH of 13.4. pH and pOH are related to each other by the expression $pH + pOH = 14.00$.

$$pOH = 14.00 - pH$$

$$pOH = 14.00 - 13.4$$

$$pOH = 0.6$$

$$[OH^-] = \text{inverse log}(-0.6) = 3 \times 10^{-1} M$$

        c.   We want to know the $[OH^-]$ of a phosphate-containing detergent with a pOH of 4.7. We must go backward from pOH to $[OH^-]$.

$$[OH^-] = \text{inverse log}(-4.7) = 2 \times 10^{-5} M$$

16.   a.   HCl is a strong acid, meaning that when HCl is dissolved in water, only H^+ ions and Cl^- ions are present. If a solution is described as 0.02 M HCl, then it actually contains 0.02 M H^+ and 0.02 M Cl^-. Because the pH depends on the hydrogen ion concentration, we can calculate the pH of a solution of HCl if we know the molar concentration of HCl.

$$0.02 \text{ mol/L HCl} = 0.02 \text{ mol/L } H^+ \text{ and } 0.02 \text{ mol/L } Cl^-$$

$$pH = -\log[H^+]$$

$$pH = -\log(0.02)$$

$$pH = 1.7$$

b. 3.5×10^{-3} mol/L HNO_3 dissolved in water produces 3.5×10^{-3} mol/L H^+ and 3.5×10^{-3} mol/L NO_3^-. Use the hydrogen ion concentration to calculate the pH.

$$pH = -\log[H^+]$$

$$pH = -\log(3.5 \times 10^{-3})$$

$$pH = 2.46$$

17.   a.   Hydrogen ions produced when HCl is dissolved in water would react with the bicarbonate ion, HCO_3^-, which has a high affinity for hydrogen ions.

$$HCO_3^- + H^+ \rightarrow H_2CO_3$$

b.   The pH of a solution is determined by the number of hydrogen ions in a solution. In a solution that contains a mixture of $NaHCO_3$ and H_2CO_3, the $[H^+]$ remains steady. H_2CO_3 is a weak acid, so most of the acid is in the undissociated form and not much hydrogen ion is produced. But most of the $NaHCO_3$ is dissociated as Na^+ and HCO_3^-. When an outside source of hydrogen ion is added to a buffered solution, the hydrogen ions are removed from the solution by reacting with the conjugate base, HCO_3^-, which has a high affinity for hydrogen ions. The hydrogen ions are removed from the solution and the pH of the solution does not change much.

CHAPTER 17

Equilibrium

Introduction

Because atoms and molecules are so tiny, it is hard to imagine what happens when they react and form new products. In this chapter you will learn what is necessary for a reaction to occur, why some reactions stop before all the reactants have been used up, and how to speed up a reaction. Learning how to control chemical reactions has led to many important applications, such as new ways to keep food from spoiling.

Chapter Discussion

The collision model says that in order for molecules to react with each other, they must first collide. Increases in the temperature and concentration of reactants bring about more collisions, and the rate of reaction increases. The collision model explains many observations about reactions.

Not all molecules that collide will react. Colliding molecules must have a minimum amount of energy in order for a reaction to occur – what we call the activation energy. As the temperature increases, molecules absorb more heat energy, move faster, and when they collide are more likely to meet the activation energy requirement. Therefore, as temperature increases, reaction rate increases. Some substances can cause the reaction rate to increase without increasing the temperature. These substances are called catalysts. Catalysts are useful because they increase the reaction rate without necessitating an increase in temperature or concentration.

Many reactions do not continue until all of the reactants have been converted to products. This is because reactions are reversible. A reversible reaction is one where reactants form products, and products can also form reactants. Both the forward and reverse reactions eventually occur at the same rate, so the concentrations of the products and reactants do not change. Equilibrium is dynamic: both reactions (forward and reverse) are always occurring, but the rates are equal. The reaction system must be in a closed container for this dynamic equilibrium to occur.

The results of measuring the concentrations of reactants and products for many reversible reactions led scientists to formulate the law of chemical equilibrium. This law can be stated mathematically as:

$$aA + bB \rightleftharpoons cC + dD$$

$$K = \frac{[C]^c[D]^d}{[A]^a[B]^b}$$

The letter K is called the equilibrium constant, and the amounts of reactants and products are measured in molarity. The equilibrium constant remains the same as long as the temperature is held constant, even though the initial concentrations may change. We can write the equilibrium expression for any equation as long as the equation is balanced.

When we write an equilibrium expression for an equilibrium involving solids or pure liquid, we do not include the solid or pure liquid because the concentrations of these are constant.

Thus, the equilibrium expression for

$$2CO_2 (g) \rightleftharpoons 2CO (g) + O_2 (g)$$

is

$$K = \frac{[CO]^2[O_2]}{[CO_2]^2}$$

while the equilibrium expression for

$$Fe_2O_3 (s) + 3H_2 (g) \rightleftharpoons 3H_2O (g) + 2Fe (s)$$

is

$$K = \frac{[H_2O]^3}{[H_2]^3}$$

Le Châtelier's principle helps us predict what happens to systems at equilibrium when conditions are changed. Le Châtelier's principle states that when a system at equilibrium is changed, the system will shift its equilibrium position in order to reduce the change. The most common changes are changes in concentration, volume and temperature.

When an equilibrium condition is changed by changing the concentration of a reactant or a product, the system will shift to counteract this change. For example, adding a reactant (or removing a product) will cause more product to be formed. Adding a product (or removing a reactant) will cause more reactant to be formed.

Decreasing the volume of a reaction vessel at constant temperature and moles of gas causes an increase in pressure. Gas molecules in a smaller volume hit the walls of the vessel more often. Le Châtelier's principle predicts that the system will act to lower the pressure. How can pressure decrease? By having fewer molecules of gas. For example, consider the equation

$$2CO_2 (g) \rightleftharpoons 2CO (g) + O_2 (g)$$

If the volume of a reaction mixture with CO_2, CO and O_2 is decreased, the system responds by shifting to the left, since 3 molecules react to form 2 molecules. K stays the same, but the concentrations change.

Temperature causes the value of K to change, but we can still use Le Châtelier's principle to predict the effect of a change in temperature. To do this, we treat heat just like a product or a reactant. If a reaction is endothermic (absorbs heat), an increase in temperature will shift the reaction to the right. If the reaction is exothermic (gives off heat), an increase in temperature will shift the reaction to the left. Decreasing the temperature has the opposite effect in each case.

Ionic compounds dissolving in water reach equilibrium. The equilibrium constant for this type of reaction is called the solubility product and is given as K_{sp}. For example, consider the following reaction:

$$Al(OH)_3 (s) \rightleftharpoons Al^{3+} (aq) + 3OH^- (aq)$$

The solubility product is given as:

$$K_{sp} = [Al^{3+}][OH^-]^3$$

Active Learning Questions

The Active Learning Questions at the end of each chapter are conceptually based questions that work well as discussion questions with a group of students. If your instructor does not assign these, consider getting together with a group of classmates and using these questions to see how well you understand the material in each chapter. While all of the questions work well, Active Learning Questions 1, 3, 6 and 10 focus on disturbing systems at equilibrium, Question 2 is a visual problem testing your conceptual understanding of the concept of an equilibrium constant, and Question 11 has you consider the concept of equilibrium from a macroscopic and microscopic perspective. You are strongly encouraged to answer these.

Learning Review

1.   Why does an increase in the concentration of reactant cause a reaction to speed up?

2.   a.   Which letter represents the energy of the products of a reaction?

        b.   Which letter represents the energy of the reactants?

        c.   Which letter represents the activation energy (E_a) of a reaction?

        d.   Which letter represents the catalyzed reaction pathway?

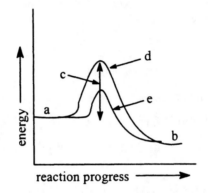

3.   What is a catalyst and how does it work?

4.   A beaker of liquid water in a sealed container is allowed to reach equilibrium vapor pressure. What happens to the concentration of water vapor in the beaker from the time the water is placed in the beaker until equilibrium is reached?

5.   Which of the following statements about equilibrium are true?

        a.   After equilibrium is established, the rate of the forward reaction is greater than the rate of the reverse reaction.

        b.   Before equilibrium is reached, the concentration of products increases as time passes.

        c.   Before equilibrium is reached, the concentration of reactants increases as time passes.

6.   Write equilibrium constant expressions for each of the reactions below.

        a. $I_2(g) + Cl_2(g) \rightleftharpoons 2ICl(g)$

        b. $2NO_2(g) + 7H_2(g) \rightleftharpoons 2NH_3(g) + 4H_2O(g)$

        c. $4NH_3(g) + 5O_2(g) \rightleftharpoons 4NO(g) + 6H_2O(g)$

7.   Write the equilibrium expression and calculate the equilibrium constant, K, for the reaction below, at each set of equilibrium concentrations.

$$C_2H_4O_2 \rightleftharpoons C_2H_3O_2{}^- + H^+$$

Experiment	Equilibrium concentrations			Eq. expression	K
	$[C_2H_4O_2]$	$[H^+]$	$[C_2H_3O_2{}^-]$		
I	1.0 M	0.0042 M	0.0042 M		
II	0.50 M	0.0030 M	0.0030 M		
III	2.0 M	0.0060 M	0.0060 M		

8.   Why do we not include the concentration of solids or pure liquids in the equilibrium expression?

9.   Write the equilibrium constant expression for each of the reactions below.

a. $Pb(OH)_2(s) \rightleftharpoons Pb^{2+}(aq) + 2OH^-(aq)$

b. $2Sb(s) + 3Cl_2(g) \rightleftharpoons 2SbCl_3(g)$

c. $Fe_2O_3(s) + 3H_2(g) \rightleftharpoons 3H_2O(g) + 2Fe(s)$

10. What would happen to the position of the equilibrium when the following changes are made to the equilibrium reaction below?

$$2SO_2(g) + O_2(g) \rightleftharpoons 2SO_3(g)$$

a. SO_2 is removed from the reaction vessel.

b. SO_3 is added to the reaction vessel.

c.   Oxygen is removed from the reaction vessel.

11. What would happen to the position of the equilibrium when the following changes are made to the reaction below?

$$2HgO(s) \rightleftharpoons Hg(l) + O_2(g)$$

a. $HgO(s)$ is added to the reaction vessel.

b.   The pressure in the reaction vessel is increased by lowering the volume.

12. When the volume of the following mixture of gases is increased, what will be the effect on the equilibrium position?

$$4HCl(g) + O_2(g) \rightleftharpoons 2H_2O(g) + 2Cl_2(g)$$

13. Predict the effect of decreasing the volume of the container on the position of each equilibrium below.

a. $SiF_4(g) + 2H_2O(g) \rightleftharpoons SiO_2(s) + 4HF(g)$

b. $2H_2(g) + 2NO(g) \rightleftharpoons 2H_2O(g) + N_2(g)$

c. $C(s) + H_2O(g) \rightleftharpoons CO(g) + H_2(g)$

14. Predict the effect of increasing the temperature on the position of each equilibrium below.

a.	$H_2(g) + Cl_2(g) \rightleftharpoons 2HCl(g) + heat$	exothermic
b.	$2NH_3(g) + heat \rightleftharpoons N_2(g) + 3H_2(g)$	endothermic
c.	$CO_2(g) + H_2(g) + heat \rightleftharpoons CO(g) + H_2O(g)$	endothermic

15.   If the equilibrium constant for the reaction below is 51.47, the concentration of HI is 0.50 M, and the concentration of H_2 is 0.069 M, what is the concentration of I_2?

$$H_2(g) + I_2(g) \rightleftharpoons 2HI(g)$$

16.   Write the balanced equation describing the dissolution of the solids below. Then write the K_{sp} expression.

   a. $Ca_3(PO_4)_2$

   b.   FeS

   c. $Al(OH)_3$

17.   The solubility of $PbSO_4(s)$ is 1.3×10^{-4} mol/L at 25°C. What is the K_{sp} of $PbSO_4(s)$?

18.   Copper(II) sulfide has a K_{sp} of 8.0×10^{-45}. What is the solubility of $CuS(s)$ in water at 25°C?

Answers to Learning Review

1.   The collision model says for reactions to occur, the reactants must first collide with each other. Higher concentrations of reactants cause the reaction rate to speed up because the number of collisions increases as the concentration of reactants increases.

2.   a.   Letter b represents the energy of the products. In this part of the graph, the reactants have achieved the activation energy, and products have formed.

   b.   Letter a represents the energy of the reactants. The average energy of the reactants is lower than the activation energy.

   c.   Letter c represents the activation energy, the minimum amount of energy needed for a reaction to occur.

   d.   Letter e represents the catalyzed reaction pathway. A catalyst lowers the activation energy for a reaction.

3.   A catalyst is a substance added to the reaction that causes the reaction to speed up. Catalysts are not used up during the reaction. They are not reactants and do not form products. A catalyst works by providing a new path for the reaction, which lowers the activation energy for that reaction.

4.   When water is first sealed in the beaker, the level of water in the beaker decreases, as water from the beaker enters the vapor phase. After some period of time, the level of water stops decreasing and stays at the same level. At this point a balance occurs between the processes of evaporation and condensation. The system is at equilibrium and the concentration of water vapor does not change.

5.   a.   This statement is false. At equilibrium the rate of forward reaction equals the rate of the reverse reaction.

   b.   This statement is true. When reactants are mixed, they continue to react to form product. The amount of product increases until equilibrium is reached.

   c.   This statement is false. The concentration of reactants decreases until equilibrium is reached, at which point the concentration of reactants remains constant.

6.   When writing equilibrium expressions, coefficients become powers. Products appear in the numerator and reactants in the denominator.

a. $K = \dfrac{[ICl]^2}{[I_2][Cl_2]}$

b. $K = \dfrac{[H_2O]^4[NH_3]^2}{[NO_2]^2[H_2]^7}$

c. $K = \dfrac{[NO]^4[H_2O]^6}{[NH_3]^4[O_2]^5}$

7.

Experiment	Equilibrium concentrations			Eq. expression	K
	$[C_2H_4O_2]$	$[H^+]$	$[C_2H_3O_2{}^-]$		
I	1.0M	0.0042M	0.0042M	$K = \dfrac{[H^+][C_2H_3O_2{}^-]}{[C_2H_4O_2]}$	1.8×10^{-5}
II	0.50M	0.0030M	0.0030M	$K = \dfrac{[H^+][C_2H_3O_2{}^-]}{[C_2H_4O_2]}$	1.8×10^{-5}
III	2.0M	0.0060M	0.0060M	$K = \dfrac{[H^+][C_2H_3O_2{}^-]}{[C_2H_4O_2]}$	1.8×10^{-5}

8.   The concentrations of pure solids and liquids are constant and do not change. They are not shown in the equilibrium expression.

9.   a. $K_{sp} = [Pb^{2+}][OH^-]^2$

b. $K = \dfrac{[SbCl_3]^2}{[Cl_2]^3}$

c. $K = \dfrac{[H_2O]^3}{[H_2]^3}$

10.   a.   The equilibrium will shift to the left and begin producing SO_2.

b.   The equilibrium will shift to the left and begin consuming SO_3.

c.   The equilibrium will shift to the left and begin producing O_2.

11.   a.   Pure solids and liquids have no effect on the equilibrium, so adding or removing $HgO(s)$ or $Hg(l)$ will not affect the position of the equilibrium.

b.   The equilibrium will shift toward the left to reduce the pressure inside the system by consuming oxygen gas.

12.   On the left side there are five gaseous molecules and on the right there are four. When the volume is increased, the pressure decreases and the equilibrium will shift toward the side that increases the pressure: to the left.

13. Decreasing the volume causes an increase in pressure. The equilibrium shifts in the direction to relieve the pressure, or toward the side with fewer numbers of gaseous molecules.

    a. The equilibrium would shift toward the left because the left has three gaseous molecules while the right has four gaseous molecules.

    b. The equilibrium would not shift in either direction because the number of gaseous molecules on the right and the left is the same.

    c. The equilibrium would shift toward the left because the left has one gaseous molecule and the right has two gaseous molecules. Solid carbon on the left does not affect the equilibrium.

14. For exothermic reactions, treat heat energy as a product of the reaction. If heat energy is added to the system by raising the temperature, then the equilibrium shifts to the left to consume the heat energy. For endothermic reactions, treat heat energy as a reactant. If heat energy is added to the system by raising the temperature, then the equilibrium shifts to the right to consume the heat energy.

    a. This is an exothermic reaction. Raising the temperature would shift the equilibrium to the left to consume the energy.

    b. This is an endothermic reaction. Raising the temperature would shift the equilibrium to the right to consume excess energy.

    c. This is an endothermic reaction. Raising the temperature would shift the equilibrium to the right to consume the energy.

15. First, write the equilibrium expression for this reaction.

$$K = \frac{[HI]^2}{[H_2][I_2]}$$

Rearrange this equation to isolate I_2 on one side. Divide both sides by $[HI]^2$.

$$\frac{K}{[HI]^2} = \frac{[HI]^2}{[HI]^2} \times \frac{1}{[H_2][I_2]}$$

$$\frac{K}{[HI]^2} = \frac{1}{[H_2][I_2]}$$

Now, multiply both sides by $[H_2]$.

$$\frac{K[H_2]}{[HI]^2} = \frac{1}{[I_2]}$$

Take the inverse of both sides.

$$[I_2] = \frac{[HI]^2}{K[H_2]}$$

Substitute values into the equation and find $[I_2]$.

$$[I_2] = \frac{[0.25 \text{ mol/L}]^2}{51.47[0.069 \text{ mol/L}]} = 0.070 \text{ mol/L}$$

16. The K_{sp} expression does not include the concentration of the solid salt, only the ions in solution.

    a. $K_{sp} = [Ca^{2+}]^3[PO_4^{3-}]^2$

    b. $K_{sp} = [Fe^{2+}][S^{2-}]$

    c. $K_{sp} = [Al^{3+}][OH^-]^3$

17. This problem asks us to calculate the K_{sp} for $PbSO_4$, given the solubility of $PbSO_4$. When $PbSO_4$ dissolves in water, lead ions and sulfate ions are released into the aqueous environment.

$$PbSO_4(s) \rightleftharpoons Pb^{2+}(aq) + SO_4^{2-}(aq)$$

The K_{sp} expression for the reaction is

$$K_{sp} = [Pb^{2+}][SO_4^{2-}]$$

We need to know the molar concentrations of Pb^{2+} and SO_4^{2-} to find the K_{sp}. We know that the solubility of $PbSO_4$ is 1.3×10^{-4} mol/L, so 1.3×10^{-4} mol $PbSO_4$ dissolves per liter of solution. Each 1.3×10^{-4} mol $PbSO_4$ produces 1.3×10^{-4} mol Pb^{2+} and 1.3×10^{-4} mol SO_4^{2-}. The concentration of Pb^{2+} is 1.3×10^{-4} mol/L and the concentration of SO_4^{2-} is 1.3×10^{-4} mol/L. We can use these concentrations to calculate the K_{sp}.

$$K_{sp} = [Pb^{2+}][SO_4^{2-}]$$
$$K_{sp} = (1.3 \times 10^{-4}\, mol/L)(1.3 \times 10^{-4}\, mol/L)$$
$$K_{sp} = 1.7 \times 10^{-8}\, mol^2/L^2$$

The units for K_{sp} are usually omitted, so the K_{sp} would be reported as 1.7×10^{-8}.

18. This problem asks us to find the solubility of copper(II) sulfide. We are given the K_{sp}, which is 8.0×10^{-45}. When CuS dissolves in water, each mole of CuS that dissolves produces one mole of Cu^{2+} and one mole of S^{2-}.

$$CuS(s) \rightleftharpoons Cu^{2+}(aq) + S^{2-}(aq)$$

The K_{sp} expression for the dissolution of CuS in water is

$$K_{sp} = [Cu^{2+}][S^{2-}]$$

$x\, \dfrac{mol}{L}$ of CuS(s) dissociates into $x\, \dfrac{mol}{L}$ $Cu^{2+}(aq)$ and $x\, \dfrac{mol}{L}$ $S^{2-}(aq)$.

At equilibrium $[Cu^{2+}] = x\, \dfrac{mol}{L}$ and $[S^{2-}] = x\, \dfrac{mol}{L}$.

We can substitute these values into the equilibrium expression.

$$K_{sp} = 8.0 \times 10^{-45} = [Cu^{2+}][S^{2-}] = (x)(x) = x^2$$

We can say that

$$x^2 = 8.0 \times 10^{-45}$$

$$x = \sqrt{8.0 \times 10^{-45}} = 8.9 \times 10^{-23}\, mol/L$$

The solubility of CuS is 8.9×10^{-23} mol/L.

CHAPTER 18

Oxidation-Reduction Reactions and Electrochemistry

Introduction

There are many important oxidation-reduction reactions. These reactions are characterized by electron transfer. One of the most annoying and costly of the oxidation-reduction reactions is the rusting of automobile bodies. In this chapter you will learn what actually happens during an oxidation-reduction reaction, and what means are available to keep your car from rusting.

Chapter Discussion

Reactions between metals and nonmetals involve the transfer of electrons. When the metal Li reacts with Br_2, the result is the ionic compound LiBr.

$$2Li + Br_2 \rightarrow 2LiBr$$

Both Li and Br_2 began as neutral species, but after the reaction both were ions. Li became the Li^+ cation and Br_2 became the Br^- anion. Electrons must have been transferred between the lithium and bromine for the reaction to have occurred. Reactions of this type are called oxidation-reduction reactions or redox reactions. In this reaction, Li lost an electron to become the Li^+ cation; this process is called oxidation. Each Br atom gained an electron to form Br^-; this process is called reduction. In every oxidation-reduction reaction, one species is oxidized, and another is reduced.

In some redox reactions it is not easy to tell which species has been oxidized and which has been reduced. The assignment of oxidation states or oxidation numbers can help you determine which species is oxidized and which reduced, and whether a reaction is really a redox reaction or not. An oxidation number is an imaginary number assigned to each element in a chemical reaction. The number comes from the charge an element would have if it were an ion. How the electrons are assigned to the atoms is governed by a set of rules, but is basically determined by the electronegativity of the atom. Some species are easy to assign oxidation states to. All of the metals that form ions with a 1+ charge have oxidation states of +1 (like K^+, Na^+). Many atoms in chemical reactions are not ions, but are covalently bonded to other atoms; that is, the electrons are shared between two atoms. Assign the electrons as though the atom were ions. The most electronegative atom is assigned both of the shared electrons. Because the molecules are electrically neutral, the sum of the oxidation states of all the atoms must be zero.

In Chapter 6 you learned how to balance simple chemical reactions by inspection. Balancing redox reactions is more difficult, and can rarely be done by inspection. Another method is needed for balancing these reactions. One method for balancing redox reactions is called the half-reaction method. A half-reaction is part of a complete chemical equation. In a redox reaction, there is always a reduction half-reaction and an oxidation half-reaction. We can write each of them separately, and balance the difference in oxidation states on each side of the equation by adding electrons to either the right or the left side. Section 18.4 in your textbook gives some general steps to be used when balancing redox reactions, and five specific steps to use when balancing redox reactions that take place in acidic solution. Questions 7 and 8 in Learning Review will test your ability to solve these types of problems.

Chemical and electrical energy can be interchanged. The study of this interchange is called electrochemistry. During a redox reaction, electrons are transferred whenever the reactants collide in solution. It is not possible to use the electron transfer to generate electrical energy under these circumstances. In order to harness the energy of a redox reaction, it is necessary to physically separate the two half-reactions in two separate containers that are connected by a wire. The electrons that are transferred between the oxidation half-reaction and the reduction half-reaction travel along the wire and produce an electrical current.

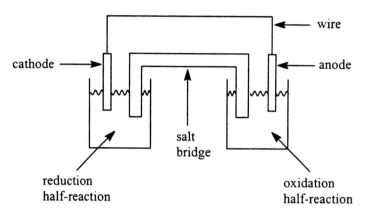

A reaction between two half-cells connected only by a wire will not happen unless there is another connection between the two containers that allows ions to flow freely back and forth. As electrons leave one container, and travel along the wire to the other container, differences in charges in the two containers would occur. The container with the oxidation half-reaction would build up a negative charge from the gain in electrons. The extra connection that contains ions allows negative ions to travel to the container losing electrons, and positive ions to travel to the container gaining electrons, so the net charge in each container is zero. This connection is called a salt bridge.

The current that is produced in a cell such as this can be used to do useful work, and is the principle upon which batteries are based. Cells powered by two separate half-reactions that are connected by a wire (and by some type of connection to allow ion exchange) are called galvanic cells. The electrode where electrons are lost is called the anode, and the electrode where electrons are gained is called the cathode. A battery is a galvanic cell.

Active Learning Questions

The Active Learning Questions at the end of each chapter are conceptually based questions that work well as discussion questions with a group of students. If your instructor does not assign these, consider getting together with a group of classmates and using these questions to see how well you understand the material in each chapter. While all of the questions work well, Active Learning Questions 3 has you identify oxidation-reduction reactions, and Questions 1 and 9 focus on electrochemical cells. You are strongly encouraged to answer these.

Learning Review

1.   For each of the partial reactions, decide whether oxidation or reduction is occurring.

a. $Li \rightarrow Li^+ + e^-$

b. $Br_2 + 2e^- \rightarrow 2Br^-$

c. $S^{2-} \rightarrow S + 2e^-$

2.   For each reaction below, identify which element is oxidized and which is reduced.

    a. $Ca(s) + I_2(g) \rightarrow CaI_2(s)$

    b. $2K(s) + S(s) \rightarrow K_2S(s)$

    c. $6Na(s) + N_2(g) \rightarrow 2Na_3N(s)$

3.   Determine the oxidation states for each element in the substances below.

    a. CH_4

    b. SO_4^{2-}

    c. $NaHCO_3$

    d. N_2O_5

    e. HIO_4

4.   Determine the oxidation state for each element in the reactions below.

    a. $4Fe(s) + 3O_2(g) + 12HCl(aq) \rightarrow 4FeCl_3(aq) + 6H_2O(l)$

    b. $Zn(s) + 2AgNO_3(aq) \rightarrow Zn(NO_3)_2(aq) + 2Ag(s)$

    c. $MgCl_2(l) \rightarrow Mg(s) + Cl_2(g)$

5.   During a redox reaction, does the reactant which is the reducing agent contain an element that is oxidized or reduced?

6.   For each of the reactions below identify which atom is oxidized and which is reduced, and identify the oxidizing and reducing agents.

    a. $2C_2H_6(g) + 7O_2(g) \rightarrow 4CO_2(g) + 6H_2O(g)$

    b. $2KNO_3(l) \rightarrow 2KNO_2(l) + O_2(g)$

    c. $3CuO(s) + 2NH_3(aq) \rightarrow 3Cu(s) + N_2(g) + 3H_2O(l)$

    d. $K_2Cr_2O_7(aq) + 14HI(aq) \rightarrow 2CrI_3(s) + 2KI(aq) + 3I_2(s) + 7H_2O(l)$

7.   Balance each of the reactions below by the half-reaction method.

    a. $Zn(s) + Cu^{2+}(aq) \rightarrow Zn^{2+}(aq) + Cu(s)$

    b. $Re^{5+}(aq) + Sb^{3+}(aq) \rightarrow Re^{4+}(aq) + SbS^+(aq)$

8.   Each of the reactions below occurs in acidic solution. Balance each one by the half-reaction method.

    a. $H_2S(aq) + NO_3^-(aq) \rightarrow S_8(s) + NO(g)$

    b. $H_5IO_6(aq) + I^-(aq) \rightarrow I_2(s)$

    c. $Cr_2O_7^{2-}(aq) + Sn^{2+}(aq) \rightarrow Sn^{4+}(aq) + Cr^{3+}(aq)$

    d. $I_2(s) + NO_3^-(aq) \rightarrow IO_3^-(aq) + NO_2(g)$

9.   Normally, when a redox reaction occurs, no useful work is produced. How can a redox reaction be made to perform useful work?

10.   Label what is needed to complete the electrical circuit and allow the redox reaction to proceed.

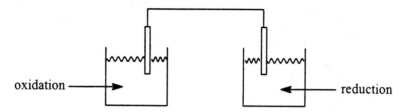

11.   Briefly explain how the lead storage battery works.

12.   Aluminum metal easily loses electrons to form Al_2O_3. How can aluminum metal be produced from its oxide?

Answers to Learning Review

1.   a.   Lithium metal loses an electron: oxidation.

        b.   Bromine gains an electron: reduction.

        c.   The sulfide ion loses two electrons: oxidation.

2.   a.   Calcium is a metal from Group 2 and forms Ca^{2+} cations. Calcium metal loses two electrons. This is oxidation. Halogens such as I_2 form anions. Each atom in a molecule of I_2 gains one electron to form $2I^-$. This is reduction.

        b.   Potassium metal from Group 1 forms K^+ cations. Potassium loses one electron so this is oxidation. Sulfur from Group 6 forms the S^{2-} anion. Sulfur gains two electrons, so it is reduced.

        c.   Sodium metal forms Na^+ cations. Sodium loses electrons so it is oxidized. Nitrogen from Group 5 forms the N^{3-} anion. Each nitrogen atom gains three electrons, so it is reduced.

3.   If you have trouble assigning oxidation states, look at the rules found in Section 18.2 of your textbook.

        a.   Rule 4 says that hydrogen bonded to a nonmetal such as carbon will have an oxidation state of 1+. There are four hydrogen atoms, so carbon must be 4− so that the sum of the charges is 0.

        b.   Rule 3 says that oxygen is usually 2−. There are four oxygen atoms, so sulfur must be 6+. The sum of the charges must be 2− because the charge on the sulfate ion is 2−.

c.   Rule 2 says that the charge on Group 1 ions is 1+ so Na^+ is 1+. Rule 4 says that hydrogen is 1+ when covalently bonded to nonmetals. In this molecule, the hydrogen atom is covalently bonded to the CO_3 part of the molecule, so the oxidation state of hydrogen is 1+. Rule 3 says that oxygen is usually 2−. There are three of them. Carbon must be 6 − (1 + 1) which is 4+.

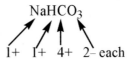

$NaHCO_3$

1+ 1+ 4+ 2− each

d.   Rule 3 says that oxygen is usually 2−. There are five oxygen atoms. There are two nitrogen atoms, so each nitrogen atom must be 5+ to counterbalance the five oxygen atoms.

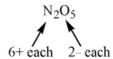

N_2O_5

6+ each   2− each

e.   Rule 4 says that hydrogen is usually 1+. Rule 3 says that oxygen is usually 2−. If hydrogen is plus one and the four oxygen atoms are 2− each, then iodine must be 7+ so that the sum is zero.

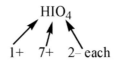

HIO_4

1+   7+   2− each

4.   a.

$$4Fe(s) + 3O_2(g) + 12HCl(aq) \longrightarrow 4FeCl_3(aq) + 6H_2O(l)$$

0   0   1+ 1−   3+ 1− each   1+ each 2−

b.

$$Zn(s) + 2AgNO_3(aq) \longrightarrow Zn(NO_3)_2(aq) + 2Ag(s)$$

0   1+ 5+ 2− each   2+ 5+ 2− each   0

c.

$$MgCl_2(l) \longrightarrow Mg(s) + Cl_2(g)$$

2+ 1− each   0   0

5.   The reducing agent contains an element that is oxidized. So, the element that loses electrons during oxidation furnishes the electrons needed for reduction.

6.   Use changes in oxidation state to determine which element is oxidized and which is reduced. Remember that the element that *increases* in oxidation state is oxidized. The oxidizing agent contains the element that is reduced, and the reducing agent contains the element that is oxidized.

a.   Carbon in C_2H_6 has an oxidation state of 3−, while carbon in CO_2 has an oxidation state of 4+. The oxidation state increases so carbon is oxidized. C_2H_6 is the reducing agent. Oxygen in O_2 has an oxidation state of 0, and in CO_2 and in H_2O oxygen has an oxidation state of 2−. The oxidation state of oxygen decreases so oxygen is reduced. Oxygen gas is the oxidizing agent.

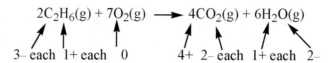

$$2C_2H_6(g) + 7O_2(g) \longrightarrow 4CO_2(g) + 6H_2O(g)$$

3– each 1+ each   0   4+ 2– each 1+ each   2–

b.   Nitrogen in KNO_3 has an oxidation state of 5+, while nitrogen in KNO_2 has an oxidation state of 3+. The oxidation state decreases from 5+ to 3+ so nitrogen is reduced. KNO_3 is the oxidizing agent. Oxygen in KNO_3 has an oxidation state of 2–, while molecular oxygen has an oxidation state of 0. The oxidation state of oxygen increases, so oxygen is oxidized. KNO_3 is the reducing agent.

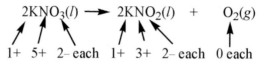

$$2KNO_3(l) \longrightarrow 2KNO_2(l) + O_2(g)$$

1+ 5+ 2– each   1+ 3+ 2– each 0 each

c.   Copper in CuO has an oxidation state of 2+, while copper metal has an oxidation state of 0. The oxidation state decreases so copper is reduced. CuO is the oxidizing agent. Nitrogen in NH_3 has an oxidation state of 3–, while molecular nitrogen has an oxidation state of 0. The oxidation state increases, so nitrogen is oxidized. NH_3 is the reducing agent.

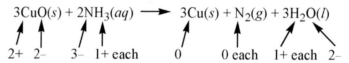

$$3CuO(s) + 2NH_3(aq) \longrightarrow 3Cu(s) + N_2(g) + 3H_2O(l)$$

2+ 2–   3– 1+ each   0   0 each   1+ each   2–

d.   Chromium in $K_2Cr_2O_7$ has an oxidation state of 6+, while chromium in CrI_3 has an oxidation state of 3+. The oxidation state of chromium decreases so chromium is reduced. $K_2Cr_2O_7$ is the oxidizing agent. Iodine in HI has an oxidation state of 1– while iodine molecules have an oxidation state of 0. Note that some of the iodine does not change oxidation state. The iodine atoms in CrI_3 and KI both have oxidation states of 1–. Because the oxidation state of some of the iodine has increased, iodine is said to be oxidized. HI is the reducing agent.

$$K_2Cr_2O_7(aq) + 14HI(aq) \longrightarrow 2CrI_3(s) + 3I_2(s) + 7H_2O(l) + 2KI(aq)$$

1+ each 6+ each 2– each 1+ 1–   3+ 1– each 0 each   1+ each   2–   1+   1–

7.   a.   To balance redox reactions that do not occur in acid solution, follow the general steps given in Section 18.4 of your textbook.

Write individual oxidation and reduction half-reactions.

$$Zn(s) + Cu^{2+}(aq) \rightarrow Zn^{2+}(aq) + Cu(s)$$

The oxidation state of zinc increases from 0 to 2+. Zinc is oxidized.

$$Zn \rightarrow Zn^{2+} \quad \text{oxidation half-reaction}$$

The oxidation state of copper decreases from 2+ to 0, so copper is reduced.

$$Cu^{2+} \rightarrow Cu \quad \text{reduction half-reaction}$$

The Cu^{2+} ion gains electrons to produce copper metal. Two electrons are gained by the Cu^{2+} ion. To balance the 2+ charge on the left side of the reduction half-reaction, add two electrons to the left side.

$$2e^- + Cu^{2+} \rightarrow Cu$$

Zinc metal loses two electrons to become the Zn^{2+} ion. To balance the 2+ charge on the right side of the oxidation half-reaction, add two electrons to the right side.

$$Zn \rightarrow Zn^{2+} + 2e^-$$

Balance the number of atoms in each half-reaction. In this reaction the number of copper atoms is the same on both sides, so the coefficients of solid copper and Cu^{2+} ion do not need to be adjusted.

Zinc metal loses two electrons to become the Zn^{2+} ion. The number of zinc atoms is the same on both sides, so the coefficients of solid zinc and Zn^{2+} ion do not need to be adjusted.

In a balanced oxidation-reduction reaction the number of electrons lost must equal the number of electrons gained. In the oxidation half-reaction two electrons are lost and in the reduction half-reaction two electrons are gained. Because the number of electrons is the same in both half-reactions, no adjustment is needed to the number of electrons.

Add the two half-reactions together.

$$2e^- + Cu^{2+} \rightarrow Cu$$

$$Zn \rightarrow Zn^{2+} + 2e^-$$

$$2e^- + Cu^{2+} + Zn \rightarrow Cu + Zn^{2+} + 2e^-$$

Now cancel the electrons that appear on both sides to give the overall reaction.

$$Cu^{2+}(aq) + Zn(s) \rightarrow Cu(s) + Zn^{2+}(aq)$$

We can check our work to make sure the elements and charges are the same on both sides. There is one copper and one zinc on each side, and the charge is 2+ on each side, so the equation is balanced.

	$Cu^{2+}(aq)$ + $Zn(s)$ → $Cu(s)$ + $Zn^{2+}(aq)$			
elements	1 Cu	1 Zn →	1 Cu	1 Zn
charge	2+	→	2+	

b.   Write the individual oxidation and reduction half-reactions.

$$Re^{5+}(aq) + Sb^{3+}(aq) \rightarrow Re^{4+}(aq) + Sb^{5+}(aq)$$

The oxidation state of rhenium decreases from 5+ to 4+. Rhenium is reduced.

$$Re^{5+} \rightarrow Re^{4+} \quad \text{reduction half-reaction}$$

The oxidation state of antimony increases from 3+ to 5+. Antimony is oxidized.

$$Sb^{3+} \rightarrow Sb^{5+} \quad \text{oxidation half-reaction}$$

The Re^{5+} ion gains an electron to become the Re^{4+} ion. To balance the 1+ charge on the left side of the reduction half-reaction, add one electron to the left side.

$$e^- + Re^{5+} \rightarrow Re^{4+}$$

The Sb^{3+} ion loses two electrons to become the Sb^{5+} ion. To balance the 2+ charge on the right side of the oxidation half-reaction, add two electrons to the right side.

$$Sb^{3+}(aq) \rightarrow Sb^{5+}(aq) + 2e^-$$

The number of rhenium atoms and antimony atoms is the same on both sides, so the coefficients of Re^{5+}, Re^{4+}, Sb^{3+} and Sb^{5+} do not need to be adjusted.

In a balanced redox reaction the number of electrons gained and lost must be equal, so multiply the reduction half-reaction by two so that both half-reactions transfer two electrons.

$$2(e^- + Re^{5+} \rightarrow Re^{4+})$$

$$2e^- + 2Re^{5+} \rightarrow 2Re^{4+}$$

Now, add the two half-reactions together.

$$2e^- + 2Re^{5+} \rightarrow 2Re^{4+}$$

$$Sb^{3+} \rightarrow Sb^{5+} + 2e^-$$

$$2e^- + 2Re^{5+} + Sb^{3+} \rightarrow 2Re^{4+} + Sb^{5+} + 2e^-$$

Cancel the electrons that appear on both sides of the equation to give the overall balanced reaction.

$$2Re^{5+}(aq) + Sb^{3+}(aq) \rightarrow 2Re^{4+}(aq) + Sb^{5+}(aq)$$

We can check our work to make sure the elements and charges are the same on both sides. There are two rheniums and one antimony on both sides, and the charge is 13+ on each side, so the equation is balanced.

	$2Re^{5+}(aq) + Sb^{3+}(aq) \rightarrow 2Re^{4+}(aq) + Sb^{5+}(aq)$			
elements	2 Re	1 Sb $\rightarrow$	2 Re	1 Sb
charge	13+	$\rightarrow$	13+	

8.   When balancing oxidation-reduction reactions in acidic solution, use the five steps given in Section 18.4 of your textbook.

a.   Step 1: Write equations for the oxidation and reduction half-reactions.

$$H_2S(aq) + NO_3^-(aq) \longrightarrow S_8(s) + NO(g)$$

1+ each   2–   5+   2– each   0 each   2+   2–

Sulfur in H_2S loses two electrons to become elemental sulfur, so sulfur is oxidized. The oxidation half-reaction is

$$H_2S \rightarrow S_8 \quad \text{oxidation half-reaction}$$

Nitrogen in NO_3^- gains three electrons to become NO, so nitrogen is reduced. The reduction half-reaction is

$$NO_3^- \rightarrow NO \quad \text{reduction half-reaction}$$

Step 2a: Balance all elements except hydrogen and oxygen.

The right side of the oxidation half-reaction has eight sulfur atoms so we will need eight on the left.

$$8H_2S \rightarrow S_8$$

The reduction half-reaction contains one nitrogen atom on both sides so no adjustment is needed.

Step 2b: Balance the oxygen atoms using H_2O.

The oxidation half-reaction contains no oxygen atoms. The reduction half-reaction has three oxygen atoms on the left and only one on the right, so add two molecules of H_2O to the right side.

$$NO_3^- \rightarrow NO + 2H_2O$$

Step 2c: Balance hydrogens using H^+.

The oxidation half-reaction has sixteen hydrogens on the left, and none on the right, so add $16H^+$ to the right side.

$$8H_2S \rightarrow S_8 + 16H^+$$

The reduction half-reaction has four hydrogens on the right, and none on the left, so add $4H^+$ to the left side.

$$4H^+ + NO_3^- \rightarrow NO + 2H_2O$$

Step 2d: Balance the charge using electrons.

To balance the 16 positive charges on the right side of the reduction half-reaction, add 16 electrons to the right side.

$$8H_2S \rightarrow S_8 + 16H^+$$

charge $0 \rightarrow 16+$

$$8H_2S \rightarrow S_8 + 16H^+ + 16e^-$$

To balance the three positive charges on the left side of the oxidation half-reaction, add three electrons to the left side.

$$4H^+ + NO_3^- \rightarrow NO + 2H_2O$$

charge $3+ \rightarrow 0$

$$3e^- + 4H^+ + NO_3^- \rightarrow NO + 2H_2O$$

Step 3: The oxidation half-reaction transfers 16 electrons and the reduction half-reaction transfers three electrons, so we must equalize the number of electrons transferred. Multiply the oxidation half-reaction by three and the reduction half-reaction by 16.

$$16(3e^- + 4H^+ + NO_3^- \rightarrow NO + 2H_2O)$$
$$48e^- + 64H^+ + 16NO_3^- \rightarrow 16NO + 32H_2O$$
$$3(8H_2S \rightarrow S_8 + 16H^+ + 16e^-)$$
$$24H_2S \rightarrow 3S_8 + 48H^+ + 48e^-$$

Step 4: Now, add the half-reactions together and cancel species that appear on both sides. The 48 electrons appear on both sides and cancel. All 48 hydrogen ions cancel on the right, and 48 cancel on the left, leaving 16 hydrogen ions on the left.

$$24H_2S \rightarrow 3S_8 + 48H^+ + 48e^-$$
$$48e^- + 64H^+ + 16NO_3^- \rightarrow 16NO + 32H_2O$$

$$48e^- + 16H^+ + 16NO_3^- + 24H_2S \rightarrow 16NO + 32H_2O + 3S_8 + 48e^-$$

The equation becomes

$$16H^+(aq) + 16NO_3^-(aq) + 24H_2S(aq) \rightarrow 16NO(g) + 32H_2O(l) + 3S_8(s)$$

Step 5: Let's check the elements and the charges on each side. There are 64 hydrogen atoms, 16 nitrogen atoms, 48 oxygen atoms, and 24 sulfur atoms on each side. The charge on each side is zero, so the equation is balanced.

	$16H^+(aq) + 16NO_3^-(aq) + 24H_2S(aq)$	$\rightarrow$	$16NO(g) + 32H_2O(l) + 3S_8(s)$
elements	64H 16N 48O 24S	$\rightarrow$	64H 16N 48O 24S
charge	0	$\rightarrow$	0

b.   Step 1: Write the equations for the oxidation and reduction half-reactions.

$$H_5IO_6(aq) + I^-(aq) \longrightarrow I_2(s)$$

1+ each 7+ 2– each 1–   0 each

Iodine in H_5IO_6 gains seven electrons to become I^-. Iodine is reduced. The reduction half-reaction is:

$$H_5IO_6 \rightarrow I_2 \quad \text{reduction half-reaction}$$

Iodide ion loses an electron to become I_2. Iodine is oxidized. The oxidation half-reaction is

$$I^- \rightarrow I_2 \quad \text{oxidation half-reaction}$$

In this oxidation-reduction reaction, iodine is both the species oxidized and the species reduced.

Step 2a: Let's balance all the elements except oxygen and hydrogen. For the reduction half-reaction there is one iodine atom on the left, and two on the right. Change the coefficient of H_5IO_6 from one to two so that the number of iodine atoms is the same on each side.

$$2H_5IO_6 \rightarrow I_2$$

For the oxidation half-reaction, put a coefficient of two on the left side to balance the two iodine atoms on the right.

$$2I^- \rightarrow I_2$$

Step 2b: There are 12 oxygen atoms on the left side of the reduction half-reaction, so put 12 molecules of H_2O on the right to balance the oxygen atoms.

$$2H_5IO_6 \rightarrow I_2 + 12H_2O$$

The reduction half-reaction contains no oxygen atoms.

Step 2c: There are 24 hydrogen atoms on the right side of the reduction half-reaction, but only 19 on the left. Add 14 hydrogen ions to the left side.

$$14H^+ + 2H_5IO_6 \rightarrow I_2 + 12H_2O$$

The oxidation half-reaction contains no hydrogen atoms.

Step 2d: To balance the 14+ charge on the left side of the reduction half-reaction, add 14 electrons to the left side.

$$14H^+ + 2H_5IO_6 \rightarrow I_2 + 12H_2O$$

charge   14+   →   0

$$14e^- + 14H^+ + 2H_5IO_6 \rightarrow I_2 + 12H_2O$$

The reduction half-reaction is now balanced.

To balance the 2− charge on the left side of the oxidation half-reaction, add two electrons to the right side.

$$2I^- \rightarrow I_2$$

charge   2− → 0

$$2I^- \rightarrow I_2 + 2e^-$$

Step 3: Because the reduction half-reaction transfers 14 electrons and the oxidation half-reaction transfers two electrons, multiply the oxidation half-reaction by seven.

$$7(2I^- \rightarrow I_2 + 2e^-)$$
$$14I^- \rightarrow 7I_2 + 14e^-$$

Step 4: Now add the half-reactions together.

$$14e^- + 14H^+ + 2H_5IO_6 \rightarrow I_2 + 12H_2O$$
$$14I^- \rightarrow 7I_2 + 14e^-$$
$$14e^- + 14H^+ + 2H_5IO_6 + 14I^- \rightarrow 8I_2 + 12H_2O + 14e^-$$

The electrons on both sides cancel, and the number of iodine molecules can be combined to simplify the equation.

$$14H^+ + 2H_5IO_6 + 14I^- \rightarrow 8I_2 + 12H_2O$$

Step 5: Let's check the elements and charges on each side. There are 24 hydrogen atoms, 16 iodine atoms and 12 oxygen atoms on each side. The charge on both sides is zero, so the equation is balanced.

	$14H^+ + 2H_5IO_6 + 14I^-$	→	$8I_2 + 12H_2O$		
elements	24H 16I 12O	→	48H 16I 12O		
charge	0	→	0		

c.   Step 1: Write equations for the oxidation and reduction half-reactions.

$$Cr_2O_7^{2-}(aq) + Sn^{2+}(aq) \longrightarrow Sn^{4+}(aq) + Cr^{3+}(aq)$$

6+ each   2− each   2+   4+   3+

Chromium in $Cr_2O_7^{2-}$ gains three electrons to become Cr^{3+}. Chromium is reduced. The reduction half-reaction is:

$$Cr_2O_7^{2-} \rightarrow Cr^{3+} \quad \text{reduction half-reaction}$$

The Sn^{2+} ion loses two electrons to become Sn^{4+}. Tin is oxidized. The oxidation half-reaction is:

$$Sn^{2+} \rightarrow Sn^{4+} \quad \text{oxidation half-reaction}$$

Step 2a: The reduction half-reaction has two chromium atoms on the left and one on the right, so change the coefficient of Cr^{3+} to two.

$$Cr_2O_7^{2-} \rightarrow 2Cr^{3+}$$

The oxidation half-reaction has one tin on each side. The coefficients need no adjustment.

Step 2b: In the reduction half-reaction there are seven oxygen atoms on the left and none on the right, so add seven molecules of H_2O to the right to balance the oxygens.

$$Cr_2O_7^{2-} \rightarrow 2Cr^{3+} + 7H_2O$$

The oxidation half-reaction contains no oxygen atoms.

Step 2c: The reduction half-reaction has 14 hydrogens on the right and none on the left, so add 14 hydrogen ions to the left side.

$$14H^+ + Cr_2O_7^{2-} \rightarrow 2Cr^{3+} + 7H_2O$$

The oxidation half-reaction needs no adjustments for hydrogens.

Step 2d: To balance the 6+ charge on the left side of the reduction half-reaction, add six electrons to the left side.

$$14H^+ + Cr_2O_7^{2-} \rightarrow 2Cr^{3+} + 7H_2O$$

$$\text{charge} \qquad 12+ \qquad \rightarrow \qquad 6+$$

$$6e^- + 14H^+ + Cr_2O_7^{2-} \rightarrow 2Cr^{3+} + 7H_2O$$

The oxidation half-reaction has a 2+ charge on the left, and 4+ charge on the right, so add two electrons to the right to balance the charge.

$$Sn^{2+} \rightarrow Sn^{4+}$$

$$\text{charge} \quad 2+ \quad \rightarrow \quad 6+$$

$$Sn^{2+} \rightarrow Sn^{4+} + 6e^-$$

Step 3: In the reduction half-reaction six electrons are gained, and in the oxidation half-reaction two electrons are lost. Multiply the oxidation half-reaction times three to equalize the number of electrons transferred.

$$3(Sn^{2+} \rightarrow Sn^{4+} + 2e^-)$$

$$3Sn^{2+} \rightarrow 3Sn^{4+} + 6e^-$$

Step 4: Now add the two half-reactions together.

$$6e^- + 14H^+ + Cr_2O_7^{2-} \rightarrow 2Cr^{3+} + 7H_2O$$

$$3Sn^{2+} \rightarrow 3Sn^{4+} + 6e^-$$

$$6e^- + 14H^+ + Cr_2O_7^{2-} + 3Sn^{2+} \rightarrow 2Cr^{3+} + 7H_2O + 3Sn^{4+} + 6e^-$$

The electrons cancel and the equation becomes:

$$14H^+ + Cr_2O_7^{2-} + 3Sn^{2+} \rightarrow 2Cr^{3+} + 7H_2O + 3Sn^{4+}$$

Step 5: Let's check the elements and charges on both sides. There are 14 hydrogen atoms, two chromium atoms, seven oxygen atoms and three tin atoms on each side. The charge is 18+ on both sides; the equation is balanced.

	$14H^+ + Cr_2O_7^{2-} + 3Sn^{2+}$	$\rightarrow$	$2Cr^{3+} + 7H_2O + 3Sn^{4+}$
elements	14H 2Cr 7O 3Sn	$\rightarrow$	14H 2Cr 7O 3Sn
charge	18+	$\rightarrow$	18+

d.   Step 1: Write equations for the oxidation and reduction half-reactions.

$$I_2(s) + NO_3^- \ (aq) \longrightarrow IO_3^- \ (aq) + NO_2(g)$$

Each atom in molecular iodine loses five electrons to become IO_3^-. Iodine is oxidized. The oxidation half-reaction is:

$$I_2 \rightarrow IO_3^- \quad \text{oxidation half-reaction}$$

Nitrogen in NO_3^- gains one electron to become NO_2. Nitrogen is reduced. The reduction half-reaction is:

$$NO_3^- \rightarrow NO_2 \quad \text{reduction half-reaction}$$

Step 2a: There are two iodine atoms on the left side of the oxidation half-reaction and one on the right. Change the coefficient of IO_3^- to two.

$$I_2 \rightarrow 2IO_3^-$$

The reduction half-reaction has one nitrogen atom on each side.

Step 2b: The oxidation half reaction has six oxygen atoms on the right, so add six molecules of H_2O to the left.

$$6H_2O + I_2 \rightarrow 2IO_3^-$$

The reduction half-reaction has three oxygen atoms on the left, but only two on the right, so add one molecule of H_2O to the right.

$$NO_3^- \rightarrow NO_2 + H_2O$$

Step 2c: The oxidation half-reaction has twelve hydrogens on the left, so add 12 hydrogen ions to the right.

$$6H_2O + I_2 \rightarrow 2IO_3^- + 12H^+$$

The reduction half-reaction has two hydrogen atoms on the right, so add two hydrogen ions to the left.

$$2H^+ + NO_3^- \rightarrow NO_2 + H_2O$$

Step 2d: To balance the 10+ charge on the right side of the oxidation half-reaction, add 10 electrons to the right side.

$$6H_2O + I_2 \rightarrow 2IO_3^- + 12H^+$$

charge   0 $\rightarrow$ 10+

$$6H_2O + I_2 \rightarrow 2IO_3^- + 12H^+ + 10e^-$$

To balance the 1+ charge on the left side of the reduction half-reaction, add one electron to the left side.

$$2H^+ + NO_3^- \rightarrow NO_2 + H_2O$$

charge   1+ $\rightarrow$ 0

$$e^- + 2H^+ + NO_3^- \rightarrow NO_2 + H_2O$$

Step 3: In the oxidation half-reaction ten electrons are lost, while one electron is gained during reduction. Multiply the reduction half-reaction by 10 to equalize the electrons transferred.

$$10(e^- + 2H^+ + NO_3^- \rightarrow NO_2 + H_2O)$$

$$10e^- + 20H^+ + 10NO_3^- \rightarrow 10NO_2 + 10H_2O$$

Step 4: Now add the two half-reactions together.

$$6H_2O + I_2 \rightarrow 2IO_3^- + 12H^+ + 10e^-$$

$$10e^- + 20H^+ + 10NO_3^- \rightarrow 10NO_2 + 10H_2O$$

$$10e^- + 8H^+ + 10NO_3^- + I_2 \rightarrow 10NO_2 + 4H_2O + 2IO_3^- + 10e^-$$

The 10 electrons on each side cancel. There are 20 hydrogen ions on the left and 12 on the right, so cancel the 12 hydrogen ions on the right and leave eight on the left. There are six water molecules on the left and 10 on the right so cancel the six molecules on the left, which leaves four on the fight. The equation becomes

$$8H^+(aq) + 10NO_3^-(aq) + I_2(s) \rightarrow 10NO_2(g) + 4H_2O(l) + 2IO_3^-(aq)$$

Step 5: Let's check the elements and charges on each side. There are eight hydrogen atoms, 10 nitrogen atoms, 30 oxygen atoms and two iodine atoms on each side. The charge on each side is 2−, so the equation is balanced.

	$8H^+(aq) + 10NO_3^-(aq) + I_2(s)$	$\rightarrow$	$10NO_2(g) + 4H_2O(l) + 2IO_3^-(aq)$
elements	8H 10N 30O 2I	$\rightarrow$	8H 10N 30O 2I
Charge	2−	$\rightarrow$	2−

9.   Usually redox reactions occur in a single container. If we separate the oxidation half-reaction from the reduction half-reaction but use a salt bridge to allow ions to flow, we can require the electron transfer to occur through a wire. The current produced can be used to do work.

10.   During oxidation, electrons are lost, so oxidation occurs in the left container and reduction in the right container.

11.   In the lead storage battery there are lead grids connected by a metal bar. Lead is oxidized to form Pb^{2+}, which combines with SO_4^{2-} from sulfuric acid (battery acid) to form solid $PbSO_4$. The

substance that gains electrons and is reduced is PbO_2, which is coated on the lead grids. Pb^{4+} in PbO_2 is reduced to Pb^{2+}, which combines with $SO_4{}^{2-}$ from H_2SO_4 to form $PbSO_4$. So the product of both oxidation and reduction is $PbSO_4$. The oxidation and reduction half-reactions are separated so that useful work, such as starting your car, can be accomplished.

12.   Aluminum metal can be produced by electrolysis of aluminum oxide. Electrolysis is the process of forcing a current through an electrochemical cell to cause a chemical change that would not occur naturally. During electrolysis, aluminum is reduced.

$$2Al_2O_3(s) \rightarrow 4Al(s) + 3O_2(g)$$

CHAPTER 19

Radioactivity and Nuclear Energy

Introduction

Most chemical properties depend on the arrangement of electrons, and many chemical reactions involve the transfer of electrons from one atom to another. But the events and reactions described in this chapter depend on the properties of the nucleus of an atom. The best known nuclear reactions produce energy in nuclear reactors and in nuclear explosions. You will learn about these reactions and other processes in this chapter.

Chapter Discussion

Not all nuclei are stable. Many decay spontaneously, producing a new nucleus, and in addition, some type of nuclear particle. The nucleus of cobalt-60 is unstable. It spontaneously decays to produce nickel-60 and an electron. The reaction can be written

$$\ce{^{60}_{27}Co} \rightarrow \ce{^{60}_{28}Ni} + \ce{^{0}_{-1}e}$$

When writing nuclear decay reactions, always show the atomic mass, A, and the atomic number, Z, for each element and each particle. Nuclear equations must be balanced. The sum of the atomic masses must be the same on both sides of the equation, and the sum of the atomic numbers must be the same on both sides. In the equation above, the atomic mass is 60 on the left side and 60 plus zero on the right. The atomic number is 27 on the left side and 28 minus one, or 27, on the right. Both properties are balanced.

Different types of radioactive decay are defined by the type of particle produced in the reaction. One type of decay produces an alpha particle, which is a helium nucleus. Beta particles are also often produced during nuclear decay. A beta particle is an electron. The net effect of beta production is to change a neutron to a proton. The atomic number in the new nucleus increases by one. The mass number does not change. Sometimes gamma rays are produced during nuclear decay, usually accompanied by another particle. A gamma ray is a high-energy photon of light with no mass or atomic number.

A positron has very little mass and a positive charge. The production of a positron does not change the mass number and decreases the atomic number by one. Sometimes the nucleus can capture one of its own inner orbital electrons. This process is called electron capture. The capture of an electron decreases the atomic number by one.

Examples of Radioactive Decay

Alpha-particle production: $\ce{^{211}_{83}Bi} \rightarrow \ce{^{4}_{2}He} + \ce{^{207}_{81}Tl}$

Beta-particle production: $\ce{^{10}_{4}Be} \rightarrow \ce{^{0}_{-1}e} + \ce{^{10}_{5}B}$

Gamma-ray production: $\ce{^{226}_{88}Ra} \rightarrow \ce{^{222}_{86}Rn} + \ce{^{4}_{2}He} + \ce{^{0}_{0}\gamma}$

Positron production: $\ce{^{15}_{8}O} \rightarrow \ce{^{15}_{7}N} + \ce{^{0}_{+1}e}$

Electron capture: $\ce{^{37}_{18}Ar} + \ce{^{0}_{-1}e} \rightarrow \ce{^{37}_{17}Cl}$

Active Learning Questions

The Active Learning Questions at the end of each chapter are conceptually based questions that work well as discussion questions with a group of students. If your instructor does not assign these, consider getting together with a group of classmates and using these questions to see how well you understand the material in each chapter. These questions cover topics from throughout the chapter and you are strongly encouraged to answer these.

Learning Review

1.   In a balanced nuclear equation, which two quantities must be the same on both sides of the equation?

2.   What is the atomic number and the mass number of each of the particles below?

    a.   gamma ray

    b.   positron

    c.   alpha particle

    d.   beta particle

3.   Write balanced nuclear equations for the decay of the radioactive particles below.

    a. $^{226}_{86}\text{Rn}$ decays to produce an α-particle and a γ-ray.

    b. $^{70}_{31}\text{Ga}$ decays to produce a β-particle.

    c. $^{144}_{60}\text{Nd}$ decays to produce a β-particle.

4.   Complete and balance these nuclear equations.

    a. $^{161}_{67}\text{Ho} + ? \rightarrow {}^{161}_{66}\text{Dy}$

    b. $^{10}_{4}\text{Be} \rightarrow ? + {}^{0}_{-1}\text{e}$

    c. $? + {}^{0}_{-1}\text{e} \rightarrow {}^{44}_{21}\text{Sc}$

    d. $^{253}_{99}\text{Es} + {}^{4}_{2}\text{He} \rightarrow {}^{1}_{1}\text{H} + ?$

    e. $^{59}_{29}\text{Cu} \rightarrow ? + {}^{59}_{28}\text{Ni}$

5.   Show the product formed when the nuclide below is bombarded with a smaller nuclide.

$$^{238}_{92}\text{U} + {}^{12}_{6}\text{C} \rightarrow ? + {}^{1}_{0}\text{n}$$

6.   Two instruments for detecting radioactivity are the Geiger counter and the scintillation counter. Briefly explain how each one works.

7.   In a sample of the nuclides below, which would exhibit the highest number of decay events during a fixed period of time?

	Name	half-life
a.	potassium-42	12.4 hours
b.	hydrogen-3	12.5 years
c.	plutonium-239	2.44×10^4 years

8. If a sample of 5.0×10^{20} iodine-131 atoms with a half-life of 8 days is allowed to decay for 48 days, how many iodine-131 atoms will remain?

9. A wooden post from an ancient village has 25 percent of the carbon-14 found in living trees. How old is the wooden post? The half-life of carbon-14 is 5,730 years.

10. Why do you think that most nuclides used in medicine as radiotracers have short half-lives?

11. What safety features should prevent a nuclear explosion in the event of a serious malfunction at a nuclear reactor?

12. Why do you think that the fusion process would supplant fission if the technology were available?

13. What differences exist between genetic and somatic damage caused by radioactivity?

14. Why is the ionizing ability of a radiation source important in determining the biological effects of radiation?

Answers to Learning Review

1. The sum of the atomic numbers (Z) and the sum of the mass numbers (A) must be the same on both sides of a nuclear equation.

2.   a. A gamma ray has a mass number of zero and an atomic number of zero.

     b. A positron has a mass number of zero and an atomic number of 1+.

     c. An alpha particle has a mass number of four and an atomic number of 2+.

     d. A beta particle has a mass number of zero and an atomic number of 1−.

3.   a. When Rn-226 decays to produce an alpha particle and a gamma particle, the mass number of the new nuclide is decreased by four to 222. The atomic number decreases by two to 84. The new nuclide would have a mass number of 222 and an atomic number of 84. The element with atomic number of 84 is polonium, so the new nuclide is Po-222.

$$^{226}_{86}\text{Rn} \rightarrow \, ^{4}_{2}\text{He} + \, ^{0}_{0}\gamma + \, ^{222}_{84}\text{Po}$$

     b. When Ga-70 decays to produce a beta particle, the mass number of the new nuclide does not change. The atomic number increases by one to 32 . The new nuclide would have a mass number of 70, and an atomic number of 32. The element with an atomic number of 32 is germanium, so the new nuclide is Ge-70.

$$^{70}_{31}\text{Ga} \rightarrow \, ^{0}_{-1}\text{e} + \, ^{70}_{32}\text{Ge}$$

     c. When Nd-144 decays to produce a beta particle, the mass number does not change. The atomic number increases by one to 61. The new nuclide would have a mass number of 144 and an atomic number of 61. The element with an atomic number of 61 is promethium, so the new nuclide is Pm-144.

$$^{144}_{60}\text{Nd} \rightarrow \, ^{0}_{-1}\text{e} + \, ^{144}_{61}\text{Pm}$$

4.   a.   This problem provides the nuclides before and after decay and asks for the identity of an unknown decay particle. Because the mass number does not change on either side, the mass number of the particle is zero. The atomic number decreases by one on the right side, so the atomic number of the unknown particle is 1− (the sum of atomic numbers on each side must be the same). The unknown particle has a mass number of zero and an atomic number of −1. It is a β-particle. This is an example of electron capture.

$$^{161}_{67}\text{Ho} + \,^{0}_{-1}\text{e} \rightarrow \,^{161}_{66}\text{Dy}$$

   b.   This problem provides a nuclide on the left that decays to an unknown nuclide and a β-particle. Because the mass number of the β-particle is zero, the mass number of the unknown nuclide must be 10 to balance the left side. The atomic number increases by one to become five to balance the four on the left side. The element with an atomic number of five is boron, so the nuclide is B-10.

$$^{10}_{4}\text{Be} \rightarrow \,^{10}_{5}\text{B} + \,^{0}_{-1}\text{e}$$

   c.   This problem provides the identity of a particle that combines with an unknown nuclide to produce the nuclide Sc-44. The β-particle has a mass number of zero, so the mass number of the unknown nuclide must be 44. The β-particle has an atomic number of 1-, so the atomic number of the unknown nuclide must be 22 (the sum of the atomic numbers must be the same on each side). The element with atomic number 22 is titanium, so the unknown nuclide is Ti-44.

$$^{44}_{22}\text{Ti} + \,^{0}_{-1}\text{e} \rightarrow \,^{44}_{21}\text{Sc}$$

   d.   This problem provides a nuclide that reacts with an alpha particle to produce a proton and an unknown nuclide. The total mass number on the left side is 257. On the right, the proton has a mass number of one, so the unknown nuclide must have a mass number of 256 so that both sides are balanced. The total atomic number on the left side is 101. On the right, the proton has an atomic number of one, so that the atomic number of the unknown nuclide must be 100. The element with an atomic number of 100 is fermium, so the nuclide is Fm-256.

$$^{253}_{99}\text{Es} + \,^{4}_{2}\text{He} \rightarrow \,^{1}_{1}\text{H} + \,^{256}_{100}\text{Fm}$$

   e.   This problem provides a nuclide that decays to an unknown particle and to a nuclide of nickel. The mass number on both sides is 59, so the mass number of the unknown particle must be zero. The atomic number of the nuclide on the left is 29 and the atomic number of the nuclide on the right is 28. The unknown particle has an atomic number of 1+. The particle with a mass number of zero and an atomic number of 1+ is a positron.

$$^{59}_{29}\text{Cu} \rightarrow \,^{0}_{+1}\text{e} + \,^{59}_{28}\text{Ni}$$

5.   The problem provides a nuclide of uranium that is bombarded with a smaller carbon nucleus to produce an unknown nuclide and four neutrons. The total mass number on the left is 238 plus 12, which is 250. Each neutron on the right has a mass number of one, so the total mass number of the neutrons is four. The mass number of the new nuclide is 246. The total atomic number on the left is 92 plus six, which is 98. Each of the four neutrons on the right has an atomic number of zero, so the atomic number of the new nuclide is 98. The element with an atomic number of 98 is californium, Cf. The new nuclide is Cf-246.

$$^{238}_{92}\text{U} + \,^{12}_{6}\text{C} \rightarrow \,^{246}_{98}\text{Cf} + 4\,^{1}_{0}\text{n}$$

6.   The Geiger-Müller counter, or Geiger counter, has a probe that is placed close to the source of radioactivity. The probe contains atoms of argon gas, which lose an electron when hit by a high-speed subatomic particle. The argon cation and accompanying electron produce a momentary pulse of electrical current that is detected by the Geiger counter. The amount of radioactive material is directly related to the number of pulses detected.

Radioactivity can also be detected with a scintillation counter. High-speed decay particles collide with a substance such as sodium iodide inside the scintillation counter. The sodium iodide emits a flash of light when struck. Each flash of light is counted, and the number of flashes is directly related to the amount of radioactivity.

7.   The half-life of potassium-42 is 12.4 hours, which means that 50 percent of a sample of potassium-42 would decay in 12.4 hours. Plutonium-239 has a half-life of 24,400 years, which means it would take 24,400 years for 50 percent of a plutonium-239 sample to decay. The shorter the half-life, the quicker a nuclide decays, so the nuclide with the smallest half-life produces the most decay events over time. Of the three nuclides, potassium-42 would produce the most decay events in any fixed amount of time.

8.   Because the half-life of iodine-131 is eight days, the number of iodine-131 atoms in any sample will decrease by 50 percent after eight days. So, after eight days there will be $(5.0 \times 10^{20})/2 = 2.5 \times 10^{20}$ iodine-131 atoms left. After another eight days (for a total of sixteen days) there would be $(2.5 \times 10^{20})/2 = 1.3 \times 10^{20}$ iodine-131 atoms left. After another eight days (for a total of 24 days) there would be $(1.3 \times 10^{20})/2 = 6.3 \times 10^{19}$ iodine-131 atoms left. After three more eight-day periods (for a total of 48 days) there would be 7.8×10^{18} iodine-131 atoms left.

9.   A piece of wood which contains 25 percent of the carbon-14 found in freshly cut wood has undergone two half-life decays. The first half-life would decrease the carbon-14 from 100 percent to 50 percent, and the second half-life would decrease the carbon-14 content from 50 percent to 25 percent. So, a piece of wood that has undergone two half-life decays would be two times 5,730, or 11,460, years old.

10.   Using any radiotracer inside the human body poses some risk of damage by the high-speed decay particles. Radiotracers with a short half-life will rapidly decay and produce many decay particles in a short period of time. Doctors can use small amounts of radiotracer and still detect their presence, because the numbers of decay particles are high at first. Because the half-life is short, most of the radiotracer decays quickly.

11.   Nuclear reactors have many safety features, including control rods that are made of substances that absorb neutrons. The control rods can be raised or lowered between the fuel rods to control how fast the nuclear reaction occurs. If a serious problem occurs with the reactor, the control rods automatically lower into the core so that the fission process slows down. The amount of fissionable fuel present in any nuclear reactor is below the critical mass, so that even in the worst possible case a nuclear explosion would not occur.

12.   Fusion would quickly supplant fission because fuel for fusion is readily available in sea water. Fusion reactors would produce helium as an end product, dangerous radionuclides. Safe disposal of the nuclear waste from fission is a concern that would not occur with fusion reactors.

13.   Somatic damage is the damage done directly to the tissues of the organism. Somatic damage usually occurs soon after exposure to the radiation source. Genetic damage is the kind of damage done to the reproductive machinery of the human body. Genetic damage occurs at the time of exposure but may not show up until the birth of offspring.

14.   When biomolecules are ionized by a radiation source, they no longer perform their functions in the body.

CHAPTER 20

Organic Chemistry

Introduction

Organic chemistry is devoted to the study of compounds and reactions of the element carbon. No other element forms as many different compounds as carbon. The compounds range from the simple molecule methane, which we burn as fuel, to the complex molecules that carry genetic information. This chapter will help you learn the language of organic chemistry by introducing you to the ways that carbon-containing molecules are formed, how they function, and how they are named.

Chapter Discussion

A carbon atom can form a maximum of four covalent bonds with other atoms. The VSEPR model tells us that electron pairs try to spread out as far as possible. The shape assumed by a carbon atom bonded to four atoms is a tetrahedron. Carbon can bond to fewer than four other atoms when it forms a double or triple bond. When carbon forms a double bond with an atom, two electron pairs are used to make the double bond. When carbon forms a triple bond, three electron pairs are used to form the triple bond. Carbons with either double or triple bonds do not have a tetrahedral shape.

Hydrocarbons are compounds composed entirely of carbon and hydrogen. Hydrocarbons are either saturated or unsaturated. A saturated hydrocarbon is one in which all of the carbons are bonded to four atoms. An unsaturated hydrocarbon has at least one carbon atom bonded to less than four atoms, that is, it has at least one double or triple bond. Alkanes are saturated hydrocarbons. Alkenes are hydrocarbons that contain at least one carbon-carbon double bond. Alkynes are hydrocarbons that contain at least one carbon-carbon triple bond. The rules for naming all of these are listed in your textbook. You can practice this in the Learning Review section, where you can also look at a discussion of the solutions.

In addition to alkanes, alkenes and alkynes, you should know how to name organic compounds that are aromatic (and substituted) or that contain functional groups. These compounds include alcohols (primary, secondary and tertiary), aldehydes, ketones, carboxylic acids and esters. Naming these compounds is quite systematic and presented quite clearly in the text. There are also many practice problems in the Learning Review section of this Study Guide, along with solutions.

Active Learning Questions

The Active Learning Questions at the end of each chapter are conceptually based questions that work well as discussion questions with a group of students. If your instructor does not assign these, consider getting together with a group of classmates and using these questions to see how well you understand the material in each chapter. These questions will test your conceptual understanding of naming compounds and isomers and you are strongly encouraged to answer these.

Learning Review

1.   Match the term below with the correct definition.

a.	hydrocarbon	contains one or more double or triple bonds
b.	alkane	an unbranched molecule
c.	normal	contains only carbon-carbon single bonds
d.	unsaturated	composed of carbon and hydrogen

2.   What is the shape of a carbon tetrachloride molecule, CCl_4?

3.   Write the condensed formula for an unbranched alkane with five carbons.

4.   A branched alkane with the formula below has seven carbons. Can this alkane be represented by the general formula C_nH_{2n+2}?

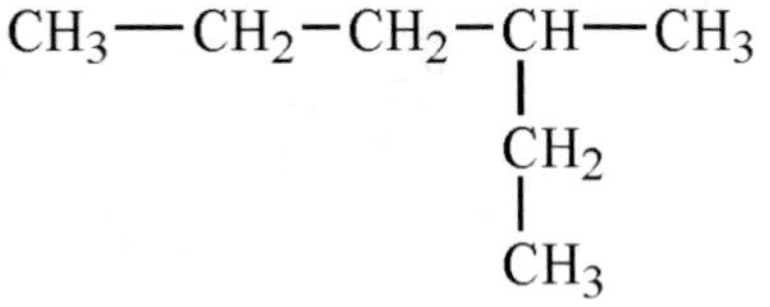

$$CH_3-CH_2-CH_2-CH-CH_3$$
$$| $$
$$CH_2$$
$$|$$
$$CH_3$$

5.   What are structural isomers?

6.   Write all structural isomers of hexane, C_6H_{14}.

7.   Name the alkanes below.

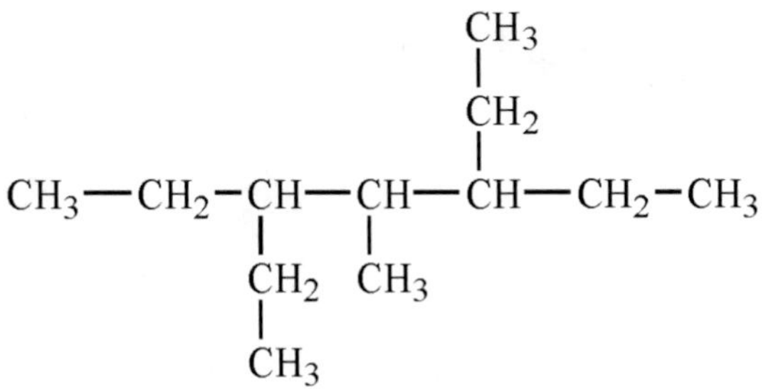

a.
$$CH_3-CH-CH-CH_2-CH-CH_3$$
$$\quad\;\; | \quad\; | \qquad\quad |$$
$$\quad\;\; CH_3\; CH_3 \qquad CH_3$$

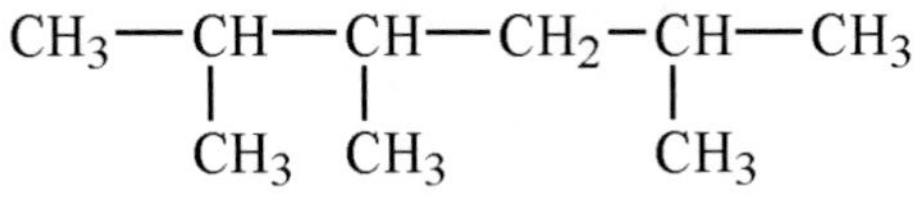

b.
$$CH_3-CH_2-CH-CH_2-CH_3$$
$$\qquad\qquad\quad |$$
$$\qquad\qquad\quad CH-CH_3$$
$$\qquad\qquad\quad |$$
$$\qquad\qquad\quad CH_3$$

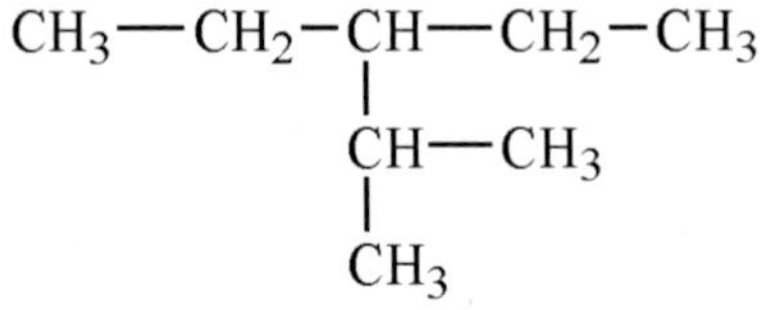

c.
$$CH_3-CH-CH-CH_3$$
$$\qquad\; |\quad\; |$$
$$\qquad\; CH_2\; CH_3$$
$$\qquad\; |$$
$$\qquad\; CH_3$$

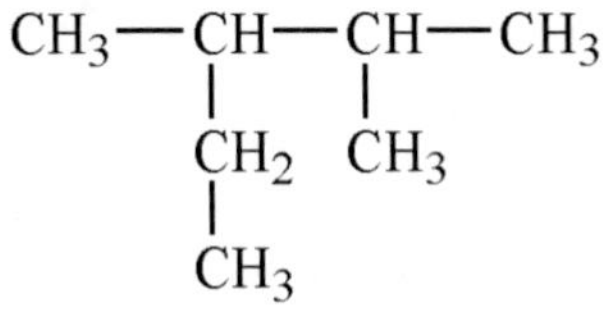

d.
$$\qquad\qquad\qquad\quad CH_3$$
$$\qquad\qquad\qquad\quad |$$
$$\qquad\qquad\qquad\quad CH_2$$
$$\qquad\qquad\qquad\quad |$$
$$CH_3-CH_2-CH-CH-CH-CH_2-CH_3$$
$$\qquad\qquad\quad |\quad\; |$$
$$\qquad\qquad\quad CH_2\; CH_3$$
$$\qquad\qquad\quad |$$
$$\qquad\qquad\quad CH_3$$

$$CH_3$$
$$|$$
$$H_3C—C—CH_3$$
$$|$$
$$CH_2$$

e.

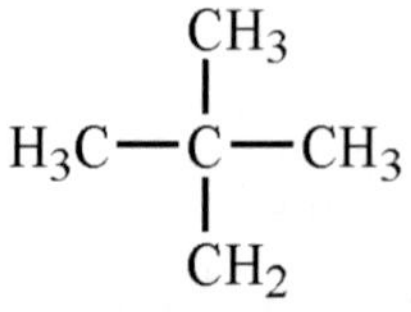

8. Are the molecules a and b structural isomers of each other?

$$CH_3—CH—CH—CH_3$$
$$|\quad\quad|$$
$$CH_3\quad CH_2-CH_3$$

a.

$$CH_3$$
$$|$$
$$CH_3—CH\quad CH_3$$
$$|\quad\quad|$$
$$CH_2-CH$$
$$|$$
$$CH_3$$

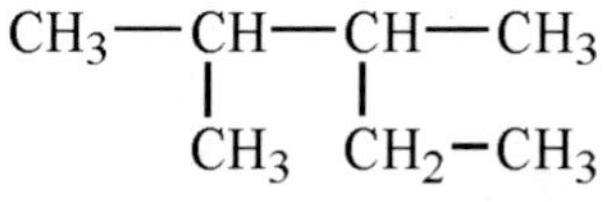

b.

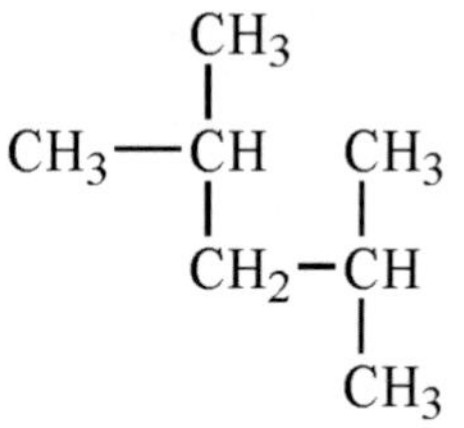

9. Write structural formulas for the molecules below.

   a. 2-methyl-4-sec-butyloctane

   b. 2-methylpropane

   c. 3-ethylpentane

   d. 2,2,4-trimethylhexane

10. Each of the alkane names below is incorrect. Write the structural formula for each molecule. Then name it correctly.

   a. 2-ethylbutane

   b. 1-methylpentane

   c. 4,4-dimethylhexane

   d. 2-ethyl-2-methylheptane

11. Petroleum itself is not very useful. It must be separated into fractions to be useful. How is petroleum separated into the fractions that have useful properties?

12. When chlorine gas reacts with pentane, one of the hydrogens is substituted by a chlorine atom. Several structural isomers are possible depending on which hydrogen atom is substituted. Show all possible structural isomers that could be produced when chlorine reacts with pentane in the presence of ultraviolet light.

13. Write the structures for the products of the reactions below.

$$CH_3—CH—CH_3 + Cl_2 \xrightarrow{h\nu}$$
$$|$$
$$CH_3$$

a.

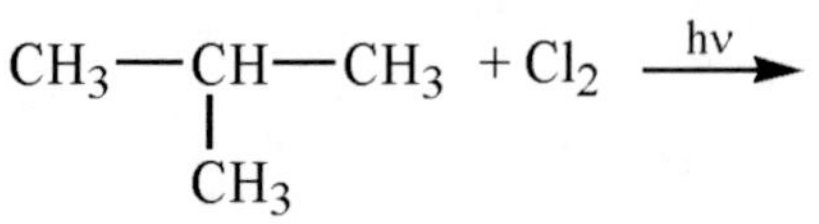

   b. $CH_4 + O_2 \longrightarrow$

c. $CH_3—CH_2—CH_3$ $\xrightarrow[500°C]{Cr_2O_3}$

14.   Name each of the molecules below.

a.
$$CH_3—CH_2—CH_2—C{=}CH_2$$
$$\overset{|}{CH_2}$$
$$\overset{|}{CH_3}$$

b.
$$CH_3—CH—C{\equiv}C—CH_2—CH—CH_3$$
$$\overset{|}{CH_3} \qquad\qquad \overset{|}{CH_3}$$

c.
$$CH_3—C{=}C—CH_3$$
$$\overset{|}{CH_3}\ \overset{|}{CH_3}$$

15.   Write structural formulas for the products of the reactions below.

a.
$$CH_3—C{=}C—CH_3 + H_2 \xrightarrow{catalyst}$$
$$\overset{|}{CH_3}\ \overset{|}{CH_3}$$

b. $CH_3—CH_2—CH_2—CH{=}CH_2 + Cl_2 \longrightarrow$

c.
$$CH_3—CH{=}C—CH_2—CH_3 + Br_2 \longrightarrow$$
$$\overset{|}{CH_3}$$

16.   Name the aromatic hydrocarbons below.

a.

b.

c.

NO$_2$

d.

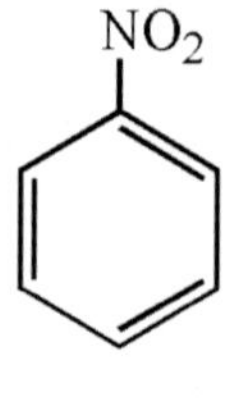

17. Name the di-substituted aromatic hydrocarbons below.

NO$_2$

NO$_2$

a.

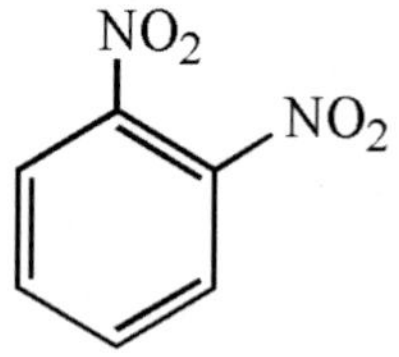

OH

Cl

b.

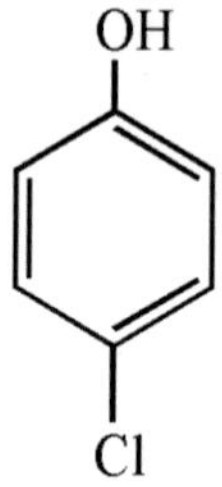

CH$_3$

CH$_2$—CH$_3$

c.

CH$_3$

Br

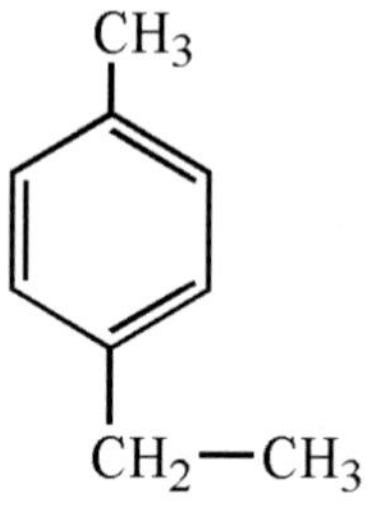

d.

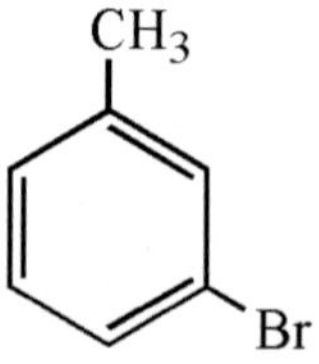

18. Name each of the alcohols below and decide whether they are primary, secondary or tertiary alcohols.

CH$_3$

H$_3$C—C—CH—CH$_2$—CH$_3$

CH$_3$ OH

a.

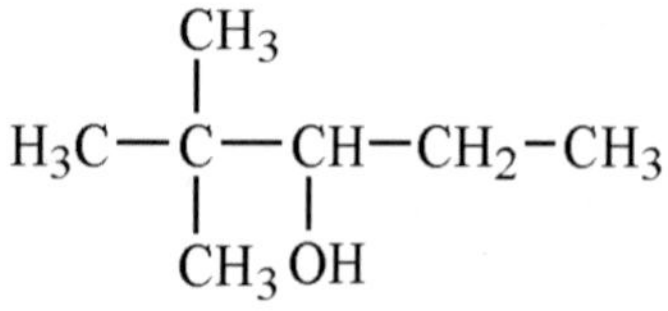

CH$_3$

CH$_3$—C—OH

CH$_2$

CH$_3$

b.

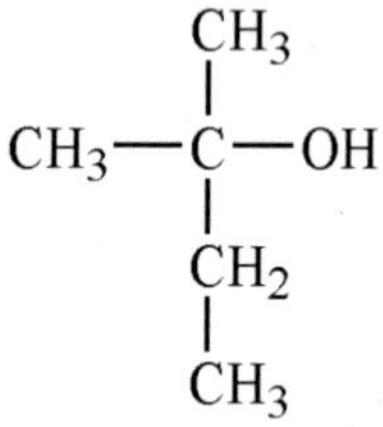

$$CH_3-CH_2-\underset{\underset{Br}{|}}{\overset{\overset{CH_3}{|}}{C}}-\underset{\underset{CH_3}{|}}{CH}-CH_2-CH_2-OH$$

c.

$$CH_3-\underset{\underset{CH_2-OH}{|}}{CH}-CH_2-\underset{\underset{|}{|}}{\overset{\overset{CH_3-CH-CH_3}{|}}{CH}}-CH_2-CH_2-CH_2-CH_3$$

d.

e. CH_3-OH

$$CH_3-CH_2-\underset{|}{CH}-CH_2-CH_3$$
$$CH_2-CH_2-\underset{\underset{CH_3}{|}}{\overset{}{CH}}-CH_2-\underset{\underset{OH}{|}}{CH}-CH_3$$

f.

19.   Match the alcohols below with the appropriate description.

a.	methanol	used in antifreeze
b.	phenol	found in alcoholic beverages
c.	ethanol	commonly known as wood alcohol
d.	ethylene glycol	used in the production of plastics

20.   Show the structures of the aldehydes and ketones that would be produced from the oxidation of the following alcohols.

a.   (benzene ring)—CH_2-OH $\xrightarrow{\text{oxidation}}$

b. $CH_3-\underset{\underset{CH_3}{|}}{CH}-CH_2-OH$ $\xrightarrow{\text{oxidation}}$

c. $CH_3-CH_2-\underset{\underset{OH}{|}}{CH}-CH_2-CH_3$ $\xrightarrow{\text{oxidation}}$

21.   Name the aldehydes and ketones below.

a. $CH_3-\underset{\underset{CH_3}{|}}{\overset{\overset{CH_3}{|}}{C}}-\underset{\underset{CH_3}{|}}{CH}-\overset{\overset{O}{\parallel}}{C}\diagdown_H$

b.

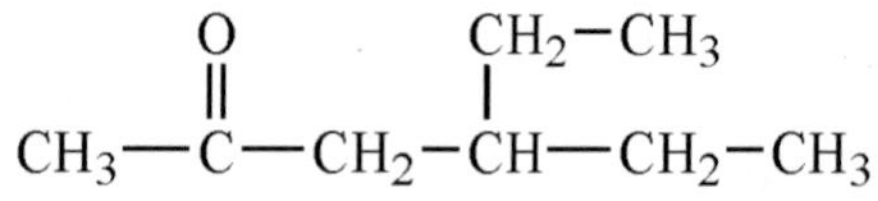

$$CH_3-\overset{\overset{\displaystyle O}{\|}}{C}-CH_2-\overset{\overset{\displaystyle CH_2-CH_3}{|}}{CH}-CH_2-CH_3$$

c.

$$\overset{\overset{\displaystyle O}{\diagdown}}{\underset{H}{C}}-\overset{\overset{}{\underset{Br}{|}}}{CH}-CH_2-CH_2-CH_2-CH_2-CH_3$$

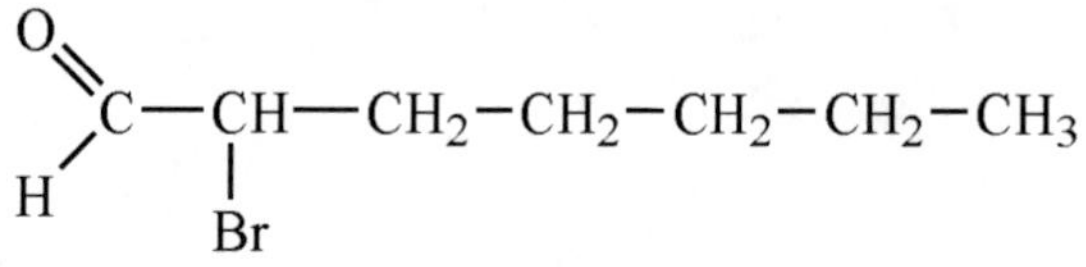

d.

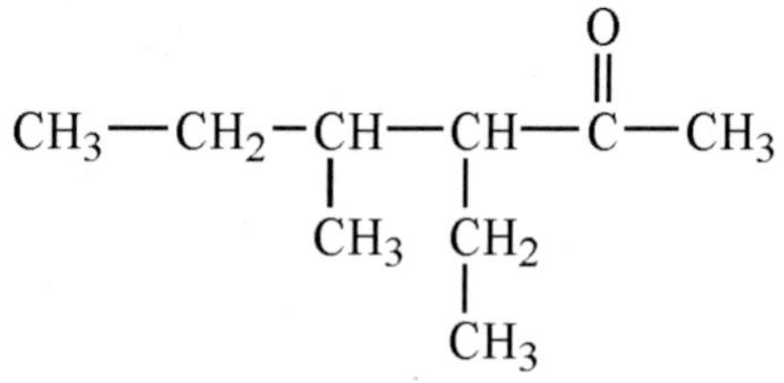

$$CH_3-CH_2-\overset{\overset{}{\underset{CH_3}{|}}}{CH}-\overset{\overset{}{\underset{\underset{\displaystyle CH_3}{\underset{|}{CH_2}}}{|}}}{CH}-\overset{\overset{\displaystyle O}{\|}}{C}-CH_3$$

e.

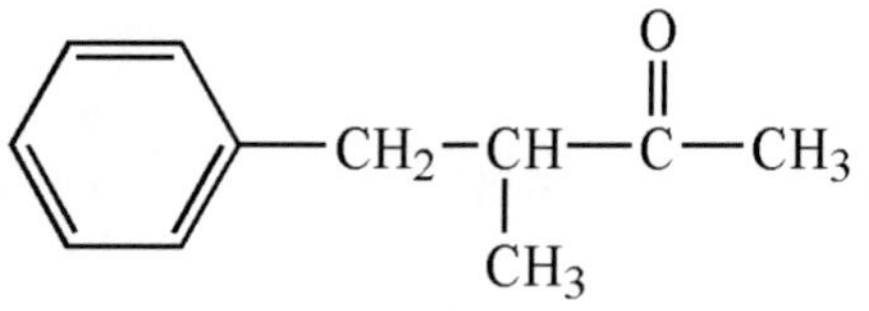

$$-CH_2-\overset{\overset{}{\underset{CH_3}{|}}}{CH}-\overset{\overset{\displaystyle O}{\|}}{C}-CH_3$$

f.

$$CH_3-\overset{\overset{\displaystyle CH_3}{|}}{\underset{\underset{\displaystyle O}{\underset{\diagdown}{C}}\diagup H}{C}}-\overset{\overset{\displaystyle Cl}{|}}{\underset{Cl}{C}}-CH_2-CH_3$$

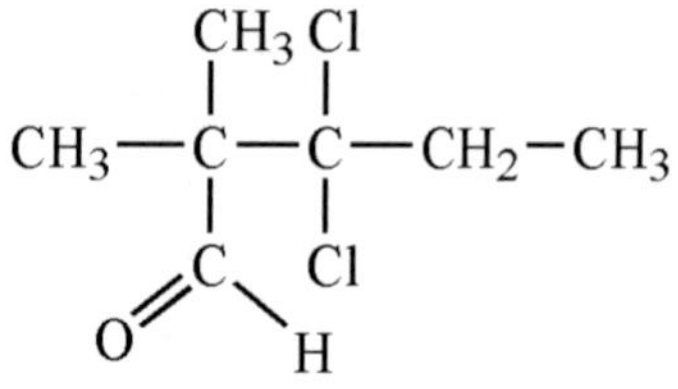

22. Match the structure with the functional group name.

a.

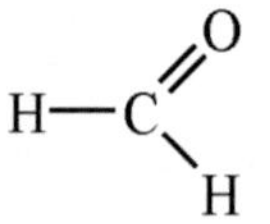

$$H-C\overset{\displaystyle \diagup O}{\diagdown H}$$

ketone

b.

$$CH_3-C\overset{\displaystyle \diagup O}{\diagdown OH}$$

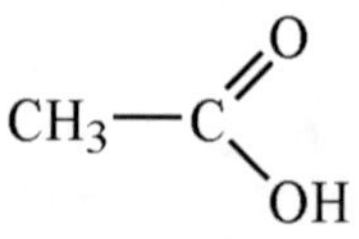

ester

c. CH_3-CH_2-OH aldehyde

d.

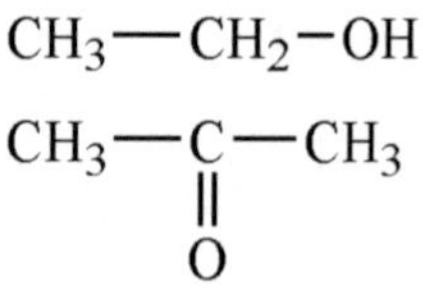

$$CH_3-\overset{\overset{}{\underset{\displaystyle O}{\underset{\|}{C}}}}{}-CH_3$$

carboxylic acid

e.

$$CH_3-C\overset{\displaystyle \diagup O}{\diagdown O-CH_3}$$

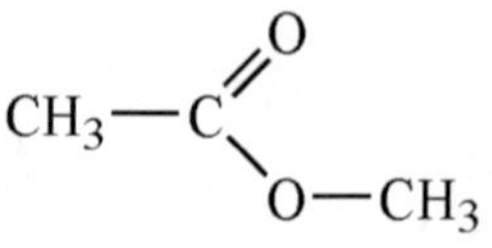

alcohol

23. Show the structure of the carboxylic acid that is produced by oxidizing the following primary alcohols.

a.

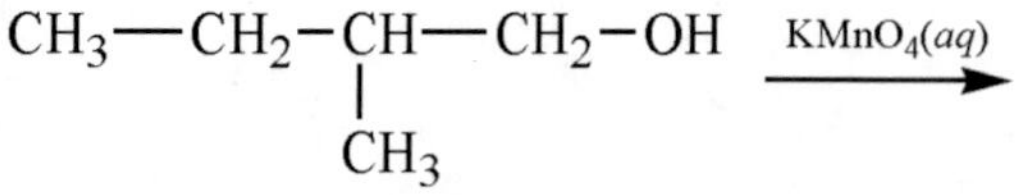

$$CH_3-CH_2-\overset{\overset{}{\underset{CH_3}{|}}}{CH}-CH_2-OH \xrightarrow{\text{KMnO}_4(aq)}$$

b.

$$CH_3-CH_2-CH_2-CH_2-CH_2-OH \xrightarrow{\text{KMnO}_4(aq)}$$

24.   a.   Show the structure of the ester formed when benzoic acid reacts with CH_3OH.

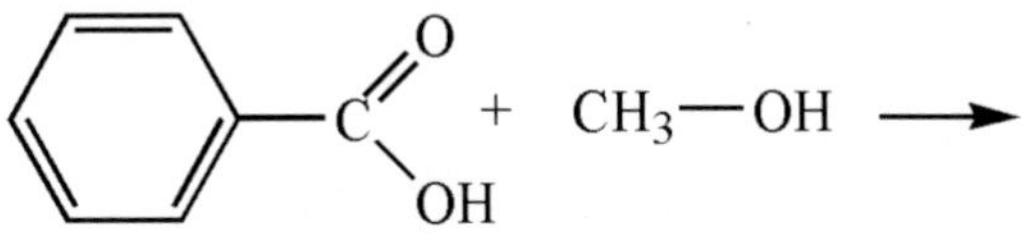

+ CH_3—OH   ⟶

b.   What is the name of the ester?

25.   Name the carboxylic acids below.

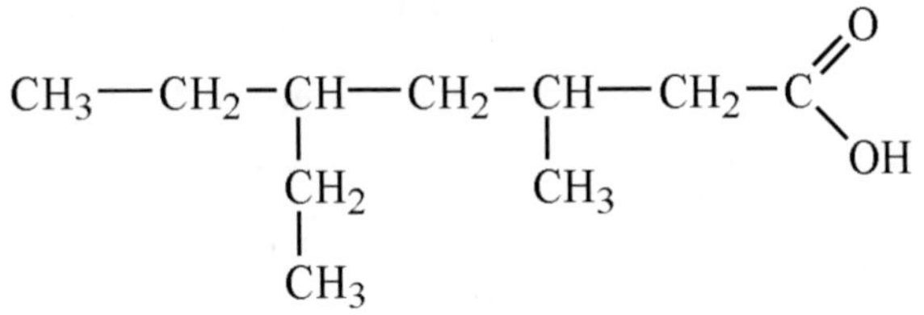

a.

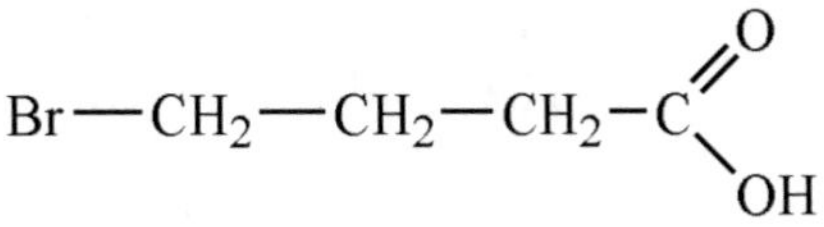

b.

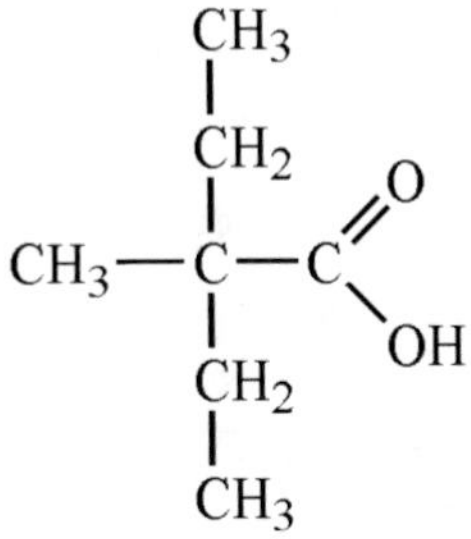

c.

26.   Show the structure of the carboxylic acid and the alcohol that reacted to make the esters below.

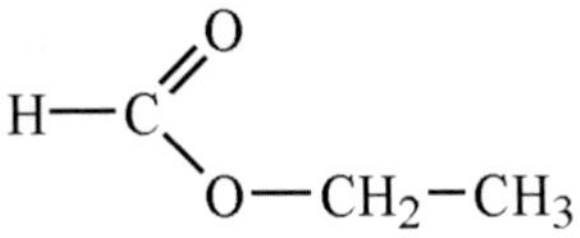

a.

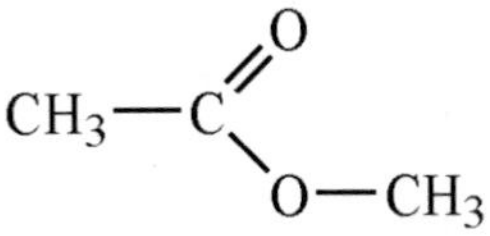

b.

27.   Show the structure of the polymer that would be produced from the monomer below.

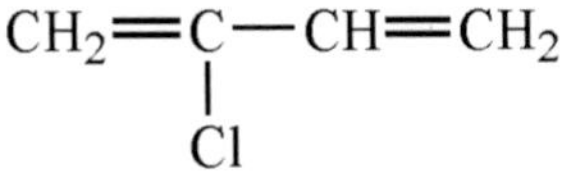

CH_2=C—CH=CH_2
　　　|
　　　Cl

Answers to Learning Review

1.   The correct matches are shown below.

a.	hydrocarbon	composed of carbon and hydrogen
b.	alkane	contains only carbon-carbon single bonds
c.	normal	an unbranched molecule
d.	unsaturated	contains one or more double or triple bonds

2.   In carbon tetrachloride, carbon is bonded to four other atoms. From the VSEPR model four pairs of bonding electrons spread out to form a tetrahedron.

3.   The condensed structure of an alkane with five carbons will have a CH_3 on each end, and three CH_2, or methylene, units. The structure is $CH_3(CH_2)_3CH_3$.

4.   This alkane has seven carbons and 16 hydrogens, so it can be represented by the general formula C_nH_{2n+2}. Both straight chain and normal alkanes are represented by the general formula C_nH_{2n+2}.

5.   Structural isomers are molecules that have the same numbers and kinds of atoms, but a different arrangement of bonds.

6.   One way to write all the structural isomers of a particular formula is to use the same system each time. Hexane has six carbons in a chain, so first write the structure of hexane itself.

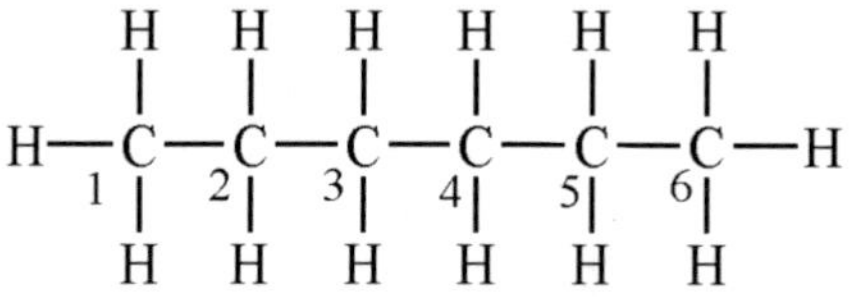

Then, remove a $-CH_3$ from the end of hexane, which leaves five carbons in the chain. Remove an $-H$ from successive carbons on the chain and replace with the $-CH_3$. If we remove an $-H$ from the end carbon, and replace with the $-CH_3$, we have not made a structural isomer, because the new molecule is just like hexane.

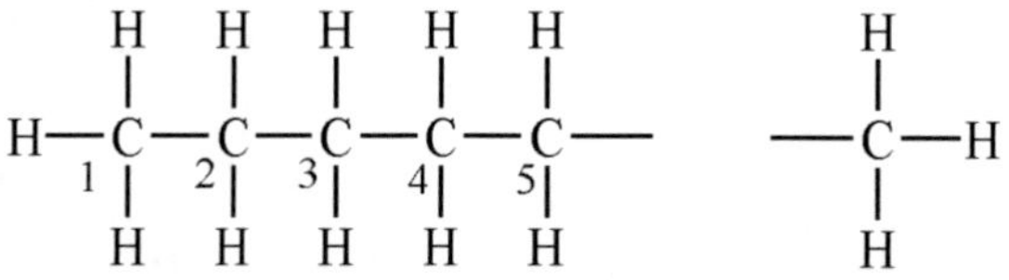

Put the $-CH_3$ on carbon number two. The $-CH_3$ is now located on the second carbon from the end. This is a new structural isomer.

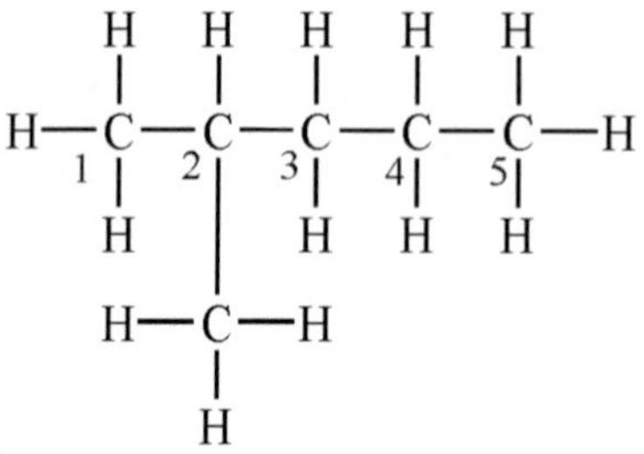

Now, move the $-CH_3$ to carbon number three.

```
        H   H   H   H   H
        |   |   |   |   |
   H — C — C — C — C — C — H
       1|  2|  3|  4|  5|
        H   H   |   H   H
                H — C — H
                    |
                    H
```

The -CH₃ is now located on the middle carbon, the third carbon from the end. We can move the
-CH₃ to carbon number four, but this move does not create a molecule with a different order. The
carbons have the same order as when the -CH₃ was on the second carbon from the left. Both
structures have -CH₃ on the second carbon from the end.

```
     H   H   H   H   H                    H   H   H   H   H
     |   |   |   |   |                    |   |   |   |   |
 H — C — C — C — C — C — H           H — C — C — C — C — C — H
    1|  2|  3|  4|  5|                   5|  4|  3|  2|  1|
     H   |   H   H   H                    H   H   H   |   H
     H — C — H                                       H — C — H
         |                                               |
         H                  same as                      H
```

We have exhausted the structural isomers that can be made by moving one -CH₃ from one
location to another. Let's now remove another carbon from the chain and see what isomers can
be made from a chain with four carbons and two -CH₃ groups.

```
      H   H   H   H          H          H
      |   |   |   |          |          |
  H — C — C — C — C —     — C —      — C — H
     1|  2|  3|  4|         5|         6|
      H   H   H   H          H          H
```

Substitute one -CH₃ on the second carbon, and one on the third carbon.

```
       H   H                   H   H
       |   |                   |   |
   H — C — C —————————— C — C — H
      1|  2|                  3|  4|
       H   |                   |   H
       H — C — H   H — C — H
           |           |
           H           H
```

Now, substitute both -CH₃ groups on the second carbon.

```
                    H
                    |
               H — C — H
       H            |        H   H
       |            |        |   |
   H — C ————— C ————— C — C — H
      1|          2|        3|  4|
       H            |        H   H
               H — C — H
                    |
                    H
```

If we put both -CH_3 groups on the third carbon, we have not created a structure with a new order of atoms. It is the same order as putting both -CH_3 groups on carbon number two.

same as

We can make no more different structural isomers with a four-carbon chain and two -CH_3 groups. Take another carbon from the chain.

With a three-carbon chain and three -CH_3 groups, there are no new structural isomers. All the combinations we can make have the same order as ones we have already made. Thus there are five structural isomers of C_6H_{14}.

7. You can name alkanes by applying the rules in Section 20.4 of your textbook.

a. The longest continuous chain of carbon atoms has six carbons so the parent alkane name is hexane.

We need to number the parent chain, assigning number one to the end that is closest to the first branch. In this case, the first branch, a -CH_3 group, would be on carbon two regardless of which end we begin numbering from. But, beginning the numbering from the left would locate the next branch, and also a -CH_3, on carbon three. If we began from the right, the second substituent would be on carbon four.

We now need to name and number each group on the main chain. All three branches are -CH_3 groups. These groups are equivalent to methane molecules with a hydrogen removed and are called methyl groups. There is a methyl group on carbons two, three and five. When there is more than one of a kind of substituent, use the prefix di, tri and so on, to indicate the number of times the substituent appears. These substituents would be named 2,3,5-thmethyl. Because there is only one kind of substituent, we do not have to list them in alphabetical order. The entire name is 2,3,5-trimethylhexane.

b.   The longest continuous chain of carbon atoms has five carbons so the parent alkane name is pentane.

$$CH_3\!\!-\!\!CH_2\!\!-\!\!CH\!\!-\!\!CH_2\!\!-\!\!CH_3$$
$$| $$
$$CH\!\!-\!\!CH_3$$
$$|$$
$$CH_3$$

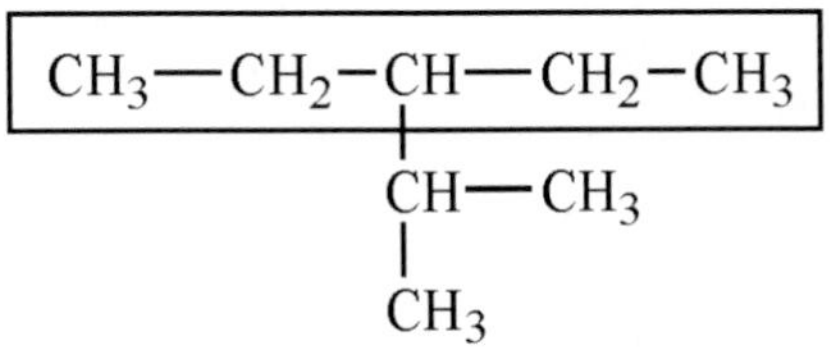

We can number this alkane from either end. There is only one substituent, and it is on the middle carbon.

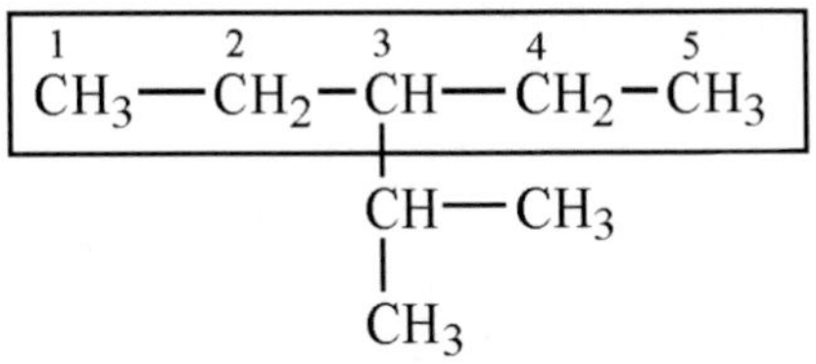

$$\overset{1}{CH_3}\!\!-\!\!\overset{2}{CH_2}\!\!-\!\!\overset{3}{CH}\!\!-\!\!\overset{4}{CH_2}\!\!-\!\!\overset{5}{CH_3}$$
$$|$$
$$CH\!\!-\!\!CH_3$$
$$|$$
$$CH_3$$

The group on carbon three is an isopropyl group, so this molecule is called 3-isopropylpentane.

c.   The longest continuous chain of carbon atoms has five carbon atoms so the parent alkane name is pentane. Remember that the longest chain will not always be drawn horizontally on the page.

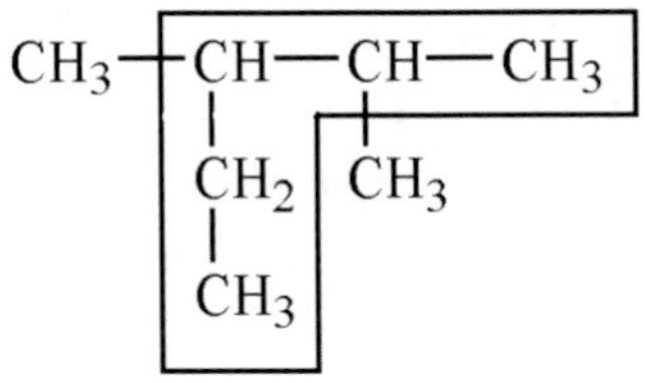

$$CH_3\!\!-\!\!CH\!\!-\!\!CH\!\!-\!\!CH_3$$
$$| \quad |$$
$$CH_2 \quad CH_3$$
$$|$$
$$CH_3$$

Number the chain beginning with the end on the right side in order to give the first substituent the lowest possible number.

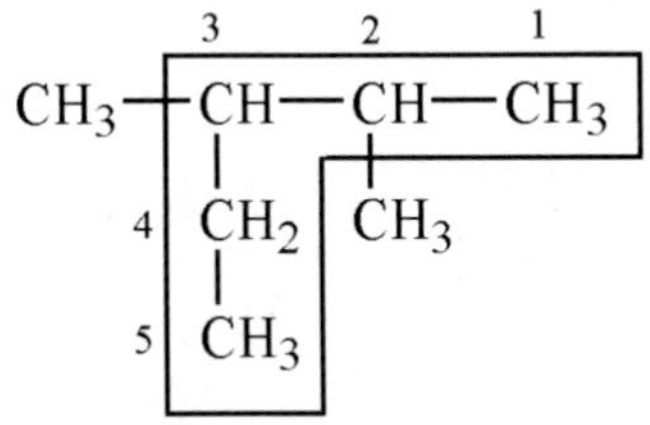

$$CH_3\!\!-\!\!\overset{3}{CH}\!\!-\!\!\overset{2}{CH}\!\!-\!\!\overset{1}{CH_3}$$
$$| \quad |$$
$$_4 CH_2 \quad CH_3$$
$$|$$
$$_5 CH_3$$

There are two substituents, both methyl groups, on carbons two and three. The substituents are named 2,3-dimethyl. The whole name is 2,3-dimethylpentane.

d.   The longest continuous chain of carbon atoms has seven carbons, so the parent alkane name is heptane.

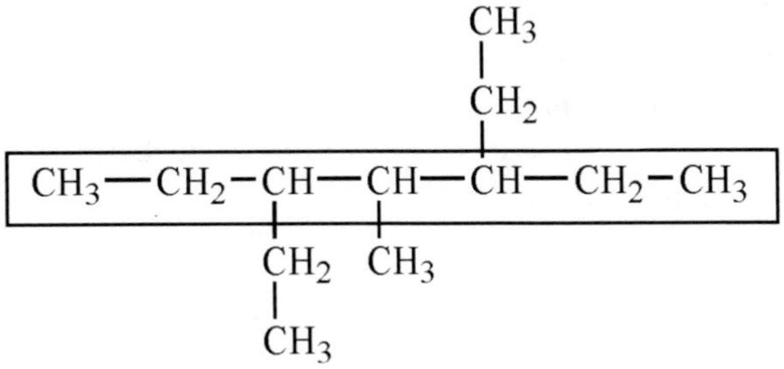

$$CH_3$$
$$|$$
$$CH_2$$
$$|$$
$$CH_3\!\!-\!\!CH_2\!\!-\!\!CH\!\!-\!\!CH\!\!-\!\!CH\!\!-\!\!CH_2\!\!-\!\!CH_3$$
$$| \quad |$$
$$CH_2 \quad CH_3$$
$$|$$
$$CH_3$$

You can also draw the box another way, which gives a chain of equal length.

$$\begin{array}{c}
1|\text{CH}_3 \\
| \\
2|\text{CH}_2 \\
5 \quad 4 \quad 3| \\
\text{CH}_3-\text{CH}_2-\boxed{\text{CH}-\text{CH}-\text{CH}}-\text{CH}_2-\text{CH}_3 \\
| \quad | \\
6|\text{CH}_2 \quad \text{CH}_3 \\
| \\
7|\text{CH}_3
\end{array}$$

Number the chain from either end.

$$\begin{array}{c}
\text{CH}_3 \\
| \\
\text{CH}_2 \\
1 \quad 2 \quad 3 \quad 4 \quad 5| \quad 6 \quad 7 \\
\boxed{\text{CH}_3-\text{CH}_2-\text{CH}-\text{CH}-\text{CH}-\text{CH}_2-\text{CH}_3} \\
| \quad | \\
\text{CH}_2 \quad \text{CH}_3 \\
| \\
\text{CH}_3
\end{array}$$

The substituents are a -CH_3, or methyl group, on carbon four, and two CH_3CH_2-, or ethyl groups, on carbons three and five. The two ethyl groups are named 3,5-diethyl. When assembling the substituent names, list ethyl before methyl because the groups must be listed alphabetically. The group names are 3,5-diethyl-4-methyl. The entire name is 3,5-diethyl-4-methylheptane.

e.   The longest continuous chain of carbons has three carbons, so the parent alkane name is propane.

$$\begin{array}{c}
\text{CH}_3 \\
| \\
\boxed{\text{CH}_3-\text{C}-\text{CH}_3} \\
| \\
\text{CH}_3
\end{array}$$

Number the chain from either end.

$$\begin{array}{c}
\text{CH}_3 \\
1 \quad 2| \quad 3 \\
\boxed{\text{CH}_3-\text{C}-\text{CH}_3} \\
| \\
\text{CH}_3
\end{array}$$

The substituents are two methyl groups on carbon number two. The substituents are named 2,2-dimethyl. The entire name is 2,2-dimethylpropane.

8.   One way to tell whether or not two molecules are structural isomers is to name them. If two molecules have the same name, they are not structural isomers – they are the same molecule. If two molecules have the same number of carbons and hydrogens and different names, they are structural isomers. Molecule **a** has five carbons in the longest chain, and molecule **b** also has five carbons in the longest chain.

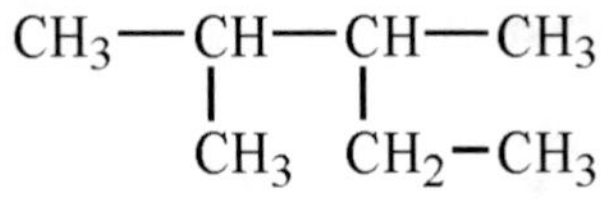

$$CH_3—CH—CH—CH_3$$
$$\quad\quad\quad | \quad\quad |$$
$$\quad\quad\quad CH_3 \quad CH_2—CH_3$$

$$CH_3$$
$$\quad\quad | $$
$$CH_3—CH \quad CH_3$$
$$\quad\quad\quad | \quad\quad\quad |$$
$$\quad\quad\quad CH_2—CH$$
$$\quad\quad\quad\quad\quad\quad |$$
$$\quad\quad\quad\quad\quad\quad CH_3$$

a 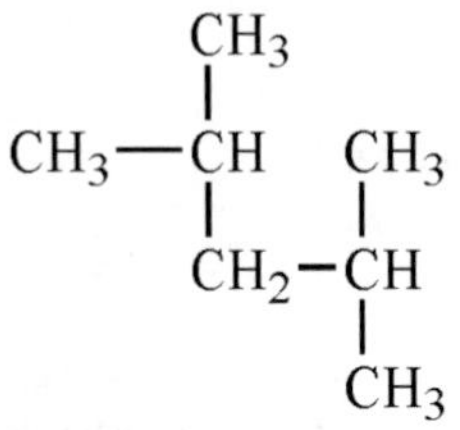   b

Number both molecules from the left. Each molecule has two substituents: two methyl groups. The substituents on molecule **a** are 2,3-dimethyl, and on molecule **b** they are 2,4-dimethyl. The entire name for molecule **a** is 2,3-dimethylpentane, and for molecule **b** it is 2,4-dimethylpentane. The names are different. Each molecule has five carbons and 12 hydrogens, so they are structural isomers.

9. Writing structural formulas from names is the reverse of writing names from formulas. First, find the parent alkane name and write a carbon skeleton with the same number of carbons. Number the chain from either direction. Determine how many substituents there are, and where they are attached, then put them on the chain. Fill in hydrogens so that each carbon is surrounded by four other atoms.

a. 2-methyl-4-sec-butyloctane has the parent alkane name octane.

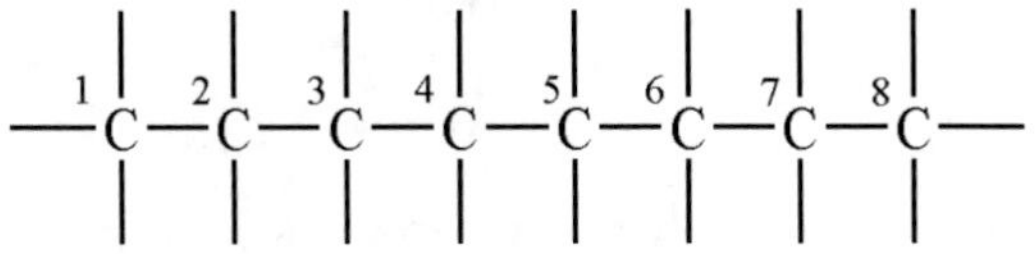

2-methyl indicates that there is a methyl group on carbon two.

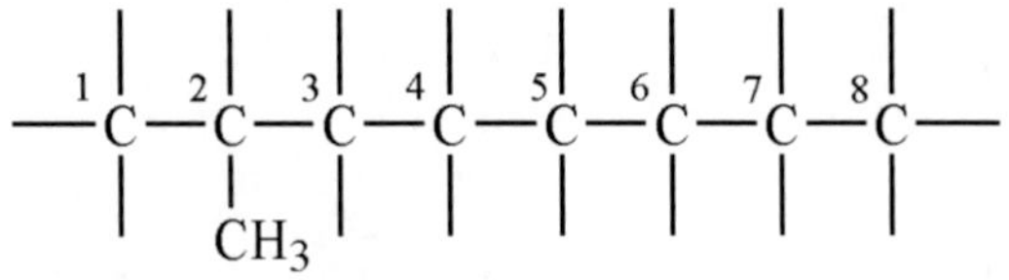

4-sec-butyl indicates that there is a sec-butyl group on carbon four.

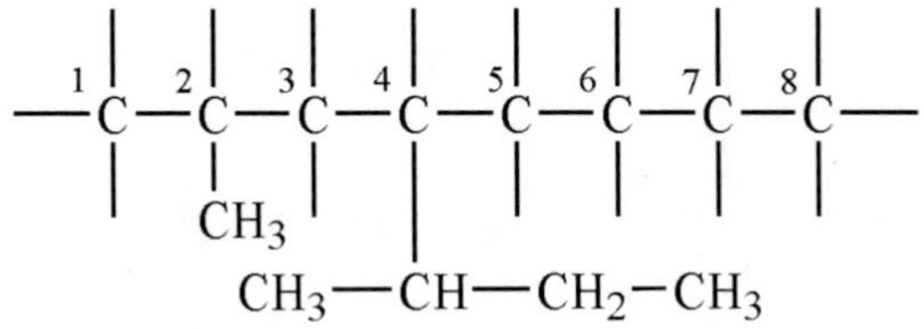

Now fill in the hydrogens so that each carbon is surrounded by four atoms.

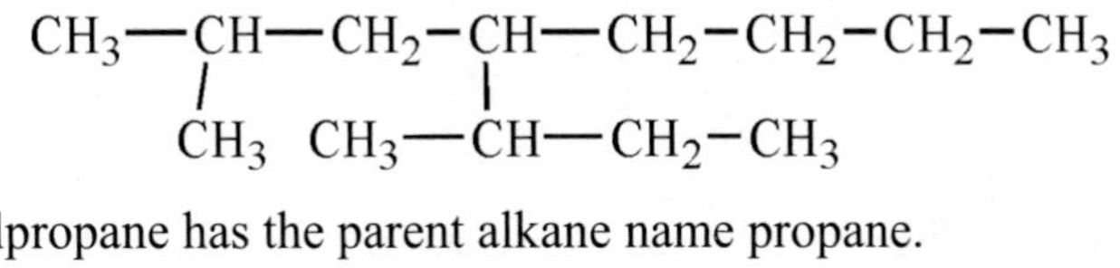

$$CH_3—CH—CH_2—CH—CH_2—CH_2—CH_2—CH_3$$
$$\quad\quad | \quad\quad\quad\quad | $$
$$\quad\quad CH_3 \quad CH_3—CH—CH_2—CH_3$$

b. 2-methylpropane has the parent alkane name propane.

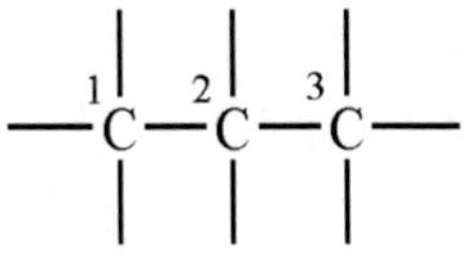

2-methyl indicates a methyl group on carbon two.

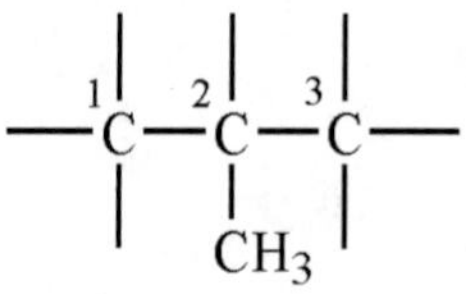

$$-\overset{1}{C}-\overset{2}{C}-\overset{3}{C}-$$
$$\qquad\qquad CH_3$$

Now fill in the hydrogens so that each carbon is surrounded by four atoms.

$$CH_3-CH-CH_3$$
$$\qquad CH_3$$

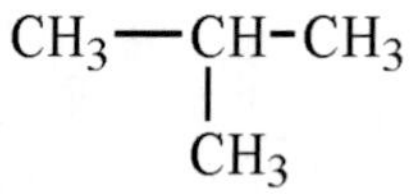

c. 3-ethylpentane has the parent alkane name pentane.

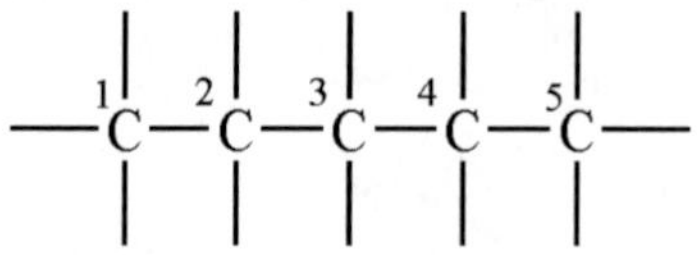

$$-\overset{1}{C}-\overset{2}{C}-\overset{3}{C}-\overset{4}{C}-\overset{5}{C}-$$

3-ethyl indicates an ethyl group on carbon three.

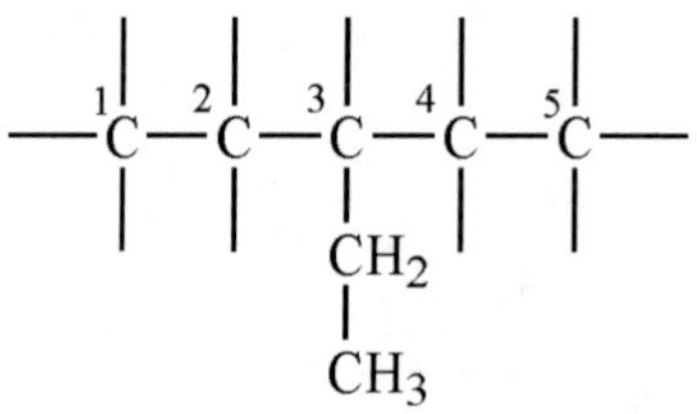

$$-\overset{1}{C}-\overset{2}{C}-\overset{3}{C}-\overset{4}{C}-\overset{5}{C}-$$
$$\qquad\qquad CH_2$$
$$\qquad\qquad CH_3$$

Now fill in the hydrogens so that each carbon is surrounded by four atoms.

$$CH_3-CH_2-CH-CH_2-CH_3$$
$$\qquad\qquad CH_2$$
$$\qquad\qquad CH_3$$

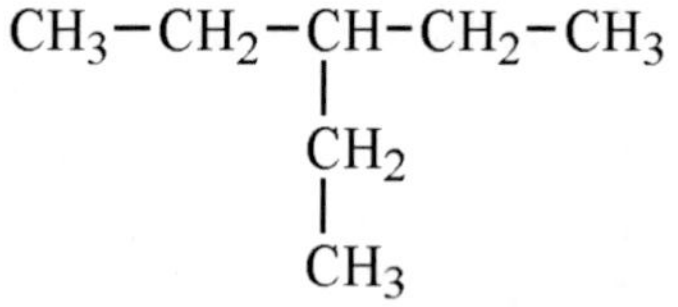

d. 2,2,4-trimethylhexane has the parent alkane name hexane.

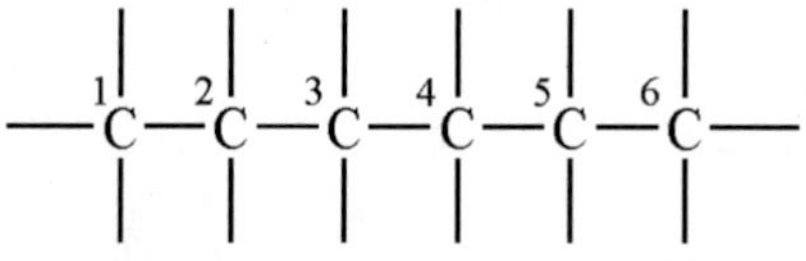

$$-\overset{1}{C}-\overset{2}{C}-\overset{3}{C}-\overset{4}{C}-\overset{5}{C}-\overset{6}{C}-$$

2,2,4-trimethyl indicates that there are three methyl groups, two on carbon two and one on carbon four.

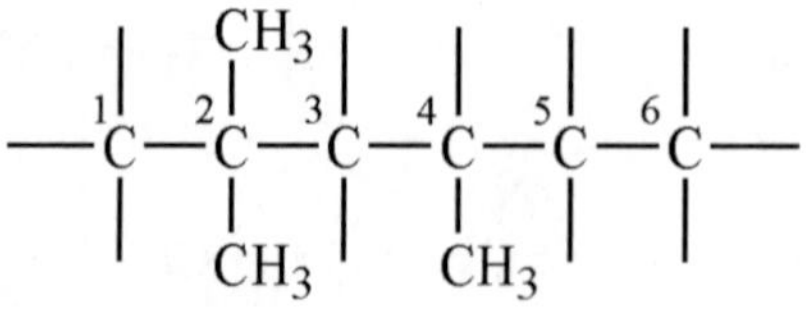

$$\qquad\quad CH_3$$
$$-\overset{1}{C}-\overset{2}{C}-\overset{3}{C}-\overset{4}{C}-\overset{5}{C}-\overset{6}{C}-$$
$$\qquad\quad CH_3 \qquad CH_3$$

Now, fill in the hydrogen atoms so that each carbon is surrounded by four atoms.

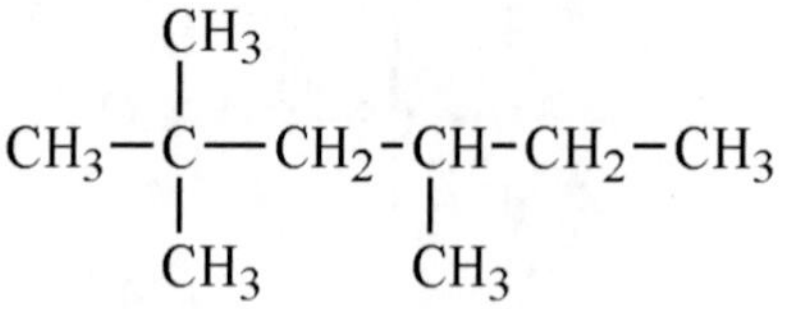

$$\qquad\quad CH_3$$
$$CH_3-C-CH_2-CH-CH_2-CH_3$$
$$\qquad\quad CH_3 \qquad CH_3$$

10. a. 2-ethylbutane has the structure:

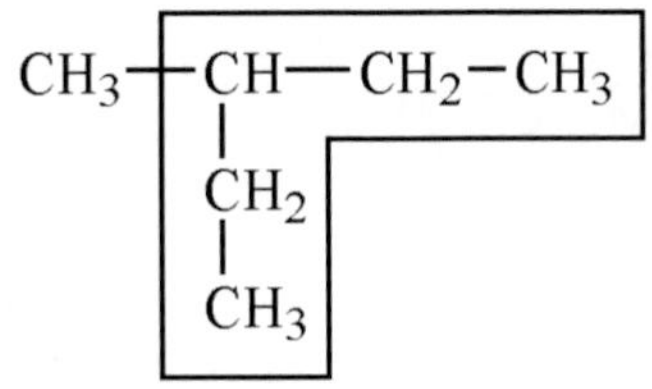

The longest carbon chain has not four, but five carbons, so the correct alkane name is pentane. There is a methyl group on carbon three, so this is 3-methylpentane.

b. 1-methylpentane has the structure

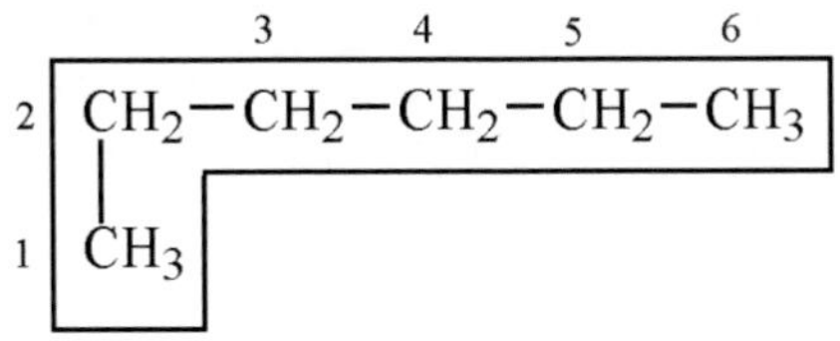

The longest chain has six carbons, not five, so the correct name is hexane.

c. 4,4-dimethylhexane has the structure

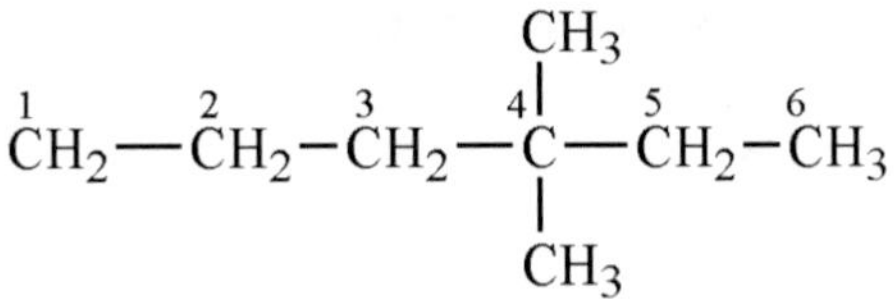

The longest chain has six carbons, so this is a hexane. The two methyl groups are on carbon four. Numbering the chain from the other end would put the methyl groups on carbon three. We want to number from the end that gives the substituents the lowest numbers, so 3,3-dimethylhexane would be the correct name.

d. 2-ethyl-2-methylheptane has the structure

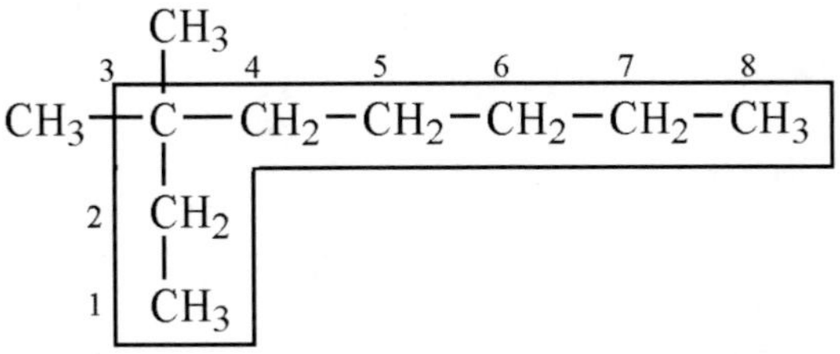

The longest chain has eight carbons, not seven, so the correct alkane name is octane. There are two methyl groups on carbon three, so this is 3,3-dimethyloctane.

11. Petroleum is a mixture of hydrocarbons containing molecules with various numbers of carbons in the chain. Usually, as the number of carbons in an alkane chain increases, the boiling point increases. Petroleum can be separated into different fractions by boiling.

12. First, draw the structure of pentane.

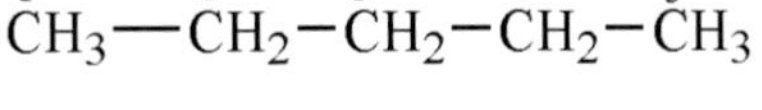

$$\overset{1}{CH_3}-\overset{2}{CH_2}-\overset{3}{CH_2}-\overset{4}{CH_2}-\overset{5}{CH_3}$$

Then, begin at one end and remove a hydrogen atom and replace it with a chlorine atom.

$$\overset{1}{C}H_2 - \overset{2}{C}H_2 - \overset{3}{C}H_2 - \overset{4}{C}H_2 - \overset{5}{C}H_3$$
$$|$$
$$Cl$$

There is only one structural isomer that can be produced from pentane by removing a hydrogen from carbon one. The order of bonding does not change by replacing either of the other two hydrogen atoms on carbon number one.

$$\overset{1}{C}H_2 - \overset{2}{C}H_2 - \overset{3}{C}H_2 - \overset{4}{C}H_2 - \overset{5}{C}H_3$$
$$|$$
$$Cl$$

same as $Cl - \overset{1}{C}H_2 - \overset{2}{C}H_2 - \overset{3}{C}H_2 - \overset{4}{C}H_2 - \overset{5}{C}H_3$

$$Cl$$
$$|$$
same as $\overset{1}{C}H_2 - \overset{2}{C}H_2 - \overset{3}{C}H_2 - \overset{4}{C}H_2 - \overset{5}{C}H_3$

Now, remove a hydrogen atom from carbon two and replace it with a chlorine atom. There is one structural isomer with a chlorine atom on carbon two.

$$\overset{1}{C}H_3 - \overset{2}{C}H - \overset{3}{C}H_2 - \overset{4}{C}H_2 - \overset{5}{C}H_3$$
$$|$$
$$Cl$$

Remove a hydrogen atom from carbon three and replace it with a chlorine atom. There is one structural isomer with a chlorine atom on carbon three.

$$\overset{1}{C}H_3 - \overset{2}{C}H_2 - \overset{3}{C}H - \overset{4}{C}H_2 - \overset{5}{C}H_3$$
$$|$$
$$Cl$$

Substituting a chlorine atom on carbon atoms four or five does not produce a new structural isomer, so there are three structural isomers.

13.   a.

$$CH_3 - CH - CH_3 + Cl_2 \xrightarrow{h\nu} CH_3 - CH - CH_2 - Cl + HCl$$
$$\qquad | \qquad\qquad\qquad\qquad\qquad | $$
$$\qquad CH_3 \qquad\qquad\qquad\qquad CH_3$$

In this reaction, a chlorine atom substitutes for a hydrogen atom.

b. $CH_4 + 2O_2 \longrightarrow CO_2 + 2H_2O$

This is an example of a combustion reaction.

c. $CH_3 - CH_2 - CH_3 \xrightarrow[500°C]{Cr_2O_3} CH_3 - CH = CH_2 + H_2$

This is an example of a dehydrogenation reaction.

14.   The rules for naming alkenes and alkynes are given in Section 20.7 of your textbook.

   a.   The longest chain that contains the double bond has five carbons.

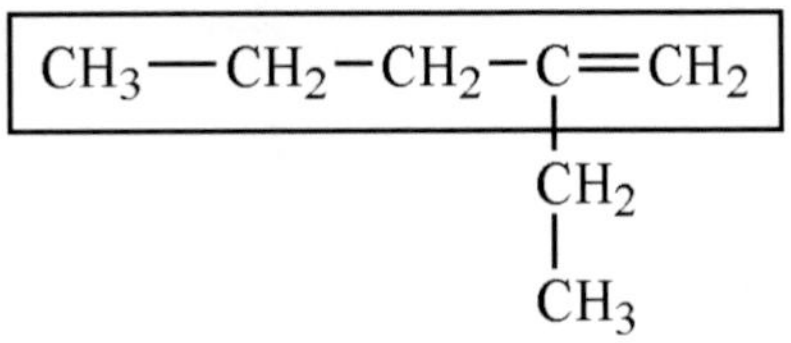

$$CH_3-CH_2-CH_2-C=CH_2$$
$$|$$
$$CH_2$$
$$|$$
$$CH_3$$

Replace the -ane ending of pentane with -ene to produce pentene. Number the carbon chain from the end closest to the double bond.

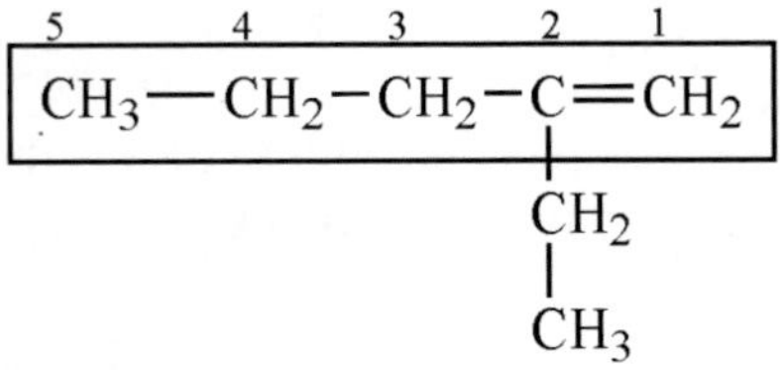

$$\overset{5}{CH_3}-\overset{4}{CH_2}-\overset{3}{CH_2}-\overset{2}{C}=\overset{1}{CH_2}$$
$$|$$
$$CH_2$$
$$|$$
$$CH_3$$

Give the location of the double bond by putting a number in front of the alkene name. This molecule is 1-pentene. There is an ethyl group on carbon two, so this molecule would be named 2-ethyl-1-pentene.

   b.   The longest chain that contains the triple bond has seven carbons.

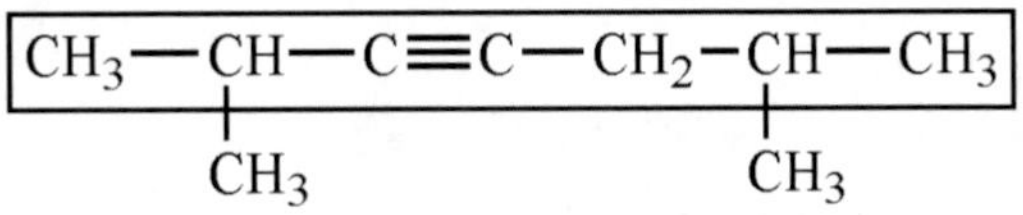

$$CH_3-CH-C\equiv C-CH_2-CH-CH_3$$
$$|\qquad\qquad\qquad\qquad |$$
$$CH_3\qquad\qquad\qquad CH_3$$

Replace the -ane ending of heptane with -yne to produce heptyne. Number the carbon chain from the end closest to the triple bond.

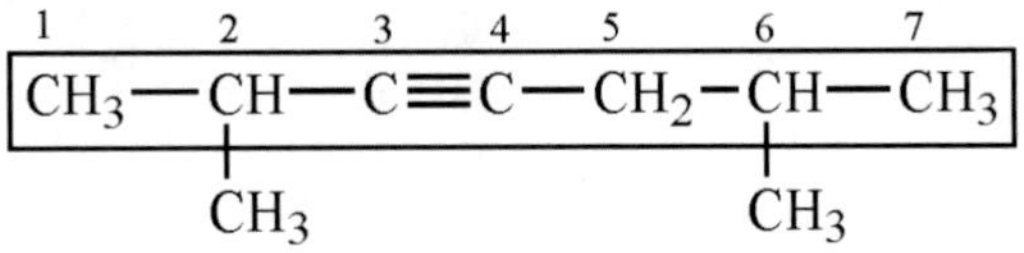

$$\overset{1}{CH_3}-\overset{2}{CH}-\overset{3}{C}\equiv\overset{4}{C}-\overset{5}{CH_2}-\overset{6}{CH}-\overset{7}{CH_3}$$
$$|\qquad\qquad\qquad\qquad |$$
$$CH_3\qquad\qquad\qquad CH_3$$

Give the location of the triple bond by putting a three in front of heptyne. There are two methyl groups attached to the chain on carbons two and six. This molecule would be named 2,6-dimethyl-3-heptyne.

   c.   The longest chain that contains the double bond has four carbons.

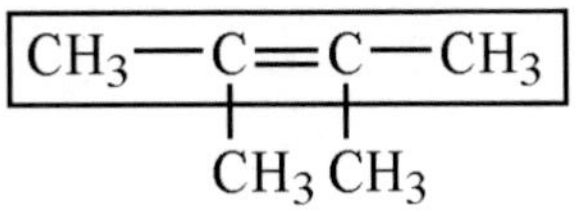

$$CH_3-C=C-CH_3$$
$$|\quad |$$
$$CH_3\ CH_3$$

Replace the -ane ending of butane with -ene to produce butene. Number the carbon chain from either end to give the location of the double bond the smallest number.

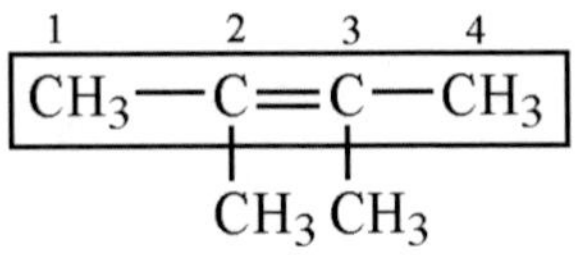

$$\overset{1}{CH_3}-\overset{2}{C}=\overset{3}{C}-\overset{4}{CH_3}$$
$$|\quad |$$
$$CH_3\ CH_3$$

Give the location of the double bond by putting a number in front of the alkene name. This molecule is 2-butene. There are two methyl groups attached to the main chain on carbons two and three. This molecule would be named 2,3-dimethyl-2-butene.

15.   a.

$$CH_3-C=C-CH_3 + H_2 \xrightarrow{\text{catalyst}} CH_3-CH-CH-CH_3$$
$$\quad\quad |\quad\quad|\quad\quad\quad\quad\quad\quad\quad |\quad\quad |$$
$$\quad\quad CH_3\ CH_3\quad\quad\quad\quad\quad\quad CH_3\ CH_3$$

b.

$$CH_3-CH_2-CH_2-CH=CH_2 + Cl_2 \longrightarrow CH_3-CH_2-CH_2-CH-CH_2$$
$$\quad\quad\quad\quad\quad\quad\quad\quad\quad\quad\quad\quad\quad\quad\quad\quad\quad\quad\quad |\quad\quad |$$
$$\quad\quad\quad\quad\quad\quad\quad\quad\quad\quad\quad\quad\quad\quad\quad\quad\quad\quad\quad Cl\quad\quad Cl$$

c.

$$CH_3-CH=C-CH_2-CH_3 + Br_2 \longrightarrow CH_3-CH-C-CH_2-CH_3$$

16.   a.   This molecule is usually called toluene.

b.   This molecule is named as a pentane with two substituents. There is a chlorine atom on carbon three and a phenyl group on carbon two. The name of this molecule is 3-chloro-2-phenylpentane.

c.   This molecule is chlorobenzene.

d.   This molecule is nitrobenzene.

17.   a.   is 1,2-dinitrobenzene or o-dinitrobenzene

b.   is 4-chlorophenol or p-chlorophenol

CH$_3$

c. CH$_2$—CH$_3$ is 4-ethyltoluene or p-ethyltoluene

d. Br is 3-bromotoluene or m-bromotoluene

18. a. The longest chain that contains the OH has five carbons.

$$\overset{CH_3}{\underset{\underset{CH_3 \; OH}{|\;\;\;\;|}}{\overset{1}{C}H_3-\overset{2}{C}-\overset{3}{C}H-\overset{4}{C}H_2-\overset{5}{C}H_3}}$$

Number the chain from the left side so that the OH group and the substituents have the lowest possible numbers. Drop the -e ending from pentane, and replace with -ol to produce pentanol. Locate the OH group with a number. This molecule would be 3-pentanol. There are two methyl groups on carbon two, so the entire name would be 2,2-dimethyl-3-pentanol. The carbon to which the OH is attached is bonded to two hydrocarbon fragments, so this is a secondary alcohol.

b. The longest chain that contains the OH has four carbons.

$$CH_3\overset{}{\underset{2}{\text{—}}}\overset{1\;CH_3}{\underset{\underset{4\;CH_3}{\overset{3\;CH_2}{|}}}{\overset{|}{C}\text{—OH}}}$$

Number the chain from the top so that the OH group has the lowest possible number. Drop the -e ending from butane and add -ol to produce butanol. Locate the OH group with a number. This molecule would be 2-butanol. There is a methyl group on carbon two, so the entire name is 2-methyl-2-butanol. The carbon to which the OH is attached is bonded to three hydrocarbon fragments, so this is a tertiary alcohol.

c. The longest chain that contains the OH group has six carbons.

$$\overset{\overset{4}{CH_3}}{\underset{\underset{Br\;\;\;CH_3}{|\;\;\;\;\;|}}{\overset{6}{C}H_3-\overset{5}{C}H_2-\overset{4}{C}-\overset{3}{C}H-\overset{2}{C}H_2-\overset{1}{C}H_2-OH}}$$

Begin numbering from the right to give the OH the lowest possible number. Drop the -e ending of hexane and add -ol to produce hexanol. Locate the OH group with a number.

This molecule would be 1-hexanol. There are two methyl groups on carbons three and four, and a bromo group on carbon four. The entire name would be 4-bromo-3,4-dimethyl-l-hexanol. The carbon to which the OH is attached is bonded to one hydrocarbon fragment, so this is a primary alcohol.

d.   The longest chain that contains the OH has eight carbons.

$$CH_3-CH-CH_3$$

$$CH_3 \overset{2}{|} CH \overset{3}{-} CH_2 \overset{4|}{-} CH \overset{5}{-} CH_2 \overset{6}{-} CH_2 \overset{7}{-} CH_2 \overset{8}{-} CH_3$$

$$\overset{1}{|} CH_2-OH$$

Begin numbering from the carbon that has the OH. Drop the -e ending of octane and add -ol to produce octanol. Locate the OH group with a number. This molecule would be 1-octanol. There is a methyl group on carbon two and an isopropyl group on carbon four. The entire name would be 2-methyl-4-isopropyl-l-octanol. The carbon to which the OH is attached is bonded to one hydrocarbon fragment, so this is a primary alcohol.

e.   The longest chain has one carbon. Assign this carbon number one.

$$CH_3OH$$

Drop the -e ending of methane and add -ol to produce methanol. Because there is only one carbon, we do not need a number to locate the OH group. It can only be found on carbon one. There are no substituents so methanol is the entire name. This molecule is also known by the common names methyl alcohol and wood alcohol. The carbon to which the OH is attached is bonded to one hydrocarbon fragment, so this is a primary alcohol.

f.   The longest chain that contains the OH has nine carbons.

$$\overset{7}{CH_3}-\overset{}{CH_2}-\overset{8}{CH}-\overset{9}{CH_2}-CH_3$$

$$\overset{6}{|} CH_2 \overset{5}{-} CH_2 \overset{4}{-} CH \overset{3}{-} CH_2 \overset{2}{-} CH \overset{1}{-} CH_3$$

$$CH_2 \qquad\qquad OH$$

$$CH_3$$

Begin numbering from the right to give the OH the lowest possible number. Drop the -e ending of nonane and add -ol to produce nonanol. Locate the OH with a number. This molecule would be 2-nonanol. There are two ethyl groups on carbons four and seven. This molecule would be named 4,7-diethyl-2-nonanol. The carbon to which the OH is attached is bonded to two hydrocarbon fragments, so this is a secondary alcohol.

19.   Match the alcohols below with the appropriate description.

a.	methanol	commonly known as wood alcohol
b.	phenol	used in the production of plastics
c.	ethanol	found in alcoholic beverages
d.	ethylene glycol	used in antifreeze

20. a.

$$\text{C}_6\text{H}_5\text{—CH}_2\text{—OH} \xrightarrow{\text{oxidation}} \text{C}_6\text{H}_5\text{—C(=O)—H}$$

b.

$$\text{CH}_3\text{—CH(CH}_3)\text{—CH}_2\text{—OH} \xrightarrow{\text{oxidation}} \text{CH}_3\text{—CH(CH}_3)\text{—C(=O)—H}$$

c.

$$\text{CH}_3\text{—CH}_2\text{—CH(OH)—CH}_2\text{—CH}_3 \xrightarrow{\text{oxidation}} \text{CH}_3\text{—CH}_2\text{—C(=O)—CH}_2\text{—CH}_3$$

21. a. The longest chain that contains the carbonyl has four carbons. Begin numbering from the end that has the aldehyde group.

$$\overset{4}{\text{CH}_3}\text{—}\overset{3}{\text{C}}(\text{CH}_3)(\text{CH}_3)\text{—}\overset{2}{\text{CH}}(\text{CH}_3)\text{—}\overset{1}{\text{C}}(\text{=O})\text{H}$$

Drop the -e ending of butane and add -al to produce butanal. Since the carbonyl in aldehydes is always found on an end, do not use a number to locate the carbonyl. There are three methyl groups, two on carbon three and one on carbon two. This molecule would be named 2,3,3-trimethylbutanal.

b. The longest chain that contains the carbonyl has six carbons. Begin numbering from the end which is closest to the ketone group.

$$\overset{1}{\text{CH}_3}\text{—}\overset{2}{\text{C}}(\text{=O})\text{—}\overset{3}{\text{CH}_2}\text{—}\overset{4}{\text{CH}}(\text{CH}_2\text{—CH}_3)\text{—}\overset{5}{\text{CH}_2}\text{—}\overset{6}{\text{CH}_3}$$

Drop the -e of hexane and add -one to produce hexanone. Locate the ketone carbonyl with a number, 2-hexanone. There is an ethyl group on carbon four, so the entire name would be 4-ethyl-2-hexanone.

c. The longest chain that contains the carbonyl has seven carbons. Begin numbering from the end which has the aldehyde group.

$$\text{O=}\overset{1}{\text{C}}(\text{H})\text{—}\overset{2}{\text{CH}}(\text{Br})\text{—}\overset{3}{\text{CH}_2}\text{—}\overset{4}{\text{CH}_2}\text{—}\overset{5}{\text{CH}_2}\text{—}\overset{6}{\text{CH}_2}\text{—}\overset{7}{\text{CH}_3}$$

Drop the -e ending of heptane and add -al to produce heptanal. There is a bromo group on carbon two, so the entire name is 2-bromoheptanal.

d. The longest chain that contains the carbonyl has six carbons. Begin numbering from the right to give the ketone the lowest number.

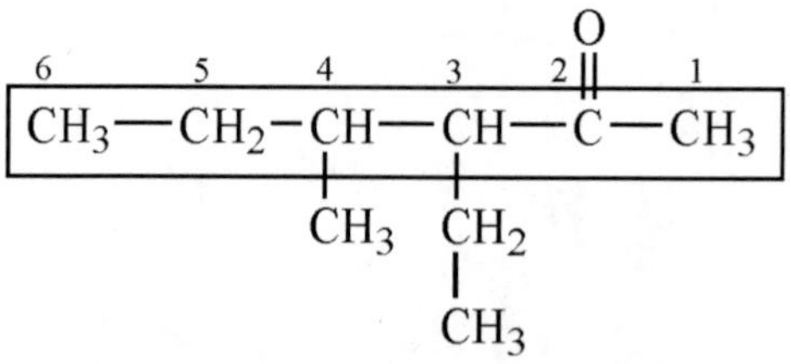

$$
\overset{6}{CH_3}-\overset{5}{CH_2}-\overset{4}{CH}-\overset{3}{CH}-\overset{2}{\overset{\displaystyle O}{\overset{\|}{C}}}-\overset{1}{CH_3}
$$

CH₃   CH₂

CH₃

Drop the -e ending of hexane and add -one to produce hexanone. Locate the ketone with a number. This molecule would be 2-hexanone. There is an ethyl group on carbon three, and a methyl group on carbon four. The entire name would be 3-ethyl-4-methyl-2-hexanone.

e.   The longest chain that contains the carbonyl has four carbons. Begin numbering from the right to give the ketone carbonyl the lowest number.

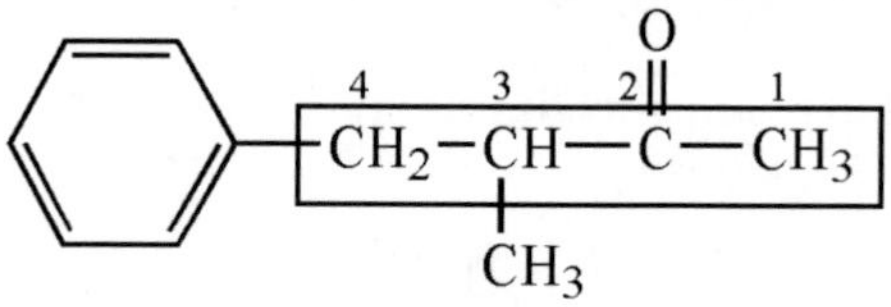

$$
\overset{4}{CH_2}-\overset{3}{CH}-\overset{2}{\overset{\displaystyle O}{\overset{\|}{C}}}-\overset{1}{CH_3}
$$

CH₃

Drop the -e of butane and add -one to produce butanone. Locate the ketone with a number. This molecule would be 2-butanone. There is a methyl group on carbon three and a phenyl group on carbon four. The name would be 3-methyl-4-phenyl-2-butanone.

f.   The longest chain that contains the carbonyl has five carbons. Begin numbering from the end with the aldehyde group.

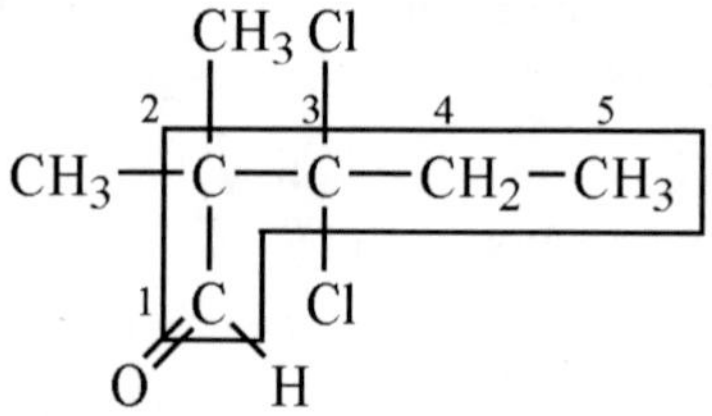

CH₃ Cl

$$
CH_3-\overset{2}{C}-\overset{3}{C}-\overset{4}{CH_2}-\overset{5}{CH_3}
$$

C   Cl

O   H

Drop the -e of pentane and add -al to produce pentanal. The aldehyde group does not need a number because it is always on the end. There are two methyl groups on carbon two, and two chloro groups on carbon three. The name would be 3,3-dichloro-2,2-dimethylpentanal.

22.   a.

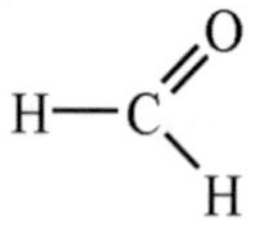

$$H-C\overset{\displaystyle O}{\underset{\displaystyle H}{<}}$$

aldehyde

b.

$$CH_3-C\overset{\displaystyle O}{\underset{\displaystyle OH}{<}}$$

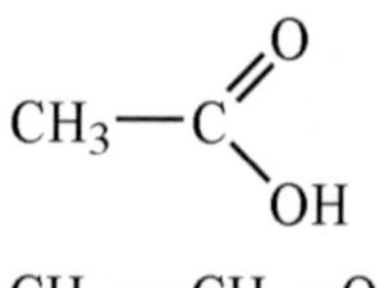

carboxylic acid

c. CH_3-CH_2-OH alcohol

d.

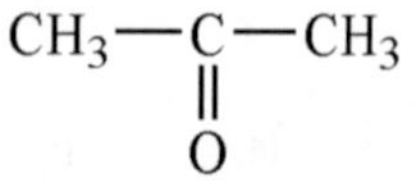

$$CH_3-\overset{\displaystyle}{\underset{\displaystyle O}{\overset{\|}{C}}}-CH_3$$

ketone

e.

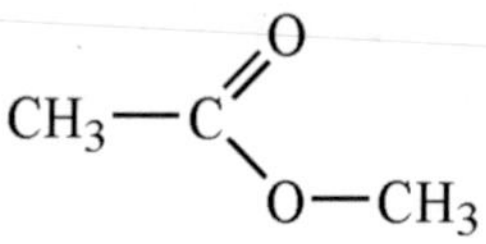

$$CH_3-C\overset{\displaystyle O}{\underset{\displaystyle O-CH_3}{<}}$$

ester

23.   a.

$$CH_3—CH_2—CH—CH_2—OH \xrightarrow{KMnO_4(aq)} CH_3—CH_2—CH—C\!\!\begin{smallmatrix}O\\ \\OH\end{smallmatrix}$$
$$\quad\quad\quad\quad|\quad\quad\quad\quad\quad\quad\quad\quad\quad\quad\quad\quad|$$
$$\quad\quad\quad\quad CH_3 \quad\quad\quad\quad\quad\quad\quad\quad\quad\quad CH_3$$

   b.

$$CH_3—CH_2—CH_2—CH_2—CH_2—OH \xrightarrow{KMnO_4(aq)} CH_3—CH_2—CH_2—CH_2—C\!\!\begin{smallmatrix}O\\ \\OH\end{smallmatrix}$$

24.   a.

   b.   The part of the ester that came from the alcohol is called methyl. The part of the ester that came from the carboxylic acid is called benzoate. The name is methylbenzoate.

25.   a.   The longest carbon chain that contains the carboxylic acid functional group has seven carbons. Number the chain from the end which has the carboxylic acid group.

Drop the -e of heptane and add -oic acid to give heptanoic acid. There is a methyl group on carbon three and an ethyl group on carbon five. The name is 5-ethyl-3-methylheptanoic acid.

   b.   The longest chain of carbons that contains the carboxylic acid functional group has four carbons. Begin numbering from the right to give the carboxylic acid functional group the lowest number.

Drop the -e ending and add -oic acid to give butanoic acid. There is a bromo group on carbon four, so the name would be 4-bromobutanoic acid.

c.   The longest chain of carbons that contains the carboxylic acid functional group has four carbons. Begin numbering from the right to give the carboxylic acid functional group the lowest number.

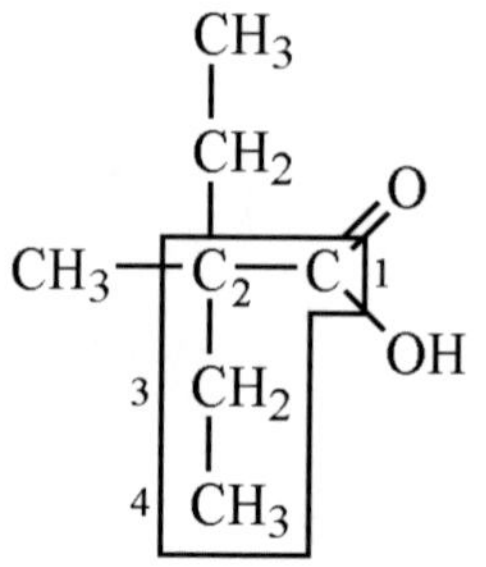

Drop the -e ending and add -oic acid to give butanoic acid. There is a methyl group and an ethyl group on carbon two. The entire name would be 2-ethyl-2-methylbutanoic acid.

26.   a.

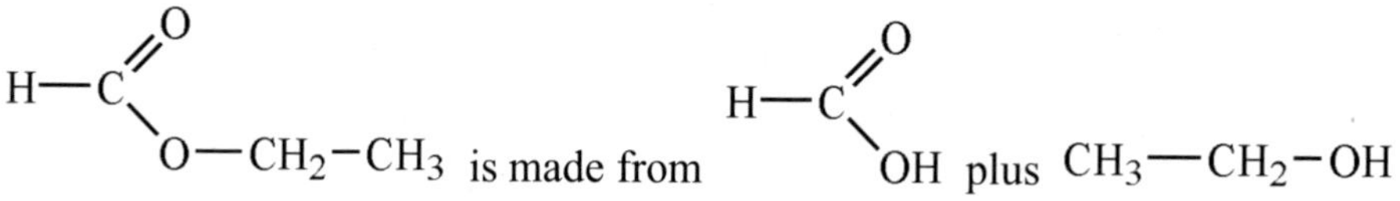

$O-CH_2-CH_3$ is made from

OH plus CH_3-CH_2-OH

b.

$O-CH_3$ is made from

OH plus CH_3-OH

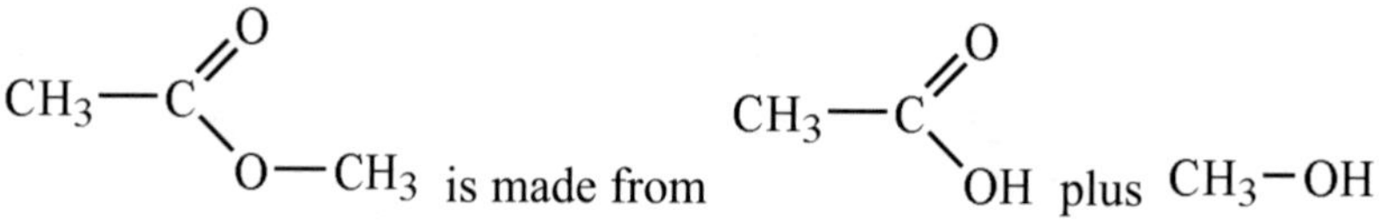

27.   The polymer would have the structure below.

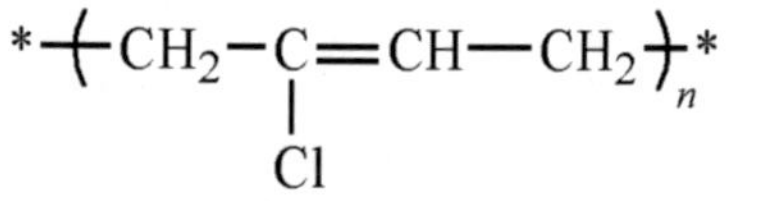

CHAPTER 21

Biochemistry

Introduction

Biochemistry, the chemistry of living systems, is a subject that concerns everyone. How do our bodies extract chemical energy from sugar and other substances? How can we find cures for diseases? The answers to these questions lie in the biochemistry of the human body. To begin to understand how the complex biochemical systems work, we need to know about the kinds of molecules that are important in living organisms. They are often large organic molecules, and they contain atoms and functional groups with characteristics with which we are already familiar.

Chapter Discussion

Proteins are made when amino acids react with each other to form peptide linkages. The carboxyl group of one amino acid reacts with the amino group of another amino acid. A water molecule is removed during the process.

The bond formed between two amino acids is called a peptide linkage. There is an almost endless number of proteins that could be formed from combinations of 20 different amino acids. Each different sequence of amino acids produces a different protein, so the order in which the amino acids occur is important. The order in which amino acids occur is called the primary structure of a protein.

The secondary structure of a protein is the shape the protein chain assumes. Two common secondary structures are the alpha-helix and the pleated sheet.

The tertiary structure of a protein is the three-dimensional shape of the protein molecule. Some proteins are globular in shape, while some are elongated. A protein can have several areas of alpha-helix that are separated from each other by bends. The protein folds at each bend, giving the molecule its tertiary structure.

Carbohydrates are a large class of biomolecules composed mainly of carbon, hydrogen and oxygen. They are a major source of food and serve as structural components in plants. Some carbohydrates are simple sugars, or monosaccharides (such as glucose), some are disaccharides (such as sucrose or table sugar), and some are polysaccharides (such as starch and cellulose).

Nucleic acids store the information necessary for life to continue from generation to generation. The nucleic acid that stores genetic information and transmits information from one generation to the next is deoxyribonucleic acid, or DNA. Another nucleic acid that helps translate the genetic information into proteins is ribonucleic acid, or RNA. Both DNA and RNA are composed of smaller building blocks called nucleotides. A nucleotide is made of three parts: a five-carbon monosaccharide, a nitrogen-containing organic base, and a phosphate group.

Active Learning Questions

The Active Learning Questions at the end of each chapter are conceptually based questions that work well as discussion questions with a group of students. If your instructor does not assign these, consider getting together with a group of classmates and using these questions to see how well you understand the material in each chapter. These questions cover topics from throughout the chapter and you are strongly encouraged to answer these.

Learning Review

1. What functions do carbon, phosphorus and magnesium perform in the human body?

2. What are two major types of proteins and how do their functions differ?

3. Which of the amino acids below have hydrophilic and which have hydrophobic side chains?

   a. $HO-\bigcirc-CH-C\overset{O}{\underset{OH}{}}$, with NH_2 on the CH

   b. $\overset{O}{\underset{HO}{}}C-CH_2-CH-C\overset{O}{\underset{OH}{}}$, with NH_2 on the CH

   c. $H_3C-CH-CH_2-CH-C\overset{O}{\underset{OH}{}}$, with CH_3 and NH_2

4. What is the structure of the dipeptide made from the two amino acids below?

   $HO-\bigcirc-CH_2-CH-C\overset{O}{\underset{OH}{}}$ (with NH_2) $+$ $HS-CH_2-CH-C\overset{O}{\underset{OH}{}}$ (with NH_2) $\rightarrow$

5. Show the sequences of all tripeptides that can be made from the amino acids phenylalanine (phe), glycine (gly), proline (pro) and aspartic acid (asp).

6. Explain the difference between the primary, secondary and tertiary structures of proteins.

7. Two types of secondary structures are the α-helix and the pleated sheet. What are the major characteristics of each?

8. Which amino acid plays a special role in maintaining the tertiary structure of proteins?

9. Use a lock and key analogy to explain how an enzyme can catalyze a reaction.

10. What two functional groups are characteristic of monosaccharides?

11. Draw the structure of a tetrose that has an aldehyde functional group.

12. The disaccharide sucrose, or table sugar, is made from which two monosaccharides?

13. What property causes starch to be a food source for humans, while cellulose is not?

14. a. What are the parts of a nucleotide?

    b. How do the nucleotides of RNA differ from nucleotides of DNA?

15.   Show the structure of a nucleotide.

16.   Show why the bases cytosine and guanine and the bases adenine and thymine pair with each other in DNA.

17.   How is it thought that DNA reproduces itself?

18.   How are proteins synthesized from the DNA code?

19.   a.   Draw the structure of the fat made from a molecule of glycerol and three molecules of oleic acid.

       b.   Would this fat likely be a solid or a liquid at room temperature?

20.   Explain in chemical terms how soap cleans away greasy dirt.

21.   Molecules with which two functional groups combine to form wax molecules?

22.   The steroids are a diverse group of molecules. What structural feature do they all have in common?

Answers to Learning Review

1.   Carbon is the backbone of all organic molecules in the body. Phosphorus is present in cell membranes and plays an important role in energy transfer in cells. Magnesium is required for proper functioning of some enzymes.

2.   The two major types are fibrous and globular. Fibrous proteins provide structure and shape, while globular proteins perform chemical work.

3.   a.   The side chain on tyrosine is a benzene ring that has an OH substituted for one of the hydrogen atoms. The OH bond is polar, just as the OH bond in water is. The polarity of the OH bond makes the side chain of tyrosine hydrophilic.

b.   Aspartic acid has a side chain that has a CH_2 and a COOH. The OH bond is polar, and so is the CO bond. The polarity of the COOH makes the side chain of aspartic acid hydrophilic.

c.   Leucine has a side chain composed entirely of carbon and hydrogen. Carbon-hydrogen bonds are not polar, so the side chain of leucine is hydrophobic.

4.

5.   To help you determine all the sequences, begin with one of the amino acids, and write all the possible sequences beginning with this one amino acid. Then choose another amino acid and write all the sequences that begin with the second amino acid. Continue until you have written sequences that begin with each of the amino acids given.

phe-gly-pro	gly-phe-pro	pro-gly-phe	asp-phe-pro
phe-gly-asp	gly-phe-asp	pro-gly-asp	asp-phe-gly
phe-pro-gly	gly-pro-phe	pro-phe-asp	asp-pro-phe
phe-pro-asp	gly-pro-asp	pro-phe-gly	asp-pro-gly
phe-asp-pro	gly-asp-pro	pro-asp-phe	asp-gly-phe
phe-asp-gly	gly-asp-phe	pro-asp-gly	asp-gly-pro

6.   The primary structure of proteins is the amino acid sequence. The secondary structure of proteins is the arrangement of the protein chain, or the arrangement of the amino acids to form an α-helix or a pleated sheet. How the α-helices or pleated sheets are bent in relation to one another is the tertiary structure of a protein.

7.   In the α-helix the amino acids are coiled like a spiral staircase. This array creates a long region of protein. Areas of protein with lots of α-helix are springy and elastic. In a pleated sheet, protein chains are bent back one or more times to form a sheet of protein chains. Pleated sheets are strong and resistant to stretching.

8.   The amino acid cysteine helps proteins maintain their unique tertiary structures. The SH side chains of two cysteine molecules can react to form a disulfide linkage that holds the protein chain in a fixed tertiary structure.

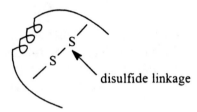

9.   For some enzymes it is believed that the enzyme has a shape that fits the shape of the substrate, just like a key fits a lock. When the enzyme and the substrate join together, a reaction occurs. The enzyme then releases the product that has formed.

10.   Monosaccharides all have hydroxyl and carbonyl functional groups. The carbonyl can either be an aldehyde or a ketone.

11.   There are several tetroses with an aldehyde group. The structure of one is presented below.

$$
\begin{array}{c}
H \diagdown \ C \diagup\!\!\!\!= O \\
| \\
H - C - OH \\
| \\
H - C - OH \\
| \\
CH_2OH
\end{array}
$$

12.   Sucrose is made from the monosaccharides glucose and fructose.

13.   Both starch and cellulose are made from glucose molecules. The way the glucose molecules are joined together in starch is different than the way they are joined in cellulose. Enzymes in our bodies can break the links between glucose molecules in starch, but not in cellulose.

14.   a.   All nucleotides are made from a phosphate group, a nitrogen-containing organic base and a five-carbon sugar.

     b.   In RNA, the sugar is ribose, while in DNA the sugar is deoxyribose. Some of the organic bases also differ between DNA and RNA. DNA and RNA have cytosine, adenine and guanine. Thymine is found only in DNA, and uracil is found only in RNA.

15.

16. Cytosine and guanine pair with each other in DNA because the hydrogen bonding sites on the molecule are complementary. The three hydrogen bonds between the two molecules hold cytosine and guanine together. Adenine and thymine molecules on complementary DNA strands are also held together by hydrogen bonds. Two hydrogen bonds form between adenine and thymine molecules.

17. There is evidence to show that two complementary DNA chains unwind, and new strands are made by pairing bases along the old chains. The end result is two new chains, each complementary to the old one.

18. DNA stores the information required to produce proteins needed by organisms. A discreet length of the DNA chain, called a gene, contains the information for one protein. The DNA transmits the information it contains by synthesizing a chain of RNA called messenger RNA (mRNA). Once the mRNA has been produced, it moves away from DNA to the site of protein synthesis. The mRNA and small bodies called ribosomes begin the synthesis of protein. Another kind of RNA, called transfer RNA (tRNA), brings up amino acids one by one to join them on the end of the growing protein chain. The mRNA contains the information that determines which amino acids join, and in what order.

19.

a.

b. Fats made of unsaturated fatty acids are often liquids at room temperature. This fat would likely be a liquid at room temperature because oleic acid is an unsaturated fatty acid.

20.   Soap molecules are the anions of long chain fatty acids. Each soap molecule has two pans. The carboxylate head has a negative charge and is attracted to polar water molecules. The remainder of the molecule is a long hydrocarbon tail that is not attracted to water. The hydrocarbon tail is hydrophobic. When soap is added to water, the hydrocarbon tail does not want to associate with the polar water molecules – so tails from soap molecules associate together to form a soap micelle in which the polar heads face outward toward the water.

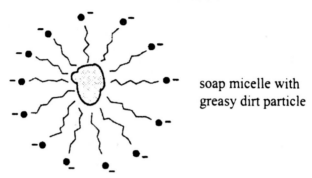

soap micelle with
greasy dirt particle

Much of the dirt we wish to remove is greasy dirt. This kind of dirt is not washed away by water, because it is hydrophobic. When soap micelles come in contact with greasy dirt, the dirt is lifted from the surface and enters the inside of the micelle. The hydrophobic dirt would rather be in contact with the hydrophobic hydrocarbon tails than with water. The soap micelles that contain the greasy dirt are washed away with water.

21.   Waxes are esters with long carbon chains. Esters are made from a carboxylic acid and an alcohol.

22.   All steroids have a basic ring structure called the steroid nucleus. Each steroid has different substituents on the rings.